MODERN COLLEGE PHYSICS

MODERN COLLEGE PHYSICS

HARVEY E. WHITE, Ph.D., Sc.D.

PROFESSOR OF PHYSICS AND DIRECTOR OF THE LAWRENCE HALL OF SCIENCE
UNIVERSITY OF CALIFORNIA

FIFTH EDITION

D. VAN NOSTRAND COMPANY, INC.

PRINCETON, NEW JERSEY
TORONTO · LONDON

Van Nostrand Regional Offices: *New York, Chicago, San Francisco*

D. Van Nostrand Company, Ltd., *London*

D. Van Nostrand Company (Canada), Ltd., *Toronto*

First Published, February 1948

Second Edition, March 1953

Third Edition, January 1956

Fourth Edition, May 1962

Fifth Edition, May 1966

PRINTED IN THE UNITED STATES OF AMERICA

Photograph of Astronaut Edward H. White II, pilot for the Gemini-Titan 4 space flight, floating under weightless conditions outside the Gemini-4 spacecraft. Note the curvature of the earth and cloud cover.

White wears a specially designed space suit and the visor of his helmet is gold plated to protect him from the unfiltered rays of the sun. In his hand he carries a Hand-Held Maneuvering Unit with which he controls his movements in space. June 3, 1965.

(Courtesy U. S. National Aeronautics and Space Administration.)

To my son, Don

PREFACE

This text book is designed primarily for the one-year college general physics course. It is particularly suitable for students who plan to major in one of the physical or life sciences, or are pursuing a liberal arts program.

Originally published in 1947, the book has been revised three times prior to this its fifth edition. The main objective in originally preparing the manuscript was to unite under one cover the elementary principles of classical physics and those branches of modern science called atomic and nuclear physics. The ever-increasing importance of space science, as well as high-energy and low-energy nuclear physics, has led to the extensive revision of many chapters and to the addition of new ones.

Included in the new or expanded material of this text are sections or chapters on mechanical energy levels; Kepler's laws and space mechanics; rocket engines; electric and magnetic dipole moments; atomic energy levels; lasers; theory of relativity; alpha, beta, and gamma rays; elementary particles; field theory and world lines; and special atomic and nuclear effects.

The mathematics of this text is confined to elementary algebra, plane geometry, and trigonometry. Although the cgs and English system of units are often used in sample calculations, the mks system is emphasized throughout the book.

Even though a large number of students who plan to major in one of the life sciences are enrolled in physics courses, the illustrations in many physics texts are almost entirely selected from the fields of engineering. It is for this reason that the author has introduced, wherever it has been convenient, illustrations of basic principles of physics from the biological and medical sciences as well as engineering.

Since instructors differ widely in their decisions as to which subjects to include or to emphasize in an introductory physics course, the book has been divided into many chapters, thus making it possible to eliminate a subject by omitting an entire chapter.

The subject matter of the entire text has been arranged in the most commonly used order of preference, and with seventy-five chapters is so divided as to lend itself to the semester or the quarter system. Where the semester system is used, the subjects divide with mechanics, properties of matter, heat, sound, electricity and magnetism in the first semester, and optics, atomic structure, nuclear physics and quantum theory in the second. For the quarter system, the first twenty-five chapters cover mechanics, properties of matter, heat and sound; the next twenty-five chapters cover electricity and magnetism, and geometrical and physical optics; and the last twenty-five chapters cover atomic structure, nuclear physics and quantum theory.

The answers to even-numbered problems have been determined by the author and checked by another physics teacher. Yet whenever a human being is involved mistakes can be made and a recorded answer may be in error. The author would, therefore, greatly appreciate his being notified of any errors, as they can be corrected in succeeding printings of this edition.

The author wishes to thank his colleagues, Messrs. L. Alvarez, R. T. Birge, R. B. Brode, R. R. Brown, O. Chamberlain, D. Cooksey, W. B. Fretter, E. W. Friesen, M. Gould, A. C. Helmholz, D. B. Judd, V. F. Lenzen, L. B. Loeb, E. M. McMillan, B. J. Moyer, W. M. Powell, A. Rosenfeld, G. T. Seaborg, E. Segré, C. D. Shane, H. Shugart, L. L. Skolil, H. Snodgrass, E. Teller, and H. Weltin for their valuable contributions to this text through discussions with the author of various special subjects. The author also wishes to thank the many teachers and students whose written comments have been most helpful throughout the years, and also the various publishers and research laboratories whose permission to reproduce certain illustrations has also been so kindly granted.

The author is particularly indebted to D. H. White for his many contributions, suggestions, and criticisms of the entire book, particularly with regard to atomic and nuclear physics; to J. P. White for his corrections in English grammar and proofreading of all galley and page proofs; and D. Aigner for his checking of the many cross references and example solutions to problems, and reading of all galley and page proofs.

Berkeley, California   HARVEY E. WHITE

CONTENTS

APPENDICES

OPTICAL ILLUSIONS

In the early dawn on the morning of July 16, 1945, there occurred in a remote spot on the desert sands of Alamogordo, New Mexico, a man-made explosion of enormous magnitude. This, the explosion of the first atomic bomb, marked the culmination of a five-year coordinated research program, the size of which in terms of manpower and material is best expressed by its total cost to the United States government of approximately two billion dollars. With the ending of World War II and the subsequent dissemination of many of the scientific and technical developments made during that war, the civilized world awakened to the realization that we stand today on the threshold of a scientific era. This is the beginning of an era in which the wonders of television, radar, electronics, atomic energy, jet propulsion, and rocket ships are already a commonplace reality.

In all of these developments in the physical sciences, as well as many others in the field of medicine and the life sciences in general, the subject we call physics has played a most important role. So important is this role that many authorities in other fields of knowledge and endeavor consider physics to be the most basic of all the sciences. A knowledge of the fundamental principles of physics is today an essential part of the education of all who desire to become proficient in the physical and medical professions.

One of the reasons physics is called an exact science is that reproducible experiments are performed and observations are made with high-precision measuring instruments. Laws and theories are formulated from the measured results of these experiments and then used to predict the results of new experiments. If these new experimental results do not agree with theory, the theory is either modified and brought into agreement or it is discarded for a new and better theory. Physics may be defined as that branch of knowledge treating the inanimate world and its phenomena and includes the subjects of:

Mechanics	**Atomic Structure**
Properties of Matter	**Quantum Mechanics**
Heat	**Wave Mechanics**
Sound	**Relativity**
Light	**Solid State Physics**
Electricity	**Nuclear Structure**
Magnetism	**Elementary Particles**

1.1 Physics as an Objective Method. It has long been known that when experiments are to be performed, one cannot rely too much upon the human senses of touch, sight, hearing, etc., to make accurate observations. Methods of measurement that rely upon the senses entirely are called *subjective methods*. Methods that make use of scientific instruments are generally called *objective methods*.

In the early history of science, laws were frequently discovered by the use of subjective methods. Progress was slow, however, until such methods were replaced by objective methods using measuring instruments devised to give greater and greater precision.

It is true that many scientific discoveries have been made in the past with what we now would call the crudest of apparatus and equipment. It is the development of precision instruments and apparatus, however, that has led, particularly within the last several decades, to discoveries that are far-reaching in their theoretical implications and are of extreme practical importance to the advancement of civilization.

As an introduction to the subject of physics, we will first consider a number of experiments illustrating the false impressions so easily arrived at from the use of subjective methods of observation. Although these experiments are of the nature of an entertainment, they do have more serious aspects, for they demonstrate the necessity for using objective methods in advancing science.

1.2. Subjective Methods. If someone asks you to determine the temperature of a pan of water, your first impulse, if the water is not too hot, is to use your hand or your finger-tips and not to bother looking for a thermometer. To illustrate the gross inaccuracy of the touch in determining temperature, consider the three pans of water as shown in Fig. 1A. If the hand is first held for

cold   warm   hot

Fig. 1A   *Experiment illustrating the uncertainty of subjective methods of measurement.*

some little time in the pan containing *cold* water and then plunged into the *warm* water, the senses tell you it is hot. If, however, the hand is first held in the *hot* water and then plunged into the *warm* water, your senses tell you it is cold. Your conclusion in either case is thus influenced by your experiences immediately preceding your determination of the temperature of the middle pan. When a thermometer is used in this experiment the same temperature will be indicated in either case. Although this latter would be called an objective method of measurement, one still relies upon the senses to obtain a reading of the thermometer scale.

If the length and breadth of a table top are to be measured, a *foot rule*, a *yardstick*, or a *meter stick* should be used and not the *span of a hand*. In a similar way the time that it takes a sprinter to run the "*one-hundred yard dash*" is measured by a *clock*, a *watch*, or a *chronometer* and not by the *heart beat* or *pulse*.

1.3. The Eye. In making many scientific measurements the eye is considered as the most useful of all recording instruments. In some instances, however, the eye is not and should not be used directly in making observations, since it cannot be relied upon to observe what is really there. To illustrate how unreliable the sense of vision can be in some cases, we will consider in the next section a number of examples commonly referred to as "optical illusions."

Despite its many and sometimes serious imperfections and limitations, the human eye is a marvelous optical instrument. It is nature's priceless gift to man, enabling him to enjoy the beauties of form, color, and motion made possible by light. Optically the eye is like an exceptionally fine camera with an elaborate lens system on the one side and a sensitive screen or photographic film, called the *retina*, on the other (see Fig. 1B). The refracting media of the eye consists of the *cornea*, the *aqueous humor*, the *crystalline lens*, and *vitreous humor*, and its function is to focus an image of the objects to be seen on the retina. Like a camera, the eye contains an *iris diaphragm* which opens wider for faint light and closes down to a bare pinhole opening for very bright sunlight. It is this iris that contains the pigment determining the color of the eye.

In the retina of the eye the light pulses are received by tiny *cones* and *rods* whose function it seems to be to change the light into electricity. Each cone and rod is connected with an individual nerve which conducts the electricity through the nerve canal to the brain. Just how these electrical impulses are produced by the cell-like structures, the cones and rods, and how they are interpreted by the brain as vision, is still only vaguely understood by scientists. Experiments seem to indicate that the cones respond only to bright light and are particularly responsible for the detection and distinction of color, whereas the rods are sensitive to very feeble light, to motion, and to slight variations in intensity.

At the very center of the retina is a small yellowish-looking spot called the *fovea*. This small region contains a large number of cones, but no rods. It is on this spot in each eye that the words and letters of this page are focused one after the other when reading. Note when scrutinizing one

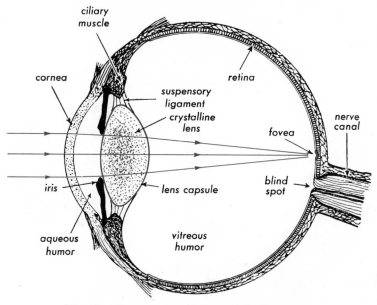

Fig. 1B *Cross-section diagram of the human eye.*

word or particularly a single letter in a word that the rest of the page and even the words and letters close by appear indistinct.

It is customary to divide into two parts all sensory data that contribute to sight perception of any object: first, the formation of the retinal image by the light coming from the object, and second, the integrative property of the brain to interpret this image.

1.4. The Blind Spot. Not far from the fovea on the retina of the eye is a small region called the *blind spot*. This spot, which is insensitive to light, is where the nerve canal joins the eyeball. The existence of the blind spot can be demonstrated by closing the right eye and holding the book at arm's length, looking continuously at the center of the circle of Fig. 1C with the left eye. Both the circle and square will be seen from this distance. If the book is now moved slowly toward the eye, still fixing the eye upon the circle,

a position (about 8 to 10 inches from the eye) will be reached where the square disappears. When both eyes are open, no position will be found where either the cross or the square disappears. One eye always sees that part of an object to which the other eye is blind. A similar experiment with the right eye focused on the square will cause the circle to disappear. A further discussion of the human eye and how it functions as an optical instrument is given in Chapter 41.

1.5. Optical Illusions. Of the hundreds of well-known optical illusions, only a few of the most interesting ones will be presented here. In Fig. 1D

Fig. 1C *Experiment illustrating the blind spot of the eye.*

Fig. 1D *Optical illusions with lines and angles.*

Fig. 1E *Which figure is tallest? Measure them.*

is a group of six figures classified as illusions due to *lines* and *angles*. In (a), the first figure, the brim of the hat is as long as the hat is high. In (b) the diagonal lines of each parallelogram are of the same length, and in (c) the perfect circle appears to be distorted. In figure (d) the two horizontal lines are parallel and straight and in (f) they are of equal length. In (e) the lower right-hand line, if extended, will intersect the left-hand line where it joins the vertical.

Figure 1E is an example of *perspective*, an illusion suggesting depth to the picture when, in reality, it is flat. Actually this figure is a rectangle showing three figures of equal height. By means of slanting lines these figures are made to appear to have different heights. Experiences from early childhood have trained us to interpret the slanting lines as depth.

The next set of illusions, shown in Fig. 1F, are classified as *equivocal figures*. These illustrate the

phenomenon of the *fluctuation* of the process of vision. In (a) six cubes may be seen stacked 3, 2, 1, or seven cubes may be seen stacked 2, 3, 2. In

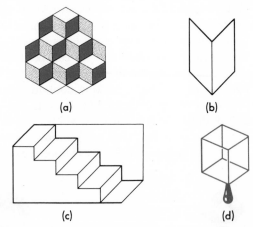

Fig. 1F *Optical illusions illustrating fluctuation of the attention.*

(b) a folded sheet of paper is seen opening either toward or away from the reader. In (c) is a flight of steps seen from above looking down, or from below looking up.

Figure 1F(d) is one of the most interesting of all illusions. To appreciate the effect fully, one must himself perform the experiment with a small wire cube about 1 in. in size. The cube is held by a small handle at one corner and viewed with one eye at a distance of from 1 to 2 ft. By the principle of fluctuation, the observer next tries to make the farthest corner of the cube appear as the nearest corner. When this condition is attained, the cube upon being turned about a horizontal or vertical axis will appear to turn in the opposite direction. A little practice in the fluctuation of the visual senses is required in this experiment, and it is well worth performing.

In Fig. 1G are two pairs of similar figures of

Fig. 1G   *Optical illusions of area.*

equal area. The slanting lines at the ends make the lower figure in each case appear to be larger than the one immediately above. Such figures should be cut from white cardboard and held one above the other. When the upper figure is interchanged with the corresponding lower figure, one figure seems to grow and the other to shrink before your eyes.

In Fig. 1H(a) are two small squares of equal size, a white square on a black background, and a black square on a white background. When an image of this is formed on the retina of the eye, the cones and rods just beyond the white edges are stimulated by those nearby, thus causing the white square to be larger than the black one. This phenomenon is called *irradiation* or *brightness contrast.* A similar phenomenon is illus-

trated in Fig. 1H(b) where gray spots are seen at the intersections of the white lines.

1.6. Color Illusions. There exist a large number of illusions that are classified as *color illusions.*

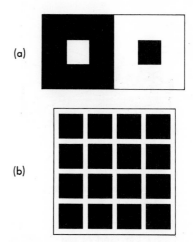

Fig. 1H   *Illustrations of irradiation.*

One of these is diagramed in Fig. 1I. A disk painted black and white as shown will appear to be colored when set rotating at a relatively low speed. The colors to be seen are rather faint

Fig. 1I   *Diagram of an experiment demonstrating color illusions.*

pastel shades of violet, blue, green, yellow, and pink. The speed of the wheel should be from about 4 to 15 revolutions per second (rps). The explanation usually given for the phenomenon is that the retina of the eye responds more quickly to some colors than to others. Since the white image of the disk moves around on the retina and since white light contains all the colors of the rainbow, some colors are perceived at each given spot on the retina sooner than others, and the effect of color is produced.

The second demonstration, as shown in Fig. 1J, illustrates the appearance of color by virtue of

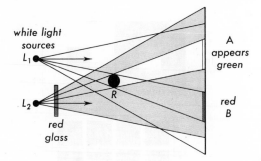

Fig. 1J   *Experimental demonstration of complementary colors attributed to background.*

contrast. If a white patch of light, for example, is seen on a background of red, it will appear to be pale green. If, on the other hand, a white patch is seen on a background of green, it will appear to be pink. The experiment may be performed with two similar arc lights producing white light. Each of these is made to cast a shadow of the same rod R on a white screen. If a piece of red glass is placed in front of light L_2 as shown in the figure, the white patch of light at A will appear to be pale green. If a green glass is inserted in its place, the region A will appear pink. In each case, A receives light from L_1 only and must therefore be really white. Red and green of the proper shades are complementary colors and when they are added together produce white light. The subject of the mixing of colors will be taken up in detail in Chapter 42.

1.7. Circles and Spirals. If this page of the book is held about 1 ft in front of the observer's eyes and the book moved rapidly in a circle about 2 to 3 in. in diameter, the spiral in Fig. 1K will appear to rotate in the direction of motion. A set of alternately dark and light concentric circles will show the same effect, the apparent rotation being due to the persistence of vision.

We have seen in the previous illustrations how some optical illusions break down or diminish under critical inspection. There are others, however, that persist. No amount of staring or thought will teach you to see the circles of Fig. 1L as anything other than spirals.

Fig. 1L   *Circles appear to be spirals.*

A first look at Fig. 1M reveals a three pronged fork, but on inspection the figure has little physical reality.

Fig. 1M   *An illusion in perspective and dimensions.*

1.8. The Trapezoidal Window. One of the most striking optical illusions in perspective is that of a slowly rotating window having the design shown

Fig. 1K   *Illusion of rotation.*

in Fig. 1N. This device is cut from a single sheet of $\frac{1}{4}$-in. plywood, painted white, grey, and black on both sides,* and mounted on a slowly rotating motor-driven shaft.

Viewed in a darkened room, with front and side illumination of the window by two lights shielded from the audience, the window appears to rotate first in one direction, then the other.

An added effect is obtained by hanging a brightly colored ball at the upper corner of the small end. The ball appears to continue around in the same direction while the window appears to oscillate back and forth.

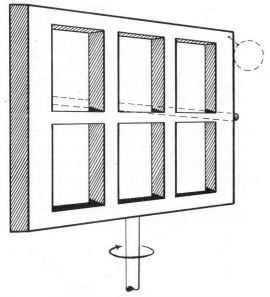

Fig. 1N *Rotating slowly and continuously in one direction, this trapezoidal-shaped window appears to oscillate back and forth.*

Another striking effect is to place a colored rod through the upper center window pane, as shown dotted in the figure. The rod's apparent behavior must be observed to be appreciated.

1.9. The Stroboscopic Effect. In moving pictures, when a wagon with spoked wheels is coming to a stop, the wheels are often noticed to

---

* In constructing such a window make all dimensions proportional to the reproduction in Fig. 1N.

stand still, then turn backward, stop, turn forward, and then stop again. This phenomenon, known as the "stroboscopic effect," is due to interrupted illumination of the moving-picture screen and can be illustrated in many ways. An interesting experiment illustrating the phenomenon is shown in Fig. 1O. Two disks are mounted on the shafts of two separate motors. The smaller disk A with a narrow slot is used to interrupt the light beam illuminating the larger disk. The disk B is green with black circles and dots arranged exactly as shown. Suppose now that disk A makes 16 rps, thus illuminating disk B with 16 short flashes of light per second. Suppose also that B makes only 1 rps, and that one flash of light comes when the disk has the position shown in the figure. If the attention is confined to the circle at position (1), the two enclosed dots are one above the other. When the second flash of light appears, the circle (2) will be in position (1) and the two dots will appear to have shifted slightly clockwise. When the next flash of light comes, the circle (3) will be in position (1) and the two dots will have shifted still farther. This process continued shows that the circles will appear to stand still and the dots to rotate within them.

If the light flashes in any such experiment as the one described above are slower than 16 per second, the illuminated object will appear to flicker badly. If, however, the flashes come at an increasingly higher rate, the flicker will soon disappear entirely and the illumination will seem to be steady. The reason for this is that each retinal image is somehow retained by the vision mechanism for about $\frac{1}{16}$ of a second. This is called the *persistence of vision*.

1.10. Fatigue and Complementary Images. When the eyes are subjected to bright light for some little time, the retina seems to show tiring or *fatigue*. Furthermore, continued subjection of any part of the retina to one particular color causes only those cones sensitive to that color to tire. When the same retinal area is subsequently subjected to white light, the previously inactive cones respond more strongly than those originally stimulated and a complementary color is

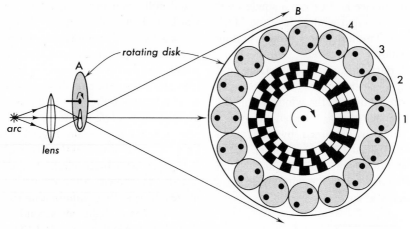

Fig. 1O   *Experimental arrangement for demonstrating the stroboscopic effect.*

seen. The following pairs of colors are complementary to each other:

red – blue-green
blue – yellow
green – magenta
black – white

To observe such colored images, fix the attention on the black star in the lower right-hand corner of the field of the flag in Fig. 1P and keep it there for about 15 to 20 seconds. Then turn the eyes toward a white wall of the room, or toward the open sky, and in one or two seconds the American flag will appear in all of its true colors. Similar effects can be observed with other color photographs.

After-images of this kind are always complementary in color to the original pictures; black becomes white, yellow becomes blue, green becomes magenta, magenta becomes green, etc.

For supplementary reading on optical illusions, see *Am. J. Phys.*, **14,** 104 (1946).

QUESTIONS

1. Briefly explain the difference between a subjective method and an objective method of measuring temperature.

2. How would you measure the length of a table using a subjective method of measurement? Assume you want to determine its length as accurately as possible and you had no ruler.

3. If you had no measuring stick or tape measure, how could you make use of a subjective capability to measure the length of a certain city block?

4. Briefly explain how the subjective method of measurement would enter into any measurement of the length of an automobile. Assume a yard stick or tape measurement is used.

5. In motion pictures the propeller of an airplane coming down the runway seems to stand still, stop, then turn backward. Explain this phenomenon.

6. Explain why the flag shown in Fig. 1P, appears to be red, white, and blue when viewed as an after-image.

7. One end of a board of unknown length is raised higher than the other to form an inclined plane. A ball started from the top is allowed to roll to the bottom. Using subjective methods alone, how would you find (a) the length of the incline, and (b) the number of seconds it takes to get to the bottom?

8. Using match sticks and some quick-drying glue, make a small cube of the kind shown in Fig. 1F(d). When the glue is dry, perform the experiment described in Sec. 1.5 and write a brief description of your observations.

9. Using the pattern of Fig. 1G(a), cut two equivalent figures from a piece of cardboard. Place one above the other, and then interchange their positions. Briefly explain why the top one always seems to be the smaller.

Fig. 1P   *Fatigue images enable the above objects to appear in their natural colors.*

10. Using Fig. 1N as a pattern, cut a trapezoidal window from a $\frac{1}{4}$-in.-thick piece of plywood, a $\frac{1}{8}$-in.-thick sheet of fiber board, or from a thick sheet of cardboard. Take exact measurements from the diagram and make the height about 1–2 ft. Paint or color the black and gray areas exactly as shown, with both sides identical. Mount the window on a metal or wooden rod and use a motor or some other means of turning it slowly. This illusion, viewed from a distance, is quite remarkable.

UNITS OF MEASUREMENT, SPEED, AND VELOCITY

Since physics is a science based upon exact measurement, it is essential that the student first become familiar with several of the more commonly used measuring devices and the units into which each is usually divided. Every measurement, whether it be a distance, a weight, an interval of time, or anything else, requires *two* things: first, a *number;* and second, a *unit*. One might, for example, obtain as the result of the measurement of different distances, *20 feet, 5 miles, 3 rods*, or as the result of the measurement of different weights, *6 pounds, 25 tons, 4½ ounces*, or as the result of the measurement of different time intervals, *7 hours, 26 seconds*, etc. As the result of some experiment or the reading of certain instruments, one might obtain the measurements, *10.7 calories, 90 horsepower, 6 volts, 12 kilowatts*, etc. In each case, the *unit* is just as essential as the *number* expressing the amount.

Although there are numerous different units, each one can be expressed in terms of not more than three special units. These three, called *fundamental units*, are the units of *length, mass*, and *time*. All other units are called *derived units* since, as we shall see later, they can always be written as some combination of the three fundamental units.

There are in general two widely used sets of fundamental units: (a) the *metric*, and (b) the *English*. Throughout the civilized world, scientific observations are nearly always expressed in terms of metric units. This set employs the *standard meter* as the unit of length, the *standard kilogram* as the unit of mass, and the *second* as the unit of time.

2.1. The Standard Meter and Yard. The standard meter is a platinum–iridium bar about 40 in. long which is kept in the vaults of the International Bureau of Weights and Measures near Paris, France. Three facsimiles of this bar are to be found at the United States Bureau of Standards in Washington, D. C. Each of these duplicate copies may be called an *International Prototype Meter* and is now the standard of length in the United States. From these prototypes, all other measuring rods and tapes are standardized.

When the standard meter was first devised, it was intended that it have a length equal to one ten-millionth part of the distance from one of the earth's poles to the equator. Although more recent measurements of the earth's dimensions have shown that the distance from pole to equator is about 10,000,880 *standard meters*, the two groove marks, one on either end of the original platinum–iridium bar, are now taken to be exactly one meter apart.

The standard meter is usually divided into 100 equal parts. Each of these parts is called a *centimeter*.

$$1 \text{ meter} = 100 \text{ centimeters}$$

or, abbreviated,

$$1 \text{ m} = 100 \text{ cm}$$

The centimeter is further divided into ten equal parts. Each of these parts is called a *millimeter* (see Fig. 2A).

$$1 \text{ centimeter} = 10 \text{ millimeters}$$
$$1 \text{ cm} = 10 \text{ mm}$$
$$1 \text{ m} = 1000 \text{ mm}$$

The millimeter is further divided into 1000 equal parts. Each of these parts is called a *micron*.

1 millimeter = 1000 microns
1 mm = 1000 μ

In civil life in the United States the *yard* is used as the standard unit of length. By an act of Congress in 1866 the standard yard to be used legally in the United States was defined as 3600/3937 part of a standard meter. Since the yard is divided into 36 in.,

1 meter = 39.37 inches
1 m = 39.37 in.

With 12 in. to 1 ft,

3 ft = 1 yd
1 ft = 30.48 cm

and   **1 in. = 2.54 cm**

The sizes of the inch and fractions of an inch relative to the centimeter and millimeter, are illustrated in Fig. 2A.

When large distances are to be measured, it is convenient as well as customary to use large units of length. Such units are the *kilometer* in the metric system and the *mile* in the English system. One kilometer is equivalent to 1000 meters, and one mile is equivalent to 5280 ft.

1000 meters = 1 kilometer
1000 m = 1 Km
1 mile = 5280 feet
1 mi = 5280 ft

The relations between units of length in the metric system and those in the English system are given in the following table:

inches

centimeters

Fig. 2A *Diagram comparing the centimeter scale with the inch scale.*

2.2. The Standard Kilogram and Pound. The standard unit of mass is the *kilogram*, a block of platinum also preserved at the International Bureau of Weights and Measures near Paris. Two copies of this kilogram (which may be called International Prototype Kilograms) are kept in the vaults of the U. S. Bureau of Standards. The kilogram is divided into 1000 equal parts called *grams*.

1000 grams = 1 kilogram
1000 g = 1 Kg

The original intent was to base the standard kilogram upon the gram, the gram being the mass of one cubic centimeter of pure water taken at a temperature of four degrees centigrade.

The standard pound is defined in terms of the standard kilogram by the relation that its mass shall equal 0.4536 kilogram.

453.6 g weighs 1 lb

Following this we have the relations

28.35 g weighs 1 oz
1 lb = 16 oz

and

1 ton = 2000 lb

The relative sizes of the kilogram, gram, and pound may be seen in Fig. 2B.

TABLE 2A. CONVERSION FACTORS FOR UNITS OF LENGTH

		Km	m	cm	in.	ft	mi
1 kilometer	=	1	1000	100,000	39370	3280.83	0.62137
1 meter	=	0.00100	1	100	39.370	3.28083	6.21×10^{-4}
1 centimeter	=	1.0×10^{-5}	0.0100	1	0.39370	0.032808	6.21×10^{-6}
1 inch	=	2.54×10^{-5}	0.02540	2.5400	1	0.08333	1.58×10^{-5}
1 foot	=	3.05×10^{-4}	0.30480	30.480	12	1	1.89×10^{-4}
1 mile	=	1.60935	1609.35	160935	63360	5280	1

Fig. 2B *The mass of a standard kilogram is 2.2 times the mass of a standard pound weight.*

2.3. Time and the Mean Solar Day. Three kinds of time are always recognized by astronomers: first, *sidereal time;* second, *apparent solar time;* and third, *mean solar time.* The last is the time used in civil life. If at any given point on the earth's surface we adjust the gnomon of a sundial to lie in the North and South vertical plane, the time interval between two successive transits of the sun's shadow over the 12 o'clock mark is called the *apparent solar day.* For several reasons, one being that the earth's orbit around the sun is elliptical, this interval of time varies slightly from day to day. An apparent solar day in December is about one minute longer than an apparent solar day in September. It is clear, therefore, why in this day of accurate timepieces we do not regulate our clocks to apparent solar time.

The *average* length of all apparent solar days throughout a solar year is called the *mean solar day.* Since there are 3600 seconds in one hour, 24 hours in one day, and 365.241 days in one tropical year, there are approximately $3600 \times 24 \times 365.241$, or 31,556,822 seconds in one year. The *tropical year* is defined as the time between two successive passages of the vernal equinox by the sun. Since tropical years vary slightly, the *second* is defined as*

$$\frac{1}{31,556,825.9747} \text{ part of tropical year 1900}$$

The second is abbreviated s.

For astronomical purposes, a different time

* International standard adopted on October 14, 1960, by the General Conference on Weights and Measures, at Paris, France.

scale known as sidereal time is used. There is one more sidereal day in one solar year than there are mean solar days. One solar year equals 366.241 sidereal days. The reason for the additional day is that in making one complete turn around the sun in its orbit the earth has actually made 366.241 rotations with respect to the fixed stars. The sidereal second as ticked off by an astronomical clock is therefore slightly shorter than the second given by an ordinary clock keeping mean solar time.

2.4. Metric Units. Nearly all scientific experiments, in the United States as well as abroad, are performed using metric units. In these units distance is usually measured in millimeters, centimeters, meters, or kilometers; mass is measured in grams or kilograms; and time is measured in seconds, minutes, or hours. In metric units the abbreviation *cgs* means *centimeter, gram, second;* and *mks* means *meter, kilogram, second.*

The English system, as already referred to, uses the foot, yard, and mile as units of length; the ounce, pound, and ton as units of force; and the second as the unit of time. We Americans inherited the English system with all of its cumbersome fractions, and because it is so firmly ingrained in our civil life it will be a difficult task ever to change over completely to the simpler metric system. There is a strong movement today, however, advocating such a change.

The chief advantage of metric units over English units is that all units are divided into 10 or 100 parts. This enables fractional distances and masses to be expressed as decimals. Decimals, it is well known, are easier to manipulate in the addition, subtraction, multiplication, and division of two or more quantities.

2.5. Speed. Mechanics is defined as that branch of physics dealing with the *motions* or *states* of material bodies. It is generally divided into two parts: the first called *kinematics*, dealing with various kinds of motion, and the second called *dynamics*, dealing with the causes for changes in motion. Dynamics is further divided into two parts, *statics* and *kinetics*.

While statics deals with bodies in a state of equilibrium, a condition brought about by balanced forces, kinetics deals with changes in motion brought about by one or more un-balanced forces. As an introduction to the kinematics of motion, the elementary concepts of speed and velocity will be taken up first.

Speed is defined as the time rate of change of position. Change of position means the *distance traveled*, and by time rate we are referring to the *elapsed time*. As an equation

$$\text{speed} = \frac{\text{change of position}}{\text{elapsed time}} \qquad (2a)$$

Change of position is illustrated in Fig. 2C. A car traveling with uniform speed along a straight

Fig. 2C   *Diagram of a body moving with constant speed and constant velocity.*

line passes the point A at one instant of time t_1 and the point B at some later instant of time t_2. If the positions of points A and B are measured from some point of origin O, the distances can be expressed as x_1 and x_2, respectively.

With these symbols, the change in position Δx is equal to $x_2 - x_1$, and the elapsed time of travel Δt is equal to $t_2 - t_1$.

$$\Delta x = x_2 - x_1$$
$$\Delta t = t_2 - t_1$$

In symbols we may therefore write Eq.(2a), as

$$v = \frac{\Delta x}{\Delta t} \qquad (2b)$$

where v is the speed, Δx is the *change in position*, and Δt is the *elapsed time* or *time of travel*.

If we measure distances and times from the point A as origin, we see that $x_1 = 0$, and $t_1 = 0$, and Eq.(2b) can be written $v = x_2/t_2$, or more simply

$$v = \frac{x}{t} \qquad (2c)$$

it being understood that x stands for Δx the distance traveled, and t stands for Δt the elapsed time interval.

Example 1. A man takes 2 hr to drive his car to a distant city 120 mi away. What is his speed?

Solution. Here the distance traveled $\Delta x = 120$ mi, and the time interval $\Delta t = 2$ hr. The speed therefore, using Eq. 2(c), is

$$v = \frac{120 \text{ mi}}{2 \text{ hr}} = 60 \frac{\text{mi}}{\text{hr}}$$

The answer is *60 mi/hr.* The units are just as important as the numbers and must be included in the answer.

If, in the answer to the above example, the time 1 hr in the denominator is replaced by its equivalent of 3600s, a speed of 60 mi/hr becomes

$$60 \frac{\text{mi}}{\text{hr}} = 60 \frac{\text{mi}}{3600 \text{ s}} = 0.0167 \frac{\text{mi}}{\text{s}} \qquad (2d)$$

If at the same time the distance 1 mi in the numerator is replaced by its equivalent of 5280 ft,

$$60 \frac{\text{mi}}{\text{hr}} = 60 \frac{5280 \text{ ft}}{3600 \text{ s}} = 88 \frac{\text{ft}}{\text{s}} \qquad (2e)$$

All three of the above answers, 60 mi/hr, 0.0167 mi/s, and 88 ft/s, are exactly equal; they are only expressed in different units. This last derived result that 60 mi/hr is equivalent to 88 ft/s should be memorized, as it is very useful in the solving of many practical problems. A speed of 120 mi/hr, for example, is equivalent to 2×88 or 176 ft/s, while a speed of 30 mi/hr is equivalent to $\frac{1}{2} \times 88$ or 44 ft/s.

Example 2. A toy train running along a straight track at a constant speed requires 8 s to travel a distance of 20 m. Find the speed.

Solution. Since $x = 20$ m and $t = 8$ s, the speed

$$v = \frac{20 \text{ m}}{8 \text{ s}} = 2.5 \frac{\text{m}}{\text{s}}$$

The answer is read *two point five meters per second.* To change this answer to centimeters per second, the unit 1 m in the numerator is changed to 100 cm, and the answer becomes

$$v = 2.5 \frac{\text{m}}{\text{s}} = 2.5 \frac{100 \text{ cm}}{\text{s}} = 250 \frac{\text{cm}}{\text{s}}$$

It should be noted that all units are indicated by roman letters, while all symbols for measurable quantities are printed in italics.

2.6. Constant (or Uniform) Speed. *A body traveling equal distances in equal intervals of time, is moving with constant speed.* Suppose, as a demonstration of the scientific method, we perform an experiment of the kind shown in Fig. 2D. A toy automobile is pulled across the

Fig. 2D *Experimental arrangement for measuring the speed of a car.*

table top by means of a cord wrapped around a drum, and a stopclock is used to measure the time. A small synchronous motor M, with a geared-down shaft making 1 rps, and a drum about 1 in. in diameter makes a suitable power unit.

Markers A and B are located a short distance apart, and the distance x between them is measured with a meter stick. The car is started, and, as it passes marker A, the clock is started; as it passes marker B, the clock is stopped. The time t in seconds, as read on the clock, is then recorded. This procedure should be repeated with the markers farther and farther apart, and the data recorded in a table. Suppose this experiment has now been performed at five different distances and the data recorded are those shown in the first three columns of Table 2B.

TABLE 2B. RECORDED DATA FOR CAR

Trial	Distance x (cm)	Time t (s)	Speed v (cm/s)
1	39.8	5.3	7.51
2	86.2	11.5	7.50
3	108.8	14.5	7.53
4	141.6	18.9	7.49
5	174.2	23.2	7.51

To find how x and t are related to each other, it is most informative to plot a graph of the two measured quantities. If we plot x vertically

and t horizontally, as shown in Fig. 2E, we obtain the points shown as X's. When a smooth line is drawn through these points it is observed to be a straight line. Furthermore, this straight

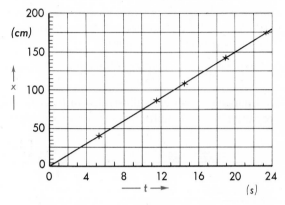

Fig. 2E *Graph of the data recorded in the car experiment.*

line passes through the origin $x = 0$ and $t = 0$. From the fact that the graph is a straight line, one concludes that the two quantities x and t are directly proportional to each other.

$$x \propto t$$

To make an equation of this, the proportionality sign is replaced by an equal sign, and a proportionality constant inserted on the right. Calling this constant v, we obtain

$$\boxed{x = vt} \qquad (2f)$$

To find the value of this constant which we call the speed, divide both sides of the equation by t and obtain

$$\frac{x}{t} = v$$

The next step is to take each value of x in Table 2B and divide by the corresponding value of t. When this is done for each of the five trials, a value near 7.50 cm/s is obtained in all cases. Note that the units are divided one by the other to obtain cm/s as shown in the last column. This then is the speed of the car, and, since all trials give nearly the same result, we say that the speed is constant, or uniform.

That the motion of the car follows the definition of constant speed, as stated at the beginning of this section, may be seen from the graph. In 10 seconds the distance traveled is 75 cm. During the next 10 seconds the distance traveled is 75 cm, making the total distance 150 cm. *In equal time intervals, the car travels equal distances.* Although this is a simple experiment illustrating a simple principle in mechanics, its purpose is that of illustrating the scientific method, namely, of making measurements of a given phenomenon and, from the recorded observations, of finding the simplest relations between them.

2.7. Distance Traveled. If the speed of a body is known, the distance traveled can be calculated for any given interval of time.

$$x = vt \tag{2f}$$

Example 3. If a body moves with a speed of 45 cm/s, how far will it travel in 2 min?
Solution. The distance traveled can be determined by Eq. (2f).

$$x = 45 \frac{cm}{s} \times 2 \text{ min} = 90 \frac{cm \text{ min}}{s}$$

In order to eliminate *time* units in this answer, they must both be expressed in the same units. To do this, the minutes may be changed to seconds as follows:

$$x = 45 \frac{cm}{s} \times 120 \text{ s} = 5400 \text{ cm}$$

Note that seconds in the numerator and seconds in the denominator are eliminated by the property of 1, i.e., s/s = 1. This leaves *cm* in the answer as the unit of length. This illustrates a common practice that should be followed in the solving of all problems. Always express like quantities in the same units.

Dividing both sides of Eq.(2f) by v we obtain

$$t = \frac{x}{v} \tag{2g}$$

This is an equation for the time of travel in terms of x and v.

Example 4. If a car travels with an average speed of 30 mi/hr, how long will it take to go 175 mi?
Solution. Using Eq. (2g), we find

$$t = \frac{x}{v} = \frac{175 \text{ mi}}{30 \text{ mi/hr}} = 5.83 \text{ hr}$$

2.8. Vectors and Scalars. Nearly all physical measurements, whether they are made with the simplest of instruments or with the most complex of apparatus, may be classified as *vector* or *scalar* quantities. *Measurable quantities that have magnitude and direction are called vectors.* Examples of vector quantities are *displacement*, *velocity*, *acceleration*, and *force*. *Measurable quantities that have magnitude only are called scalars.* Examples of scalar quantities are *speed*, *volume*, *area*, and *mass*.

The importance of this seemingly trivial distinction between quantities that have direction and those that do not, is realized when in solving certain problems the simple process of the addition of two or more like quantities becomes necessary.

No difficulty is generally encountered with scalars since such quantities are added algebraically. For example, in the addition of volumes, the sum of 2 gal and 3 gal is 5 gal. The addition of two vectors, on the other hand, is more complicated and requires a special process called *vector addition*. (This process will be treated in detail in Chap. 6.)

2.9. Speed and Velocity. The terms *speed* and *velocity* are often used synonymously. Strictly speaking, however, *speed is a scalar quantity and velocity is a vector quantity*.

Speed is a term applied only to the magnitude of velocity and does not specify the direction of motion. In moving along a straight line, *speed* and *velocity* are numerically equal to each other. If, however, the speed along a curved path is constant, the velocity is not considered to be constant because of its changing direction.

When a body moves with constant speed along a straight line whose direction is specified, it is customary to speak of its *velocity*. Movement along a straight or curved path, with no reference being made to direction, is properly referred to as *speed*.

A body moving along the same straight line, traveling equal distances in equal intervals of time, is moving with constant velocity.

Speed and velocity always have the *dimensions* of *length divided by time*, i.e., *L/T*, and both are given by the Eqs.(2a) through (2g).

TABLE 2C. CONVERSION FACTORS FOR SPEED

Speed		m/s	ft/s	Km/hr	mi/hr	knots
1 m/s	=	1	3,281	3.600	2.240	1.940
1 ft/s	=	0.30480	1	1.0973	0.6818	0.5921
1 Km/hr	=	0.27778	0.9113	1	0.6214	0.5396
1 mi/hr	=	0.44704	1.4667	1.6093	1	0.8684
1 knot	=	0.51480	1.689	1.853	1.152	1

A set of conversion factors as given in Table 2C can be very useful in converting any speed or velocity in one set of units to the speed or velocity in another set.

Example 5. Change 30 mi/hr to kilometers per hour.

Solution. From Table 2C, 1 mi/hr in the left-hand column is (read across to the fourth column) equal to 1.6093 Km/hr. Therefore,

$$30 \times 1.6093 = 48.279 \frac{Km}{hr}$$

Upon dropping off the last two figures, we find the answer, to three significant figures:

$$30 \frac{mi}{hr} = 48.3 \frac{Km}{hr}$$

The *knot* is a nautical unit of speed, about 15% greater than speed in miles per hour. It is *not* correct to say the speed of a ship is 10 10 knots/hr; it is correct to say the speed is 10 knots.

2.10. Constant and Variable Velocity. In mechanics, it is often convenient to neglect the size and shape of a body and to consider its motion as that of a small *particle* of negligible size. For example, in describing the motion of an airplane flying between two cities, it is not necessary to give a detailed description of the plane in order to give its position and progress. Hence, it is customary to speak of the motion of a body as the motion of a particle.

If the statement is made that a particle travels 30 mi in 1 hr, it does not necessarily mean that its speed or velocity is constant. Moving due East in a straight line, the particle either moved with a *constant velocity* or with a *variable velocity*. A constant velocity is defined as one in which

equal displacements are traversed in equal intervals of time and the direction is at all times that of the same straight line. In other words, the distance traveled in any 1 second is equal to that traveled in any other second.

A particle has a *variable velocity* when, in equal intervals of time, its displacements are unequal. In such cases it is customary to speak of the *average velocity*. Average velocity, $\bar{v}$, is defined by

$$\bar{v} = \frac{x}{t} \tag{2h}$$

where t is the total time required to travel the total distance x.

2.11. Curvilinear Motion. Motion along a curved path is called curvilinear motion. When a particle moves along a curved path as shown in Fig. 2F, it may have a constant or variable

Fig. 2F   *Motion along a curved path.*

speed. The term *speed* is used here in place of velocity since the path is not straight. A *constant speed* is defined as one in which the distances traveled in equal intervals of time are equal, the distances being measured along the curved path.

A *variable speed* means that the distances traveled in equal intervals of time are different. It follows from these definitions, by comparison with those for linear motion in the preceding section, that all of the equations in this chapter apply equally well to constant and average speed.

2.12. Instantaneous Velocity. In describing the curvilinear motion of a particle, it sometimes

Fig. 2G   *Arrows indicate instantaneous velocity.*

becomes necessary to specify its *instantaneous velocity.* As shown in **Fig. 2G**, the instantaneous velocity of a particle at any given point in its path is obtained by drawing a tangent to the curve at the point in question. The magnitude of the instantaneous velocity is equal to the speed of the particle as it passes that point, and the direction is that of the tangent to the curve at that point.

PROBLEMS

The first 10 problems are exercises in the use of *powers of ten* notation. For an explanation see Appendix XIII.

1. Write each of the following in powers of ten notation, and then express the answers in powers of ten notation: (a) $2000 \times 40,000$, (b) $16,000 \times 0.005$, (c) $690 \times 0.004 \div 0.0023$, (d) $0.0048 \times 0.00006 \div 0.0016$.

2. Solve each of the following problems and find the answers in powers of ten notation: (a) $6 \times 10^4 \times 5 \times 10^7$, (b) $4.8 \times 10^5 \times 5.5 \times 10^{-2}$, (c) $4.6 \times 10^4 \times 2.5 \times 10^5 \div 2 \times 10^{-3}$, (d) $1.2 \times 10^{-4} \times 5 \times 10^{12} \div 4 \times 10^3$. [*Ans.* (a) 3×10^{12}, (b) 2.64×10^4, (c) 5.75×10^{12}, (d) 1.5×10^5.]

3. The mass of the planet Jupiter is 1.9×10^{27} Kg. Find the ratio of the mass of Jupiter to the mass of the Earth (see Fig. 7B).

4. Calculate the number of seconds in one year and express the answer in powers of ten. Give your answer to three significant figures. [*Ans.* 3.16×10^7 s.]

5. Calculate the number of seconds in a man's lifetime if he lives to be 100 years old.

6. Calculate the distance to the moon in meters if the distance in miles is 239,000. [*Ans.* 3.85×10^8 m.]

7. The following measurements were made in the performance of a laboratory experiment: $m = 5$ Kg, $v = 24$ m/s, and $t = 6$ s. If the known relation between these quantities is given by $Ft = mv$, what is the experimental value of F?

8. The following values have been determined by a laboratory experiment: $m = 9.1 \times 10^{-31}$ Kg, $c = 3 \times 10^8$ m/s, and $e = 1.6 \times 10^{-19}$ coulomb. If the known relation between these quantities is given by $Ve = mc^2$, find the value of V. [*Ans.* $V = 5.12 \times 10^5$ Kg m²/s² coulomb.]

9. Find the difference between 100 miles and 100 kilometers, in (a) miles, and (b) kilometers.

10. Find the circumference of the earth in meters if it were a perfect sphere and the radius were 3960 mi. [*Ans.* 4.00×10^7 m.]

11. In the Olympic games of 1960 the 1600-meter relay was won by the United States in 3 min 2.2 s. Find the average speed of the four runners in m/s.

12. In the 1960 Olympic games the 50,000 meter walk was won by Donald Thompson of Great Britain in 4 hr 26 min and 30 s. Find the average speed in (a) m/s, and (b) mi/hr. [*Ans.* (a) 3.13 m/s, (b) 7.01 mi/hr.]

13. In the 1960 Olympic games all but one of the following races set a new world record. The times for these races were: 100 m in 10.2 s, 200 m in 20.5 s, 400 m in 44.9 s, 800 m in 1 min 46.3 s, 1500 m in 3 min 35.6 s, 5000 m in 13 min 43.4 s, and 10,000 m in 28 min 32.2 s. (a) Calculate the average speed of each runner in m/s. (b) Make a graph of these results by plotting speed vertically, and distance horizontally.

14. An astronaut in a space capsule circles the earth 440 miles above the surface in 1 hr 38.8 min. If the earth's radius is 3960 mi, find the speed of the astronaut in (a) mi/hr, (b) mi/s, and (c) m/s. [*Ans.* (a) 16,800 mi/hr, (b) 4.67 mi/s, (c) 7,510 m/s.]

15. In the 1960 Olympic games the men's 400-meter free-style swimming race was won by Murray Rose of Australia in 4 min 18.3 s. Find the average speed in (a) m/s, and (b) mi/hr.

16. How long will it take a ship traveling at 18 knots to go 1000 mi? [*Ans.* 48.2 hr.]

17. Find the cruising range of a plane if its fuel tank contains 50 gal of gasoline. Assume that a cruising speed of 135 mi/hr requires 10.5 gal/hr.

18. A jet passenger plane crosses the United States from San Francisco to Washington, D.C., a distance of 2800 mi, in 4 hr 22 min. Calculate the average speed (a) in mi/hr, and (b) m/s. [*Ans.* (a) 641 mi/hr, (b) 286 m/s.]

19. How long will it take a ship traveling at 22 knots to sail from San Francisco to Hawaii, a distance of 2200 mi?

20. An automobile leaving a railroad station averages 45 mi/hr along a highway that follows a railroad track. If a train leaves the station one-half hour later and travels at the rate of 60 mi/hr, (a) how much time will it take the train to overtake the automobile? (b) What will be the distance traveled? [*Ans.* (a) 1.5 hr, (b) 90 mi.]

21. A propeller-driven plane leaving a New York airport for Los Angeles maintains a constant speed of 385 mi/hr. A jet plane leaving the same airport 1 hr later has a speed of 625 mi/hr. (a) How long will it take the second plane to overtake the first plane, and (b) how far will they both have traveled?

22. Two airplanes leave the same airport at the same

time to fly to a distant city. One has a speed of 320 mi/hr and the other a speed of 480 mi/hr. If the faster plane arrives at the distant city 45 min ahead of the other, (a) how far is it to the distant city, and (b) what are the two flight times? [*Ans.* (a) 720 mi, (b) 1.5 hr; 2.25 hr.]

23. Two planes leave the same airport at the same time to fly to the same distant city. One has a speed of 360 mi/hr, and the other a speed of 520 mi/hr. How long will it take the faster plane to get 200 mi ahead of the other?

ACCELERATION

One of the most important concepts in mechanics is that part of kinematics called *acceleration*. Acceleration refers to the speeding up and slowing down of an object and is concerned with changes in speed and velocity.

3.1. Uniform Acceleration, or Constant Acceleration. *Acceleration is defined as the time rate of change of velocity.* A car "picking up speed" has a *positive acceleration*, while another car slowing down has a *negative acceleration*. If standing still or moving with constant velocity a car has zero acceleration.

By the above definition of acceleration we may write as an equation

$$\text{acceleration} = \frac{\text{change in velocity}}{\text{elapsed time}} \qquad (3a)$$

Consider as an illustration of accelerated motion the car shown in Fig. 3A. Due to a constantly acting force, exerted by the motor through the drive wheels, this car is continually accelerated as it moves along the straight line AB. As it passes A it has a relatively low velocity v_0, while farther along its path at the point B it is moving faster and has a velocity v. With this symbolism, v_0 is called the *initial velocity*, and v is called the *final velocity*.

If we let Δv represent the change in velocity, we can write

$$\Delta v = v - v_0 \qquad (3b)$$

If the instant the car passes point A is called the *initial time* t_0, and the instant the car passes point B is called the *final time* t, the elapsed time Δt is given by

$$\Delta t = t - t_0 \qquad (3c)$$

By letting a represent the acceleration we can now write Eq.(3a) in the form,

$$a = \frac{\Delta v}{\Delta t} \qquad (3d)$$

or,

$$a = \frac{v - v_0}{t - t_0} \qquad (3e)$$

In making *time* measurements one would normally start his timer when the car passed point A and stop it when it passed point B. When this is done $t_0 = 0$, and Eq.(3d) becomes

$$a = \frac{v - v_0}{t} \qquad (3f)$$

Example 1. Suppose at A, in Fig. 3A, that the velocity of the car is 20 ft/s, that at B it has increased

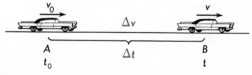

Fig. 3A   *A car is accelerated for a period of time Δt.*

to 40 ft/s, and that it takes 4 s to go from A to B. What is the acceleration?

Solution. By direct substitution in Eq. (3f), we obtain

$$a = \frac{40 \text{ ft/s} - 20 \text{ ft/s}}{4 \text{ s}} = \frac{20 \text{ ft/s}}{4 \text{ s}} = 5 \frac{\text{ft}}{\text{s s}}$$

The answer is read *five feet per second per second* and means that the velocity increases 5 ft/s every second of time. Initially, that is at

Fig. 3B *Diagram showing instantaneous velocity at end of each second for uniformly accelerated car (see Example 1).*

time $t_0 = 0$, the velocity as shown in Fig. 3B is 20 ft/s. An increase of 5 ft/s every second means that at the end of 1 s the velocity is 25 ft/s, at the end of 2 s it is 30 ft/s, at the end of 3 s it is 35 ft/s, and at the end of 4 s it is 40 ft/s. Uniform or constant acceleration is, therefore, one in which *the velocity changes by equal amounts in equal intervals of time.*

3.2. Negative Acceleration. When a body is slowing down, the initial velocity is greater than the final velocity, and the acceleration as given by Eq.(3a) is negative.

Example 2. In going up a long steep hill a car slows down from 60 mi/hr to 30 mi/hr in 2 min. Find the acceleration.

Solution. Substitute the foregoing values in Eq. (3f); then

$$a = \frac{30 \text{ mi/hr} - 60 \text{ mi/hr}}{2 \text{ min}} = -15 \frac{\text{mi}}{\text{hr min}}$$

The velocity thus decreases by 15 mi/hr each minute of time. During the first minute it drops from 60 mi/hr to 45 mi/hr, and during the next minute from 45 mi/hr to 30 mi/hr.

The above answer, as written, has two different units of time in the denominator. It can be left this way or changed to the same units as follows: replace 1 hr in the denominator by its equality, 60 min, so that

$$a = -15 \frac{\text{mi}}{60 \text{ min min}} = -0.25 \frac{\text{mi}}{\text{min}^2}$$

To express this answer in feet and seconds, 1 mi in the numerator is replaced by its equivalent, 5280 ft, and (1 min)² in the denominator by (60 s)², to give

$$a = -0.25 \frac{5280 \text{ ft}}{3600 \text{ s}^2} = -0.367 \frac{\text{ft}}{\text{s}^2}$$

This answer is read *minus zero point three six seven feet per second per second,* or *per second squared.*

3.3. Distance Traveled during Uniform Acceleration. As a demonstration of the scientific method we may perform an experiment of the kind shown in Fig. 3C. Here a toy truck T with

Fig. 3C *Demonstration experiment with a toy truck.*

ball-bearing, steel-rimmed wheels is shown free to roll with a minimum amount of friction along a level glass plate.

Uniform acceleration is brought about by a thin cord passing over two pulleys P_1 and P_2 to a small mass m. We now wish to accelerate the truck and find the relation between the *distance traveled* and the *time of travel*. Markers A and B are located a short distance apart, and the distance x between them is measured with a meter stick. With the front bumper at marker A, the truck is released and the clock is started. As the truck reaches marker B, the clock is stopped and the time is recorded. This procedure should be repeated with the markers farther and farther apart, and the data recorded in a table. Suppose this experiment has been performed at five different distances and the data recorded are as shown in the first three columns of Table 3A.

To find how x and t are related to each other, we can follow the procedure used in Chapter 2, namely, that of plotting a graph of the measured quantities. If we plot x vertically and t horizontally as shown in the graph in Fig. 3D, we obtain the points marked X. When a smooth

TABLE 3A. RECORDED DATA FOR TRUCK

Trial	Distance x (cm)	Time t (s)	x/t^2 (cm/s²)
1	17.5	1.6	6.8
2	39.2	2.4	6.8
3	98.1	3.8	6.8
4	163.4	4.9	6.8
5	213.3	5.6	6.8

line is drawn through these points, it is definitely not a straight line. The curve must be drawn through the origin $x = 0$ and $t = 0$, since this is an observed point. In zero time, the distance traveled is zero.

Fig. 3E *Straight-line graph for the toy-truck experiment.*

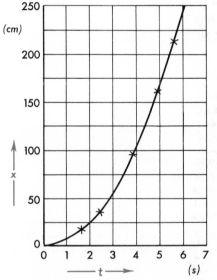

Fig. 3D *Graph of measurements made with a toy truck.*

Since the graph does not yield a straight line, x is not proportional to t. The problem then becomes one of seeing if either or both of the measured quantities can be modified to produce a straight-line graph. A few trials of plotting such quantities as $2x$, x^2, $\sqrt{x}$, $2t$, t^2, $\sqrt{t}$, etc., will show that if x is plotted against t^2, a straight line like that shown in Fig. 3E will be the result. From this graph we can conclude that x is proportional to t^2, and we can write

$$x \propto t^2$$

To make an equation of this relation, the proportionality sign is replaced by an equal sign, and a proportionality constant inserted on the right. Calling this constant k, we write

$$x = kt^2$$

To find the value of k in this particular experiment, divide both sides of the equation by t^2 and obtain

$$\frac{x}{t^2} = k$$

If we divide each of the measured values of x in Table 3A with the corresponding value of t^2, we find the values given in column 4.

$$k = 6.8 \frac{\text{cm}}{\text{s}^2}$$

This result we will see in Sec. 3.7 is just one-half the quantity called the acceleration a.

$$a = 2k = 13.6 \frac{\text{cm}}{\text{s}^2}$$

One who is familiar with analytical geometry will recognize the curve at the left in Fig. 3D, as a parabola, and that $x = kt^2$, the equation above, is its algebraic representation.

If this experiment were to be repeated with a different mass m, the graph shown in Fig. 3D could well be expected to change. It will be left for the student to determine by experiment, or by reasoning, what the new graph might look like, and whether the value of k would be different.

3.4. Final Velocity. Return now to the definition of acceleration introduced at the beginning of this chapter. If both sides of Eq.(3f) are multiplied by t,

$$v - v_0 = at$$

Solving for v, we obtain

$$\boxed{v = v_0 + at} \qquad (3g)$$

Here the final velocity v of a body is given as the sum of two terms, the initial velocity v_0 plus the increase in velocity at.

Example 3. A body with an initial velocity of 50 cm/s is subject to an acceleration of 8 cm/s² for 5 s. What is its final velocity?

Solution. Use Eq. (3g). The known quantities for direct substitution are: $v_0 = 50$ cm/s, $a = 8$ cm/s², and $t = 5$ s.

$$v = 50\,\frac{cm}{s} + 8\,\frac{cm}{s^2} \times 5\,s = 50\,\frac{cm}{s} + 40\,\frac{cm}{s} = 90\,\frac{cm}{s}$$

Note that the product at has the dimensions of a velocity; *length* divided by *time*. It can therefore be added to v_0 because it is expressed in the same units (cm divided by s). It is a rule well worth remembering when solving a problem by the substitution of known quantities in an equation, that quantities can be added or subtracted only when they are like quantities; that is, they have the same dimensions and the same units.

3.5. Average Velocity. While the velocity of an accelerated body is continually changing, the distance traveled in any given time t may be described in terms of its *average velocity*. The average velocity of a particle moving with uniform acceleration is given by

$$\bar{v} = \frac{v + v_0}{2} \qquad (3h)$$

The bar over the v indicates an average value. The equation $x = vt$ already given in Chapter 2 to hold for constant velocity, also holds for

uniform acceleration if v is replaced by $\bar{v}$. Thus

$$x = \bar{v}t$$

or

$$\boxed{x = \frac{v + v_0}{2}\,t} \qquad (3i)$$

Example 4. If 5 s are required to increase the velocity of a body from 2 m/s to 5 m/s, what is (a) the average velocity, and (b) the distance traveled?

Solution. The given quantities are $t = 5$ s, $v_0 = 2$ m/s, and $v = 5$ m/s. By direct substitution in Eq.(3h),

$$\bar{v} = \frac{5\,m/s + 2\,m/s}{2} = \frac{7\,m/s}{2} = 3.5\,\frac{m}{s}$$

Substitute this answer in Eq.(3i). Then

$$x = \bar{v}t = 3.5\,\frac{m}{s} \times 5\,s = 17.5\,m$$

For the special case of a body starting from rest, $v_0 = 0$; and Eq.(3h) for the average velocity becomes

$$\bar{v} = \frac{v}{2} \qquad (3j)$$

3.6. Derived Equations. By combining Eq. (3f) with Eq.(3i), a new and useful equation is obtained. To do this each of the two equations is solved for t as the unknown.

$$t = \frac{v - v_0}{a} \quad \text{and} \quad t = \frac{2x}{v + v_0}$$

Since the left-hand sides of these equations are equal, the right-hand sides must be equal. By setting them equal, we obtain

$$\frac{v - v_0}{a} = \frac{2x}{v + v_0}$$

Since the product of the extremes equals the product of the means, we obtain,

$$(v - v_0)(v + v_0) = 2ax$$

Multiplying, and solving for v^2, we obtain

$$v^2 - v_0^2 = 2ax$$

$$\boxed{v^2 = v_0^2 + 2ax} \qquad (3k)$$

Another useful equation is obtained by eliminating v from the same two original equations.

Solving each of the Eqs.(3f) and (3i) for v we obtain separately

$$v = v_0 + at \quad \text{and} \quad v = \frac{2x}{t} - v_0$$

If the right-hand sides of these two equations are set equal to each other, we obtain

$$\frac{2x}{t} - v_0 = v_0 + at$$

Multiplying both sides of the equation by $t/2$, and solving for x, we obtain

$$x = v_0 t + \tfrac{1}{2}at^2 \qquad (3l)$$

These equations, (3k) and (3l), are called *derived equations*. They give no additional information to that given by Eqs.(3f) and (3i); they are only rearrangements of the same quantities. In their new form, however, they are more readily applied to certain types of problems.

Example 5. A train is traveling 15 mi/hr when the throttle is suddenly opened full and kept open for a distance of 1 mi. If the acceleration is 0.5 ft/s², what is the final velocity?

Solution. Since a velocity of 60 mi/hr is equivalent to 88 ft/s, the given velocity of 15 mi/hr is only one-quarter of 60 mi/hr, and is therefore equivalent to 22 ft/s. By direct substitution in Eq.(3k), we obtain

$$v^2 = (22 \text{ ft/s})^2 + 2 \times 0.5 \text{ ft/s}^2 \times 5280 \text{ ft}$$
$$v^2 = 484 \text{ ft}^2/\text{s}^2 + 5280 \text{ ft}^2/\text{s}^2 = 5764 \text{ ft}^2/\text{s}^2$$
$$v = 75.9 \text{ ft/s}$$

3.7. Starting from Rest. When a body starts from rest and undergoes uniform acceleration, the initial velocity v_0 is zero. The acceleration a as defined by Eq.(3f) can therefore be simplified by placing $v_0 = 0$. Making this substitution, we obtain

$$a = \frac{v}{t} \qquad (3m)$$

Solving for v, we obtain

$$v = at \qquad (3n)$$

Example 6. An airplane starting from rest at one end of a runway acquires its take-off speed of 60 mi/hr in 8 s. What is its acceleration?

Solution. The acceleration is obtained from Eq. (3m).

$$a = \frac{60 \text{ mi/hr}}{8 \text{ s}} = 7.5 \frac{\text{mi}}{\text{hr s}}$$

The answer is read *seven point five miles per hour per second.*

Remembering that 60 mi/hr is equivalent to 88 ft/s, we can express this same acceleration as

$$a = \frac{88 \text{ ft/s}}{8 \text{ s}} = 11 \frac{\text{ft}}{\text{s}^2}$$

read *eleven feet per second squared.*

The other equations involving uniformly accelerated motion, and derived in the preceding sections of this chapter, are also simplified if a body starts from rest. With $v_0 = 0$, Eq.(3i) becomes

$$x = \frac{v}{2} t \qquad (3o)$$

Eq. (3k) becomes

$$v^2 = 2ax \qquad (3p)$$

and Eq.(3l) becomes

$$x = \tfrac{1}{2}at^2 \qquad (3q)$$

Compare this last equation with the conclusions reached with the toy-truck experiment in Sec. 3.3. The constant k derived from experiment, and equal to 6.8 cm/s², is just $\tfrac{1}{2}a$.

Because of the importance of the equations developed in this chapter, the student would do well to memorize the four general equations for uniformly accelerated motion, Eqs.(3g), (3i), (3k), and (3l). The special equations need not be memorized, since they are just special cases for starting from rest and are obtained by placing $v_0 = 0$.

TABLE 3B. FORMULAS FOR UNIFORMLY
ACCELERATED MOTION

General Equations	Special Equations
$v = v_0 + at$	$v = at$
$x = \dfrac{v + v_0}{2} t$	$x = \dfrac{v}{2} t$
$v^2 = v_0^2 + 2ax$	$v^2 = 2ax$
$x = v_0 t + \tfrac{1}{2}at^2$	$x = \tfrac{1}{2}at^2$

PROBLEMS*

1. Starting from rest at the end of a runway, a jet airliner acquires its take-off speed of 90 m/s in a time of 52 s. Find (a) the acceleration, (b) the distance traveled, and (c) the speed at the end of the first 30 s.

2. A rocket starting from rest on the launching pad acquires a vertical velocity of 120 m/s in 8.6 s. Find (a) the acceleration, (b) the height above the ground, and (c) the velocity acquired at the end of the first 5 s. [*Ans.* (a) 13.9 m/s², (b) 516 m, (c) 69.7 m/s.]

3. A car starting from rest acquires a speed of 40 m/s in a distance of 80 m. Calculate (a) the time elapsed, (b) the acceleration, and (c) the speed at the end of 3 s.

4. A jet airliner starting from rest at the end of a runway acquires a speed of 180 mi/hr in a distance of 6200 ft. Calculate (a) the time in seconds, (b) the acceleration in ft/s², and (c) the speed acquired at the end of 30 s. [*Ans.* (a) 47.0 s, (b) 5.62 ft/s², (c) 168.6 ft/s.]

5. A car starting from rest acquires a speed of 25 m/s in 10 s, after which it maintains constant speed for 10 s. Find (a) the acceleration, (b) the distance traveled during acceleration, and (c) the total distance traveled.

6. A freight train with a speed of 15 mi/hr at the top of a long down grade acquires a speed of 60 mi/hr when it reaches the bottom of the grade 3 min later. Assuming constant acceleration, find (a) the acceleration in ft/s², (b) the distance traveled during these 3 min, in feet, and (c) the same distance in miles. [*Ans.* (a) 0.367 ft/s², (b) 9900 ft, (c) 1.875 mi.]

7. A passenger car starting from rest has an acceleration of 2 m/s² for 15 s, after which time it continues at constant speed. After 6 s at this constant speed the brakes are applied bringing the car to rest in 8 s. Find (a) the constant speed acquired, (b) the acceleration during the time the brakes are being applied, (c) the distance traveled during the first 15 s, (d) the distance traveled at constant speed, and (e) the distance traveled during the last 8 s.

8. A locomotive starting from rest travels with an acceleration of 2 ft/s² for 8 s. After traveling at the acquired speed for 10 s, the brakes are applied, stopping the locomotive in 6 s. Find (a) the speed acquired as a result of acceleration, (b) the acceleration while the brakes are applied, (c) the distance traveled during acceleration, (d) the distance traveled at constant speed, and (e) the distance traveled while the brakes are applied. [*Ans.* (a) 16 ft/s, (b) −2.67 ft/s², (c) 64 ft, (d) 160 ft, (e) 48 ft.]

9. A shell from a naval gun barrel 3 m long has a muzzle velocity of 820 m/s. Find (a) the average speed of the shell while being accelerated in the gun barrel, (b) the time taken to travel the length of the barrel, and (c) the acceleration. Assume uniform acceleration.

10. A train starting from rest maintains a constant acceleration of 0.28 ft/s². How long will it take to go 1 mi? [*Ans.* 3 min 14 s.]

11. The engine of a train 2000 ft long stands at a road crossing. If the train starts up and maintains an acceleration of 0.18 ft/s², how long must a motorist wait for the end of the train to cross the intersection?

12. A man driving a truck at a constant speed of 20 m/s, suddenly applies the brakes bringing the truck to a stop in 5 s. Find (a) the acceleration, (b) the total distance traveled, (c) the speed at the end of 2 s, and (d) the distance traveled during the first 2 s. [*Ans.* (a) −4 m/s², (b) 50 m, (c) 12 m/s, (d) 32 m.]

13. A jet fighter plane initially at rest is catapulted from an aircraft carrier to a speed of 60 m/s in 3 s. Calculate (a) the acceleration, and (b) the length of the catapult. Assume the aircraft carrier is moving in the same direction at a constant velocity of 15 m/s.

14. A photo-reconnaissance plane, initially at rest, is catapulted from the deck of an aircraft carrier to a speed of 42 m/s in 2.8 s. Calculate (a) the acceleration, and (b) the length of the catapult. [*Ans.* (a) 15 m/s², (b) 58.8 m.]

15. A car starts from rest and undergoes an acceleration of 2.5 m/s². A motorcycle starts from rest at the same point 5 s later, and maintains an acceleration of 5.5 m/s². Find (a) the time it takes the motorcycle to overtake the car, (b) the distance both have traveled, and (c) the speed of the motorcycle the instant it passes.

16. A box accidentally falls from a truck traveling 15 m/s, and slides along the ground for a distance of 45 m. Find, (a) the acceleration, (b) the time to come to rest, and (c) the velocity of the box at the end of 2 s. [*Ans.* (a) −2.5 m/s², (b) 6.0 s. (c) 10 m/s.]

17. A plane coming in for a landing travels a distance of 1200 m along the runway before coming to rest. Assuming constant acceleration and a landing speed of 40 m/s, find (a) the acceleration, (b) the total time for stopping, and (c) the distance traveled during the first 15 s.

18. Starting from rest a plane takes off after traveling 700 m along a runway. If the plane becomes airborne at a speed of 35 m/s, find (a) the acceleration, (b) the total time of take-off, and (c) the distance traveled during the last 2 s. [*Ans.* (a) 0.875 m/s², (b) 40 s, (c) 68.2 m.]

---

* For quadratic equations use $x = (-b \pm \sqrt{b^2 - 4ac})/2a$.

GRAVITY AND
FALLING BODIES

Neglecting friction, all bodies, large and small, fall with the same acceleration. This, the law of falling bodies, is a physical paradox for it contradicts the conclusion the average person might reach from general observations. This is not to be wondered at, for centuries ago the great philosopher Aristotle* (384–322 B.C.) taught that heavy bodies fall proportionately faster than lighter ones.

It took the world nearly 2000 years to produce a challenger of Aristotle's scientific teachings. In the year 1590, Galileo† was pondering over the question of falling bodies and found apparent inconsistencies in Aristotle's teachings. As tests, he is said to have dropped various kinds of objects from different levels of the leaning tower of Pisa and to have timed their fall and measured their velocities.

* Aristotle (384–322 B.C.), famous Greek philosopher, logician, moralist, political thinker, biologist, and founder of literary criticism, spent his early years as a student and fellow worker with Plato. While practically all of Aristotle's teachings concerning physical principles are now known to be erroneous, his contributions to other fields of knowledge have placed him high among the great men of ancient Greece.

† Galileo Galilei (1564–1642), Italian mathematician, astronomer, and experimental physicist, who at the early age of twenty-four wrote a treatise on the center of gravity of solids. This led the following year to his appointment as professor of mathematics at the University of Pisa. A rumor that a Dutch lens grinder had observed that two lenses used together make distant objects appear close at hand led Galileo to construct the first telescope. Successful telescopes of greater and greater magnification enabled him eventually to observe, for the first time, the mountains on the moon, the major satellites of Jupiter, and sunspots. While at Pisa, Galileo carried out many experiments and public demonstrations of principles which laid the foundations of mechanics and the laws of projectiles and falling bodies.

On one occasion, Galileo is alleged to have attracted a large crowd to the leaning tower, where he climbed the spiral staircase to the bell chamber at the top and there through an open archway dropped two stones, one large and one small. These two bodies fell side by side and struck the ground together, thus sounding the death knell of an old hypothesis and the birth of a new era in science.

Whether this particular incident is true or not, the importance of Galileo's many authentic experiments lies not in the fact that they demonstrated the fallacy of Aristotle's reasoning, but that they presented to the world a new and more reliable scientific method, the method of experimentation.

4.1. Gravitation. The principle that all objects fall with the same acceleration can be demonstrated in various ways. One of these is illustrated in Fig. 4A where two steel balls, one large and one small, are supported in the groove of a wooden block 10 or 20 ft above the ground. When the block is tipped by pulling the cord, both balls fall together and strike the ground together. Dropped from a height of 16 ft, the time of fall is just 1 sec. The shaded circles in the figure show the position of the two bodies at the end of each quarter second.

If the balls in the experiment are replaced by two marbles of the same size, one steel and the other wood, they too will fall side by side and strike the ground together. In this case, the steel marble weighs fifteen times as much as the wood. (Density of steel 7.8 g/cm³; density of wood, 0.5 g/cm³.)

The question of air friction usually arises in

this latter experiment, for careful observation will show that the wooden ball lags ever so slightly behind the steel ball. This lagging due to air friction increases the farther they fall, and

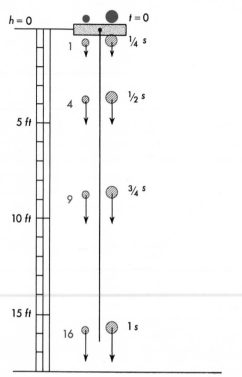

Fig. 4A *All bodies falling freely under the constant pull of gravity fall a distance of 16 ft in the first second.*

is even more pronounced when a still lighter object, like a feather or leaf, is allowed to fall at the same time. Due to its large surface area, a feather or leaf flutters to the ground, being held back by the large amount of air that must be pushed aside to let it by.

In the absence of air, even a feather will fall with the acceleration of a solid steel ball. An experiment illustrating just this is shown in Fig. 4B. A long glass cylinder containing a feather and silver coin is connected by a flexible tube to a vacuum pump. If after evacuation the tube is turned upside down, the feather and the coin will be observed to fall together. When the air is once more admitted to the cylinder, the feather will again flutter slowly to the bottom.

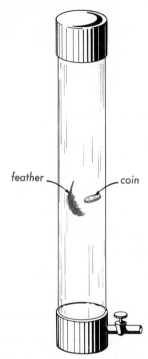

Fig. 4B *In a vacuum, a feather and coin fall with the same acceleration and strike the bottom together.*

In the absence of air friction, all bodies fall with the same acceleration.

In the treatment of falling bodies given in the remainder of this chapter, air friction is entirely neglected. The formulas presented and used in working problems are known to hold only approximately. In most practical cases, however, the calculated results are so nearly realized experimentally that corrections for air friction need only be made where the distances and velocities involved are large. A detailed discussion of the effects of air friction on falling bodies is given in Chapter 8.

4.2. Free Fall. Let us perform an experiment on free fall and, by making quantitative measurements, apply the graphical method of analysis to determine a relation between *distance* and *time of fall*. The experimental arrangement to be used is shown in Fig. 4C. A small steel ball is dropped from different fixed positions, and its time of fall is determined for each distance. Because the time of fall is less than a second, for the heights to be used, an electrically operated stop-clock

Fig. 4C   *Falling-body experiment.*

with one-hundredth of a second divisions around its dial is used. To reduce the subjective errors introduced by the observers' having to start and stop the clock, electric switching is employed. Repeated falls from the same height will then show that interpolations between marks on the clock dial are significant, and the time averages can be given to thousandths of a second.

When the switch K is in position A, an electric current supplied by the battery C energizes the electromagnet E and holds the steel ball suspended ready for dropping. When switch K is snapped to position B, the electromagnet circuit is opened, releasing the ball, and the clock circuit is closed, starting the clock. When the ball strikes the lower switch L, contacts D are instantly opened, stopping the clock. The time t is then recorded, along with the distance of fall h. By dropping the ball a number of times, the slight differences will not only demonstrate the reliability of the timing mechanism but enable good average values to be obtained.

This procedure should be repeated with the electromagnet higher and higher, and the measurements of distance and time recorded in a table. Suppose this experiment has been performed at five different heights and the data recorded as shown in Table 4A.

TABLE 4A. RECORDED DATA FOR THE FREELY
FALLING STEEL BALL

Trial	Distance h (m)	Time t (s)
1	0.356	0.270
2	0.824	0.410
3	1.262	0.508
4	1.867	0.616
5	2.362	0.694

To see how h and t are related to each other, we shall follow the analytical method described in the preceding chapter. First we plot h vertically and t horizontally, as shown in Fig. 4D.

Fig. 4D   *Graph for the freely falling body experiment.*

When a smooth line is drawn through these points (dots with circles), the curve obtained has the general appearance of a parabola. Taking the same steps described in detail in Sec. 3.3, we next try plotting h against t^2, as shown in Fig. 4E. The fact that this graph yields a straight line shows that h is proportional to t^2.

$$h \propto t^2$$

Replacing the proportionality sign by an equal sign, and putting in a proportionality constant, we obtain

$$h = kt^2 \qquad (4a)$$

This result shows clearly that, with little or no air friction, a falling body has a uniform down-

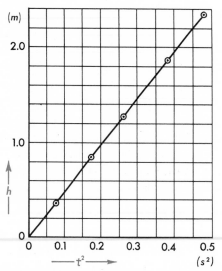

Fig. 4E   *Straight-line graph for free-fall experiment.*

ward acceleration, and that this acceleration is given by an equation of the form of Eq.(3q).

$$h = \tfrac{1}{2}at^2$$

For free fall it is convenient to represent the acceleration due to gravity by the letter g. Starting from rest,

$$\boxed{h = \tfrac{1}{2}gt^2} \qquad (4b)$$

for free fall only

To determine the value of g from the above experiment, we first solve Eq.(4b) for g.

$$g = \frac{2h}{t^2} \qquad (4c)$$

The result of substituting values of h and t from Table 4A, in Eq.(4c), is shown in Table 4B.

The average value of these five determinations of the acceleration due to gravity is

$$g = 9.80 \, \frac{m}{s^2}$$

TABLE 4B. CALCULATED RESULTS OF FREE FALL EXPERIMENT

Trial	Acceleration g (m/s²)
1	9.77
2	9.80
3	9.78
4	9.84
5	9.81

When different-sized masses are used in an experiment of this kind, the final result, within the limits of experimental error, is the same. It is for this reason that the special letter g is often used in formulas to represent free-fall acceleration.

If for example an object falls from rest and we wish to calculate the velocity acquired by falling a distance h, Eq.(3p) may be used. Replacing a by g, and x by h, we obtain,

$$v^2 = 2gh$$

which, upon taking the square roots of both sides, becomes

$$\boxed{v = \sqrt{2gh}} \qquad (4d)$$

4.3. The Acceleration Due to Gravity. Experiments carried on at many points over the earth show that the acceleration due to gravity is not everywhere the same; there are slight variations. Although these variations are small and are not of any consequence in most practical problems, they do exist and should be mentioned.

In general, the values of g lie between a minimum of 32.09 ft/s² or 9.7804 m/s² at the equator and a maximum of 32.26 ft/s² or 9.8321 m/s² at the North and South poles. Referring here to the equator and the poles is only a generalization, for not all points on the equator have the same values as quoted above, nor do all points on any one latitude have the same value. Irregularities of the earth's structure give rise to minute random differences.

The International Committee on Weights and Measures has adopted as a standard or accepted value, 9.80665 m/s² or 32.174 ft/s². For practical purposes, however, it is customary to use the even-numbered values 9.80 m/s² and 32 ft/s². For freely falling bodies, then, we shall assume that

$$g = 9.80 \frac{m}{s^2}$$

$$g = 980 \frac{cm}{s^2} \qquad (4e)$$

$$g = 32 \frac{ft}{s^2}$$

The formulas developed for accelerated motion, given at the end of Chapter 3, with the distance x replaced by the letter h, and a replaced by g, are

$$v = v_0 + gt \qquad (4f)$$

$$h = \frac{v + v_0}{2} t \qquad (4g)$$

$$v^2 = v_0^2 + 2gh \qquad (4h)$$

$$h = v_0 t + \tfrac{1}{2}gt^2 \qquad (4i)$$

All four of these equations apply to freely falling bodies.

Example 1. A boy standing on a bridge 200 ft above a river throws a stone straight downward with a velocity of 50 ft/s. (a) With what speed will the stone strike the water, and (b) how long will it take to descend?

Solution. To find the answer to (a), use the general Eq.(4h). The known quantities are $v_0 = 50$ ft/s, $h = 200$ ft, and $g = 32$ ft/s². Direct substitution gives

$$v^2 = \left(50 \frac{ft}{s}\right)^2 + 2 \times 32 \frac{ft}{s^2} \times 200 \text{ ft}$$

$$v^2 = 2500 + 12{,}800 = 15{,}300 \text{ ft}^2/\text{s}^2$$

If the square roots of both sides of the equation are taken, we obtain

$$v = 123.7 \text{ ft/s}$$

For the answer to (b) use Eq.(4f). The known quantities are $v = 123.7$ ft/s, $v_0 = 50$ ft/s, and $a = g = 32$ ft/s². By solving the general Eq.(4f) for t, we obtain

$$t = \frac{v - v_0}{g}$$

Substituting known values in this equation gives

$$t = \frac{123.7 \text{ ft/s} - 50 \text{ ft/s}}{32 \text{ ft/s}^2} = \frac{73.7 \text{ ft/s}}{32 \text{ ft/s}^2} = 2.3 \text{ s}$$

The stone, therefore, hits the water with a speed of 123.7 ft/s, 2.3 s after it leaves the boy's hand.

4.4. Projection Straight Upward. When a body is projected straight upward, its speed will rapidly diminish until at some point it comes momentarily to rest and then falls back toward the earth, acquiring again at the ground the same speed it had upon projection. Experiment shows that the time taken to rise to the highest point of its trajectory is equal to the time taken to fall from there to the ground. This implies that the upward motions are just the same as the downward motions, but in reverse, and that the time and speed for any point along the path are given by the same equations for free fall, Eqs.(4f), (4g), (4h), and (4i).

In Fig. 4F, a particle is shown projected upward with a velocity of 128 ft/s. After each second's time, its speed on the way up is shown to be the same as its speed at the same level on the way down.

To treat the motion mathematically, it is convenient to use Eqs.(4f), (4g), (4h), and (4i), taking the point of projection as the *origin*, and adopting the following convention of signs, for projection upward:

(1) Distances above the origin are positive.
(2) Distances below the origin are negative.
(3) Velocities upward are positive.
(4) Velocities downward are negative.
(5) Acceleration downward (gravity) is negative.

Whether a body is moving up or down, the acceleration g is always downward. Using the above sign conventions, with Eqs.(4f) to (4i), the value of g should always be substituted with a minus sign.

Example 2. A stone is projected upward with a speed of 128 ft/s. Calculate the time required to reach the highest point.

Solution. The known quantities in this problem are $v_0 = 128$ ft/s, $g = -32$ ft/s², and at the highest point $v = 0$. Since t is the unknown, general Eq.(4f) may be used.

$$v = v_0 + gt$$

Direct substitution gives

$$0 = 128 \text{ ft/s} + (-32 \text{ ft/s}^2)t$$

Fig. 4F   *The upward motion of a body is just the same as the downward motion, but in reverse. A stone thrown upward returns to the ground with the same speed.*

Fig. 4G   *A body projected upward rises to a predetermined height, then falls with increasing speed.*

Solving for *t*, we obtain

$$t = \frac{128 \text{ ft/s}}{32 \text{ ft/s}^2} = 4 \text{ s}$$

In 4 s, therefore, the stone will reach its highest point. In another 4 s it will fall to the ground, as shown in Fig. 4F.

Example 3. A baseball is thrown upward with a speed of 80 ft/s from a point 224 ft above the ground as shown in Fig. 4G. Find (a) the maximum height to which the ball rises, (b) the total time required to reach the point of projection again, (c) the time required to reach a height of 64 ft above the origin, (d) the velocity upon arrival at the ground, and (e) the total time in the air.

Solution. (a) The given quantities for part (a) are

$v_0 = 80$ ft/s, and $g = -32$ ft/s^2. At the highest point of the path $v = 0$. Since h is the unknown, general Eq.(4h) may be used. By direct substitution,

$$v^2 = v_0{}^2 + 2gh$$
$$0 = (80 \text{ ft/s})^2 + 2(-32 \text{ ft/s}^2)h$$

Solving for *h*, we find

$$h = \frac{(80 \text{ ft/s})^2}{2 \times 32 \text{ ft/s}^2} = \frac{6400 \text{ ft}^2/\text{s}^2}{64 \text{ ft/s}^2} = 100 \text{ ft}$$

(b) Upon returning to its starting point, *the origin*, the ball is at $h = 0$. Since *t* is the unknown, general Eq.(4i) may be used.

$$h = v_0 t + \tfrac{1}{2}gt^2$$

By direct substitution, we obtain,

$$0 = (80 \text{ ft/s})t + \tfrac{1}{2}(-32 \text{ ft/s}^2)t^2$$

which leads to

$$(16 \text{ ft/s}^2)t^2 = (80 \text{ ft/s})t$$

Dividing both sides by $16t$, we find that

$$t \text{ ft/s}^2 = 5 \text{ ft/s} \qquad \text{or} \qquad t = 5 \text{ s}$$

(c) Here the given quantities are $h = 64$ ft, $v_0 = 80$ ft/s, $g = -32$ ft/s², and the unknown is t. Inspection of equations shows that general Eq.(4i) may be used. Direct substitution gives

$$64 \text{ ft} = (80 \text{ ft/s})t + \tfrac{1}{2}(-32 \text{ ft/s}^2)t^2$$

which leads to

$$(16 \text{ ft/s}^2)t^2 - (80 \text{ ft/s})t + 64 \text{ ft} = 0$$

and dividing both sides by 16 ft/s²,

$$t^2 - 5 \text{ s} + 4 \text{ s}^2 = 0$$

Upon factoring, we get

$$(t - 1 \text{ s})(t - 4 \text{ s}) = 0$$

from which, we obtain

$$t = 1 \text{ s} \qquad \text{and} \qquad t = 4 \text{ s}$$

Both of these answers are correct. The first answer, 1 s, is the time required for the ball to reach the 64-ft level on its way up, whereas the second answer, 4 s, is the time required to reach the 64-ft level on the way down.

(d) Upon reaching the ground, the ball is below the origin making $h = -224$ ft. Since v is the unknown, general Eq.(4h) may be used. Substituting directly, we get

$$v^2 = (80 \text{ ft/s})^2 + 2(-32 \text{ ft/s}^2)(-224 \text{ ft})$$
$$v^2 = 20{,}736 \text{ ft}^2/\text{s}^2$$
$$v = \pm 144 \text{ ft/s}$$

Of these two answers only the one $v = -144$ ft/s is correct; the ball is moving downward. The answer $+144$ ft/s means that the baseball could have been thrown upward from the ground level with this velocity, to acquire the same height.

(e) To find the total flight time we may use general Eq.(4f). The known quantities are $v_0 = 80$ ft/s, $g = -32$ ft/s², and $v = -144$ ft/s.

$$-144 \text{ ft/s} = 80 \text{ ft/s} + (-32 \text{ ft/s}^2)t$$

from which

$$t = \frac{224 \text{ ft/s}}{32 \text{ ft/s}^2} = 7 \text{ s}$$

Or we may use general Eq.(4i), and obtain

$$-224 \text{ ft} = (80 \text{ ft/s})t + \tfrac{1}{2}(-32 \text{ ft/s}^2)t^2$$

from which

$$(16 \text{ ft/s}^2)t^2 - (80 \text{ ft/s})t - 224 \text{ ft} = 0$$

Dividing by 16 ft/s², we find

$$t^2 - 5 \text{ s} - 14 \text{ s}^2 = 0$$

Factoring, we obtain

$$(t - 7 \text{ s})(t + 2 \text{ s}) = 0$$

which gives

$$t = 7 \text{ s} \qquad \text{and} \qquad t = -2 \text{ s}$$

Only the answer $t = 7$ s is a real answer for this problem. The question of what the answer $t = -2$ s means is left to be answered by the student.

PROBLEMS

1. A stone is dropped from a bridge 220 ft above the water. (a) How long is the stone in the air, and (b) with what velocity does it hit the water?

2. A workman, working on a steel tower 320 ft above the ground, drops a Crescent wrench. (a) How long is the wrench in the air, and (b) with what speed does it hit the ground? [*Ans.* (a) 4.47 s, (b) 143.1 ft/s.]

3. A sandbag, dropped as ballast from a balloon, hits the ground with a speed of 60 m/s. (a) How high is the balloon, and (b) how long is the sandbag in the air?

4. A stone dropped into a well hits the water in 4 s. (a) How deep is the well, and (b) with what speed does the stone hit the water? Give answers in the metric system of units. [*Ans.* (a) 78.4 m, (b) 39.2 m/s.]

5. A ball is thrown straight upward with a velocity of 121.6 ft/s. Find (a) the time to reach the highest point, (b) the maximum height reached, (c) the total time in the air, and (d) the velocity at the end of 3 s.

6. An arrow is shot upward with a velocity of 63.7

m/s. Find (a) the time to reach the highest point, (b) the maximum height reached, (c) the total time of flight, (d) the velocity at the end of 5 s, and (e) the velocity at the end of 8 s. [*Ans.* (a) 6.5 s, (b) 207 m, (c) 13.0 s, (d) $+14.7$ m/s, (e) -14.7 m/s.]

7. A stone thrown straight upward reaches a height of 100 m. Calculate (a) the time to reach the highest point, (b) the velocity upon reaching the ground, and (c) the velocity at the end of 4 s.

8. An arrow shot straight upward reaches a height of 480 ft. Calculate (a) the time to reach the highest point, (b) the velocity upon arrival at the ground, and (c) the velocity at the end of 6 s. [*Ans.* (a) 5.48 s, (b) -175.3 ft/s, (c) -16.7 ft/s.]

9. A ball is thrown straight upward with a speed of 24.5 m/s. Find (a) the height to which it rises, (b) the total time it is in the air, (c) its height above the ground at the end of 4 s, and (d) its velocity at the end of 2 s.

10. A baseball player hits a ball straight upward with

an initial velocity of 60 mi/hr. Find (a) the height to which it rises, (b) the total time it is in the air before it is caught, (c) its height at the end of 5 s, and (d) its velocity at the end of 3.5 s. [*Ans.* (a) 121 ft, (b) 5.50 s, (c) 40.0 ft, (d) −24.0 ft/s.]

11. A ball thrown straight upward returns to the ground again after a total flight time of 8 s. Find (a) the initial velocity in m/s, (b) the maximum height reached in meters, (c) its height above ground at the end of 5.5 s, and (d) its velocity at the end of 6 s.

12. A dart shot straight upward returns to the ground again after a total flight time of 12 s. Find (a) the initial velocity in m/s, (b) the maximum height reached in meters, (c) its height above ground at the end of 9 s, and (d) its velocity at the end of 9 s. [*Ans.* (a) 58.8 m/s, (b) 176.4 m, (c) 132.3 m, (d) −29.4 m/s.]

13. A stone fired straight upward by a catapult reaches a height of 29.4 m in 1 s. Find (a) the maximum height reached, (b) the time of flight, and (c) the initial speed of projection.

14. An arrow shot straight upward reaches a height of 39.2 m in 1 s. Find (a) the maximum height reached, (b) the total time of flight, and (c) the speed of projection. [*Ans.* (a) 99.2 m, (b) 9.0 s, (c) 44.1 m/s.]

15. A stone is thrown upward from the edge of a cliff with a speed of 31.4 m/s. Find (a) the maximum height reached, (b) the height at the end of 2 s, (c) the velocity at the end of 5 s, and (d) the height at the end of 7 s.

16. A ball is thrown upward from a bridge with an initial velocity of 144 ft/s. If the bridge is 150 ft above the river flowing under it, find (a) the height to which the ball rises, (b) the time to reach the highest point, (c) the total time to reach the water, and (d) the velocity with which it hits the water. [*Ans.* (a) 324 ft, (b) 4.5 s, (c) 9.94 s, (d) −174 ft/s.]

17. Arrows are shot upward at 1 s intervals with an initial speed of 44.1 m/s. After several arrows have been shot, how long will each arrow be in the air before another passes it, and (b) at what distances above the origin will arrows be passing each other?

18. Darts are shot vertically upward at 2 s intervals with an initial speed of 160 ft/s. After several darts have been shot, (a) how long will each dart be in the air before another passes it, and (b) at what distances above the origin will darts be passing each other? Check your answers by plotting a graph with distances vertical and time horizontal. [*Ans.* (a) 1 s, (b) 144 ft, 256 ft, 336 ft, and 384 ft.]

19. A stone thrown vertically upward reaches a height of 39.2 m the first second on its way to a higher altitude. Find (a) the time to reach the maximum height, (b) the maximum height, and (c) the velocity of projection.

20. An arrow shot vertically upward reaches a height of 128 ft during the first second of its flight. Find (a) the time to reach the highest point, (b) the maximum height, and (c) the velocity of projection. [*Ans.* (a) 4.5 s, (b) 324 ft, (c) 144 ft/s.]

21. Calculate the value of g in mi/hr^2.

NEWTON'S FIRST AND
SECOND LAWS OF MOTION

In the preceding chapters the motions of bodies have been described in terms of *distance*, *speed*, *velocity*, *acceleration*, and *time*. The definitions of these quantities, and the laws and formulas relating to them, are classified as belonging to that branch of mechanics called "kinematics." Here, and in later chapters, the cause of motion is to be treated. Such a treatment involves the introduction of *mass* and *force* into the equations already presented.

To Isaac Newton* goes the credit of having been the first to systematically introduce these concepts into mechanics and to formulate the fundamental laws governing all motion. These laws constitute the fundamental principles of that branch of mechanics called "dynamics" and resolve themselves into three laws commonly referred to as "Newton's laws of motion."

5.1. Newton's First Law. *A body at rest or in uniform motion will remain at rest or in uniform motion unless some external force is applied to it.*† This law can be demonstrated by many simple experiments. In Fig. 5A a tablecloth is shown in the process of being removed from under the dishes and silverware on a table without disturbing their original setting. In Fig. 5B a small car is shown free to move on a smooth hard track. If If the track is jerked quickly to right or left, the wheels of the car will turn, but the car itself will tend to remain at rest.

In both of these experiments the dishes and the car are at rest. They tend to remain at rest because the sudden motion of the objects on which they are resting exerts no large force for any appreciable length of time. Actually, the dishes and the car do move slightly because of frictional forces between the moving parts in contact. The tendency for each body to remain at rest is due to that property, common to all material bodies, called *inertia*.

The inertia of a body may be defined as that property of a body which tends to resist a change in its state of rest or motion. Mass is defined as a quantitative measure of inertia.

---

* Sir Issac Newton (1642–1727), English physicist and mathematician, was born in England on Christmas day, 1642. He obtained his education at Trinity College, Cambridge, where in 1665 he was awarded the Master of Arts degree. At just this time, the prevalence of the black plague forced him into retirement at his old home in Woolsthorpe where, in two years 1665 and 1666, his genius developed. In this period he invented the calculus, discovered the composition of white light, and conceived the idea of universal gravitation. In the years that followed, he published much of his work on optics and developed his ideas on gravitation which were published in 1687 in his *Principia*. At the age of fifty he suffered a nervous breakdown, and never again did any extensive scientific work, but devoted his time to theology. He became very absent-minded and slovenly in his personal appearance. He never married. His *Principia* is considered to be one of the greatest monuments of the human intellect. In it, Newton lays the foundations of mechanics which are broad enough to include all future developments, and these he applies to the motions of heavenly bodies under the law of gravitation. He was elected to Parliament, was president of the Royal Society for twenty years, and was knighted by Queen Anne in 1705. The greatness of this modest man is illustrated by a remark of his made on his deathbed, "If I have seen farther than others, it is by standing on the shoulders of giants."

† Newton's first law of motion is given in Latin in his famous book *Principia*. Lex. I. Corpus omne perseverare in statu suo quiesendi vel movendi uniformiter in directum, nisi quatenus illud a viribus impressis cogitur statum suum mutare.

Fig. 5A   *A tablecloth can be pulled from a table without dislodging the dishes.*

Inertia and mass are both measured in the same units, in grams, or kilograms.

Fig. 5B   *The smooth track can quickly be moved so as not to set the car in motion.*

A third experiment illustrating inertia, and Newton's first law, is illustrated in Fig. 5C. A mass M of 1000 g is suspended by a piece of thread A, then pulled downward by another piece of the same thread B. If the force F is a slow steady pull, the thread will always break at A; whereas if it is a sudden jerk, it will always break at B. In the first case, the tension in the upper thread is greater and is equivalent to the force F plus the weight of the mass M. In the second case, the force F is momentarily very large, causing the thread to break before the mass M has had time to move down far enough to stretch and break the upper thread. It is the inertia of M that permits the very large force F to be momentarily applied to the lower thread only.

5.2. Inertia and Motion. The three preceding demonstrations are concerned with bodies at rest. The second part of Newton's first law of motion is concerned with moving bodies, and a restatement of the law confined to this aspect would change the law to read:

A body in uniform motion will remain in uniform motion unless some external force is applied to it.

Fig. 5C   *A slow, steady pull at F breaks the thread at A, while a quick pull at F breaks the thread at B.*

This aspect of Newton's first law was first recognized by Galileo. In order to study the acceleration due to gravity, he used an inclined plane to reduce the acceleration due to gravity, thereby permitting better measurements. He observed that a ball rolling down one incline would roll up another to approximately the same height regardless of the inclination of the second plane. Furthermore, if the ball were allowed to roll out on a level plane when it reached the bottom of the incline, it could never achieve its original height but tended to roll on and on. Due to friction it would eventually stop.

A most striking demonstration of this property of inertia is provided by a "dry ice disk" as shown in Fig. 5D. Here, friction is reduced to

Fig. 5D   *Demonstration of the inertia of a body moving with uniform velocity.*

practically zero by a metal disk that rides over a glass plate and literally floats on a thin layer of carbon dioxide gas. When this body is given a very slight push, it rides across the plate and seems to keep going on and on, with constant velocity, as if by magic. What keeps the body moving in the same straight line is its inertia.* The above law, of course, neglects friction, for we know that, left to itself, friction will eventually bring the body to rest. The greater the friction, the sooner it will stop. The smaller the friction, the longer it will move. If friction could be entirely eliminated, the *inertia* of the body would keep it moving indefinitely with constant velocity.

5.3. Inertia and Mass. Mass is a measure of inertia. In the metric system, inertia and mass are measured in *grams* and *kilograms*. In the

* A cross-section diagram of this dry ice disk is shown in Fig. 5E. A thin-walled, brass or copper ball about 10 cm in diameter is soldered to a flat, circular brass disk about 2 cm thick and 15 cm in diameter. Thin-walled vessels of this kind are used as floats in certain plumbing utilities and may be purchased in most hardware stores. Dry ice is available in almost every drugstore soda fountain, and one loading will last a couple of hours. The bottom surface of the disk is undercut several thousandths of a centimeter, and a hole about 0.5 cm in diameter is drilled through the center. A short section of metal tubing is mounted directly above this center and prevents the dry ice from clogging the hole. A larger hole in the top is provided for the insertion of dry ice, and a tight-fitting cork closes the opening.

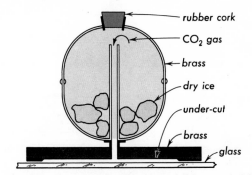

Fig. 5E   *Cross-section diagram of "dry ice disk."*

English system they are both measured in *slugs*. Fig. 5F is a diagram illustrating the relative sizes of these three units. They are shown in a hooked weight form convenient for use in experiments.

Fig. 5F   *Units of mass are also units of inertia.*

If one were to weigh these three fundamental units of mass, 1 slug would weigh 32 lb, 1 Kg would weigh 9.8 newtons, and 1 g would weigh 980 dynes. The difference between mass and weight will be taken up in detail in Sec. 5.6.

5.4. An Experiment on Accelerated Motion. Newton's first law of motion, concerning bodies at rest or in uniform motion, assumes that no forces are acting to change them. Newton's second law of motion, however, assumes that a force is acting, and the law describes exactly how the motion changes. To learn just how the motion of a body changes and how this change is related to its mass and to the force acting upon it, we may perform an experiment like that shown in Fig. 5G.

A "dry ice disk" of the kind described in the preceding section is accelerated along a level plane (a long glass plate) by means of a thread, a pulley, and a small mass m_2. A switching circuit, like that shown in Fig. 4C is used to time the moving mass m_1 as it starts from position A and passes position B.

Fig. 5G *Diagram of apparatus for acceleration experiment.*

After weighing and recording its mass m_1, the body is held in position A by the small electromagnet E, acting on a small piece of iron attached to the copper ball for this purpose. With the snap of a switch the electromagnet circuit is opened releasing the disk, and the clock circuit is closed starting the clock. When the top edge of the body m_1 strikes the switch L, contacts D are instantly opened, stopping the clock. The time t is then recorded, along with the distance x. By repeating this procedure several times, a good average of the time is obtained.

A number of different trials should be performed with this experiment, first by adding masses to the moving body, and then by increasing the accelerating mass m_2. The mass m_1 should be reweighed with each trial since the loss of CO_2 will change the value. Furthermore, for trials 4, 5, 6, and 7, the mass m_2 added to m_1 should be adjusted so that $m_1 + m_2$ remains constant. If done correctly, the first set of measurements can be used to determine how acceleration changes with increasing mass, and the second set to determine how acceleration changes with increasing force.

Suppose we have performed this experiment and have recorded the data shown in Table 5A.

To find the acceleration for each of the seven trials we make use of the kinematic Eq.(3n).

$$x = \tfrac{1}{2}at^2$$

Upon solving for the unknown a, we get

$$a = \frac{2x}{t^2} \qquad (5a)$$

TABLE 5A. RECORDED DATA FOR ACCELERATION EXPERIMENT

Trial	Mass m_1 (Kg)	Mass m_2 (Kg)	Distance x (m)	Time t (s)
1	0.560	0.020	1.00	2.45
2	0.965	0.020	1.00	3.18
3	1.460	0.020	1.00	3.91
4	1.980	0.020	1.00	4.51
5	1.960	0.040	1.00	3.20
6	1.940	0.060	1.00	2.61
7	1.920	0.080	1.00	2.27

Substituting the recorded values of x and t in this relation, we obtain the values of a shown in the first column of Table 5B. Since m_1 and m_2 both undergo the same acceleration, the total mass being accelerated is $m_1 + m_2$. This sum is shown as m in the third column of the table. Here we have assumed that the mass of the thread and the effective mass of the pulley are negligibly small.

TABLE 5B. CALCULATIONS FOR ACCELERATION EXPERIMENT

Trial	Acceleration a (m/s²)	Mass m (Kg)	Reciprocal $1/m$ (1/Kg)
1	0.333	0.580	1.72
2	0.198	0.985	1.02
3	0.131	1.480	0.676
4	0.098	2.000	0.500
5	0.195	2.000	0.500
6	0.294	2.000	0.500
7	0.388	2.000	0.500

To see how the acceleration a is related to the mass of the accelerated body, we use the first four trials, for which the applied force is constant, and plot a graph. Plotting m vertically and a horizontally, we obtain the graph in Fig. 5H. Since this is not a straight line, we should try modifying a and m to see if a straight-line plot can be obtained.

With the graph for a guide, we note that as the mass increases the acceleration decreases. This suggests the possibility that an inverse ratio

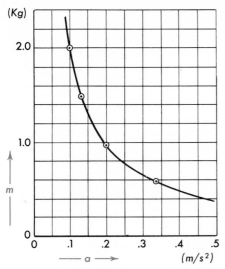

Fig. 5H   *Graph for the acceleration experiment.*

exists between the two quantities, that is, that one of the quantities might be proportional to the reciprocal of the other. Assuming this as a possibility, the values of $1/m$ are given in Table 5B. When these reciprocal values are plotted against a, as shown at the right in Fig. 5I, a straight line is the result.

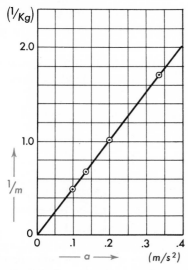

Fig. 5I   *Straight-line graph for acceleration experiment.*

The conclusion to be drawn from this straight-line graph is that a is proportional to $1/m$.

$$a \propto \frac{1}{m} \qquad (5b)$$

Replacing the proportionality sign by an equal sign and a constant, we can write

$$a = F\frac{1}{m} \qquad (5c)$$

from which

$$F = ma$$

The constant F is called the *force* and has the units of *mass times acceleration.*

To find how the acceleration changes with the applied force, the value of a given in Table 5B can be plotted against m_2 from Table 5A. The plotting of this graph, and the conclusions to be drawn from it, are left as an exercise for the student.

5.5. Newton's Second Law of Motion. *When a body is acted upon by a constant force, its resulting acceleration is proportional to the force and inversely proportional to the mass.* The experiment described in the preceding section verifies this statement and leads us to the so-called force equation.

$$\boxed{F = ma} \qquad (5d)$$

force = mass × acceleration

Example 1. If we neglect friction, what constant force will give a mass of 4 Kg an acceleration of 3.8 m/s²?

Solution. Apply the force equation, Eq.(5d).

$$F = 4\,\text{Kg} \times 3.8\,\frac{\text{m}}{\text{s}^2} = 15.2\,\frac{\text{Kg m}}{\text{s}^2}$$

The answer is a force of 15.2 Kg m/s². Thus force is not as simple a concept as it might seem at first hand; it involves all three of the fundamental units, *length*, *mass*, and *time*.

By definition, 1 Kg m/s² is a unit of force called the *newton*. According to this definition the answer to the above problem could have been written 15.2 newtons.

The newton is a force which, acting on a 1-Kg mass, will give it an acceleration of 1 m/s².

$$1\ \text{newton} = 1\ \text{kilogram} \times 1\,\frac{\text{meter}}{\text{second}^2}$$

This is the unit of force expressed in the mks system of units.

The newton is named in honor of Sir Isaac Newton, and is abbreviated N.

In the cgs system of units Eq.(5d) becomes

$$1 \text{ dyne} = 1 \text{ gram} \times 1 \frac{\text{centimeter}}{\text{second}^2}$$

Example 2. Neglecting friction, what constant force will give a mass of 50 g an acceleration of 5 cm/s²?

Solution. By substituting the given values into the force equation, Eq.(5d), we obtain

$$F = 50 \text{ g} \times 5 \frac{\text{cm}}{\text{s}^2} = 250 \frac{\text{g cm}}{\text{s}^2}$$

The answer is a force of $250 \frac{\text{g cm}}{\text{s}^2}$.

By definition

$$1 \text{ dyne} = 1 \frac{\text{g cm}}{\text{s}^2}$$

According to this definition, the answer to the above problem is written

$$F = 250 \text{ dynes.}$$

To the above statement of Newton's second law of motion should be added the statement that the acceleration takes place in the direction of the force. If the force is toward the north the acceleration is toward the north, and if the force is up the acceleration is up, etc.

Newtons and dynes are absolute units of force. They arise from the force equation when the absolute units of *mass* and *time* are used.

Since 1 Kg = 1000 g, and 1 m = 100 cm,

$$1 \text{ newton} = 10^5 \text{ dynes}$$

5.6. Weight and Mass. When a mass *m* is allowed to fall freely, it is the constant downward force of gravity on the mass that gives rise to its constant downward acceleration. If Newton's second law is applied to this motion, the force *F* is none other than the weight F_g of the body, and the acceleration *a* is the acceleration due to gravity *g*. For falling bodies, the force equation, $F = ma$, is written in different symbols.

$$\boxed{F_g = mg} \qquad (5e)$$

weight = mass × acceleration

In absolute units, the weight of a body is expressed in newtons or dynes.

Weight and *force* have both magnitude and direction and are therefore vector quantities. Mass, on the other hand, is a scalar quantity since it has only magnitude. The distinction between *weight* and *mass* is illustrated by imagining a given body to be carried out into free space far removed from other bodies and their gravitational attraction. There, a body at rest will still have its mass but it will have no weight. That such a body has its mass would be demonstrated if another mass were to bump into it. The smaller the mass of the incoming body, the less would be the recoil of the first mass from the impact.

Weight here on the earth is due to the gravitational attraction of the earth upon a mass at its surface and will be treated in detail in the next chapter. In the equation $F_g = mg$ we may define *g* as the *weight per unit mass*. F_g is equal to the *mass* times the *weight per unit mass*.

Example 3. Calculate the weight of a body having a mass of 1 Kg.

Solution. By Eq.(5e),

$$F_g = 1 \text{ Kg} \times 9.80 \frac{\text{m}}{\text{s}^2} = 9.80 \frac{\text{Kg m}}{\text{s}^2} = 9.80 \text{ N} \quad (5f)$$

This answer shows that to lift a mass of 1 Kg requires an upward force of 9.80 N and that the weight and mass differ from each other numerically by a ratio equal to the acceleration due to gravity. By similar calculations to the above, the weight of a 1-g mass is found to be 980 dynes. See Fig. 5J.

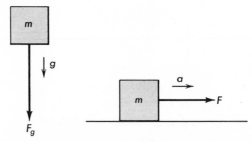

Fig. 5J   *A mass m falling freely has an acceleration g; pulled by a force F it has an acceleration a.*

5.7. The Engineering System of Units. The engineer seldom uses metric units as described above. He finds it more convenient to measure forces in *pounds* or *tons*. In the construction of buildings, bridges, airplanes, and all kinds of machines, the loads to be carried are usually specified in pounds. To apply Newton's second law of motion, as expressed by the force equation $F = ma$, it is necessary to modify one of the two factors, *mass* or *acceleration*.

It is general engineering practice to modify *mass* by defining it not in pounds but in *slugs*. To see how these units are derived from the "force equation," Eqs.(5d) and (5e) are both solved for m, and then set equal to each other.

$$\frac{F}{a} = \frac{F_g}{g} \tag{5g}$$

The justification for this is that Newton's second law of motion applied to a given mass holds for any force, whether it be its own weight F_g due to the earth's downward pull or any other applied force F. If the force is F the acceleration is a; if the force is F_g the acceleration is g (see Fig. 5J). The engineer's form of the force equation evolves from Eq.(5g). By solving for F, we obtain,

$$\boxed{F = \frac{F_g}{g}\, a} \tag{5h}$$

In this relation F and F_g are to be considered as forces, both measured in pounds, while the accelerations g and a are both measured in the customary units ft/s². $g = 32$ ft/s².

Example 4. A small wagon weighing 80 lb stands at rest on a level road. What force is required to give it an acceleration of 3 ft/s²?
Solution. By direct substitution in the force equation, Eq.(5h),

$$F = \frac{80 \text{ lb}}{32 \text{ ft/s}^2} \times 3 \text{ ft/s}^2 = 7.5 \text{ lb}$$

The answer is a force of 7.5 lb.

The term F_g/g represents mass in the engineering or British system of units. Such units are called *slugs*. The slug is abbreviated sl. *Mass in slugs is always obtained by dividing the weight in pounds by the acceleration due to gravity, 32 ft/s².*

In turning this around, we may *define unit force (the pound) as that force which, applied to a mass of one slug, will give it an acceleration of one*

foot per second per second. Consider now a mass of one slug falling freely under the pull of gravity with an acceleration of 32 ft/s². By the above definition of unit force, such an acceleration of unit mass (1 slug) could be caused only by a force

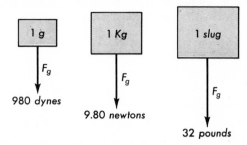

Fig. 5K *Weight is a force equal in magnitude to the mass multiplied by the acceleration due to gravity.* $F_g = mg$.

of 32 lb. In other words, one slug weighs 32 lb. (see Fig. 5K).

$$
\begin{aligned}
1 \text{ newton} &= 0.225 \text{ lb} \\
1 \text{ dyne} &= 2.25 \times 10^{-6} \text{ lb} \\
1 \text{ slug} &= 14.6 \text{ Kg}
\end{aligned}
$$

5.8. Change in Velocity. In Chapter 3, acceleration was defined as the rate of change of velocity and written as

$$a = \frac{\Delta v}{\Delta t}$$

or

$$a = \frac{v - v_0}{t}$$

If the acceleration a, in the force equation $F = ma$, is replaced by either of these expressions, Newton's second law of motion takes on a new form.

$$F = m\frac{\Delta v}{\Delta t}$$

or

$$F = m\frac{v - v_0}{t} \tag{5i}$$

This equation is used in solving problems where the initial and final velocities are involved.

Example 5. A 2000-Kg automobile is moving with a velocity of 12 m/s. What constant force, applied for a period of 8 s, will increase its velocity to 40 m/s?
Solution. The given quantities are $m = 2000$ Kg, $v = 40$ m/s, $v_0 = 12$ m/s, and $t = 8$ s. By direct substitution in Eq.(5i), we obtain

$$F = 2000 \text{ Kg} \frac{40 \text{ m/s} - 12 \text{ m/s}}{8 \text{ s}} = 7000 \frac{\text{Kg m}}{\text{s}^2}$$

The answer is 7000 N.

5.9. Momentum. When Eq. (5i) is multiplied out, we obtain an equation involving a new concept: namely, that of *momentum*.

$$F = \frac{mv - mv_0}{t} \qquad (5j)$$

Momentum is defined as the product *mass times velocity*. According to this definition, all moving bodies have momentum. In Fig. 5G, the dry ice disk m_1 at the left has momentum $m_1 v_0$. Under the action of a force F, it gains in momentum, acquiring, after a time of t seconds, a greater momentum $m_1 v$. Two masses, one large and one small, moving with the same velocity, have quite different momenta: the larger mass has a proportionately larger momentum.

Newton's second law of motion was originally stated in terms of momentum.*

The rate at which the momentum of a body changes is proportional to the impressed force and takes place in the direction of the straight line in which the force acts.

As an equation in words,

$$\text{force} = \frac{\text{change in momentum}}{\text{change in time}}$$

or in symbols

$$F = \frac{\Delta(mv)}{\Delta t} \qquad (5k)$$

assuming the mass to remain unchanged

$$F = m \frac{\Delta v}{\Delta t} \qquad (5l)$$

5.10. Impulse. Multiplying both sides of Eq.(5j) by t, we find

$$\boxed{Ft = mv - mv_0} \qquad (5m)$$

This is called the "impulse equation." $F \times t$ is the *impulse* and $mv - mv_0$ is the *change in momentum*. Its meaning is illustrated in Fig. 5L

* Newton's second law of motion is stated in Latin in his *Principia*. Lex. II. Mutationem motus, proportionalem esse vi motrici impressae, et fieri secundum lineam rectam qua vis illa imprimitur.

Fig. 5L   *The impulse of a hammer drives a nail into a block of wood.*

where a hammer is shown driving a nail into a block of wood. Moving with a velocity v, the hammer head of mass m strikes the nail a blow of force F. Lasting for only a fraction of a second, this force has by an impulse driven the nail a short distance into the wood. If F represents the average force, and t the time interval during which the force acts,

$$\text{impulse} = F \times t \qquad (5n)$$

When a body starts from rest, the initial velocity v_0 of Eq.(5m) is zero, and

$$Ft = mv \qquad (5o)$$

As the result of an impulse Ft, a body initially at rest acquires a momentum mv. Conversely, a body moving with a momentum mv can be brought to rest by an impulse $-Ft$. The minus sign indicates that the force is opposite in direction to the velocity.

Example 6. A hammer weighing 2 lb, moving with a velocity of 20 ft/s, strikes the head of a spike and drives it into a block of hard wood. If the hammer comes to rest in 0.001 s, find (a) the impulse, (b) the average force, and (c) the distance the nail is driven into the wood.

Solution. By direct substitution in Eq.(5o),

(a) $\qquad Ft = -\dfrac{2 \text{ lb}}{32 \text{ ft/s}^2} \times 20 \text{ ft/s} = -1.25 \text{ lb s}$

The average force is

(b) $$F = -\frac{1.25 \text{ lb s}}{0.001 \text{ s}} = -1250 \text{ lb}$$

That such a large force as this is really exerted is due in part to the very short time in which the force acts and its reality can be demonstrated by trying to push a nail into a block of wood by piling weights on top of it. The minus sign indicates that the force stopping the hammer is opposite in direction to the motion. The hammer velocity is down and the stopping force is up.

To find the distance the nail is driven into the wood in the above example, the equations for accelerated motion may be used. From Eq.(3l),

$$x = \frac{v}{2} t$$

Substitution of the known quantities gives

(c) $$x = 10 \text{ ft/s} \times 0.001 \text{ s} = 0.01 \text{ ft}$$

which is about $\frac{1}{8}$ in.

PROBLEMS

1. What force is required to give a mass of 4.5 Kg an acceleration of 2.4 m/s².

2. A mass of 8.5 Kg is to be given an acceleration of 2.4 m/s². What force is required? [Ans. 20.4 N.]

3. What force in pounds is required to give a car with a mass of 120 sl an acceleration of 2.8 ft/s².

4. A mass of 16 sl is to be given an acceleration of 1.25 ft/s². What force is required? [Ans. 20 lb.]

5. What force in pounds is required to accelerate a small truck from rest to 60 mi/hr in 15 s. Assume the mass of the truck to be 180 sl.

6. What force in newtons is required to accelerate a car from rest to 30 m/s in 12 s. Assume the mass of the car to be 2100 Kg. [Ans. 5250 N.]

7. Starting from rest, a 5600-lb truck acquires a speed of 45 mi/hr in 8 s. Find (a) the mass of the truck, (b) the average acceleration, and (c) the applied force.

8. Starting from rest, a car of 1200 Kg acquires a speed of 42 m/s in 15 s. Find (a) the weight of the car, (b) the average acceleration, and (c) the average accelerating force. [Ans. (a) 11,760 N, (b) 2.80 m/s², (c) 3360 N.]

9. A small car of 1000 Kg starts from rest and acquires a speed of 25 m/s in 7 s. Find (a) the weight of the car, (b) the average acceleration, (c) the average force in newtons, and (d) the average force in dynes.

10. A golf ball of 20 g, moving with a speed of 25 m/s lands on a pile of soft dirt and becomes embedded a distance of 8 cm. Assuming constant deceleration during impact, find (a) the acceleration, (b) the time interval during impact, (c) the force, and (d) the momentum before impact. [Ans. (a) 3910 m/s², (b) 0.00639 s, (c) 78.2 N, (d) 0.50 Kg m/s.]

11. A 5-Kg shell is fired with a muzzle velocity of 700 m/s from a gun barrel 2.4 m long. Calculate the average value of (a) the acceleration, (b) the time, (c) the force, (d) the impulse, and (e) the momentum.

12. A mortar shell weighing 3.2 lb is fired from a mortar 2.8 ft long. If the muzzle velocity is 148 ft/s, find the average (a) acceleration, (b) time, (c) force, (d) impulse, and (e) momentum. [Ans. (a) 3910 ft/s², (b) 0.0378 s, (c) 391 lb, (d) 14.8 sl ft/s, (e) 14.8 sl ft/s.]

13. A 0.25-Kg shell is shot from a gun with a velocity of 1200 m/s. If the gun barrel is 1.2 m long, find (a) the

time, (b) the acceleration, (c) the force, (d) the impulse, and (e) the momentum of the shell.

14. A sledge hammer with a steel head of 4 Kg, moving downward with a speed of 5 m/s, strikes the head of a railroad spike driving it 8 mm into a redwood railroad tie. Assuming constant deceleration during impact, find (a) the time, (b) the acceleration, (c) the force, (d) the impulse, and (e) the momentum. Neglect the mass of the spike, and use the mks system of units. [Ans. (a) 0.0032 s, (b) −1560 m/s², (c) 6250 N, (d) 20 N s, (e) 20 Kg m/s.]

15. The steel head of a hammer, with a mass of 1.2 Kg and moving with a speed of 6 m/s, strikes the head of a nail driving it 0.5 cm into a block of hardwood. Neglecting the mass of the nail, calculate (a) the momentum of the hammer before impact, (b) the acceleration during impact, (c) the force, (d) the impact time, and (e) the impulse.

16. A jet passenger plane with a mass of 50,000 Kg requires a 1500 m runway to attain its take-off speed of 50 m/s. Assuming constant acceleration, calculate (a) the time of take-off, (b) the acceleration, (c) the thrust of the jet engines, (d) the impulse, and (e) the total momentum. [Ans. (a) 60 s, (b) 0.833 m/s², (c) 41,700 N, (d) 2.50 × 10⁶ N s, (e) 2.50 × 10⁶ Kg m/s.]

17. A small private plane with a mass of 1500 Kg requires a minimum runway 200 m long to acquire its take-off speed of 28 m/s. Assuming constant acceleration, find by calculation, (a) the time of take-off, (b) the acceleration, (c) the thrust of the propeller, (d) the impulse, and, (e) the momentum.

18. A 90-mm gun fires a 4 Kg shell with a muzzle velocity of 1000 m/s. Assuming uniform acceleration in the 2-m-long gun barrel, find (a) the acceleration, (b) the time, (c) the force, (d) the impulse, and (e) the momentum. [Ans. (a) 250,000 m/s², (b) 0.004 s, (c) 1.00 × 10⁶ N, (d) 4000 N s, (e) 4000 Kg m/s.]

19. A 15-g bullet with a speed of 1000 m/s strikes a wooden target and penetrates a distance of 10 cm. Find (a) the acceleration, (b) the time, (c) the force, (d) the impulse, and (e) the momentum during impact.

20. How large a force is required to give a mass of 20 Kg an acceleration of 2.45 m/s² (a) horizontally, and (b) vertically upward ? Neglect all friction. [Ans. (a) 49 N, (b) 245 N.]

VECTOR ADDITION AND COMPOSITION OF FORCES

An introduction to the concepts of *vector* and *scalar quantities* is given in Sec. 2.9. Vector quantities have *magnitude* and *direction*, while scalar quantities have *magnitude* only. Although scalar quantities are added arithmetically, vector quantities are added by a more complicated process called *vector addition*.

In vector addition it is necessary to take into account the directions as well as the magnitudes of all quantities to be added. Of the following list of vector quantities commonly used in mechanics, *displacement* and *force* will be taken up in this chapter.

displacement	momentum
force	torque
velocity	angular momentum
acceleration	angular velocity

6.1. Vector Addition. The process of vector addition will first be illustrated by an example involving two displacements. Suppose that a ship starts from a point A as diagramed in Fig. 6A, and sails due north for a distance of 6 mi to a point B, where it changes course and sails due east for a distance of 4 mi to a point C. Although the ship has sailed a total distance of 6 + 4 or 10 mi, it is obvious that its distance from the starting point is not given by this arithmetic sum.

To find the actual displacement, that is, the distance from the starting point, a diagram like that shown may be drawn to some selected scale. With a pencil and a ruler (a centimeter scale) a vertical line AB, 6 cm long, is drawn to represent the displacement *6 miles north*. The line BC is next drawn to the right from B and 4 cm long to

represent the *4 miles east*. The triangle is finally completed by joining A and C. With an arrowhead at C, the hypotenuse *R*, measuring 7.2 cm, represents the resultant displacement of 7.2 mi.

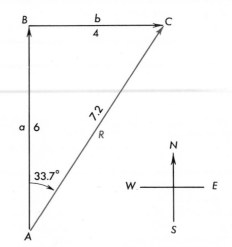

Fig. 6A   *Diagram illustrating vector addition as applied to displacements.*

Vectorially, we write

$$\vec{AB} + \vec{BC} = \vec{AC} \qquad \text{or} \qquad \boxed{\vec{R} = \vec{a} + \vec{b}}$$

Using a protractor, the angle A is measured to be 33.7°. The direction of the resultant vector *R* is therefore 33.7° east of north.

It is customary in any vector diagram to represent all vector quantities by arrows, each arrow being drawn in the proper direction and to the proper length. A little practice in drawing will show that, regardless of what scale is used to make the diagram, the resultant must be the same in magnitude and direction, and that the more carefully the diagram is drawn, the more accurate will be the measured result.

To calculate the magnitude of the resultant R in Fig. 6A, use is made of the Pythagorean theorem in geometry that, for any right triangle, *the square of the hypotenuse is equal to the sum of the squares of the other two sides.*

$$R^2 = a^2 + b^2$$

Substitute the two values of a and b.

$$R^2 = (6)^2 + (4)^2 = 52$$

By taking the square root* of 52, we obtain

$$R = 7.21 \text{ mi}$$

Example 1. A man walks east for a distance of 10 mi, then turns and walks north-east for a distance of 5 mi. Find the resultant displacement.

Solution. Following the procedure outlined above, a horizontal line AB is first drawn 10 cm long and labeled as shown in Fig. 6B. The second vector, BC,

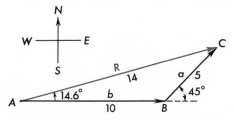

Fig. 6B *Vector diagram for Example 1.*

is next drawn north-east in direction, i.e., at 45°, and 5 cm long. The resultant R is then drawn and measured; its length is found to be 14 cm which represents a displacement of 14 mi. The angle at A measured with a protractor is found to be 14.6°. The answer, therefore, is 14 mi in a direction 14.6° north of east.

To calculate the magnitude of R, it is seen that a right triangle can be formed as shown in Fig. 6C.

* A simplified method for finding the square root of a number to an accuracy of three figures is the following. By inspection, a guess of the square root is made to two figures. For example, if the number is 685, inspection shows that it lies between $(20)^2 = 400$ and $(30)^2 = 900$, and that a reasonable guess might be 25. The original number is then divided by 25 and gives 27.4. The average of these two numbers, 26.2, is then the square root to three figures. If greater accuracy is desired, the averaged number may be assumed to be an original guess and the process repeated.

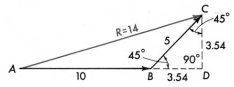

Fig. 6C *Vector diagram for Example 1.*

The right triangle theorem is then applied to the triangle BCD

$$(BC)^2 = (BD)^2 + (CD)^2$$

Since two angles of BCD are equal to each other, the triangle is isosceles and the sides BD and CD are equal. BD = CD. Therefore,

$$(BC)^2 = 2(BD)^2 = 25$$

from which $(BD)^2 = 25/2$

and $BD = \sqrt{12.5} = 3.54$

Applying the same theorem to the right triangle ADC, we get

$$R^2 = (3.54)^2 + (13.54)^2 = 195.8$$

from which $R = 14.0 \text{ mi}$

6.2. The Parallelogram Method of Vector Addition. There are two generally accepted methods of vector addition; namely, the triangle method described in the preceding section and shown in Figs. 6A and 6B, and the parallelogram method described below. Consider, as an illustration of the latter, the addition of the same two vectors given in Fig. 6B, $b = 10$ mi and $a = 5$ mi, the two making an angle of 45° with each other.

As shown at the left in Fig. 6D, the vectors are first drawn outward from the same origin A. From D a dotted line is next drawn parallel to vector b, and from B a dotted line is drawn parallel to vector a, as in diagram (b). From the point C, where these two lines cross, the diagonal line AC is drawn in and labeled with an arrowhead as the resultant R.

A comparison of the parallelogram with the triangle in Fig. 6B shows that if the same scale is used the triangle ABC in both diagrams is identical. Both methods, regardless of the scale used, lead to the same numerical result. In solving certain problems, the triangle method will be found more convenient, while in solving others, the parallelogram is more readily applicable.

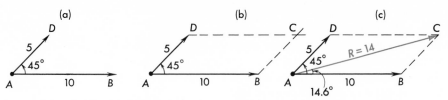

Fig. 6D   *Diagram illustrating the parallelogram method of vector addition.*

There are two common systems by which the directions of vector quantities are designated: one is to refer all angles to the points of the compass as in Figs. 6A and 6B; and the other is to specify all angles with reference to the *x* axis,

As illustrated in Fig. 6G, gravitational forces always act in the direction of a line joining the body and the center of the earth and they are, therefore, perpendicular to the earth's surface at the body.

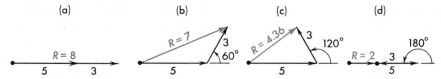

Fig. 6E   *Diagram illustrating the triangle method of vector addition.*

as in Fig. 6D and 6E. In navigation, for example, the *true bearing* of a ship is measured from the *north* clockwise around the compass. To sail east is to have a true bearing of 90°, and to sail south-west is to have a true bearing of 225°.

When directions are referred to the *x* axis, angles measured in a counterclockwise direction from the +*x* axis are called +; those measured clockwise from the same line are called −. For example, the direction-angle for the second vector in Fig. 6E(b) is +60°, or −300°.

6.3. Weight is a Vector. Everyone knows that, when he weighs himself as illustrated in Fig. 6F, he is measuring the downward force he exerts on the foot board of the scales, and that this force causes some mechanism within the scales to indicate his weight. The greater the downward force, the greater is the indicated weight. We are not interested here in the system of levers, weights, or springs within the scales, but rather with the downward force we call our *weight*.

Weight, as explained in detail in the next chapter, is due to the gravitational attraction of the earth for all bodies, and is given by Eq.(5e), in the previous chapter as

$$F_g = mg$$

The term "force" is not confined to weight alone but to the action of any one body upon another. For example, in towing an automobile

Fig. 6F   *Weight is a downward force. The earth attracts all bodies toward its center.*

as shown in Fig. 6H, there are two forces acting: (1) a downward force F_g due to gravity, and (2) a horizontal force F due to a pull on the towline.

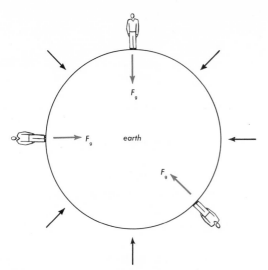

Fig. 6G   *Weight is a force due to gravitational attraction, and gravitational force acts in the direction of a line joining the body and the center of the earth.*

Fig. 6H   *Illustration of two independent forces acting on the same body.*

The latter force is supplied by some external object or machine. In pushing a lawnmower there are also two forces: (1) the downward force F_g due to gravity and (2) a diagonal force F due to some person pushing on the lawnmower handle.

Regardless of the direction in which a force may act, its magnitude may be expressed in *newtons*, *dynes*, or *pounds*. The justification for this is illustrated in Fig. 6I where spring scales are used to measure forces. In diagram (a), the

3-lb weight exerts a downward force of 3 lb. A horizontal force of the same magnitude is produced by running the cord over a pulley as in diagram (b).

This is not to imply that gravitational attraction is responsible for all forces, for it is not; it is only to indicate that all forces, whatever their origin or direction, may be expressed in terms of weight.

6.4. Forces Are Added Vectorially. Since forces have both magnitude and direction, they are vector quantities and, therefore, subject to the rules of *vector addition*. Consider the diagram in Fig. 6J, illustrating a heavy trunk being pulled along the floor by two ropes. With steady pulls of 25 lb and 40 lb exerted in directions at 90° from each other, the trunk moves in a direction indi-

Fig. 6I   *All forces, whether they are vertical, horizontal, or at any angle, may be expressed in terms of weight.*

Fig. 6J   *Two forces acting at an angle to each other are equivalent to a single force acting in a direction between them.*

cated by the dotted arrow. By vector addition, a *resultant* force R can now be found which, upon taking the place of the two forces shown, will produce the same motion.

The addition of the two force vectors of Fig. 6J is illustrated in Fig. 6K. Starting at O, the two

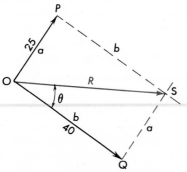

Fig. 6K   *Diagram illustrating the addition of two forces acting at an angle of 90° with each other.*

vectors a and b are first drawn to scale and in their proper directions. The dotted lines QS and PS are next drawn in to complete the parallelogram, and then followed by the diagonal R. With an arrowhead at S, the diagonal represents the resultant whose magnitude R and direction θ is to be calculated by trigonometry.

Since a and b make an angle of 90° with each other, OQS is a right triangle with the sides a, b, and R. By definition from trigonometry,

$$\frac{a}{b} = \tan \theta$$

In this equation, substitute known values, as follows:

$$\frac{25}{40} = 0.6250 = \tan \theta$$

Look up 0.6250 in the tangent column of the table of trigonometric functions, Appendix III. We find that $\theta = 32°$.

Again, by definition,

$$\frac{b}{R} = \cos \theta$$

Since R is the unknown to be calculated, multiply both sides by $R/\cos \theta$, and obtain

$$\frac{b}{\cos \theta} = R$$

Look up the natural cosine of 32° in Appendix III; then, by substitution,

$$R = \frac{40}{0.8480} = 47.2 \text{ lb}$$

The resultant force is, therefore, equal to 47.2 lb at an angle of 32° with OQ.

Example 2. A boat is being towed through a canal by two ropes, one on either side of the canal, as shown at the left in Fig. 6L. If the applied forces are 400 and 600 N, respectively, and the angle between the ropes is 60°, find the magnitude of the resultant force on the boat and the angles the ropes make with the canal. Assume the resultant force to be parallel to the canal.

Fig. 6L   *The pull of two ropes at an angle on a canal boat is equivalent to a single force straight along the canal.*

Solution. The triangle method is applied to the solution of this problem at the right in Fig. 6L. First a vector *b*, 6 cm long, is drawn down and to the right to represent the one force of 600 N. From the end of this vector, and at an angle of 60°, the second vector *a*, 4 cm long, is drawn to represent the other force of 400 N. The line *R* is then drawn in with an arrowhead to represent the resultant force on the boat.

By trigonometry the unknown quantities, (1) the magnitude of *R*, (2) the angle *θ*, and (3) the angle *φ*, can be calculated as follows.

Use the law of cosines for an oblique triangle. (See Appendix VI.)

$$R^2 = a^2 + b^2 + 2ab \cos 60° \qquad (6a)$$

Look up the cosine of 60° in tables and substitute the value in this equation.

$$R^2 = (400)^2 + (600)^2 + 2(400)(600) \times 0.500$$

from which

$$R^2 = 160,000 + 360,000 + 240,000$$

so that

$$R^2 = 760,000 \quad \text{and} \quad R = 872$$

The resultant force $R = 872$ N.

To find angles *φ* and *θ*, either the law of sines or the law of cosines may be used (see Appendix VI). Using the law of cosines to find angle *φ*,

$$\cos \phi = \frac{b^2 + R^2 - a^2}{2bR} = \frac{(600)^2 + (872)^2 - (400)^2}{2 \times 600 \times 872}$$

Thus

$$\cos \phi = 0.9178$$

which from the tables of cosines gives

$$\phi = 23.4°$$

Use the law of sines to find the angle *θ*.

$$\frac{a}{\sin \phi} = \frac{b}{\sin \theta} \qquad (6b)$$

Solving for sin *θ*, and substituting, we find

$$\sin \theta = \frac{b \sin \phi}{a} = \frac{600 \times 0.3971}{400} = 0.5957$$

From the tables of natural sines, we obtain

$$\theta = 36.6°$$

6.5. Force Polygon. When three or more forces act simultaneously upon a body, a single force, called their resultant, can be found which acting alone upon that body will produce the same result. To find such a resultant force, the *polygon method* of vector addition is often employed. In principle, this is an extension of the triangle method and consists of placing the tail of one vector at the head of the one preceding it, and continuing this process until all vectors have been added.

An illustration of the polygon method applied to five forces is given in Fig. 6M. The space diagram at the left shows the forces acting on a body at P, while the *vector diagram* at the right shows the vector addition and the resultant force *R*. Starting at A as the origin, vector AB is drawn 8 cm long, parallel to the 8-lb vector in diagram (a). Vector BC is next drawn 7 cm long and parallel to the 7-lb vector. These are followed in succession by vectors CD, DE, and EF, respec-

(a)

(b)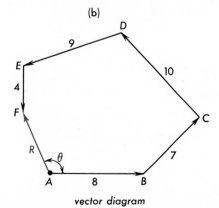

space diagram   vector diagram

Fig. 6M   *Diagrams illustrating the graphical addition of five forces to find their resultant. (The polygon method.)*

tively. With all five vectors added, the resultant R is found by joining the last arrowhead F with the origin A.

Drawn to scale, the measured length of R will give the magnitude of the resultant force, and the measured angle θ will give the direction in which it acts.

To calculate the resultant force R in such a problem, the polygon may be divided up into triangles and all sides and angles of the triangles calculated in their turn.

It is important to know that regardless of the order in which the vectors are drawn to form the force polygon the resultant must, of necessity, be the same. For example, if the vectors were added in the order 4 lb, 7 lb, 9 lb, 8 lb, and 10 lb, each to scale and in its proper direction, the resultant would have the direction and magnitude of R in Fig. 6M. It would be well for the student to construct such other diagrams and find to his own satisfaction that the resultant always comes out the same.

6.6. Resolution of a Force into Components. Many of the problems in mechanics are most easily solved by the so-called "*method of components.*" To apply this method to typical problems, it is necessary that we first see how a single vector may be resolved into two components. Consider as an illustration the known force F, making an angle of θ degrees with the x axis as shown in Fig. 6N.

By dropping lines from A, perpendicular to the x and y axes, the component forces F_x and F_y are equivalent to the original force F, since by adding them vectorially they give F as a resultant.

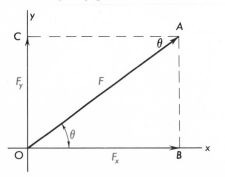

Fig. 6N *The resolution of a vector into two rectangular components.*

With F_x and F_y perpendicular to each other, triangles OAB and OAC are equivalent right triangles with corresponding sides equal. $F_y =$ AB and $F_x =$ AC.

By trigonometry, then,

$$\frac{F_x}{F} = \cos \theta,$$

$$\frac{F_y}{F} = \sin \theta, \qquad (6c)$$

$$\frac{F_y}{F_x} = \tan \theta$$

Since F and θ are usually the known quantities, the first two equations are the most useful in finding the magnitudes of force components. These may be rewritten,

$$\boxed{\begin{aligned} F_x &= F \cos \theta \\ F_y &= F \sin \theta \end{aligned}} \qquad (6d)$$

Example 3. A force of 50 lb is applied to the handle of a 150-lb lawn roller. See Fig. 6O. Calculate

Fig. 6O *The force on the handle of a lawn roller is resolved into two components.*

(a) the horizontal and vertical components of this force if the handle makes an angle of 40° with the horizontal, and (b) the force exerted by the roller on the ground.

Solution. The graphical solution to (a) is shown at the right in Fig. 6O. The magnitudes of the two components F_x and F_y are calculated by direct substitutions in Eq.(6d).

$$F_x = 50 \text{ lb} \times \cos 40°$$
$$F_y = 50 \text{ lb} \times \sin 40°$$

From the tables of natural sines and cosines, substitution gives

$$F_x = 50 \times 0.7660 = 38.3 \text{ lb}$$
$$F_y = 50 \times 0.6428 = 32.1 \text{ lb}$$

The horizontal component, $F_x = 38.3$ lb, is the force causing the roller to move, while the vertical component, $F_y = 32.1$ lb, acting straight downward must be added to the weight of the roller to find the total force exerted by the roller on the ground.

Total downward force = 150 + 32.1 = 182.1 lb

6.7. The Sailboat.

A problem that puzzles many people, particularly those more or less familiar with sailboats, is that of sailing across the water into the wind. This phenomenon, commonly known as *tacking*, is another illustration of the resolution of a force into rectangular components.

As shown in Fig. 6P, the wind is from the east

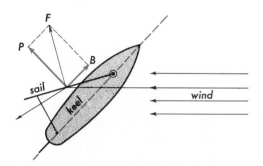

Fig. 6P *A boat sailing into the wind. An example of the resolution of a force F into two rectangular components, P and B.*

and the boat is headed north-east. When the sail is properly set, the wind, in blowing across the canvas, is deflected away in such a way that it exerts a force F normal to the surface as shown. By resolving this force into two rectangular components, one parallel and the other perpendicular to the keel, the force B, responsible for the boat's motion, is found.

The other component, P, has little effect upon the boat since it is perpendicular to the motion. It is a useless force which tends to tip the boat and move it to leeward. To reduce tipping or being pushed sideways, sailboats are equipped with a deep heavy keel. By increasing the angle

between the sail and the wind, the force F will increase but the forward component will decrease. If the boat is headed more directly into the wind, without changing the relative position of the sail and the keel, the useful component B will again decrease. Most rapid progress upwind is attained when the wind and keel make an angle of 45° and the sails are so rigged that the rudder is parallel to the keel.

6.8. Conditions for Equilibrium.

When one or more forces act upon a body at rest, and their resultant sum is not zero, the body will be set into motion. Under such conditions there is an *unbalanced force* acting, and this force alone accounts for the acceleration. If, however, the vector sum of all the forces acting is zero, the body is in equilibrium and the body will either remain at rest or, if moving, maintain constant velocity. To turn this statement around is to say that *"Any object remaining at rest, or moving with uniform motion, is in equilibrium and the resultant of all forces acting upon it is zero."*

If two and only two forces act upon a body in equilibrium, a little study will show that they must be equal in magnitude and opposite in direction. A book lying on the table or a lamp hanging from the ceiling are good examples of dual forces in equilibrium. See Figs. 6Q and 6R.

Fig. 6Q *A book lying on a table is in equilibrium.*

The two forces acting on the book are F_g, the downward pull of the earth, called the *weight*, and F, the upward thrust of the table. Since the book is in equilibrium, the force F is equal in magnitude to the weight F_g. For the lamp in Fig. 6R, the downward force or weight F_g is counterbalanced by the upward force T exerted

Fig. 6R *A lamp hanging from the ceiling is in equilibrium.*

by the cord. Here again, the forces are equal in magnitude and opposite in direction.

It is important to note that a body moving with constant velocity is in equilibrium: since there is no acceleration, there is no unbalanced force.

In the game of tug-of-war, when two opposing teams are pulling with equal but opposite forces at the ends of a rope, a condition of equilibrium exists. As illustrated in Fig. 6S, the force F of

$$-F \quad\quad\quad K \quad\quad\quad F$$
1000 *lb* 〰〰〰〰〰〰〰〰 1000 *lb*

Fig. 6S *The tension in the rope is 1000 lb.*

1000 lb acting to pull the knot K to the right is counterbalanced by an equal but opposite force $-F$ of 1000 lb pulling it to the left. If the two forces become unequal, equilibrium will no longer exist and the knot K will move in the direction of the greater force. It should be noted in the equilibrium case that the tension in the rope is 1000 lb and not 2000 lb. This apparent paradox can be explained away by supposing that one team ties its end of the rope to a post. The other team, still pulling with its 1000 lb, maintains the same equilibrium conditions as before and in so doing maintains the tension of 1000 lb. One team can be looked upon as holding the rope so the other team can pull.

6.9. Three Forces in Equilibrium. When, as the result of the action of three forces, a body is in equilibrium, the *resultant* of all three forces must

be zero. In other words, *to be in equilibrium, the vector sum of the three forces must be zero.* This means that if we draw vectors to scale and add them in their respective directions we will obtain a closed polygon. In this case of three forces the polygon is a triangle. As an illustration, consider the street light suspended from two poles as shown in Fig. 6T.

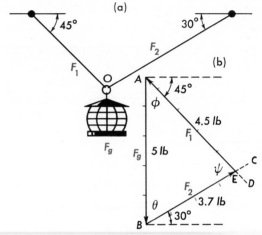

Fig. 6T *Three forces produce equilibrium if their vector sum is zero.*

The three forces acting through the common point O are F_g, the weight of the lamp (5 lb) acting straight downward; F_1, the pull of one rope at 45° up and to the left; and F_2, the pull of the other rope at 30° up and to the right. The force triangle is shown in diagram (b), where vectorially

$$\boxed{\vec{F_g} + \vec{F_1} + \vec{F_2} = 0} \quad\quad (6e)$$

In constructing this diagram, the conditions of equilibrium are imposed as a means of determining the magnitude of the forces F_1 and F_2. The graphical procedure is as follows: a vector of length 5 units is first drawn straight downward to represent F_g, the weight of the light. To the head of this vector at B, a dotted line BC is drawn parallel to the rope exerting the force F_2. From A, another dotted line AD is drawn parallel to the rope exerting the force F_1. At E, where these two lines intersect, the vectors F_1 and F_2 are terminated and arrowheads inserted in the directions shown. The solid lines AE and BE, when measured, are found to have lengths of 4.48 and 3.66 units and represent the forces $F_1 = 4.48$ lb and $F_2 = 3.66$ lb, respectively.

To solve the same problem analytically, the internal angles of the triangle ABE are first determined and then the law of sines is applied to find the lengths of the sides AE and BE. Using the angles given in diagram (b), subtraction gives angle $\phi = 45°$, angle $\theta = 60°$, and angle $\psi = 75°$. By the law of sines,

$$\frac{AE}{\sin \theta} = \frac{F_g}{\sin \psi} \quad \text{or}$$

$$AE = \frac{F_g \sin 60°}{\sin 75°} = \frac{5 \times 0.866}{0.966} = 4.48 \text{ lb}$$

and

$$\frac{BE}{\sin \phi} = \frac{F_g}{\sin \psi} \quad \text{or}$$

$$BE = \frac{F_g \sin 45°}{\sin 75°} = \frac{5 \times 0.707}{0.966} = 3.66 \text{ lb}$$

The magnitudes of the forces are therefore $F_1 = 4.48$ lb and $F_2 = 3.66$ lb.

6.10. The Inclined Plane. As another illustration of the resolution of a force into rectangular components and the principle of equilibrium, consider the following problem. A boy wishes to pull a small 100-lb wagon up a 50% grade. Such a grade, as shown in Fig. 6U, is one in which for every 100 ft measured along the horizontal there is a vertical rise of 50 ft. The angle θ of such an incline is given by

$$\tan \theta = \frac{50}{100} = 0.500$$

from which $\qquad \theta = 26.5°$

To find how hard the boy must pull on the wagon, the downward force F_g, called the weight, is resolved into two components, one a force Q parallel to the inclined plane and the other N perpendicular to it. Resolution is shown graphically in diagram (b). The component N, being perpendicular to the inclined plane, neither aids nor hinders the motion up or down. The component Q represents the force which, in the absence of a counterbalancing force, would accelerate the wagon down the incline. To pull the wagon the boy must, therefore, exert a force P up the incline equal to or greater than Q. Once the wagon is started, a force P, equal to Q, will keep it moving with constant velocity.

To find the magnitudes of Q and N, it will be noted that the triangle NOF_g at the right and the triangle CAB at the left are similar triangles. The side ON is perpendicular to AB, and OF_g is perpendicular to AC. This relation makes angles θ equal. Since both triangles are right triangles we can write

$$\sin \theta = \frac{Q}{F_g}$$

$$\cos \theta = \frac{N}{F_g}$$

Solving for Q and N, we obtain,

$$Q = F_g \sin \theta$$
$$N = F_g \cos \theta$$

If we substitute known values for F_g and θ, we obtain,

$$Q = 100 \times 0.4462 = 44.6 \text{ lb}$$
$$N = 100 \times 0.8949 = 89.5 \text{ lb}$$

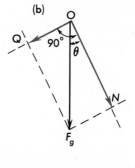

Fig. 6U   *The resolution of a force into components.*

Fig. 6V *Experiment illustrating equilibrium conditions for a car on an inclined plane.*

An experiment illustrating the above example and its solution is shown in Fig. 6V. A car with a mass of 1000 g is held in equilibrium on a 26.5° inclined plane by two cords passing over pulleys to masses of 446 g and 895 g. One cord runs parallel and the other perpendicular to the incline. If P is increased or decreased slightly the car will move up or down the plane, whereas if M is increased slightly the car will be lifted from the plane. The removal of the inclined plane entirely does not alter the equilibrium of the suspended mass. The three forces acting to maintain equilibrium are P, M, and F_g.

Gram masses may be used as weights in this experimental demonstration since the respective forces they exert are obtained by multiplying each mass by the same factor g ($g = 980$ cm/s²). The resultant three forces of 437,000 dynes, 877,000 dynes, and 980,000 dynes respectively, when added vectorially will form a closed triangle. Although mass is a scalar and not a vector, the masses are directly proportional to their weights, and their numbers 446, 895, and 1000 can be used just as well in drawing the vectors to scale to form a closed triangle. This is left as an exercise for the student.

PROBLEMS

1. Two forces of 45 N and 72 N, respectively, are exerted at the same time to pull a log over the ground. If the angle between the forces is 50°, find their resultant and specify the angle it makes with the larger force (a) graphically, and (b) by calculation.

2. Two forces of 38 lb and 64 lb, respectively, act on a trunk to pull it across the floor of a warehouse. If the angle between the forces is 65°, find their resultant and specify the angle it makes with the larger force, (a) graphically, and (b) by calculation. [*Ans.* (a) 87.2 lb at 23.3°].

3. A canal boat is being pulled by two ropes making an angle of 30° with each other. If the forces are 220 lb and 280 lb, respectively, what is the magnitude and direction of the resultant force? Specify the angle with respect to the larger force. Draw a vector diagram to scale to check your answer.

4. Determine the resultant of two forces, (a) 60 N at 30°, and (b) 80 N at 150°. Directions are specified with respect to the +x axis. Make a vector diagram. [*Ans.* 72.1 N at +103.9°.]

5. Find the magnitude and direction of the resultant of two forces, (a) 42 N at 45°, and (b) 56 N at 120°. Directions are specified with respect to the +x axis. Make a vector diagram to scale.

6. Calculate the magnitude and direction of the resultant of two forces: (a) 52 N at 150°, and (b) 36 N at 225°. Directions are specified with respect to the +x axis. Make a vector diagram. [*Ans.* 70.5 N at 179.5°.]

7. Find the resultant of two forces, one of 38 N vertically upward, and the other of 25 N making an angle of 75° with the vertical. Specify the resultant with respect to the horizontal. Make a vector diagram to scale.

8. Two forces of 12 N and 8 N, respectively, are exerted at direction angles of 210° and 300°, respectively. Find the magnitude and direction of the resultant force. Draw a vector diagram. [*Ans.* 14.4 N at 243.7°.]

9. A vertically upward force of 25 N is combined with a second force directed at an angle of 20° with the horizontal. If their resultant has a direction of 50°, find (a) the magnitude of the second force, and (b) the magnitude of the resultant. Make a vector diagram.

10. Find the resultant of the following three forces: (a) 60 N at 20°, (b) 39 N at 110°, and (c) 45 N at 170°. Check your answer by a vector diagram drawn to scale. [*Ans.* 65 N at 91.2°.]

11. Find the x and y components of a force of 56 N acting in a direction of 32° with respect to the +x axis. Draw a vector diagram.

12. Find the x and y components of a force of 12 lb acting in a direction making an angle of 68° with respect to the +x axis. Make a scale diagram. [*Ans.* $F_x = 4.50$ lb, and $F_y = 11.1$ lb.]

13. A force F of 60 N is to be resolved into two components at right angles to each other. (a) What are the magnitudes of the two forces if one is four times the other, and (b) what is the angle between the force F and the larger component?

14. A heavy box weighing 150 lb is pulled along a station platform by a 75-lb force applied at an angle of 30° with the horizontal. Find (a) the horizontal component, (b) the vertical component, and (c) the resultant downward

force on the floor. Draw a graph. [*Ans.* (a) 64.9 lb, (b) 37.5 lb, (c) 112.5 lb.]

15. A sailboat is tacking at 45° into the wind. If the resultant force exerted by the wind on the sail is 240 lb, and the boom makes an angle of 25° with the keel, find the forward thrust on the boat. Make a diagram.

16. A tractor with a mass of 4500 Kg stands idle on the side of a hill where the slope makes an angle of 28° with the horizontal. Find the component of the tractor's weight (a) in a direction parallel to the slope, and (b) perpendicular to the slope. [*Ans.* (a) 20,700 N, (b) 38,900 N.]

17. A car on an incline going up a mountain has a mass of 2400 Kg when fully loaded. (a) What is the tension in the cable to hold the car stationary on the track if the angle the incline makes with the horizontal is 30°? (b) What are the magnitudes of the three forces acting on the car that keep it in equilibrium? Make a diagram.

18. A boy weighing 90 lb sits in a swing. (a) With what force should he pull on a horizontal rope to keep the swing at 20° to the vertical? (b) Find the tension in the rope. Make a diagram. [*Ans.* (a) 32.8 lb, (b) 95.8 lb.]

19. The two ends of a chain 6 m long are fastened to hooks that are 4 m apart in the ceiling of a garage. A car motor with a mass of 160 Kg hangs from the midpoint of the chain. Find the tension in the chain. Make a diagram.

20. What single force will balance the following two forces and produce equilibrium: (a) 65 N at 40°, and (b) 45 N at 110°. [*Ans.* 90.8 N at 247.8°.]

21. A man with a sailboat wishes to go 5 mi down a river in which the water flows at 5 mi/hr. When on shore he notes that there is no wind. Should he use his sail to shorten the time of his trip? If so, how should he set his sail?

22. A body is acted upon by the two following forces: 45 N at +60°, and 34 N at +330°. Find (a) the sum of the x components, and (b) the sum of the y components. Calling these two sums X and Y respectively, find (c) the vector sum of X and Y. Make a force diagram to scale. [*Ans.* (a) +51.9 N, (b) +22.0 N, (c) 56.4 N at 23°.]

NEWTON'S LAW OF GRAVITATION AND THIRD LAW OF MOTION

Nearly everyone has heard the story of how young Isaac Newton, while sitting under an apple tree one day, was struck on the head by a falling apple. This incident set Newton to thinking about falling bodies and led him at the early age of twenty-three to the discovery of the law of gravity.

7.1. Newton's Law of Gravitation. It has often been said incorrectly that Newton discovered gravity. What Newton discovered was the *universal law of gravitation. Any two bodies attract each other with a force proportional to the product of their masses and inversely proportional to the square of the distance between them.* Written in algebraic symbols,

$$F \propto \frac{m_1 m_2}{d^2}$$

As illustrated in Fig. 7A, F is the force of attraction, m_1 and m_2 are the two masses, and d is the distance between them. Mass m_1 pulls on m_2 with a force F to the left and m_2 pulls on m_1

To make an equation of this symbolism it is only necessary to replace the proportionality constant above by an equal sign and insert a constant on either side of the equality.

$$F = -G \frac{m_1 m_2}{d^2} \qquad (7a)$$

The minus sign signifies the force is one of attraction.

Experiment shows that, if F is measured in newtons, m_1 and m_2 in kilograms, and d in meters, the "Newtonian constant of gravitation" G has the value

$$G = 6.66 \times 10^{-11} \frac{\text{m}^3}{\text{Kg s}^2} \qquad (7b)$$

If F is in dynes, m_1 and m_2 in grams, and d in centimeters,

$$G = 6.66 \times 10^{-8} \frac{\text{cm}^3}{\text{gm s}^2}$$

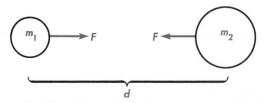

Fig. 7A *The gravitational attraction of one body of mass m_1 for another of mass m_2.*

with an equal force F to the right. These two forces are equal in magnitude but opposite in direction.*

* Newton's law of gravitation is presented before his third law of motion since gravitational forces always exist in pairs, and are needed to explain action and reaction forces as they apply to bodies at rest and in motion.

If F is in pounds, m_1 and m_2 in slugs, and d in feet,

$$G = 3.41 \times 10^{-8} \frac{\text{ft}^3}{\text{sl s}^2} \qquad (7c)$$

To obtain some idea of the magnitude of gravitational forces, consider the following example:

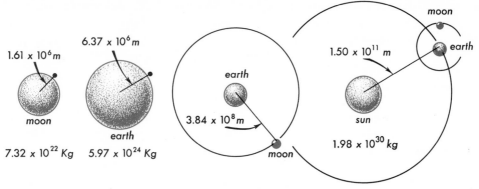

Fig. 7B   *Gravitational attraction keeps the moon in its orbit around the earth, and the earth in its orbit around the sun.*

Example 1. Calculate the force of attraction between two masses of 1 Kg each, held in the hands 10 cm apart.

Solution. By substitution in Eq.(7a),

$$F = -6.66 \times 10^{-11} \frac{m^3}{Kg\,s^2} \cdot \frac{1\,Kg \times 1\,Kg}{(0.1\,m)^2}$$

$$F = -6.66 \times 10^{-9} \frac{Kg\,m}{s^2}$$

$$F = -6.66 \times 10^{-9}\,N$$

This force is far too small to be detected by the muscle senses of the hands or arms.

7.2. The Cavendish Experiment. This famous experiment was performed by Henry Cavendish* in the year 1797 to 1798, and is frequently referred to as "weighing the earth." The principal features of the experiment consisted of determining the attracting forces between two pairs of lead spheres by means of a torsion balance and from these measurements determining the value of *G*. A diagram of the apparatus is shown in Fig. 7C. A rod 6 ft long was supported at its

* Henry Cavendish (1731–1810), English chemist and physicist, elder son of Lord Charles Cavendish, brother of the third duke of Devonshire, and Lady Anne Grey, daughter of the duke of Kent, was born at Nice on October 10, 1731. Although one of the richest men of his time through inheritance, he devoted his life to scientific work. He had little interest in society, always avoided the attention of his fellows, and never married. He was a member of the Royal Society and is best known for his experiments on gravitational attraction. He is also noted for his contributions to the chemistry of gases, and for his work on electrical capacitors and the inverse square law of force between electrical charges.

center by a long wire P. At the ends of the rod were two lead balls, m_1 and m_2, each 2 in. in diameter. Two lead spheres, M_1 and M_2, each 12 in. in diameter, were then placed on either

Fig. 7C   *The Cavendish experiment. Weighing the earth.*

side as shown. Gravitational attraction between m_1 and M_1 and between m_2 and M_2 caused the rod C to turn through a small angle and come to rest in some position like that shown by the solid line.

The shifting of M_1 and M_2 to the opposite sides of m_1 and m_2 caused the rod C to turn to a new position indicated by the dotted line. The angle through which the rod turned was measured by a small telescope or by reflection of a beam of light from a small mirror R onto a distant scale. From previous measurements of the stiffness of the supporting wire P, and a measure of the angle turned through, the force of attraction between the masses could be calculated.

If we neglect cross attractions of the right sphere on the left ball and the left sphere on the right ball, this angle between the two positions is assumed to be four times as great as that caused by the deflection of the rod, due to the attraction force of only one sphere on one ball.

It will now be shown how this measured force F in such an experiment makes it possible to calculate the earth's mass. If we know the masses of m_1 and M_1 by weighing, and the distance between them, d, from measurement, these known values can be substituted in Eq.(7a) and the only unknown quantity, G, calculated. The value which will be found is that given in Eqs.(7b) and (7c).

Consider now the attraction between the earth, of unknown mass M, and a 1-Kg mass on its surface, as shown in Fig. 7D. In this instance,

Fig. 7D *The earth exerts a downward force of 9.80 newtons on each kilogram of mass on its surface.*

the force on the 1-Kg mass is known. The force is just 9.8 N, for it can be calculated from Newton's second law, Eq.(5e), using the measured acceleration due to gravity $g = 9.8$ m/s^2 (see Fig. 5K).

From experimental measurements and calculations, the following quantities are therefore known.

$m = 1$ Kg $G = 6.66 \times 10^{-11}$ m^3/Kg s^2
$F = -9.8$ N $d = 3960$ mi $= 6.37 \times 10^6$ m

Substituting these values in Eq.(7a), the only unknown quantity, the mass of the earth M, can be calculated. Letting $m_1 = m$ and $m_2 = M$,

$$F = -G \frac{m \times M}{d^2}$$

Solving for M, and substituting the known quantities, we obtain

$$M = \frac{F \times d^2}{m \times G} = \frac{9.8 \times (6.37 \times 10^6)^2}{1 \times 6.66 \times 10^{-11}}$$
$$= 5.97 \times 10^{24} \text{ Kg}$$

This is a reasonable value for the earth's mass, for if it is divided by the earth's volume, $\frac{4}{3}\pi r^3$, the average density of 5400 Kg/m^3 or *5.4 g/cm^3* is obtained. The average density of the rocks found at and near the earth's surface is 2700 Kg/m^3 or 2.7 g/cm^3. This means, therefore, that deep within the earth's body the average density must rise to 8000 to 10,000 Kg/m^3. Such values are entirely reasonable since most metals have just such densities.

The above experiment is assumed, therefore, to be correct in principle and to be a means for determining the mass of the earth.

Earth's mass $M = 5.97 \times 10^{24}$ Kg

7.3. Newton's Third Law of Motion. Of Newton's three laws of motion the third is the least understood. This is probably due to the fact that it is seldom used in solving problems, and often when it is used it is incorrectly applied. The law states:

*To every action force there is an equal and opposite reaction force.**

The principle of action and reaction may be illustrated by a bat striking a ball, Fig. 7E. During impact the bat exerts a force F on the ball, and the ball exerts an equal but opposite force B on the bat. The force F being exerted on the ball gives it an acceleration to the right, while the force B being exerted on the bat gives it an acceleration to the left. The ball speeds up during the impact and acquires a high velocity, while the bat in the same time interval slows down to a lower velocity. The impulse Ft from the bat gives the ball a momentum mv [see Eq.(5m)]. The impulse Bt from the ball decreases the momentum of the bat from a higher value to one of lower value.

* Newton's third law, as published in Latin in his "Principia" is, Lex. III. Actioni contrariam semper et aequalem esse reactionem; sive corporum duorum actiones in se mutuo semper esse aequales et in partes contrarias dirigi.

Fig. 7E   *A bat at all times exerts a force on the ball equal in magnitude to the force that the ball exerts on the bat.*

Consider the second example of a block hanging by a cord as illustrated in Fig. 7F. The weight of the block F_g is the force with which the earth pulls downward on the block, while the equal and opposite force X is the upward force exerted by the block on the earth.

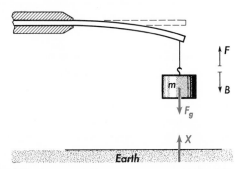

Fig. 7F   *Diagram illustrating Newton's third law of motion. Forces always exist in pairs.*

In addition to this pair of forces, the block exerts a downward force B on the cord, while the cord pulls upward with the reaction force F. Although to many people these forces may seem confusing, it should be pointed out that Newton himself had some difficulty in applying his third

law to certain problems. The difficulty arises from trying to apply action and reaction forces to the same body when in reality they apply to different ones.

It is important to note that the action force and the reaction force in Newton's third law of motion act on different bodies.

Whether a body is at rest or in motion, the state of that body depends upon the forces acting on it and not upon the forces it exerts on something else. So far as the body is concerned, the latter do not determine its motion.

7.4. Isolating a Body. Forces are vector quantities and must be added by the principles of vector addition. To illustrate, the block in Fig. 7F remains at rest because two equal and opposite forces are acting upon it. To see what these forces are, the body is isolated by drawing a dotted line around it as shown in Fig. 7G.

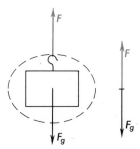

Fig. 7G   *Balanced forces produce equilibrium.*

Only those forces acting on the body from outside this boundary determine its state or motion. The earth is pulling down on the block with a force F_g while the cord is pulling up on the block with an equal but opposite force F. By vector addition shown at the right, the resultant force must be zero. (It should be noted that F and F_g are not an action and reaction pair, even though they happen here to be equal.)

Suppose in Fig. 7F that the force F is increased to a value greater than F_g. The block will then have an unbalanced force acting and it will be accelerated upward. By vector addition, as shown in Fig. 7H, the resultant upward force is equal to $F - F_g$. The acceleration can be calculated by applying Newton's second law, $F = ma$, the force here being $F - F_g$.

$$F - F_g = ma \qquad (7d)$$
resultant force = mass × acceleration

If, on the other hand, the force F is smaller than the weight F_g, the body will be accelerated

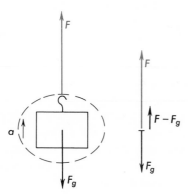

Fig. 7H   *Because of a resultant force, $F - F_g$, the body is accelerated upward.*

downward and $F_g - F$ is the resultant force acting. Again applying Newton's second law,

$$F_g - F = ma \qquad (7e)$$
resultant force = mass × acceleration

In each case, the smaller force is subtracted from the larger to make the acceleration come out with a positive sign in the direction of motion.

Example 2. An elevator weighing 1000 lb is raised and lowered by a cable fastened at the top. Calculate the upward force exerted by the cable when the elevator (a) starts up with an acceleration of 2.4 ft/s²; (b) is rising with constant velocity; (c) starts down with an acceleration of 2.4 ft/s²; and (d) goes down with constant velocity.

Solution. (a) For acceleration upward, Eq.(7d) is applied. By direct substitution,

$$F - 1000 \text{ lb} = \frac{1000}{32} \text{ sl} \times 2.4 \text{ ft/s}^2$$

Hence

$$F = 1000 \text{ lb} + 75 \text{ lb} = 1075 \text{ lb}$$

(b) Moving upward with constant velocity, the elevator has no acceleration. With $a = 0$, Eq.(7d) becomes

$$F - F_g = 0 \qquad \text{or} \qquad F = F_g$$

The upward force, or tension, in the cable equals the weight of the elevator, 1000 lb.

(c) For acceleration downward, Eq.(7e) is used. By direct substitution,

$$1000 \text{ lb} - F = \frac{1000}{32} \text{ sl} \times 2.4 \text{ ft/s}^3$$

so that

$$F = 1000 \text{ lb} - 75 \text{ lb} = 925 \text{ lb}$$

(d) Moving downward with constant velocity, the elevator has no acceleration, and the tension in the cable is 1000 lb.

7.5. The Train-and-Track Experiment. Another illustration of Newton's third law is that of a train on a track, both of which, the track as well as the train, are free to move. The drive wheels push back on the track with a force B, and the track pushes forward on the wheels with an equal and opposite force F. These two form an action and reaction pair.

In Fig. 7I, the track is mounted on a large wheel with its axis of rotation vertical. With the

Fig. 7I   *Demonstration of Newton's third law of motion. The train moves forward, and the track, if free to move, moves backward.*

track free to move, both forces of the pair are seen to be real; the track moves backward and the train moves forward. The track moves backward because the wheels exert a force B upon it in that direction, and the train goes forward because the track exerts a force F upon it in that direction. If, when the train acquires a certain velocity, the power is shut off, the force F *vanishes*—so also does B—and by Newton's first law of motion the train and track would be expected to continue to move with constant speed.

In a practical case, however, the track is not only fastened down, but there is some frictional resistance to motion. Because of this friction the track pushes backward on the wheels with a force b, and the wheels push forward on the track with an equal but opposite force f.

In order to keep a train moving with constant speed, a minimum force B great enough to overcome friction must continually be supplied to the locomotive drive wheels. The two forces acting on the train, then, are F and b, and if these are equal and opposite they have a zero resultant. There being no resultant force, there is no acceleration, and the train continues to move with constant velocity.

To start the train moving, and to maintain an acceleration, F must be greater than b. Under these conditions the acceleration, by Newton's second law, is

$$F - b = ma$$
resultant force = mass × acceleration

7.6. The Atwood Machine. The Atwood Machine is a contrivance often used in the physics laboratory for determining the acceleration of gravity. The experiment involves the application of Newton's Second Law to the acceleration of a set of masses, as shown in Fig. 7J. Two equal

Fig. 7J *Schematic diagram of the Atwood machine.*

masses are fastened to the ends of a long cord which passes over a light-weight ball-bearing pulley P. At a given instant, a small mass, called a rider, is added to one side, thus setting the system moving with an acceleration a.

By measuring the distances moved in 1, 2, 3, 4, and 5 s, and knowing the values of the masses m_1 and m_2, the acceleration a can be calculated.

The first step in deriving the appropriate equation to be used for this experiment is to use the *force equation*, $F = ma$. On the left side of Fig. 7J there is the downward force due to gravity, acting on mass m_1.

$$F_{g1} = m_1g \qquad (7f)$$

Similarly, on the right side, there is the downward pull on m_2.

$$F_{g2} = m_2g \qquad (7g)$$

Since these two forces oppose each other, the resultant force F, causing the acceleration of the system, is their difference $F_{g2} - F_{g1}$.

$$F = F_{g2} - F_{g1} \qquad (7h)$$

From Eqs.(7f) and (7g), and subtracting equals from equals, we obtain,

$$F_{g2} - F_{g1} = m_2g - m_1g$$

By the distributive law, this gives,

$$F_{g2} - F_{g1} = (m_2 - m_1)g \qquad (7i)$$

Neglecting the mass of the cord and pulley, the total moving mass is $m_2 + m_1$. Therefore, by substituting in the force equation,

$$(m_2 - m_1)g = (m_2 + m_1)a$$
force = mass × acceleration

which upon solving for g, becomes

$$g = \frac{m_2 + m_1}{m_2 - m_1} a \qquad (7j)$$

To calculate the tension in the cord passing over the pulley, the force equation can be applied to either one of the masses separately. For example the forces acting on m_1 are F_{g1} acting downward, and T acting upward. Since m_1 is moving upward with the acceleration a, the tension T is greater than F_{g1}. The resultant of these two forces is therefore upward and equal to $T - F_{g1}$. By the force equation, we can write,

$$T - F_{g1} = m_1a$$

Knowing F_{g1}, m_1, and a from Eq.(7j), the tension T can be calculated.

PROBLEMS

1. Two large bronze spheres, each with a mass of 10,000 Kg, are located side by side with their centers 2 m apart. Calculate the force of attraction between them.

2. A space ship with a mass of 20,000 Kg circles the earth at a distance of 6.3×10^5 m above the surface. (a) Calculate the gravitational pull the earth exerts on the ship at that distance. (b) What would be the gravitational pull when the ship is on the earth's surface? [*Ans.* (a) 1.62×10^5 N, (b) 1.96×10^5 N.]

3. A 16-lb lead shotput used in track and field meets has a mass of 7.26 Kg and a diameter of 10.7 cm. If two such balls are lying on a shelf with their centers 20 cm apart, what is the magnitude of the gravitational force between them?

4. Two army tanks each with a mass of 50,000 Kg pass each other. If the distance between their centers at closest approach is 6 m, what is the gravitational force between them in (a) newtons, and (b) pounds? [*Ans.* (a) 0.00462 N, (b) 0.00104 lb.]

5. From the values given in Fig. 7B, find the gravitational pull of the earth on the moon. Compare your result with the answer to Problem 6.

6. From the values given in Fig. 7B, find the average gravitational pull of the sun on the moon. [*Ans.* 4.29×10^{20} N.]

7. A man whose mass is 75 Kg stands in an elevator rising at constant speed of 2 m/s. With what force is (a) the earth pulling down on him, and (b) the elevator pushing up on his feet?

8. A man weighing 160 lb is driving a car along a straight and level highway at a speed of 60 mi/hr. What are the magnitudes, directions, and sources of the two forces acting on him? [*Ans.* (a) Earth pulling down with 160 lb, and (b) car seat pushing up with 160 lb.]

9. An elevator car of 500 Kg contains 5 persons whose average mass is 70 Kg. Find the tension in the cable supporting this total load if it is (a) standing still, (b) moving upward with an acceleration of 0.5 m/s², and (c) starting downward with the same acceleration.

10. Three solid steel spheres, each with a mass of 30 Kg, are located at the corners of an equilateral triangle. Find the gravitational force on each sphere if each side of the triangle is 25 cm. [*Ans.* 1.66×10^{-6} N.]

11. Four solid lead spheres, each with a mass of 8 Kg, are located with their centers at the corners of a square. Find the gravitational force on each sphere if the sides of the square are 20 cm.

12. The concrete bucket of a hoist has a mass of 950 Kg when fully loaded. If it is given an initial upward acceleration of 0.40 m/s², what is the tension in the cable in (a) newtons, and (b) pounds? [*Ans.* (a) 9690 N, (b) 2180 lb.]

13. A man weighing 160 lb stands on a spring scale which is itself resting on the floor of an elevator car. What will the scale read when (a) the elevator car starts up with an acceleration of 2 ft/s², and (b) starts down with the same acceleration?

14. Two masses of 3.5 Kg and 4.5 Kg, respectively, are fastened to opposite ends of a strong cord, and the cord hung over a pulley. Neglecting the mass of the cord and pulley, calculate (a) the resultant force acting to accelerate the system, (b) the acceleration of the system, and (c) the tension in the cord. [*Ans.* (a) 9.8 N, (b) 1.225 m/s², (c) 38.6 N.]

15. A 6-Kg mass and a 9-Kg mass are fastened to opposite ends of a cord, and the cord hung over a pulley. Neglecting the mass of the cord and pulley, find (a) the resultant force accelerating the system, (b) the acceleration of the system, and (c) the tension in the cord.

16. A small car with ball-bearing wheels and a mass of 4 Kg rests on a level table top. A string fastened to the car passes over a pulley at the end of the table, and a mass of 1 Kg hangs from the end of the string. Assume the string between the car and the pulley is horizontal. Upon release of the car, find (a) the resultant force accelerating the system, (b) the acceleration of the car, and (c) the tension in the string. Neglect the mass of the cord and pulley. Make a diagram. [*Ans.* (a) 9.8 N, (b) 1.96 m/s², (c) 7.84 N.]

FRICTION AND STREAMLINING

In the preceding chapters on mechanics, the formulas presented, the experiments described, and the problems solved were idealized to the extent that all friction was neglected. Since friction does exist, and in some cases is not negligibly small, a quantitative treatment of friction becomes a necessity in the solving of many problems.

8.1. Friction. Whenever one body slides over another, frictional forces opposing the motion are developed between them. Such forces are due largely to the atomic and molecular attractive forces at the small *contact areas* (see Fig. 8A). Within limits, the smoothness of the

Fig. 8A *The relatively small contact areas between two bodies have a much larger apparent contact area.*

surfaces does not greatly affect *f*, the force of sliding friction. If the surfaces are smooth there will be many small areas in contact, while if they are rough there may be fewer but larger ones. It is well known that surfaces of the same material show greater friction than do surfaces of different materials. This is one of the reasons why machine bearings are often made of one metal like bronze while their rotating shafts are made of another like steel.

Experiments show that to start a body sliding requires a greater force than that needed to keep it moving. In other words *static friction*, or *starting friction*, is greater than *kinetic friction*. Once a body is moving, however, the force of sliding friction increases only slightly with increasing speed and then remains nearly constant over a moderate range of speeds.

Recent experiments,* particularly with metals in contact, show that, when one surface is pressed against another and sliding is brought about, the enormous pressures existing at the tiny contact areas cause a kind of welding of the two materials. With all materials in general, the atoms and molecules are so close together at the contact areas that strong mutual attractive forces often pull microscopic bits of material from one body to the other as they move along. To start a body moving is to break these bonds simultaneously, while to keep it moving is to break them smoothly and continuously.†

The general statement can be made that wherever there is motion there is friction. All forms of friction may be classified as one of three kinds—

sliding friction
rolling friction
fluid friction

Sliding and rolling friction are usually confined to solids while fluid friction applies to liquids and gases. Generally speaking, sliding friction

* Review by Frederic Palmer, *Am. J. Phys.*, **17**, 327 (1949).

† For details on all kinds of friction origins see *Am. J. Phys.*, **31**, No. 12, 1963.

is greater than fluid friction at low speeds, while the reverse is true at high speeds.

8.2. Sliding Friction. A quantitative treatment of sliding friction will be given here as the result of a simple laboratory experiment illustrated in Fig. 8B. In diagram (a), a block of wood of mass

Fig. 8B *Sliding friction is proportional to the normal force pushing the surfaces together and is independent of the apparent area of contact.*

500 g is shown being pulled with uniform speed across a table top by the weight F_g of a 100-g mass. The latter force has been arrived at by trying different loads on the hook at the right. A load greater than 100 g will accelerate the block, while a load smaller than 100 g will allow it to stop. Moving with constant speed, the applied force F_g is just counterbalanced by f, the force of sliding friction.

In diagram (b), a second block of mass 500 g is added to make the sliding mass 1000 g. By experiment, the force required to pull the two with constant speed is given by the weight of a 200-g mass. Should a third and then a fourth block be added successively, the weights of 300- and 400-g masses, respectively, will be found necessary to pull them. From these results we can draw the following conclusions:

The force of sliding friction f is directly proportional to the total downward or normal force N.

$$f \propto N \qquad (8a)$$

When the two blocks in diagram (b) are connected in tandem, one behind the other as in diagram (c), the force of friction is still the weight of a 200-g mass.

Again, if the single block in diagram (a) is turned on edge as in diagram (d), the weight of a 100-g mass is just enough to slide it with constant speed. These observations, along with the results of other similar experiments, may be explained largely in terms of molecular attractive forces. In general, the total contact area where molecular attraction is effective (see Fig. 8A) is small compared with the total apparent area. When a greater force is applied normal to the surfaces, the contact areas increase in size and number, and the following relations are found to hold reasonably true.

(1) The total contact area is proportional to the total normal force.

(2) The total contact area is independent of the total apparent area.

(3) The force of sliding friction is proportional to the total contact area.

(4) The force of sliding friction is proportional to the total normal force.*

Introducing the Greek letter μ as a constant of proportionality, Eq.(8a) becomes

$$f = \mu N \qquad (8b)$$

μ is called the *coefficient of sliding friction*, and is defined as the ratio

$$\boxed{\mu = \frac{f}{N}} \qquad (8c)$$

By knowing the value of μ for a given pair of surfaces, one is able to calculate the force of friction f in terms of the normal force N. Average values of μ for a number of surfaces are given in Table 8A.

As an illustration of the general use of the coefficient of sliding friction, consider the following problem, diagramed in Fig. 8C.

* Curiously enough, an increased normal force increases the pressure over the apparent area but not over the contact area. The proportionate increase in total contact area with increased force means that the force of friction on unit contact area is independent of apparent pressure.

TABLE 8A. COEFFICIENTS OF SLIDING FRICTION
FOR A FEW COMMON MATERIALS
(AVERAGE VALUES FOR DRY SURFACES)

Material	μ
Oak on oak.	0.25
Rubber on concrete.	0.70
Metals on oak.	0.55
Metals on elm.	0.20
Hemp on oak.	0.53
Pine on pine.	0.35
Steel on steel.	0.18
Greased surfaces.	0.05
Iron on concrete.	0.30
Leather on metals.	0.56
Steel on babbit.	0.14
Rubber on oak.	0.46

Example 1. What force is required to pull an iron box weighing 60 lb across a smooth oak floor?

Solution. From Table 8A, μ for metals on oak is 0.55. The normal force N is the weight of the box, or 60 lb. Substituting in Eq.(8b), the force of friction is found to be

$$f = 0.55 \times 60 \text{ lb} = 33 \text{ lb}$$

The general observation that sliding friction increases only slightly at low speeds and levels

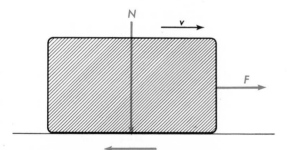

Fig. 8C *Sliding friction f is proportional to the normal force N pushing the surfaces together.*

off to become practically constant at higher speeds is illustrated by the experimental values given in Table 8B.

If the force F applied to a body is greater than that required to overcome friction f, the resultant force $(F - f)$ is effective in producing acceleration. As an equation of motion, Newton's force equation takes the form

$$\boxed{F - f = ma} \qquad (8d)$$

resultant force = mass $\times$ acceleration

Solving for F, we get

$$F = f + ma$$

or,

$$F = \mu N + ma$$

8.3. Angle of Uniform Slip. One method of measuring the coefficient of sliding friction is to

TABLE 8B. COEFFICIENT OF SLIDING FRICTION OF
PINE ON WALNUT WOOD

Speed (cm/s)	μ
0	0.210
1.00	0.142
2.30	0.154
3.87	0.163
6.21	0.172
8.54	0.177
10.00	0.179
11.50	0.181
12.81	0.183
17.50	0.184

place a block on an inclined plane and then tilt the plane until the block slides down with constant speed (see Fig. 8D). When this condition exists, Eq.(8b) can be imposed directly

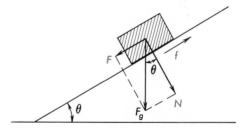

Fig. 8D *Illustration of the angle of uniform slip for a block on an inclined plane.*

upon the components of the weight F_g. The component F is equal in magnitude to f, the sliding friction, and the component N is the normal force pushing the two surfaces together. If θ is the angle of the incline, then

$$\mu = \frac{f}{N} = \frac{F}{N} = \frac{F_g \sin \theta}{F_g \cos \theta} = \tan \theta$$

which gives

$$\mu = \tan \theta \qquad (8e)$$

The coefficient of friction μ equals the tangent of the angle of uniform slip. The angle of uniform slip is defined as that angle of an incline that will keep a body sliding down it with constant speed. At a steeper angle the force component F down the plane is greater than that required to overcome friction f, and the difference between them produces an acceleration as given by Eq.(8d).

8.4. Rolling Friction. A comparison of the force required to slide a heavy box along the ground with the force required to move it on rollers shows that sliding friction is many times greater than rolling friction. It is for this reason that wheels are used on vehicles instead of runners, and that ball-bearings are employed in some machines in place of sleeve-bearings.

A comparison of the sleeve type of bearing with a ball-bearing is made in Fig. 8E. The

Fig. 8E   *Sleeve bearings and ball bearings illustrate the two kinds of friction: (a) sliding friction, and (b) rolling friction. (Note: the clearance in the sleeve bearing is exaggerated.)*

rotating axle, as shown at the left, slides on the bottom of the sleeve at low speeds and climbs

part way up the side as the speed increases. The purpose of lubricating such bearings with oils and greases is to keep the two metal surfaces from coming into direct contact. Properly lubricated, the axle rides on a thin film of oil. In diagram (b) it may be seen how the axle rolls around on the balls with little or no possibility for sliding. The balls themselves roll in a groove called a "race."

The harder a rolling wheel or ball, and the harder the surface over which it rolls, the less is the force of rolling friction. A better understanding of the origin of rolling friction is to be had by a comparison of the different kinds of wheels shown in Fig. 8F. For a hard wheel on a soft dirt road, as shown in (a), the applied force is continually pulling the wheel over a mound developed in the ground. For a soft wheel on a hard paved road, as in (b), the road is continually pushing the wheel out of shape. For a hard wheel on a hard road, both wheel and road are distorted ever so little, so that the force of friction is exceedingly small.

The same equations that hold for sliding friction also hold for rolling friction, the only difference being that the coefficients for rolling friction are exceedingly small.

$$f = \mu N \qquad (8f)$$

TABLE 8C. COEFFICIENTS OF ROLLING FRICTION

Cast iron on rails. . . . . $\mu = 0.004$
Rubber tires on concrete. . . . . $\mu = 0.030$
Ball-bearing on steel. . . . . $\mu = 0.002$

(a)   (b)   (c)

Fig. 8F   *Rolling friction between soft and hard surfaces: (a) wagon wheel, (b) soft automobile tire, and (c) locomotive drive wheel.*

8.5. Fluid Friction. Friction in a gas or liquid manifests itself when the fluid is made to flow around a stationary obstacle or an object is made to move through a previously stationary fluid. Such friction is involved in the propulsion of ships through the water, and automobiles, trains, and airplanes through the air. In any discussion or treatment of fluid friction, it makes no difference whether the fluid is considered as moving and the object as standing still, or vice versa. It is only necessary to specify that there is a relative motion between the two.

Experiments show that, at relatively low speeds, the flow of fluid around an object is smooth and regular and that fluid friction is proportional to the speed [see Fig. 8G(a)].

$$f \propto v \quad \text{or} \quad f = Kv \quad (8g)$$

where K is a constant of proportionality.

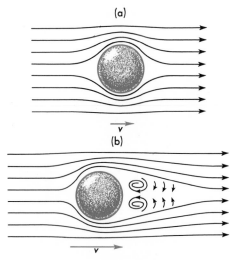

(a)

(b)

Fig. 8G　(a) *Low-velocity fluid showing laminar flow.* (b) *High-velocity fluid showing turbulent flow.*

If, initially, $v = 0$, frictional resistance to motion is zero and an applied force is entirely effective in producing acceleration. As the speed increases, however, friction increases proportionally so that less and less force is available for acceleration. Newton's second law, applied to motion through a fluid, therefore takes the same form as Eq.(8d) where f is given by Eq.(8g).

$$F = Kv + ma \quad (8h)$$

The above equations hold only for "laminar flow," that is, for relatively low velocities. As the speed increases, a point is reached where "turbulence" sets in and the force of friction increases rapidly and becomes proportional to the square of the velocity.

$$f \propto v^2 \quad \text{or} \quad f = Tv^2 \quad (8i)$$

Turbulent flow is characterized by small eddy currents that form behind the object as shown in Fig. 8G(b). Not only does the fluid have to move out and around the obstacle quickly, but considerable energy is taken up by the eddies. This, of course, results in greater loss of energy and therefore greater friction. When the velocity is increased still further, the eddies, instead of forming symmetrical pairs, form alternately on one side and then on the other, leaving a long trail of vortex motions like those shown in Fig. 8H. These strings of whirlwinds or whirlpools are commonly referred to as *Kármán trails.*

Fig. 8H　*Eddies set up by drawing an obstacle through still water form a Kármán trail.*

The existence of such trails is illustrated by the flapping of the rope on a flagpole. The waving of the flag at the top of the pole is direct evidence of the whirlwinds that follow each other alternately along the sides. As the speed of a streamlined body approaches the speed of sound, friction again increases rapidly, becoming proportional to the cube of the speed: $f \propto v^3$.

8.6. Terminal Velocity. It is well known that raindrops fall with a speed that depends upon their size and not upon the height from which they fall. Starting from rest, a particle falling in a gas or a liquid increases in velocity until the retarding force of friction becomes as great as the downward force of gravity. When this condition is reached, the body is in equilibrium and falls with a constant velocity called its *terminal velocity.*

The terminal velocity for small particles like fog drops is so low that the air stream around them is one of *laminar flow.* It was Stokes who first discovered that the terminal velocity of small particles is proportional to their weight. This relation is known as *Stokes' law.**

For increasingly larger bodies, terminal velocity increases and turbulent flow sets in, to eventually be the predominating part of frictional resistance. Under these conditions, both the resistance to laminar flow and the resistance to turbulent flow exist, so that, equating downward forces to upward forces of friction,

$$F = Kv + Tv^2 \tag{8j}$$

This equation applies not only to falling bodies but to airplanes in the air and ships in the water. Their speed remains constant where the resistance is just equalized by the forward thrust of the propellers.

If a parachutist delays the opening of his chute long enough, he will attain a terminal velocity of from 130 to 150 mi/hr. At such speeds wind resistance pushes upward with a

* Sir George G. Stokes (1819–1903), British mathematician and physicist, is well known for his fundamental contribution to hydrodynamics, diffraction, double refraction, and the polarization of light. He received the Rumford Medal in 1852 and the Copley Medal in 1893, and was one time president of the Royal Society.

total force equal to his weight, with the result that he is no longer accelerated.

8.7. Streamlining. By shaping a body to the streamlines of the fluid through which it is moving, the retarding force of friction may be greatly reduced. This is particularly effective at high speeds where the conditions of turbulent flow would otherwise predominate.

Referring to Fig. 8G(b) it may be seen that by adding a tail to an object, so that its cross-section has the form shown in Fig. 8I, the

Fig. 8I   *The flow of air or water around a properly shaped body may be smooth and steady.*

tendency to form eddy currents can be reduced and the body made to slip through the fluid with a minimum disturbance.

The experiment diagramed in Fig. 8J shows

Fig. 8J   *Diagram of a wind tunnel for testing the air friction of an airfoil or streamlined body.*

that a long pointed tail and a rounded or pointed nose are both effective in cutting down resistance. The diagrams picture a small wind tunnel through which a stream of air is drawn by a fan F. Objects for which wind resistance is to be measured are suspended from a support connected at the center to a spring balance. Parts of a streamlined body are tested in the order shown in Fig. 8K. Their wind resistance changes in the order indicated. Note that it is greatest for the top figure and smallest for the bottom one.

The bodies of airplanes, torpedoes, and ships are streamlined to cut down resistance and hence permit higher speed with the same forward thrust of the propellers. Bombs are streamlined

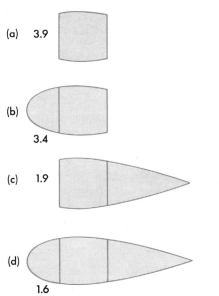

(a)   3.9

(b)

3.4

(c)   1.9

(d)

1.6

Fig. 8K   *Test bodies for the wind tunnel shown in Fig. 8J.*

to enable them to acquire higher terminal velocities. Automobiles, if they are to travel at high speeds, should be streamlined to make more efficient use of gasoline.

Experiments with airplane and automobile models in wind tunnels show the importance of streamlining for speeds as low as 30 mi/hr. The findings from such tests are confirmed by full-sized planes in the air and by cars on the speedway or open road.

8.8. Airplanes. The necessity for streamlining all outside structures of an airplane where high speeds must be maintained is quite clear. For land planes, *solid friction* is of importance only during take-off. Once a plane is in the air, friction is almost entirely due to turbulent flow and is approximately proportional to the square of the velocity.

In Fig. 8L a streamlined plane is shown in a climb. If the plane rises with constant velocity, the conditions of equilibrium exist and all forces acting form a closed polygon. The external forces acting on an airplane may be reduced to three: *weight, thrust,* and *friction* (see Fig. 8M).

The weight F_g may be assumed to act vertically downward through the center of gravity of the plane. The thrust T is the result of the push of the exhaust gases leaving the jet engine and acts in the direction of the plane axis. The friction f is the resultant force of air friction on the plane and acts in a direction upward and back as shown in Fig. 8M. The angle between the plane's *attitude* and the horizontal is called the *angle of attack*. Note that the line of flight, the path along which the plane is flying, is not quite the same as the plane's attitude.

It is customary to resolve the frictional force into two components: one, a useful component perpendicular to the line of flight and called *lift,* and the other a detrimental component parallel to the line of flight called the *drag.* The conditions of equilibrium require that these combined forces form a closed polygon as shown in Fig. 8N. The latter polygon is often used to determine certain factors in the performance of a plane. For example, if the forward thrust and

Fig. 8L   *Diagram of a plane in a climb.*

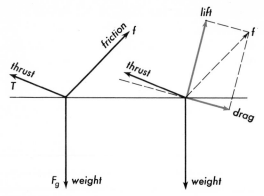

Fig. 8M   *Force diagrams for an airplane, showing the origin of lift and drag.*

weight are known, and the line of flight determined, the force polygon may be used to find the lift L and the drag D.

When a plane is in level flight and has constant velocity, T and D are practically horizontal, equal in magnitude, and opposite in direction, while F_g and L are vertical, equal in magnitude, and opposite in direction. With the motor throttled down and the plane in a dive at constant velocity, equilibrium conditions exist again and the forces form a closed polygon.

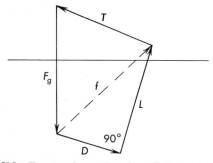

Fig. 8N   *Force polygon for plane flying at constant velocity, in a climb, as shown in Fig. 8L.*

8.9. Supersonic Speeds. The rapid development of rockets and jet-propelled planes, all capable of acquiring and maintaining speeds greater than the speed of sound, has increased the importance of studying high-speed air flow around bodies of different size and shape. The

flow of air around missiles moving with *supersonic speed*, that is, a speed greater than the speed of sound, is characterized by the existence in the air of discontinuities known as *shock waves*.

These sudden discontinuities, shown in Fig. 8O, are the result of sudden encounters of the

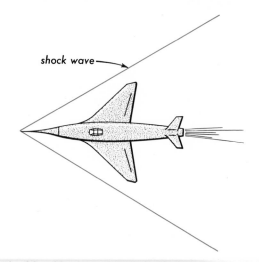

Fig. 8O   *Shock wave produced by jet or rocket plane at supersonic velocity.*

air with an impenetrable body. At subsonic speeds the fluid seems to be forewarned and begins its outward flow in advance of the arrival of the leading edge. With supersonic speed, however, the fluid in front of the missile is undisturbed, while immediately behind the missile it is moving sideways. The sudden impulse at the nose creates a high-pressure region which, traveling outward with the speed of sound, creates the conical-shaped shock wave that changes the direction of air flow.

It is customary in supersonic studies to specify the speed of a body relative to the speed of sound. The ratio between these two speeds is called the *Mach number*.

$$\text{Mach number} = \frac{\text{speed of body}}{\text{speed of sound}} \qquad (8k)$$

PROBLEMS

1. A metal box with a mass of 50 Kg is pulled along the floor by a force of 200 N, applied at an angle of 30° with the horizontal. Find (a) the horizontal component of the force, (b) the vertical component of the force, (c) the

resultant normal force on the floor, and (d) the coefficient of sliding friction.

2. A large trunk with a mass of 75 Kg is pulled along a wooden floor by a force of 320 N, applied at an angle of 28° with the horizontal. Find (a) the horizontal component of the force, (b) the vertical component of the force, (c) the resultant normal force on the floor, and (d) the coefficient of sliding friction. [Ans. (a) 283 N, (b) 150 N, (c) 585 N, (d) 0.483.]

3. A leather-soled shoe is placed on a wooden plank. The plank is tilted to different angles until the angle of uniform slip is found to be 26.5°. What is the coefficient of sliding friction?

4. The angle of uniform slip for a large metal block on an oak plank is 22°. What is the coefficient of sliding friction? [Ans. 0.404.]

5. A constant horizontal force of 120 N is applied to slide a 25-Kg box along a concrete sidewalk. If the coefficient of sliding friction is 0.32, find (a) the force required to overcome friction, (b) the accelerating force, and (c) the acceleration of the box.

6. A tractor exerts a force of 1200 N to pull a felled tree along the ground. If the tree's total mass is 320 Kg, and the coefficient of sliding friction is 0.35, find (a) the force of sliding friction, (b) the accelerating force, and (c) the acceleration of the tree. [Ans. (a) 1098 N, (b) 102 N, (c) 0.319 m/s².]

7. A 20-Kg wooden crate falls from a truck when it is traveling along a straight and level road at 25 m/s. If the crate slides for a distance of 80 m in coming to rest, find (a) the acceleration, (b) the force of friction, and (c) the coefficient of sliding friction.

8. A 96-lb box falls from a truck going 60 mi/hr. If the box slides for a distance of 300 ft before coming to rest, find (a) the acceleration, (b) the force of friction, and (c) the coefficient of sliding friction. [Ans. (a) −12.9 ft/s², (b) 38.7 lb, (c) 0.403.]

9. The angle of uniform slip for a 40-Kg metal box sliding down a wooden plank is 23°. (a) Find the coefficient of sliding friction. If the plank is tilted up to 30° with the horizontal, find (b) the normal component of the weight of the box, (c) the parallel component of the force, (d) the retarding force of friction, (e) the resultant accelerating force down the plank, and (f) the acceleration of the box.

10. The angle of uniform slip of a 100-Kg wooden crate on a metal chute is 24.5°. (a) Find the coefficient of sliding friction. If the chute is tilted up to 32°, find (b) the normal force N, (c) the parallel force F, (d) the retarding force of friction f, (e) the resultant accelerating force down the chute, and (f) the acceleration of the crate. [Ans. (a) 0.456, (b) 831 N, (c) 519 N, (d) 379 N, (e) 140 N, (f) 1.40 m/s².]

11. A jet plane of 20,000 Kg goes into a power climb just after takeoff. It maintains a constant velocity when its angle of attack is 15° and its line of flight is 10°. Assuming a lift of three times the drag, calculate the combined forward thrust of the jet engines.

12. A jet passenger plane of 40,000 Kg maintains a constant velocity in a power climb. If the angle of attack is 16°, the line of flight 10°, and the combined thrust of the engines 250,000 N, find (a) the lift and (b) the drag. [Ans. (a) 360,000 N, (b) 180,300 N.]

13. A motor car of 1600 Kg is traveling along a straight and level highway at 30 m/s when the clutch is depressed permitting the car to coast. If the car comes to rest after traveling 300 m, find (a) the acceleration, (b) the rolling force of friction, and (c) the coefficient of rolling friction.

14. A boy on a bicycle is pedalling along a straight and level road at 8 m/s. When he stops pedalling to coast he finds he travels at distance of 250 m before coming to rest. Assuming boy and bicycle to have a total mass of 65 Kg, find (a) the acceleration, (b) the rolling force of friction, and (c) the coefficient of rolling friction. [Ans. (a) −0.128 m/s², (b) 8.32 N, (c) 0.0131.]

15. The engine of a small sports plane stalls while in straight and level flight. The pilot sets the plane attitude into a glide preparatory to landing. When the gliding velocity of the plane is constant the angle of attack is 14° below the horizontal, and the line of flight is 20° below the horizontal. If the plane weighs 4800 lb, find (a) the lift, and (b) the drag.

16. The motor of a propeller-driven airplane stalls when in straight and level flight, and the pilot drops the nose of the ship into a glide preparatory to making a forced landing in a field. The plane glides with constant velocity when the attitude is held at 12° below the horizontal. Under these conditions the line of flight is 18° below the horizontal. If the plane weighs 6400 lb, find (a) the lift, and (b) the drag. [Ans. (a) 6090 lb, (b) 1980 lb.]

17. Plot a graph showing the variation of the *coefficient of sliding friction* with the *speed* using the experimental values given in Table 8B. Plot μ vertically, the scale extending from 0.120 to 0.220, and speed horizontally, the scale extending from zero to 20 cm/s. What would you predict for the coefficient of sliding friction for these same surfaces at speeds greater than 20 cm/s?

PROJECTILES

We have seen in Chapter 4 how objects projected vertically upward or downward, or released from rest at some point above the ground, move along a vertical path subject at all times to the downward acceleration due to gravity. If an object is projected at some angle other than 90° with the horizontal it will, neglecting air friction, follow a parabolic path. It is with the paths of such objects that we are concerned in this chapter.

9.1. Horizontal Projection. If one body falls freely from rest at the same time that another is projected horizontally from the same height, the two will strike the ground simultaneously. An experimental proof of this fundamental observation may be obtained by an experiment of the type diagramed in Fig. 9A.

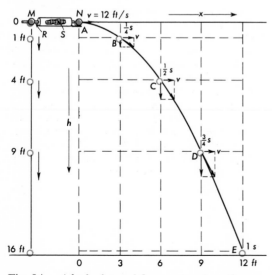

Fig. 9A *A body dropped from rest and another projected horizontally strike the ground at the same time.*

Two identical marbles, M and N, are supported by a rod and trough, respectively, in such a way that when the compressed spring S is released the rod R springs to the right, dropping M and projecting N horizontally. Marble M, falling with the acceleration g due to gravity, and marble N, traversing the longer path ABCDE, strike the ground at the same time. Repetition of the experiment with higher or lower projection velocities and from different heights always ends with the same result: both marbles hit the ground together.

The first conclusion that may be drawn from this experiment is that the downward acceleration of any projectile is the same as that of a freely falling body and takes place independently of its horizontal motion. Furthermore, an experimental measurement of *times* and *distances* shows that the horizontal velocity of projection continues unchanged and takes place independently of the vertical motion.

In other words, a projectile carries out two motions independently: (1) a constant horizontal velocity v; and (2) a vertically downward acceleration g.

With an initial horizontal velocity v, the horizontal distance x traveled is proportional to the time t and is given by the equation

$$x = vt \qquad (9a)$$

As the marble falls at the same time with an acceleration g, the vertical distance h is proportional to the square of the time and is given by

$$h = \tfrac{1}{2}gt^2 \qquad (9b)$$

where g is given by Eq.(4e).

An experimental verification of these two

equations is illustrated by the numerical values given in the diagram. With an initial velocity of 12 ft/s, marble N falls a distance of 1 ft in $\frac{1}{4}$ s and at the same time travels a horizontal distance of 3 ft. In $\frac{1}{2}$ s it falls 4 ft and travels horizontally 6 ft, etc. Since the motion obeys both formulas at the same time, the path traversed is a *parabola*.

As a proof, Eq.(9a) is first solved for t, then both sides of the equation squared to obtain

$$t^2 = \frac{x^2}{v^2}$$

If we substitute x^2/v^2 for t^2 in Eq.(9b), we obtain

$$h = \frac{1}{2} g \frac{x^2}{v^2}$$

which can be written

$$h = \left(\frac{g}{2v^2}\right) x^2 \qquad (9c)$$

For any specified value of the velocity v, the terms in parentheses are all constants, and we may write

$$h = kx^2$$

which is the equation of a parabola.

Figure 9A is a graph of this equation, in which $g = 32$ ft/s^2, and $v = 12$ ft/s. For example, for $x = 12$ ft, substitution in Eq.(9c) gives $h = 16$ ft.

For the purposes of solving problems, the motions of projectiles are usually determined by calculating the horizontal and vertical motions separately and combining the results by vector addition.

For the vertical motions it is convenient to use the equations for uniform acceleration given by Eqs.(4f), (4g), (4h), and (4i). The *special equations* given in Table 3B are the simplest to use, and may be written,

$$v = gt \qquad (9d)$$

$$h = \frac{v}{2} t \qquad (9e)$$

$$v^2 = 2gh \qquad (9f)$$

$$h = \tfrac{1}{2}gt^2 \qquad (9g)$$

Example 1. A stone is thrown horizontally with a velocity of 50 ft/s from the top of a tower 100 ft high. How long will it take to reach the ground, and with what velocity will it strike?

Solution. The time to reach the ground is the time of free fall given by Eq.(9g). By solving for t, we obtain

$$t = \sqrt{\frac{2h}{g}} = \sqrt{\frac{2 \times 100 \text{ ft}}{32 \text{ ft/s}^2}} = \sqrt{6.25 \text{ s}^2} = 2.5 \text{ s}$$

Upon striking the ground, the stone will have a horizontal velocity, $v_x = 50$ ft/s, and a vertical velocity given by Eq.(9d),

$$v_y = gt$$

By direct substitution, we obtain,

$$v_y = 32 \frac{\text{ft}}{\text{s}^2} \times 2.5 \text{ s} = 80 \frac{\text{ft}}{\text{s}}$$

Combining these two velocities vectorially as shown in Fig. 9B, we find

$$v = \sqrt{v_x^2 + v_y^2} = \sqrt{(50)^2 + (80)^2} = 94.5 \frac{\text{ft}}{\text{s}}$$

The angle θ is seen from the right triangle to be given by

$$\tan \theta = \frac{80}{50} = 1.60, \text{ or } \theta = 58°$$

Another illustration of horizontal projection is to be found in the dropping of mailbags, or

$$v_x$$
50 ft/s

v_y 80 ft/s

94.5 ft/s

θ

Fig. 9B *Combined velocities of a projectile.*

other loads by a low-flying plane in level flight. See Fig. 9C. Sweeping down in a dive from a greater height, a plane may level off at a low elevation and, sighting on a target, release a mailbag when the proper angle θ is reached. As the bag falls with increasing speed, its horizontal velocity remains constant and equal to the velocity of the plane.

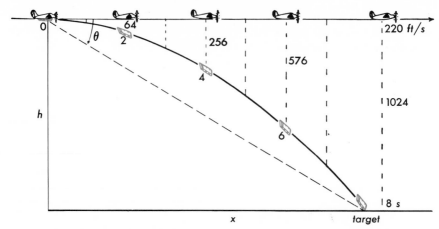

Fig. 9C   *For the first few seconds after release, a falling body remains directly beneath the plane. Later, wind resistance causes it to lag farther and farther behind.*

If air friction is neglected, the mailbag should stay directly beneath the plane at all points along its path. To find the angle θ at which the bag should be released, two factors must be taken into account: (1) the speed of the plane, and (2) the height above the target. From the height h, the time of fall can be calculated, and from the time of fall the horizontal distance can be computed.

If x represents the horizontal distance traveled and h the vertical height, the right triangle in Fig. 9C gives

$$\tan \theta = h/x \qquad (9h)$$

where x and h are given by Eqs.(9a) and (9b).

9.2. Projectiles. Many missiles when projected into the air follow a parabolic path. Such is the case only for low speeds where the retarding force of air friction is negligible. For high-speed projectiles the air continually slows the motion down and the path departs from a parabola as indicated in Fig. 9D. The higher the velocity, the

greater is the force of air friction and the greater is the departure from a parabolic path.

In general, it is convenient to neglect air friction, calculate the theoretical path of a projectile, and then if necessary make corrections for air friction. As a rule, the known factors concerning a given projectile are v, the initial velocity of projection, and θ the angle of departure. The latter is always measured from the horizontal, and in the case of bullets and shells is the *elevation angle* of the gun. The factors to be calculated are: (1) the *time of flight*, (2) the *maximum height* reached, and (3) the *range* attained.

The time of flight of a projectile will here be defined as the time required for it to return to the same level from which it was fired. The maximum height, called the summit, is defined as the greatest vertical distance reached, as measured from the horizontal projection plane, while the range is the horizontal distance from the point of projection to the point where the projectile returns again to the projection plane.

9.3. Calculation of Trajectories. To calculate the height and range of a projectile, the initial velocity of projection is resolved into two components, one vertical and the other horizontal. This is illustrated in Fig. 9E. Calling v the velocity of projection and θ the elevation angle, the x and y components of velocity are given by the following trigonometric functions,

Fig. 9D   *Projectiles tend to follow a parabolic path. Because of air friction, they fall short.*

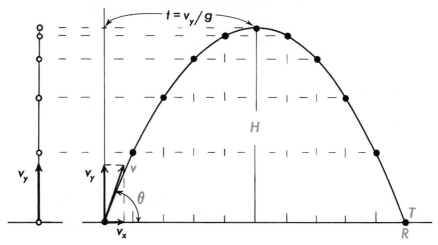

Fig. 9E *The path of a projectile showing H the maximum height reached, T the time of flight, and R the range.*

$$\sin \theta = \frac{v_y}{v} \quad \text{and} \quad \cos \theta = \frac{v_x}{v}$$

Solving for v_y and v_x we obtain,

$$v_y = v \sin \theta \qquad (9i)$$
$$v_x = v \cos \theta \qquad (9j)$$

The traversal of the actual trajectory is a combination of two motions, one the motion of a particle projected vertically upward with an initial velocity v_y, the other a horizontal velocity v_x that remains constant. In other words, a particle projected vertically upward with a velocity of v_y will rise to the same height and in the same time as another projected at an angle θ with a velocity v.

Since the time required to reach the highest point is equal to the time required to fall the same distance, the formula for free fall may be employed. The formula for an object falling from rest is Eq.(9d).

$$v_y = gt$$

By solving for t, and substituting from Eq.(9i), we find

$$t = \frac{v_y}{g} = \frac{v \sin \theta}{g} \qquad (9k)$$

Because t is the time to rise, or the time to fall, the total time of flight will be $2t$. Therefore, the time of flight T is,

$$\boxed{T = \frac{2v \sin \theta}{g}} \qquad (9l)$$

time of flight

To find the height H, Eq.(9f) is used. The letter h is replaced by H, and the letter v by v_h.

$$(v_h)^2 = 2gH$$

Solving this equation for H, we obtain:

$$H = \frac{(v_h)^2}{2g}$$

Using Eq.(9i) substitute $v \sin \theta$ for v_h, and we have,

$$\boxed{H = \frac{(v \sin \theta)^2}{2g}} \qquad (9m)$$

maximum height

To find the range R, the equation for constant velocity, $x = vt$, is used. Replacing the letter x by R, v by $v \cos \theta$, and t by the total time of flight, $T = 2v \sin \theta/g$, we obtain

$$R = v \cos \theta \times \frac{2v \sin \theta}{g}$$

or

$$R = \frac{2v^2 \sin \theta \cos \theta}{g}$$

To put this formula into another form,

Fig. 9F *Diagram illustrating the shape of the trajectories of objects projected at different elevation angles. The vertical and horizontal scales are for the special case where the velocity of projection is 80 ft/sec.*

use is made of the trigonometric relation that $2 \sin \theta \cos \theta = \sin 2\theta$. Substitution gives

$$R = \frac{v^2}{g} \sin 2\theta \qquad (9n)$$

range

In this form it is seen at once that, for a given velocity v, the range is a maximum when the $\sin 2\theta$ is a maximum. Since the sine has its maximum value of unity for an angle of 90°, the angle θ above will be 45°. Furthermore, the range for any angle any number of degrees greater than 45° will be equal to the range for an equal number of degrees less than 45°. This is illustrated in Fig. 9F, for example, by the equal ranges of 100 ft for the 15° and 75° projections, and the equal ranges of 173 ft for the 30° and 60° projections.

Example 2. A baseball is thrown with a velocity of 50 ft/s at an angle of 60° with the horizontal. Calculate (a) the time of flight, (b) the maximum height, and (c) the range.

Solution. To find the time of flight, direct substitution of the given quantities in Eq.(9l) gives

$$T = \frac{2v \sin \theta}{g} = \frac{2 \times 50 \times 0.866}{32} = \frac{86.6}{32} = 2.71 \text{ s}$$

To find the maximum height, Eq.(9m) is used.

$$H = \frac{(v \sin \theta)^2}{2g} = \frac{(50 \times 0.866)^2}{2 \times 32} = 29.3 \text{ ft}$$

For the range, Eq.(9n) is used.

$$R = \frac{v^2}{g} \sin 2\theta = \frac{(50)^2 \times 0.866}{32} = 67.6 \text{ ft}$$

9.4. Monkey and Hunter Experiment. A hunter aims and shoots an arrow at a monkey in a tree. At the instant the arrow leaves the bow, the monkey drops from the branch upon which he has been sitting. The two should meet in mid-air regardless of the speed of the arrow.

If gravity could be eliminated, the arrow, as shown in Fig. 9G, would travel the straight line path AM, and the monkey would stay at M and be hit there. With gravity acting, however, the arrow travels the path ABC and the monkey drops from M to C. During each fraction of a second, indicated by $t = 1, 2, 3,$ and 4, both fall the same distance from their gravity-free positions and collide at C. The greater the speed of the missile, the shorter will be the distance MC.*

9.5. Rocket Flights into Space. The first American man to be launched into space by a rocket was carried aloft in a Mercury capsule boosted by a Redstone rocket from Cape Canaveral,

* This experiment may be performed by blowing a small wooden marble through a tube (about a foot long). A toy monkey is released at M by a small electromagnet. Two fine copper wires completing the electric circuit are crossed just in front of the tube at A. When the projectile passes this point the circuit is broken, releasing M. The mass M should have a small piece of iron at the top for the magnetic attraction.

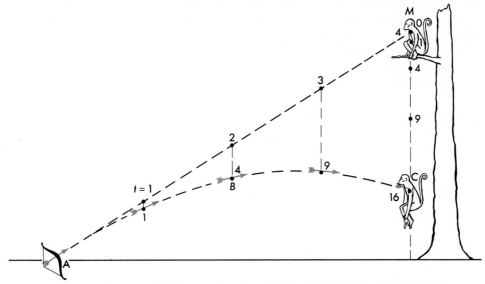

Fig. 9G *Diagram illustrating the monkey and hunter experiment.*

Florida, on May 5, 1961. The astronaut, Alan Shepard, who piloted the pressurized space capsule in which he was jettisoned, followed a path similar to that shown in Fig. 9H.

to which the rocket and astronaut were subjected at several points of the flight, will be presented. The following cases are typical of space flight in general, and the equations can be

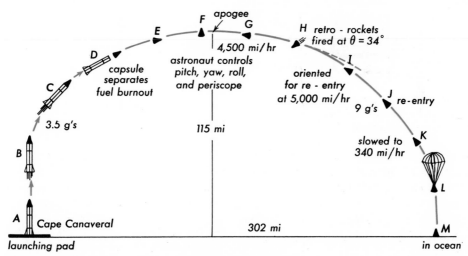

Fig. 9H *Diagram of the flight path taken by the first American astronaut to be launched into space, May 5, 1961.*

Although the details of this history-making event will not be given here,* an analysis of some of the forces, velocities, and accelerations,

* For details of Alan Shepard's space flight, see *Life Magazine*, May 12 and 19, 1961.

applied equally well to orbiting satellites and to flights to the moon and planets.

Since the value of g in Shepard's flight diminished by less than 5% at an altitude of 115 mi, and its direction changed by less than

5 degrees over the 302-mi range, it will be assumed that g remains constant over the entire flight path.

Case A. Before Vertical Launch. When the entire rocket assembly is at rest on the launching pad, just prior to take-off, all velocities and accelerations are zero, and all forces are in equilibrium (see Fig. 9I). At this time there are

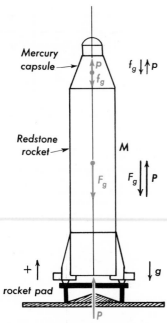

Fig. 9I　*Diagram of a rocket and its manned space capsule at rest on its launching pad and ready for vertical take-off.*

two equal forces acting on the rocket, F_g the downward pull of the earth and P the upward push of the launching pad. The downward force is given by

$$F_g = Mg \qquad (9o)$$

where M is the total mass of the rocket and its payload.

Assuming the upward direction as positive, g the acceleration due to gravity is negative, and so is F_g. Since the upward force P on the total mass M must be equal to F_g in magnitude,

$$P = -Mg \qquad (9p)$$

In a similar way the two equal but opposite forces acting on the astronaut are f_g, the down-

ward pull of the earth, and p, the upward thrust of his supporting cradle. These forces are given by

$$f_g = mg \qquad (9q)$$
$$p = -mg \qquad (9r)$$

showing that for each kilogram mass of the rocket structure, or its contents, the force p is equal to 9.8 N, and for each slug of mass it is 32 lb. Under these conditions the force is said to be "1 g."

Case B. Vertical Climb. When the rocket is accelerating vertically upward after launching (see Fig. 9J), the two forces acting on the total

Fig. 9J　*Force diagram for a rocket and its astronaut pilot during vertical flight under rocket thrust.*

mass M are P, the upward thrust of the rocket engines, and F_g, the downward pull of the earth. The force F giving rise to the upward acceleration a is the vector resultant of these two forces

$$\vec{P} + \vec{F_g} = \vec{F}$$

where

$$F_g = Mg$$

To lift the rocket from the ground, P must be greater than F_g, and their vector resultant F will be the force that produces the upward acceleration.

$$F = Ma$$

Applying these same principles to the astronaut in the capsule shown at the top in Fig. 9J, we observe that

$$\vec{p} + \vec{f_g} = \vec{f} \qquad (9s)$$

where p is the thrust of the cradle on the astronaut's body and f_g is the downward pull of the earth on the same mass. The resultant f is the force that gives the astronaut the same upward acceleration as the rocket.

$$.f = ma \qquad (9t)$$

Example 3. A 40-ton rocket with an astronaut of 160 lb aboard is climbing vertically upward with an acceleration of 96 ft/s². Find the total force of the cradle on the man's body (a) in g's and (b) in lb.

Solution. Solving Eq.(9s) for p, we obtain for the thrust

$$\vec{p} = \vec{f} - \vec{f_g}$$

and substituting Eq.(9q) and Eq.(9t), we have

$$\vec{p} = \vec{ma} - \vec{mg} \qquad (9u)$$

Assuming $g = -32$ ft/s², the astronaut's acceleration of 96 ft/s², is just $-3 \times g$.

$$a = -3g$$

Direct substitution in Eq.(9u) gives for the thrust

$$p = -m(3g) - mg \qquad (9v)$$
or
$$p = -m(4g)$$

Ans. (a) The astronaut is said to be "taking 4 g's." This also means that all parts of his body are subjected to a force of four times their normal weight.

To find the thrust in pounds, direct substitution in Eq.(9v) gives

$$p = -\frac{160 \text{ lb}}{32 \text{ ft/s}^2}\left(-4 \times 32 \frac{\text{ft}}{\text{s}^2}\right)$$

$$p = 5 \text{ sl} \times 128 \text{ ft/s}^2$$
$$p = 640 \text{ lb}$$

Ans. (b) The astronaut's apparent weight is four times normal.

Case C. Inclined Rocket Thrust. When the rocket elevation angle θ is slowly altered from 90° to give the missile a predetermined direction at burnout, the rocket thrust is not directed along the flight path. In Fig. 9K the rocket is shown prior to burnout and at the instant its center of mass M passes a point (1) in its flight path.

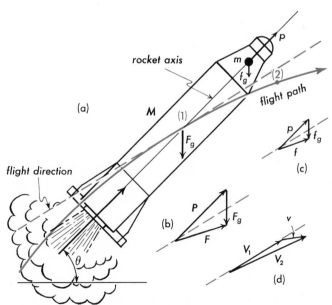

Fig. 9K   *Force and velocity diagrams for a rocket and its astronaut pilot under rocket thrust at an angle.*

Although the rocket axis determines the direction of total thrust P, the downward force F_g continually changes the direction of motion. The dashed green line, tangent to the flight path at (1), represents the instantaneous direction as the center of mass passes that point.

The two forces P and F_g acting on the rocket, and their resultant F, are shown in diagram (b). This resultant force gives rise to the acceleration a, in the direction of F, thus altering both in magnitude and direction the missile's velocity V.

$$F = Ma \qquad (9w)$$

The two forces p and f_g acting on the astronaut, and their resultant f, are shown in diagram (c). This resultant force gives the astronaut the same acceleration as the rocket.

$$f = ma \qquad (9x)$$

A vector diagram of velocities is shown in diagram (d), where V_1 represents the instantaneous velocity of the missile as it passes point (1), v the additional velocity imparted by F during the time t it takes to go from point (1) to point (2), and V_2 the instantaneous velocity as it passes point (2). This added velocity v is given by

$$v = at$$

Note that p represents the force of the cradle on the astronaut's body mass m, and the magnitude of this force gives his apparent weight.

Case D. Free Jettisoned Space Capsule.
After the space capsule carrying the astronaut has been jettisoned from the rocket, as shown at D in Fig. 9H, the vehicle becomes a free projectile. From point D to point H, where the retrorockets are fired, the downward pull of the earth F_g is the only force acting on the body. This force gives rise to a downward acceleration g and is responsible for the continually changing

direction of the capsule as it travels along its flight path.

In the velocity diagram, Fig. 9L(b), V_1 represents the instantaneous velocity of the capsule

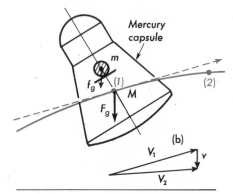

Fig. 9L   *Diagram of a free jettisoned space capsule as it travels without rocket thrust along its flight path.*

as it passes point (1); v is the change in velocity imparted by F_g during the time it takes to reach point (2); and V_2 is the instantaneous velocity as it passes point (2).

$$v = gt$$

Since there is no thrust P from rocket motors for this part of the flight, the cradle exerts no force on the astronaut, and he exerts no force on the cradle. While the capsule, the astronaut, and the cradle fall with the same acceleration g, the concept of weightlessness prevails throughout the moving system.

When the velocity of the capsule is great enough (about 17,500 mi/hr), it will orbit the earth as a satellite. In orbital flight the retrorockets are necessary, to deflect and slow the capsule to begin its return to earth. In this particular flight of Shepard's, however, the retrorockets were used only as a test of this manned capability.

PROBLEMS

1. A mail plane cruising at 80 m/s comes down to an elevation of 100 m where, in straight and level flight, it releases a mail bag to be caught in a net on the ground. Find (a) the time of fall, (b) the horizontal distance between the plane and the net when the bag is released, (c) the vertical velocity acquired, and (d) the velocity of impact.

2. A boy standing on a bridge 120 m above the water throws a stone horizontally outward with a velocity of 20 m/s. Find (a) the time it takes to hit the water, (b) the distance away from the foot of the bridge, (c) the vertical velocity with which it hits the water, and (d) the velocity of impact. [*Ans.* (a) 4.95 s, (b) 99.0 m, (c) 48.5 m/s, (d) 52.5 m/s at 67.6° with the horizontal.]

3. A stream of water from the nozzle of a fire hose emerges horizontally with a speed of 16 m/s. If the nozzle is 20 m above the ground, find (a) the time required for the stream of water to hit the ground, (b) the horizontal distance the water travels after leaving the nozzle, (c) the vertical velocity with which it hits the ground, and (d) the velocity of impact.

4. A small plane flying food to a snow-bound herd of cattle comes down to a 320-ft elevation where, traveling at 90 mi/hr in straight and level flight, it releases a bail of hay. Find (a) the time required to hit the ground, (b) the horizontal distance traveled, (c) the vertical velocity acquired, and (d) the velocity of impact. [*Ans.* (a) 4.47 s, (b) 590 ft, (c) 143 ft/s, (d) 195 ft/s at 47.4° with the horizontal.]

5. An arrow is shot into the air with a velocity of 100 m/s at an elevation angle of 45°. Find (a) the time of flight, (b) the maximum height reached, and (c) the range.

6. A baseball is hit with a velocity of 30 m/s at an elevation angle of 58°. Find (a) the time of flight, (b) the maximum height reached, and (c) the range. [*Ans.* (a) 5.20 s, (b) 33.1 m, (c) 82.6 m.]

7. A stone is thrown from a sling with a velocity of 36 m/s at an elevation angle of 54°. Find (a) the time of flight, (b) the maximum height reached, and (c) the range.

8. A World's record for the javelin throw was made by Egil Danielsen of Norway in 1956 with a throw of 281 ft 2¼ in. Photographs show the initial elevation angle was 45°. Assuming the start and finish was at the same level, find (a) the velocity of projection, (b) the time of flight, and (c) the maximum height reached. [*Ans.* (a) 94.9 ft/s, (b) 4.19 s, (c) 70.3 ft.]

9. A World's record for the 16-lb shotput was made by Wm. Nieder of the U.S. in 1960 with a toss of 64 ft 6¾ in. Photographs show the initial elevation angle was 45°. Assuming the start and finish of the flight of the shot was at the same level, find (a) the time of flight, (b) the maximum height reached, and (c) the initial velocity.

10. A shotput is tossed for a distance of 18 m. If the elevation angle is 45°, find (a) the velocity of projection, (b) the time of flight, and (c) the maximum height reached. [*Ans.* (a) 13.3 m/s, (b) 1.92 s, (c) 4.52 m.]

11. A mortar hurls a 5-Kg shell with a speed of 220 m/s. Neglecting friction, at what angle with the horizontal should it be aimed to hit a target on the ground at the same level 500 m away?

12. An arrow shot into the air has a flight time of 5 s and a range of 200 m. Find (a) the maximum height reached, (b) the vertical component of the projection velocity, (c) the horizontal component, (d) the elevation angle, and (e) the initial velocity. [*Ans.* (a) 30.6 m, (b) 24.5 m/s, (c) 40 m/s, (d) 31.5°, (e) 46.9 m/s.]

13. An arrow shot with a speed of 50 m/s reaches a maximum height of 100 m. Find (a) the time of flight, (b) the angle of departure, and (c) the range.

14. A catapult hurls a stone with a speed of 40 m/s.

If the maximum height reached is 70 m, find (a) the elevation angle, (b) the time of flight, and (c) the range. [*Ans.* (a) 67.8°, (b) 7.56 s, (c) 114.2 m.]

15. A 30,000-Kg rocket with an astronaut of 75 Kg aboard is climbing vertically upward with an acceleration of 36 m/s². Calculate the total force of the cradle on the man's body, (a) in newtons, and (b) in pounds.

16. A 45,000-Kg rocket with an 80-Kg astronaut aboard is under full thrust of its rocket motors and climbing vertically upward with an acceleration of 40 m/s². Calculate the total thrust of the rocket motors in (a) newtons, and (b) in pounds. Find the thrust of the cradle on the man's body in (c) newtons, and (d) in pounds. [*Ans.* (a) 2.24×10^6 N, (b) 5.04×10^5 lb, (c) 3.98×10^3 N, (d) 896 lb.]

17. A 64,000-lb rocket with a 160-lb astronaut aboard is under full thrust of its rocket motors with its axis and flight path vertically upward. If the astronaut finds his apparent weight to be 4 g's, find (a) the upward acceleration of the rocket in ft/s², (b) the thrust of the cradle against the astronaut's body in pounds, and (c) the total thrust of the rocket motors.

18. A 48,000-lb rocket with a 196-lb astronaut aboard is under full thrust of its rocket motors with its axis inclined at 60° with the horizontal. If the pilot finds his apparent weight to be 4 g's, find (a) the thrust of the cradle against the astronaut's body, and (b) the resultant force on the astronaut's body. [*Ans.* (a) 784 lb, (b) 621 lb at 50.9° with the horizontal.]

19. An arrow is shot with a speed of 40 m/s at an elevation angle of 40°. Find (a) the initial vertical component of velocity, and (b) the horizontal component. After 2 s have elapsed, find (c) the height of the arrow, (d) the horizontal distance it has traveled, and (e) the maximum height reached.

20. A baseball is hit with a velocity of 30 m/s at an elevation angle of 38°. Find (a) the vertical component of this velocity, and (b) the horizontal component. After 2 s have elapsed, find (c) the height of the ball, (d) the horizontal distance it has traveled, (e) its vertical component of velocity, and (f) its horizontal component. Find (g) the maximum height reached. [*Ans.* (a) 18.5 m/s, (b) 23.6 m/s, (c) 17.4 m, (d) 47.2 m, (e) −1.11 m/s, (f) 23.6 m/s, (g) 28.9 m.]

21. Plot a graph of Eq.(9c). Assume values of $v = 8$ ft/s, and $g = -32$ ft/s², and calculate values of h for all even integral values of x from −6 ft to +6 ft.

22. An arrow is shot with a velocity of 33.95 m/s at an elevation angle of 60°. Calculate its (a) vertical distance, and (b) horizontal distance, at the end of each of the first 6 s. (c) Plot a graph of these distances and draw a smooth curve through the points to represent the trajectory, starting with the origin at $t = 0$. [*Ans.* (a) 24.5 m, 39.2 m, 44.1 m, 39.2 m, 24.5 m, 0, (b) 17.0 m, 34.0 m, 51.0 m, 68.0 m, 85.0 m, 102 m.]

WORK, ENERGY, AND POWER

There is little doubt that the most important concept in all nature is energy. It is important because it represents a fundamental entity common to all forms of matter in all parts of the known physical world. Closely associated with energy is another concept, *work*, a term used in civil life to describe the expenditure of one's stored-up bodily energy. Because energy is most easily described in terms of work, this latter concept will first be treated in detail.

10.1. Work. In its simplest mechanical form, *work* is defined as *the force times the distance* through which the force acts.

$$\text{work} = \text{force} \times \text{distance}$$

Algebraically, we write*

$$W = F \times h \tag{10a}$$

Consider the general problem of calculating the work done in lifting a mass m to a height h above the ground (see Fig. 10A). By Newton's second law of motion ($F = ma$), the force required to lift any mass m is equal to its own weight.

$$F_g = mg$$

If we substitute the weight mg for F in Eq.(10a),

$$W = mg \times h \tag{10b}$$

To give numerical values, assume that a mass of 5 Kg is lifted vertically a distance of 2 m. By direct substitution in Eq.(10b),

$$W = 5 \text{ Kg} \times 9.8 \frac{\text{m}}{\text{s}^2} \times 2 \text{ m} = 98 \frac{\text{Kg m}^2}{\text{s}^2}$$

* Equation (10a) can also be written as $W = F \times x$, where x designates distance traveled while overcoming friction (see Sec. 10.3).

Since *force*, in *newtons*, has the units Kg m/s^2, the answer can also be written

$$W = 98 \text{ newton meters}$$

Work in the mks system is seen to have the absolute units $\text{Kg m}^2/\text{s}^2$, which are equal to the

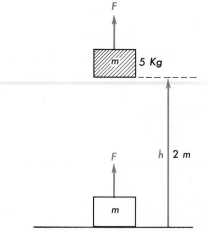

Fig. 10A   *Work is defined as force × distance.*

derived units, *newton meters* (Nm). In the cgs system, the corresponding absolute units are $\text{g cm}^2/\text{s}^2$, which are equal to the derived units *dyne centimeters* (dyne cm). In the English, or engineering system, the units of work are *foot-pounds* (ft-lb).

Example 1. Find the work done in lifting a weight of 5 lb to a height of 10 ft.
Solution. By direct substitution in Eq.(10a), we obtain
$$W = 5 \text{ lb} \times 10 \text{ ft} = 50 \text{ ft-lb}$$

10.2. Joules and Ergs. In the mks system of units, a force of 1 *newton* acting through a distance of 1 m performs an amount of work equivalent to *1 joule*.

$$\boxed{1 \text{ newton meter} = 1 \text{ joule}} \quad (10c)$$

In the cgs system, the *dyne cm* as a unit of work is called the *erg*.

$$1 \text{ dyne cm} = 1 \text{ erg} \quad (10d)$$

A force of 1 dyne acting through a distance of 1 cm does 1 erg of work.

Example 2. Calculate the work done in lifting a mass of 8 Kg to a height of 2.5 m.
Solution. The known quantities are $m = 8$ Kg, $x = 2.5$ m, and $g = 9.8$ m/s². Substitution in Eq. (10b) gives

$$W = 8 \text{ Kg} \times 9.8 \frac{\text{m}}{\text{s}^2} \times 2.5 \text{ m}$$

$$W = 196 \frac{\text{Kg m}}{\text{s}^2} \text{ m}$$

$$W = 196 \text{ Nm}$$
$$W = 196 \text{ joules}$$

The joule as a unit of work is abbreviated J. Hence the work done in this example is 196 J.

10.3. Work Done Against Friction. In sliding a mass of 5 Kg along a horizontal plane a distance of 2 m (see Fig. 10B) the work done *will not* in

Fig. 10B   *To slide a body horizontally, work must be done against friction.*

general be as great as that required to lift the same mass 2 m vertically.

Suppose, for example, that the coefficient of sliding friction for the block in the diagram is $\mu = 0.25$. By calculation then, the force of friction is [see Eq.(8b)]

$$f = \mu N = 0.25 \times 5 \text{ Kg} \times 9.8 \text{ m/s}^2$$
$$= 12.25 \text{ N}$$

Since a force of 12.25 newtons will slide the block, the work done, by Eq.(10a), will be

$$W = 12.25 \text{N} \times 2 \text{ m}$$
$$= 24.5 \text{ Nm}$$
$$= 24.5 \text{ J}$$

This is only one-quarter as much work as that required to lift the same 5 Kg mass an equal vertical distance of 2 m (see Fig. 10A). By reducing the friction between the block and the plane, the force F can be reduced still further. Such a reduction can be accomplished by smoothing and lubricating the sliding surfaces, or better by mounting the block on wheels. Could the friction be eliminated entirely, the work done in moving any object in a horizontal direction would be practically zero, for once started it would continue moving with constant velocity. A vertical lift, however, requires at least an amount of work equal to the weight mg times the height h.

When a force acting on an object is applied at angle with the direction of motion, only the component of the force in the direction of motion is effective in doing work. This is illustrated in Fig. 10C where a force of 100 N applied at an angle

Fig. 10C   *Force and distance are measured in the same direction in calculating work.*

of 30° moves a 20 Kg mass a distance of 5 m. In the bottom diagram, F is resolved into two components, F_x horizontally and F_y vertically.

By calculation or by graphical construction,

$$F_x = F \cos 30° = 100 \times 0.866 = 86.6 \text{ N}$$
$$F_y = F \sin 30° = 100 \times 0.500 = 50.0 \text{ N}$$

The vertical force of 50 N, being perpendicular to the direction of motion, does no work since the distance moved upward is zero. Work is done only by the horizontal force F_x.

$$W = 86.6 \text{ N} \times 5 \text{ m} = 433 \text{ J}$$

While the vertical force does not enter directly into the calculation of work, it does help to lift the body and thereby reduce the friction between the sliding surfaces. As an illustration, consider the following problem.

Example 3. A trunk with a mass of 100 Kg is pulled 20 m across the floor by a rope making an angle of 35° with the horizontal (see Fig. 10D). If

Fig. 10D　*Work is done in sliding a trunk along the floor.*

the coefficient of sliding friction is 0.25, find (a) the tension in the rope, and (b) the work done.

Solution. The force F is resolved into two components,

$$F_x = F \cos 35° = 0.819 \, F$$
$$F_y = F \sin 35° = 0.574 \, F$$

To find the horizontal force of friction ($f = \mu N$), the normal force N is calculated as the resultant of two forces acting on the block; mg downward due to gravity and F_y upward due to the pull of the rope. Therefore,

$$N = mg - F_y$$

and the force of friction is

$$f = \mu N = 0.25 \, (mg - F_y)$$

To overcome friction and slide the body, the component F_x must be at least equal to f. Set $f = F_x$,

$$F_x = 0.25 \, (mg - F_y)$$

Substitute for F_x and F_y from the above relations, and multiply out,

$$0.819 \, F = 0.25 \, mg - 0.25 \times 0.574 \, F$$

Collect factors containing F, on the left, and substitute for m and g,

$$0.962 \, F = 0.25 \times 100 \text{ Kg} \times 9.8 \frac{\text{m}}{\text{s}^2}$$

Therefore
(a)　　　　　　　$F = 255 \text{ N}$

By Eq.(10a) the work done is $F_x \times x$,

$$W = 0.819 \times 255 \text{ N} \times 20 \text{ m}$$
(b)　　　　　　　$W = 4177 \text{ J}$

10.4. Work in the Engineering System of Units. Because it is customary in engineering design and construction to measure loads and forces in pounds, it is proper to calculate work in *foot-pounds*, i.e., *force in pounds × distance in feet*. As an illustration consider the following problem.

Example 4. When loaded, the small car of a hoist weighs 240 lb. How much work is done in lifting this load 35 ft?

Solution. By Eq.(10a),

$$W = F \times h = 240 \text{ lb} \times 35 \text{ ft} = 8400 \text{ ft-lb}$$

10.5. Potential Energy. Mechanical energy is divided into two categories, *potential energy* (E_p) and *kinetic energy* (E_k). A body is said to have potential energy if by virtue of its position or state it is able to do work. A car at the top of a hill or a wound clock spring is an example of an object with potential energy. The clock spring may keep a clock running for a certain length of time, and a car may, by coasting downhill, travel a great distance. Potential energy is measured by the amount of work that is available. It is therefore measured in *ergs, joules,* or *foot-pounds*.

If a given mass m is raised to a specified height h, as illustrated in Fig. 10E, it then has potential

Fig. 10E　*A body has potential energy by virtue of its position.*

energy $F \times h$ by virtue of its position above the ground level from which it has been lifted. The *work done* in lifting it has been stored up as potential energy in the block. This energy can be regained by dropping the mass back to the ground, for in so doing it can be made to perform some kind of work. By definition,

$$\text{potential energy} = F \times h \qquad (10e)$$

or, in absolute units,

$$\boxed{\text{potential energy} = mg \times h}$$

Example 5. A mass of 5 Kg is raised to a height of 2.5 m above the ground. Calculate its potential energy.

Solution. If we substitute the known quantities in Eq.(10g),

$$E_p = 5 \text{ Kg} \times 9.8 \frac{\text{m}}{\text{s}^3} \times 2.5 \text{ m} = 122.5 \text{ J}$$

If a body is lifted straight upward, carried up a staircase, or pulled up an inclined plane, the potential energy acquired is given by the *weight $\times$ vertical height* to which it is raised.

The meaning of positive, zero, or negative potential energy is illustrated in Fig. 10F. Located at any point above the *base plane* a body has positive potential energy, while at points below

that line it has negative potential energy. To lift the mass m from A to B, work is done, and the mass acquires a potential energy to the amount of mgh_1.

In returning from B to A, the mass loses potential energy, performing $work = mgh_1$ on some other body. Similarly, in going from A to C, the body loses energy and ends up at C with mgh_2 less energy than it had at A. To raise it again to A, an equivalent amount of work mgh_2 will have to be done on the body.

The choosing of a *base plane* as a zero energy level is a purely arbitrary selection. In most practical applications it is customary to select the lowest point to be reached by a body as the zero level, so that all displacements from there will be positive in sign. In the engineering system of units, *potential energy*, like *work*, can be expressed in foot-pounds, i.e., *pounds $\times$ vertical distance in feet*.

When a force is applied to a body to slide or roll it along the ground, the *work done* is not stored up as potential energy. Because of friction, the energy is transformed into heat, and as a practical matter is considered lost for further use. If the body ends up at the same level at which it started, all of the energy has gone into heat and the potential energy remains unchanged.

If a body is pulled up an inclined plane, on the other hand, part of the energy goes into heat and part into potential energy. The potential energy as illustrated in Fig. 10G is given by mgh, while

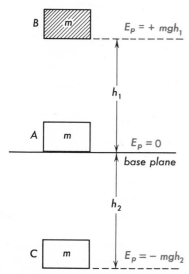

Fig. 10F *Potential energy with respect to a base plane may be plus or minus.*

Fig. 10G *Part of the work done in sliding a mass up an incline goes into friction, and part into potential energy.*

the work done is given by $F \times s$ and the frictional energy by $f \times s$.

$$F \times s = f \times s + mgh$$

work done = frictional energy

+ potential energy

10.6. Kinetic Energy. The kinetic energy of a moving body is defined as its ability to do work by virtue of its motion. A car moving along the highway has kinetic energy of translation, and a rotating wheel on a machine has kinetic energy of rotation. For a given mass m, moving in a straight line with constant speed v, the kinetic energy is given by

$$\boxed{\text{kinetic energy} = \tfrac{1}{2}mv^2} \qquad (10f)$$

Example 6. Calculate the kinetic energy of a 20-Kg mass, moving with a speed of 4 m/s.
Solution. By direct substitution in Eq.(10f),

$$E_k = \frac{1}{2} \times 20 \text{ Kg} \times \left(4\frac{\text{m}}{\text{s}}\right)^2 = 160\frac{\text{Kg m}^2}{\text{s}^2}$$

This answer has exactly the dimensions of *work*, and *potential energy*, and can be written in the same derived units.

$$E_k = 160 \text{ J}$$

A moving body has energy, because in being brought to rest it must exert a force F on some other object, and this force acting through a distance x does work. In other words, work can be done by a moving body. Conversely, by applying a constant horizontal force F on a body of

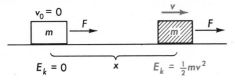

Fig. 10H   *A body has kinetic energy by virtue of its motion.*

mass m for a distance x, it will be given a kinetic energy $\tfrac{1}{2}mv^2$ (see Fig. 10H).

$$F \times x = \tfrac{1}{2}mv^2 \qquad (10g)$$

The above equation is known as the "work equation." In it, friction is entirely neglected and the body is presumed to start from rest. To derive Eq.(10g) from previous principles, Newton's second law of motion will serve as a starting point.

$$F = ma$$

Upon multiplying both sides of the equation by x,

$$F \times x = max \qquad (10h)$$

For the product ax on the right, Eq.(3k) is used. The equation $v^2 - v_0^2 = 2ax$ is solved for ax, and gives,

$$ax = \frac{v^2 - v_0^2}{2}$$

which, substituted in Eq.(10h), gives

$$F \times x = m\frac{v^2 - v_0^2}{2}$$

Then,

$$F \times x = \tfrac{1}{2}mv^2 - \tfrac{1}{2}mv_0^2, \qquad (10i)$$

In the special case that a body starts from rest, $v_0 = 0$, the last term drops out and the equation becomes Eq.(10g).

Example 7. A constant horizontal force of 25 lb acts for a distance of 20 ft on a 500-lb box. If friction is neglected and the box starts from rest, what is its velocity?
Solution. The known quantities are $v_0 = 0$, $m = 500$ lb/32 ft/s^2, $x = 20$ ft, and $F = 25$ lb. The special Eq.(10g) may, therefore, be applied. Solving for v^2, and substituting the known values, we obtain,

$$v^2 = \frac{2(F \times x)}{m} = \frac{2(25 \text{ lb} \times 20 \text{ ft})}{500 \text{ lb}/32 \text{ ft/s}^2},$$

$$v^2 = 64 \text{ ft}^2/\text{s}^2 \quad \text{and} \quad v = 8\frac{\text{ft}}{\text{s}}$$

Note that in solving this problem the mass m must be in slugs, i.e., pounds weight divided by g in ft/s^2.

10.7. Power. Power is defined as the rate of doing work or the rate at which work is being done.

$$\text{Power} = \frac{\text{work}}{\text{time}} \qquad (10j)$$

$$\boxed{P = \frac{F \times x}{t}} \qquad (10k)$$

The faster a given amount of work is done, the greater is the power. In other words, the smaller the time t in the above equation, the greater is the fraction $F \times x/t$ and the power P.

In the metric system, with work measured in *joules*, power is expressed in *joules per second*. One joule per second is called the *watt*, a unit of power.

$$\boxed{1 \text{ joule/second} = 1 \text{ watt}} \qquad (10l)$$

The *kilowatt* is another unit of power and is equal to *1000 watts*.

$$1 \text{ kilowatt} = 1000 \text{ watts}$$
$$1 \text{ KW} = 1000 \text{ W}$$

In the engineering system, with work measured in foot-pounds, power is expressed in foot-pounds per second, and in horsepower (hp).

$$1 \text{ hp} = 550 \text{ ft-lb/s} \qquad (10m)$$

Example 8. Find the power of an engine capable of lifting 200 lb to a height of 55 ft in 10 s.

Solution. By Eq.(10k),

$$P = \frac{200 \text{ lb} \times 55 \text{ ft}}{10 \text{ s}} = 1100 \frac{\text{ft-lb}}{\text{s}}$$

Divide this answer by 550 to get the horsepower,

$$\frac{1100}{550} = 2 \text{ hp}$$

If 550 ft-lb/s is changed to the metric system (1 ft = 0.305 m, and 1 lb = 4.45 N),

$$1 \text{ hp} = 746 \frac{\text{joules}}{\text{second}} = 746 \text{ watts} \qquad (10n)$$

$$1 \text{ hp} = 746 \frac{\text{J}}{\text{s}} = 746 \text{ W}$$

PROBLEMS

1. A 2200-Kg car is lifted by an elevator a distance of 28 m. Find (a) the force required, (b) the work done, and (c) the potential energy.

2. A small amphibious plane of 3500 Kg is lifted from the water to the deck of a naval aircraft carrier, a vertical distance of 16.5 m. Find (a) the force required, (b) the work done, and (c) the potential energy. [*Ans.* (a) 34,300 N, (b) 5.66 × 10⁵ N m, (c) 5.66 × 10⁵ J.]

3. A jet airliner of 320,000 lb climbs to a height of 3600 ft. Find the stored potential energy.

4. A 24,000-Kg rocket takes off from its launching pad and acquires a vertical velocity of 4000 m/s at an altitude of 30,000 m. Calculate (a) the potential energy, and (b) the kinetic energy. [*Ans.* (a) 7.06 × 10⁹ J, (b) 1.92 × 10¹¹ J.]

5. A 4800-lb car travels along a highway at 80 mi/hr. Find the kinetic energy.

6. A car with a mass of 1500 Kg climbs to the top of a grade where the road levels out at a height of 230 m. If the car maintains a constant velocity of 30 m/s, find (a) the potential energy, (b) the kinetic energy, and (c) the total energy. [*Ans.* (a) 3.38 × 10⁶ J, (b) 6.75 × 10⁵ J, (c) 4.055 × 10⁶ J.]

7. A small plane with a mass of 3500 Kg is in straight and level flight with a speed of 200 Km/hr at a height of 480 m. Find (a) the potential energy, (b) the kinetic energy, and (c) the total energy.

8. A small plane weighing 4800 lb climbs to a height of 6000 ft in 4 min, where it levels out into straight and level flight at 150 mi/hr. Find (a) the potential energy, (b) the kinetic energy, (c) the total energy, and (d) the power developed. [*Ans.* (a) 2.88 × 10⁷ ft-lb, (b) 3.63 × 10⁶ ft-lb, (c) 3.24 × 10⁷ ft-lb, (d) 245 hp.]

9. A car weighing 4200 lb climbs to the top of a grade 1600 ft above the bottom in 2.5 min. Neglecting friction, calculate (a) the potential energy, and (b) the horsepower developed.

10. A fully loaded elevator car has a total mass of 1800 Kg. If it rises 28 floors, a distance of 120 m in 30 s, find (a) the potential energy, and (b) the power developed. [*Ans.* (a) 2.12 × 10⁶ J, (b) 70.6 KW.]

11. Water is pumped from the ocean into a reservoir, a total lift of 86 m, at a rate of 20 m³/hr. What is the minimum power required? One cubic meter of sea water has a mass of 1025 Kg.

12. Oil is pumped from the tanks of a ship, through a large pipe to a storage tank on land 200 ft higher in elevation. What is the minimum horsepower required to pump 8000 gallons per hour, if one gallon of oil weighs 6.2 lb. [*Ans.* 50.1 hp.]

13. A 35,000-Kg rocket takes off vertically from a launching pad and acquires a vertical velocity of 600 m/s at an altitude of 5000 m. Assuming the acceleration due to gravity to be constant at 9.8 m/s², find (a) its potential energy, (b) its kinetic energy. Assuming constant upward acceleration, find (c) the acceleration, (d) the total upward thrust of the rocket motors, and (e) the power developed.

14. A 64,000-lb rocket takes off vertically from its launching pad and acquires a velocity of 1200 mi/hr at an altitude of 40,000 ft. Assuming the acceleration due to gravity to be constant at 32 ft/s², find (a) its potential energy, and (b) its kinetic energy. Assuming constant acceleration of the rocket, find (c) the acceleration, (d) the total thrust of the rocket motors, (e) the total energy, (f) the time from take-off, and (g) the power developed. [*Ans.* (a) 2.56 × 10⁹ ft-lb, (b) 3.10 × 10⁹ ft-lb, (c) 38.7 ft/s², (d) 1.41 × 10⁵ lb, (e) 5.66 × 10⁹ ft-lb, (f) 45.5 s, (g) 2.26 × 10⁵ hp.]

15. A 48,000-Kg jet plane, starting from rest at one end of a runway, acquires its takeoff speed of 42 m/s in a distance of 2000 m. Assuming constant acceleration, find (a) the acceleration, (b) the force, (c) the acquired kinetic energy, and (d) the power developed.

16. A steam-operated catapult 125 m long launches a

30,000-Kg jet photo-reconnaissance plane from the deck of an aircraft carrier. Starting at rest at one end, the plane acquires its takeoff speed of 100 m/s at the other. Find (a) the acceleration, (b) the average force, (c) the work done in newton meters, (d) the time to accelerate, and (e) the power developed. [*Ans.* (a) 40.0 m/s^2, (b) 1.20 $\times$ 10^6 N, (c) 1.50 $\times$ 10^8 N m, (d) 2.50 s, (e) 6.0 $\times$ 10^4 KW.]

CONSERVATION OF ENERGY

Most important of all the laws of nature is the law of the conservation of energy. Although the law has been stated in almost as many different ways as there are books written on the subject, they all have in reality the same meaning. The following three examples are typical statements:

(1) *In transforming energy from one form to another, energy is always conserved.*
(2) *Energy is never created or destroyed.*
(3) *The sum total of all energy in the universe remains constant.*

Everyone should be aware of the fact that there are many forms of energy. The most important forms are:

FORMS OF ENERGY

Mechanical	*Light*
Electrical	*Atomic*
Chemical	*Molecular*
Heat	*Nuclear*

In this chapter we are concerned with the law of conservation of energy only as it applies to the two forms of mechanical energy, *potential* and *kinetic.* The law will again be encountered in connection with the other forms in the chapters on heat, electricity, and atomic structure.

11.1. Energy Levels. In the preceding chapter we have seen that *potential energy* is one of the two forms of mechanical energy and is defined as *the energy a body has by virtue of its position or state.* In terms of *work done,*

$$W = F \times h$$

Calling the potential energy E_p, we write,

$$E_p = F \times h \qquad (11a)$$

A simple example is that of lifting a mass m against the pull of gravity as shown in Fig. 11A. An upward force F is applied to raise the mass m to a height h_1. By definition the *work done* is

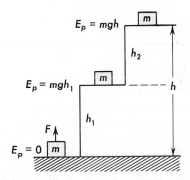

Fig. 11A   *An illustration of potential energy, E_p.*

equal to the force times the distance moved, $W = F \times h_1$. Since the force is equal to mg, the work done is stored as potential energy and we can write

$$E_1 = mgh_1 \qquad (11b)$$

If the mass is lifted to the top level, an additional distance h_2, the work done $F \times h_2$, is stored as an additional amount of potential energy mgh_2. The total stored energy is then given by

$$E_2 = mgh \qquad (11c)$$

where $h = h_1 + h_2$.

The horizontal lines E_0, E_1, and E_2 in Fig. 11B constitute an energy-level diagram in which stored energy in joules is plotted vertically. The up arrows indicate the storing of energy by raising the mass m, and the down arrows the release of energy when m is allowed to come down.

Fig. 11B   *An energy-level diagram for the mass m in Fig. 11A.*

Example 1. A 6-Kg mass is raised to a height of 5 m. Find the potential energy.

Solution. By direct substitution in Eq.(11a) we obtain

$$E_p = 6 \text{ Kg} \times 9.8 \frac{\text{m}}{\text{s}^2} \times 5 \text{ m}$$

$$E_p = 294 \frac{\text{Kg m}^2}{\text{s}^2}$$

$$E_p = 294 \text{ J}$$

If we select a base plane, such as sea level, as a level of zero potential energy, an object may have positive potential energy $+ mgh_2$, or negative potential energy mgh_1 as shown in Fig. 11C. Lo-

Fig. 11C   *Potential energy with respect to a base plane may be plus or minus.*

cated at any point above the base plane, a body has positive potential energy; at points below that level it has negative potential energy. In lifting the mass m from A to B, work is done. In returning from B to A, the mass releases energy. Similarly in going from A to C, the mass releases energy and ends up at C with less than it had at A. To raise it again to A, energy will have to be provided to do work.

From these considerations it is clear that we are free to choose the base plane of zero potential energy at any level and at the same time retain, unchanged, the energy differences between levels.

The other form of mechanical energy presented in the last chapter is called *kinetic energy*. *The kinetic energy of a moving mass is defined as the energy a body possesses by virtue of its motion.* An airplane in straight and level flight has kinetic energy of translation, and a spinning wheel has kinetic energy of rotation. For a given mass m moving in a straight line with constant velocity v, the kinetic energy E_k is given by

$$E_k = \tfrac{1}{2}mv^2 \qquad (11d)$$

Example 2. Calculate the kinetic energy of a 12-Kg mass moving with a velocity of 3 m/s.

Solution. By direct substitution in Eq. (11d), we obtain

$$E_k = \frac{1}{2} 12 \text{ Kg} \left(3 \frac{\text{m}}{\text{s}} \right)^2$$

$$E_k = 54 \frac{\text{Kg m}^2}{\text{s}^2}$$

$$E_k = 54 \text{ J}$$

Note, as pointed out in the last chapter, that kinetic energy has the same fundamental units as potential energy, and in the mks system is in joules.

At times it is convenient to express the kinetic energy of a body in terms of *momentum*. In Chapter 5 we have seen that the momentum p of a moving body is defined as the mass m multiplied by the velocity v:

$$p = mv \qquad (11e)$$

Multiplying numerator and denominator of Eq.(11d) by m and substituting p^2 for m^2v^2, we obtain for the kinetic energy

$$E_k = \frac{p^2}{2m} \qquad (11f)$$

11.2. Total Energy. When a body moves on an elevated plane, it possesses kinetic energy by virtue of its motion and potential energy by virtue of its position. The total energy of such a body is the sum of its separate energies:

$$\text{Total energy} = E_k + E_p$$

abbreviated

$$E_t = E_k + E_p \qquad (11g)$$

As an illustration consider a car moving on different floor levels in a modern auto parking building (see Fig. 11D). Starting at rest at A,

Fig. 11D *A moving car at different levels has different amounts of energy.*

where the ground level is selected as the base plane, the velocity $v = 0$, the height $h = 0$, and both E_k and E_p are zero. The total mechanical energy is therefore zero:

$$E_0 = 0$$

When the car is at B and moving with a velocity v_0 at the ground level, $h = 0$, the total energy is all kinetic:

$$E_1 = \tfrac{1}{2}mv_0{}^2 + 0$$

When the car is at C, moving with a velocity v_1 at a height h_1 above the ground level, the total stored energy is

$$E_2 = \tfrac{1}{2}mv_1{}^2 + mgh_1$$

and when the car is moving with a velocity v_2 at D on the next floor up, the total energy is

$$E_3 = \tfrac{1}{2}mv_2{}^2 + mgh_2$$

If we assign specific values to m, v, and h in these equations, we can calculate each specific energy and construct an energy-level diagram of the kind shown in Fig. 11E. Energy in joules E_t is plotted vertically upward from zero and horizontal lines are drawn at the appropriate values. The up arrows show the energy stored as the car goes up from one level to the other, while the down arrows show the energy being liberated as the car descends. Note that although the floor levels might be equally spaced the energy levels need not be.

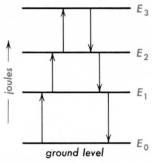

Fig. 11E *Energy-level diagram for the total mechanical energy of the car shown in Fig. 11D.*

11.3. Conservation of Energy. As an illustration of the transformation of one form of mechanical energy into another, consider the demonstration experiment shown in Fig. 11F.

Fig. 11F *Demonstration of energy transformation.*

Water in a tank escapes through an outlet pipe and falls on the blades of a paddle wheel. The water in the tank has potential energy mgh. As it falls with ever-increasing speed, that energy is converted into kinetic energy $\tfrac{1}{2}mv^2$. In turning the paddle wheel this energy of motion can be utilized to do mechanical work of one kind or another. On the other hand, it might well be made to turn an electric generator and convert mechanical energy into electrical energy. The electrical generator in turn can be connected to a toaster and convert electrical energy into heat, etc.

Consider the energy involved in a waterfall as shown in Fig. 11G. The water at the top of the fall has potential energy by virtue of its position above the base. As it falls over and then down-

potential energy

$\frac{1}{2} E_p + \frac{1}{2} E_k$

kinetic energy

Fig. 11G   *All the available energy at the top of a waterfall is potential. At the bottom it is kinetic.*

ward with ever-increasing speed, the kinetic energy $\frac{1}{2}mv^2$ increases, while the potential energy decreases. At the bottom of the fall, the potential energy approaches zero and the kinetic energy approaches its maximum value. At the top, the energy was practically all potential, while near the bottom it is mostly kinetic. Assuming the water to start from rest at the top and that no energy is lost in falling, the E_p at the top of the falls equals the E_k at the bottom.

$$E_p \text{ at top} = E_k \text{ at bottom}$$

$$F \times h = \tfrac{1}{2}mv^2 \qquad (11h)$$

or

$$mgh = \tfrac{1}{2}mv^2 \qquad (11i)$$

Divide both sides of the equation by m and solve for v.

$$v^2 = 2gh$$

or

$$\boxed{v = \sqrt{2gh}} \qquad (11j)$$

This is the same equation that is derived for uniformly accelerated motion in Chapter 3, used for freely falling bodies in Chapter 4, and applied to projectiles in Chapter 9 [see Eqs.(4d) and (9f)]. Here the equation has been derived from the law of conservation of energy.

Example 3. A mass of 25 Kg is dropped from a height of 5 m. Find the kinetic energy and velocity just as it reaches the ground.

Solution. Since the E_p at the top is equivalent to the E_k at the bottom,

$$E_p = 25 \text{ Kg} \times 9.8 \, \frac{\text{m}}{\text{s}^2} \times 5 \text{ m}$$

$$= 1225 \text{ joules} = E_k$$

The velocity is found by Eq.(11j),

$$v = \sqrt{2 \times 9.8 \times 5} = 9.9 \text{ m/s}$$

When the falling body in the above problem is part way down, it has some E_p and some E_k. Its total energy E_t is therefore given by Eq.(11g).

$$E_t = \tfrac{1}{2}mv^2 + mgh$$

At the instant the body reaches the ground, it is suddenly stopped and all of the energy is quickly transformed into heat. The transformation of mechanical energy into heat is often demonstrated in the physics laboratory by an experiment in which a quantity of lead-shot is dropped from a height of several feet and its temperature measured before and after falling. By raising the shot and dropping it many times, the rise in temperature amounts to several degrees.

11.4. The Inclined Plane. It can be shown that a body sliding without friction down an incline of height h should acquire at the bottom a velocity $v = \sqrt{2gh}$. This equation is readily derived from the law of conservation of energy.

Consider the demonstration experiment shown in Fig. 11H in which a small truck is pulled up

Fig. 11H   *Conservation of energy.*

an incline. The work done to reach the top is given by the product of force F times the distance s. By conservation of energy, this must be equal to the stored-up potential energy mgh at the top. Therefore

$$F \times s = mgh \qquad (11k)$$

Now, if the truck is released, it will accelerate back down the incline, thereby converting the potential energy mgh into kinetic energy $\frac{1}{2}mv^2$. By conservation of energy we can write the more general form

total E at top = total E at bottom

$$E_p + E_k = E_p + E_k$$
$$mgh + 0 = 0 + \tfrac{1}{2}mv^2$$

$$mgh = \tfrac{1}{2}mv^2$$

Since the m on both sides refers to the same mass, we can divide by m and obtain

$$gh = \tfrac{1}{2}v^2,$$
$$v = \sqrt{2gh} \qquad (11l)$$

A comparison of this last equation with Eq.(11j) shows that neglecting friction, an object acquires the same speed at the bottom of an incline as that of a body falling freely from the same height. In effect, the speed at the bottom of an incline does not depend upon its steepness, but upon the height alone.

When sliding friction is not negligibly small, Eq.(11k) must include an additional term. At the top of the incline the total energy E is all potential and $E = mgh$. In sliding down, part of this available energy, to the amount of $f \times s$, is used up in overcoming friction, and the rest goes into kinetic energy, $\frac{1}{2}mv^2$. By conservation of energy,

E_p at top = frictional energy + E_k at bottom
$$mgh = f \times s + \tfrac{1}{2}mv^2$$

In applying this formula to the solving of problems, the force of friction, $f = \mu N$, is found by resolving the weight mg into components.

11.5. The Simple Pendulum. A similar energy treatment can be given for the swinging of a simple pendulum (see Fig. 11I). At the extreme

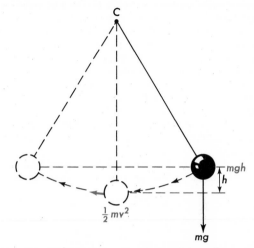

Fig. 11I *Potential energy of a pendulum changes to kinetic energy and back again.*

ends of each swing the bob comes momentarily to rest, and the energy E is all potential and equal to mgh. At the bottom of the swing the energy E is all kinetic and equal to $\frac{1}{2}mv^2$.

The motion of the pendulum bob is like that of a body sliding, without friction, down an inclined plane of changing angle. The kinetic energy acquired in going down one side is just sufficient to carry it up to an equal height on the other. Equation (11l) therefore applies equally well to a swinging pendulum.

PROBLEMS

1. A 1000-Kg car drives from the street level to the fourth floor of a car-parking building. The car maintains a speed of 3 m/s on the ramps as well as on the floor levels. The latter are spaced 3 m apart, with the first floor at street level. (a) Calculate the total energy at each floor level. (b) Plot an energy-level diagram for the car while moving on each of the floor levels.

2. An elevator car of 800 Kg goes from the basement level 4 m below street level to the fourth floor of an apartment house. The first floor is at the street level and all floors are 4 m apart. Starting from rest at the basement the elevator passes floors 1, 2, and 3 at the same speed of 4 m/s, and stops at the fourth floor. Calculate (a) the potential energy at each floor level and (b) the kinetic energy at each floor level. (c) Plot an energy-level diagram for the total energy at each floor if we select the base plane at the street level. [*Ans.* (a) −31,360 J, 0, +31,360 J, +62,720 J, and +94,080 J, respectively. (b) 0, 6400 J, 6400 J, 6400 J, and 0, respectively. (c) −31,360 J, +6400 J, +37,760 J, +69,120 J, and +94,080 J, respectively.]

3. A jet plane with a weight of 160 tons takes off from the Denver Airport where the elevation is 1 mi above sea level. Climbing to a height of 5 mi it acquires a cruising

speed of 480 mi/hr in straight and level flight. Approaching a storm over the mid-west it now climbs to a height of 8 mi, where it levels with a cruising speed of 540 mi/hr. Approaching New York City the plane descends to a height of 2 mi where its cruising speed is reduced to 240 mi/hr. The plane lands at International Airport where it comes to rest at the air terminal, altitude approximately sea level. Calculate (a) the total energy at each level, and (b) plot an energy-level diagram.

4. A 75-Kg box falls from a bridge and lands in the water 35 m below. Find (a) its initial potential energy, (b) its velocity of impact on the water, (c) the maximum kinetic energy, (d) the kinetic energy 15 m above the water, and (e) the potential energy 15 m above the water. [*Ans.* (a) 2.57×10^4 J, (b) 26.2 m/s, (c) 2.57×10^4 J, (d) 1.47×10^4 J, (e) 1.10×10^4 J.]

5. If 20 m³ of water go over a waterfall 25 m high every minute, find the power equivalent in (a) kilowatts, and (b) horsepower.

6. A girl of 60 Kg slides down a swimming-pool slide which is 10 m long. The upper end is 5 m above the water and the lower end is at the water. Assuming a coefficient of sliding friction to be 0.22, find (a) the potential energy of the girl at the top, (b) the force of friction, (c) the energy loss overcoming friction, (d) the maximum kinetic energy of the girl, and (e) the girl's maximum velocity. [*Ans.* (a) 2940 J, (b) 112 N, (c) 1120 J, (d) 1820 J, (e) 7.78 m/s.]

7. A boy of 55 Kg slides down a playground slide which is 8 m long. The upper end is 4 m above the ground and the lower end is on the ground. Assuming a coefficient of sliding friction of 0.3, find (a) the potential energy of the boy at the top, (b) the force of friction, (c) the energy loss overcoming friction, (d) the maximum kinetic energy acquired, and (e) the boy's maximum velocity.

8. A mass of 3 Kg is suspended as a pendulum by a fine wire 6 m long. If the mass is pulled back, and released from rest when the wire makes an angle of 30° with the vertical, find (a) the potential energy stored in raising the mass, (b) the maximum kinetic energy attained by the mass, and (c) its maximum velocity. [*Ans.* (a) 23.6 J, (b) 23.6 J, (c) 3.96 m/s.]

CONSERVATION OF MOMENTUM

In order to provide an accurate description of many of the events that occur in nature, the laws of conservation of energy and conservation of momentum are most important. While these two laws involve different concepts, both are implicated and both are generally applied to practical problems.

When two or more bodies collide with each other, or some internal changes occur within a body or system of bodies, it is common practice to first apply the law of conservation of momentum.

12.1. The Law of Conservation of Momentum. The law of conservation of momentum applies to all collision phenomena whether they involve the largest astronomical bodies or the smallest atomic particles. This universal law of nature may be stated as follows:

The total momentum before impact equals the total momentum after impact.

Consider as an example the "head-on" encounter of two balls as shown in Fig. 12A. Before impact the mass m_1 is moving with a velocity u_1 and has a momentum m_1u_1, while m_2 is moving with a velocity u_2 and has a momentum m_2u_2. The total momentum before impact is therefore equal to the sum of the two momenta, $m_1u_1 + m_2u_2$.

By similar reasoning it is clear that after impact, m_1 and m_2, with their new velocities v_1 and v_2 have a total momentum $m_1v_1 + m_2v_2$. The law of conservation of momentum requires that

$$m_1u_1 + m_2u_2 = m_1v_1 + m_2v_2 \qquad (12a)$$

$$\frac{\text{total momentum}}{\text{before impact}} = \frac{\text{total momentum}}{\text{after impact}}$$

During impact, two equal but opposite forces are set up between the bodies, one the force exerted by m_1 on m_2, and the other the force exerted by m_2 on m_1. These two equal but opposite forces are an action and reaction pair as specified by Newton's third law of motion. Each force acts for the same short interval of time, giving equal impulses Ft to both bodies. By Newton's second law, as expressed by the im-

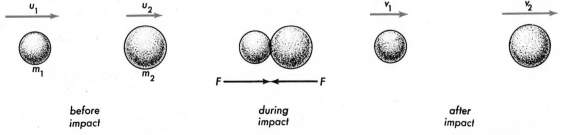

before impact   during impact   after impact

Fig. 12A   *The total momentum of two bodies before impact is equal to the total momentum after impact.*

pulse equation $Ft = mv - mv_0$, equal impulses produce equal changes in momentum. One body gains as much momentum as the other loses. In other words, the total momentum remains constant.

Example 1. A ball with a mass of 5 Kg moving with a velocity of 20 m/s, collides with another ball with a mass of 10 Kg moving in the same direction along the same line with a velocity of 10 m/s. After impact the first mass is still moving in the same direction but with a velocity of 8 m/s. Calculate the velocity of the second mass after impact.

Solution. By direct substitution in Eq.(12a), we obtain,

$$(5 \times 20) + (10 \times 10) = (5 \times 8) + (10 \times v_2)$$
$$200 = 40 + 10v_2$$
$$10v_2 = 160 \qquad v_2 = 16\,\text{m/s}$$

After impact, the second mass has a velocity of 16 m/s.

If, in the above example, the total kinetic energy after impact is calculated and compared with the total kinetic energy before impact, the two will not be found equal. Employing the equation $E_k = \frac{1}{2}mv^2$, we obtain

before impact

$$E_k = \frac{1}{2}(5 \times 20^2) + \frac{1}{2}(10 \times 10^2)$$
$$= 1500\,\text{J}$$

after impact

$$E_k = \frac{1}{2}(5 \times 8^2) + \frac{1}{2}(10 \times 16^2)$$
$$= 1440\,\text{J}$$

The difference in energy, to the amount of 60 J, has disappeared as mechanical energy and gone into heat. During impact, both masses were slightly deformed in shape due to the mutually acting forces and a small amount of heat was generated internally. This heat raised the temperature of the two colliding bodies. It is only by including this heat energy of 60 J with the mechanical energy after impact that makes it possible to retain the law of conservation of energy.

This is just another way of stating that collisions in general are not perfectly elastic. If they were perfectly elastic, conservation of mechanical energy would hold, as well as conservation of momentum.

An interesting experiment that illustrates conservation of momentum is shown in Fig. 12B. Two small cars of equal mass, $m_1 = m_2$, are tied together with a compressed spring between them.

Fig. 12B   *Conservation of momentum demonstration experiments.*

Then, when the cord is burned with a match, releasing the spring, the two cars fly apart with equal velocities. Before the spring is released, the cars are at rest and the total momentum is zero. After the spring is released the total momentum is still zero because the two velocities are oppositely directed. Momentum being a vector quantity,

$$m_1v_1 + m_2v_2 = 0 \qquad (12b)$$

With motions to the right taken as positive, v_2 is positive and v_1 negative, and the two momenta cancel.

If the experiment above is repeated with one of the cars heavily loaded as shown in diagram (b), the two fly apart as before but with unequal velocities. The lighter mass moves away with a high velocity while the heavier mass recoils with a low velocity. The product $m_1 \times v_1$, however, is equal in magnitude to the product $m_2 \times v_2$, and the sum of the two momenta is zero.

Example 2. A 60-Kg shell is shot with an initial velocity of 500 m/s, from a gun having a mass of 2000 Kg. What is the initial velocity with which the gun recoils?

Solution. Applying Eq.(12b), and substituting directly the known quantities, we find

$$60\,\text{Kg} \times 500\,\text{m/s} + 2000\,\text{Kg} \times v_2 = 0$$
$$30{,}000\,\text{Kg m/s} + 2000\,v_2\,\text{Kg} = 0$$

$$v_2 = \frac{30{,}000\,\text{Kg m/s}}{-2000\,\text{Kg}} = -15\,\text{m/s}$$

The gun recoils with a velocity of 15 m/s.

The law of conservation of momentum can be derived from Newton's second law as shown by Eqs.(5k) or (5m). An unbalanced force F acting on a body for a time t changes the momentum from its initial value mv_0 to a final value mv,

$$Ft = mv - mv_0 \qquad (12c)$$

If no external unbalanced forces are applied to a body, or system of bodies, $F = 0$, and the impulse $Ft = 0$.

$$0 = mv - mv_0$$
or $$mv = mv_0$$

Forces between individual parts of a system of bodies are internal forces and always exist in pairs. Each pair gives rise to equal and opposite impulses so that no resultant momentum is imparted to the system as a whole.

Another interesting experiment illustrating conservation of momentum may be performed with six or seven large balls or small marbles and a grooved board as shown in Fig. 12C. When

hard bodies in collision are highly resilient and rebound from each other quite rapidly, while many soft bodies are less resilient and rebound much more slowly. *Resilience is defined as the ability of a body to undergo a compression, or rapid deformation, without the development of permanent deformation.* The vigor with which a body restores itself to its original shape after a deformation is called *restitution*.

The coefficient of restitution r is defined as a number expressing the ratio of the velocity with which the two bodies separate after collision to the velocity of their approach before collision.

$$r = \frac{\text{velocity of separation}}{\text{velocity of approach}} \qquad (12d)$$

Referring to the two bodies in Fig. 12A,

$$r = \frac{v_2 - v_1}{u_1 - u_2} \qquad (12e)$$

One method of determining r for two bodies in collision is to employ spheres of the material

Fig. 12C　*Experiment with the duckpin balls, illustrating the law of conservation of momentum.*

one ball is rolled up to the others, it will be stopped by collision with the others and the one on the extreme right-hand end will roll out with the same velocity. If two balls are rolled up as indicated in the diagram, two will roll out on the other end, and if three are rolled up, three will roll out. (Glass or steel marbles work best in this experiment, as they are highly elastic.)

When the two balls are rolled up, why doesn't just one roll off on the other side with twice the velocity, thus conserving momentum? The answer to this question involves conservation of energy, for if only one came off with twice the velocity to conserve momentum, its kinetic energy would be twice the energy available from the original two.

12.2. Resilience, and the Coefficient of Restitution. Experimental observations show that most

and mount them as pendulums, as shown in Fig. 12D. With m_2 hanging freely at rest, m_1 is raised to a height h_1 and released. From the rebound heights h_2 and h_1' the velocities before and after collision can be determined from the equation $v = \sqrt{2gh}$ [see Eq.(4d)]. By substitution of the calculated velocities in Eq.(12e), the value of r is found.

The simplest method of finding the coefficient of restitution for two bodies at impact is shown in Fig. 12E. Spheres of different substances are dropped successively, all from the same height, onto the smooth top surface of a large anvil and allowed to bounce to their various heights. Contrary to one's preconceived ideas of elasticity, a glass or steel marble will bounce to a greater height than will a ball made of the best Pará or India rubber. A lead ball or lead marble, on the other hand, hardly bounces at all.

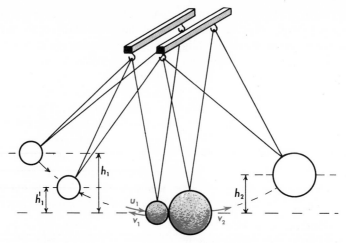

Fig. 12D   *Experiment for determining the coefficient of restitution.*

If we apply Eq.(12a) to these bouncing marbles, we note that the very great mass of the anvil reduces its recoil velocity v_2 to practically zero. Under these conditions we can write $u_2 = 0$ and $v_2 = 0$, and u_1 and v_1 are given by the law of freely falling bodies,

$$u_1 = \sqrt{2gH} \qquad v_1 = \sqrt{2gh}$$

Upon substitution in Eq.(12e), we obtain

$$r = \frac{\sqrt{2gh}}{\sqrt{2gH}}$$

or, simply

$$r = \sqrt{\frac{h}{H}} \qquad (12f)$$

As illustrated in Fig. 12E, H is the height from which a marble falls and h is the height to which

it rebounds. For a very elastic substance, like glass or steel colliding with steel, r has a value of 0.95 or better, whereas for a very inelastic substance, like lead colliding with steel, r is extremely small. It is seen from Eq.(12e) that the smallest value that r can have is zero, while the largest value is unity.

Curves showing how the coefficient of restitution varies with impact velocity are given in Fig. 12F. These curves show that at moderate to high velocities the coefficient of restitution shows little change and is nearly constant, while for very low velocities r increases and approaches *unity*. Note for example the low value of r at moderate velocities, and how at extremely low velocities r approaches 1.0. This means that a lead ball dropped onto an anvil from a height of a meter or more would hardly bounce at all,

Fig. 12E   *The bouncing marble experiment, illustrating the resilience of different substances.*

Fig. 12F *Coefficients of restitution measured for the impact of two spheres of similar mate-rial. Dotted curves at top are for small spheres dropped on thick flat plates of similar material.*

but dropped from a low height of 1 mm would bounce to a height of almost 1 mm. Such behavior involves going beyond the elastic limit of the solid, and is a subject treated in Chapter 18.

Approximate values of the coefficient of restitution for the impact at moderate velocities of pairs of spheres of the same material are given in Table 12A.

TABLE 12A. APPROXIMATE VALUES OF THE
COEFFICIENT OF RESTITUTION

Material	r	Material	r
brass	0.30	iron	0.67
bronze	0.52	ivory	0.78
copper	0.22	lead	0.16
cork	0.60	maple	0.65
elm	0.48	rubber	0.75
glass	0.96	steel	0.90

12.3. Head-on Collisions. We have seen in Sec. 12.1, that when two bodies collide head-on the law of conservation of momentum as given by Eq.(12a) applies. This law is not sufficient, however, to determine the recoil velocities of each of the two bodies after impact. Different kinds of materials have different elastic properties and do not behave alike during impact, and for this reason will move apart with different velocities.

Combining Eq.(12a) with the coefficient of restitution, as given by Eq.(12c), provides a means for determining the recoil velocities of all objects.

Suppose for example that the masses of two bodies, their initial velocities, and the coefficient of restitution are known. With two equations and two unknowns, the recoil velocities of the two bodies can be calculated.

By solving Eq.(12e) for v_2, and substituting for v_2 in Eq.(12a), we obtain the equation

$$v_1 = u_1 - \frac{m_2}{m_1 + m_2}(u_1 - u_2)(1 + r) \quad (12g)$$

By solving Eq.(12e) for v_1 and substituting for v_1 in Eq.(12a), we obtain the equation

$$v_2 = u_2 - \frac{m_1}{m_1 + m_2}(u_2 - u_1)(1 + r) \quad (12h)$$

Example 3. A 2-Kg steel ball moving with a velocity of 8 m/s, collides head-on with a 5-Kg steel ball moving in the same direction and along the same straight line at 1 m/s. If the coefficient of restitution is 0.90, find the recoil velocity of the two balls.

Solution. By direct substitution in Eq.(12g), we obtain,

$$v_1 = 8\,\frac{m}{s} - \frac{5\,Kg}{7\,Kg}\left(8\,\frac{m}{s}\right) - 1\,\frac{m}{s}(1 + 0.90)$$

$$v_1 = -1.5\,\frac{m}{s}$$

By direct substitution in Eq.(12h), we obtain,

$$v_2 = 1\,\frac{m}{s} - \frac{2\,Kg}{7\,Kg}\left(1\,\frac{m}{s} - 8\,\frac{m}{s}\right)(1 + 0.90)$$

$$v_2 = 4.8\,\frac{m}{s}$$

As a check on the law of conservation of momentum, we can apply these values by direct substitution in Eq.(12a).

$$2 \times 8 + 5 \times 1 = 2(-1.5) + 5 \times 4.8$$
$$16 + 5 = -3 + 24$$

The above equations are particularly important in atomic and molecular structure collisions where perfectly elastic impacts are the common occurrence. In this special case the velocity of separation equals the velocity of approach and the coefficient of restitution $r = 1$.

For perfectly elastic collisions that are head-on, $r = 1$, Eqs.(12g) and (12h) simplify, and the law of conservation of energy applies as well as the conservation of momentum.

$$\tfrac{1}{2}m_1u_1^2 + \tfrac{1}{2}m_2u_2^2 = \tfrac{1}{2}m_1v_1^2 + \tfrac{1}{2}m_2v_2^2 \qquad (12i)$$

total kinetic energy   **total kinetic energy**
before impact $=$ **after impact**

It is important to note from the discussion above that, for all impact problems whether perfectly elastic or not, the law of conservation of momentum applies, and that if the bodies are perfectly elastic, then and only then does the conservation of kinetic energy apply.

12.4. The More General Problem of Impact. In general, the impact between two bodies is not a head-on collision but one in which a moving body collides with another body initially at rest, and the two bodies recoil in different directions. The diagram in Fig. 12G shows a mass m_1 mov-

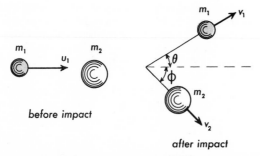

before impact

after impact

Fig. 12G   *Diagram of the impact between two bodies in which the collision is not head-on.*

ing with an initial velocity u_1 and colliding with a mass m_2 initially at rest.

After impact, mass m_1 recoils in a direction θ with a velocity v_1 while mass m_2 recoils in a different direction ϕ with a velocity v_2. Since momentum is a vector quantity, we can draw arrows to represent the momentum of bodies before impact, and after impact as shown in Fig. 12H.

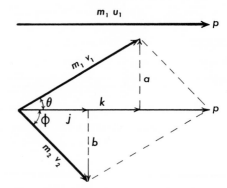

Fig. 12H   *Momentum diagram for the impact of two bodies as shown in Fig. 12G.*

Before impact, the total momentum p is that of the moving mass m_1 and is simply

$$p = m_1u_1$$

After impact the total momentum p is unchanged and is composed of two parts, m_1v_1 and m_2v_2. The momentum m_1v_1 is resolved into two components, component a perpendicular to p and component k parallel to p. Similarly, the momentum m_2v_2 is resolved into two components, component b perpendicular to p and component j parallel to p.

By the conservation of momentum, the sum of the vectors j and k must be equal to the initial momentum p.

$$m_1u_1 = m_1v_1 \cos \theta + m_2v_2 \cos \phi \qquad (12j)$$

Since the initial momentum m_1u_1 has no component perpendicular to its direction of motion, the two components a and b must be equal in magnitude and opposite in direction.

$$m_1v_1 \sin \theta = m_2v_2 \sin \phi \qquad (12k)$$

Hence, in any impact between two bodies, one initially at rest, these two equations must hold.

In the special case of a gas, where the collisions between atoms and molecules are perfectly elastic, conservation of energy also applies. If one of the particles is initially at rest, as shown in Fig. 12B, Eq.(12i) can be written

$$\tfrac{1}{2}m_1u_1{}^2 = \tfrac{1}{2}m_1v_1{}^2 + \tfrac{1}{2}m_2v_2{}^2 \qquad (12l)$$

It can be shown that for perfectly elastic collisions, Eqs.(12j), (12k), and (12l) may be combined to obtain the relation that

$$\cos\theta = \frac{u_1{}^2 + v_1{}^2 - \dfrac{m_2}{m_1}(u_1{}^2 - v_1{}^2)}{2u_1v_1} \qquad (12m)$$

and that

$$v_2{}^2 = \frac{m_1}{m_2}(u_1{}^2 - v_1{}^2) \qquad (12n)$$

To derive Eq.(12m), see Problem 18 at the end of this chapter.

For collisions between solid spheres of tempered steel or glass, the coefficient of restitution is so nearly unity that all five of the last equations can be assumed to hold.

12.5. Ballistics. The term ballistics is applied to that branch of science dealing with the measurement of bullet velocities and the effects of bullets upon targets of various kinds. A major part of the activity of this science is concerned with the determination of what is called the *muzzle velocity* of guns.

One of the procedures commonly employed for small-arms measurements consists of mounting the gun in a horizontal position, with the barrel aimed directly at a large rectangular block of wood directly in front of the muzzle. The block is usually suspended as a pendulum by four long cords of equal length. As the bullet leaves the gun barrel it becomes embedded in the wood block, and the momentum of this recoiling mass causes it to swing back and up to some maximum height. By measuring the masses of the bullet and block, and the height the combined mass recoils, the muzzle velocity can be calculated.

A similar method may be employed whereby the gun is mounted with the gun barrel pointing straight upward, and the bullet is fired directly into a block of wood resting on a support as shown in Fig. 12I(a).

The penetration of the bullet into the block of wood is a collision event and the law of conservation of momentum applies. With the wood

Fig. 12I   *Rifle arrangement with attachments for ballistics experiment.*

block initially at rest, the total momentum before impact is just that of the incoming bullet, m_1u [see Fig. 12I(b)]. After impact the bullet and the block, with a total mass $m_1 + m_2$, recoil upward with a velocity v, and the total momentum $(m_1 + m_2)v$. We can therefore write

$$m_1u = (m_1 + m_2)v \qquad (12o)$$

Since u is the unknown, we divide both sides of the equation by m_1, and obtain

$$u = \frac{m_1 + m_2}{m_1}v \qquad (12p)$$

The recoil velocity v can be determined from the maximum height h to which the block and embedded bullet rise. By the principle of conservation of energy applied to falling bodies, we may use Eq.(11j),

$$v = \sqrt{2gh}$$

and substitute $\sqrt{2gh}$ for v in Eq.(12j), and obtain

$$u = \frac{m_1 + m_2}{m_1}\sqrt{2gh} \qquad (12q)$$

All quantities on the right in this equation can be measured by experiment, and the substitution of any set of measurements will give the muzzle velocity u. It should be noted that since the velocity of separation between the bullet and block is zero, the coefficient of restitution $r = 0$.

A good laboratory demonstration of ballistics measurements can be performed with a wood block* as shown at the right in Fig 12I, and a .22-calibre rifle as shown at the left. Typical bullets, shells, and assembled cartridges to be used, commonly available in sporting-goods stores, are shown in Fig. 12J. The .22-short, .22-long, and .22-high-velocity cartridges shown at the right are combinations of two bullet sizes with two shell sizes shown at the left.

* Appropriate wood blocks for this experiment may be made of hardwood, about 2 in. in diameter and 4.5 in. long, with one or two tightly fitted metal bands to prevent splitting. The same block can be used for several firings. Hardwood balls 3 in. in diameter are sometimes available in lumberyards or hardware stores, and may be used in place of cylinders.

Fig. 12J *Bullets, shells, and assembled cartridges for a .22-rifle.*

Typical measured values and calculated velocities are given in Table 12B.

TABLE 12B. BALLISTICS MEASUREMENTS AND CALCULATED MUZZLE VELOCITIES FOR A .22-CALIBRE RIFLE

Cartridge desig.	.22-S	.22-L	.22-HV
m_1 (Kg)	0.0018	0.0026	0.0018
m_2 (Kg)	0.227	0.229	0.231
h (m)	0.57	1.25	0.81
v (m/s)	3.34	4.95	3.98
u (m/s)	425	441	515

PROBLEMS

1. A 12-Kg ball moving with a velocity of 15 m/s, collides head-on with a 4-Kg ball initially at rest. After impact the velocity of the 12-Kg mass is 9 m/s. Find (a) the velocity of the 4-Kg mass after impact, (b) the initial kinetic energy, (c) the total kinetic energy after impact, (d) the energy loss due to impact, (e) the relative velocity of approach before impact, and (f) the relative velocity of separation after impact.

2. A 5-Kg ball moving with a velocity of 8 m/s collides head-on with another ball of 2-Kg mass and initially at rest. After impact the first mass is still moving in the same direction, but with a velocity of 4 m/s. Calculate (a) the velocity of the second mass after impact, (b) the initial kinetic energy, (c) the total kinetic energy after impact, (d) the energy loss during impact, (e) the relative velocity of approach before impact, and (f) the velocity of separation after impact. [*Ans.* (a) 10 m/s, (b) 160 J, (c) 140 J, (d) 20 J, (e) 8 m/s, (f) 6 m/s.]

3. A rifle pointing straight upward has a 1.2-Kg block of wood resting on the muzzle end of the barrel. When the rifle fires a 50-gm bullet into the block, it becomes embedded in the wood, and the block rises to a maximum height of 30 m. Find the muzzle velocity of the bullet.

4. A 5-Kg block of wood hangs as a pendulum by a string 4 m long. When a 30-gm bullet is fired at close range into the block and becomes embedded, the block swings to a height where the string makes an angle of 30° with the vertical. Find (a) the recoil height of the block,

(b) the recoil speed of the block, and (c) the recoil speed of the bullet. [*Ans.* (a) 0.536 m, (b) 3.24 m/s, (c) 543 m/s.]

5. A 40-gm bullet, fired from a gun with a speed of 500 m/s, embeds itself in a 1.5-Kg block of wood suspended from the lower end of a 16-m-long cord. What is (a) the recoil velocity of the block, and (b) how high does it swing when it swings back?

6. An ivory ball with a mass of 0.4 Kg, moving with a speed of 6 m/s, collides head-on with another ivory ball of the same mass and size, at rest. If the coefficient of restitution is 0.65, find the velocity of each ball after collision. [*Ans.* 1.05 m/s, and 4.95 m/s.]

7. A wooden ball with a mass of 0.25 Kg and a velocity of 4 m/s, collides with a 1.50-Kg iron ball at rest. If the coefficient of restitution is 0.50, find the velocity of both masses after impact.

8. An atom of mass 8×10^{-25} Kg, moving with a velocity of 2×10^7 m/s, makes a head-on collision with another atom of mass 36×10^{-25} Kg, at rest. Assuming a perfect elastic collision, what are the two velocities after impact? [*Ans.* -1.273×10^7 m/s, and $+0.727 \times 10^7$ m/s.]

9. A ball with a mass of 0.50 Kg, moving with a velocity of 16 m/s, makes a head-on collision with a mass of 0.12 Kg initially at rest. If the coefficient of restitution is 0.80, what is the final velocity of each mass?

10. A 25-gm bullet, moving with a velocity of 700 m/s,

passes through a 1-Kg block of wood lying on a fence post. If the bullet leaves the other side with a velocity of 200 m/s (a) what is the velocity of the block, and (b) how much energy goes into heat? [*Ans.* (a) 12.5 m/s, (b) 5547 J.]

11. An 8-lb ball moving with a velocity of 20 ft/s makes a head-on collision with a 24-lb ball initially at rest. If the coefficient of restitution is 0.8, find (a) the total momentum before impact, (b) the velocity of m_1 after impact, (c) the velocity of m_2 after impact, (d) the total kinetic energy before impact, (e) the kinetic energy of m_1 after impact, (f) the kinetic energy of m_2 after impact, and (g) the energy loss during impact.

12. An atomic particle of mass 16×10^{-28} Kg, moving with a velocity of 3×10^7 m/s, collides head-on with a second atomic particle of mass 3.2×10^{-28} Kg initially at rest. If the coefficient of restitution is $r = 1$, find (a) the total momentum before impact, (b) the velocity of m_1 after impact, (c) the velocity of m_2 after impact, (d) the total kinetic energy before impact, (e) the kinetic energy of m_1 after impact, (f) the kinetic energy of m_2 after impact, and (g) the total energy after impact. [*Ans.* (a) 4.8×10^{-20} Kg m/s, (b) 2×10^7 m/s, (c) 5×10^7 m/s, (d) 7.2×10^{-13} J, (e) 3.2×10^{-13} J, (f) 4.0×10^{-13} J, (g) 7.2×10^{-13} J.]

13. A 15-Kg steel sphere, moving with a velocity of 12 m/s, collides with a 20-Kg steel sphere initially at rest. If after impact the velocity of m_1 is 8 m/s, find (a) the angle of recoil θ, (b) the recoil velocity of m_2, and (c) the recoil angle ϕ.

14. A 10-Kg steel sphere, moving with a velocity of 20 m/s, collides with an 8-Kg steel sphere initially at rest. If after impact the velocity of m_1 is 16 m/s, find (a) the angle θ, the velocity of m_2, and (c) the angle ϕ. [*Ans.* (a) 32.33°, (b) 13.42 m/s, (c) 52.85°.]

15. A glass marble with a mass of 8 gm, and moving with a velocity of 0.60 m/s, collides with another glass marble of the same mass but initially at rest. If the marbles bounce off in directions $\theta = 41.4°$, and $\phi = 48.5°$, respectively, find the recoil velocity of (a) the incident marble, and (b) the second marble. Assume perfect elasticity. Find the kinetic energy of (c) the first marble, and (d) the second marble.

16. A steel ball of 8 Kg, moving with a velocity of 12 m/s, collides with another steel ball of 32 Kg initially at rest. If the balls bounce off in directions $\theta = 73.5°$ and $\phi = 46.3°$, respectively, find the recoil velocity of (a) the incident ball, and (b) the second ball. Assume perfect elasticity. Find the kinetic energy of (c) the first ball, and (d) the second ball. [*Ans.* (a) 10.0 m/s, (b) 3.32 m/s, (c) 400 J, (d) 176 J.]

17. An atomic particle with a mass of 3.4×10^{-26} Kg, and moving with a velocity of 3×10^6 m/s, collides with another with ten times the mass and initially at rest. If the incident particle recoils with a velocity of 2.8×10^6 m/s, find (a) the recoil angle θ, (b) the recoil velocity of the heavier particle, and (c) the recoil angle of the heavier particle.

18. Solve Eq.(12k) for $\sin \phi$, then square to find $\sin^2 \phi$. Solve Eq.(12j) for $\cos \phi$, then square to find $\cos^2 \phi$. Since by trigonometry $\sin^2 \phi + \cos^2 \phi = 1$, add the right hand sides of the two derived equations and set equal to unity. Solve this equation for v_2^2. Solve Eq.(12l) for v_2^2 also, and put right-hand sides of both equations equal to each other. Solve for $u_1^2 - v_1^2$, multiply out the term $(u_1 - v_1 \cos \theta)^2$, noting that $\sin^2 \theta + \cos^2 \theta = 1$, and simplify by solving for $\cos \theta$. [*Ans.* This is Eq.(12m)].

19. Solve Eq.(12g) for u_1.

20. Solve Eq.(12h) for u_2.

13

CIRCULAR MOTION AND
KEPLER'S LAWS

When a rigid body is set into rotation, its motion is generally described with reference to the axis about which it revolves. The *axis of rotation*, as it is generally called, is sometimes fixed within the body and sometimes beyond its outermost boundary. In the case of most wheels of machinery, for example, the axes of rotation are lines through the geometrical centers perpendicular to the planes of rotation. For a stone whirled on the end of a string, however, the axis is at the opposite end of the string, remote from the stone itself.

13.1. Rotational Speed and Angular Velocity. The speed with which a body rotates is called its rotational speed, or *frequency*. Either of these terms refers to the number of complete revolutions a body makes in unit time and is designated by the letter n.

n = number of revolutions per second

A flywheel, for example, might be said to have a rotational speed of 10 revolutions per second (10 rps). This is equivalent to a rotational speed or frequency of 600 revolutions per minute (600 rpm), and to a speed or frequency of 36,000 revolutions per hour (36,000 rph).

For formulating the laws of mechanics it will be found convenient to express all rotation in radians, not in degrees or revolutions. *The radian* (rad) *is a unit of angular measure* just as the centimeter is a unit of linear measure. It is defined as the angle subtended by the arc of a circle whose length is equal to the radius of the same circle. Referring to Fig. 13A the distance x measured along the arc is equal to the radius r, and the angle θ = 1 radian.

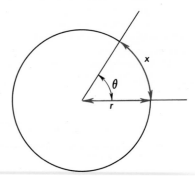

Fig. 13A *The radian is a unit of angular measure. When the arc equals the radius r, the angle θ equals one radian.*

Since the entire circumference of a circle is just 2π times the radius r, there are 2π radians in one complete circle.

$$2\pi \text{ radians} = 360°$$

Since $\pi = 3.1416$,

$$1 \text{ radian} = 57.3°$$

It follows from the above relations that the angle θ in radians between any two points on the circumference of a circle is given by x, the length of the arc between the two points, divided by the radius r. In other words,

$$\text{angle in radians} = \frac{\text{arc length}}{\text{radius}}$$

or, in algebraic symbols,

$$\theta = \frac{x}{r} \qquad (13a)$$

The reason for measuring angles in radians is

that it simplifies all formulas for rotary motion. As an illustration, consider the speed of a stone being whirled on the end of a string as shown in Fig. 13B. The angular velocity of the motion is

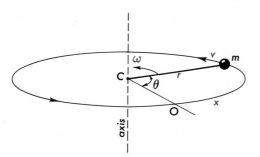

Fig. 13B *An illustration of circular motion.*

defined as the angle turned through, divided by the elapsed time.

$$\text{angular velocity} = \frac{\text{angle turned through}}{\text{time}}$$

In algebraic symbols,

$$\omega = \theta/t \qquad (13b)$$

and is to be compared with the corresponding definition of linear velocity,

$$v = x/t \qquad (13c)$$

Angular velocity ω corresponds to linear velocity v, and angular displacement θ corresponds to linear displacement x. With θ measured in radians and t in seconds, the angular velocity ω has the units of radians per second, (rad/s).

As a problem, suppose that a stone, when it is whirled on the end of a string 0.50 m long, makes 8 complete revolutions in 2 s, and we wish to find the angular velocity in radians per second. To employ Eq.(13b) the angle θ is first calculated as follows. Since 1 revolution = 2π rad, 8 revolutions are equivalent to

$$\theta = 2\pi \times 8 = 50.2 \text{ rad}$$

Substitution in Eq.(13b) gives

$$\omega = \frac{\theta}{t} = \frac{50.2 \text{ rad}}{2 \text{ s}} = 25.1 \frac{\text{rad}}{\text{s}}$$

To find the linear speed of the stone along its curved path, Eqs.(13a), (13b), and (13c) can be used by combining them as follows. Solving Eq.(13a) for x, we obtain

$$\boxed{x = r\theta} \qquad (13d)$$

Substitute $r\theta$ for x in Eq.(13c).

$$v = \frac{r\theta}{t} = r\frac{\theta}{t}$$

Replace θ/t by ω from Eq.(13b).

$$\boxed{v = r\omega} \qquad (13e)$$

From the problem of the stone on a string in Fig. 13B, we can now calculate the speed of the stone from the known values of r and ω. Since the angular velocity $\omega = 25.1$ rad/s, and the length of the string r is 0.50 m, then in 1 s ($t = 1$ s) the angle turned through will be 25.1 rad, and the velocity will be

$$v = 0.50 \text{ m} \times 25.1 \frac{\text{rad}}{\text{s}} = 12.55 \frac{\text{m}}{\text{s}}$$

If it is required to find the distance traveled in 5 s, Eq.(13c) can be used as follows:

$$x = vt = 12.55 \frac{\text{m}}{\text{s}} \times 5 \text{ s} = 62.75 \text{ m}$$

To find the total angle turned through in 5 sec, Eq.(13a) can be used.

$$\theta = \frac{x}{r} = \frac{62.75}{0.50} = 125.5 \text{ rad}$$

Likewise, Eq.(13b) can be used to find the angle turned through.

$$\theta = \omega t = 25.1 \frac{\text{rad}}{\text{s}} \times 5 \text{ s} = 125.5 \text{ rad}$$

Note that all equations are consistent with each other and that the radian as a unit has no dimensions. The radian is the ratio between two lengths and therefore has the same value in all systems of units. It is for this reason that it can be canceled out where it is not needed, or added where necessary in the above answers.

13.2. Centripetal Force. When a stone is whirling on the end of a string, there is an inward force exerted by the string on the ball. This force is called the *centripetal force* (see Fig. 13C). Since the only force acting on the ball is inward, the ball is not in equilibrium but is being continually accelerated in the direction of the force, that is, toward the center.

This appears to be a physical paradox, for here is a body moving with constant speed in a circle and yet being accelerated toward the center of the circle without getting any closer to it. If

Fig. 13C   *A mass m, moving in a circle, experiences an acceleration toward the center.*

the string were to break suddenly, the ball would fly off on a tangent to the circle and move with constant velocity according to Newton's first law.

To obtain a clearer picture of centripetal force and acceleration toward the center, motion in a

The instantaneous velocity is shown at two points, A and B, in diagram (a) of Fig. 13D. The velocity, as indicated by the vectors v, is seen to be changing in direction but not in magnitude. Diagram (b) is a velocity diagram showing v' as the change in velocity that occurs in going from A to B. Since this velocity triangle is similar to triangle ABC in diagram (a), corresponding sides are proportional to each other, and the following can be written:

$$\frac{x}{r} = \frac{v'}{v}$$

Since the velocity v' is changing and is due to an acceleration, it can, by the equation $v = at$, be replaced by at. During the time t, the body moves from A to B a distance $x = vt$. For small angles θ the distance measured along the arc AB is approximately equal to the chord x, so

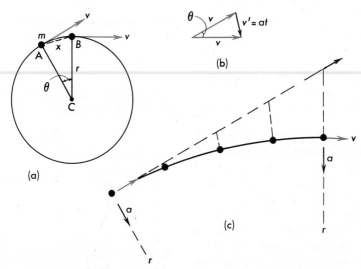

(b)

(a)

(c)

Fig. 13D   *A body moving in a circle is continually being accelerated toward the center.*

circle, as illustrated in Fig. 13D(c), is to be compared with the motion of a projectile accelerated downward by the pull of gravity as shown in Fig. 9G. Due to the earth's attraction of all bodies, a projectile is continually accelerated downward, away from the straight line of its original projection. In circular motion the mass is continually accelerated toward the center, always at right angles to its instantaneous velocity and away from any straight-line tangent along which it would travel if suddenly released.

that for a close approximation, x can be replaced by vt. These two substitutions made in the equation above give

$$\frac{vt}{r} = \frac{at}{v}$$

Dividing both sides by t, and solving for v, we obtain the relation

$$a = \frac{v^2}{r} \qquad (13f)$$

Thus, the *centripetal acceleration* is given by v^2/r.

As the angle θ in Fig. 13D is made smaller and smaller, the arc distance x becomes more and more nearly equal to the chord, while the change in velocity v', which gives the direction of the acceleration a, becomes more nearly perpendicular to v. In the limit when θ becomes zero, Eq.(13f) holds true exactly and the acceleration is perpendicular to v.

If we substitute $r\omega$ for v [see Eq.(13f)], the centripetal acceleration can be expressed in terms of the angular velocity ω.

$$a = r\omega^2 \qquad (13g)$$

Centripetal force is defined as that constant force which, acting continuously at right angles to the motion of a particle, causes it to move in a circle with constant speed. Since by Newton's second law of motion $F = ma$, the centripetal force is given by

$$\boxed{F = m\frac{v^2}{r}} \qquad (13h)$$

or in angular quantities by

$$\boxed{F = mr\omega^2} \qquad (13i)$$

Example 1. A mass of 5 Kg is moving in a circle of 1-m radius with an angular velocity of 2 rad/s. Find the centripetal force.

Solution. The known quantities substituted directly in Eq.(13i) give

$$F = 5 \text{ Kg} \times 1 \text{ m} \times \left(2\frac{\text{rad}}{\text{s}}\right)^2 = 20\frac{\text{Kg m}}{\text{s}^2} = 20 \text{ N}$$

Note: Radians have no dimensions and are therefore dropped out in arriving at the force.

By Newton's third law of motion, centripetal force has a *reaction force*. This oppositely directed force is called the *centrifugal force*. Referring to Fig. 13C, the centrifugal force, equal in magnitude to the centripetal force, is an outward force exerted by the ball on the string. The string in turn transmits this outward force to the center pin C. It should be emphasized, however, that the centrifugal force does not act on the ball. Only one force acts on the ball and that is the one shown, the centripetal force.

13.3. Experiments Demonstrating Centripetal Force. Many interesting experiments can be performed to illustrate centripetal force. In Fig. 13E mercury and water have been placed in a

Fig. 13E *Mercury and water rotate in a dish; the water is inside the mercury. Centripetal force, like gravitational force, is greater for the more dense substance.*

dish and the dish set rotating rapidly about a vertical axis. Since mercury is 13.6 times as heavy as an equal volume of water, the centripetal force F on each cm^3 of mercury is 13.6 times larger than on each cm^3 of water. The mercury therefore takes the outermost position in the dish. This is the principle of the centrifuge and ultracentrifuge, a spinning device used for separating materials having different densities.

Although the earth is often said to be spherical, it is in reality an oblate spheroid, that is, a slightly flattened sphere. Accurate measurements show that the earth's diameter is 28 mi greater through the equator than it is through the poles. The cause for this flattening is illustrated in Fig. 13F by two circular metal strips. Diagram (a) shows the strips to be round when at rest, while (b) shows the flattening due to rapid rotation. The flattening of the earth is due to its own rotation of 2π rad every 24 hr. It is the enormous size of the earth and its lack of greater rigidity that makes it behave as though it were soft and semiplastic.

Mud or water clings to an automobile tire

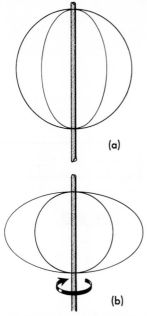

(a)

(b)

Fig. 13F   *The flattening of the earth is due to its rotation about the polar axis.*

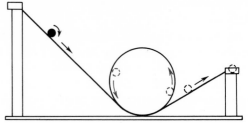

Fig. 13H   *The ball will loop the loop if it starts rolling from a point high enough on the incline.*

over the head and down, at arm's length, without spilling it. To find the critical velocity at the top of the circle, the centripetal force mv^2/r is equated to the body's weight mg. This is the same as equating the centripetal acceleration v^2/r to the acceleration of gravity g. For any given radius r, the critical speed becomes fixed by the equation

$$g = \frac{v^2}{r} \qquad (13j)$$

When a stone on the end of a string is whirled in a vertical circle, gravity acts downward upon it at all times. At the bottom of its path, the weight must be added to the centripetal force to obtain the tension in the string, while at the top of its path the weight must be subtracted.

When a stone on the end of a string is whirled in a horizontal circle, the stone's weight is at all times perpendicular to centripetal force, and the string describes a cone. The *centripetal force F* is the resultant of two forces, the *tension T* in the string and the *weight F_g*. The forces F and F_g are at right angles.

The opening of the loop in a lariat as whirled and thrown by a cowboy is due to centripetal force (see Fig. 13I). Because of rotation, each small section of the rope, acting as an individual mass m, tends to fly off on a tangent and thus get as far from the center of rotation as possible. The average distance from the center of all sections of the rope is a maximum when the loop takes the form of a circle rotating about an axis perpendicular to the plane of the loop.

until the speed becomes too high and then it flies off on a tangent, as shown in Fig. 13G. To remain with the tire the required centripetal force cannot exceed the force of adhesion.

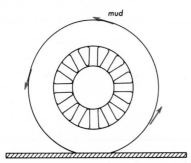

mud

Fig. 13G   *Mud or water on a fast-turning wheel flies off on a tangent.*

Figure 13H shows a ball rolling down a looped track. The ball will stay with the track even at the top of the loop if the required centripetal force there is equal to or greater than the downward force of gravity. This means that the speed v must be greater than a certain critical speed or the ball will fall. Such a behavior is similar to that of whirling a bucket of water in a circle up

When a small chain, as shown in Fig. 13J, is set rotating at high speed by an electric motor and then set free, it will roll along the floor as though it were a rigid metal hoop. Upon bump-

Fig. 13I *A lariat takes a circular form because each small part tries to fly off on a tangent, thus getting as far from the center as possible. Centripetal force is responsible for keeping it in a circle.*

Fig. 13J *A chain turning at high speed will roll along the level as a rigid wheel.*

ing into an obstacle, it will bounce into the air, and upon coming down, will retain its circular form as it rolls on. The rigidity of the hoop is due to the enormous centripetal force attained at high angular velocities.

13.4. Planetary Motion. According to astronomical history, it was the early Greek philosopher Pythagoras (530 B.C.) who said "the world is round and hangs in space." "The earth," he said, "does not stand still but revolves around a central fire, called Hestia. This fire is not the sun, for the sun is illuminated, as are the planets, by reflection from Hestia."

This idea lay dormant for 2000 years before Copernicus, at the beginning of the 16th century, said "the sun stands still and the earth and planets move in orbits around it." The observational and mathematical proof that all the planets move in elliptical orbits was first presented in 1609 when John Kepler* published a book containing two of his three laws which are now

*John Kepler (1571–1630), German astronomer and philosopher. Born in Weil of a poor but noble family, Kepler was educated at the University of Maulbroon. It was in his position as professor of astronomy at Gratz that he first became interested in the planets. When he heard that Tycho Brahe had recorded great quantities of data on the motions of hundreds of stellar objects, Kepler went to Prague. There he became a close and devoted friend of Tycho Brahe, and promised this grand old man, on his deathbed, that he would tabulate and publish the recorded observations. In 1609 Kepler published his *Commentaries on Mars*, in which his first two laws of planetary motion are to be found. The third law came a little later. Kepler was a religious, but sickly, man for most of his 59 years. He was twice married, but had no children of his own. He died penniless.

known as Kepler's laws of planetary motion.

13.5. Kepler's First Law. *The planets move in elliptical orbits with the sun at one of the foci.*

An ellipse can be constructed by fastening the two ends of a piece of string to two pins, F_1 and F_2, as shown in Fig. 13K. By keeping the string

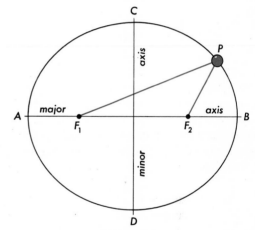

Fig. 13K *An ellipse can be drawn with two pins, a string, and a pencil.*

tight with a pencil at P, the complete arc can be swung around, much the same as one draws a circle with a compass.

If the length of the string remains unchanged, and the foci F_1 and F_2 are brought closer and closer together, the major axis AB and the minor axis CD become more and more nearly equal; in the limit when the foci coincide, the axes are equal and the ellipse becomes a circle. The real orbits of the planets are so nearly circular, however, that if they were drawn with a compass, the ellipse would differ from the circle by less than the thickness of the pencil line.

The eccentricity e of an ellipse is defined as

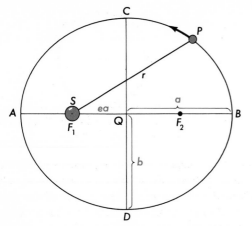

Fig. 13L   *Elliptical orbit with an eccentricity e = 0.5.*

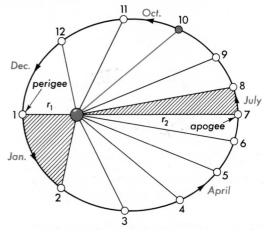

Fig. 13M   *Elliptical orbit of a planet, or satellite, showing equal areas swept out by the radius vector in equal intervals of time.*

the ratio of the distances SQ and AQ (see Fig. 13L).

$$e = \frac{SQ}{AQ} \qquad (13k)$$

where AQ is the semimajor axis *a*, and SQ is equal to *ea*. With the sun at one focus, the distance of closest approach AS is called *perigee*, and the greatest distance BS is called *apogee*. A little study of Fig. 13L will enable the reader to find that

$$\text{apogee} = a(1 + e)$$
$$\text{perigee} = a(1 - e) \qquad (13l)$$
$$b = a\sqrt{1 - e^2}$$

where *b* is the semiminor axis DQ.

These equations are readily derived by noting that if straight lines are drawn from F_1 and F_2 to the point D, the distance F_1DF_2 equals the length of the major axis 2*a*, and that these two lines form right triangles with *a* as the hypotenuse for each.

13.6. Kepler's Second Law. *The straight line joining the sun and any planet sweeps out equal areas in equal intervals of time.*

As shown in Fig. 13M, the straight line referred to is called the *radius vector;* it varies in length from a minimum at perigee to a maximum at apogee. Although the orbit of the earth is nearly circular, the numbers 1, 2, 3, 4, etc., corre-

spond to the position of the earth at the end of each 12 equal months.

To cover these unequal orbital distances in equal intervals of time, the speed must be a maximum at perigee and a minimum six months later at apogee. During the periods 1 to 2 and 7 to 8, for example, the areas swept out are equal.

As the earth moves along its orbit in September, October, November, etc., the attractive force of the sun causes it to speed up. Upon reaching perigee at the end of December its speed is a maximum, and too fast to remain at this distance r_1 from the sun. During the months of March, April, May, etc., the earth is receding from the sun, and the attractive force of the sun slows the earth down. Upon reaching apogee at the end of June the speed of the revolving earth is a minimum, too slow to keep it at this greater distance r_2 from the sun. The average distance from the sun is 92,900,000 mi while the average orbital speed of the earth is 18.5 mi/s.

13.7. Kepler's Third Law. *The squares of the orbital periods of the planets are proportional to the cubes of their mean distances from the sun.*

The period *T* of a planet, or satellite, is defined as the time required to make one complete trip around its orbit; the mean distance *r* is defined as the average distance away from the sun. Important data on the eight major planets of the solar system are given in Table 13A. The con-

TABLE 13A. MEASURED CHARACTERISTICS OF THE PLANETS

Name	Period T (years)	Mean distance (mi $\times 10^6$)	(Km $\times 10^6$)	$\dfrac{T^2}{r^3}$	Mean radius (mi)	(Km)	Mass (Kg 10^{24})
Mercury	0.241	36.0	57.9	1.245	1504.3	2421.1	0.3244
Venus	0.615	67.1	108.1	1.252	3828.2	6161.0	4.861
Earth	1.000	92.9	149.5	1.247	3958.9	6370.0	5.975
Mars	1.881	141.5	227.8	1.249	2070.5	3332.1	0.6387
Jupiter	11.862	483.3	777.8	1.246	43429.0	69892.0	1902.1
Saturn	29.458	886.1	1426.0	1.247	35748.5	57532.0	569.4
Uranus	84.015	1783.0	2869.0	1.245	14727.0	23701.0	87.1
Neptune	164.790	2793.0	4496.0	1.246	13381.0	21535.0	103.1
Pluto	247.700	3665.0	5899.0	1.246	1781.4	2867.0	0.5?

stant ratios in column five verify Kepler's third law.

While Kepler's laws were originally derived from Tycho Brahe's careful observations, they are readily derived from the basic laws of classical mechanics.

For simplicity we will assume that the orbit of the earth is circular, as shown in Fig. 13N. In

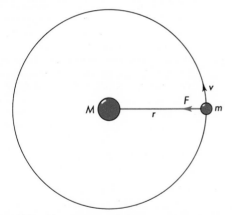

Fig. 13N   *The gravitational force of attraction F is the centripetal force that keeps the earth in its nearly circular orbit around the sun.*

this diagram, M is the mass of the sun, m is the mass of a planet like the earth, and r is the distance between their centers. The centripetal force F, as given by Eq.(13h), is just the force of gravitational attraction given by Eq.(7a). These are

$$F = m\frac{v^2}{r} \qquad F = G\frac{Mm}{r^2} \qquad (13m)$$

centripetal force   **Newton's law of gravitation**

where $$G = 6.66 \times 10^{-11}\,\frac{m^3}{Kg\,s^2}$$

Since these two equations are different expressions for the same force F, the right-hand sides may be placed equal to each other, which gives

$$G\frac{Mm}{r^2} = m\frac{v^2}{r}$$

Upon simplifying, this equation becomes

$$\frac{GM}{r} = v^2 \qquad (13n)$$

In mechanics the velocity of a body is given by $v = x/t$. If we choose the distance x to be once around the orbit, the time t then becomes the period T, and we obtain

$$v = \frac{2\pi r}{T} \qquad (13o)$$

By squaring both sides of this equation, and substituting the right-hand side for v^2 in Eq.(13n), we can write

$$\frac{GM}{r} = \frac{4\pi^2 r^2}{T^2}$$

or

$$T^2 = \left(\frac{4\pi^2}{GM}\right) r^3 \qquad (13p)$$

Since all quantities in parentheses are constants, $T^2 \propto r^3$, and Kepler's third law is consistent with the laws of classical mechanics.

PROBLEMS

1. A mass of 0.5 Kg is whirled at 120 rpm in a horizontal circle at the end of a string 2 m long. Neglecting the force due to gravity, find (a) the angular velocity, (b) the centripetal acceleration, and (c) the centripetal force.

2. A 2500-Kg car going 72 Km/hr rounds a curve of 250-m radius. What is (a) the angular velocity in rad/s, (b) the centripetal acceleration, and (c) the centripetal force? [Ans. (a) 0.08 rad/s, (b) 1.60 m/s², (c) 4.0 × 10³ N.]

3. A motorcycle and rider going 60 mi/hr round a curve of 300-ft radius. Find (a) the centripetal acceleration, and (b) the angle they must lean from the vertical.

4. A 30-Kg box rests on the floor of a merry-go-round 5 m from the center. If the coefficient of static friction is 0.25, find (a) the force of friction, (b) the angular velocity at which the box will just start to slide, and (c) the speed of the box at that moment. [Ans. (a) 73.5 N, (b) 0.700 rad/s, (c) 3.50 m/s.]

5. A car with a mass of 2600 Kg and traveling at 100 Km/hr rounds a curve of 150-m radius. At what angle should the road be banked in order that there be no tendency to slip?

6. A pail of milk held at arms length is swung overhead and down in a vertical circle of 0.80-m radius. What is (a) the minimum speed v at the top to assure that no milk spills out, and (b) the corresponding angular velocity. [Ans. (a) 2.80 m/s, (b) 3.50 rad/s.]

7. A curve in the highway has a radius of 22 m, and the surface is banked at 15° with the horizontal. At what speed should a car go around this curve if there is to be no tendency to slip? Find the speed in (a) m/s, (b) Km/hr, and (c) mi/hr.

8. A stone of 6.4 lb is whirled at 60 rpm in a circle at the end of a wire 1 m long. If the plane of the circle is vertical, what is the tension in the wire (a) at the top of the circle, and (b) at the bottom? Assume constant speed. [Ans. (a) 1.5 lb, (b) 14.3 lb.]

9. A stone attached to a wire 1.5 m long moves in a horizontal circle, the wire describing the surface of a cone. If the wire stands out at an angle of 70° with the vertical, find (a) the speed, and (b) the angular velocity.

10. A man living at the equator accurately weighs himself and finds his mass is 70.0 Kg. What correction must be made for the earth's rotation? [Ans. +0.241 Kg.]

11. An ellipse is drawn with two common pins 5 cm apart and a string 10 cm long. Find (a) the major axis, (b) the minor axis, (c) the eccentricity, (d) the apogee distance, and (e) the perigee distance.

12. An ellipse is to be drawn with a major axis of 18 cm and a minor axis of 10 cm. Find (a) the eccentricity, (b) the apogee distance, (c) the perigee distance, (d) the distance between foci, and (e) the length of the string required to draw this ellipse on paper. [Ans. (a) 0.831, (b) 16.48 cm, (c) 1.52 cm, (d) 14.96 cm, (e) 18.0 cm.]

13. The Bell Telephone Telestar I satellite, put into orbit on July 10, 1962 for the purpose of demonstrating that radio and television waves could be relayed by an active satellite, was 592 mi above the earth's surface at perigee, and 3531 mi at apogee. Find (a) the major axis, (b) the minor axis, and (c) the eccentricity.

14. The Bell Telephone Telestar II satellite, put into orbit on May 7, 1963 for the purpose of relaying radio and television signals to remote areas of the earth, was 600 mi above the earth's surface at perigee, and 6700 mi at apogee. Find (a) the semimajor axis, (b) the perigee distance, (c) the apogee distance, (d) the eccentricity, and (e) the semiminor axis. [Ans. (a) 7609 mi, (b) 4559 mi, (c) 10,659 mi, (d) 0.401, (e) 7010 mi.]

15. Draw straight lines from F_1 to C and C to F_2 in Fig. 13L, and show that F_1C is equal to the semimajor axis a.

16. Using the defining equation, Eq.(13k), and the result of Problem 15, derive the equation $b = a\sqrt{1 - e^2}$.

GRAVITATIONAL FIELDS,
AND ORBITING SATELLITES

We are living today on the threshold of the space age, an age in which each planned space flight brings together, in one project after the other, all of the known science and technology at our command. Such large-scale operations illustrate not only the unity of science but the importance of understanding the basic principles of each of the separate sciences.

As each space ship leaves or approaches an astronomical body, such as the earth, the moon, or the planets, it is subject to gravitational forces of great magnitude. Since these forces vary with distance along each flight path, we find it most convenient to take them into account, describing them in terms of what are called *gravitational fields* and *gravitational potentials*.

14.1. Gravitational Fields. The concept of a gravitational field begins with Newton's Universal Law of Gravitation (see Sec. 7.1). In Fig. 14A a mass M is shown exerting a gravita-

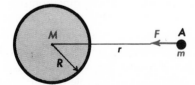

Fig. 14A *Gravitational forces are always those of attraction.*

tional force F on a small mass m. The magnitude of this force is

$$F = -G \frac{Mm}{r^2} \qquad (14a)$$

where M and m are in kilograms, r is in meters,

F is in newtons, and the universal constant of gravitation G is given by

$$G = 6.670 \times 10^{-11} \frac{m^3}{Kg\ s^2} \qquad (14b)$$

The minus sign in Eq.(14a) signifies the force is one of attraction.

The field intensity I at any point A, in free space surrounding any mass M, is defined as the force per unit mass acting on any object placed there.

$$I = \frac{F}{m} \qquad (14c)$$

The small mass is used in this definition only as a means of detecting and measuring the gravitational field at A. Whether m is large or small, the force per unit mass at the point is exactly the same. Double the mass m and F will be doubled, triple the mass m and F will be tripled, etc.

To develop an equation for the field intensity I, we obtain a value for F/m from Eq.(14a). Dividing both sides of the equation by m, we obtain

$$\frac{F}{m} = -\frac{GM}{r^2}$$

which gives,

$$I = -\frac{GM}{r^2} \qquad (14d)$$

gravitational field intensity

A diagram of the gravitational field around a spherical mass M is shown in Fig. 14B. The arrows show the direction of the field as every-

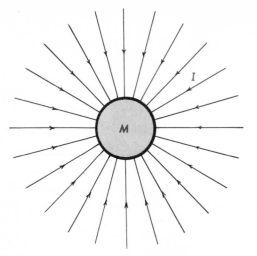

Fig. 14B *The gravitational field around a spherical mass M is radially inward.*

where radially inward, and the spacing of the lines shows the field is strongest at the surface. For every point at the same distance from the center, the field intensity I has the same magnitude, but as the distance increases, the field intensity decreases.

It is to be noted that as many radial lines as desired can be drawn to represent the field but they must be equally spaced. Furthermore, the lines themselves are imaginary and do not actually exist; they are introduced here as an aid to the understanding of gravitational phenomena.

Multiplying both sides of Eq.(14c) by m, we obtain the relation that

$$F = mI \qquad (14e)$$

This equation says that any mass m placed in a gravitational field of intensity I experiences a force given by the product $m \times I$.

While Eqs.(14a) through (14e) apply to all masses m, we may use Eq.(5e) and obtain a special case for the earth. The downward force on any mass m at the earth's surface is given by

$$F = mg \qquad (14f)$$

Since by Eq.(14e), $F = mI$, we obtain the equality

$$mI = mg$$

or,

$$I = g$$

at the earth's surface

Although the field intensity has the dimensions of an acceleration, it is more meaningful to express I, through Eq.(14c), as a force per unit mass:

$$1 \frac{\text{newton}}{\text{kilogram}} = 1 \frac{\text{meter}}{\text{second}^2}$$

Over a small volume of space, the gravitational field can be assumed to be constant. Throughout the space of one cubic mile at or near the earth's surface, for example, the direction of the field at all points is practically parallel, and the magnitude of I is practically constant (see Fig. 14C).

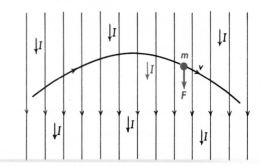

Fig. 14C *The path of a projectile in a uniform gravitational field is a parabola.*

Such a field is said to be *uniform*. The path taken by a mass m projected through a uniform gravitational field is the result of a constant downward force F; and if air friction is negligibly small, the path is a parabola, as shown in the diagram.

14.2. Satellites. When a space vehicle takes off from the ground to orbit the earth as a satellite, its initial take-off direction is vertically upward (see Fig. 9H). As the rocket gains height, control fins or jets are set to make it turn slowly toward a horizontal trajectory (see Fig. 9K). To find the velocity that a space vehicle must acquire to circle the earth, consider the details of Fig. 14D.

Imagine a tower several hundred miles high, from the top of which projectiles are launched in a horizontal direction. With a low initial velocity the projectile will follow a nearly parabolic path as shown at A. At a somewhat higher velocity the trajectory will be that of path B. At a still higher velocity, the projectile in falling

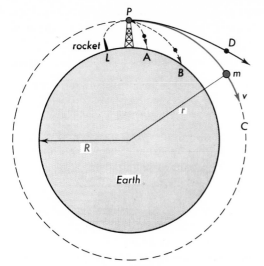

Fig. 14D   *Horizontal projection from P with a high velocity v can cause a projectile m to circle the earth.*

toward the earth will follow a circular path of radius *r*. This particular velocity is called the *oribiting velocity*. At still higher velocities, such as shown at D, the projectile will follow an elliptical path or escape from the earth completely.

We have seen in the preceding chapter that the force *F* required to make a mass *m* move in a circle of radius *r*, is the *centripetal force*, and that its magnitude is given by the relation

$$F = m \frac{v^2}{r} \qquad (14g)$$

where *v* is the velocity. Since this inward force for a satellite is the gravitational force *F* given by Newton's Universal Law of Gravitation Eq.(14a), we may equate the right-hand terms of both equations, and obtain

$$m \frac{v^2}{r} = G \frac{Mm}{r^2} . \qquad (14h)$$

Dividing both sides of the equation by *m*, and multiplying both sides by *r*, we find

$$v^2 = \frac{GM}{r}$$

and taking the square root of both sides, we find for the orbiting velocity

$$\boxed{v = \sqrt{\frac{GM}{r}}} \qquad (14i)$$

orbiting velocity

This equation holds for any satellite moving in a circular orbit around any astronomical body throughout the universe.

In the special case of a satellite circling the earth close to the surface, the orbital radius is approximately the radius of the earth *R*. Under these conditions the centripetal force *F* is just *mg*, and we may write Eq.(14h) in the form

$$mg = G \frac{Mm}{R^2}$$

Solving this equation for *GM*, we obtain,

$$GM = gR^2 \qquad (14j)$$

where *R* is approximately 4000 mi, and

$$g = 9.80 \text{ m/s}^2 = 32.15 \text{ ft/s}^2$$

or,   (14k)

$$g = 78,920 \text{ mi/hr}^2$$

If we now substitute gR^2 for *GM* in Eq.(14i), we find,

$$\boxed{v = \sqrt{g \frac{R^2}{r}}} \qquad (14l)$$

**orbiting velocity
for the earth
only**

Example 1. A satellite orbits the earth 500 mi above the surface. Find its velocity in mi/hr.

Solution. To find the answer we may use the earth's mass given in Table 13A, and substitute in Eq.(14i), or we may use the value of *g* at the earth's surface, and substitute in Eq.(14l). Choosing the latter, we obtain

$$v = \sqrt{\frac{78,920 \text{ mi/hr} (3960 \text{ mi})^2}{4460 \text{ mi}}}$$

$$v = 16,700 \text{ mi/hr}.$$

If a satellite orbits the earth at an altitude of only 100 mi, air friction is still extremely small, and a fairly stable orbit is sustained. For such a special case we can substitute *R* for *r* in Eq.(14l) and obtain the very simple relation that

$$v = \sqrt{gR} \qquad (14m)$$

If the orbit of a satellite is not circular, but elliptical, the magnitude of the orbital velocity changes from one point to another. As shown

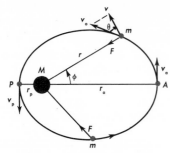

Fig. 14E *Diagrams of the elliptical orbit of a satellite showing the different orbital speeds and velocities.*

in Fig. 14E the velocity v_p at perigee P is a maximum.

As the satellite m recedes from its perigee position P, the backward gravitational pull of the mass M slows it down until at apogee A the orbital speed is a minimum. As the satellite moves along the opposite side of its orbit, the gravitational pull F speeds it up again until at perigee P its speed becomes a maximum.

The general formula for the speed of a satellite is quite complicated, but for the maximum and minimum positions, where the *instantaneous velocity* is perpendicular to the radius vector r, it simplifies and gives

$$v_{\text{perigee}} = \sqrt{\frac{GM}{a}\left(\frac{1+e}{1-e}\right)}$$
$$v_{\text{apogee}} = \sqrt{\frac{GM}{a}\left(\frac{1-e}{1+e}\right)} \qquad (14n)$$

where a is the semimajor axis, and e is the eccentricity given by Eqs.(13l).

It can be shown for satellite motion that the angular momentum is constant. The angular momentum p of a satellite is given by the product

$$p = mvr \qquad (14o)$$

where, as shown in Fig. 14E, r is the distance to the satellite, m is the mass, and v is the perpendicular component of the orbital velocity v_0.

14.3. Gravitational Potential. The gravitational potential P of a point in a gravitational field may be defined as the work done W, or potential energy stored E_p, per unit mass in carrying any mass m from infinity up to that point.

$$P = \frac{E_p}{m}$$

We have seen in Chapter 10 that the work done in raising a body of mass m to a height h is given by the product, force times distance.

$$W = Fh \qquad (14p)$$

where the force F is given by Newton's second law, $F = mg$,

$$W = mgh$$

As a result of doing work on a body, we have stored within it, by virtue of its new position, an equivalent amount of potential energy.

$$E_p = mgh$$

In setting up these defining equations in Chapter 10, it was assumed that the gravitational field intensity g is constant over the distance h through which the force acts. If the distance is large, however, the field intensity I is not constant, but varies inversely as the square of the distance from the center of the earth [see Eq.(14d)].

To calculate the work done by means of the defining equation, Eq.(14p), and with a continuously changing force, a mathematical procedure called *the calculus* is required. The calculus shows that the *work done* in carrying a mass m from a point at a distance r from the center of M to a distance so great that the gravitational field is negligibly weak, is given by

$$W = G\frac{Mm}{r} \qquad (14q)$$

This relation can also be derived by an approximation method using simple algebra. The work done in lifting a body from the surface of a planet of radius R to a distance r from the center of the planet, is shown graphically in Fig. 14F.

Imagine that we divide the distance from R to r into a number of small intervals, so that over each interval the gravitational force will be practically constant, and given by a kind of average force over that interval. We can then calculate the work done for each interval and then add them all together to get the total.

At the surface the force is $F_0 = GMm/R^2$, while at r_1 it is $F_1 = GMm/r_1^2$. We may therefore write for the average force in the first interval R to r_1

$$F_1 = G \frac{Mm}{Rr_1}$$

and for the work done

$$W_1 = G \frac{Mm}{Rr_1} (r_1 - R)$$

or, by the distributive law,

$$W_1 = GMm \left(\frac{1}{R} - \frac{1}{r_1} \right)$$

In a similar way the work done lifting the

Fig. 14F *Diagram showing how to calculate the work done in lifting a mass m from the surface of a planet like the earth to a height r.*

mass through the second interval r_1 to r_2 is found to be

$$W_2 = GMm \left(\frac{1}{r_1} - \frac{1}{r_2} \right)$$

and similarly for the third interval

$$W_3 = GMm \left(\frac{1}{r_2} - \frac{1}{r_3} \right)$$

If we add all these W's from R to r, all intermediate values cancel out and we obtain for the total

$$W = GMm \left(\frac{1}{R} - \frac{1}{r} \right)$$

If we now choose r to be at infinity, $r = \infty$, the value $1/r = 0$ and we obtain

$$W = G \frac{Mm}{R}$$

We can see from this simple result that *to carry a mass m from any point A at a distance r to infinity where $r = \infty$, the energy expended is given by*

$$W = G \frac{Mm}{r}$$

Since the work done is stored as potential energy, the potential energy of a mass m at any point A is, therefore,

$$E_p = -G \frac{Mm}{r} \qquad (14r)$$

The minus sign establishes the zero level of potential energy at infinity, that is, in free space. Lifting a mass against the pull of a gravitational field requires the expenditure of energy, and when $r = \infty$, Eq.(14q) gives $E_p = 0$.

We now define the gravitational potential P of any point in the space around a mass M as the potential energy per unit mass of any mass m located there.

$$P = \frac{E_p}{m} \qquad (14s)$$

Dividing both sides of Eq.(14r) by m and substituting from Eq.(14s), we obtain

$$P = -\frac{GM}{r} \qquad (14t)$$

gravitational potential

TABLE 14A. CONSTANTS FOR THE PLANETS

	GM (m³/s²)	GM/R (m²/s²)
Mercury	2.160×10^{13}	8.921×10^6
Venus	3.237×10^{14}	5.254×10^7
Earth	3.979×10^{14}	6.245×10^7
Mars	4.254×10^{13}	1.277×10^7
Jupiter	1.267×10^{17}	1.813×10^9
Saturn	3.792×10^{16}	6.591×10^8
Uranus	5.801×10^{15}	2.448×10^8
Neptune	6.866×10^{15}	3.188×10^8

moon mass = 7.32×10^{22} Kg
moon radius = 1.740×10^6 m

Any mass m located at or near the surface of the earth M can be looked upon as being in a hole where the potential energy is negative, and to lift it out into free space (r infinite, and $E_p = 0$) requires an amount of energy W.

$$W = -mP \qquad (14u)$$

We therefore arrive at the very simple result that the force on any mass is given by

$$F = mI$$

and its potential energy is given by

$$E_p = mP$$

14.4. Escape Velocity. For a satellite to escape from the earth and never return, it must be launched with a velocity greater than that required to make it orbit. To find the *minimum escape velocity*, we make use of the gravitational potential as given in the preceding section.

To lift a mass m from any point at a distance r from the center of M requires the expenditure of energy in the amount given by Eq.(14q) (see Fig. 14G). If we impart this energy by giving

Fig. 14G *The potential energy of a mass m near the earth is negative with respect to its potential energy at infinity.*

the mass a velocity, the total energy expended will be kinetic, $\frac{1}{2}mv^2$. By direct substitution in Eq.(14q) of $\frac{1}{2}mv^2$ for W, we obtain

$$\frac{1}{2} mv^2 = m\frac{GM}{r}$$

Upon solving for v, we find

$$v = \sqrt{2\frac{GM}{r}} \qquad (14v)$$

escape velocity

If we launch the mass m from the earth's surface, where $r = R$, we write

$$v = \sqrt{2\frac{GM}{R}} \qquad (14w)$$

If we wish to express this escape velocity in terms of g at the earth's surface, we can make use of Eq.(14j), and substitute gR^2 for GM in Eq.(14w) and obtain

$$v = \sqrt{2gR} \qquad (14x)$$

**escape velocity
from earth's surface**

Note that the escape velocity from a point at any distance r from any body M, as given by Eq.(14v), is just $\sqrt{2}$ greater than the orbiting velocity at the same distance r, as given by Eq.(14i).

$$v_{escape} = 1.41v_{orbit} \qquad (14y)$$

This relation holds for any value of r.

14.5. Mechanical Well Model. The preceding sections of this chapter show that we on the surface of the earth are living at the bottom of a "gravitational well" thousands of miles deep. To reach the moon, the planets, or other worlds, we must climb out of this well onto a horizontal plane we call *gravitationless free space*.

To see what is meant by a well, we plot a potential-energy graph for the gravitational field around the earth like that shown in Fig. 14H. Such a graph is obtained by using Eq.(14t) and plotting the potential P vertically and the dis-

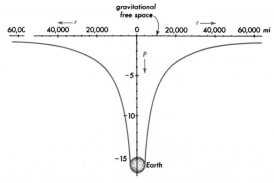

Fig. 14H *Potential-energy graph illustrating the "well" analogy of the earth's gravitational field.*

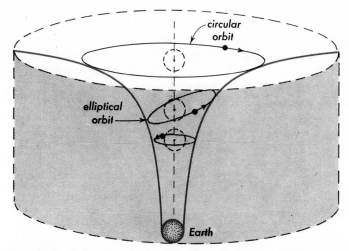

Fig. 14I   *Mechanical well model for demonstrating elliptical and circular orbits.*

tance from the center of the earth *r horizontally.*

For a distance *r* that is infinitely far away, $P = 0$. At smaller and smaller distances *P* increases, but is negative. The green curve in the diagram comes down to the earth's surface where *r* has the value of the earth's radius *R*.

A mechanical well model for demonstrating satellite orbits is obtained by rotating this potential-energy graph around the vertical axis. In so doing, the curve describes a cone-like surface as shown in Fig. 14I. If we make a solid body of some hard material with the shape of the shaded section, a small steel or glass marble can

be rolled around in the cone to describe satellite orbits.

A great variety of orbits can be generated simply by varying the initial velocity of the marbles. When viewed from directly overhead, most orbits are elliptical or circular. Orbital distortion arising from rolling friction can be held to a minimum by using hard materials with smooth surfaces.

If orbits including the moon are desirable, a small potential crater, far out on the periphery of the earth model, can be made (see Fig. 14J). The rolling of a marble toward this crater, away

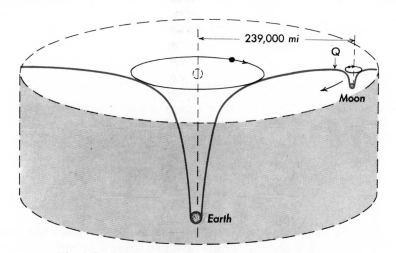

Fig. 14J   *Mechanical well model for the earth and moon.*

from the earth, is analogous to the path of an earth-based satellite on its projected trip to or around the moon. At the saddle point Q the gravitational pull of the earth and moon are equal and opposite.

14.6. Simulated Weight in Space Vehicles. Biological records on astronauts circling the earth indicate that prolonged exposure of the body to weightless conditions will cause permanent health damage. This is not surprising when it is realized that evolutionary processes have taken place in the earth's gravitational field over millions of years, and bodily functions rely greatly upon the ever-present gravitational forces.

If, therefore, extended space travel is to become a common-place reality, it would appear that weightlessness must be replaced by centripetal and centrifugal forces. Gravitational mass m, and weight mg, would be replaced by inertial mass m, and centripetal force mv^2/r.

Figure 14K shows two widely separated space

directed as to set the system rotating. Connecting cables are simultaneously reeled out until the two bodies are several hundred feet apart.

If the centripetal force $mr\omega^2$ is to be equal to the astronauts weight mg, we may write

$$mr\omega^2 = mg$$

where ω is the angular velocity in radians per second.

Solving for ω, we obtain,

$$\omega = \sqrt{\frac{g}{r}} \qquad (14z)$$

If we make $r = 128$ ft, direct substitution in Eq.(14z) gives,

$$\omega = \sqrt{\frac{32 \text{ ft/s}^2}{128 \text{ ft}}} = 0.5 \frac{\text{rad}}{\text{s}}$$

This is a relatively low angular speed and means that the system would make one revolution every 12.5 s. To the standing astronaut in the space vehicle the force on his body, exerted by the floor, would seem to be straight up. An

Fig. 14K *Two separated space vehicles bound together by cables, and rotating, simulate normal astronaut weight conditions.*

capsules rotating around their common center of mass. After being launched close together in orbit, small rockets on each capsule may be so

object released from the hand of the astronaut would fall to the floor but its path would be slightly curved (see Chapter 56 and Fig. 56I).

PROBLEMS

1. A satellite is to orbit the earth 2000 mi above the surface. Calculate (a) its speed, and (b) its period of revolution in minutes.

2. A satellite orbits the earth 640 mi above the surface. Find (a) its speed, and (b) its period in minutes. [*Ans.* (a) 1.64×10^4 mi/hr, (b) 106 min.]

3. (a) What must be the speed of a satellite if it is to orbit the earth 6000 mi above the surface? (b) What will be its period?

4. Find the gravitational-field intensity 3000 Km above the surface of the earth. [*Ans.* 4.54 m/s².]

5. A satellite is to orbit the earth at a height of 241 mi.

Calculate (a) its speed, and (b) its period of revolution in minutes.

6. What must be the speed of a 1000-Kg satellite if it is to orbit the earth 1000 Km above the surface? (b) What will be its period? (c) What will be its kinetic energy? [Ans. (a) 7.35×10^3 m/s, (b) 105 min, (c) 2.70×10^{10} J.]

7. Calculate (a) the speed of a satellite orbiting the planet Mars 100 Km above the surface, and (b) its period (see Table 13A).

8. Calculate (a) the speed of a satellite orbiting the planet Saturn 1000 Km above the surface. (b) Find its period (see Table 13A). [Ans. (a) 2.55×10^4 m/s, (b) 1.44×10^4 s, or 4.0 hr.]

9. With what speed must a 500-Kg satellite be launched from the earth's surface (a) to escape into interplanetary space? (b) What is the kinetic energy required?

10. (a) Find the speed of a 2000-Kg satellite orbiting the moon 50 Km above the surface. Find (b) the period, and (c) the kinetic energy (see Table 13A). [Ans. (a) 1.65×10^3 m/sec, (b) 113.6 min, (c) 2.72×10^9 J.]

11. With what speed must an 800-Kg satellite be launched from the moon's surface (a) to escape into interplanetary space? (b) What is the kinetic energy required (see Table 13A)?

12. A 500-lb satellite is to orbit the earth in a circular orbit 541 mi above the surface. Calculate (a) its speed in mi/hr, (b) its period of revolution, and (c) its kinetic energy. [Ans. (a) 16,580 mi/hr, (b) 102.3 min, (c) 4.62×10^9 ft-lb.]

13. Calculate (a) the gravitational-field intensity, and (b) the gravitational potential 6000 Km above the earth's surface.

14. (a) Calculate the gravitational-field intensity, and (b) the gravitational potential on the surface of the moon. [Ans. (a) 1.91 N/Kg, (b) 3.05×10^6 J/Kg.]

15. (a) Calculate the acceleration due to gravity on the moon, and (b) the relative weight of a man on the moon as compared with his weight on the earth (see Table 13A).

16. A satellite orbits the earth 20,000 mi above the surface. Find (a) its speed, and (b) the gravitational-field intensity. [Ans. (a) 7.19×10^3 mi/hr, (b) 0.874 lb/sl.]

17. Calculate the orbiting speed of a satellite in a circular orbit 200 Km above the surface of the planet Mars (see Table 13A).

18. Calculate the speed of a satellite orbiting the planet Jupiter at a distance of 500 Km above the surface (see Table 13A). [Ans. 4.24×10^4 m/s.]

19. Calculate the escape velocity of a missile leaving the planet Jupiter.

20. Find the escape velocity of a missile leaving the surface of Mars. [Ans. 5050 m/s.]

21. What is the orbital radius of a satellite that will remain fixed over the same point on the earth's equator?

22. A rocket engine with a mass of 25×10^3 Kg is to be launched vertically upward and then turned horizontally at burnout to orbit the earth at a height of 300 Km above the surface. Find (a) the orbiting speed in m/s, (b) the kinetic energy in joules, (c) the gravitational potential at the orbit height, and (d) the total energy expended. [Ans. (a) 7.72×10^3 m/s, (b) 7.46×10^{11} J, (c) -5.96×10^7 J/Kg, (d) 8.16×10^{11} J.]

23. An anti-aircraft missile with a mass of 50 Kg, fired vertically upward from a big gun, rises to a height of 200 Km. Find (a) the gravitational potential at the highest point, (b) the potential energy, and (c) the initial velocity.

24. A rocket missile with a mass of 30 Kg, fired vertically upward from the ground, rises to a height of 200 Km. Find (a) the gravitational potential at the highest point, (b) the potential energy, and (c) the initial velocity. [Ans. (a) -6.05×10^7 m²/s², (b) -1.815×10^9 J, (c) 1.97×10^3 m/s.]

25. A rocket engine with a mass of 20×10^3 Kg is launched vertically upward and then turned into a horizontal direction at burnout, to orbit the earth at a height of 500 Km above the surface. Find (a) the orbiting velocity, (b) the kinetic energy, (c) the gravitational potential at the orbit, and (d) the stored potential energy measured from the ground up.

26. A satellite launched from the earth is found to be 630 Km above the earth's surface at its lowest point, and 21,630 Km above the surface at its highest point. Find (a) the perigee, (b) apogee, (c) semimajor axis, (d) eccentricity, (e) maximum satellite speed, and (f) maximum satellite speed. [Ans. (a) 7×10^6 m, (b) 2.8×10^7 m, (c) 1.75×10^7 m, (d) 0.600, (e) 9.54×10^3 m/s, (f) 2.38×10^3 m/s.]

27. A satellite circles the earth at a height of 630 Km above the surface. (a) Find its orbital speed. Rocket engines are now turned on to speed it up so that it will orbit the earth with a perigee of 7000 Km and an apogee of 70,000 Km. Find (b) the added speed that must be given the satellite, and (c) the speed of the satellite at apogee.

28. A satellite circles the earth 50,000 Km above the surface. Find (a) its orbiting speed. By firing retrorockets for a few seconds the satellite is to be slowed down to a speed where its height of 50,000 Km is now at apogee, and perigee is to be 300 Km. Find (b) the apogee speed, (c) the change in speed required, and (d) the perigee speed. [Ans. (a) 2.66×10^3 m/s, (b) 1.23×10^3 m/s, (c) 1.43×10^3 m/s, and (d) 10.2×10^3 m/s.]

CENTER OF MASS AND ROTATIONAL EQUILIBRIUM

In the kinematics and dynamics of motion, one often neglects the size and shape of a body and speaks of the object as if it were located at a point. Of course, this is done for convenience only and is justified as long as one's interests are not centered on structural details. Under certain conditions it is found necessary to take into account the structural details and still make use of the simplest forms of Newton's laws of motion.

15.1. Center of Mass. *The center of mass of any given body, or system of bodies, is a point such that, if any plane is passed through it, the mass moments on one side of the plane are equal to the mass moments on the other.*

Consider, for example, two spheres of mass m_1 and m_2 as shown in Fig. 15A. The center of

Fig. 15A *The center of mass of two bodies is located at some point on a line joining their centers of mass.*

mass (c of m) P lies on a line connecting the centers of the two bodies and in such a position that

$$m_1 \times r_1 = m_2 \times r_2 \qquad (15a)$$

For a vertical plane through P, perpendicular to the line AB, $m_1 \times r_1$ is the mass moment of

m_1, and $m_2 \times r_2$ is the mass moment of m_2. The mass moment of a body about any chosen plane is given by the mass of the body multiplied by its perpendicular distance to the plane.

Example 1. Find the c of m of two bodies $m_1 = 2$ Kg, and $m_2 = 5$ Kg, placed 14 m apart.
Solution. Given is the distance $r_1 + r_2 = 14$ m, from which

$$r_2 = 14 - r_1$$

Substitute all known quantities in Eq.(15a).

$$2r_1 = 5(14 - r_1) \qquad \text{or} \qquad 2r_1 = 70 - 5r_1$$

and

$$7r_1 = 70 \qquad \text{or} \qquad r_1 = 10$$

The substitution of this value of r_1 in Eq.(15a) gives

$$r_2 = 4 \text{ m}$$

The c of m of a three-body system is found by an extension of the above principle (see Fig. 15B). To illustrate, two of the masses like A

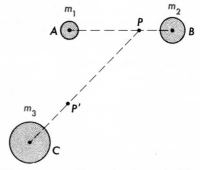

Fig. 15B *Diagram illustrating the method for finding the center of mass of a three-body system.*

and B are first selected and their *c of m* found by use of Eq.(15a). These two bodies are then treated as though they were one body located at P. With one mass $(m_1 + m_2)$ located at P and a second mass m_3 located at C, Eq.(15a) is applied to find P′, the resultant *c of m*. If a system consists of more than three bodies, the above process is continued until all masses have been included.

The *c of m* of all regularly shaped bodies like those shown in Fig. 15C is at their geometrical

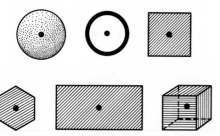

Fig. 15C   *Illustrating the center of mass of regularly shaped objects.*

center. A plane passed through the center of any of these figures will divide the body into two equal parts. Consider, for example, a thin ring of mass M as shown in Fig. 15D(a). By drawing

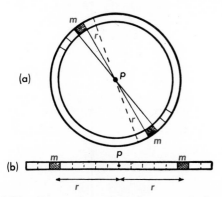

(a)

(b)

Fig. 15D   *Center of mass is at the geometrical center: (a) uniform ring, (b) uniform rod.*

straight lines through the geometrical center, the total mass can be divided up into pairs of small but equal masses. Since the masses m of each pair are equidistant from the center, their *c of m* is at their midpoint P, and this is common to all pairs.

A similar process can be applied to a long thin rod or pole of equal cross section. Dividing the rod into an equal number of parts as shown in Fig. 15D(b) permits the pairing off of equal parts at equal distances from the center. Since the geometrical center is the *c of m* of each pair, it is also the *c of m* of the entire rod. It is now clear why the distances in Fig. 15A must be measured from the centers of the spheres; their centers give their *c of m*.

15.2. Rotation about the Center of Mass. In Fig. 15E two masses m_1 and m_2 are shown

Fig. 15E   *Diagram illustrating the smooth rotation of two bodies around their center of mass.*

supported at the ends of a thin rod and rotating smoothly around a pin through the *c of m*. If the pin is located at any other point, for example halfway between the two masses, the experimenter will experience an unbalanced force on his hand, tending to make it "wobble."

Should the two-body system be thrown spinning into the air as shown in Fig. 15F, it will be

Fig. 15F   *A body thrown spinning into the air rotates smoothly about its center of mass, while the center of mass traces out the smooth trajectory of a projectile.*

observed to rotate about its *c of m* while the *c of m* traces out the smooth trajectory of a projectile.

The earth and the moon serve as a good

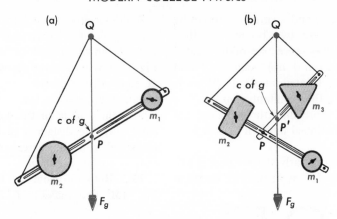

Fig. 15G   *Demonstration of an experiment for finding the center of gravity of a system of bodies.*

illustration of two bodies rotating freely about their *c of m*. The mass of the earth is 81 times the mass of the moon, and the distance between them is approximately 240,000 mi. A calculation, as in Example 1, gives $r_2 = 2927$ mi; nearly 3000 mi from the center of the earth and 1000 mi below the earth's surface.

In a similar manner the earth and moon, considered as a single body, rotate with the sun as the second body about their *c of m*. Relatively, the bodies are similar to those in Fig. 15B, with m_1 and m_2 rotating about P, and the point P and mass m_3 rotating more slowly around P'.

15.3. Center of Gravity. The *c of m* of the two bodies in Fig. 15A is the one and only point about which the two bodies will, if pivoted, balance under the earth's gravitational pull. Furthermore, a single upward force applied at C, equal in magnitude to the weight of the two bodies, will maintain equilibrium; the system will not tend to move in any direction nor will it tend to rotate.

The *c of m* is therefore a point at which all of the weight can be considered as concentrated. For this reason, the *c of m* is often called the center of gravity (*c of g*).

The *c of g* of a system of bodies may be found by suspending it from a pivot point as shown in Fig. 15G. Both of these systems of masses may be turned to differently oriented positions by sliding the supporting string on the pin Q. No matter what orientation is assigned, the line

of the plumb *F* will pass through the same point. The rigid system in diagram (b) is convenient for demonstrations since the rotation of m_1, m_2, or m_3 about their own centers of mass, or the turning of either bar at P to a new angle, will not shift the *c of g* from P'.

The *c of g* of any regular or irregular shaped body of uniform or nonuniform density can be found by suspending it from one pivot point and then another, as shown in Fig. 15H. With

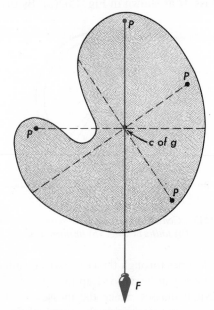

Fig. 15H   *The center of gravity of any freely suspended object lies at, or directly beneath, the point of suspension.*

each suspension from a point P near the periphery, the body will hang with its *c of g* directly under that point. Lines drawn along the string supporting the plumb for each suspension will all cross at the common point, the *c of g*.

If pivoted at this point and set turning, or thrown spinning into the air, the rotation will be smooth about the *c of g*. (*Note:* Because the force of gravity decreases with altitude, the *c of g* of a body is not always at exactly the same point as the *c of m*. The lower part of a mass, for example, is closer to the earth's center than the upper part and therefore has a greater weight per unit mass. For all practical purposes, however, the two terms *c of g* and *c of m* are considered synonymous.)

15.4. Equilibrium. In Chapter 6 it was shown how *a body acted on by any number of forces is in equilibrium if the vector sum of all the forces is zero.* If each of these forces is resolved into *x* and *y components* and the conditions of equilibrium applied, the summation of all the *x components* of force must be zero, and the summation of all the *y components* must be zero. Symbolically,

$$\Sigma F_x = 0$$
$$\Sigma F_y = 0 \qquad (15b)$$

The capital Greek sigma represents "*summation.*"

If all of the forces acting on a body lie in one plane, the fulfillment of these two conditions is all that is necessary to assure *translational equilibrium*. These equations are commonly referred to as *the 1st condition of equilibrium.*

When a rigid body is acted upon by a number of forces, complete equilibrium is not assured with the satisfying of the 1st condition of equilibrium alone. In Fig. 15I, for example, a body is shown acted upon by two equal but opposite forces. While Eq.(15b) is satisfied, the body is not in complete equilibrium; it is acted upon by a *couple* which tends to set it into rotation. To prevent this turning, the rigid body must be acted upon by another equal but opposite couple. In other words, to be in rotational equilibrium, couples must be balanced.

A couple is defined as two equal but op-

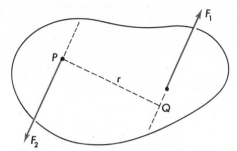

Fig. 15I   *A "couple" acting on a rigid body tends to set it in rotation.*

positely directed forces not acting along the same line. The magnitude of a couple is given by the product of one of the forces and the perpendicular distance between them. From the diagram,

$$\text{couple} = F_1 \times r \qquad (15c)$$

A couple made up of large forces close together may have the same magnitude as a pair of small forces farther apart.

A rigid body is defined as one whose various parts do not change their relative positions when forces are applied at different points. Actually, no known bodies strictly satisfy this condition, but for practical purposes most solid bodies may be regarded as rigid.

15.5. Torque. When a single force acting on a body tends to produce rotation, it is said to exert a *torque* or *force moment*. Torque is synonymous with force-moment and is defined as the product of force times lever arm, the lever arm being the perpendicular distance from the pivot point to the force. In Fig. 15J a body is shown acted upon by a torque. The force *F* is

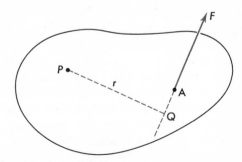

Fig. 15J   *A single force acting on a rigid body pivoted at some point P exerts a torque L = F × r.*

applied at the point A while the body is pivoted at the point P. The perpendicular distance r is equal to the line PQ, and the torque L is given by

$$\boxed{L = F \times r} \qquad (15\text{d})$$

If $F = 5$ N, and $r = 3$ m,

$$L = 5\text{ N} \times 3\text{ m} = 15\text{ N m}$$

The dimensions *"newton meters"* should not be confused with the units of *work* and *energy*. In the calculation of work, force and distance are measured in the same direction, while in torque the two are measured at right angles.

It is customary to ascribe a positive sign to all torques acting to turn a body counterclockwise and a minus sign to all torques tending to turn it clockwise.

15.6. Rotational Equilibrium. Consider the rigid body in Fig. 15K, pivoted by a pin at the

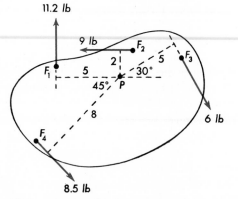

Fig. 15K   *Diagram illustrating a rigid body in equilibrium under the action of four forces.*

point P and acted upon by four forces F_1, F_2, F_3, and F_4. With lever arms of 5, 2, 5, and 8, respectively, these forces constitute torques L_1, L_2, L_3, and L_4. For this body to be in translational equilibrium, the summation of all the forces, or the sums of their x and y components, must be zero. To be in rotational equilibrium, the summation of all the *torques* must be zero. This latter condition, the 2nd condition of equilibrium, can be expressed symbolically as

$$\boxed{\Sigma L = 0} \qquad (15\text{e})$$

It will now be shown that the four forces in Fig. 15K are in translational as well as rotational equilibrium. To apply the 1st condition of equilibrium, each of the forces is resolved into x and y *components* and each group added separately. From the angles given in the figure, and using Eq. (6d), we obtain

x components

F_1,		0 lb
F_2,		-9 lb
F_3,	$6 \quad \cos 60° =$	3 lb
F_4,	$8.5 \cos 45° =$	6 lb
	$\Sigma F_x = 0$	

y components

F_1,		11.2 lb
F_2,		0 lb
F_3,	$6 \quad \sin 60° =$	-5.2 lb
F_4,	$8.5 \sin 45° =$	-6 lb
	$\Sigma F_y = 0$	

Since $\Sigma F_x = 0$, and $\Sigma F_y = 0$, the conditions for translational equilibrium are satisfied.

Applying the 2nd condition of equilibrium,

L_1	$11.2 \times 5 =$	-56
L_2	$9 \quad \times 2 =$	$+18$
L_3	$6 \quad \times 5 =$	-30
L_4	$8.5 \times 8 =$	$+68$
	$\Sigma L = 0$	

Because the sum of all the torques is zero, rotational equilibrium is assured. Since the body is in complete equilibrium, the pin P, acting as a pivot, cannot be exerting a force of any kind and it can therefore be removed. After removal it can be placed at any other point in the body and equilibrium is still assured. In other words, *if all of the forces acting on a rigid body maintain complete equilibrium about one pivot point, they also are in equilibrium about any other pivot point.*

Although the body in Fig. 15J is acted upon by a single torque and is set into rotation, the pin keeps it from being moved away. In other words, the body is in translational equilibrium; the pin is exerting a force on the body equal in magnitude to F and opposite in direction. Or, in other words, the force F, and the force exerted by the pin, constitute a couple.

15.7. Anatomical Mechanics. In the preceding chapters it has been seen that, to obtain a solution to many problems in mechanics, it is customary to neglect certain minor details like the weight of a bridge girder or the friction in a bearing, in order to simplify a problem and to arrive at some approximate yet practical numerical answer.

Although complicated, the general principles of muscle function in animals as well as in living human beings may also be simplified in much the same way by neglecting certain minor parts. As a result of such simplification, the bones of the body and the muscles that move them form the compression and tension members, respectively, of mechanical systems already classified as levers and machines. It is, therefore, the purpose of this chapter to show in what way some of the principles of mechanics may be found in, and applied to, the human anatomy.

One significant fact concerning muscles and their action is that their lever arms, that is, the perpendicular distance from some joint as a fulcrum to the line of action of the muscle, is relatively short. This means that, to overcome a relatively slight resistance at the extremity of some bone system, a muscle must be capable of exerting far greater forces than those offering the resistance to motion. It will be seen in what follows, therefore, that the large force of a muscle exerted through a short distance moves a lesser load through a greater distance. In other words, motion is magnified while the mechanical advantage is diminished.

When one part of the body is bent toward another, the action is called *flexion*, that is, bending; when the parts are straightened out, the motion is called *extension*. Even though a number of muscles are involved in the flexion of a joint, and another group in its extension, it is often true that some one particular muscle group may be considered to be the *prime mover* for flexion and another as the prime mover for extension.

Muscles that perform a minor role in any action are called *assistors*. The function of assistor muscles is to prevent undesired actions of the prime mover, such as inward and outward rotation.

15.8. Mechanics of the Foot. An elementary example of anatomical mechanics is found in an analysis of foot movement (see Fig. 15L). In the

Fig. 15L   *Skeleton diagram of the lower leg and foot showing the muscles and tendon used in rising on tiptoe.*

flexion and extension of the whole foot, the ankle acts as a hinge or pivot about which rotation in a vertical plane takes place. The top of the *astragalus* is like a ball fitting into and free to turn in the socket formed by the ends of the *fibula* and *tibia* bones of the leg. When a person attempts to rise on tiptoe, the strong muscles, the *gastrocnemius* and *soleus* forming the calf of the leg, act as prime movers. A sufficient tightening of these muscles causes the heel to rise, and the foot to bend at C where the *phalanx* of the toes join the *metatarsals*.

A simple space diagram shown in Fig. 15M illustrates how rising on tiptoe involves the simplest type of torque action with a fixed pivot at C. The horizontal member AC represents the foot skeleton from A to C in Fig. 15L, and

Fig. 15M *Schematic diagram showing the mechanical principle of the human foot when rising on tiptoe.*

the vertical member (BD) the leg skeleton (BD) supporting the body. To calculate the tension required of the muscles and the load to be carried by the leg bones, the foot member A to C is drawn as a rigid body and all forces acting upon it are taken into account.

There are three forces acting on the horizontal member, an upward force at A due to tension in the muscles, a downward force at B due to the leg bones, and an upward force at C due to the floor. As a problem, let it be assumed that a person weighing 150 lb *stands on one foot* and then rises on tiptoe. Assign the dimensions of 2 in. for AB and 6 in. for BC, and calculate the tension force T and the compression force P as follows:

By taking moments about A, the counter-clockwise torque is $F_g \times 8$ in. and the clockwise torque $P \times 2$ in.

Apply the 2nd condition of equilibrium.

$$F_g \times 8 \text{ in.} - P \times 2 \text{ in.} = 0$$

Substitute $F_g = 150$ lb and solve for P.

$$P = \frac{150 \text{ lb} \times 8 \text{ in.}}{2 \text{ in.}} = 600 \text{ lb}$$

Take moments about B, and apply the 2nd condition of equilibrium.

$$F_g \times 6 \text{ in.} - T \times 2 \text{ in.} = 0$$

Substitute and solve for T.

$$T = \frac{150 \text{ lb} \times 6 \text{ in.}}{2 \text{ in.}} = 450 \text{ lb}$$

If we now apply the 1st condition of equilibrium, it is observed that the total upward force $F_g + T$ of 600 lb equals the total downward force P of 600 lb.

It should be pointed out that tension is produced by a contraction of the large part or "belly" of a muscle, and not by the narrow section called the *tendon*.

15.9. Mechanics of the Lower Jaw. The *mandible*, or lower "jawbone," is a large, strong, horseshoe-shaped bone, forming the lower third of the facial skeleton [see Fig. 15N(a)]. A pair

Fig. 15N (*a*) *Diagram of a human skull.* (*b*) *Schematic diagram showing the mechanics involved in chewing.*

of *condyles* at the ends fit into sockets, one on either side of the skull just in front of the auditory canal, and act as hinges about which the lower jaw pivots.

The *masseter* or "chewing muscle" is one of the strongest muscles in the body. As illustrated in the figure, it is located in the back part of the side of the face. Originating on the lower margin of the *zygoma*, the masseter passes downward to where it terminates on the lower edge of the *ramus* of the mandible.

The action of the two masseters, one on either side of the face, is such as to lift the lower jaw and at the same time draw it slightly forward. In principle, this is a torque action with a pivot at C, an upward force at B, and a load force at A introduced when chewing takes place between the teeth of the upper and lower jaws.

A schematic diagram of the torque action is shown in Fig. 15N(b), with selected values of the dimensions given in inches. When the mandible is selected as the rigid body, all of the acting forces, due to symmetry, are reduced to three, F_g, T, and P. To calculate the magnitudes of these forces, at least one of them must be known.

As a problem, let it be assumed that the lower jaw, in chewing with the front teeth, is able to exert a measured force of 20 lb. To calculate the tension T exerted by the two masseters, the point C is assumed as pivot, and the torques are equated as follows:

$$F_g \times 5 \text{ in.} = T \times 1.5 \text{ in.}$$

Inserting $F_g = 20$ lb, and solving for T,

$$T = \frac{20 \text{ lb} \times 5 \text{ in.}}{1.5 \text{ in.}} = 66.7 \text{ lb}$$

Equating downward forces to upward forces,

$$P + F_g = T$$

from which

$$P = T - F_g = 66.7 - 20 = 46.7 \text{ lb}$$

Each masseter therefore exerts $\frac{1}{2}$ of 66.7 lb or 33.35 lb, while the condyles each press against their sockets with a force of $\frac{1}{2}$ of 46.7 lb, or 23.35 lb.

15.10. The Biceps. The above procedure of solution will be applied to the muscle problem involved in the flexion of the lower arm. In

Fig. 15O(a) a skeleton of the forearm is shown in a horizontal position supporting a stone in the palm of the hand. With a pivot point at the elbow joint, the forearm and hand form a

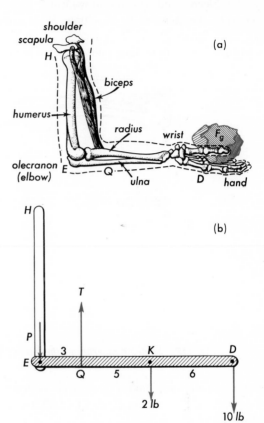

Fig. 15O   (a) *Skeleton diagram of the arm and hand showing the biceps used in lifting a load.* (b) *Mechanics of the forearm.*

compression member like the boom of a crane, while the *biceps* which assume the duty of prime mover in any flexor movement become the tension member.

The biceps originate on the *scapula* or shoulder, from where they pass downward and forward to terminate on the *radius* near the elbow.

A schematic diagram of this force problem is shown in Fig. 15O(b); the vertical member (EH) represents the *humerus;* the horizontal member (ED), 14 in. in length, the forearm and hand; and the tension member (TQ), the biceps. A weight of 10 lb is assumed held in the hand, while the weight of the forearm and hand is taken to be 2 lb and applied at the center of mass 8 in. from the elbow.

The problem to be solved resolves itself into one of calculating (a) the upward force exerted by the biceps and (b) the downward force exerted by the humerus on the elbow. With two unknown forces P and T, either one can be determined by eliminating one of them from

15.11. The Quadriceps. The mechanics concerned with the extension of the lower limb involves a four-branched muscle called the *quadriceps*. One of the branches of this muscle originates above the hip on the anterior inferior spine of the ilium, and the other three on the front and two sides of the *femur*, respectively (see Fig. 15P). All four unite around the small

Fig. 15P   *Skeleton diagram of the human leg (above) and its mechanical analog (below).*

torque calculations. Taking E as a pivot point and applying the 2nd condition of equilibrium, we write

$$10\ \text{lb} \times 14\ \text{in.} + 2\ \text{lb} \times 8\ \text{in.} - T \times 3\ \text{in.} = 0$$

Multiplying out and solving for the unknown T, we obtain

$$T = \frac{140\ \text{lb in.} + 16\ \text{lb in.}}{3\ \text{in.}} = 52\ \text{lb}$$

If Q is chosen as the pivot point, the 2nd condition of equilibrium gives

$$10\ \text{lb} \times 11\ \text{in.} + 2\ \text{lb} \times 5\ \text{in.} - P \times 3\ \text{in.} = 0$$

Multiplying out and solving for the unknown P, we find

$$P = \frac{110\ \text{lb in.} + 10\ \text{lb in.}}{3\ \text{in.}} = 40\ \text{lb}$$

The 1st condition of equilibrium is satisfied, since the only upward force is equal to the total of the downward forces, 40 lb + 2 lb + 10 lb.

kneecap bone, the *patella*, and terminate as a strong tendon near the upper end of the *tibia*.

If, while the body is in a sitting position, the leg is extended as shown in the diagram, contraction in the quadriceps pulls the patella up over the knee joint. The action is similar to that of a pulley, as indicated in Fig. 15P. As a mechanical problem it is desired to find the tension required of the quadriceps to hold the lower part of the leg at any given angle with the horizontal, and the force exerted by the femur on the knee joint.

To make these calculations it is necessary to know the weights of the foot and lower leg, their centers of gravity, and the geometry involved at the knee joint. When these are known, the lower leg from B to C may be isolated and solved as a rigid body with a pivot at B. Such solutions will be left as problems on the following pages.

PROBLEMS

1. Two bodies, 20 Kg and 36 Kg, respectively, are located 4 m apart. Find their center of mass.

2. Three bodies, each with a mass of 5 Kg, are located at the three corners of a right triangle with sides of length 3 m, 4 m, and 5 m, respectively. Find the center of mass. [Ans. On the line joining the midpoint of the 3 m side and the third mass, and 1.42 m from the midpoint.]

3. Three masses 5 Kg, 5 Kg, and 12 Kg are located at the corners of an equilateral triangle whose sides are 4 m long. Find the center of mass from the 12 Kg mass.

4. Two lead spheres of 6 Kg and 9 Kg, respectively, are tied 2 m apart at opposite ends of a wire. This system is projected whirling into space with an angular speed of 240 rpm. Find (a) the center of mass, (b) the angular velocity in radians per second, (c) the centripetal acceleration of each mass, and (d) the centripetal force on each mass. [Ans. (a) 0.8 m from 9-Kg mass, (b) 25.1 rad/s, (c) 756 m/s², and 504 m/s², (d) 4536 N, and 4536 N.]

5. A uniform bar MN, 5 m long, has a mass of 4 Kg and supports two masses: 8 Kg at M, and 15 Kg at N. Find their center of mass.

6. A uniform ladder 7 m long has a mass of 15 Kg. Find the center of mass if an 80 Kg man is standing on the ladder (a) 2 m from the bottom, and (b) 1 m from the top. [Ans. (a) 2.24 m from the bottom, (b) 5.61 m from the bottom.]

7. Two stones with masses of 3 Kg and 5 Kg, respectively, are tied 1.5 m apart at opposite ends of a wire and are projected into space with a rotational speed of 180 rpm. Find (a) the center of mass, (b) the angular velocity, (c) the centripetal acceleration of each mass, and (d) the centripetal force on each mass.

8. The two ends of a uniform pole 8 ft long and weighing 30 lb, rest on the shoulders of a man and his son. Where should a 150 lb load be suspended from the pole if the man is to carry twice the load carried by the boy? [Ans. 2.4 ft from the man.]

9. The center of gravity of an empty truck weighing 6200 lb is 12 ft in front of the rear axle. The truck carries a solid block of steel weighing 2 tons, which is placed with its center of gravity 3.5 ft in front of the rear axle. If the front and rear wheels of the truck are 20 ft apart, find (a) the center of gravity, (b) the load carried by the rear wheels, and (c) the load carried by the front wheels.

10. A man weighing 180 lb, holding a 50-lb boy in his arms, is able to rise on one tiptoe with the other foot off the ground. Find (a) the tension in the Achilles' tendon, and (b) the compressional force in the bones of the leg. Referring to Figs. 15L and 15M, assume AB = 2.2 in. and AC = 9.0 in. [Ans. (a) 711 lb, (b) 941 lb.]

11. A girl pedaling a bicycle weighs 80 lb. When she puts all of her weight on the ball of one foot, what is (a) the tension in the Achilles' tendon, and (b) the compressional force in the leg bones? Referring to Figs. 15L and 15M, assume AB = 1.7 in. and AC = 7.5 in.

12. When chewing on a piece of dried salmon, an Eskimo exerts a force of 16 lb with his front teeth. Find (a) the tension in each masseter, and (b) the force on each condyle, if the mandible dimensions are: AB = 2.5 in., BC = 2.8 in., and $\theta = 50°$. [Ans. (a) 17.3 lb, (b) 9.34 lb.]

13. In biting down hard on a piece of candy with his front teeth a boy exerts a force of 18 lb. Calculate (a) the tension in the masseter, and (b) the force on each condyle, if the mandible dimensions are: AB = 2.9 in., BC = 3.2 in., and $\theta = 54°$.

14. A man holds a 7.7-Kg bowling ball in the palm of his hand. If his forearm is in the median position, as shown in Fig. 15O, find (a) the tension exerted by the biceps, and (b) the compressional force in the humerus. The dimensions of his forearm are EQ = 6 cm, and ED = 38 cm. Assume the forearm and hand to have a mass of 2.0 Kg, with the center of mass 20 cm from the elbow. [Ans. (a) 543 N, (b) 448 N.]

15. An athlete holds a 16-lb shot-put in his hand with his forearm flexed to the median position as shown in Fig. 15O. Calculate (a) the force exerted by the biceps, and (b) the compressional force on the humerus. The dimensions of his forearm are: EQ = 2.2 in., and ED = 17 in.

16. A uniform ladder 6 m long and mass of 25 Kg makes an angle of 70° with the rough floor on which it stands. The upper end rests against a smooth round horizontal bar so that the force exerted by the bar is normal to the ladder. A man whose mass is 75 Kg stands on a rung 1 m from the top. Find the force exerted on the upper end of the ladder. [Ans. 267 N.]

17. The uniform boom of a crane is 30 ft long and has a mass of 400 lb. One end of the boom is pivoted at the base of a vertical mast, or king post, and the other end is held up by a tie rope, or cable, to the top of the mast. The boom is horizontal, and the tie rope makes an angle of 45° with the mast. If a 600-lb load hangs from the far end of the boom, find the tension in the tie rope.

18. Two uniform timbers each 15 ft long and weighing 30 lb, form a lifting frame in the shape of a capital A. The two timbers make an angle of 90° with each other, and a load of 500 lb is supported from the peak or vertex. A steel cable with its ends fastened 5 ft from the lower end of each timber forms the horizontal member of the A frame. Find the tension in the cable. Neglect the weight of the cable. (Note. Find forces on one side, assume half the load is carried by each side, and the force on the lower end is vertical.) [Ans. 397 lb.]

19. Two sections of a space ship like that shown in Fig. 14K are maintained 480 ft apart, and turning. If the vehicle housing the astronauts has one-quarter the mass of the other vehicle, and they are to experience normal weight forces, what should be (a) the angular speed, and (b) the period of revolution?

KINEMATICS AND
DYNAMICS OF ROTATION

When a rigid body is acted upon by an unbalanced torque, it is set into rotation. Free to turn about an axis, such a body increases in angular velocity and acquires, when the torque ceases to act, some final angular speed (see Fig. 16A).

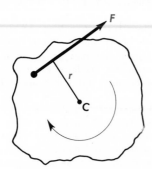

Fig. 16A   *A rigid body is acted upon by a torque,* $F \times r$.

16.1. Angular Acceleration. Just as the acceleration of a body in linear motion is defined as the rate of change of velocity, so the angular acceleration of a body in rotation is defined as the rate of change of angular velocity. By comparison, these two definitions are expressed the same mathematically [see Eq.(3a)].

$$a = \frac{v - v_0}{t} \qquad \alpha = \frac{\omega - \omega_0}{t} \qquad (16a)$$
linear motion   **angular motion**

In the equations above, α represents the angular acceleration and is analogous to the linear acceleration a; ω_0, the initial angular

velocity, is analogous to v_0; and ω, the final angular velocity, is analogous to v. If the above equations are solved for v and ω respectively, they become

$$v = v_0 + at \qquad \omega = \omega_0 + \alpha t \qquad (16b)$$
linear motion   **angular motion**

Angular velocity ω [see Eq.(13b)] is defined as θ, the angle turned through, divided by t the time.

$$v = \frac{x}{t} \qquad \omega = \frac{\theta}{t} \qquad (16c)$$
linear motion   **angular motion**

The following example will illustrate the meaning, as well as an application, of the above angular formulas.

Example 1. A flywheel starting from rest acquires, in 10 s, a speed of 240 rpm. Find the acceleration.
Solution. Since the wheel starts from rest, $\omega_0 = 0$. The final velocity in radians per second is calculated by the use of Eq.(16c). Since there are 2π rad in 1 revolution,

$$\omega = \frac{2\pi \times 240}{60} = 25.1 \frac{\text{rad}}{\text{s}}$$

Using Eq.(16a), we find that

$$\alpha = \frac{25.1 - 0}{10} = 2.51 \frac{\text{rad}}{\text{s}^2}$$

It is clear from the above formulas that linear quantities x, v, and a in the linear equations have only to be replaced by the corresponding angular quantities, θ, ω, and α, to obtain the angular equations. This direct correspondence is the result of using the radian as a unit of angular measure and holds throughout all of the formulas in mechanics.

To derive a formula for the linear acceleration of a point around the periphery of an accelerated wheel, it is convenient to start with the definition of acceleration given by Eq.(16a) and substitute for the velocities v and v_0 the equality given by Eq.(13e), $v = r\omega$, and $v_0 = r\omega_0$ (see Fig. 16B).

$$a = \frac{v - v_0}{t} = \frac{r\omega - r\omega_0}{t} = r\left(\frac{\omega - \omega_0}{t}\right) = r\alpha$$

The result, $a = r\alpha$, is to be compared with two previous formulas, Eqs.(13d) and (13e). The

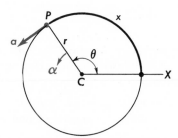

Fig. 16B   *A wheel free to rotate about its center is given an angular acceleration.*

similarity is more conspicuous when written together.

$$\begin{array}{|c|} \hline x = r\theta \\ v = r\omega \\ a = r\alpha \\ \hline \end{array} \qquad (16d)$$

These transformation equations are well worth remembering, for they are found to be quite useful in the solving of many problems.

16.2. Average Angular Velocity. To calculate the total angle turned through by a rigid body undergoing constant angular acceleration, use is made of the *average angular velocity*. By analogy with linear motion [see Eq.(3b)], the *average angular velocity is defined as $\frac{1}{2}$ the sum of the initial and final angular velocities.*

Symbolically, we write

$$\bar{v} = \frac{v + v_0}{2} \qquad \bar{\omega} = \frac{\omega + \omega_0}{2} \qquad (16e)$$

linear motion   angular motion

Since $x = \bar{v}t$, and $\theta = \bar{\omega}t$, direct substitution gives

$$x = \frac{v + v_0}{2}t \qquad \theta = \frac{\omega + \omega_0}{2}t \qquad (16f)$$

linear motion   angular motion

Example 2. An airplane motor, while idling at 300 rpm, is suddenly accelerated. At the end of 3 s it has acquired its maximum speed of 2400 rpm. Assuming constant acceleration, find (a) the average angular velocity, and (b) the total angle turned through.

Solution. We begin by changing the given speeds to radians per second.

$$\omega_0 = \frac{300}{60} \times 2\pi = 31.4 \frac{\text{rad}}{\text{s}}$$

$$\omega = \frac{2400}{60} \times 2\pi = 251.3 \frac{\text{rad}}{\text{s}}$$

To find (a), direct substitution in Eq.(16e) gives

$$\bar{\omega} = \frac{251.3 + 31.4}{2} = 141.4 \frac{\text{rad}}{\text{s}}$$

To find (b), direct substitution in Eq.(16f) gives

$$\theta = 141.4 \times 3 = 424.2 \text{ rad}$$

16.3. Kinematics of Rotation. The term "kinematics of rotation" refers to a quantitative description of motion such as that given above. By combining two of the equations already studied, Eqs.(16b) and (16f), two other useful formulas may be derived.* Each of these is written here beside their analogous linear motions.

$$\begin{array}{ll} x = v_0 t + \frac{1}{2}at^2 & \theta = \omega_0 t + \frac{1}{2}\alpha t^2 \quad (16g) \\ v^2 = v_0^2 + 2ax & \omega^2 = \omega_0^2 + 2\alpha\theta \quad (16h) \end{array}$$

linear motion   angular motion

Again note here that angular quantities θ, ω, and α take the place of the corresponding linear quantities x, v, and a.

Example 3. An automobile engine running at 300 rpm is given an angular acceleration of 20 rad/s² for 10 s. Find (a) the angle turned through, and (b) the total number of revolutions.

Solution. First change 300 rpm to radians per second.

$$\omega_0 = \frac{300}{60} \times 2\pi = 31.4 \frac{\text{rad}}{\text{s}}$$

---

* The derivations of Eq.(16g) and (16h) follow exactly the steps taken in obtaining the corresponding linear formulas, Eqs.(3i) and (3h).

Using Eq.(16g), we obtain

$$\theta = 31.4 \frac{rad}{s} \times 10\,s + \frac{1}{2} 20 \frac{rad}{s^2} \times (10\,s)^2 = 1314\,rad$$

$$\theta = \frac{1314}{2\pi} = 209\,rev$$

The four basic equations most useful in dealing with the kinematics of rotational motion are:

$$\omega = \omega_0 + \alpha t$$

$$\theta = \frac{\omega + \omega_0}{2} t$$

$$\theta = \omega_0 t + \tfrac{1}{2}\alpha t^2$$

$$\omega^2 = \omega_0^2 + 2\alpha\theta$$

16.4. Dynamics of Rotation. In the treatment of angular acceleration given in the preceding sections of this chapter, neither the torques causing the acceleration, nor the mass of the rotating body, entered into the calculations. When these two factors are introduced into the equations the treatment is referred to as the *dynamics of rotation.*

When a specified torque is applied to a body free to rotate about some axis, the angular acceleration produced depends not only upon the size and shape of the body, but also upon the distribution of the mass with respect to the axis of rotation. To see how these factors are taken into account, consider the simplest kind of example, namely, that of a small mass m fastened to the end of a string and set into rotation as shown in Fig. 16C.

By Newton's second law of motion, the acceleration a of the mass around the periphery of the circle should be given by

$$F = ma$$

Multiply both sides of this equation by the radius of the circle r.

$$F \times r = ma \times r$$

The product $F \times r$ on the left side represents the applied torque L. If we replace the acceleration a on the right by its equal, $r\alpha$, from Eq.(16d), the result is

$$L = mr^2\alpha \qquad (16i)$$

Since m and r for a given body are both constants, they may be replaced by a single constant I, and the equation written

$$L = I\alpha \qquad (16j)$$

where $I = mr^2$, and is called the *moment of inertia.* By the following comparison with the force equation,

$$F = ma \qquad\qquad L = I\alpha$$
linear motion   angular motion

the torque L is seen to be analogous to F, the angular acceleration α analogous to a, and the moment of inertia I analogous to m.

According to Eq.(16i), the angular acceleration α is inversely proportional to r^2. An experiment illustrating this fact is shown in Fig. 16D. Two masses m threaded on light

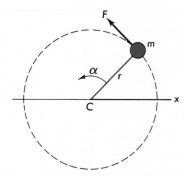

Fig. 16C   *Angular acceleration depends upon torque and moment of inertia.*

Fig. 16D   *An experimental demonstration of moment of inertia.*

horizontal arms, free to turn about a vertical axis, are acted upon by a constant torque $L = F \times R$.

When the masses are clamped at equal distances from, and halfway out on the arms, the angular acceleration is relatively large, and the weight F_g exerting the constant torque L quickly drops from A to B. When the masses m are moved to the outer ends of the arms where their distance r is doubled, the angular acceleration is reduced to $\frac{1}{4}$ and the weight F_g takes 2 times as long to go from A to B. By measuring the distance of each mass from the center, and the time of fall of the weight F_g for each part of the experiment, the product αr^2 is found to be constant.

16.5. Moment of Inertia. The moment of inertia of a body with respect to any axis is the sum of the products obtained by multiplying each elementary mass by the square of its distance from the axis. To illustrate, consider the uniform ring and the thin rod as shown in Fig. 16E.

(a)

(b)

Fig. 16E *Diagram showing the division of (a) a ring, and (b) a rod, into small masses for calculating their moments of inertia.*

Both the ring and the rod are divided into small parts, as shown by the dotted lines and shaded areas, and the moment of inertia I is calculated from the formula

$$I = m_1 r_1^2 + m_2 r_2^2 + m_3 r_3^2 + \ldots \quad (16k)$$

where m_1, m_2, m_3, ... represent the masses of each small part, and r_1, r_2, r_3, ... their respective distances from the axis of rotation.

Since r has the same value for all masses around the ring, the subscripts on the r's can be dropped,

$$I = m_1 r^2 + m_2 r^2 + m_3 r^2 + \ldots$$

and the common factor r^2 taken out as follows:

$$I = (m_1 + m_2 + m_3 + \ldots)r^2$$

Because the sum of all the masses $m_1 + m_2 + m_3 + \ldots$ equals M, the total mass of the ring,

$$I_{\text{ring}} = Mr^2$$

This is the same as the formula for a mass on the end of a string.

When the same procedure is applied to the rod in Fig. 16E, the values of r vary from mass to mass, and the calculations, using Eq.(16k), give only an approximate value of its moment of inertia. It is not difficult to show that the larger the number of parts into which the rod is divided, the more nearly will Eq.(16k) give the true moment of inertia. A derivation of the formula by which the true moment of inertia is usually calculated requires the integral calculus and gives

$$I_{\text{rod}} = \tfrac{1}{12} M l^2$$

where M is the total mass of the rod and l its total length. Because the calculus method is beyond the scope of this book, this formula should be assumed to be correct.

The true moments of inertia of a number of regular-shaped solid bodies are given in Fig. 16F. Diagram (a) represents a thin ring or hoop of radius r, (b) a disk of uniform density, (c) a solid sphere with an axis through the center, etc.

Two common moments of inertia not given in the figure are

Thin spherical shell—around any diameter,

$$I = \tfrac{2}{3} M r^2$$

Uniform ring—around any diameter,

$$I = \tfrac{1}{4} M (r_1^2 + r_2^2)$$

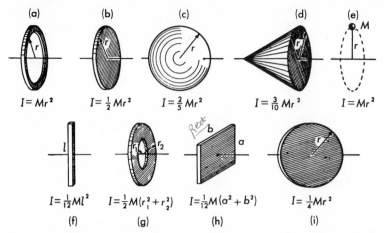

Fig. 16F   *Formulas for the moment of inertia of certain regularly shaped bodies.*

In the *mks system*, the moment of inertia has the units of Kg m²; and in the *fps* system, the units are lb-ft s²

16.6. Angular Momentum. *Angular momentum* and *rotational kinetic energy* are to all rotating bodies what *linear momentum* and *kinetic energy* are to all bodies moving along a straight line. By definition, the angular momentum p of a rotating body is equal to the product of its moment of inertia about the axis of rotation and its angular velocity.

$$p = I\omega \qquad (16l)$$

In the special case of a small mass moving in

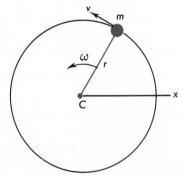

Fig. 16G   *Angular momentum of a small mass m is given by mvr, or by mr²ω.*

a circle, as shown in Fig. 16G, the moment of inertia equals mr^2, and

$$p = mr^2\omega \qquad (16m)$$

If ω is replaced by its equivalent, v/r,

$$p = mvr \qquad (16n)$$

The first of the above equations applies to any rotating body regardless of size or shape, while the last two apply only to bodies considered small with respect to their distance from the center of rotation. To illustrate, consider the following example.

Example 4. A boy whose mass is 50 Kg rides at the outer edge of a merry-go-round, 12 m in diameter. Calculate his angular momentum if the merry-go-round is making 3 rpm.

Solution. Since the boy is small compared with his distance from the center of rotation, Eq.(16m) can be used. First the angular velocity ω is found by Eq. (16c).

$$\omega = \frac{3 \times 2\pi}{60} = 0.314 \,\frac{\text{rad}}{\text{s}}$$

Substitution of known values in Eq.(16m) gives

$$p = 50 \text{ Kg} \times (6 \text{ m})^2 \times 0.314 \,\frac{\text{rad}}{\text{s}}$$

$$p = 565 \,\frac{\text{Kg m}^2}{\text{s}}$$

16.7. Theoretical Considerations. To understand why angular momentum is defined as $I\omega$, return to the fundamental equation for torque, $L = I\alpha$. If in this equation the angular acceleration is replaced by its defining equation, $\alpha = (\omega - \omega_0)/t$,

$$L = I\frac{\omega - \omega_0}{t} \qquad (16o)$$

Solving for the product Lt, we obtain an equation analogous to the impulse equation in translational motion.

$Ft = mv - mv_0$	$Lt = I\omega - I\omega_0$ (16p)
linear motion	**angular motion**

In linear motion, Ft is called the impulse and $mv - mv_0$, the change in momentum. By analogy, therefore, it is logical that Lt be called the *angular impulse* and $I\omega - I\omega_0$ the *change in angular momentum*. $I\omega_0$ is the initial angular momentum and $I\omega$ the final value.

16.8. Conservation of Angular Momentum. If no external torque acts upon a body or system of bodies already in rotation, the angular momentum remains constant. Setting the torque L in Eq.(16p) equal to zero, $0 = I\omega - I\omega_0$, from which

$$I\omega = I\omega_0 \qquad (16q)$$

In words, the final angular momentum is always equal to the initial angular momentum.

An experiment illustrating a system of bodies in rotation is diagramed in Fig. 16H. Two equal masses m are mounted on a rod AB which is capable of rotation about a vertical axis MN. Cords fastened to each mass and leading over pulleys at P to the ring R enable the radial distance to be changed from r_1 in (a) to r_2 in (b) by simply pulling up on the ring R. The swivel S prevents the cords from twisting.

When the system is first set rotating as in (a) with an angular velocity ω_1, the angular momentum of each mass is $I\omega_1$. On pulling up on the ring R, the radius decreases to r_2 and the angular velocity ω_2 increases. Conservation of angular momentum requires that, for each mass m,

$$I_1\omega_1 = I_2\omega_2 \qquad (16r)$$

In terms of speed v,

$$mv_1r_1 = mv_2r_2 \qquad (16s)$$

Since the mass is not altered in value, the conservation of angular momentum requires that any decrease in r must be compensated for by an increase in speed. This is necessary to keep both sides of the above equation equal to each other.

Equation (16s) shows for example that, if r is reduced to half value, the velocity v must double.

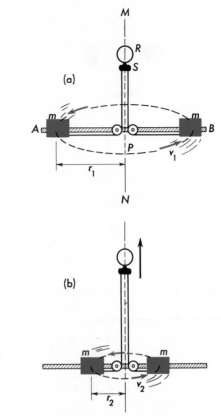

Fig. 16H   *Experimental demonstration of the conservation of angular momentum.*

With v doubled and the circle only half as large, the angular velocity increases fourfold.

Example 5. Suppose in Fig. 16H that $m = 10$ g, $v_1 = 20$ cm/s, and $r_1 = 16$ cm. What will be the new speed if the radius r_1 is decreased to half value, i.e., $r_2 = 8$ cm?

Solution. By direct substitution in Eq. (16s),

$$10 \text{ g} \times 20 \frac{\text{cm}}{\text{s}} \times 16 \text{ cm} = 10 \text{ g} \times v_2 \times 8 \text{ cm}$$

$$3200 \frac{\text{cm}}{\text{s}} = 80 \, v_2$$

$$v_2 = 40 \frac{\text{cm}}{\text{s}}$$

An interesting experiment illustrating the same principle is diagramed in Fig. 16I. An observer stands on a turntable with weights in each hand. With arms fully extended horizontally, he is first set rotating slowly. Upon drawing the hands and

Fig. 16I *Experiments illustrating conservation of angular momentum.*

weights in toward the chest, as shown, the angular velocity is considerably increased. This experiment is best appreciated by the turning observer who feels himself speeded up by what seems to be a mysterious force.

This principle is used by expert figure skaters on the ice. They start into a whirl with their arms, and perhaps one leg extended, and then upon drawing the arms and leg in, obtain a greatly increased angular velocity.

16.9. Kinetic Energy of Rotation. In a previous chapter on linear motion, kinetic energy was seen to be given by $\frac{1}{2}mv^2$. By analogy the kinetic energy of a rotating body is given by $\frac{1}{2}i\omega^2$:

$$E_{k \text{ trans}} = \tfrac{1}{2}mv^2 \qquad E_{k \text{ rot}} = \tfrac{1}{2}I\omega^2 \qquad (16t)$$
linear motion   angular motion

As a hoop rolls along a level road it has both kinetic energy of rotation and kinetic energy of translation (see Fig. 16J). In rotating about its geometrical center, it has a moment of inertia I and kinetic energy $\frac{1}{2}I\omega^2$, while the center of

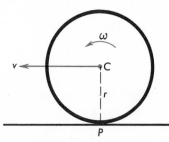

Fig. 16J *A rolling hoop has kinetic energy of rotation and kinetic energy of translation.*

gravity C, moving along a straight line with velocity v, has kinetic energy $\frac{1}{2}mv^2$. The total kinetic energy is, therefore,

$$E_{k \text{ total}} = \tfrac{1}{2}I\omega^2 + \tfrac{1}{2}mv^2 \qquad (16u)$$

Total E_k = rotational E_k + translational E_k

16.10. Angular Momentum a Vector. Angular momentum, as illustrated by the rotating wheel in Fig. 16K, may be treated as a vector quantity.

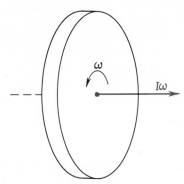

Fig. 16K *Angular momentum may be represented by a vector.*

To obtain an angular momentum vector, imagine grasping the axis of rotation with the right hand, the fingers pointing in the direction of rotation, the thumb then pointing in the direction of the vector. The length of the vector is given by the magnitude of $I\omega$.

The advantage of representing angular momentum and angular impulse by vectors becomes apparent when attempting to determine the resultant motion of a body that undergoes rotation about two or more axes simultaneously. The gyroscope in some of its varied forms serves as a good illustration of this.

16.11. The Gyroscope. A common top, set spinning like the one shown in Fig. 16L, is but one of the many forms of a gyroscope. Spinning about its axis, the top precesses about its peg or pivot point, the line AB describing an inverted cone about the vertical line AC. If, when looking down from above, such a top is seen to be spinning in a clockwise direction, the precession is clockwise; spinning counterclockwise the precession is counterclockwise.

A fundamental study of gyroscopic precession

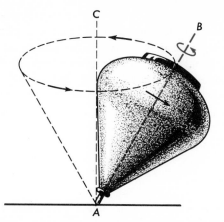

Fig. 16L   *A spinning top precesses around a vertical axis.*

may be readily made by the use of a top similar to those found in toy shops, and diagramed in Fig. 16M. The wheel is designed to have a large moment of inertia, and is often ball-bearing

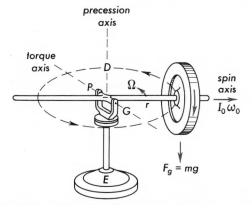

Fig. 16M   *Experimental gyroscope for demonstrating precession.*

mounted. Free rotation in any direction is permitted by the double pivot at the top of the stand E.

When the wheel is set spinning at high speed and released with its axis in a horizontal position, a smooth precession takes place around the vertical axis. This precessional motion is due to the external force exerted by the earth's gravitational pull downward on the wheel. Acting through the wheel's center of gravity, this downward force F_g, equal to mg, exerts a torque about a horizontal axis through PG. This torque L, given by

$r \times F_g$, and acting for a time t, constitutes a torque impulse Lt and gives rise to a corresponding angular momentum $(I\omega)'$ about the same axis.

$$Lt = (I\omega)' \qquad (16v)$$

The top therefore has two angular momenta, one $I_0\omega_0$ due to spin and the other $(I\omega)'$ about a horizontal axis PG. Combining these vectorially, as shown in Fig. 16N, we obtain a resultant R

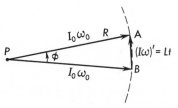

Fig. 16N   *Vector diagram for precession of a gyroscope.*

equal in magnitude to the original $I_0\omega_0$ and now making an angle ϕ with its direction. In other words, there has been a precession, a change in the direction of the spin axis. The angular momentum $I_0\omega_0$ is called the *spin vector.*

In the vector diagram the spin vector $I_0\omega_0$ is changing in direction by an amount $(I\omega)'$. Since $(I\omega)'$ is increasing with time and is due to a torque L, it can, by Eq.(16v), be replaced by Lt. For small angles ϕ, the distance measured along the arc AB is approximately equal to Lt and we can write

$$\phi = \frac{Lt}{I_0\omega_0}$$

Because the action gives rise to a uniform precession, angle ϕ is increasing at a uniform rate and may be written

$$\phi = \Omega t$$

where Ω is the precessional angular velocity.

Solving these as simultaneous equations, we obtain

$$\Omega = \frac{L}{I_0\omega_0} \qquad (16w)$$

This, the precessional angular velocity in radians per second, is given by the torque L divided by the spin angular momentum.

By analogy, the treatment above is similar to that of circular motion given in Fig. 14D. There, a mass moves in a circle at constant speed because a constant inward force is exerted upon it. Although the acceleration is toward the center, the radius remains constant while only the direction of v changes.

In precessional motion, the magnitude of the angular momentum remains constant while its direction changes smoothly and continuously. And similar to the treatment of circular motion, as the angle ϕ is made smaller and smaller in Fig. 16N, the arc AB becomes more and more nearly equal to the chord AB, and the change is nearly perpendicular to the spin axis. In the limit when ϕ becomes zero, Eq.(16w) holds exactly and the spin vector and torque vector are mutually perpendicular.

PROBLEMS

1. When the electric power is turned off, an electric motor turning over at 1800 rpm is slowed down to 300 rpm in 5 s. Find (a) the angular acceleration, (b) the angular velocity at the end of 4 s, and (c) the total angle turned through during the 5 s.

2. An automobile engine is idling at 150 rpm. Upon acceleration it acquires a speed of 3000 rpm in 3 s. Calculate (a) the angular acceleration, (b) the angular velocity at the end of 2 s, and (c) the total angle turned through during the 3 s. [*Ans.* (a) 99.5 rad/s², (b) 215 rad/s, (c) 495 rad.]

3. A 2-Kg stone on the end of a wire 0.75 m long is whirled in a circle at 150 rpm. Find (a) the moment of inertia, (b) the angular velocity, (c) the angular momentum, (d) the centripetal force, and (e) the rotational kinetic energy.

4. An atom with a mass of 1.8×10^{-25} Kg moves in a circular path of radius 1×10^{-10} m. If it makes 6×10^{10} rpm, find (a) the moment of inertia, (b) the angular velocity, (c) the angular momentum, (d) the centripetal force, and (e) the rotational kinetic energy. [*Ans.* (a) 1.8×10^{-45} Kg m², (b) 6.28×10^9 rad/s, (c) 1.13×10^{-35} Kg m²/s, (d) 7.10×10^{-16} N, (e) 3.55×10^{-26} J.]

5. A uniform ring with a mass of 5 Kg, and a diameter of 0.40 m, rotates about its geometrical center at 2100 rpm. Find (a) the moment of inertia, (b) the angular velocity in radians per second, (c) the angular momentum, and (d) the rotational kinetic energy.

6. A uniform disk with a mass of 2.5 Kg and a diameter of 0.35 m rotates at 2700 rpm. Calculate (a) the moment of inertia, (b) the angular velocity, (c) the angular momentum, and (d) the rotational kinetic energy. [*Ans.* (a) 3.83×10^{-2} Kg m², (b) 283 rad/s, (c) 10.8 Kg m²/s, (d) 1530 J.]

7. A bowling ball with a mass of 4.5 Kg and a diameter of 0.25 m is pivoted to rotate about an axis through its center. If it rotates at 1500 rpm, find (a) the angular velocity in radians per second, (b) the moment of inertia, (c) the angular momentum, and (d) the rotational kinetic energy.

8. A uniform disk with a mass of 4 Kg and a diameter of 0.30 m, starts from rest and acquires a speed of 1800 rpm in 5 s. Find (a) the moment of inertia, (b) the angular acceleration, (c) the applied torque, (d) the final angular momentum, and (e) the kinetic energy. [*Ans.* (a) 0.045 Kg m², (b) 37.7 rad/s², (c) 1.70 N m, (d) 8.48 Kg m²/s, (e) 799 J.]

9. Two masses of 5 Kg each are fastened to opposite ends of a wire so their centers are 2 m apart. If this system is projected into space rotating at 1200 rpm, calculate (a) the moment of inertia, (b) the angular velocity, (c) the angular momentum, (d) the rotational kinetic energy, and (e) the tension in the wire.

10. A uniform disk with a mass of 2 Kg and a diameter of 0.10 m, is mounted as a gyroscope as shown in Fig. 16M. If it spins at 2400 rpm, and the pivot P is 0.05 m from the center of the wheel, find (a) the moment of inertia of the wheel, (b) the angular velocity of the wheel about its axis, (c) the torque exerted by gravitation, and (d) the precessional angular velocity. [*Ans.* (a) 2.5×10^{-3} Kg m², (b) 251 rad/s, (c) 0.98 N m, (d) 1.56 rad/s.]

11. A uniform disk with a mass of 4 Kg and a diameter of 0.20 m, is mounted as a gyroscope as shown in Fig. 16M. If it spins at 6000 rpm, and the distance from the center of the wheel to the pivot point is 0.12 m, find (a) the moment of inertia, (b) the angular velocity, (c) the torque, and (d) the precessional angular velocity.

12. Two masses of 50 Kg each are fastened to opposite ends of a wire 4 m long. If this system is projected into space rotating at 120 rpm, find (a) the moment of inertia, (b) the angular velocity, (c) the angular momentum, (d) the rotational kinetic energy, and (e) the tension in the wire. [*Ans.* (a) 400 Kg m², (b) 12.6 rad/s, (c) 5040 Kg m²/s, (d) 3.17×10^4 J, (e) 1.58×10^4 N.]

13. A wheel with a moment of inertia of 500 Kg m², and rotating at a speed of 3000 rpm, is brought to rest in 20 s by applying a brake. Find (a) the angular velocity, (b) the angular acceleration, and (c) the torque applied by the brake.

14. The two atoms of a diatomic molecule each have a mass of 2.6×10^{-26} Kg. If the distance between their centers is 3×10^{-10} m, and they rotate around their center of mass with an angular momentum of 2.5×10^{-34} Kg m²/s, find (a) the moment of inertia of the molecule, and (b) the angular speed in revolutions per second. [*Ans.* (a) 1.17×10^{-45} Kg m², (b) 2.13×10^{11} rps.]

15. Two atoms of a diatomic molecule of sodium chloride, NaCl, have masses of 3.8×10^{-26} Kg and 6.0×10^{-26} Kg, respectively. If the distance between their centers is 2.5×10^{-10} m, and they rotate around their center of mass with an angular momentum of 5×10^{-35} Kg m²/s, find (a) the center of mass, (b) the moment of inertia of the molecule, and (c) the angular speed in revolutions per second.

16. The two atoms of a diatomic molecule of sodium iodide, NaI, have masses of 3.8×10^{-26} Kg and 21.0×10^{-26} Kg, respectively. If the distance between their centers is 2.9×10^{-10} m, and they rotate around their center of mass with an angular momentum of 1.5×10^{-35} Kg m²/s, find (a) the center of mass, (b) the moment of inertia, and (c) the angular speed in revolutions per second. [Ans. (a) 2.46×10^{-10} m from Na, (b) 27.1×10^{-46} Kg m², (c) 8.80×10^{8} rps.]

17. An electron with a mass of 9.1×10^{-31} Kg moves in a circular orbit around a nucleus with a mass of 1.67×10^{-27} Kg. If the radius of the orbit is 5.0×10^{-11} m, and the angular momentum is 1.05×10^{-34} Kg m²/s, find (a) the moment of inertia, and (b) the frequency of rotation in revolutions per second.

18. The moon and the earth, with masses of 7.32×10^{22} Kg and 5.97×10^{24} Kg, respectively, rotate around their center of mass making one revolution every 27.3 days. If the distance between their centers is 3.84×10^{8} m, find (a) the distance from the center of the earth to the center of mass, (b) the angular velocity around the center of mass, (c) the centripetal force, and (d) the gravitational attractive force exerted on the moon by the earth. [Ans. (a) 4.65×10^{6} m, or 2888 mi, (b) 2.66×10^{-6} rad/s, (c) 1.97×10^{20} N, (d) 1.97×10^{20} N.]

PROPERTIES OF SOLIDS AND LIQUIDS

Of all the properties of solids and liquids that are known and studied, only a few of the more important characteristics will be given in this chapter. In the order of their presentation these are: *density, elasticity, pressure, buoyancy,* and *surface tension.*

17.1. Density and Specific Gravity. The density of matter, whether in the solid, liquid, or gaseous state, is defined in metric units as the mass per unit of volume. Algebraically, this may be expressed as

$$\text{density} = \frac{\text{mass}}{\text{volume}} \qquad \boxed{\rho = \frac{M}{V}} \qquad (17a)$$

The Greek letter ρ is commonly used to represent density. In the *cgs* system, density is given in *grams per cubic centimeter.* Since the gram is defined as the mass of 1 cm³ of water, the density of water is 1 gm/cm³. In the *mks* system, density is given in *kilograms per cubic meter.*

Example 1. If 25 cm³ of mercury have a mass of 340 g, what is the density?
Solution. Direct substitution in Eq.(17a) gives

$$\rho = \frac{340 \text{ gm}}{25 \text{ cm}^3} = 13.6 \frac{\text{gm}}{\text{cm}^3}$$

If the volume and density of a body are known, the mass is given by Eq.(17a) as

$$M = V \times \rho \qquad (17b)$$

Specific gravity is another term frequently used to express the relative weights of matter. *Specific gravity is defined as the ratio of the weight of a given volume of substance to the weight of an equal volume of water.*

Specific gravity

$$= \frac{\text{weight of a given substance}}{\text{weight of equal volume of water}} \qquad (17c)$$

According to this definition, the specific gravity of a substance is given by the same numerical value as the density in the *cgs* system. Since it is the ratio between like quantities, specific gravity has no dimensions and is therefore the same in all systems of units. For example, the specific gravity of aluminum is 2.7, which means that any solid piece of aluminum weighs 2.7 times as much as an equal volume of water.

TABLE 17A. DENSITIES AND WEIGHT-DENSITIES OF A FEW COMMON SUBSTANCES

Material	Kg/m³	g/cm³	lb/ft³
Liquids			
alcohol	790	0.79	49.3
benzine	900	0.90	56.2
blood	1,040	1.04	65.0
gasoline	690	0.69	41.2
ice	910	0.91	57.2
mercury	13,600	13.6	849
olive oil	918	0.918	57.3
water	1,000	1.000	62.4
Metals			
aluminum	2,700	2.7	168.7
brass	8,500	8.5	530
copper	8,900	8.9	556
gold	19,300	19.3	1205
iron	7,900	7.9	493
lead	11,400	11.4	712
platinum	21,500	21.5	1342
silver	10,500	10.5	655
tin	7,300	7.3	456
zinc	7,100	7.1	446

For convenience only, engineers, as well as others, in this country usually employ the quantity *weight per unit volume* for the term *density*. For example the density of water is commonly said to be 62.4 lb per cubic foot. Since the pound is a unit of force, it is proper to distinguish such a quantity from density as defined by Eq.(17a) by calling it *weight-density*.

$$\text{weight-density} = \rho g \qquad (17d)$$

where ρ in the Engineering system is the density in *slugs/ft³*, and g is the acceleration due to gravity, 32 ft/s².

17.2. Stretching of a Spring. If a vertically mounted rod, wire, or spring is supported rigidly at its upper end, and weights are added to its lower end, the amount by which it is stretched is found to be proportional to the weight applied. This is an example of Hooke's law.

The stretching of a spring is illustrated in Fig. 17A. Due to an added weight F_g, the spring is stretched a distance x.

If a second equal weight is added, the total distance stretched will be twice that for the first one. If a third weight is added, the total distance stretched will be three times that for the first one, etc. These observations are illustrated by the graph shown at the right in Fig. 17A. Each

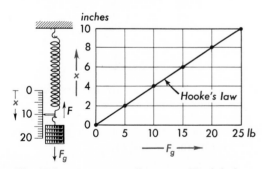

Fig. 17A *Experiment illustrating Hooke's law.*

value of x is plotted vertically and the corresponding loads F_g are plotted horizontally.

More specifically, when the first 5-lb weight is added, the stretch or elongation is 2 in. With two 5-lb weights the total elongation is 4 in., and with three weights $x = 6$ in., etc. A continuation of this shows as does the graph at the right in Fig.

17A, that each 5-lb weight produces an added elongation of 2 in. To make an equation of these observations, we write

$$F_g = kx$$

where k is a constant and equal in this experiment to 2.5. Each value of x multiplied by 2.5 gives the corresponding weight F_g. When the spring in Fig. 17A is stretched a distance x, the spring itself exerts an upward force F equal but opposite in direction to F_g. For the spring, then,

$$F = -kx \qquad (17e)$$

The minus sign indicates that x and F are in opposite directions. This equation is often referred to as Hooke's law.*

17.3. The Stretching of a Wire. Because a wire or rod will not stretch very far before reaching the breaking point, one must, in order to check Hooke's law, resort to some method of measuring extremely small changes in length. This is frequently done by means of a device known as the optical lever. As shown by the experiment diagramed in Fig. 17B, a beam of light is reflected from a small mirror M mounted on a small three-legged stool, two legs of which rest on a stationary platform, as shown, and the third on a small clamp C at the lower end of the wire. As the wire stretches under an added weight F_g, the mirror tips back and the light beam is reflected up a measurable amount on the distant scale.

Like the stretching of a spring described in the preceding section, the stretching of a wire obeys Hooke's law. The amount stretched is directly proportional to the force applied and is illustrated by the straight part of the graph AE in Fig. 17C. If the weights are removed, the wire will return to its original length. If weights are continually added, the forces applied will even-

* Robert Hooke (1635–1703), English experimental physicist known principally for his contributions to the wave theory of light, universal gravitation, and atmospheric pressure. He originated many physical ideas but perfected few of them. Hooke's scientific achievements would undoubtedly have received greater acclaim had his efforts been confined to fewer subjects. He had an irritable temper, and made many virulent attacks on Newton and other men of science, claiming that work published by them was due to him.

Fig. 17B *The stretching of a wire under increasing tension can be measured by an optical lever.*

ment, diagramed in Fig. 17B, where a wire or rod is clamped at one end and a load is applied at the other. Let *l* represent the wire's original length, *A* its cross-sectional area, and *e* the elongation produced by the applied load F_g. The reaction force *F* exerted by the wire is always equal but opposite to the action force F_g.

By definition the applied *stress* is the force per unit area and the resultant *strain* is the elongation per unit length (see Fig. 17D).

$$\text{stress} = F/A \qquad (17f)$$
$$\text{strain} = e/l \qquad (17g)$$

Since *A* and *l* are constants, and by Hooke's

tually become too great, and Hooke's law will no longer hold as the elongation will increase too rapidly. This is the region EP on the graph. Carried too far in this direction, the wire will break.

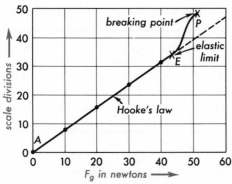

Fig. 17C *A graph of the stretching of a wire showing Hooke's law, the elastic limit, and the breaking point.*

The point E at which Hooke's law ceases to hold is called the *elastic limit*. If the wire is stretched beyond this point, it will be permanently stretched and will not return to its original length when the weights are removed.

17.4. Young's Modulus. Consider the experi-

Fig. 17D *Young's modulus for the stretching of a wire or rod is given by Fl/Ae.*

law *F* is proportional to *e*, stress is proportional to the strain, and we can write

$$\frac{F}{A} \propto \frac{e}{l}$$

By inserting a constant *Y* we obtain the relation

$$\frac{F}{A} = Y\frac{e}{l}$$

$$Y = \frac{Fl}{Ae} \qquad (17h)$$

The proportionality constant is called Young's modulus.*

Young's modulus is a very practical constant, for, if its value is known for any given material, the amount of stretch produced in any size of wire or rod of that material can be calculated. Careful laboratory experiments have established such values for many common substances. See columns 2 and 3 in Table 17B.

TABLE 17B. YOUNG'S MODULUS

| Material | Young's modulus Y | |
	N/m²	lb/in.²
Aluminum	7×10^{11}	10.2×10^6
Brass	9.02 "	13.09 "
Copper	12.5 "	18.0 "
Iron	21.0 "	30.0 "
Steel (mild)	19.2 "	27.9 "
Tendon (human)	1.6 "	2.3 "
Muscle (human)	0.009 "	0.013 "
Bone (tension)	22 "	32 "
Bone (compression)	22 "	32 "
Nerve	0.1850 "	0.2680 "
Vein	0.0085 "	0.0123 "
Artery	0.0005 "	0.0007 "

Example 2. A copper wire 3 m long and 2 mm² in cross-sectional area hangs from the ceiling. What will be its elongation if a 2-Kg mass is suspended from the lower end?

Solution. Solving Eq.(17h) for e,

$$e = \frac{Fl}{AY}$$

and substituting the known dimensions and Young's modulus for copper from Table 17B, we obtain,

$$e = \frac{2 \, Kg \times 9.8 \, m/s^2 \times 3 \, m}{2 \times 10^{-6} \, m^2 \times 12.5 \times 10^{10} \, n/m^2}$$

$$e = 2.35 \times 10^{-4} \, m$$

or $e = 0.235 \, mm$

* Thomas Young (1773–1829), English scientist. Born of a Quaker family, young Thomas had read the Bible twice through at the age of four and at fourteen could speak seven languages. He studied medicine in London, Edinburgh, Göttingen, and Cambridge, and at twenty-eight he was appointed professor of physics at the Royal Institution. Young is best known for his experiments proving the wave theory of light, but he also made valuable contributions to mechanics, medicine, and to the mechanism of sight and vision. He was one of the first to decipher successfully Egyptian hieroglyphic inscriptions.

17.5. Compression. When a load F_g is applied to the ends of a rod to compress it as shown in Fig. 17E, the decrease in length is the same in amount as the elongation it would acquire when

Fig. 17E   *Young's modulus for the compression of a rod is given by Fl/Ae.*

the same load is applied as a tension. In other words, Hooke's law applies to compression, the values of Young's modulus for stretching are valid, and Eq.(17h) can be used for all calculations within the elastic limit.

The simple proportionality between the force applied to a body and the amount stretched or compressed is consistent with the intermolecular force diagram of Fig. 47C. The straightness of the graph for a short distance on each side of the equilibrium position E is an indication of why Hooke's law holds for limited amounts of stretch or compression.

17.6. Pressure. *Pressure is defined as the force per unit of area.* Written in the form of an equation,

$$\text{pressure} = \frac{\text{total force}}{\text{area}},$$

$$P = \frac{F}{A} \tag{17i}$$

As an illustration of the distinction between pressure and total force, consider the two aluminum metal blocks in Fig. 17F. Block (a) stands

Fig. 17F   *A block standing on end exerts a greater pressure than when it is lying on its side.*

Fig. 17G   *The pressure at any depth in a free-standing liquid is given by the weight per unit area of the liquid above that level.*

on one end where the area is 200 in.^{2}, while block (b) stands on one edge where the area is 400 in.^{2} Weighing 1000 lb, each block separately exerts the same downward force. Standing on end as in (a), the downward pressure is given by Eq.(17i) as

$$\text{pressure} = \frac{1000 \text{ lb}}{200 \text{ in.}^2} = 5 \frac{\text{lb}}{\text{in.}^2}.$$

This is read *5 pounds per square inch.* Standing on edge as in (b), on the other hand, the pressure is only one-half as great.

$$\text{pressure} = \frac{1000 \text{ lb}}{400 \text{ in.}^2} = 2.5 \frac{\text{lb}}{\text{in.}^2}.$$

Over each square inch in the first case there is a downward force equivalent to 5 lb while in the second case there is only 2.5 lb. The pressure in (a) is, therefore, twice as great as the pressure in (b), but the total downward force is the same.

Transposing A to the other side of Eq.(17i) gives:

$$F = P \times A. \qquad (17j)$$

Total force equals pressure times area.

In the case of liquids it is frequently desirable to know the pressure on the bottom of a containing vessel, or at some depth within a body of liquid.

The rule regarding pressure states that the magnitude of the pressure at any depth is equal to the weight of a column of liquid of unit cross section reaching from that point to the top of the liquid.

At a depth of l_1, as illustrated in Fig. 17G (a), the pressure P_1 is given by the weight of a column of liquid 1 cm^2 in cross section and l_1 cm in height. At a greater depth of l_2, the pressure P_2 is given by the weight of a column of liquid 1 cm^2 in cross section and l_2 cm in height.

This can be demonstrated with a glass cylinder and a thin lightweight disk as shown in Fig. 17H. With water surrounding the empty cylinder, the force F pushing up, holds the disk tightly against

Fig. 17H   *The pressure at any given depth in a liquid is equal to the weight per unit cross section of the liquid directly above.*

the end. If the cylinder is gradually filled with water, an increasing downward force is exerted on the disk. Just as the water inside reaches the level of the water outside, the disk drops from the end of the cylinder, showing that the downward force and upward force at that point and at that instant become equal. We can conclude from this experiment that not only is the pressure at any given point in a liquid given by the weight of the liquid per unit area above it, but that the pressure at one point is equal to the pressure at any other point at the same level.

Pressure in a liquid is defined as the normal force exerted by the liquid per unit area and is usually measured in *pounds per square inch*, or *newtons per square meter*. Because of its dimensions, pressure is not a force, and it is not a vector.

17.7. The Ocean Depths. Only recently has man descended to very great depths in the ocean to observe one of the most interesting regions of the earth's crust. The *bathysphere*, a hollow but thick-walled steel sphere about 4½ ft in diameter, descended with its two American observers, Beebe and Barton, in 1931, to a depth of 1400 ft, and in 1934 to a depth of 3000 ft.

Auguste Piccard, the Swiss professor who once set a balloon record into the stratosphere (see Fig. 18B of the next chapter), set another record in 1953 by diving into the Mediterranean, just off the coast of Italy. Accompanied by his son Jacques, they descended in their *bathyscaph* to a depth of 10,300 ft.

In January of 1960, Jacques Piccard and Lt. Donald Walsh, U.S.N., descended into the Pacific, just off the coast of the island of Guam, to a depth of 37,800 ft. The pressure at this great depth of over seven miles amounts to 16,400 lb/in.² (see Fig. 17I). These bathyscaphs had steel walls 3 to 5 in. thick and small portholes through which observations and photographs could be made.

17.8. Archimedes' Principle. Archimedes' principle states that *a body floating or submerged in a*

Fig. 17I *A diagram of the bathyscaph, an underwater vessel in which Jacques Piccard and Lt. Donald Walsh, U.S.N., descended to an ocean depth of 7 mi, in January 1960. The bathyscaph operates much the same as a balloon. The main part of the vessel is a thin-walled, multiple-celled tank, supporting a small, thick-walled passenger gondola at the bottom. While the buoyancy of a balloon is due to the lightweight gas it contains, the bathyscaph obtains its buoyancy by being filled with lighter-than-water gasoline. To descend, the divers release gasoline; to rise, they release ballast. Propellers on top permit the vessel to maneuver for short periods of time.*

liquid is buoyed up by a force equal to the weight of the liquid displaced. For example, if a block of wood is floating in water, as shown in Fig. 17J, the buoyant force F holding the block up is equal

Fig. 17J *A block of wood lowered into the water sinks until the buoyant force of the water equals the weight of the block.*

to the weight of the water displaced (shaded area). When the block is first placed in the water it sinks until the buoyant force F becomes great enough to equalize the downward force, the weight of the block F_g.

An experimental demonstration of the truth of Archimedes' principle is shown in Fig. 17K. A

Fig. 17K *Illustrating the four steps in an experiment demonstrating Archimedes' principle.*

small cylindrical cup containing a close-fitting solid metal cylinder is accurately balanced by a set of weights on an equal-arm balance. No change in balance occurs when in diagram (b) the cylinder has been removed from the cup and suspended from a hook underneath. In diagram (c) a beaker of water has been raised until the cylinder is completely submerged. Balance is now destroyed because of the upward buoyant force of the water on the cylinder.

If Archimedes' principle is correct, the buoyant force is equal to the weight of a volume of

water exactly equal to the volume of the cylinder. A slow addition of water to the cup in diagram (d) shows that at the very instant the cup becomes filled, exact balance of the beam is restored. The restoring of balance confirms the principle.

One of the many ways of measuring the density of solids or liquids is by the use of Archimedes' principle. An experiment in which the density of a solid (aluminum) and of a liquid (kerosene) may be determined is shown in Fig. 17L. A solid

Fig. 17L *The buoyant effect of water may be used as a means of determining the density of solids or liquids.*

aluminum cylinder is weighed with spring scales (a) in air, (b) in water and (c) in kerosene.

Diagram (a) gives directly the mass of the cylinder as 1400 g. When submerged in water the scales indicate a mass of only 880 g. The difference $1400 - 880 = 520$ g multiplied by g is the buoyant force and therefore the weight of the displaced fluid. But since the density of water is equal to 1 g/cm³, 520 g of water will have a volume of 520 cm³. Therefore 520 cm³ is the volume of the cylinder. By Eq. (17a) the density of the aluminum cylinder is

$$\rho = \frac{M}{V} = \frac{1400 \text{ g}}{520 \text{ cm}^3} = 2.7 \frac{\text{g}}{\text{cm}^3}.$$

Submerged in kerosene, the scale shows a weight of 1040 g, indicating a buoyant force equal to the weight of a 360-g mass. Since the cylinder displaces its volume 520 cm³ of liquid, and this liquid has a mass of 360 g, the density of the kerosene is

$$\rho = \frac{M}{V} = \frac{360 \text{ g}}{520 \text{ cm}^3} = 0.69 \frac{\text{g}}{\text{cm}^3}.$$

17.9. Adhesion and Cohesion. All matter is composed of atoms and molecules of one kind or another. As already stated, these ultramicroscopic particles attract each other with forces which depend upon the kinds of atoms or molecules involved and upon the distance between them. The closer two atoms or molecules are together, the greater is the attractive force between them. The attractive force between different kinds of molecules is called *adhesion*, and the attractive force between two like kinds of molecules is called *cohesion*.

Although the force of attraction between two molecules is extremely small, the combined attraction of billions of molecules contained within a very small bit of matter is astonishingly great. A steel cable 1 in. in diameter, for example, will support a maximum load of 25 or more tons without breaking. This is a direct measure of the cohesive forces between hundreds of billions of atoms.

The difference between adhesion and cohesion can be demonstrated by an experiment diagramed in Fig. 17M. A glass plate G is supported

Fig. 17M *Experiment illustrating the forces of adhesion between glass and water.*

by one arm of a beam balance. The plate, after being balanced by weights on the left-hand scale pan, is brought into contact with the surface of water, as shown. Additional weights are next added at F_g until the plate breaks free from the water surface. Upon examining the glass, water is found clinging to the under-surface, showing that the break came between water molecules only. The adhesive forces between glass and

water molecules therefore exceed the cohesive forces between water molecules. The weight added in the experiment is therefore a measure of the cohesive forces among water molecules.

If mercury is substituted for the water in the above experiment and the glass plate pulled away from the mercury surface, the added weights will measure adhesion, the force of attraction between the glass and mercury molecules. This is shown by the fact that no mercury clings to the bottom of the glass plate. Thus the cohesion between the mercury molecules is greater than the adhesion between mercury and glass.

17.10. Surface Tension. The cohesion of molecules gives rise in liquids to a phenomenon called surface tension. According to this aspect of molecular attraction, the surface of a liquid acts at all times as thought it has a thin membrane stretched over it, and this membrane is under tension and trying to contract. It is for this reason that fogdrops, raindrops, soap bubbles, etc., assume a spherical shape as they fall through the air. For any specified volume of matter, a sphere has a smaller surface area than any other geometrical figure.

An experiment designed to illustrate the spheroidal state of a liquid drop is shown below in Fig. 17N. Alcohol and water are poured care-

Fig. 17N *Demonstration of the spheroidal state.*

fully into a glass vessel where they form a separation boundary, the water with its greater density going to the bottom. Olive oil, which is not soluble in either water or alcohol, is then dropped into the liquid. The drops quickly take on a spherical form and, due to their intermediate density, settle slowly to the boundary level where they remain suspended.

Another illustration of surface tension is the

floating needle experiment. A common sewing needle lowered horizontally to the surface of water in an open dish wil be found to float as shown in Fig. 17O. If the needle is first drawn

Fig. 17O   *A steel needle can float on water because of surface tension.*

Fig. 17P   *A simple laboratory experiment for measuring surface tension.*

through the fingers, a thin film of grease is deposited on the surface, making it easier to float. The adhesion between water and grease is very weak.

For the needle to break through the surface, water molecules must be pulled apart. Rather than do this, the surface becomes depressed until the upward buoyant force F is equal in magnitude to F_g, the weight of the needle. Surface tension T keeps the film intact.

An interesting experiment is performed by fastening a bit of soap to the back of a small wooden boat and then placing the boat on the surface of a pond of water. As the soap goes into solution, the surface tension of the water is greatly weakened behind the boat and surface tension in front pulls the boat forward. As soon as a soap film covers the whole of the water surface, the boat will stop.

A similar experiment is to scrape small bits of camphor into a dish of water. Like the boat, each tiny camphor flake is propelled rapidly around on the surface of the water. The camphor, going into solution most rapidly at the pointed end of each flake, reduces surface tension more at that point than at any other.

Surface tension in the laboratory is usually measured by an arrangement illustrated in Fig. 17P. A small wire frame of length *l* is dipped into water and then pulled slowly out. As a result of both cohesion and adhesion, a thin film of water is formed in the frame. This film pulls down by a

force which can be measured by suspending the frame from the arm of a beam balance. Weights are slowly added to the other scale pan (not shown), until the film breaks. The maximum weight added without breaking the film is a direct measure of surface tension, which arises from the cohesive forces of the water molecules.

Surface tension is defined as the force of contraction across a line of unit length, the line and the force being perpendicular to each other, both lying in the plane of the liquid film. If F is the maximum force applied in the above experiment and *l* is the length of the wire frame, the surface tension T is given by

$$T = \frac{F}{2l} \qquad (17\text{k})$$

The factor 2 enters because there are two surfaces to a thin film, thus making the effective length of the surface equal to 2*l*.

TABLE 17C. SURFACE TENSION OF A FEW LIQUIDS

Liquid	0°C	T in N/m 20°C	50°C
acetone	0.0263	0.0237	0.0199
alcohol	0.0240	0.0223	0.0198
benzine	0.0315	0.0289	0.0250
mercury	0.5080	0.4800	0.4450
water	0.0756	0.0727	0.0679

It was Laplace who first proved by a mathematical analysis that the pressure P on the concave side of a single curved surface of radius r is greater than the pressure P' on the convex side by the factor $2T/r$.

$$P - P' = \frac{2T}{r}$$ (171)

The pressure inside a fog particle or raindrop is, therefore, greater than the pressure outside.

Furthermore, the smaller the drop, the smaller is the radius, and the greater is the internal pressure. Due to this large pressure, tiny fogdrops have rigidity properties like those of solids. A good illustration is to be found in the ease with which ice skates slide over the surface of smooth ice. Under the enormous pressures exerted on the ice by the sharp metal edges of the skate, ice melts, and the runners run along on the tiny drops as if they were on ball bearings.

PROBLEMS

1. A solid sphere of iron has a diameter of 20 cm. Find its mass in kilograms.

2. A cylindrical tank 2 m in diameter and 2 m tall is filled with olive oil. Find the mass of the olive oil. [Ans. 5.77×10^3 Kg.]

3. If the Hooke's law constant for the stretching of a spring is 260 N/m, what mass in Kg, suspended from the lower end, will stretch the spring 4.5 cm?

4. A 6-Kg mass suspended from the lower end of a spring, stretches it a distance of 0.12 m. Find the value of Hooke's law constant in N/m. [Ans. 490 N/m.]

5. A steel wire 3 m long and cross-sectional area 0.04 cm² is subjected to a tension of 50 N. Calculate the elongation.

6. A steel wire 5 ft long and cross-sectional area of 0.006 in.² is subjected to a tension of 50 lb. Calculate its elongation. [Ans. 0.0179 in.]

7. A brass wire 1.2 m long and 0.40 mm in diameter hangs from the ceiling. If a mass of 4 Kg is suspended from the lower end, what will be the elongation?

8. Find the elongation of a tendon 4 cm long and 6 mm in diameter if it is put under a tension of 1600 N. Assume Young's modulus to be 1.6×10^{10} N/m². [Ans. 0.141 mm, or 0.000141 m.]

9. An artery has a length of 12 cm and a cross-sectional area of 0.40 cm². Find the elongation under a tension of 60 N.

10. A blood vein has a length of 5 cm and a cross-sectional area of 0.25 cm². Find the elongation under a tension of 85 N. [Ans. 0.20 cm.]

11. A water tank is 4 ft in diameter and 12 ft tall. Find (a) the pressure on the bottom, and (b) the total weight of the water it contains when full.

12. What pressure must a diver withstand when he dives 100 ft deep in the ocean? Assume the specific gravity of sea water to be 1.03. [Ans. 44.6 lb/in².]

13. An iron casting, suspected of having a hole inside due to faulty casting practice, weighs 48.0 lb in air and 41.0 lb when submerged in water. Find the volume of the cavity.

14. A solid brass cylinder weighs 9 lb in air and 8 lb in liquid. Calculate the density of the liquid. [Ans. 58.9 lb/ft³.]

15. A stone on being weighed is found to have a mass of 2.70 Kg in air, 2.2 Kg in water, and 2.4 Kg in oil. Find the density of (a) the stone, and (b) the oil.

16. An aluminum casting is suspected of containing holes due to gas bubbles that formed when the molten metal was poured into the mold. When the casting is weighed in air it is found to have a mass of 3.12 Kg. When weighed in water its mass appears to be 1.60 Kg. Find the volume of the holes. [Ans. 364 cm³.]

17. A solid cylinder 30 cm in diameter and 30 cm high floats in water with its top 6.5 cm above the surface. (a) What is the density of the solid, and (b) what is the mass of the solid?

18. A solid metal casting is found by weighing to have a mass of 7.0 Kg in air, 6.0 Kg in water, and 6.4 Kg in oil. Find (a) the density of the metal, and (b) the density of the oil. [Ans. (a) 7000 Kg/m³, (b) 600 Kg/m³.]

19. A wooden timber 12 in. by 12 in. by 6 ft, floats with half of its volume above the surface. Find the maximum weight this timber can support before sinking.

20. A U-shaped wire having a length of 6.2 cm is lowered into benzine at 0°C. What force is required to break the film that forms as the wire is slowly raised through the surface? [Ans. 3.91×10^{-3} N.]

21. A fogdrop, as seen under a microscope with a micrometer eyepiece, is found to have a diameter of 2×10^{-6} m. Calculate the pressure inside this drop, in atmospheres, if the temperature is 20°C. Assume the air pressure outside the drop is one atmosphere and equal to $1,013 \times 10^5$ N/m².

22. A spherical drop of mercury has a diameter of 5×10^{-4} m. Find the difference in pressure between the inside and the outside if the temperature is 20°C. [Ans. 3840 N/m².]

23. Find the difference in air pressure between the inside and outside of a soap bubble 6 mm in diameter. Assume the surface tension to be 1.6 N/m².

PROPERTIES OF GASES, AND FLUIDS IN MOTION

We on the earth's surface, although little conscious of the fact, are submerged in a great sea of air called the atmosphere. This air, which to the earth is the most common of all gases, is really a mixture of well-known gases: about 77% nitrogen, 21% oxygen, and 1% argon. The remaining 1% includes small quantities of such gases as carbon dioxide, hydrogen, neon, krypton, helium, ozone, and xenon.

Being most dense at sea level (see Fig. 18A),

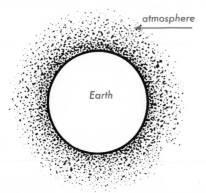

Fig. 18A *Illustration of the air surrounding the earth. The height is exaggerated to bring out the decrease in density with altitude. (If drawn to scale, the earth's atmosphere would form a layer much thinner than the line shown here representing the earth's surface.)*

the atmosphere extends upward to a height of many miles. The air gets thinner and thinner the the higher one goes and finally thins out into interstellar space. Observations show that even interstellar space, which is often referred to as the most perfect vacuum, contains a small but definite amount of matter: several atoms or molecules per cubic centimeter.

18.1. The Earth's Atmosphere. Figure 18B is a schematic cross section of the atmosphere up to a height of 25 miles. It will be noted on the right-hand side of the diagram that 50% of the earth's atmosphere lies below $3\frac{1}{2}$ mi, and that 99% lies below 20 mi. While this accounts for most of the atmosphere, experiments with radio waves show that the small amount of air existing at a height of several hundred miles is sufficient to reflect radio waves back to the earth.

Living as most of us do near sea level, we are constantly subjected to an enormous pressure due to the weight of the air above us. Unbelievable as it may seem, the air exerts a pressure of close to 15 lb for every square inch of surface. This, the atmospheric pressure, is given by the weight of a column of air 1 in.² in cross section and reaching from sea level to the top of the atmosphere.

A pressure of one atmosphere is defined as the average atmospheric pressure at sea level. This is taken to be 14.7 lb/in.², or 101,300 N/m².

18.2. The Density of Air. That air has weight may be shown by one of the simplest of experiments. A hollow brass ball with a volume of 1 liter (1 liter = 1000 cm³) is first weighed when it is filled with air, and again when it is evacuated (see Fig. 18C). With the air removed, the vessel is found to be lighter than before by 1.29 g. If

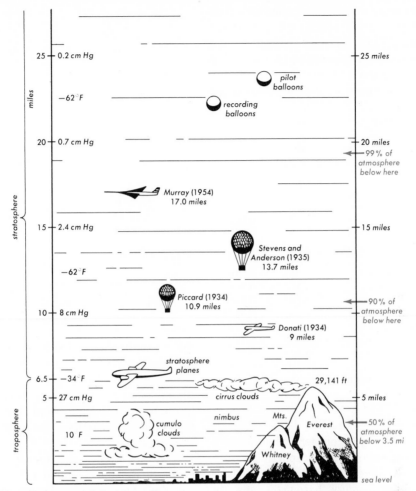

Fig. 18B   *Illustration of important facts concerning the troposphere and the stratosphere and the relative heights reached by man in balloons and airplanes.*

the scales are first balanced with the sphere evacuated, and then the air is allowed to enter, a mass of 1.29 g must be added to the opposite scale pan to restore balance. Since this is the mass of 1000 cm³ of air, the mass of 1 m³ will be 1.29 Kg. This is the density of air.

If the above experiment is repeated at an elevation of 5 mi, the air in the brass vessel will weigh only one third as much as at sea level. The reason for this is that the lower pressure at a height of 5 mi admits only one-third as much air to an evacuated vessel.

If, on the other hand, air is pumped into the hollow sphere, the weight can be made to increase considerably, thus giving a greater than

normal density. The density of a gas is therefore standardized and defined as the mass of 1 m³ of the gas measured at standard pressure and tem-

Fig. 18C   *The weighing of air.*

perature. Standard pressure is defined as a pressure of one atmosphere and is explained in Sec. 18.5. Standard temperature is defined as zero degrees centigrade. The densities of a few common gases are given in Table 18A. The reason for specifying temperature is that gases expand with a rise in temperature. This subject will be treated in Chapter 21 on expansion.

TABLE 18A. DENSITIES OF COMMON GASES

Gas, and chemical symbols		Kg/m^3 or g/liter	$\dfrac{lb}{ft^3}$
Air	N_2, O_2	1.293	0.0800
Ammonia	NH_3	0.771	0.0483
Butane	C_4H_{10}	2.519	0.157
Carbon dioxide	CO_2	1.980	0.124
Carbon monoxide	CO	1.250	0.078
Chlorine	Cl	3.214	0.201
Helium	He	0.180	0.0113
Hydrogen	H_2	0.090	0.0056
Hydrogen bromide	HBr	3.641	0.228
Krypton	Kr	3.708	0.232
Neon	Ne	0.900	0.056
Nitrogen	H_2	1.250	0.078
Nitrous oxide	N_2O	1.978	0.124
Oxygen	O_2	1.430	0.088
Sulfur dioxide	SO_2	2.927	0.183

18.3. The Mercury Barometer. A barometer is a device for measuring the atmospheric pressure. There are in common use today two kinds of barometers—the mercury barometer and the aneroid barometer. The mercury barometer was invented by the Italian physicist, Evangelista Torricelli, some 300 years ago. Torricelli's experiment is illustrated in Fig. 18D. A long glass tube open at one end only, is filled with mercury as shown in diagram (a). With one finger over the open end, the tube is inverted, the open end is immersed in a dish of mercury, and the finger is removed as in diagram (b). At the instant the finger is removed, the mercury level drops in the tube to a height *h* as shown. The mercury drops until the pressure due to its own weight inside the tube (at the level P) is equal to the atmospheric pressure outside.

At sea level the height at which the mercury column stands is about 76 cm or 30 in. This height at any given point, and any given time,

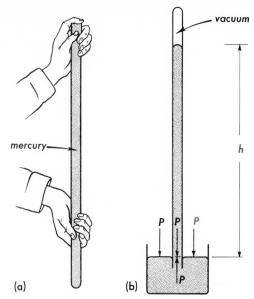

Fig. 18D   *Torricelli's experiment. The making of a mercury barometer.*

will be the same regardless of the diameter of the tube or the length of the vacuum space at the top. Torricelli's experiment shows that a column of air 1 cm² in cross section and reaching to the top of the atmosphere is equal in weight to a column of mercury of the same cross section and 76 cm high.

It was the French philosopher and mathematician, Blaise Pascal, who first showed that when a mercury barometer is taken to a high elevation like the top of a mountain, the height of the mercury column drops considerably. It drops because there is less air above that point and hence a lesser downward pressure on the free mercury surface.

Figure 18E is a diagram of an experiment demonstrating that it is the atmosphere outside of a barometer pushing down on the exposed mercury surface which supports the mercury column inside, and not the vacuum in the space above drawing it up. An entire barometer is placed in a tall cylinder and the air removed by means of a vacuum pump. As the air slowly leaves, the mercury column drops steadily. When the cylinder is well evacuated, the level of the mercury inside the tube is the same as the level in the small reservoir outside. A return of the air

Fig. 18E *Experimental arrangement demonstrating that atmospheric pressure supports the column of mercury in a barometer tube. When the air is removed, the mercury column drops from its normal height.*

ures directly the atmospheric pressure. Instead of specifying the pressure in lb/in.² or in dynes/cm², it is customary to give the height of the mercury column in inches or centimeters. The pressure so expressed in centimeters of Hg (the chemical symbol for mercury is Hg) is given at each 5-mi interval at the left in Fig. 18B.

If a barometer were made to employ water in place of mercury, the barometer tube would have to be at least 13.6 times as high, or 10.34 m. This is equivalent to about 34 ft. Such an instrument would be too cumbersome to be of much practical value.

18.4. The Aneroid Barometer. The desirability of a small portable pressure-measuring instrument has led to the development of the aneroid barometer. This device is frequently used as an altimeter and barometer combined. A cross-sectional diagram of such an instrument is shown in Fig. 18F and photographs are reproduced in Fig. 18G. A small flat metal box, evacuated and with a flexible top, is attached at A to a multiplying system of levers. The end of the lever system is connected to a small cable C which is wrapped around a spindle N, carrying a pointer, I. If the atmospheric pressure P increases, the

forces the mercury back into the tube and up to its original height h.

The height of the mercury in a barometer meas-

Fig. 18F *Schematic diagram and cross section of an aneroid barometer.*

Fig. 18G　(*a*) *Aneroid barometer used for measuring atmospheric pressure.* (*b*) *Self-recording aneroid barometer, or barograph.* (Courtesy, Central Scientific Co.)

flexible boxtop is pushed down at A. This lowers the end of the lever system at B, and with a pivot at D raises the point C. The cable winds up on the spindle N, turning the pointer I to the right to a scale reading of higher pressure. The scale of the aneroid is calibrated by a standard mercury barometer, so the pressure is always given in centimeters or inches of mercury.

Since the atmospheric pressure decreases as one goes to higher altitudes, a barometer is often used to determine elevation. As a matter of fact, aneroid barometers are frequently made with an altitude scale attached. Such instruments, called *altimeters*, are to be found on the instrument panel of every airplane. Some of these instruments are small enough to be carried in the pocket like a watch, and others are so sensitive that they will indicate a change in elevation of 1 ft. The altitude scale usually has its zero mark near the sea-level pressure as shown in Fig. 18F.

18.5. Standard Atmospheric Pressure. Standard atmospheric pressure is defined as the pressure equivalent to a column of mercury 76 cm high when the temperature is 0°C. This is equivalent to 29.92 in. of mercury at 32°F. Standard atmospheric pressure is equivalent to 14.7 lb/in.² The approximate value of 15 lb/in.² is frequently quoted and used.

To calculate the equivalent pressure in newtons per square meter, multiply by the density of mercury and the acceleration of gravity (see Table 17A).

$$0.76 \text{ m} \times 13{,}600 \text{ Kg/m}^3 \times 9.8 \text{ m/s}^2$$

$$1 \text{ atm} = 1.013 \times 10^5 \text{ N/m}^2$$
$$1 \text{ atm} = 1.013 \times 10^6 \text{ dynes/cm}^2$$

It is common practice in meteorology to measure atmospheric pressure in bars and millibars.

$$1 \text{ bar} = 100{,}000 \text{ N/m}^2$$
$$1 \text{ millibar} = 100 \text{ N/m}^2$$

On this basis,

$$1 \text{ atm} = 1.013 \text{ bars} = 1013 \text{ millibars}$$

The United States Weather Bureau obtains daily records of the barometric pressure from hundreds of weather stations over the country. These records are obtained automatically at each station by means of a specially designed aneroid like the one shown in Fig. 18G(b). A pen or stylus from the barometer itself moves up and down on a slowly rotating drum, thus recording the pressure at every instant. These records are then compiled by the United States Weather Bureau, and maps are published daily of the equal pressure areas over the country (see Fig. 18H).

18.6. Experiments Illustrating Atmospheric Pressure. Normal atmospheric pressure of 14.7 lb/in.² does not ordinarily impress a person as being very great. Taken over a considerable area, however, such a pressure gives rise to a tremendous force. Consider the evacuated glass picture tube of the average home TV receiver. The circular face of a tube 21-in. diameter has an area of 360 in.², and hence withstands a total inward force of 360 × 14.7 or 5,290 lb. The glass walls

warm front
cold front
occluded front
stationary front
precipitation

Fig. 18H *Typical daily U. S. weather map showing barometric pressures, warm and cold air fronts, and precipitation.*

can withstand this because the force is distributed uniformly over the whole surface. If it were all applied at one small point, the tube would surely break. A spherical or cylindrical vessel can have thin walls and yet stand enormous pressures whereas a vessel with flat sides may not. It is for this reason that all large vessels used for storing liquids or gases have curved walls instead of flat ones.

An experiment illustrating atmospheric pressure is diagramed in Fig. 18I. In diagram (a) a

Fig. 18I *Experiments illustrating the magnitude of atmospheric pressure.*

thin sheet of rubber is first tied over the top end of a jar. When this is done, the air pressure inside is the same as that outside. If now the inside force, upward on the rubber, is removed by means of a vacuum pump, the outside force

pushes the rubber down inside as shown in diagram (b).

The principles of breathing in the human body are demonstrated in Fig. 18J. Muscular con-

Fig. 18J *Experimental demonstration of the principles of breathing by the human body.*

traction in pulling down on the *diaphragm* creates a low pressure around the lungs and atmospheric pressure pushes air into the lungs. Retraction of the diaphragm raises the pressure and compresses the lungs, forcing air and carbon dioxide out.

In the year 1654, Otto von Guericke* performed before the Emperor Ferdinand III, at Regensburg, the celebrated experiment of the "Magdeburg hemispheres." Two copper hemispheres, about 22 in. in diameter, were placed together to form a sphere as shown in Fig. 18K.

Fig. 18K   *The Magdeburg hemisphere designed by Otto von Guericke.*

A ring of leather soaked in oil and wax was set between them to make an airtight joint. When the sphere was evacuated, two teams, consisting of eight horses each, were unable to pull the hemispheres apart. This is not to be wondered at, for the force required to pull them apart is easily calculated; it amounts to nearly three tons.

18.7. Fluids in Motion. The term fluid applies to any substance capable of flowing and includes gases as well as liquids. Since all fluids have mass, Newton's second law of motion implies that unbalanced forces are required to set them in motion. As a matter of practical interest, we shall consider the various means by which such forces are obtained, how they are applied to fluids, and what factors control the resultant motion. In these discussions the student would do well to keep in mind the fact that liquids are practically incompressible.

* Otto von Guericke (1602–1686), German philosopher, lawyer, physicist, and magistrate. Incited by the discoveries of Galileo, Pascal, and Torricelli, he produced the first vacuum and made the first air pump. From researches in astronomy he predicted the periodic return of comets.

Many city water supply systems store water in reservoirs on some hilltop or in a nearby water tower and from these sources run the water through pipes into houses, stores, and factories in and around the city. Such an arrangement is called a "gravity system."

When a hole is opened in the side of a vessel containing a liquid, the velocity of flow through the orifice increases with depth. Here the unbalanced force setting the liquid in motion is gravity acting through the liquid as pressure. We have already seen how the pressure at any given depth is given by $P = h\rho g$ and is the same in all directions. At a depth h_1 (see Fig. 18L), the liquid

Fig. 18L   *The velocity of efflux through a hole in the side of a vessel of water increases with depth.*

exerts a pressure P_1 against the walls, and the walls exert an equal and opposite pressure against the liquid.

The instant an opening is made in the side of the vessel, the wall pressure is destroyed at that point and the liquid pressure inside pushes the liquid directly in front of the hole, giving it an acceleration outward and normal to the plane of the opening. To find the velocity of escape, consider the potential energy of the liquid body in the vessel when the hole is first opened and then a short time later when a small amount of liquid has escaped, dropping the surface level a distance t.

As far as energy is concerned, the change is the same as though the top layer of water had fallen a distance h_1 and its potential energy mgh_1 converted into kinetic energy $\frac{1}{2}mv_1^2$ as it becomes the emerging stream. By conservation of energy,

$$mgh_1 = \tfrac{1}{2}mv_1^2 \qquad (18a)$$

Since m is the same on both sides, one may divide by m, and solve for v to give

$$v = \sqrt{2gh_1} \qquad (18b)$$

the same as the law of falling bodies. In other words, the velocity of efflux at any depth, h, is

proof of this will be left as a problem for the student.

18.8. Flow Through a Pipe. One of the factors determining the flow of water, oil, or gas through a pipe, or the flow of blood through the arteries and veins of the body is the resistance to flow offered by the confining walls. Consider the experiment shown in Fig. 18M in which water from a vertical tank at the left is made to flow through a horizontal glass tube at the bottom. The pres-

Fig. 18M *Flow of water through a pipe showing the velocity head h_v, the friction head h_f, and the pressure head h_p.*

equivalent to the velocity acquired by free fall from the same height. This relation, first discovered by Torricelli,* is known as Torricelli's theorem.

It is interesting to note that the parabolic path followed by an emerging stream of liquid is such that the greatest horizontal range R (see diagram) is obtained from an orifice midway between any base level and the top surface of the liquid and that holes equidistant above and below this point have lesser but equal ranges. The

* Evangelista Torricelli (1608–1647). An Italian physicist and mathematician and disciple of Galileo. He is most noted for his scientific articles on fluid motion, on the theory of projectiles, and on geometrical optics.

sure at five equally spaced points along the tube is measured by vertical standpipes, and the velocity of flow is controlled by the valve at the right. By means of a "water supply" and "over-flow" pipe, the water level in the tank is maintained at a constant level, thus assuring a constant pressure and hence a steady flow.

With the valve closed, the water "seeking its own level" soon brings all standpipes to the same level, sr. Their heights thereby indicate equal pressures at all points along the pipe from A to E. When the valve is partially opened and a steady flow is attained, the water in each pipe drops to different levels similar to those shown. The more the valve is opened, the more rapid is the flow and the steeper is the straight line abcde.

Since at all times the heights of columns aA, bB, cC, dD, and eE measure the pressures at the points A, B, C, D, and E respectively, the straight line ae indicates a smooth and uniform drop in pressure all along the pipe from A to E. Such a drop in pressure, designated h_f in the figure, is due to *fluid friction* in the pipe and is called the *friction head*. By measuring the friction head for different rates of flow, a comparison of the results will show that h_f is proportional to the square of the velocity. This may be expressed as an equation:

$$h_f = Kv^2 \qquad (18c)$$

where K is the proportionality constant.

The pronounced drop in level from s in the tank to a in the first standpipe measures the drop in pressure at A where the water is practically at rest in the tank and is then speeded up to a velocity v upon entering the pipe. Just as in Torricelli's theorem, the drop in potential energy from s to a

is converted into kinetic energy in the stream, and by Eqs.(18a) or (18b),

$$h_v = v^2/2g \qquad (18d)$$

Here h_v equals sa and is the *velocity head*.

The final pressure at the point E, where the water is being drawn from the pipe is directly measured by the height of the liquid column eE, and is called the *pressure head*, h_p. Thus, with a total pressure, h available at the tank, there is first a velocity-head drop of h_v, and then a friction-head drop h_f, giving as the final pressure $h_p = h - h_v - h_f$. For all points along a uniform pipe, the velocity head is constant while the friction head increases proportionally with the distance from the source.

The above equations also apply to the flow of gas through a pipe provided that the pressure is relatively small. If the pressure is large, the formulas must be modified to allow for the compressibility of the gas.

18.9. Bernoulli's Principle. When a river runs through broad open country, the water runs slowly, but when it comes to a narrow rocky

Fig. 18N   *Where the velocity of a fluid increases, the pressure drops; and where the velocity of a fluid decreases, the pressure rises.*

gorge its velocity increases many fold. Similarly, when a gas or liquid flowing through a pipe comes to a narrow constricted section, the velocity increases as it enters the constriction and decreases again as it leaves the other end. This is illustrated by an experiment diagramed in Fig. 18N.

The arrangement is the same as in Fig. 18M except that the horizontal flow pipe contains a short section DE having only half the cross-sectional areas as elsewhere. When the valve is opened and a condition of steady flow exists, the water in the standpipes will have dropped from sr to new levels like a, b, d, etc., as shown. It is to be noted that, as the water enters the con-

striction at C, the velocity of flow increases and the pressure drops from c to l. Farther along where it leaves the narrow tube at F, the velocity decreases and the pressure rises from f to k.

This illustrates Bernoulli's principle which may be stated as follows: "where the velocity of a fluid is high the pressure is low, and where the velocity of a fluid is low the pressure is high." The drops in pressure from a to b, d to e, and g to h represent friction heads for the pipe sections AB, DE, and GH, respectively. The drop from s to a gives directly the velocity head $v_1^2/2g$ for the pipe sections, AB and GH, and to this must be added the drop from c to l to obtain the velocity head $v_2^2/2g$ for the narrow pipe section, DE. The simplest of laboratory measurements confirm the result that narrowing the tube to half the cross section doubles the velocity and quadruples the velocity head.

18.10. Experiments Illustrating Bernoulli's Principle. Bernoulli's principle is often referred to as a physical paradox and is the basis of many interesting phenomena. Seven experiments involving this principle are diagramed in Fig. 18O. In the first illustration (a) a blast of air from a nozzle is blown between two sheets of cardboard suspended about 3 in. apart by cords. Instead of being blown apart, as one might expect, they come together. The reason for this action is that between the two sheets where the velocity of the air is high the pressure p_2 is low. On the two outside surfaces where the air is not moving, the pressure p_1 (atmospheric pressure) is high and pushes the two sheets together.

In the second diagram (b) air is blown through a hole in the center of a disk AB as shown. When a piece of paper CD is placed close to the opening, it is not blown away but is drawn toward the disk. Where the velocity of air between the disk and paper is high, the pressure is low, and the higher pressure p_1 on the underside of the paper pushes it up against the disk.

One often hears it said that, during a certain wind storm, tornado, or hurricane, the roofs of one or more houses were blown off without otherwise damaging the house. This is not as freakish an accident as one might think, for there is a simple explanation. A high wind blowing

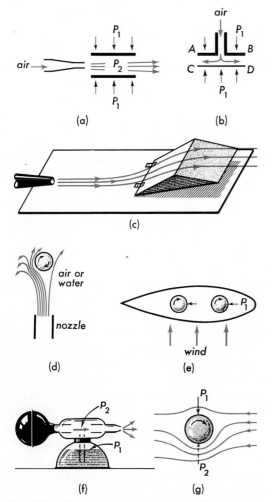

Fig. 18O *Demonstrations of Bernoulli's principle.*

over the roof, as shown in Fig. 18O(c), creates a low pressure p_2 on top, and the atmospheric pressure p_1 inside, where the wind is not blowing, lifts the roof off.

If a small "ping-pong" ball is placed in a vertical stream of air or water, it will rise to a given height above the nozzle and stay at that level, spinning and bobbing around without falling. If the ball goes to one side as illustrated in diagram (d), the fluid going by on the left side causes the ball to spin as shown. Since the velocity is high on the left there is a low pressure. The higher pressure on the right where the velocity is low pushes the ball back into the stream.

The same principle has been applied to the historical *Flettner rotor ship* which, instead of using sails, employed two tall rotating cylinders, motor-driven. As shown by the top view diagram (e), a wind from broadside the ship produces a forward force. Such a ship, carrying a cargo, crossed the Atlantic twice not many years ago. Although the trips were successful, the uncertainty of a strong wind makes shipping with such boats unreliable.

The sixth diagram (f) represents a common form of perfume atomizer. Squeezing the bulb sends a stream of air through the central tube, which creates a low pressure p_2 inside. The atmospheric pressure p_1 on the liquid surface pushes the liquid up the stem to be blown out the right-hand tube with the air stream.

Most of the baseballs thrown by a pitcher are curves, some up or down, and others in or out, i.e., to right or left. This is an art, accomplished by throwing the ball so that it spins rapidly about some particular axis. To produce a downward curve, i.e., a *drop ball*, the ball is given a top spin as shown in diagram (g). Here, instead of having the ball moving to the right, we can imagine the ball standing still, but spinning, and the air to be moving from right to left. At the top surface where the wind and ball are moving in opposite directions, the air is slowed down by friction, giving rise to a high-pressure region. On the underside the surface moving with the wind keeps the velocity high, thus creating a low-pressure region. The resultant downward force

thus causes the ball to drop faster than usual.

18.11. Blood Circulation in the Human Body. It has been estimated that the circulation of blood through the human body involves a vessel system containing several thousand arteries and veins and well over one billion capillaries. Any attempt to analyze the mechanical principles involved in circulation, therefore, must of necessity simplify the problem in one way or another. While this has been done successfully by numerous research studies, only the most elementary considerations can be presented here.

A schematic diagram of the circulation is given in Fig. 18P, and shows a combination of series and parallel paths between the *left ventricle* where the blood leaves the heart and the right *atrium* where it enters again. The pulsating heart is a force pump that contains two chambers, the right and left ventricles, joined into a single unit and pumping in synchronism. During the compression stroke of the heart, called *systole*, the blood in the *right ventricle* is forced out through the valve above into the lungs, while the blood in the left ventricle is forced into the *aorta*. During the filling stroke, called *diastole*, blood from the veins and right atrium enters the right ventricle while blood from the lungs enters the left atrium and left ventricle.

The entrance and exit valves of the right and left ventricles consist of two to three flaps or leaves attached to the edge of each opening and meeting at the center. These cusps are free to move apart when the flow is in one direction, but are forced together and thus close the opening when the flow attempts to reverse.

Upon leaving the largest artery, the aorta, the blood enters the main arteries leading to all parts of the body. After branching into smaller *arterioles*, and then into the numerous small capillaries, the blood emerges into the many small venous branches, the *venules*, and finally into the large veins where it is returned to the heart.

While passing through the capillaries of the lungs the red corpuscles in the blood stream take in oxygen by diffusion, while upon passing through the capillaries in other parts of the body, they give it up and acquire carbon dioxide by

head

arms

lungs

aorta

la   ra
                v

heart   lv   rv

spleen   P liver
   r   c   n

intestines
kidney

trunk

legs   v
            v

~ 27 in.

~ 45 in.

arteries

veins

ra - right atrium
rv - right ventricle
la - left atrium
lv - left ventricle
p - pericardium
v - valves
a - aorta
r - arterioles
c - capillaries
n - venules

Fig. 18P   *Schematic diagram of blood circulation, showing the series and parallel circuits between the large systemic arteries and the large veins.*

diffusion through the cell walls. The tubular capillaries in man are about 8 microns in diameter and the red blood cells average 7.5 microns (1 micron = 10^{-4} cm).

During systole the maximum pressure reached in the aorta (called *systolic pressure*) is about 120 mm, while during diastole the pressure (called *diastolic pressure*) drops to about 80 mm. Both of these extreme pressures vary considerably with the health and age of the individual.

In considering variations in blood pressure throughout the entire circulation system, it should be kept in mind that all vessels are semi-elastic tubes instead of rigid pipes. The two principal functions of this elasticity are (1) to smooth out the pulsating outflow from the heart into a more steady flow through the arteries and capillaries, and (2) to allow contraction by muscles, thus diverting blood through some channels in preference to others when conditions require it.

As the blood is forced out of the heart, the aortic wall expands under the pressure, and part of the energy of the ejected blood is stored momentarily as potential energy in the distended wall. This distension travels along the aortic wall and arteries as a kind of transverse wave.

As the wave passes by, the stored potential energy is returned to the blood, thereby smoothing out the flow.

A patient's blood pressure is generally measured at the same horizontal level as the heart by means of a thin-walled rubber tube wrapped around the upper arm. As air is pumped in, the expansion of the tube squeezes the arm until the *brachial artery* is collapsed. The pressure of the air in the tube is then measured with an attached U-tube mercury manometer or a Bourdon gauge. When the air pressure in the tube is slowly reduced by means of an escape valve, a point will be reached (about 110 to 120 mm) where small pressure pulses due to the heart action may be observed on the gauge. The gauge reading is then taken to be the systolic blood pressure.

The effect of gravity on venous pressure in different parts of the body differs markedly between *prone*, *sitting*, and *standing positions*. Pressure in the arteries varies too, but not to so great a degree, for muscular action partially compensates for hydrostatic pressure differences. Laboratory experiments on blood pressure measured with the body in the prone position have resulted in the pressure curve shown in Fig. 18Q. The

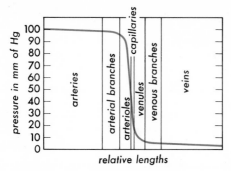

Fig. 18Q *Blood-pressure curve for the average human body in a prone position. (Lengths of capillaries greatly exaggerated.)*

very small pressure drop through the arteries and veins as compared with the long drop through the capillaries is readily understood from the relative diameters, as may be seen from the following tabulated data.

Note the enormous cross section of a large vein or artery as compared with a capillary. Maximum flow velocity in the aorta may reach as high as 40 cm/s.

When the body is upright, the variations in blood pressure with height above or below the heart level are quite appreciable. First of all, the pressure developed by the heart must be sufficient to pump blood to the top of the head, overcoming gravity as well as friction. Gravity alone is sufficient to return the blood through the veins. The vessels leading to the lower extremities and back again are like an inverted siphon.

The pressure gained in the arteries leading to the feet is transmitted through the capillaries to the veins where it is used to raise the blood again to the heart level.

Example 1. What minimum pressure is required to force blood from the heart to the top of the head

if the vertical distance is 27 in.? Assume the density of blood to be 1.04 g/cm³, and neglect friction.

Solution. The pressure will be equivalent to the weight of a column of liquid 27 in. in height. Changing inches to centimeters gives

$$27 \times 2.54 \times 1.04 = 71.3 \text{ g/cm}^2$$

Divide by the density of mercury to convert this to an equivalent mercury column.

$$\frac{71.3}{13.6} = 5.24 \text{ cm} = 52.4 \text{ mm}$$

The following observation will demonstrate the wide variation in blood pressure with elevation above or below the heart. With the hand

TABLE 18B. BLOOD CIRCULATION IN THE HUMAN BODY

	Number	Diameter, mm	Length, cm
Aorta and large arteries	40	3–10	40–20
Arterial branches	2400	0.6–1.0	1–10
Arterioles	40,000,000	0.02	0.2
Capillaries	1,200,000,000	0.008	0.1
Venules	80,000,000	0.03	0.2
Venous branches	24,000	1.5–2.4	1–10
Vena cava and large veins	40	6–12	40–20

held palm down at waist level, observe the bulging of the veins on the back of the hand. Now slowly raise the hand higher and higher and notice carefully the height at which the bulges disappear. At this height the pressure in the veins has become zero at the hand level and, due to gravity, the blood flows downward through the arm to the heart.

PROBLEMS

1. If a barometer contains water in place of mercury, how high will the water column be (a) at sea level, and (b) at an altitude of 15 mi?

2. A jet airplane maintains standard atmospheric pressure inside the cabin when flying at an altitude of 5 mi. If a mercury barometer were exposed to the air

pressure outside, what would be the mercury column height, *h*? [*Ans.* 27 cm.]

3. Magdeburg hemispheres with an internal diameter of 8 cm are put together and thoroughly evacuated. What minimum force will pull them apart at (a) sea level, and (b) 5-mi elevation?

4. Magdeburg hemispheres 0.16 m in diameter are thoroughly evacuated. Calculate the minimum force required to pull them apart (a) at sea level, and (b) at an altitude of 5 mi. [Ans. (a) 2036 N, (b) 723 N.]

5. The original Magdeburg hemispheres had an internal diameter of 22 in. Find the force in lb required to pull them apart if they were highly evacuated. Assume the atmospheric pressure to be 14.7 lb/in.^{2}

6. A circular screen of a television tube is 24 in. in diameter. With the tube thoroughly evacuated and with standard atmospheric pressure outside, what is the total inward force on the screen? Assume the screen to be flat and standard atmospheric to be 14.7 lb/in.^{2} [Ans. 6650 lb.]

7. If a jet airplane maintains standard atmospheric pressure inside the cabin when flying at an altitude of 5 mi, Fig. 18B, what would be the total outward force on a window having an area of 2 ft^2? Assume standard atmospheric pressure to be 14.7 lb/in.^{2}

8. One Magdeburg hemisphere 20 in. in diameter has a thick glass plate placed over the opening and then evacuated. Calculate the total inward force on the glass plate. [Ans. 4620 lb.]

9. If a cylindrical tin can 8 cm in diameter and 12 cm tall were thoroughly evacuated, what would be the force on each end?

10. A cylindrical pipe 14 in. in diameter has flat brass plates clamped on the ends. If the pipe is thoroughly evacuated, find the total inward force exerted by the outside air on each plate. [Ans. 2260 lb.]

11. At what speed will alcohol emerge from a hole in the side of a tank if the hole is 4 m below the liquid surface?

12. A pipe enters a water tank at a point 12 ft below the surface of the contained water. What is the water pressure in this pipe? [Ans. 5.2 lb/in.^{2}]

13. A cylindrical tank 8 m high and full of water develops a hole in its side 2 m below the top. How far from the base of the tank will the emerging water strike the ground?

14. At what speed will the velocity head of a stream of water be equal to 32 cm of mercury? [Ans. 9.24 m/s.]

15. Assuming the blood in a large artery to have a velocity of 46 cm/s, what pressure drop is attributed to the velocity head? Express your answer in millimeters of mercury.

16. Assuming the aorta to be a rigid pipe 1.2 cm in diameter, how much blood would be pumped through the heart with each pulse? Assume a pulse rate of 60 per min and an average velocity of flow through the aorta of 25 cm/sec. [Ans. 28.2 cm^3.]

17. Water flowing with a velocity of 3 m/s in a 4-cm-diameter pipe enters a short section having a diameter of only 2 cm and then a section having a diameter of 8 cm. Calculate (a) the velocity in the last two pipes, and (b) the velocity head in all three.

18. Water flowing in a 3-in. pipe at the rate of 4 ft/s comes to a small 1-in. pipe, and then a 2-in. pipe. Find (a) the velocity in the last two pipes, and (b) the velocity head in all three pipes. [Ans. (a) 36 ft/s, and 9 ft/s, (b) 3 in., 20.2 ft, 1.27 ft.]

19. A water tank is located on a platform 6 m above the ground. If the water is 4 m deep at the time that a hole develops in the side of the tank 1.5 m from the bottom, how far away from the platform and tank will the escaping stream of water strike the ground?

20. A pressure gauge on a pipe leading from the bottom of a water tank indicates a pressure of 25 lb/in.^{2} When a valve in the pipe is opened to let water flow out, the gauge pressure drops to 20 lb/in.^{2} Find the speed of the water in the pipe. [Ans. 27.1 ft/s.]

21. If the internal diameter of a water pipe is 2 in., and 20 ft^3 of water flow through in 2 min, what is (a) the velocity, and (b) the velocity head?

22. A gauge on a water pipe shows a pressure of 50 lb/in.^{2} When a valve is opened, the gauge reading drops to 40 lb/in.^{2} (a) What is the water velocity? (b) How long will it take for 2 ft^3 of water to flow out if the internal pipe diameter at the gauge is 1 in.? [Ans. (a) 38.4 ft/s. (b) 9.55 s.]

TEMPERATURE, SPECIFIC HEAT, AND THERMAL EXPANSION

The first authentic record of a thermometer dates back to the time of Galileo. Galileo's thermometer, as illustrated in Fig. 19A, consists of a

Fig. 19A *Air on heating expands and pushes the water down in the tube. On cooling, the air contracts and the water rises.*

narrow glass tube with an opening at one end and a bulb at the other. The open end of the tube is filled with colored water and inverted in a dish of water. When the temperature of the surrounding air rises, the air within the bulb expands, forcing the water down the tube. If the bulb is cooled, the air inside contracts, drawing the water up. To be exact, atmospheric pressure outside pushes the water up. A scale attached to the narrow tube can be calibrated to any temperature scale, low temperatures at the top and high temperatures at the bottom.

Of the many forms of temperature-measuring devices, the mercury thermometer is the most common. A mercury thermometer, as shown in Fig. 19B, consists of a narrow glass tube (called a capillary), the bottom end sealed to a small bulb and the top end closed. The bulb and part of the capillary are filled with mercury, and the remaining section is evacuated. When the temperature rises, the mercury and the glass bulb both expand. The mercury, however, expands more than the glass, forcing a small part of the mercury up the narrow capillary. A scale is engraved on the glass to read temperature.

19.1. Temperature Scales. There are in general use today four different temperature scales. These are the Fahrenheit, Rankine, Centigrade, and Kelvin or Absolute. Each scale is shown by a diagram in Fig. 19C. The thermometers are all identically made but each has a different scale. In the United States, the Fahrenheit scale is commonly used in civil life, and the Rankine scale

Fig. 19B *On heating a thermometer, the mercury expands more than the glass tube and the mercury level rises.*

is used by engineers. The Centigrade and Kelvin scales are used in all countries for scientific measurements.

Most of the manufactured thermometers are calibrated to one of these four scales. To calibrate a thermometer, the bulb is first placed in a mixture of ice and water, and the height of the mercury column marked on the side of the stem.

It is next placed in steam just above boiling water and again marked. These two marks then determine two points for whatever scale is to be used.

The lowest temperature ever reached is approximately −273.16°C, or −459.69°F. For theoretical reasons, this is the lowest temperature that can ever be attained. The Kelvin and Rankine scales start with the lowest possible temperature as *absolute zero*. On the basis of the Centigrade and Farenheit scale divisions, this locates the freezing point of water, to the nearest whole number, at 273°K or 492°R, and the boiling point at 373°K or 672°R.

A more detailed diagram of the two absolute temperature scales in common use is given in Fig. 19D. The zero point of both these scales is called *absolute zero* and represents the temperature at which all molecular motion ceases. While all molecular motion is said to cease at absolute zero, the atoms of which some substances are composed would still have inherent motions that cannot be eliminated.

On the Kelvin scale, water boils at 373°K and ice melts at 273°K. Air becomes a liquid at 82°K and a solid at 61°K. Hydrogen gas becomes a liquid at 20°K and freezes at 14°K. Helium liquefies at 4°K.

Between the temperatures of melting ice and

Fig. 19C *Mercury thermometers illustrating the four common temperature scales.*

boiling water there are 180° on the Fahrenheit and Rankine scales, as compared with 100° on the Centigrade and Kelvin scales. The ratio of these numbers is 9:5. This comparison shows that a temperature rise of 9°F, or 9°R, is equivalent to a rise of only 5°C, or 5°K.

Fig. 19D   *Rankine and Kelvin, or Absolute, temperature scales.*

It is frequently necessary to change temperature readings from one temperature scale to another. Rather than develop formulas for such changes, it is more convenient to work out the simple mathematical steps by the inspection of a diagram like Fig. 19C.

19.2. Electrical Thermometers. If very low or very high temperatures are to be measured, other than mercury thermometers must be employed. At temperatures below −39°C, mercury freezes

and becomes a solid; at high temperatures, glass melts and becomes a liquid. For both of these temperature extremes, electrical thermometers are commonly used. These instruments operate upon the principle that the resistance a wire offers to a flow of electric current through it changes with temperature. The higher the temperature, the greater is the resistance.

A diagram of an electrical thermometer is shown in Fig. 19E. A fine piece of platinum wire

Fig. 19E   *Electrical-resistance thermometer showing connections between the platinum wire coil, the battery, and the ammeter.*

is wound around a small spool made of silica. The ends of this wire are connected to a battery and an ammeter. The purpose of the battery is to supply the electric current, and the ammeter is used to determine its exact value. When the temperature of a hot body like a furnace is to be measured, the spool of platinum wire is placed inside the furnace and the battery and ammeter outside. A rise in temperature causes the resistance of the platinum wire to increase, and the current, therefore, to decrease. When the platinum wire reaches the temperature of the furnace, its resistance reaches a constant value and the ammeter pointer indicates a steady current. In many cases the ammeter scale is calibrated to give the temperature directly in degrees.

Another form of electrical temperature-measuring device, called a *thermocouple*, is illustrated in Fig. 19F. This device is based upon a principle, discovered in 1821 by Seebeck, known as the *thermoelectric effect*. Two pieces of wire, one copper and one iron, are joined together at the ends to form a complete loop. When one junction is heated and the other kept cool, an electric current flows around the loop in the direction indicated by the arrows. The greater the differ-

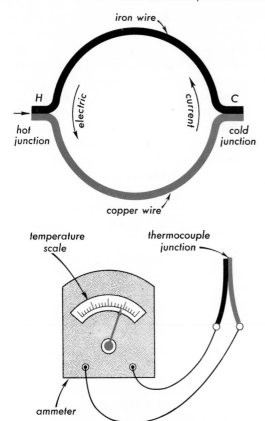

scale readings of the ammeter can be marked 0°C and 100°C at the appropriate points. These determine the scale of the instrument, making of it a direct-reading thermometer.

Thermocouples are not always made of copper and iron as shown in Fig. 19F. Any two different metals when brought into contact will exhibit a thermoelectric effect. Some combinations of two metals, however, produce larger currents than others. For very high temperature measurements, platinum and platinum–iridium alloys are used, owing to their very high melting-point temperatures.

A set of thermocouples, when connected as shown in Fig. 19G, form what is commonly called a *thermopile*. Small rods of two different metals are joined alternately as shown in diagram (b). One set of junctions is usually protected by placing them at the back of a small box container, and the other set is exposed to heat rays through the opposite side which is left open. A funnel or horn-shaped reflector mounted over the open side will collect more heat rays from a distant hot object and thereby increases the electric current. Thermocouples containing several hundred elements can be made so sensitive that they will detect the heat of a candle flame several hundred feet away.

Fig. 19F *Above, a thermocouple. Below, a thermocouple thermometer circuit diagram.*

ence in temperature between the two junctions, the greater is the electric current.

Figure 19F (below) represents a thermocouple connected by wires to an ammeter. If the junction of the thermocouple is first placed in melting ice and then in boiling water, the two

19.3. Specific Heat. According to the kinetic theory of matter, the individual atoms of which all substances are made are in a state of rapid motion. As a body is heated to a higher temperature this atomic motion increases and the body expands. As a body cools, the atomic motions decrease and the body shrinks. That heat

Fig. 19G *Cross section of a thermopile for measuring heat radiation from hot bodies.*

is a form of energy and is due to the kinetic energy of molecular motion was first proposed by Count Rumford in the latter part of the 18th century.*

It is not always clear to the beginning student that the temperature and the quantity of heat are different entities. The difference between the two can be illustrated by the heating of two pans of water. More gas must be burned to heat a large pan of water than a small pan. Although both are started at the same temperature and both are raised to the same boiling point, 100°C, the larger pan has required more thermal energy, called heat.

(a)

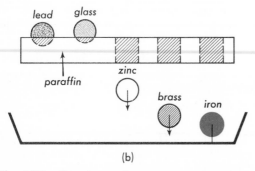

(b)

Fig. 19H *Experiment demonstrating the different heat capacities of different substances of the same size.*

The difference between the temperature and quantity of heat is well illustrated by the following experiment (see Fig. 19H). Five marbles, all of the same size but made of different materials,

are heated in boiling water to a temperature of 100°C. At a given instant they are all placed on a sheet of paraffin about 0.5 cm thick and permitted to melt their way through. The iron and brass marbles are observed to drop through first, but the lead and glass marbles never do. This illustrates the fact that the heat content of the iron and brass, even though raised to the same temperature as the others, is considerably greater than the heat content of the glass and lead.

In order to determine the exact heat capacity of a substance, we must first define the *kilocalorie, calorie* and the *British thermal unit.*

The amount of heat required to raise 1 Kg of water 1C° is called a kilocalorie (Kcal, or Cal).

The amount of heat required to raise the temperature of 1 g of water 1C° is called the calorie (cal).

The quantity of heat required to raise the temperature of 1 lb of water 1F° is called the British thermal unit (Btu.)

The ratio between units is readily computed and found to be

$$1 \text{ Kcal} = 1000 \text{ cal}$$
$$1 \text{ Btu} = 0.252 \text{ Kcal}$$
$$1 \text{ Btu} = 252 \text{ cal} \qquad (19a)$$

Once the kilocalorie of the Btu is defined, the amount of heat required to raise any amount of water from one temperature to another may be calculated by simply multiplying the mass of water by the temperature rise. For example, to raise the temperature of 25 Kg of water from 10°C to 50°C requires $25 \times 40 = 1000$ Kcal, or to raise the temperature of 6 lb of water from 32°F to 60°F requires $6 \times 28 = 168$ Btu.

While 1 Kcal of heat will raise the temperature of 1 Kg of water 1C°, a different number of Kcal will be required to raise the temperature of 1 Kg of some other substance 1C°. For example, to raise the temperature of 1 Kg of iron 1C° requires only $\frac{1}{10}$ of a Kcal, while to raise 1 Kg of lead 1C° requires only $\frac{1}{30}$ of a Kcal. In other words, the thermal capacities of equal masses of different materials have different values.

The thermal capacity of a substance is defined as the number of kilocalories required to raise the temperature of 1 Kg of that substance through

$1C°$, or the amount of heat to raise the temperature of 1 lb $1F°$.

The ratio between the thermal capacity of a substance and the thermal capacity of water is called specific heat.

Numerically, specific heat has the same value as thermal capacity; being a ratio, however, it is like *specific gravity* and has no units.

The specific heats or thermal capacities of a few common substances are given in the following table.

TABLE 19A. SPECIFIC HEATS, OR
THERMAL CAPACITIES IN KCAL/KG C°

Material	c
Aluminum	0.220
Brass	0.092
Copper	0.093
Glass	0.160
Gold	0.031
Glycerine	0.60
Ice	0.50
Iron	0.105
Lead	0.031
Mercury	0.033
Silver	0.056
Zinc	0.092
Steam	0.50
Water	1.000

To illustrate the use of this table, consider the calculation of the heat content of the marbles used in the above experiment. The measured mass of each marble is given in the second row of the following tabulation and the corresponding thermal capacity or specific heat in the next row. The product of these two quantities gives the values shown in the third row; they represent the amount of heat in Kcal required to raise that marble $1C°$. Since all marbles were raised from room temperature 20°C to the boiling point of water, 100°C, the values in the third row have been multiplied by the rise in temperature $80C°$ to obtain the total heat values in the last row.

These numbers clearly indicate that, in the experiment above, iron and brass should melt through the paraffin first: they have available within them the largest amounts of stored thermal energy, 0.235 and 0.221 Kcal, respectively.

The definition of thermal capacity and the calculation of total heat content may be summarized by a generally useful formula of the following form:

$$H = m \times c \times \Delta t \qquad (19b)$$

H represents the total amount of heat in Kcal, m the mass of the body in Kg, c the thermal capacity in Kcal/Kg C° and Δt the rise in temperature in C°.

19.4. Change of State. The continuous addition of heat to a solid or liquid mass will eventually bring about a change of state. The general behavior of many substances can be illustrated by a detailed description of the changes that occur with the most common of all liquids, water. If a block of ice at a temperature of $-50°C$ is placed in a pan and put on a stove to heat, its temperature will rise slowly until it reaches 0°C.

At 0°C the temperature stops rising and the ice begins to melt. More and more ice is melted as heat is continually added; not until it has all turned to water does the temperature begin to rise. As the water becomes hotter and hotter, it eventually reaches a temperature of 100°C where vigorous boiling sets in. Here again the tempera-

TABLE 19B. TABULATED RESULTS OF THE MARBLE EXPERIMENT

	Lead	Glass	Zinc	Brass	Iron
Mass (Kg)	0.045	0.010	0.024	0.030	0.028
Thermal capacity, (Kcal/Kg C°)	0.031	0.160	0.092	0.092	0.105
Heat to raise 1 C° (Kcal)	0.00139	0.00160	0.00220	0.00276	0.00294
Heat to raise 80 C° (Kcal)	0.111	0.128	0.176	0.221	0.235

Fig. 19I   *Heat–temperature graph for one kilogram of ice starting at −50°C, illustrating the latent heat of fusion and vaporization.*

ture stops rising and, as heat is added, more and more water is boiled away to become steam. Finally, when all has become steam at 100°C the temperature begins to rise once more.

All of these changes of temperature and changes of state are shown by a graph in Fig. 19I. The horizontal sections represent changes of state without change in temperature, while the slanted sections on either side represent changes in temperature without abrupt changes in state.

19.5. Thermal Expansion of Solids. In general, when an object is heated, whether it be a solid, liquid, or gas, it expands. There are only a few known exceptions to this. The expansion of a solid with a rise in temperature can be demonstrated by heating a long wire and measuring its over-all elongation. One experimental arrangement for demonstrating this is shown in Fig. 19J.

An iron wire about 2 m in length is fastened to a hook A at one end and to a weight W at the other. Between these two points the wire passes over three pulleys B, C, and D. The wire is heated by connecting it to a battery and sending an electric current through it from end to end.

As the wire is heated and lengthens, the weight slowly falls, thus turning the pulleys as well as the pointer P. When the current is turned off by opening the switch, the wire cools and at the same time contracts to its original length. In the well-equipped laboratory, accurate measurements of the rise in temperature and the lengthening of a solid rod are readily made. The graph at the right in Fig. 19J illustrates the straight-line relation between the rise in temperature and the elongation. By the elongation is meant the increase in length and not the total length of the wire. For an iron wire 2 m long, a rise in temperature of 50°C produces an elongation of 1 mm, 100°C produces an elongation of 2 mm, 150°C an elongation of 3 mm, etc. The straight line means, therefore, that the elongation is directly proportional to the rise in temperature.

There are many instances in engineering where the expansion of solids is an important factor in design and construction. This is particularly true in the construction of suspension bridges and railroads. When the steel rails of the early railroads were first put in place, small gaps were left at every union. The reason for this is that in summer, when the temperature rises, the rails

Fig. 19J   *Experiment illustrating the expansion (elongation) of a wire due to a rise in temperature.*

expand and close these gaps. If the gaps are not large enough in cold weather, the track may buckle up in summer and cause serious accidents. In winter when the rails contract and the gaps are wider, they become noisy to travel as the car wheels roll over them.

Not all substances expand by the same amount when heated through the same difference in temperature. This is illustrated by the linear coefficients of thermal expansion of a few common substances given in Table 19C.

TABLE 19C. LINEAR COEFFICIENTS OF
THERMAL EXPANSION (CENTIGRADE)

Material	α per °C
Aluminum	25×10^{-6}
Brass	18×10^{-6}
Copper	17×10^{-6}
Glass (soda)	17×10^{-6}
Glass (pyrex)	3×10^{-6}
Gold	14×10^{-6}
Iron	11×10^{-6}
Platinum	9×10^{-6}
Silver	18×10^{-6}
Quartz	0.4×10^{-6}
Pine wood (along grain)	5×10^{-6}
Pine wood (across grain)	30×10^{-6}

The linear coefficient of thermal expansion α is defined as the change in length per unit length of a substance per 1° rise in temperature. Once

In this equation t_1 is the original temperature of the body, t_2 the final temperature to which it is raised, and L its original length.*

Example 1. A pyrex glass rod is accurately ground and polished to a length of 2.0000 m when the room temperature is 20°C. If this same rod is heated to a temperature of 420°C, how much does it elongate?
Solution. From the above equation we write

$$e = 3 \times 10^{-6} \times 2 \times (420 - 20)$$
$$= 3 \times 10^{-6} \times 2 \times 400 = 0.0024 \text{ m}$$
$$= 2.4 \text{ mm}$$

The rod thus lengthens by only 0.0024 m to give an over-all length of 2.0024 m. It should be noted that had the length of the rod been given as 2 in. the elongation would have been 0.0024 in. In other words, e and L are always in the same units, so that the coefficients of thermal expansion are valid in the metric as well as the English system. The coefficients given in Table 19C, however, are for the centigrade temperature scale only. Should the known temperature be Fahrenheit or Rankine, the change in temperature should be converted to the Centigrade scale.

19.6. Differential Expansion. In the previous section it was stated that all substances do not expand alike. Some metals like brass and aluminum expand twice as much as others, like iron and platinum (see Table 19C). This difference in expansion is demonstrated by the heating of a bi-metallic strip as shown in Fig. 19K. Two thin

Fig. 19K   *Different substances expand by different amounts. (a) Bi-metallic strip, (b) balance wheel of a watch, (c) a thermostat.*

this constant is known, the linear expansion for any sized object made of that same material can be calculated for any rise in temperature by the following formula:

$$\text{elongation} = \alpha \times \text{length} \times \text{rise in temperature}$$
$$e = \alpha L(t_2 - t_1). \tag{19c}$$
$$e = \alpha L \, \Delta t$$

strips of different metal are placed side by side and welded together over their entire length. When heated, one metal expands more than the other, causing the strip to bend. The hotter it

* It is customary in formulas to use the letter t for temperature on either the Centigrade or Fahrenheit scale. When absolute temperature must be used, however, the capital letter T is used.

becomes the more it bends. When it cools down to its original temperature the strip becomes straight again, and if cooled still further it bends in the opposite direction.

Differential expansion as shown by this experiment finds many practical applications in industry. Bi-metallic strips are used, for example, in the making of balance wheels for fine watches and in thermostats for refrigerators, hot-water heaters, and car radiators. When on a hot day the spokes of the balance of a watch expand, they shift the weight of the rim farther from the center, causing the balance wheel to oscillate more slowly. By making the rim of the wheel of

break the electrical contact at A and B thus turning off the furnace. As the air cools the strip straightens out and makes contact, again turning on the furnace.

19.7. Thermal Expansion of Liquids. Accurate measurements of the expansion of liquids with a rise in temperature are made difficult by the simultaneous expansion of the containing vessel. This difficulty can be overcome, however, and one finds that most liquids, like solids, expand by an amount which is proportional to the rise in temperature. This is illustrated by the straight-line graphs for alcohol and mercury in Fig. 19L(a).

Fig. 19L *Volume–temperature graphs of the thermal expansion of liquids.*

two bi-metallic strips, this can be compensated for as shown in Fig. 19K(b). With a rise in temperature the ends of the spokes S move out and the free ends R of the bi-metallic strips bend in closer to the axis of rotation. One expansion compensates the other, keeping the watch running at the same rate.

Thermostats are so commonly employed in electrical devices today that their explanation will be given here. An electrical thermostat is an automatic electric switch which closes when the temperature reaches one desired temperature and opens when it reaches another. One type of switch is shown in Fig. 19K(c). If the temperature is low the bi-metallic strip is straight and makes electrical contact between the points A and B. This operates an electrical device which, for argument's sake, might open a gas valve of a furnace in the basement of a house. When the air in the house rises to the desired temperature the bi-metallic strip has bent far enough away to

A straight-line graph here means that with each degree rise in temperature the increase in volume due to expansion is exactly the same. If 1 m^3 of mercury at 0°C is heated to a temperature of 1°C its volume will be 1.00018 m^3, or an increase of 0.00018 m^3. At 10° the increase will be ten times this amount, or 0.0018 m^3. Thus for each degree rise the increase is the same and equal to 0.00018. This number is called the volume coefficient of thermal expansion of mercury. For alcohol the coefficient is 0.0011 per degree centigrade.

TABLE 19D. VOLUME COEFFICIENTS OF EXPANSION FOR FOUR COMMON LIQUIDS

Liquid	per °C	per °F
Alcohol	11.0×10^{-4}	6.6×10^{-4}
Glycerine	5.3×10^{-4}	2.9×10^{-4}
Mercury	1.8×10^{-4}	1.0×10^{-4}
Turpentine	10.5×10^{-4}	5.8×10^{-4}

The volume expansion of liquids like mercury or alcohol is given by a formula of exactly the same form as the one for solids [see Eq.(19c)].

$$v = \beta V \Delta t \tag{19d}$$

where v is the change in volume, β the volume coefficient of thermal expansion, V the original volume, and Δt is the difference in temperature.

19.8. Anomalous Expansion of Water. Over a large range in temperature, liquids do not expand linearly. Actually their graphs curve slightly upward, indicating a more rapid rise at higher temperatures. The extent of the departure from a straight-line graph differs considerably with liquids. At 100°C, for example, alcohol expands about 20% more for each degree rise than it does at 0°C. Mercury, on the other hand, varies by less than one hundredth of 1% and may be assumed accurately linear between these two temperatures.

Starting at its freezing temperature of 0°C, and being slowly heated, water contracts until it reaches a temperature of 4°C and then expands. At 4°C where it reaches its minimum volume it has its maximum density. It might be considered fortunate that water expands on being cooled from 4°C to 0°C. If this were not the case and it contracted the way most liquids do, ice would form at the bottom of lakes instead of at the top.

When a pond of water cools toward the freezing point, the surface water next to the cold air cools first. Having cooled and contracted it has a greater density than the water below and it sinks. This process continues until all the water reaches 4°C. Now, as the surface water cools below 4°C it expands, and, becoming less dense, floats. The water on the surface therefore reaches 0°C first and freezes. In freezing, the water expands still more to become ice. Ice floats on water because its density is less than that of water. When 1.00000 m³ of water at 4°C is cooled down to 0°C, it expands to a volume of 1.00013 m³, and when it freezes its new volume as a solid is 1.09051 m³.

PROBLEMS

1. If a centigrade thermometer is found to show the following series of temperatures, what are the corresponding temperatures on the Fahrenheit scale? (a) 25°C, (b) 65°C, (c) 82°C, (d) 122.3°C, (e) −40°C.

2. If a Fahrenheit thermometer shows the following series of temperatures, what are the corresponding values on the centigrade scale? (a) 50°F, (b) 77°F, (c) 140°F, (d) 194°F, and (e) −40°F. [*Ans.* (a) 10°C, (b) 25°C, (c) 60°C, (d) 90°C, (e) −40°C.]

3. If the following temperatures are recorded on the Fahrenheit thermometer, find the corresponding temperatures on the Kelvin scale. (a) 41°F, (b) 131°F, (c) −103°F, (d) 239°F, and (e) 392°F.

4. The following temperatures are recorded with a centigrade thermometer. Find the corresponding temperatures on the Rankine scale. (a) 150°C, (b) 85°C, (c) 15°C, (d) −80°C, and (e) −180°C. [*Ans.* (a) 762°R, (b) 645°R, (c) 519°R, (d) 348°R, (e) 168°R.]

5. Find the number of Kcal required to raise the temperature of 5 Kg of lead from 25°C to 260°C.

6. How much heat is required to raise the temperature of 2.4 Kg of gold from 28°C to 143°C ? [*Ans.* 8.56 Kcal.]

7. How many Btu are required to raise the temperature of 5 lb of silver from 32°F to 212°F.

8. The temperature of a block of iron weighing 16 lb is raised from 200°R to 950°R. Find the number of Btu required. [*Ans.* 1260 Btu.]

9. Calculate the heat required to change 5 Kg of ice from −30°C to steam at 100°C.

10. The iron rails used in building railroads are 20 m in length. If at the time they are nailed in place the temperature is 25°C, how large will the gaps between the rails be when the temperature drops to −40°C? [*Ans.* 0.0143 m, or 1.43 cm.]

11. A standard gauge block, made of brass, is exactly 10 cm long at 20°C. Calculate its length when the temperature is 50°C.

12. A pine wood meter stick is exactly 1 m long when the temperature is 50°F. Find its length when the temperature is 86°F. [*Ans.* 1.000100 m.]

13. The Eiffel Tower in Paris is 984 ft high and is made of iron. Calculate its change in height when the temperature changes from 32°F to 113°F.

14. A brass disk at 25°C has a diameter of 60 cm and a hole cut in the center that is 40 cm in diameter. Calculate the diameter of the hole when the temperature is raised to 125°C. [*Ans.* 40.072 cm.]

15. A pine board is cut and carefully planed so that it is exactly 30 cm wide and 3 m long when the temperature is 20°C. If the temperature is raised to 60°C, find (a) the increased length of the board, (b) its increased width, and (c) its increased area.

16. An iron wire 1 m long hangs from the ceiling. To the lower end is fastened an aluminum wire 2 m long, and

to the lower end of the aluminum wire a small weight. How far will the weight descend if the temperature is raised from 0°C to 40°C? [*Ans.* 0.00244 m, or 0.244 cm.]

17. A silver strip of metal is made into a ring whose inside diameter is 25 mm at 25°C. Find the inside diameter when the temperature rises to 45°C.

18. The iron rim of a wagon wheel has an internal diameter of 1.2 m when the temperature is 180°C. What is its internal diameter when the temperature is lowered to 30°C? [*Ans.* 1.001980 m.]

19. A standard platinum meter bar at the Bureau of Standards is exactly 1 m long at 25°C. Find the distance between the end marks when the temperature is 45°C.

HEAT TRANSFER
AND THE ATMOSPHERE

There are numerous methods by which heat may be transmitted from one place to another. Some of these methods are slow and roundabout, while others are very fast and straight to the point. A careful study of all known methods has led to the realization that there are only three general types of heat transfer: *conduction, convection*, and *radiation*. Conduction is a slow process by which heat is transmitted through a substance by molecular activity. Convection is a more rapid process involving the motion of heated matter itself from one place to another. Radiation of heat from one place to another takes place in the same manner and with the same speed as light, 186,000 mi/sec.

20.1. Conduction. Not all bodies are good conductors of heat. Metals like copper and silver are much better for this purpose than are other substances like wood, glass, paper, and water. The ability of a given substance to conduct heat is called its *thermal conductivity.*

The relative conductivities of different substances can be illustrated by an experiment performed as follows: Similar rods of six different metals, copper, aluminum, brass, tin, german silver, and lead, are coated with a special yellow paint and arranged as shown in Fig. 20A. The ends of the rods, mounted in rubber corks, project through holes in a metal tube where their lower ends are heated to 100°C by steam passing through the tube. As the heat travels slowly up each rod, the yellow paint turns to red. After 5 or 10 min of heating, the height to which the paint has turned color is approximately as shown by the stippled areas in the figure. Of these six

metals, copper is observed to be the best conductor and lead the poorest.

In order to heat an object, it is customary to bring it into contact with some other body at a

Fig. 20A *Experiment illustrating the relative heat conductivities of six different metals: copper, aluminum, brass, tin, German silver, and lead.*

higher temperature. A pan of water, for example, is generally heated by placing it over an open flame. The combustion of natural gas first sets the gas molecules into a rapid state of motion. These molecules, striking the bottom of the pan, set the molecules of the metal into rapid vibration. They in turn strike other metal molecules, thus transferring the motion through to the other side. This is called heat conduction. The metal molecules set the first layer of water molecules moving, and they in turn set others moving. Thus molecular motion, called heat, has been given to the body of water.

Laboratory experiments show that the amount of heat flowing through a rod is proportional to the time, the cross-sectional area, and the difference in temperature between the ends, and is inversely proportional to the length.

Using appropriate symbols for each of these factors and inserting a proportionality constant, we can set up the following equation:

$$H = k \frac{A \, \Delta t}{L} \Delta \tau \qquad (20a)$$

H is the amount of heat flowing through the body of length L and cross section A, k is the thermal conductivity, $\Delta \tau$ is the time interval of flow, t_2 is the temperature of the hot end, and Δt is the temperature difference between the ends. It is quite clear that if the temperature difference Δt, or the area A is increased, the amount of heat passing through is increased (see Fig. 20B). It is

Fig. 20B   *Diagram illustrating the various measurable factors involved in the flow of heat through a body by conduction.*

not as obvious, however, that an increase in the length L causes a decrease in the heat flow, or that a decrease in length produces an increase. The latter will be illustrated by two experiments.

Although paper is a poor conductor, the flow of heat through it can be made very great by increasing A, the cross-sectional area, and decreasing L, the distance it has to flow. Diagram (a) in Fig. 20C illustrates thermal conductivity by the boiling of water in a paper cup. Although

Fig. 20C   *Illustration of the conduction of heat through paper.*

the gas flame plays directly against the surface of the paper, the cup will not burn. The reason for this is that the heat from the lower surface of the paper is conducted through to the water

fast enough to keep the temperature of the paper from rising too high. If the paper is thick, the lower surface will burn. Strange as it may seem, the thinner the paper, the less is the chance of burning.

In diagram (b) of Fig. 20C, a thin piece of paper is wrapped once around a rod made half of wood and half of copper. When the flame is brought up, as shown, the paper burns only where it is in contact with the wood, and not at all where it is in contact with the copper. Copper, being a good conductor, carries the heat into the interior of the metal and away from the metal surface. Since wood is a poor conductor it cannot conduct the heat away from the surface fast enough, and the paper heats up and soon burns.

The thermal conductivities of a few common substances are given in Table 20A.

TABLE 20A. THERMAL CONDUCTIVITIES, k, IN KCAL/M²S C°

Substance	k
Silver	970×10^{-4}
Copper	920×10^{-4}
Aluminum	500×10^{-4}
Brass	260×10^{-4}
Iron	160×10^{-4}
Lead	80×10^{-4}
German Silver	100×10^{-4}
Mercury	20×10^{-4}
Tile	2×10^{-4}
Glass	2.5×10^{-4}
Water	1.4×10^{-4}
Wood	0.5×10^{-4}
Paper	0.3×10^{-4}
Felt	0.04×10^{-4}

The number k is the quantity of heat in Kcal that in 1 s will pass through a 1-m cube when two opposite faces are maintained at 1C° difference in temperature. Knowing the value of k for a given substance, it is possible to calculate, by means of Eq.(20a), the amount of heat flowing through any sized object made of that same material.

Example 1. One end of an aluminum rod 40 cm long and 5 cm² in cross section is maintained at a temperature of 100°C, and the other end at 20°C.

Find the amount of heat that will flow through the rod in 2 min.

Solution. Substitution in Eq.(20a) gives

$$H = 500 \times 10^{-4} \frac{5 \times 10^{-4}(100 - 20)}{0.40} 120$$

$$H = 0.6 \text{ Kcal}$$

20.2. Convection. Why is it that a poor conductor of heat like water can be heated so quickly when it is placed in a pan over a hot fire? It is due to the second method of heat transfer known as *convection*. Water on the bottom of a pan is heated first. Because of a rise in temperature it expands. Being lighter than the cold water above, it then rises to the top, permitting cold water to come to the bottom from the sides. This action sets up a flow of water called a *convection current* (see Fig. 20D). Convection currents thus keep the water stirred up as it heats.

Fig. 20D *Convection currents in a pan of water being heated over a stove burner.*

A convection current set up in the heating of a vessel of water is illustrated in Fig. 20E. A glass tube in the shape of a letter O is filled with water and then heated at one of the lower corners as indicated. A drop of ink admitted at the top opening will mix with the water and quickly flow around the tube in a counterclockwise direction. This circulation is the basis of the hot-water heating systems used in some houses. As illustrated in Fig. 20F, hot water from a supply tank in a lower room or basement rises and flows through several radiators, only to return, somewhat cooled, to the tank where it is reheated.

Convection currents in the atmosphere are quite noticeable and account for the wind. Along the sea coast, cool air from over the ocean comes as a sea breeze due to convection. The sun's rays are absorbed more readily by the land than they are by water, and the warmed air over the land

Fig. 20E *Demonstration experiment showing convection in water.*

rises while cooler air from the ocean comes in to take its place.

At night the land cools quickly by radiation back toward the cold sky and soon the air over the water is the warmer, and rising it causes a reversal in air movement. The wind blows from the land to the sea. These air currents are easily observed by smoke from a fire built on the seashore. During the day the smoke blows inland, and at night it blows seaward.

Fig. 20F *Illustrations of heat convection by the circulation of water in a pipe and air in a room.*

Fig. 20G   *A Crooke's radiometer.*

Pilots are well aware of rising air currents over certain local areas of ground. Solar radiation being absorbed more completely by a newly plowed field, for example, will warm the air sufficiently to cause convection. Flying into such an upward draft of air, the plane receives a sudden lift. During certain seasons these updrafts of warm air are cooled by the air layers above and water vapor is condensed to form clouds.

20.3. Radiation. When the sun comes over the horizon in the early morning, the heat can be felt as soon as the sun becomes visible. This heat, called radiant heat or radiation, travels with the speed of light, 186,000 mi/s.

radiometer, thermocouple, thermister, thermometer, etc. A Crooke's radiometer, shown in Fig. 20G, will often be found in a jewelry store window. In daylight or under a bright light the little pinwheel, made of very thin mica, will be found spinning around as if by perpetual motion.

Each vane of such a radiometer is shiny on one face, and blackened on the other. The black faces absorb more radiant energy than the polished surfaces, so that the adjacent air is heated. The faster recoiling air molecules therefore exert a larger force on the blackened sides, driving them around.

Should a radiometer be so highly evacuated that little air remains inside, light waves in bouncing off the polished surfaces will exert twice the force they do in being absorbed on the blackened side, and the pinwheel will spin the other way.

Radiant heat rays, like visible light, are electromagnetic waves and have all the general properties known to visible light. The essential difference between the two is that heat waves, sometimes called *infrared rays*, are not visible to the human eye.

A demonstration of the reflection of infrared rays is diagramed in Fig. 20H. A candle flame

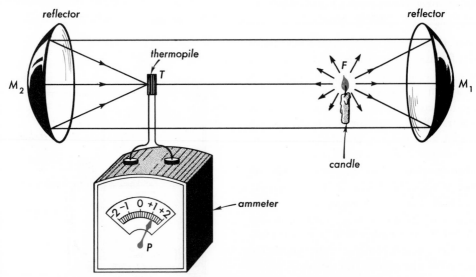

Fig. 20H   *Reflection of heat rays by concave mirrors.*

Radiant heat is only one of the many forms of energy and is readily detected by means of a

acting as a source at F emits light and heat rays in all directions. Of these rays, only the ones traveling toward the concave mirror M_1 are reflected into a parallel beam. Arriving at the second concave mirror M_2, these rays are again reflected, being brought together to a focus on the exposed junctions of a thermopile T. As the junctions of the thermopile warm up, an electric current is produced, which causes the ammeter pointer P to move to the right. When the candle is removed, the pointer returns to zero.

A practical example of heat radiation is to be found in every home where a fireplace is used as a means of heating. Contrary to most beliefs, the heat entering a room from a fireplace is practically all in the form of infrared rays originating in the flames, the coals, and the hot stone or brick walls. The air that is heated within the fireplace does not enter the room but is carried up the chimney as a convection current (see Fig. 20I). This rising current of air draws fresh air

Fig. 20I *A fireplace heats a room by radiation from the flame, the coals, and the stove walls. Convection currents set up a draft and carry warm air and smoke out the chimney.*

into the room and into the fire, thus supplying fresh oxygen to the burning wood or coal.

A Dewar-flask or "Thermos bottle" is an example of a practical device in which the conduction, convection, and radiation of heat are reduced as much as possible. As shown by the cross-sectional diagram in Fig. 20J, a Thermos bottle consists of a double-walled glass vessel silvered on the inside. The purpose of the silvering is to reflect all radiant heat attempting to enter or leave the vessel. The space between the

walls is highly evacuated to prevent convection, and the glass, being a poor conductor, minimizes conduction through the walls of the neck. With the exception of the vacuum space between walls, a calorimeter of the type commonly used in laboratories is similar to a Dewar-flask.

Fig. 20J *The Dewar-flask, or "Thermos" bottle, minimizes conduction by using glass, convection by evacuating, and radiation by silvering.*

Another type of heating system for public buildings and private dwellings has recently been developed. Known to engineers as *panel heating*, this system heats the walls of the rooms by hot air or water pipes that run through them. Even though the windows are open on the coldest days, radiant heat keeps the occupants warm.

20.4. Emission and Absorption. The rate at which a body radiates or absorbs heat depends not only upon the absolute temperature, but upon the nature of the exposed surfaces as well. Objects that are good emitters of heat are also good absorbers of the same kind of radiation. This is known as *Kirchhoff's law of radiation*. A body whose surface is blackened is an excellent emitter as well as an excellent absorber. If the same body is chromium plated, it becomes a poor emitter and a poor absorber.

If the outside surface of a hot coffee cup were painted a dull black, the rate of cooling would be more rapid than if it were chromium plated. A highly polished surface, as in the Dewar-flask, would help by reflection to keep radiant heat from crossing the boundary.

Black clothes should not be worn on a hot day since black is a good absorber of the sun's radiant heat. While black is also a good emitter, the external temperature is higher than the body temperature and the exchange rate is therefore such as to heat the body. White clothes are worn in hot climates because white is a good reflector and therefore a poor absorber.

20.5. Black-Body Radiation. The relation between the radiant heat E emitted by a body and its temperature was first made through the extensive laboratory experiments of Josef Stefan. The same law was later derived from theoretical considerations by Ludwig Boltzmann, and is now known as the *Stefan–Boltzmann law* *

$$E = kT^4 \qquad (20b)$$

Here E represents the energy radiated per second by a body at an absolute temperature T, and k is a proportionality constant. The law applies only to so-called "black bodies."

A black body is defined as one that absorbs all of the radiant heat that falls upon it.

Such a perfect absorber would also be a perfect emitter.

If E represents the heat in kilocalories radiated per second per square meter of a black-body, then $k = 1.36 \times 10^{-11}$. If E is measured in joules/meter^2 second, then $k = 5.7 \times 10^{-8}$.

The best laboratory approach to a black-body is a hole in a blackened box. Practically all heat

---

* Ludwig Boltzmann (1844–1906), Austrian theoretical physicist, was educated at Linz and Vienna. At 23 he was appointed assistant at the physical institute in Vienna. Later he became professor at Graz, then at Munich, and finally back at Vienna. His first publication was on the second law of thermodynamics, and was followed by numerous papers on molecular motion, on viscosity and diffusion of gases, on Maxwell's electromagnetic theory, on Hertz's electrical experiments, and on Stefan's law for black-body radiation.

entering such a hole would be absorbed inside. Black velvet cloth or a surface painted dull with lampblack will absorb about 97% of the radiant heat falling on it, and may for many purposes be considered a black-body. Polished metal surfaces, however, are far from black-bodies; they absorb only about 6% of the incident energy and reflect the remainder. Most other substances have absorption ratios between these two extremes.

20.6. Prevost's Law of Heat Exchange. Laboratory experiments, as well as the Stefan–Boltzmann law, show that all bodies, whether they are hot or cold, radiate heat. The words "hot" and "cold" are only relative terms, since even ice radiates heat. The greater the absolute temperature of a body, the greater is the rate at which it radiates, and ice at 0°C is 273° above absolute zero.

If a cold block of metal is brought into a warm room, it radiates heat to the walls of the room and the walls of the room radiate heat to the block. Because the walls are at a higher temperature, they give more heat per second to the block than the block gives up in return (see Fig. 20K).

Fig. 20K   *A cold body warms up to room temperature.*

Due to this unequal exchange of heat, the temperature of the cold block rises until it comes to the same temperature as the room, at which time it radiates and absorbs at exactly the same rate.

Prevost's law of heat exchange states that a body at the temperature of its surroundings is radiating and receiving heat at equal rates.

When a person stands near a fireplace, he feels warm because his body receives more heat from the fire than he emits. If he stands next to a cold window, he feels chilly because he radiates more heat than he absorbs. The side of his body facing the window gets noticeably colder than the other.

20.7. Radiant Heat from the Sun. Instruments designed to measure solar radiation are called pyroheliometers (see Fig. 20L). A beam of sun-

Fig. 20L   *Abbot's pyroheliometer for measuring the heat radiated by the sun.*

light of known cross-sectional area is allowed to fall upon the blackened surface of a silver disk where it is absorbed. A drill hole in the metal disk admits the narrow bulb of a sensitive mercury thermometer, the latter being bent and threaded through a hole in the heat-insulated box as shown in the diagram. Knowing the heat capacity of the metal and its rise in temperature, the total number of calories per minute can be calculated.

Measurements of this kind by various observers are in remarkable agreement with each other and give a value of 19.38 Kcal/m² min. This number, called *the solar constant*, is defined as the average amount of energy falling in 1 min on 1 m² of surface placed at right angles to the sun's rays. Multiplying the solar constant by the area of a sphere 93 million mi in radius, we obtain the figure 9×10^{22} Kcal/s as the total heat radiated by the sun.

An appreciation of these figures can be had by the following comparison. If all of the energy radiated by the sun could be used to heat the oceans of the earth, the temperature would rise from the freezing point to the boiling point in less than 2 s. Where all this heat comes from within the sun has long been a puzzle to astronomer and physicist alike. A satisfactory answer to the problem has recently been found and will be given in Sec. 72.7.

20.8. The Seasons. The reason for the earth's polar ice caps and warm equator, as well as the

difference in temperature between winter and summer, is to be attributed to the different angles at which the sun's rays arrive at the earth's surface. When it is summer in the northern hemisphere the sun's rays strike the earth's surface from the direction shown in Fig. 20M. It will be

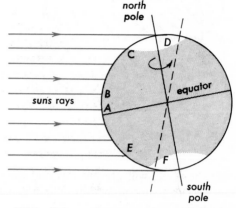

Fig. 20M   *Solar radiation is spread over a bigger area at the earth's poles than it is at the equator.*

noted that a given bundle of rays near the poles is spread over a much larger area C to D and E to F, than an equal bundle of rays near the equator A to B.

With the arrival of less heat per unit area, the resulting temperature will be lowest near the poles and highest near the equator. As the earth moves slowly in its orbit around the sun, the South Pole is in darkness for many months and it is winter in the southern hemisphere; the North Pole is in the light and it is summer. Six months later, when the orientation of the sun's rays with respect to the earth is like that shown by the dotted axis in the diagram, the conditions and the seasons are reversed.

Not all of the solar radiation coming toward the earth gets through the atmosphere to be absorbed by the surface. While a small percent is absorbed by the atmosphere on the clearest of days, fog and clouds in regions away from the equator and toward the polar caps often absorb 30% to 40% and reflect a similar amount back into space. Under such conditions only a small amount of heat may get to the ground.

On clear cold nights the temperature at the

earth's surface drops rapidly, because of direct heat radiation into space. An intervening cloud

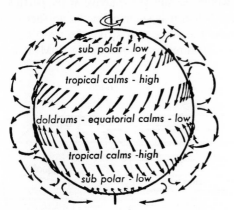

Fig. 20N *Air-current pattern for the earth, due to convection and the earth's rotation.*

blanket, however, will prevent this and the resultant surface temperature will remain considerably higher.

20.9. Convection Currents of Air Around the Earth. The earth's atmosphere is not a stationary body of air but one that is continually moving. A "wind pattern" showing the average air currents around the earth is given in Fig. 20N. Warm air masses at the equator rise because of convection and colder air from both sides rushes in to take its place. The rising currents divide high up in the atmosphere and return to the earth at other regions north and south.

This circulation of air is altered by the earth's rotation from west to east about its polar axis. The air masses that move north and south from the regions of tropical calms move to a region of lower or higher ground speeds with the result that the air gets ahead of the earth's rotation or behind, respectively. This gives rise to the diagonal movements of the trade winds which are good illustrations of what are called coriolis forces. Where the air currents rise at the equator, the average barometric pressure is less than in

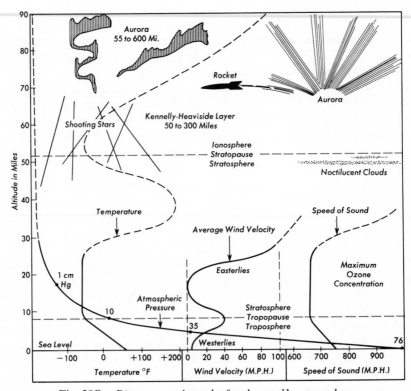

Fig. 20O *Diagrams and graphs for the earth's atmosphere.*

the regions of tropical calms where the currents are down.

The absorption of the sun's rays by the earth and its lower atmosphere causes the temperature at sea level to be greater than the temperature at higher altitudes. Normally the temperature decreases steadily with height until an altitude is reached beyond which the temperature remains constant at −67°F (see Fig. 20O). This altitude, which is about 5 mi at the poles and 10 mi at the equator, is the upper limit of the so-called *troposphere*. This layer contains about 80% of the atmospheric mass.

PROBLEMS

1. An iron rod is 10 cm long and 4 cm in diameter. How much heat will flow through this rod in 6 min if one end is maintained at 0°C and the other end at 100°C?

2. One end of a copper rod 40 cm long and with a cross-sectional area of 10 cm² is maintained at 10°C and the other end at 390°C. How much heat will flow through in 1 hr? [*Ans.* 31.5 Kcal.]

3. A glass window pane 1 m by 1 m is 25 mm thick. If the snow outside maintains the outer surface at 0°C, and the heat of the room maintains the inner surface at 6°C, how much heat will be conducted through the glass in 24 hr?

4. The bottom of a round aluminum pan is 1 mm thick and has a diameter of 20 cm. If the upper surface is maintained at 35°C and the gas flames keep the under surface of 42°C, how much heat will flow through in 1 min? [*Ans.* 659 Kcal.]

5. A large water tank with a bottom 1.60 m in diameter is made of iron boiler plate 5 mm thick. As the water is being heated, the gas burner underneath is able to maintain a temperature difference of 2 C° between the surfaces. How much heat flows through to the water in 5 min?

6. A silver rod is 10 cm long and 2 cm² in cross section. One end is maintained at 10°C and the other end at 65°C. How much heat will flow through in 30 min? [*Ans.* 19.2 Kcal.]

7. A large window contains 16 panes of glass, each one of which is 25 cm by 40 cm and 3 mm thick. If the snow outside maintains the outer surface at 0°C and the heat of the room maintains the inner surface at 4°C, how much heat will flow through the glass in 1 hr?

8. The bottom of an aluminum pan is 2 mm thick and has a cross-sectional area of 50 cm². If the pan is filled with water to be heated, and the hot-plate on which it is placed maintains a temperature difference of 5°C between the two surfaces, how much heat will flow through each minute? [*Ans.* 37.5 Kcal.]

9. The wooden handle of a frying pan is 4.0 cm in diameter and 18 cm long. If the pan temperature is 200°C and the free end of the handle is at 35°C, how much heat will flow through in 30 min?

10. A small copper ball 6 cm in diameter is coated with lampblack and heated to a temperature of 727°C. How much heat is radiated from this sphere in 1 min? [*Ans.* 9.22 Kcal.]

11. A silver ball 8 cm in diameter is coated with lampblack and its temperature maintained at 327°C. (a) How much heat will this body radiate each second of time? (b) If the walls of the room are maintained at 27°C, how much heat will this body absorb each second of time? Assume black-body surfaces.

12. The coil heater of an electric hot-plate has a surface area of 350 cm², and when heated maintains a temperature of 627°C. (a) How much heat will this unit give off each minute of time? (b) If the walls of the room are maintained at 27°C, how much heat will this unit absorb each minute of time? Assume all surfaces to be black-bodies. [*Ans.* (a) 18.7 Kcal, (b) 0.231 Kcal.]

13. In cold climates where the temperature falls below freezing, the touching of an iron railing with the bare hands tends to make the fingers stick to the metal. This does not happen so readily when the railing is made of wood. Explain.

14. The rear wall of a brick fireplace has an effective open area of 1 m². Find the number of calories radiated per minute if this area is maintained at 227°C. Assume the surface to be a black-body. [*Ans.* 51.0 Kcal.]

15. A small iron cube 4 cm on a side is raised to a temperature of 1227°C. Assuming black-body radiation, how much energy is radiated per second (a) in joules, and (b) in kilocalories?

16. A thin square sheet of iron 5 cm on a side is heated to a temperature of 1427°C. Assuming black-body radiation, find the energy radiated per second in (a) joules, and (b) kilocalories. [*Ans.* (a) 2380 J, (b) 0.569 Kcal.]

THERMODYNAMICS, AND ROCKET ENGINES

Thermodynamics is that branch of physics dealing with the conversion of mechanical energy into thermal energy, and the reverse process, heat into work. There are numerous ways of carrying out either of these transformations. By rubbing the palms of the hands together, for example, heat is produced; by rubbing two sticks of wood together a fire may be started. If a weight falls freely from some height, heat is developed when the weight strikes the ground. The bearings of a car motor or the wheels of a freight car, if not lubricated, will get hot and either "burn out" or lock together, as in a "hot box." These are all examples of mechanical energy being transformed into heat.

The reverse process of transforming heat into mechanical energy is illustrated by present-day steam, diesel, gasoline, and jet-propulsion engines. In all of these engines, fuel is burned to produce heat and by expanding gases the heat is turned into mechanical energy. Jet propulsion is not a new idea. A simple device based upon the principle of jet propulsion is to be found in the writings of some of the ancient philosophers of Archimedes' time.

An interesting demonstration is shown in Fig. 21A. A small hollow brass tube, mounted on the shaft of an electric motor, has a few drops of water in the base and a cork driven into the open end. A wooden clamp, like the one shown at the lower right, is squeezed tightly around the tube as it spins. Because of friction the tube gets hot, boils the water, and steam pressure suddenly blows the cork out as if from a gun.

21.1. The First Law of Thermodynamics. The first law of thermodynamics is frequently referred to as *the mechanical equivalent of heat*. It is to the painstaking work of Joule (1843)* that we attribute this fundamental verification of the uni-

Fig. 21A   *Cork gun. Friction heat boils water, and steam blows cork out.*

versal law of conservation of energy. With his apparatus he was able to show that, when a moving body is brought to rest, the energy that disappears is directly proportional to the amount of heat produced. In his most famous experiment, he set water into motion in a bucket by means of rotating paddles and then brought the water to rest by stationary paddles. He was able to show that, if all of the work used in churning the water goes into producing heat, then the same amount of work will always produce the same amount of heat regardless of the method used to carry out

* James Prescott Joule (1818–89), English physicist, was born on December 24, 1818, near Manchester. Although he owned a large brewery, he devoted his life to scientific research. At the age of 22, he discovered the law giving the relation between electrical energy and heat, and a short time later the law known as the first law of thermodynamics.

the transformation. In other words, the calorie, which is a unit of heat energy, is equivalent to a definite number of joules of mechanical energy.

The number of energy units, which upon conversion gives one heat unit, is called the mechanical equivalent of heat. By experiment

and
$$1 \text{ Kcal} = 4.186 \times 10^3 \text{ J}$$
$$1 \text{ Btu} = 778 \text{ ft-lb} \qquad (21a)$$

As an equation,

$$\frac{\text{work}}{\text{heat}} = \text{mech. equiv. of heat}$$

$$\boxed{\frac{W}{H} = J} \qquad (21b)$$

Because of the fundamental importance of this relation, many experimenters have devoted considerable time and effort to obtain a more accurate value of the constant J. In 1879, the famous American physicist Rowland, using an improved form of Joule's apparatus, obtained the value

$$J = 4.179 \times 10^3 \frac{\text{J}}{\text{Kcal}}$$

Since that time, simpler experiments have been devised that make use of a method first employed by Joule, namely, that of heating by electric currents. Such an experiment will be described in Chapter 31.

21.2. Experiments on Mechanical Equivalent of Heat. There are numerous ways of transforming mechanical energy into heat. By rubbing the palms of the hands together, for example, heat is produced by friction. Again, if a weight is dropped from any height, heat is developed when it strikes the ground. A 1-lb weight dropped from a height of 3085 ft will, on stopping, produce 1 Kcal of heat.

One simple laboratory method of measuring the mechanical equivalent of heat is to place a measured amount of lead shot (about 100 g) in a tube about 5 cm in diameter and about 1 m long. After reading the temperature of the shot with a thermometer, the tube is turned end for end about 50 to 200 times, stopping each time in a vertical position to allow the shot to fall the full distance and strike the bottom (see Fig. 21B). The temperature of the shot is then measured

again. From the known mass of shot, m, its specific heat c, and the rise in temperature, $t_2 - t_1$, the total *heat gained* can be calculated, $H = mc(t_2 - t_1)$. From the mass of the shot m, the

Fig. 21B *Experiment for determining the mechanical equivalent of heat.*

acceleration due to gravity g, the number of tube inversions n, and the length of the tube l, the input energy is calculated. Since *work done* equals *force times distance*, $W = mg \times nl$. Substituting in Eq.(21b), we obtain

$$J = \frac{W}{H} = \frac{mg \, nl}{mc \, \Delta t} = \frac{g \, n \, l}{c \, \Delta t} \qquad (21c)$$

The disappearance of m is to be expected since, for example, the dropping of twice the amount of shot will produce twice as much heat, but this will be divided between twice the amount of lead.

Consider as a problem the calculation of the mechanical equivalent of heat from the following data taken in such a laboratory experiment.

Initial temperature of lead shot . . . . 23.0°C
Final temperature of lead shot . . . . 30.9°C
Length of tube . . . . 1.05 m
Number of falls 100

By substituting these values in Eq. 21c and the specific heat of lead from Table 19A we obtain

$$J = \frac{9.80 \times 100 \times 1.05}{0.031(30.9 - 23.0)}$$

$$J = 4.20 \times 10^3 \frac{J}{Kcal}$$

The transformation of potential energy into heat usually occurs by first changing it into kinetic energy. In the above experiment, for example, the lead shot acquired a velocity in falling and its kinetic energy $\frac{1}{2}mv^2$ was changed into heat at the bottom. Due to the impact the molecules of the colliding bodies were given additional kinetic energy.

Example 1. A 1-Kg hammer, moving with a velocity of 50 m/s, strikes a 200-g iron stake driving it into the ground. If half of the energy goes into heating the iron rod, what will be its rise in temperature?
Solution.

E_k of hammer $= \frac{1}{2}mv^2 = \frac{1}{2} \times 1$ Kg $\times$ (50 m/s)^2
$\qquad\qquad\qquad\qquad = 1250$ J

From Eq.(21c), the heat produced will be

$$H = \frac{W}{J} = \frac{1250 \text{ J}}{4.18 \times 10^3 \text{ J/Kcal}} = 0.298 \text{ Kcal}$$

Since one-half goes to heat 200 g of iron with a thermal capacity of 0.105 Kcal/Kg C°, we use Eq.(19b) to obtain

$$0.149 \text{ Kcal} = 0.200 \text{ Kg} \times 0.105 \frac{\text{Kcal}}{\text{Kg C}°} \Delta t$$

Solving for the rise in temperature Δt gives

$$\Delta t = 7.1°C$$

21.3. Kinetic Theory of Gases. According to the kinetic theory of matter, the pressure exerted by a gas upon the walls of the containing vessel is due to the continual bombardment of the walls by the rapidly moving gas molecules. If the temperature of the gas is raised, the molecules move faster and the pressure rises, whereas if it is lowered they move slower and the pressure decreases. The absolute temperature of a gas is proportional to the average kinetic energy of translation of the molecules.

The more gas that is pumped into a vessel of constant volume, the more molecules there are to bombard the walls per second and the greater is the resultant pressure. At any given instant of

time some molecules are moving in one direction and some in another; some are traveling fast, some slow, and a few are momentarily at rest.

In any reasonably large volume of gas, there are many molecules (about 10^{24} molecules/ft³ at normal atmospheric pressure and room temperature) and, according to the mathematical laws of probability, some average speed can be determined which, if possessed by all the molecules, would correspond to the same temperature and would give rise to the same wall pressure. Denoting this average speed by $\bar{v}$, we shall now derive a formula for the pressure.

Consider a cubical vessel whose volume, as shown in Fig. 21C, is l^3. Because the total number

Fig. 21C *Gas molecules in a closed compartment create pressure by virtue of their impact against the walls.*

of molecules present N is very large, the calculations are simplified by assuming that one-third are moving in the x direction, one-third in the y direction, and one-third in the z direction.

Select now the one-third that are moving in the x direction. Each molecule as it approaches the right-hand wall of the vessel is moving with a velocity $\bar{v}$ and after collision it rebounds with a velocity $-\bar{v}$. There has been a change in velocity of $2\bar{v}$. Since the impulse Ft exerted on the wall is given by the change in momentum, we may write

$$Ft = 2m\bar{v} \qquad (21d)$$

Bouncing back and forth between opposite walls of the vessel, each molecule will make many impacts on the same wall in unit time. Now, t is the average time required for the molecule to make the round trip, $2l$, from the right-hand wall to the left-hand wall and back. Therefore

$$t = 2l/\bar{v}$$

Since the impulse Ft is given by the change of momentum, we may write

$$F \times 2l/\bar{v} = 2m\bar{v} \qquad \text{or} \qquad F = m\bar{v}^2/l$$

For $\frac{1}{3}N$ molecules, then, the force will be $N/3$ times that for one molecule, or

$$F = \frac{Nm\bar{v}^2}{3l}$$

Since pressure is the force per unit area, and the area of the wall is l^2

$$P = \frac{F}{l^2} = \frac{Nm\bar{v}^2}{3l^3} \tag{21e}$$

Since the number of molecules N multiplied by the mass of a single molecule gives the total mass of the gas, and l^3 gives it volume, the density ρ is given by

$$\rho = \frac{Nm}{l^3}$$

By substituting ρ for Nm/l^3 in Eq.(21e), we obtain for the pressure

$$P = \frac{1}{3}\rho\bar{v}^2 \tag{21f}$$

The average velocity of molecules in a gas of density ρ, under an absolute pressure P, is given by rearranging the terms.

$$\boxed{\bar{v} = \sqrt{3P/\rho}} \tag{21g}$$

Example 2. Calculate the average velocity of hydrogen molecules in a gas of normal atmospheric pressure and room temperatures.

Solution. From the gas densities in Table 18A and the value for standard atmospheric pressure,

$$\bar{v} = \sqrt{\frac{3 \times 1.013 \times 10^5 \, \text{N/m}^2}{0.090 \, \text{Kg/m}^3}}$$

$$\bar{v} = 1844 \, \frac{\text{m}}{\text{s}}$$

This is considerably faster than a rifle bullet or the shells from the largest guns.

The formula above shows that the greater the density of a gas, the lower is the average speed of its molecules. For a gas like oxygen, with 16 times the density of hydrogen, the molecules will be moving with only one-quarter the average speed of the hydrogen molecules. This is well

illustrated by the mechanical model shown in Fig. 47D, representing the case of a mixture of two gases of different density.

It should be noted that a pressure gauge reads zero when the gas in a tank reaches atmospheric pressure. In solving problems, therefore, standard atmospheric pressure should be added to all gauge readings to obtain the true gas pressure.

21.4. The General Gas Law. This is a law dealing with the compression and expansion of a gas at different temperatures. It states that the pressure of a given quantity of gas is proportional to the *absolute temperature* and inversely proportional to the *volume*. As an equation

$$P = R\frac{T}{V} \tag{21h}$$

or

$$\boxed{PV = RT}$$

general gas law

The proportionality constant R is called the *gas constant*, and is given by

$$R = \frac{PV}{T}$$

An experiment illustrating the expansion or compression of a gas is shown in Fig. 21D, along

Fig. 21D *Adiabatic compression and expansion of gas.*

with a *pressure* vs *volume* graph of the results. A heat-insulated cylinder with a movable piston is arranged with a mercury manometer and a sensitive thermometer. The gas pressure P is determined by adding the manometer height h to the atmospheric pressure P_0, the volume by multiplying the length of the gas column and the piston cross sectional area, and the gas temperature by reading the thermometer in °C and adding 273°.

For position A the pressure is represented by P_1, the volume by V_1, and the temperature by T_1. Moving the piston to position B is called an *adiabatic expansion:* the pressure decreases to a lower value P_2, the volume increases to a higher value V_2, and the temperature drops to T_2. A further expansion bringing the piston to C lowers the pressure to P_3, raises the volume to V_3, and lowers the temperature to T_3.

When the piston is pushed in from position C to position A the gas undergoes an *adiabatic compression:* the volume decreases, the pressure increases, and the temperature rises. Experimentally it is found that

$$\frac{P_1 V_1}{T_1} = \frac{P_2 V_2}{T_2} = \frac{P_3 V_3}{T_3} \qquad (21i)$$

Example 3. A balloon in a partially filled condition contains 1000 ft³ of helium gas at ground level where the pressure is 14.7 lb/in.², and the temperature is 27°C. Calculate the gas volume when this balloon rises into the stratosphere to a height of 10 mi where the pressure drops to 1.5 lb/in.² and the temperature to −55°C.

Solution. The above values may be substituted directly into the gas formula, Eq.(21i),

$$\frac{P_1 V_1}{T_1} = \frac{P_2 V_2}{T_2}$$

$$\frac{14.7 \text{ lb/in.}^2 \times 1000 \text{ ft}^3}{(273 + 27)\,°\text{Abs}} = \frac{1.5 \text{ lb/in.}^2 \times V_2}{(273 - 55)\,°\text{Abs}}$$

Solving for V_2 gives

$$V_2 = \frac{14.7 \times 218 \times 1000 \text{ ft}^3}{1.5 \times 300} = 7120 \text{ ft}^3.$$

The value of the gas constant R in Eq.(21h) depends upon many factors, including units of measurement. It is common practice to choose an amount of gas equal to one *mole*. The mole is defined in chemistry as that weight of a substance equal to its *molecular weight*. For one mole of any gas

$$R = 8.3170 \; \frac{\text{joules}}{\text{C}° \text{mole}} \qquad (21j)$$

One mole of any gas at 0°C and 76 cm of mercury pressure occupies a volume of 22,400 cm³, and contains a number of molecules equal to

$$N_0 = 6.0254 \times 10^{23} \qquad (21k)$$

This is called *Avogadro's number* and follows from *Avogadro's hypothesis* which states that *equal volumes of different gases at the same temperature and pressure contain equal numbers of molecules* (see Fig. 21E).

Hydrogen   Oxygen   Carbon dioxide

Fig. 21E *Equal volumes of different gases at the same temperature and pressure contain equal numbers of molecules.*

21.5. Rocket Engines. The thrust of a rocket engine is readily explained in terms of gas pressure and Newton's Third Law of Motion. Consider a hollow vessel having the shape of a cylindrical tin can and containing a mixture of combustible fuels as shown at the top in Fig. 21F.

Fig. 21F *Diagram illustrating the thrust arising from the gas exhausted from a hole in a tank containing gas under pressure.*

When the fuel is ignited the high pressure developed inside exerts outward forces normal to the walls as shown. The forces F on the two ends are equal and opposite, as are also the forces on opposite sides. All of these forces are balanced out and the net resultant force is zero.

Imagine that we now remove a circular section of area from the center of the right-hand end as shown below in Fig. 21F. The container now experiences an unbalanced force F to the left given by the product of the pressure P and the exit area A.

$$F = P \times A \qquad (21l)$$

At the earth's surface the atmosphere outside the container exerts inward forces on all the walls and must be taken into account (see Fig. 21G). The pressure P in Eq.(21l) then becomes

Fig. 21G   *Illustration of internal and external gas pressures on the walls of a gas container and the thrust from an exhaust jet.*

the difference between the inside pressure P_i and the outside or ambient pressure P_o. The pressure thrust on the rocket becomes, therefore,

$$F = (P_i - P_o)A \qquad (21m)$$

The principal elements of a typical liquid propellant rocket engine are shown by a cross-section diagram in Fig. 21H. Oxidizer and fuel,

and at the same time to direct their motion into a smoothly flowing exhaust stream.

As the gases approach the throat of the nozzle the decreasing cross sectional area causes the molecules to speed up. Once they are through the narrowest section the low pressure of free space provides an additional acceleration.

Out in free space, far removed from all external forces, the resultant accelerating force acting upon a rocket is due entirely to the momentum change of the mass of the particles it ejects through the exhaust. Applying Newton's Second Law of Motion to these gases the force on them equals the rate of change of their momentum. The total thrust of the rocket engine may be written

$$F = \frac{\Delta(mv)}{\Delta t} \qquad (21n)$$

Assuming steady burning of the fuel the exhaust velocity v of the waste products is constant and Eq.(21n) may be written

$$F = -\frac{\Delta m}{\Delta t} v \qquad (21o)$$

The minus sign indicates that v is oppositely directed to the force F. The velocity v is measured with respect to the rocket, and F is called the *momentum thrust*.

The exit pressure P_i of the gas from within the rocket is usually quite different from the ambient

Pump Combustion chamber Throat Nozzle

Fig. 21H   *Schematic diagram of a liquid rocket motor.*

kept in separate tanks, are pumped into the combustion chamber where they are sprayed out of jets to form an efficient combustible mixture. Burning at a steady rate, liquid fuel and oxidizer not only expand into a gas but rise in temperature to a very high value.

The purpose of a well-designed nozzle is to accelerate the gas particles to still higher velocity

pressure P_o of the surrounding gas. Although P_i may stay fairly constant as a rocket climbs through the atmosphere, the ambient pressure P_o will decrease and become practically zero in free space.

To take these varying conditions into account, it is convenient to write for the total thrust of the rocket engine

$$F = -\frac{\Delta m}{\Delta t} v_{\text{eff}}$$ (21p)

Total thrust

where v_{eff} is called the *effective exhaust velocity*. As the rocket climbs through the atmosphere where the ambient pressure P_o decreases and becomes zero, the effective velocity v_{eff} increases and approaches v, while the thrust F increases and becomes constant in free space.

21.6. Specific Impulse. Specific impulse is the term applied to the performance of a rocket engine, and is given by the total thrust divided by the weight of the propellant consumed per second.

$$I_s = \frac{F}{\Delta w/\Delta t}$$ (21q)

Since F and w are both measured in the same units, newtons or pounds, specific impulse is in seconds. Since total thrust varies with altitude, the value of F given by Eq.(21p) may be substituted in Eq.(21q).

$$I_s = \frac{\Delta m/\Delta t}{\Delta w/\Delta t} v_{\text{eff}}$$

By Newton's law, weight = mass × acceleration due to gravity, $\Delta w = \Delta m \times g$. Direct substitution gives

$$I_s = \frac{\Delta m/\Delta t}{\Delta m/\Delta t} \times \frac{v_{\text{eff}}}{g}$$

$$I_s = \frac{v_{\text{eff}}}{g}$$ (21r)

Specific impulse

The value of g is assumed to be a constant and equal to 9.80 m/s², or 32 ft/s², wherever the rocket is located. Specific impulse can be found either by dividing the thrust by the fuel consumption, or by dividing the exhaust velocity by the constant g.

Another relation for the specific impulse can be derived from the kinetic theory of gases Eq.(21g) and the general gas law Eq.(21h). Since $P = RT/V$, and the density $\rho = M/V$, direct substitution in Eq.(21g) gives

$$v = \sqrt{3R\frac{T}{M}}$$

Assuming this to give the theoretical gas velocity from the rocket nozzle, direct substitution in Eq.(21r) gives

$$I_s = k\sqrt{\frac{T}{M}}$$

where T is the absolute temperature of combustion, M is the mass of the exhaust particles or molecules, and

$$k = \frac{\sqrt{3R}}{g}$$

The higher the temperature reached through combustion, and the lower the mass of the propellant molecules, the greater will be the exhaust velocity v, and the greater will be the specific impulse I_s.

Typical values of these two quantities for a number of liquid propellants are given in Table 21A.

TABLE 21A. PERFORMANCE OF LIQUID PROPELLANTS CALCULATED FOR EXPANSION FROM 20 ATM TO 1 ATM PRESSURE

Propellant	Exhaust velocity v (Km/s)	Specific impulse I_s (s)
Oxygen and hydrogen	3.30	338
Oxygen and ethyl alcohol	2.34	240
Oxygen and kerosene	2.43	248
Nitric acid and analine	2.00	204
Hydrogen and fluorine	3.80	388
Hydrogen and ozone	3.60	368
Hydrazine and oxygen	2.22	227

These are theoretical values only and are not fully realized in practice. A specific impulse of 240 means that a thrust of 240 lb is obtained per pound of propellant consumed per second, or a thrust of 240 N per newton of propellant consumed per second. A mass of 1 Kg has a weight of 9.8 N.

21.7. The Turbo Jet. This engine, used extensively in high-speed aircraft, is shown schematically in Fig. 21I. Air needed for combustion enters the nose of the *shroud* where it is com-

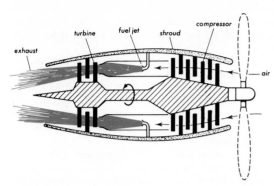

Fig. 21I Cross-section diagram of a turbo-jet engine used principally in aircraft (propeller optional). Top speed probably 600 mi/hr.

pressed by a fan-like centrifugal *compressor*. This air along with the fuel to be burned is injected into a *combustion chamber* and there the mixture ignited. The rapidly expanding gases drive a fan-like *turbine* wheel and at the same time create a forward thrust on the walls by exhausting through the rear as shown.

While the principal function of the turbine is to drive the compressor and small auxiliary equipment like fuel pumps, generators, etc., some aircraft installations employ a propeller to assist take-off. At high speeds such propellers may be stopped and "feathered" by a suitable clutch mechanism and all forward thrust comes from the exhaust jet.

PROBLEMS

1. The water flowing over a waterfall drops a distance of 120 ft. Assuming all the available energy goes into heat, find the temperature difference between the water at the top of the fall and that at the bottom.

2. A 7.2-Kg lead ball is dropped from a tower 200 m tall. Assuming half the energy goes into heating the lead, find (a) the total heat produced, and (b) the rise in temperature. [*Ans.* (a) 3.37 Kcal, (b) 7.55 C°.]

3. A trunk with a mass of 150 Kg is pulled along the floor for 20 m. If the coefficient of sliding friction is 0.35, how much heat is developed?

4. A horizontal force of 50 lb is required to pull a heavy box along the floor. How much heat is developed for each 50 ft it slides? [*Ans.* 3.21 Btu.]

5. A boy weighing 80 lb, riding a bicycle weighing 20 lb, is going 20 mi/hr. When the brakes are applied to come to a stop, how much heat is developed?

6. A train weighing 1200 tons and traveling 45 mi/hr is brought to a stop by applying the brakes. Find the total heat developed. [*Ans.* 2.1 × 10⁵ Btu.]

7. A 25-gm iron bullet, having a velocity of 700 m/s, is shot into the ground. Find (a) the total heat produced, and (b) its rise in temperature if half the heat energy goes into the bullet.

8. A large 10-Kg shell from a naval gun hits the ground in front of its target. If its speed is 500 m/s, how much heat is developed? [*Ans.* 2.99 Kcal.]

9. An automobile tire has a gauge pressure of 24 lb/in.² when the temperature is 40°F. After running at high speed on a hot pavement the temperature of the tire rises to 160°F. Find the gauge pressure at this temperature assuming the volume has not changed.

10. A cylindrical tank with a piston contains 8 m³ of nitrogen gas at 30°C. If the pressure on the piston is held constant, what will be its volume when the temperature is lowered to 5°C. [*Ans.* 7.34 m³.]

11. A tank contains helium gas at a gauge pressure of 525 lb/in.² when the temperature is 10°C. Calculate the gauge pressure when the temperature goes up to 50°C.

12. A deep-sea diver exhales air at a depth of 20 m where the temperature is 15°C. If the bubbles formed have a diameter of 3 cm, what will be their diameter at the surface where the temperature is 25°C? [*Ans.* 4.35 cm.]

13. If a gas has a volume of 5 m³ at a gauge pressure of 100 cm of Hg, and a temperature of 40°F, what volume will it occupy when the gauge pressure is doubled and the temperature is raised to 200°F?

14. A rubber balloon 4 ft in diameter is inflated with hydrogen gas at 25°C at sea level and a gauge pressure of 0.3 lb/in.² Find the diameter of the balloon at an altitude of 30,000 ft where the atmospheric pressure is 4.4 lb/in.², the gauge pressure is 0.3 lb/in.², and the temperature is −40°C. Assume standard atmospheric pressure to be 14.7 lb/in.² [*Ans.* 5.42 ft.]

15. A tank of compressed oxygen has a volume of 12 ft³, and its gauge shows a pressure of 600 lb/in.² If the valve is opened until the gauge pressure reading is down to 300 lb/in.², how many cubic feet of oxygen measured at normal pressure of 14.7 lb/in.² have escaped? Assume constant temperature.

16. A volume of 50 m³ of nitrogen gas at normal atmospheric pressure is compressed to a volume of 10 m³. Find the resulting absolute pressure if the compression is isothermal. [*Ans.* 380 cm of Hg.]

17. Find the average velocity of the oxygen molecules in the air at normal pressure and a temperature of 0°C.

18. Calculate the average velocity of helium atoms in a gas at normal temperature and pressure. [*Ans.* 1.31 × 10³ m/s.]

19. Find the average velocity of carbon dioxide molecules in a gas at normal temperature of 0°C and a pressure of 152 cm of Hg.

20. The combustion chamber of a rocket engine maintains an internal pressure of 300 lb/in.^{2}, when at sea level where atmospheric pressure is 15 lb/in.^{2} If the exit area has a diameter of 6 in., find the thrust. [*Ans.* 8060 lb.]

21. A rocket engine using liquid oxygen and liquid hydrogen as propellant developes a specific impulse of 300 s. If propellant is consumed at the rate of 100 Kg/s, find (a) the effective exhaust velocity, and (b) the total thrust in newtons.

22. A rocket engine using nitric acid and analine as oxidizer and fuel has a total weight of 5 tons. If propellant is consumed at the rate of 200 lb/s, what is, (a) the specific impulse, (b) the effective exhaust velocity, (c) the total thrust, and (d) the vertical acceleration as it leaves the ground? [*Ans.* (a) 204 s, (b) 6560 ft/s, (c) 40,800 lb, (d) 98.6 ft/s^2.]

23. A rocket engine using liquid oxygen and hydrogen as a propellant, has a total weight of 50 tons. If propellant is consumed at the rate of 500 lb/s, what is (a) the specific impulse, (b) the effective exhaust velocity, (c) the total thrust, and (d) the vertical acceleration as it leaves the ground?

24. A rocket engine using liquid oxygen and kerosene as propellant, has a total weight of 25,000 Kg. If propellant is consumed at the rate of 200 Kg/s, what is (a) the effective exhaust velocity, (b) the specific impulse, (c) the total thrust, and (d) the vertical acceleration as it leaves the ground? [*Ans.* (a) 2.43 Km/s, (b) 248 s, (c) 486,000 N, (d) 9.64 m/s^2.]

25. A rocket using liquid oxygen and hydrazine as propellant has a total weight of 15 tons. If propellant is consumed at 150 lb/s, what is (a) the specific impulse, (b) the effective exhaust velocity, (c) the total thrust, and (d) the vertical acceleration as it leaves the ground?

VIBRATIONS AND WAVES

Any motion, simple or complex, which repeats itself in equal intervals of time, is called *periodic motion*. There are many examples in everyday life which give rise to a special kind of periodic motion called *simple periodic motion*. The swinging of the clock pendulum, the turning of the balance wheel of a watch, or the vibration of a tuning fork, are good examples of such motions. The term "simple periodic motion" applies to these because each can be described in terms of one of the simplest known types of periodic motion—namely, *uniform circular motion*.

22.1. Simple Harmonic Motion. *Simple harmonic motion is defined as the projection on any diameter of a point moving in a circle with uniform speed.*

This motion is illustrated in Fig. 22A. The

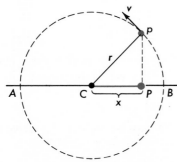

Fig. 22A *Diagram illustrating simple harmonic motion along a straight line.*

point p moves around the circle of radius r with uniform speed v. If at every instant a perpendicular is drawn from p to the diameter AB, the intercept P will move with simple harmonic motion. Moving back and forth along the straight

line from A to B, the velocity v_x is continually changing. At the center point C it has its greatest velocity, while at A and B it is momentarily at rest. Starting from either end of its path, the velocity increases until it reaches C; from there it slows down again, coming to rest at the opposite end of its path.

The *displacement* of a simple harmonic motion is defined as the distance from the center C to the point P. As shown in Fig. 22A, the displacement x varies in magnitude from zero at C up to r, the radius of the *circle of reference*, at A or B.

The *amplitude* r is defined as the maximum value of the *displacement* x, and the *period* is defined as the time required to make one complete vibration.

If a vibration starts at A, it is not completed until the point moves across to B and back again to A. If it starts from C and moves to B and back to C, only half a vibration has been completed. The amplitude r is usually measured in centimeters and the period T in seconds.

The frequency of a harmonic motion is defined as the number of complete vibrations per second. For example, if a particular vibrating object completes one vibration in one-half second (the period $T = \frac{1}{2}$ s), then it will make two complete vibrations in 1 s (the frequency $v = 2$ vib/s). If again a body completes one vibration in one-tenth of a second, $T = \frac{1}{10}$ s, it will make ten vibrations in 1 s, $v = 10$ vib/s. In other words, v and T are reciprocals of each other.

$$\text{Period} = \frac{1}{\text{frequency}}$$

or

$$\text{frequency} = \frac{1}{\text{period}} \tag{22a}$$

In algebraic symbolism,

$$T = \frac{1}{\nu} \qquad \nu = \frac{1}{T}$$ (22b)

22.2. Theory of Simple Harmonic Motion. It is intended here to derive a general formula for the period of vibrating bodies executing simple harmonic motion. Referring to Sec. 22.1, the period T is defined as the time required to make one complete vibration. Referring to Fig. 22B,

Fig. 22B *In any simple harmonic motion, the acceleration is always toward the central equilibrium position.*

the point p, moving with a speed v, will travel once around the circle of reference, a distance $2\pi r$, in a time T. Applying the relation that *time equals distance divided by velocity*, we get

$$T = \frac{2\pi r}{v}$$ (22c)

We have seen in Sec. 13.2 that an object moving in a circle with uniform speed v has a constant acceleration toward the center given by Eq.(13f) as

$$a_c = \frac{v^2}{r}$$

As this acceleration a_c changes in direction, its component a along the x axis changes in magnitude and is given by $a_c \cos \theta$. Making this substitution, we obtain

$$a = \frac{v^2}{r} \cos \theta$$

Since $\cos \theta = x/r$

$$a = \frac{v^2}{r} \cdot \frac{x}{r} \qquad a = \frac{v^2}{r^2} x$$

Multiplying both sides of the equation by $\frac{r^2}{av^2}$, and taking the square root, we obtain

$$\frac{r^2}{v^2} = \frac{x}{a} \qquad \text{and} \qquad \frac{r}{v} = \sqrt{\frac{x}{a}}$$

Substituting $\sqrt{x/a}$ for r/v in Eq.(22c) gives

$$T = 2\pi \sqrt{\frac{x}{a}}$$

When the displacement is $+$, the acceleration a is toward the center and therefore $-$. Conversely when x is $-$, a is $+$. For this reason the period should be written,

$$T = 2\pi \sqrt{-\frac{x}{a}}$$ (22d)

This is a useful equation because it gives the period of vibration in terms of the displacement x and the corresponding acceleration.

22.3. Vibrating Spring. Any elastic body may be set into a state of vibration by first distorting it in some way and then releasing it. This is demonstrated by a weight on the end of a spring as shown in Fig. 22C. In diagram (a), the spring

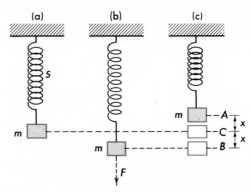

Fig. 22C *A mass on the end of a spring executes simple harmonic motion.*

S and mass m hang in a state of equilibrium. At (b) a force F has been applied to stretch the spring, displacing the mass a distance x. After being released, the mass m moves up and down with simple harmonic motion. In diagram (c) the spring is shown compressed with m at its highest point. The maximum displacement x of the vibration is determined by the original distance to which the spring is stretched, and the period T is given by the algebraic equation:

$$T = 2\pi \sqrt{m/k} \qquad (22e)$$

where m is the mass of the vibrating body and k a number expressing the stiffness of the spring. The constant k is the force in dynes required to stretch the spring 1 cm. This formula shows that, if m is made larger, the period is increased and that, when a stiffer spring is used (k being in the denominator), the period is decreased.

In accordance with Hooke's law [see Eq. (17e)], the stretch of a spring is given by the relation

$$F = -kx$$

where F is the restoring force, x the displacement, and k the same as above. Since a force of magnitude F acts to accelerate the mass m, $F = ma$ gives

$$ma = -kx \qquad \text{or} \qquad -x/a = m/k$$

The substitution of m/k for $-x/a$ in Eq. (22d) gives Eq.(22e).

22.4. Vibrating Strips. If a strip of wood or metal is clamped tightly at one end, as shown in Fig. 22D, it may be set into a natural state of

Fig. 22D *A weighted leaf spring, or reed, and a tuning fork vibrate with simple harmonic motion.*

vibration. Pulled to one side and then released, the free end of the strip will move back and forth with simple harmonic motion. If the mass m clamped to the free end is increased, the fre-

quency of vibration will decrease; whereas, if the strip is made stiffer either by increasing its thickness or decreasing its length, the frequency will increase.

Also shown in Fig. 22D is a tuning fork used by musicians to determine pitch. Striking one prong of a fork against some object sets both prongs vibrating simultaneously in opposite directions. The thinner the prongs of the fork, the lower is the frequency of vibration; the shorter the prongs of the fork, the higher is the frequency of vibration.

Besides being used as standards of pitch by musicians, tuning forks are used for scientific purposes. As scientific instruments they perform one very useful function of marking off short but equal intervals of time. A common fork used for this purpose has a frequency of 1000, $\nu = 1000$ vib/s, and is frequently kept vibrating by means of an electrical circuit similar to that of a doorbell.

22.5. The Simple Pendulum. If a simple pendulum, as shown in Fig. 22E, is set swinging in an

Fig. 22E *A pendulum bob executes simple harmonic motion along a curved path.*

arc which is not too big, its period T is given by the following formula,

$$T = 2\pi \sqrt{\frac{l}{g}} \qquad (22f)$$

T is the time of one complete vibration, l is the length of the pendulum, and g is the acceleration due to gravity. If the angle of swing is much greater than 5°, the period will be slightly increased.

The statement can now be made that the bob of a simple pendulum moves along its arc with *simple periodic motion*. At the ends of its swing the velocity is momentarily zero and at the center is a maximum. The driving force which starts the bob at one end of its path and accelerates it until it reaches the center and then decelerates it, bringing it to rest at the other end, is the component F of the force of gravity F_g. The component F_2 is the tension in the cord supporting the mass m.

The fact that the mass of a pendulum bob does not appear in Eq.(22f) signifies that pendulums of equal length but different mass should have the same period T. Started together, and with small amplitudes, simple pendulums of different mass will swing in synchronism (see Fig. 22F).

gravity

electromagnet

Fig. 22G   *An increase in gravitational attraction, like the downward pull of the magnet, will shorten the period of a simple pendulum.*

Fig. 22F   *Two simple pendulums of the same length but different mass have the same period of vibration.*

The effect of the acceleration of gravity g on the period is illustrated in Fig. 22G. If the pull of gravity could be increased, the period of all pendulums would decrease, that is, they would swing faster. If gravity could be decreased, the periods would be greater, that is, they would swing more slowly. In the diagram the pull of gravity is imitated by means of an electromagnet. When the magnet is turned on, it pulls down on the iron bob and makes it swing more quickly.

The effect of the length l on the period is shown in Fig. 22H. Two pendulums of lengths l and $4l$

are shown at the same instant a short time after having started simultaneously at their respective origins S. While the pendulum of length l has made one complete swing, the pendulum of length $4l$ has made only half a swing. This shows

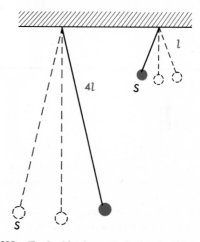

Fig. 22H   *To double the period of a simple pendulum, the length must be increased fourfold.*

that to double the time of swing the length must be made four times as large. This is in agreement with Eq.(22f) in which the length occurs under the square root sign.

A derivation of Eq.(22f) can be obtained from Fig. 22E as follows. The downward pull of gravity on the bob of mass m is F_g, and this has been resolved into two components, one parallel to the support l and the other F perpendicular to it. Because of equal angles θ in the two right triangles and the theorem that corresponding sides of similar triangles are proportional, we may write

$$\frac{F}{F_g} = \frac{x}{l}$$

Since the force F accelerates the mass m in the direction opposite to x, and the weight F_g is equal to mg, substitution in the above proportionality gives

$$\frac{ma}{mg} = \frac{-x}{l} \quad \text{or} \quad -\frac{x}{a} = \frac{l}{g}$$

Substituting l/g for $-x/a$ in Eq.(22d), we obtain

$$T = 2\pi\sqrt{l/g}$$

22.6. Sources of Waves. The motion of any material object may be considered as a source of waves. A board striking the water, the snap of a finger, or a bowed violin string are examples of this.

Suppose that the far end of a rope is fastened to a post, as shown in Fig. 22I, and that the

Fig. 22I *Examples of transverse waves sent out along a rope.*

other end (a), which is held in the hand, is given a sudden flip up and down. The disturbance sent out along the rope travels down the rope to the post, as shown, and is then reflected back again toward the hand. This kind of wave is called a *single-wave pulse*. If instead of a sudden pulse the hand is moved up and down with simple

harmonic motion, a *train of waves*, like that shown in diagram (b), travels down the rope.

When the prongs of a tuning fork are made to vibrate, they set the surrounding air into periodic motions. Each prong periodically strikes the air molecules next to it and these molecules in turn strike others, thus transmitting the disturbance outward. Traveling outward in all directions, such periodic disturbances constitute sound waves.

22.7. Transverse Waves. Transverse waves are those in which each particle vibrates along a line perpendicular to the direction of propagation. Along any one line of travel all particles are vibrating in one plane only. Such waves are illustrated in Fig. 22J by means of a wave machine

Fig. 22J *Diagram of a wave machine for demonstrating transverse waves.*

designed for this purpose. As the handle H is turned one way or the other, the small round balls at the top move up and down with simple harmonic motion. As they move up and down, each along its own line, the wave form ABCDEF will move to the right or to the left. Light is an example of transverse wave motion.

22.8. Longitudinal Waves. Longitudinal waves are those in which the vibrations of the particles are along straight lines parallel to the direction of propagation. This type of wave is illustrated in Fig. 22K by another wave machine. As the

Fig. 22K *Diagram of a wave machine for demonstrating longitudinal waves.*

handle is turned, each small ball moves horizontally and in the plane of the page with simple harmonic motion. In so doing, the regions of rarefaction B and D and the regions of condensation A, C, and E move to the right, always keeping their same relative distances.

Sound waves in air are examples of longitudinal waves. Each air molecule vibrates back and forth about some equilibrium position as the wave train passes by.

22.9. Standing Waves. Nearly all sounds emanating from musical instruments are the result of standing waves. Standing waves may be produced in any substance, whether it is a solid, liquid, or gas, by two wave trains of the same frequency traveling in the same medium in opposite directions. One of the ways in which this is done is illustrated in Fig. 22L. One end of a rope

quency, the waves traveling to the right in meeting the reflected waves traveling to the left set up *nodes* and *anti-nodes*. The nodes N correspond to points where there is no motion, and the anti-nodes L to points where the motion is a maximum. The dots in diagram (b) show the relative positions and motions of each individual coil of the spring at nine different times during one complete vibration. The dots at the nodes remain fixed at all times while those at the anti-nodes move back and forth as shown by the arrows in diagram (c). At one instant (3), compressions are formed at the odd-numbered nodes N_1, N_3, and N_5 and rarefactions at the even-numbered nodes N_2, N_4, and N_6. Half a vibration later (7), they change; the nodes of compression become nodes of rarefaction, and vice versa.

A direct comparison of standing transverse

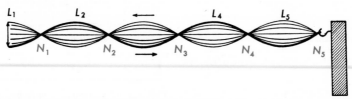

Fig. 22L   *Standing waves produced by reflecting a train of transverse waves from the fixed end of a rope.*

is fastened to a post, and the other end, held taut, is moved up and down with simple harmonic motion. As the waves reach the fixed end of the rope, they are reflected back to meet succeeding waves just coming up. If the waves have just the right frequency, the rope will sustain both wave trains by dividing into sections as shown. The points L_1 to L_5, where the rope has a maximum up and down motion, are called *anti-nodes*, and the points of no motion halfway between are called *nodes*. The heavy line represents the rope at one instant and the other lines represent it at other instants. The entire wave section between two consecutive nodes is called a *loop*.

Standing waves with longitudinal vibrations may be demonstrated with a long flexible spring as shown in Fig. 22M(a). The right-hand end of the spring is fixed and the left-hand end is moved back and forth with simple harmonic motion. If the impressed vibration has the proper fre-

and standing longitudinal waves is given by diagrams (b), (c), (d), and (e) in Fig. 22M. The numbers (1), (2), (3), etc., indicate the corresponding states in the vibrations of each. Diagram (c) indicates the amplitudes of the longitudinal motions at the anti-nodes of the spring, and diagram (e) the transverse motions at the anti-nodes of the rope.

It should be explained that the dots in diagram (b) also represent the motions of air molecules when sound waves are reflected from a flat wall, back on themselves, to produce standing waves. As we shall see in the next chapter, these are like the sustained vibrations of the air in an organ pipe, a flute, or some other musical wind instrument.

While sound waves in air are longitudinal vibrations, it is customary, for convenience only, to draw them as transverse waves. It is for this reason that the comparisons in Fig. 22M are

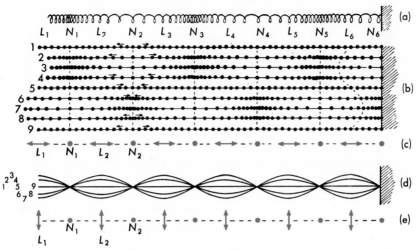

Fig. 22M *Illustration of standing waves as they are produced with (a) the longitudinal waves of a spring, (b) the longitudinal waves of sound in the air, and (d) the transverse waves of a rope. (c) and (e) indicate the direction of vibration at the antinodes.*

made here. In the following two chapters, therefore, sound waves will usually be drawn as though they were transverse.

22.10. Wavelength. When a vibrating object sends out waves through a homogeneous medium, the waves travel with constant velocity. If the source vibrates with simple harmonic motion and the waves are transverse, they have the general appearance of the waves shown in Fig. 22N. The *wavelength* is defined as the distance between two similar points of any two consecutive waves, and is represented by the Greek letter lambda, λ. The distance between two consecutive wave crests, for example, is equal to one wavelength.

The amplitude of a wave is defined as the maximum value of the displacement. This is illustrated by r in Fig. 22N, the amplitude of the waves being proportional to the amplitude of the source. The frequency of a train of waves is defined as the number of waves passing any given

point per second. This is equal to the frequency of the source and is usually designated by ν. It is customary to express frequency in *vibrations per second* or in *cycles per second*.

From the definitions of velocity, frequency, and wavelength, the following very simple relation exists among them:

$$V = \nu\lambda \qquad (22g)$$

The length of one wave, λ, times the number of waves per second, ν, equals the total distance traveled in 1 s, V.

Since the period is defined as the time required for one wave to pass by a given point, the relation between frequency and period given for vibrating sources in Eq.(22b) also applies to waves.

Example 1. If a train of waves moving along a rope has a speed of 100 ft/s and a wavelength of 20 ft, what is the frequency and period of the source?

Fig. 22N *Illustration of the wavelength λ as the distance between corresponding points on two consecutive waves, and the amplitude r as the maximum displacement.*

Fig. 22O   *Illustration of a mass m between two identical springs, vibrating with simple harmonic motion.*

Solution. By inserting these values in the proper places in Eq.(22g), we obtain

$$100 \text{ ft/s} = \nu \times 20 \text{ ft} \quad \text{or} \quad \nu = {}^{100}\!/_{20} = 5 \text{ vib/s}$$

By Eq.(22b),

$$T = \tfrac{1}{5} = 0.2 \text{ s}$$

The frequency is 5 vib/s, and the period is 0.2 s.

22.11. Vibration Energy. When an object or medium is set into vibration, energy is not only expended in setting up the vibration, but the motion of each element of mass constitutes a form of stored energy. As an illustration consider the simple case of a mass vibrating back and forth between two identical springs as shown in Fig. 22O.

Starting from its equilibrium position at C, a force F is applied to move the mass m a distance x to the right. Since the stretching and compressing of each spring obeys Hooke's law, the required force is proportional to the distance x. Hooke's law graphically leads to a straight line

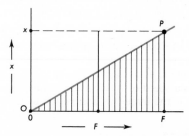

Fig. 22P   *Graph showing Hooke's law and the work done in stretching and compressing of two identical springs.*

as shown in Fig. 22P, and analytically to the equation

$$F = kx \qquad (22h)$$

To calculate the work done, the distance x must be multiplied by the average force. Since the force is not constant but is proportional to the displacement, the average force $\overline{F}$, for any given value of x is just the value of F divided by 2.

$$\overline{F} = \frac{F}{2}$$

The work done is, therefore, given by

$$W = \overline{F} \times x = \tfrac{1}{2}Fx \qquad (22i)$$

If the applied force F were constant, the work done in moving a distance x would be given by $F \times x$, the area of the rectangle xPFO, Fig. 22P. With a linearly increasing force F, however, the actual work done is given by the triangular shaded area, and this is seen to be just $\tfrac{1}{2}$ the area of the rectangle.

If we now substitute the value of F from Eq.(22h), in Eq.(22i) we obtain

$$W = \tfrac{1}{2}kx^2 \qquad (22j)$$

This work done is stored in the spring as potential energy, and when the mass is released it vibrates back and forth with simple harmonic motion.

As the mass passes through its equilibrium position C, the stored energy is all kinetic and we can write

$$E = \tfrac{1}{2}kr^2 = \tfrac{1}{2}mv^2 \qquad (22k)$$

where x is the maximum displacement r, and is called the *amplitude*. This derived equation is basic in principle to all kinds of waves and vibrations for it shows that *vibrational energy is proportional to the square of the amplitude*. To double the amplitude is to increase the vibrational energy four fold.

PROBLEMS

1. The amplitude of an object executing simple harmonic motion is 12 mm, and the period is 0.25 s. Calculate (a) the maximum acceleration, and (b) its maximum speed.

2. The maximum speed of a particle moving with simple harmonic motion is 0.25 m/s. If its period of vibration is 0.6 s, what is (a) the amplitude, and (b) the maximum acceleration? [*Ans.* (a) 2.39 cm, (b) 2.61 m/s².]

3. A particle moves with simple harmonic motion with an amplitude of 4 cm and a period of 0.05 s. Find (a) its maximum speed, and (b) its maximum acceleration.

4. When a mass of 40 gm is suspended from a spring as shown in Fig. 22C, it stretches the spring a distance of 8 cm. If the 40 g mass is now replaced by one of 100 g, and then set vibrating up and down, what will be the frequency [*Ans.* 1.11 vib/s.]

5. When a 12-lb weight is suspended from a spring as shown in Fig. 22C, the spring stretches 3 in. After the 12-lb weight is removed, a man jumps up and hangs on the lower end. If in so doing he is set vibrating with a period of 2.5 s, how much does he weigh?

6. A mass of 0.2 Kg, fastened to the end of a light-weight spring and set vibrating up and down, is found to have a frequency of 1.8 vib/s. Calculate the frequency when the mass is decreased to 0.08 Kg. [*Ans.* 2.85 vib/s.]

7. When a 2.5-Kg mass is fastened to the lower end of a spring as shown in Fig. 22C, it stretches a distance of 0.04 m. If the suspended mass is then set vibrating, what will be its frequency?

8. A mass of 0.25 Kg is suspended from a spring as shown in Fig. 22C. If the mass is set vibrating and the frequency is found to be 8 vib/s, what is the value of the spring constant? [*Ans.* 632 N/m.]

9. A clock pendulum swings with a period of 1 s where $g = 32.15$ ft/s². How many seconds will it lose in 24 hr if it is taken to a high mountain where $g = 32.00$ ft/s²?

10. A clock pendulum swings with a period of 1 s where $g = 9.82$ m/s². How many seconds will it lose in 24 hr if it is taken to a high mountain where $g = 9.80$ m/s²? [*Ans.* 88 s.]

11. A simple pendulum, generally called a Foucault pendulum, is 25 m long and hangs from the dome of a museum. With such a long pendulum the effect of the earth's rotation can be observed. Find the period of the pendulum.

12. A tiny pendulum 4 cm long is made of a fine silk thread and a quartz bead. Calculate (a) its period, and (b) its frequency. [*Ans.* (a) 0.401 s, (b) 2.49 vib/s.]

13. A pendulum has a length of 68.00 cm. Find its period and frequency to four significant figures. Assume $g = 9.822$ m/s².

14. A simple pendulum is to have a period of ⅛th of a second. How long should it be if $g = 9.820$ m/s²? [*Ans.* 3.88 mm.]

15. A train of waves moves along a cable with a speed of 18 ft/s. Find (a) the frequency, and (b) the period of the source if their wavelength is 4 in.

16. A vibrating source with a frequency of 22 vib/s sends waves along a rope with a velocity of 4 m/s. Find (a) the period of the source, and (b) the wavelength of the waves. [*Ans.* (a) 0.0454 s. (b) 18.2 cm.]

17. The velocity of radio waves is 3×10^8 m/s. What is the wavelength of the waves from a station broadcasting on a frequency of 860 Kc/s?

18. A radio station broadcasts on a wavelength of 5 m. What is the frequency in Mc/s, if the velocity of radio waves is 3×10^8 m/s? [*Ans.* 60 Mc/s.]

19. A mass of 2 Kg suspended from the end of a coiled spring, as in Fig. 22C, stretches the spring 4 cm. If the mass is then pulled downward an additional distance of 5 cm and released, find (a) its period, (b) its frequency, (c) the total vibrational energy, and (d) the maximum velocity acquired.

20. A mass of 5 Kg suspended from a spring as in Fig. 22C, stretches the spring 15 cm. If this mass is then pulled down an additional distance of 10 cm, and then released, find (a) its period, (b) its frequency, (c) its total vibrational energy, and (d) its maximum velocity. [*Ans.* (a) 0.777 s, (b) 1.29 vib/s, (c) 1.63 J, (d) 0.81 m/s.]

SOUND:
ITS TRANSMISSION AND DETECTION

The transmission of sound from one place to the other, from source to receiver, requires a material medium through which to travel. This is to be contrasted with light which travels best through a vacuum.

23.1. Sound Transmission. That sound is transmitted by air, or any other gas, may be demonstrated by placing a small bell in an evacuated jar. This is illustrated in Fig. 23A. As the air is

in turn strike others. Upon reaching the side of the jar, the glass walls are periodically bombarded by the molecules and set vibrating. The walls in turn set the outside air vibrating. Arriving at the observer's ear, the disturbance strikes the eardrum, setting it into motion. Without air to transmit the vibrations from the bell to the inside surface of the glass jar, no sound could ever leave the jar.

The transmission of sound by liquids may be illustrated by an experiment shown in Fig. 23B.

Fig. 23A *A bell ringing in a vacuum cannot be heard.*

Fig. 23B *Demonstration of sound waves traveling through water.*

slowly removed from the jar, the ringing of the bell grows fainter and fainter until, when a good vacuum is obtained, no sound can be heard. As soon as the air is admitted, however, the ringing becomes clearly audible again. The vibrating bell strikes air molecules, knocking them away from the metal surface. These fast-moving molecules strike the adjacent air molecules and they

A tuning fork with a disk attached to its base is set vibrating and then touched to the surface of a dish of water. The vibrations of the fork and disk travel through the water to the bottom of the dish and to the table top. The table top itself is set into vibration with the same frequency as the fork, thus acting like a *sounding board* to make the sound louder.

The transmission of sound by solids is illustrated in Fig. 23C. A vibrating tuning fork is

Fig. 23C *Demonstration of sound waves traveling through wood.*

brought into contact with the end of a long wooden rod. The longitudinal vibrations travel down the length of the rod, which causes the hollow wooden box at the other end to vibrate. Sound is clearly heard coming from the box.

Sound waves, whether they travel through solids, liquids, or gases, are longitudinal in character. In Fig. 23D the prongs of a tuning fork are

Fig. 23D *Sound waves are longitudinal waves.*

shown vibrating back and forth with simple harmonic motion. By collisions with air molecules, each one sends out longitudinal waves through the atmosphere.

23.2. Speed of Sound. Although light and sound both travel with a finite speed, the speed of light is so great in comparison that an instantaneous flash may be regarded as taking no time to travel many miles. When we see the light of a distant lightning flash and hear the thunder later, we know that the difference in time is due to the relatively low speed of sound. Knowing that sound requires 5 s to travel 1 mi, the distance of a passing thunderstorm can be noted by the second hand of a watch. Similarly, when a distant train starts up and we watch for the first puff of smoke as it starts out, the arrival of the accompanying sound is not heard until an appreciable time afterward.

The earliest successful attempts to measure the speed of sound in air were made in 1640 by Marin Mersenne, a French physicist, and in 1656 by Giovanni Borelli and Vincenzo Viviani, Italian physicists. Since that time many experimenters have improved upon these earliest measurements by using various different methods and devices. The most recent and probably the most accurate measurements are those made in 1934 by Miller.* With coast defense guns as a source of sound and a set of receivers located at certain distances apart, very accurate speed determinations were made. The results gave a speed of 331 m/s at a temperature of 0°C. This is equivalent to 1087 ft/s.

As a general rule, sound travels faster in solids and liquids than it does in gases. This is illustrated by the measured speeds for a few common substances given in Table 23A.

TABLE 23A. SPEED OF SOUND IN
DIFFERENT SUBSTANCES

Substance	Speed (m/s)	Speed (ft/s)
Air (at 0°C)	331	1,087
Carbon dioxide	258	846
Carbon monoxide	337	1,106
Hydrogen	1,269	4,165
Alcohol	1,213	3,890
Benzine	1,166	3,826
Turpentine	1,326	4,351
Water	1,435	4,708
Aluminum	5,104	16,704
Copper	3,560	11,670
Glass	5,500	18,050
Iron	5,130	16,820
Ivory	3,013	9,886
Nickel	4,973	16,320
Oak (w grain)	3,850	12,620

* Dayton C. Miller (1866–1940), American physicist, noted for his experiments on the quality of musical sounds and on the ether drift. He collected and had in his possession the largest collection of flutes in the world. These instruments he turned over to the Smithsonian Institute in Washington, D.C., where they are now on exhibit. A member of the National Academy of Sciences, and one-time president of the American Physical Society, he has been awarded the Elliott Cresson Medal and the Cleveland Distinguished Service Medal.

It is well known that the temperature has a small but measurable effect upon the speed of sound. For each degree centigrade rise in temperature, the speed in air increases by 61 cm/s, or its equivalent of 2 ft/sec. Written as an equation,

$$V = V_0 + 0.61t \qquad (23a)$$

Centigrade

where V_0 is the speed in m/s at 0°C, and t is the temperature in °C. For each degree on the Fahrenheit scale, the speed increases by 1.1 ft/s.

$$V = V_0 + 1.1(t - 32) \qquad (23b)$$

Fahrenheit

A speed of 1087 ft/s is equivalent to 740 mi/hr. High in the stratosphere where the daytime temperature reaches 200°F, the speed of sound increases 168 ft/s. There the speed of 1255 ft/s is equivalent to 856 mi/hr (see Fig. 20O).

23.3. Pitch. The pitch of a musical note refers to its position on a musical scale, and is determined by the frequency of the sound impulses sent out by the vibrating source. The dependence of pitch upon frequency can be demonstrated in many ways. Diagram (a) of Fig. 23E represents a

Diagram (b) is a siren similar to those commonly used as factory whistles. The energy as well as the sound is derived from compressed air which is blown through small holes in the hollow container C. The air issuing from these jets passes through similar holes in a rotating disk W. With the holes drilled at an angle as shown in detail in (d), the air blasts from the stationary holes below exert a force on one side of the holes in W, causing the disk to turn. As the disk turns, each blast of air is momentarily cut off until another hole arrives just above it. The intermittent pulses of air issuing from the disk give rise to a musical note.

Diagram (c) in Fig. 23E represents a siren in which a single blast of air is interrupted by a rotating disk containing several rings of holes. Detailed experiments with many musically trained and untrained observers alike show that pitch and frequency are not identical.

Pitch is a *subjective* measurement and is therefore a sensory magnitude depending upon the individual, while frequency is a *physical* measurement of the number of vibrations per second. As the intensity of a pure tone of 300 vib/s is increased, for example, it appears to most observers to change in quality and at the same time

Fig. 23E *Sound demonstrations illustrating the relation between pitch and frequency.*

toothed wheel (called Savart's wheel) rotating at high speed. A small card held against the teeth is set into vibration, giving out a musical note. As the wheel slows down, the vibration frequency of the card decreases and the note lowers in pitch.

to decrease slightly in pitch. Conversely, at a high frequency, an increase in the intensity seems to increase the pitch.

23.4. Detection of Sound. By far the most important instrument by which sound is detected is the ear. This hearing mechanism, which is sensitive to very faint as well as loud sounds and to very high as well as low frequencies, is treated in detail in Sec. 23.7.

Various electrical devices, commonly called

Fig. 23F *Diagram of a gas flame, sensitive to high-pitched sound waves. As the waves pass the tip of the nozzle, the flame dips down.*

microphones, have been invented for detecting sound waves and transforming them into varying electric currents. These currents may then be amplified, transmitted long or short distances, and then reconverted into sound. Sometimes

they are fed into an oscilloscope for a study of wave motion, a "cutting head" for recording, a light source for sound recording on film, or an electromagnet for recording on wire or tape. Some of these devices are considered in detail in later chapters.

Sound may also be detected by a rather interesting but impractical device known as the sensitive flame. This detector, as illustrated in Fig. 23F, consists of a tall, thin gas flame produced by gas issuing from a small nozzle. As sound waves pass by the tip of the nozzle, the gas stream is disturbed and the flame becomes unstable and drops in height. This action is particularly noticeable with high-pitched sounds like those from a blowing whistle, or those from a jingling bunch of keys.

23.5. Reflection of Sound. The reflection of sound waves may be demonstrated in various ways. One arrangement is shown in Fig. 23G in which a Galton whistle sounding a high-pitched note acts as a source of sound and a sensitive flame as the receiver. A solid screen between the two casts a "sound shadow," thus permitting only the reflected waves from the wall of the room to reach it.

When the whistle, blown by compressed air, is sounded continuously, the flame will remain unstable. If, under these conditions, the experimenter walks beside the wall through the sound

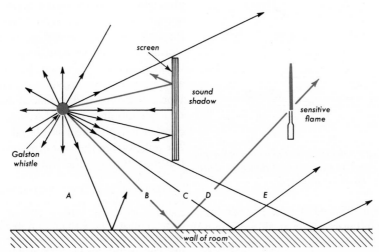

Fig. 23G *Experiment demonstrating the reflection of sound waves from the wall of a room.*

path, the flame will be quite unstable when he reaches A, C, or E, but will burn smoothly when he intercepts the beam at B or D.

Sound shadows of the kind shown in this experiment are characteristic of high-pitched notes only and demonstrate that short waves tend to travel in straight lines. The longer waves of low-pitched sounds, however, tend to bend around corners. This latter effect, known as *diffraction*, is quite noticeable where a carillon of large bells is being played. On walking around the corner of a nearby building, one notices that the sharp cutoff in the intensity of the high-pitched bells is quite marked, while the low-pitched bells continue in good strength. It should be pointed out that high-pitched notes also show diffraction, but to a lesser degree. This phenomenon is due to the wave nature of sound, and will be explained in principle in the case of light waves in another chapter.

Fig. 23H *The higher velocity of sound waves in warm air causes sound waves to be refracted down at night and up in the daytime.*

23.6. Refraction of Sound Waves. The bending of sound waves in layers of air at different temperatures is called *refraction*. The phenomenon, which can be observed in various ways, is due

to the greater speed of sound in warm air than in cold (see Sec. 23.2).

A good illustration is found in the frequent observation, while boating on a lake or river of being able to hear the music from a quite distant radio or phonograph at night but not in the daytime. The reason for this is shown in Fig. 23H. At night, the air near the water is colder than it is higher up, so that the higher speed in the warmer air bends the waves back down. During the day, the air close to the water is warmer and the waves bend up away from the water as shown.

Recent experiments of this kind have been perfomed with the very loud sounds from big guns. Sound waves refracted back from high up in the stratosphere indicate with some degree of certainty the existence of very warm layers of air at altitudes of 25 to 40 mi. Refraction in such cases as this is similar to reflection from a mirror surface, since the waves travel in more or less straight lines, going up and back, but bend over when they enter, more or less abruptly, a warmer layer.

23.7. Intensity of Sound. There are three fundamental characteristics of all sounds:

Objective	Subjective
intensity	loudness
frequency	pitch
wave form	tone quality

The intensity of sound is characterized by its loudness and is measured scientifically by the amount of energy in a given volume of the space through which the sound is traveling. In other words, sound waves constitute a flow of energy through matter. This may be demonstrated by an experiment, arranged as shown in Fig. 23I. A vibrating tuning fork is placed near one opening of a Helmholtz* resonator, and a very lightly constructed pinwheel is placed near the other. Air pulses from the vibrating prongs of the fork traveling through the resonator come out rein-

* Hermann Helmholtz (1821–1894), noted German physicist, who during his lifetime made outstanding contributions to the subjects of light, sound, and electricity. Probably his greatest contribution was his explanation of tone quality in musical notes. He demonstrated that quality depends upon the number and intensity of the overtones or harmonies present in the musical tone.

Fig. 23I   *A pin wheel may be set rotating by sound waves from a tuning fork, demonstrating that sound waves have energy.*

forced at the other opening and strike the vanes of the pinwheel. When the fork is removed the pinwheel stops rotating. *Loudness is a subjective measurement of sound power and is therefore a sensory magnitude. Intensity, on the other hand, is an objective measurement of the sound power being delivered.*

One method of specifying the intensity of a sound is to state the amount of energy flowing through unit area per second. Since the rate of flow of energy in most common sounds is extremely small, the ordinary unit of power, the *watt*, is too large to be practical. Consequently, a unit one million times smaller, the *microwatt* (μW), is used (see Fig. 23J).

1 microwatt = 10^{-6} watt
1 microwatt = 10^{-6} joules/second

Sound intensity is defined as the power flowing through one square meter of area, taken normal to the direction of the waves.

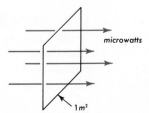

Fig. 23J   *Sound intensity is measured in microwatts flowing through 1 m² of area.*

A common method of specifying intensity is to compare the power in a given sound with the power in another. *When the power in one sound is ten times that in another, the ratio of intensity is said to be 1 bel.* The *bel* is so called in honor of Alexander Graham Bell, the inventor of the electric telephone. According to this definition, an intensity scale in bels is a logarithmic scale of power.

$$B = \log_{10} \frac{P_1}{P_2} \qquad (23c)$$

B in bels

where P_1 is the intensity, or power, of one sound and P_2 that of another. The following tabulation will illustrate this equation.

TABLE 23B. SOUND INTENSITY SCALE IN BELS

Relative Power (P_1/P_2)	Relative Intensity (bels)
1	0
10	1
100	2
1000	3
10000	4

The numbers at the right are just the logarithms of those at the left. According to these figures, a sound with 1000 times the power of another is 3 bels louder.

Because the *bel* represents large differences in intensity, a smaller unit, the *decibel* (db), has been introduced and used by telephone and radio engineers, as well as by physicians (ear specialists). According to this smaller unit, the bel is divided into ten equal ratios by the following equation.

$$b = 10 \log \frac{P_1}{P_2} \qquad (23d)$$

b in decibels

The following tabulation will illustrate specific values from this equation.

Each power ratio in the left column is 26% greater than the preceding value. Because such a change is just detectable by the human ear, the decibel is considered a practical unit. The sounds

TABLE 23C. SOUND INTENSITY SCALE IN DECIBELS

Relative power (P_1/P_2)	Relative intensity (db)
1.00	0
1.26	1
1.58	2
2.00	3
2.51	4
3.16	5
3.98	6
5.01	7
6.31	8
7.94	9
10.00	10

from several common sources are compared in different units in Table 23D.

TABLE 23D. COMMON SOUND LEVELS

	Intensity $(\mu W/m^2)$	Sound level (b)	Sound level (db)
Threshold of hearing	10^{-6}	0	0
Rustling leaves	10^{-4}	2	20
Talking (at 3 ft)	10^{-2}	4	40
Noisy office or store	1	6	60
Subway car	10^4	10	100
Threshold of pain	10^6	12	120

Example 1. The sound intensity received from a nearby jet plane is 12.6 $\mu W/m^2$, and that from another plane some distance away is 0.45 $\mu W/m^2$. Find the relative loudness of the two in decibels.

Solution. By direct substitution in Eq.(26d) we obtain

$$b = 10 \log_{10} \frac{12.6}{0.45}$$

$$b = 10 \log_{10} 28.0$$

Using the log table in Appendix IV, we look up the mantissa for 28.0 and find 4472. Since the characteristic of a common logarithm of a number greater than 1 is one less than the number of integral figures, and 28 has two integral figures, we obtain,

$$b = 10 \times 1.4472$$
$$\text{or} \quad b = 14.472 \text{ db}$$
to three figures $b = 14.5$ db.

23.8. Human Audiogram. An audiogram for the normal human ear is given in Fig. 23K. The lower curve gives the faintest sounds that can be heard, and the upper curve the loudest that can be heard without pain. It will be noted that the ear is most sensitive to frequencies between 2000 and 4000 cycles and that the sensitivity diminishes rapidly at higher and lower frequencies.

As a practical matter, sound experts have adopted as a zero level of sound intensity, $P_0 = 10^{-6} \mu W/m^2$ at a frequency of 1000 c/s. This is the limit of audibility of the average human being for a 1000 c/s note.

To see how intensity affects the frequency limits of audibility, consider the horizontal line at 20 db. At this intensity level, with a flow of energy 100 times that necessary to hear the faintest 1000 c/s note, frequencies below about 200 c/s and above 15,000 c/s cannot be heard. At 40 db with a flow of energy 10,000 times the threshold of audibility at 1000 c/s, the lowest frequency to be heard is about 100 c/s, whereas the upper limit may be as high as 20,000 c/s.

The amplitude of the sound waves at the threshold of audibility at 1000 c/s has been determined and found to be about 1 × 10^{-10} m. This is about the diameter of a hydrogen atom and gives some idea of the enormous sensitivity of the human ear. When a sound becomes so loud that it is painful to the ear, the amplitude is of the order of 1–2 mm.

23.9. Inverse Square Law. Theory indicates, and experiments prove, that the intensity of sound is inversely proportional to the square of the distance from the source. As an equation,

$$\boxed{\frac{P_1}{P_2} = \frac{d_2^2}{d_1^2}} \tag{23e}$$

where P_1 and P_2 are the intensities of the same sound at the two different distances d_1 and d_2, respectively. This is called the *inverse square law*.

If S in Fig. 23L represents a source of sound, the waves travel outward in straight lines. Whatever sound energy flows through area A at 1 m, the same energy will flow through area B at 2 m, and area C at 3 m. Since these areas have the ratios 1:4:9, the energy flow per second, through unit area at each distance, will be $P_1, \frac{1}{4}P_1$ and $\frac{1}{9}P_1$, respectively.

Fig. 23K   *Audiogram of the average human being, showing the threshold of hearing for different frequencies of sound.*

Example 2. The noise from an airplane engine 100 ft from an observer is found to have an intensity of 45 db. What will be the intensity when the plane flies overhead at an altitude of 1 mi?

Fig. 23L   *Illustration of the inverse square law.*

Solution. By direct substitution in Eq.(23e), we obtain for the ratio of the sound intensities

$$\frac{P_1}{P_2} = \frac{(5280 \text{ ft})^2}{(100 \text{ ft})^2} = 2788$$

Using the log table in the Appendix IV we look up the mantissa for 2788 and find 4453. Since the number 2788 has four integral figures, the characteristic is one less, or 3, and substituting in Eq.(23d), we write

$$db = 10 \log_{10} 2788$$
$$db = 10 \times 3.4453$$
$$\text{or,} \quad db = 34.453 \text{ decibels}$$
$$\text{to three figures} \quad db = 34.5 \text{ db}$$

Subtracting this relative loudness from the original 45 db we obtain for the plane 1 mi overhead,

$$db = 10.5 \text{ db.}$$

PROBLEMS

1. Calculate the speed of sound in air when the temperature is 40°C.

2. Find the speed of sound in air when the temperature is 100°F. [*Ans.* 1162 ft/s.]

3. Determine the speed of sound in air if the temperature is 27°C.

4. Determine the speed of sound in air at an altitude of 12.5 mi, where the temperature is −62°F (see Fig. 17B). [Ans. 984 ft/s.]

5. At a distance of 20 m from a jet plane, the noise level on open throttle is 80 db. What is the noise level when the plane flies overhead at an altitude of 2800 m?

6. The noise from a racing-car motor is 50 db at a distance of 20 ft. What is the noise level at 240 ft? [Ans. 38.4 db.]

7. If one sound is 28 db louder than another, what are the relative powers?

8. At $\frac{1}{2}$ mi the sound level of a fire siren is 15 db. What is the intensity at a distance of only 20 ft? [Ans. 57.4 db.]

9. If one sound is 32 db louder than another, what are their relative energies?

10. Two feet in front of a radio loud-speaker the sound level is 32 db. Calculate the intensity at a distance of 15 ft. [Ans. 14.5 db.]

11. To an observer standing in front of a flight of steps, a sharp clap of the hands will produce a sound that is reflected back to the observer from each step. If the step treads are 15 in. deep, what frequency is heard by the observer? Assume a temperature of 75°F.

12. If one sound is 42 db more intense than another, what are their relative powers? [Ans. 1.58 × 10⁴.]

13. If the intensity of a sound 2 m from a radio is 1 × 10⁻² μW/m², what is the intensity at a distance of 10 m?

14. If the intensity of a sound from an outdoor public address loudspeaker is 2 μW/m² at 3 m, what is the intensity at a distance of 120 m? [Ans. 1.25 × 10⁻³ μW/m².]

15. The noise from the engine of a racing car is 50 db at a distance of 2 m. How loud is it at a distance of 50 m?

16. If one sound is 36 db louder than another, what are their relative powers? [Ans. 3.98 × 10³.]

17. The volume of a public address system is adjusted to a level of 40 db for people at a distance of 125 m. What will be the level of sound at a distance of 10 m?

RESONANCE, BEATS,
DOPPLER EFFECT, AND INTERFERENCE

When sound waves from one or more sources fall on the ears of an observer the resultant sound that is heard depends upon many factors. The source of sound or the observer may be moving, two or more sources may have the same or different frequencies, or one train of waves may interfere with another. These are the subjects to be considered in this chapter.

24.1. Resonance. An experimental demonstration of resonance is easily set up, as shown in Fig. 24A. Two simple pendulums are suspended

Fig. 24A *A demonstration of resonance can be performed with two pendulums.*

from a flexible support. One, A, has a heavy bob made of metal, and the other, B, a bob made of wood.

The heavy bob A is pulled to one side and released to swing freely. The horizontal support responds to the motion and, in swaying back and forth in step with A, acts to set the other pendulum swinging. The response of pendulum B to

these forced vibrations depends upon the relative lengths of the two pendulums. If there is considerable difference in their lengths, the response is ever so slight, and the closer they are to the same length the greater is the response.

When A and B have the same length, their natural periods become equal, and B responds to the swaying support and swings with a large amplitude. It responds in sympathy, or resonance, to the driving pendulum A.

If two violin strings are tuned to the same frequency and one is set vibrating, the other stationed some distance away will soon pick up the vibrations and give out the same note. This too is a case of resonance, a phenomenon which occurs only if two objects have the same natural frequency of vibration.

Another experimental demonstration of resonance is illustrated in Fig. 24B. Two tuning forks

Fig. 24B *Tuning forks mounted on resonator boxes for demonstrating resonance.*

with exactly the same pitch are mounted on separate hollow boxes as shown. Fork A is first set vibrating for a moment and then stopped by touching the prongs with the fingers. Fork B will then be found vibrating. If we take into account the hollow boxes, whose purpose it is to act as sounding boards and thus intensify the sound, we find that the explanation is quite simple. Each sound pulse that emerges from the box with each vibration of fork A passes into the other box, pushing out the sides at just the right time to make the prongs of fork B move in the proper direction.

24.2. Beat Notes. When two notes of slightly different pitch are sounded at the same time, beats are heard. This phenomenon is used in organ pipes to produce the familiar vibrato effect. Two pipes tuned to slightly different frequencies are used for every note.

The phenomenon of beats may be demonstrated by two tuning forks mounted as shown in Fig. 24B. One fork is made slightly out of tune with the other by looping rubber bands *tightly* around the prongs. If the two forks are sounded simultaneously, the intensity of the sound rises and falls periodically. This is illustrated by means of vibration graphs as shown in Fig. 24C. The

$$\boxed{\text{beat frequency } N = \nu_2 - \nu_1} \quad (24a)$$

When the beat frequency lies between about 1 and 6 vib/s, the ear perceives a single intertone halfway between the two sounded, but periodically waxing and waning in intensity. As the beat frequency increases, the smooth rise and fall gives way to a succession of pulses, then to a sensation of roughness, and finally to two clearly perceived tones.

24.3. The Doppler Effect. Nearly everyone has at some time, perhaps without realizing it, observed the *Doppler effect*. The sounding horn of a car passing at high speed on the highway exhibits the phenomenon. The pitch of the horn, as the car goes by, drops as much as two whole notes on the musical scale. A similar observation can be made by listening to the roar of the motor of a racing car as it approaches and recedes from an observer at the race track. The motor seems

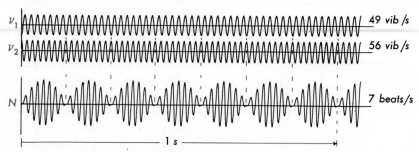

Fig. 24C   *Wave graphs illustrating how beat notes are produced by two different frequencies.*

upper curve represents the sound vibrations arriving at the ear from one fork, and the second curve the vibrations from the other. Both waves arriving at the ear are first in phase, i.e., in step with each other, then out of phase, then in phase, then out of phase, etc.

The resultant action of these two waves on the eardrum is represented by the third line. When the waves are in phase, the resultant has a large amplitude equal to the sum of the amplitudes of the two. When they are out of phase the amplitude becomes zero. The number of beats per second, N, is determined by the difference between ν_2 and ν_1, the respective frequencies of the two sources producing the sound.

to slow down as it passes by. Again, the pitch of the whistle on a fast-moving train sounds higher as the train approaches the observer than it does after the train has passed by.

This change in pitch is due to the relative motions of the source of sound and the observer. To see how this produces the effect, consider the following example. When the whistle on a train at rest is blown, it sends out waves traveling with the same velocity in all directions. To all stationary observers, no matter in what direction they are located, the true pitch of the whistle is heard, since just as many waves arrive at the ear per second as there are waves leaving the whistle.

If, on the other hand, the train is moving as

Fig. 24D *The Doppler effect. The pitch of a whistle on a fast-moving train sounds higher to an observer in front of the train, lower to an observer in back, and normal to observers off at the sides.*

shown in Fig. 24D, the whistle is moving away from the waves traveling to the rear and toward the waves traveling forward. The result is that the waves behind are considerably drawn out while those in front are crowded together. With each new wave sent out by the source, the train is farther from the preceding wave sent out to the rear and nearer to the one sent out ahead. Since the velocity of sound is the same in all directions, an observer at O_1 therefore hears more waves per second and an observer at O_2 hears fewer.

To an observer O_3 or O_4, at right angles and at some little distance from the moving source, the pitch remains unchanged. For these side positions the source is neither approaching nor receding from the observer, so that approximately the same number of waves are received per second as there are waves leaving the source.

The general relations for the Doppler effect are given by the following single equation:

$$\frac{\nu_o}{V - v_0} = \frac{\nu_s}{V - v_s} \qquad (24b)$$

where ν_s is the frequency of the source, ν_o is the frequency heard by the observer, V is the velocity of sound, v_s the velocity of the source, and v_o the velocity of the observer. *The direction of the velocity of sound V at the observer is positive, and its direction is taken as the positive direction for all velocities. Either v_o or v_s is positive if it is directed along the positive direction, and negative if it is oppositely directed.*

Case 1. If the source and observer are approaching each other, v_s is $+$, and v_o is $-$.

Case 2. If the source and observer are moving in the same direction, v_s and v_o are both $+$.

Case 3. The observer is at rest and the source is approaching at a velocity $v_s = 2V$. Here $v_o = 0$ and v_s is $+$. This is an interesting case since ν_o is the negative of ν_s. The observer hears the sound backward, as if played backward on a tape recorder, and it is heard after the source has passed him.

Example 1. A racing car passes the grandstand traveling at a speed of 150 mi/hr. If the noise from the exhaust has a frequency of 540 vib/s, what frequency is heard by the audience as the car approaches the grandstand? Assume the speed of sound to be 1120 ft/s.

Solution. Employing the Doppler formula, Eq. (24b), we solve for the unknown ν_o, and write

$$\nu_o = \frac{\nu_s(V - v_o)}{V - v_s}$$

Since the source of the sound is moving in the same direction as the sound waves arriving at the grandstand, V_s is $+150$ mi/hr, or $+220$ ft/s. Substituting the known quantities, we obtain

$$\nu_o = \frac{540(1120 - 0)}{1120 - 220}$$

and

$$\nu_o = \frac{540 \times 1120}{900} = 672 \frac{\text{vib}}{\text{s}}$$

24.4. Interference. Everyone has at one time or another dropped a stone in a still pond of water and watched the waves spread outward in ever-widening circles. Such waves are represented by concentric circles as shown in Fig. 24E. The solid-line circles represent crests of waves and are therefore one wavelength apart, while the dotted-line circles represent the troughs of the waves, which are also one wavelength apart.

If two stones are dropped simultaneously into the water, two sets of waves will spread outward as shown in Fig. 24F. As these waves cross each other, they act one upon the other, producing what is called an *interference pattern*. Where the crests of two waves come together at the dotted intersections, they are *in step*, or in phase, and the amplitude of the water surface is increased. Where the crest of one wave and the trough of another come together, they are out of step, or

Fig. 24E *Concentric waves traveling outward from a single source S.*

out of phase, and the amplitude of the water surface is reduced. The *in-phase* regions of the waves move outward along the dotted lines, such as x, y, and z, and we have what is called *constructive interference*. The *out-of-phase* regions move outward along the solid lines, such as a and b, and we have what is called *destructive interference*.

An instantaneous photograph of such a wave pattern is shown in Fig. 24G. Note how clearly the interference regions of the waves stand out.

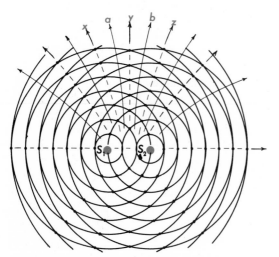

Fig. 24F *Concentric waves traveling outward from a double source, producing what is called an interference pattern.*

Photographs of this kind, as well as direct observations of such wave patterns, are readily made as follows. A glass tray for maintaining a shallow water layer can be made from a piece of window glass and a wooden frame.

Fig. 24G *Ripple-tank photograph of the interference of water waves from two sources.* (Courtesy, Physical Sciences Study Committee Project.)

A thin metal strip, clamped at one end and set vibrating up and down over the water, is used as a source. A piece of wire, fastened to the vibrating end of this strip, should have one wire end dipping into the water for a single-wave source, and both ends dipping into the water for a double source. Intermittent viewing of the waves through a slotted disk, or illumination by means of a stroboscopic light source, enables one to make the wave pattern appear to stand still, or to progress in *slow motion*.

An experiment for demonstrating the interference of sound waves is shown in Fig. 24H. Two small radio loudspeakers S_1 and S_2 are mounted, about 150 cm apart, in a hollow box. The box is free to pivot about a vertical axis

Fig. 24H *Experiment for demonstrating the inter-ference of sound waves from two sources.*

midway between the speaker centers. When both speakers are connected to an electronic sound generator, G, the speakers vibrate in phase and send out identical waves into the surrounding air. A microphone, M, about 2 m away, is an excellent detector, and an oscilloscope connected to it will indicate the relative amplitudes of the resultant sound waves arriving at M.

As the box is turned slowly in one direction, the amplitude of the oscilloscope signal P rises and falls periodically, indicating constructive and destructive interference. As it is turned slowly back again, maxima and minima are again observed at the same angle positions.

An instructive diagram showing the arrival of pairs of waves at the microphone, for maximum

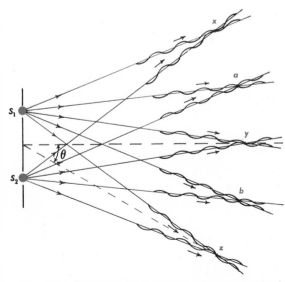

Fig. 24I *Diagram showing the in-phase and out-of-phase of waves at certain points.*

and minimum response positions, is shown in Fig. 24I. Points x, y, and z correspond to points x, y, and z in Fig. 24F, where the waves arrive in phase, while points a and b correspond to those where they arrive out of phase.

By measuring the angles, θ, at which maximum response occurs for the experiment shown in Fig. 24H, as well as the distance d between S_1 and S_2, and the distance D, the wavelength of the sound waves can be calculated. The geometry for this calculation is shown in Fig. 24J.

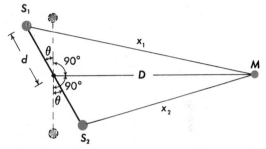

Fig. 24J *Geometrical relations for finding the wave-length of sound waves from a double source.*

When the line between the two speakers makes an angle of 90° with the perpendicular bisector D, the sources are equidistant from M, the waves arrive in phase, and we have point y of Figs. 24F and 24I. When the sources are turned to position z, the line between the speakers has been turned through an angle θ, the waves arrive in phase again, but the path x_1 is exactly one wavelength longer than the path x_2.

At some greater angle θ, the path x_1 can be made exactly two wavelengths longer than x_2, and at some still greater angle it can be made three wavelengths longer, etc. For all these particular angles where the waves are in phase, we can write the single equation

$$x_1 - x_2 = n\lambda \qquad (24c)$$

where $\qquad n = 0, 1, 2, 3, \ldots \qquad$ (24d)

We can now apply the law of cosines to the two large triangles in Fig. 24J, and calculate the distances x_1 and x_2.

For the upper triangle, we write

$$x_1{}^2 = d^2 + D^2 - 2dD \cos(90° + \theta) \quad (24e)$$

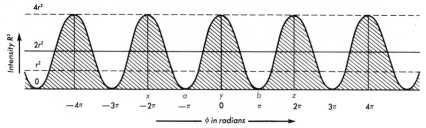

Fig. 24K   *Interference pattern for two waves of equal amplitude as produced in an experiment like that shown in Fig. 24I.*

and for the lower triangle, we write

$$x_2^2 = d^2 + D^2 - 2dD \cos (90° - \theta) \quad (24f)$$

By substituting the measured values of D, d, and θ in these two equations, the values of x_1 and x_2 can be calculated. Substituting these values in Eq.(24c), along with the appropriate value of n, makes it possible to calculate the wavelength λ.

If the intensities for the sound waves arriving at the microphone in Fig. 24J are plotted for a large number of angles θ, we obtain a graph of the kind shown in Fig. 24K. The maxima and minima are seen to be special points of a smooth and continuous curve. The central solid line represents the intensity graph one would expect if both sources were sounded and interference did not occur. The effect of interference, therefore, is seen to give rise to an angular redistribution of sound energy. The shaded areas above the dotted line fit exactly into the unshaded spaces below. The intensity at the peaks is double the average of the sum of the two.

24.5. Phase Angles. The instantaneous displacement and direction of motion of an object vibrating with simple harmonic motion is readily described by specifying the position of a graph point on a circle of reference (see Fig. 22B). The angle θ specifying the position is called the *phase angle*, and the maximum possible displacement r is called the *amplitude*.

Consider as another example an object vibrating up and down along the y axis as shown in Fig. 24L. The instantaneous position of the mass point m is given by the projection of the graph point P on the y axis. From the right triangle PQO in the figure,

$$y = r \sin \theta \quad (24g)$$

Here again the phase angle θ is measured from the $+x$ axis. Since the graph point is moving with constant speed v, and constant angular velocity ω, we can write for any angle θ,

$$\theta = \omega t$$

By substituting ωt for θ in Eq.(24g), we obtain,

$$y = r \sin \omega t \quad (24h)$$

This equation assumes that at time $t = 0$, the graph point is at $+X$, and the mass point is at O.

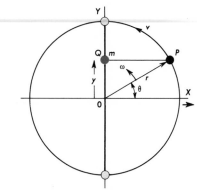

Fig. 24L   *Circle of reference for a simple harmonic motion along the y axis.*

If we start counting time when the mass point is at Q, and the graph point is at P, Eq.(24h) must be modified by adding the starting angle θ as follows:

$$y = r \sin (\omega t + \theta_1) \quad (24i)$$

The angle θ_1 is a constant and is called the *initial phase angle*. As the point P moves around the circle, the angle ωt increases uniformly and is always measured from the starting angle θ_1. The total quantity in parenthesis represents the total angle measured from the $+x$ axis.

Although ω can be given in degrees per second, and θ in degrees, it is customary to express both in radian measure.

Example 2. An object vibrating with simple harmonic motion has a period of 4 s, an amplitude of 5 cm, and an initial phase angle of $\pi/6$ rad. ($\pi/6$ rad = 30°.) Find (a) the initial displacement, and after a time of 6 s, (b) the phase angle, and (c) the displacement.

Solution. Since the graph point of this motion makes one revolution in 4 s, the angular velocity ω is 2π rad in 4 s, or $\pi/2$ rad/s. At time $t = 0$, direct substitution in Eq. (24i), gives,

$$y = 5 \sin\left(\frac{\pi}{2}0 + \frac{\pi}{6}\right)$$

$$y = 5 \sin\frac{\pi}{6} = 5 \times 0.500$$

giving $y = +2.50$ cm

At time $t = 6$ s, substitution in Eq. (24i), gives,

$$y = 5 \sin\left(\frac{\pi}{2}6 + \frac{\pi}{6}\right)$$

$$y = 5 \sin\left(3\pi + \frac{\pi}{6}\right)$$

This phase angle of $3\pi + \pi/6$ is equivalent to 570°, and measured from the $+x$ axis places the graph point 30° below the $-x$ axis on the circle of reference. This angle gives

$$\sin \theta = -0.500,$$
$$y = 5 \times (-0.5)$$
or $$y = -2.5 \text{ cm}$$

A graphical representation of this example is shown by the sine curve in Fig. 24M. The displacement y is plotted vertically and time t is plotted horizontally for the first two complete vibrations, or 8 s. On such a time graph the up

and down motion is traced out to show the starting point, the times at which each reaches its maximum displacement, and when it crosses the centerpoint. The amplitude r at the right is seen to be the radius of the circle of reference even though the mass point starts at $+2.5$ cm.

24.6. Superposition of Two Vibrations. We have seen in the last chapter that the intensity of sound, in any medium through which waves are traveling, is proportional to the flow of energy per unit area per unit time. When a number of waves of the same frequency fall on a receiver or a detector, the resultant intensity depends upon the amplitudes of all of the individual waves, and upon the phase differences between them.

In Sec. 22.11 it is shown that *the energy of a vibrating mass is proportional to the square of the amplitude.*

Combining all these relations we find that the resultant intensity due to any number of waves falling on a detector of any kind is proportional to the square of the resultant amplitude.

$$\text{intensity} \propto (\text{amplitude})^2$$
$$I = kR^2 \tag{24j}$$

where k is a proportionality constant. The resultant amplitude is given by the vector sum of all the individual amplitudes.

Consider as a practical example the coming together of two sound waves of the same frequency at regions along a smooth line drawn through x a y b z as in Fig. 24I. To find the resultant amplitude R, due to the two vibrations they produce at any given point, we add their respective amplitudes as shown in Fig. 24N. The equation of motion at that point, due to the two waves separately, may be written

Fig. 24M   *Time graph for the vibration of a point along the vertical line, the y axis.*

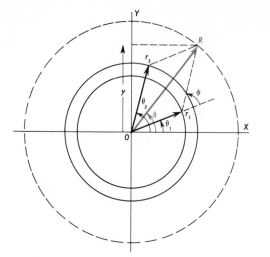

Fig. 24N   *Graphical composition of two amplitudes*
as vectors.

$$y_1 = r_1 \sin(\omega t + \theta_1)$$
$$y_2 = r_2 \sin(\omega t + \theta_2)$$ (25k)

where r_1 and r_2 are the two amplitudes, and θ_1 and θ_2 their respective initial phase angles. Together they produce the resultant amplitude R, and give rise to a resultant vibration along the y axis given by

$$y = R \sin(\omega t + \theta)$$

where ω is the same as for the two individual vibrations, and the maximum value of y is R.

From the graph it can be seen that θ represents the initial phase angle of the amplitude R, and that the phase difference ϕ between the two separate vibrations is given by

$$\phi = \theta_2 - \theta_1$$ (24l)

Since the two vibrations have the same frequency, we can visualize the vector diagram rotating around the center point O, unchanged in shape, and with the tips of the arrows tracing out their respective circles of reference.

To analytically find R we make use of the lower right triangle of the vector parallelogram, and from the law of cosines write

$$R^2 = r_1^2 + r_2^2 + 2r_1r_2 \cos\phi$$ (24m)

In most practical cases the amplitudes r_1 and r_2 are equal and Eq.(24m) simplifies. Replacing r_1 and r_2 by r, we obtain,

$$R^2 = 2r^2(1 + \cos\phi)$$

From an often used relation in trigonometry, $1 + \cos\phi = 2\cos(\phi/2)$, we obtain

$$R^2 = 4r^2 \cos^2 \frac{\phi}{2}$$ (24n)

If the phase difference is such that $\phi = 0, 2\pi,$

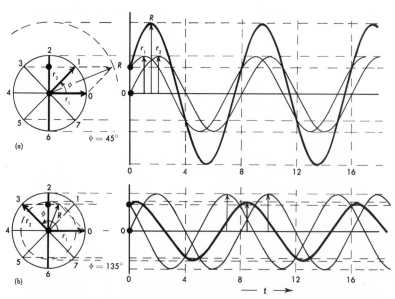

Fig. 24O   *Superposition graphs for two vibrations of equal amplitude and the same frequency,*
(a) with a phase difference of $\pi/4$ or 45°, and (b) $3\pi/4$ or 135°.

$4\pi, \ldots, \cos^2(\phi/2) = +1$, and $R^2 = 4r^2$. This means that *the resultant intensity is four times* r^2, *the intensity of either wave alone.* If $\phi = \pi, 3\pi, 5\pi, \ldots, \cos^2(\phi/2) = 0$, and the intensity is zero. For intermediate values, the intensity varies between these limits according to the square of the cosine. This is well illustrated by the intensity graph in Fig. 24K.

Two cases of the superposition of two vibrations of the same frequency and same amplitude are shown in Fig. 24O. The top graph is drawn for a phase angle difference $\phi = 45°$, and the second is for $\phi = 135°$. In the right-hand graphs it will be seen that at any instant of time t the sum of the vertical displacements of the two separate vibrations is just equal to the displacement of the resultant.

Furthermore, the resultant vibration is a smooth curve having the same frequency as the separate vibrations. As the angle ϕ approaches $0, 2\pi, 4\pi, \ldots$ rad, R approaches $2r$, and as ϕ approaches $\pi, 3\pi, 5\pi, \ldots$ rad, R approaches zero.

PROBLEMS

1. Two violin strings have frequencies of 330 and 495 vib/s, respectively. What is their beat frequency?

2. Three tuning forks with frequencies of 440, 352, and 264 vib/s, respectively, are sounded at the same time. What are the frequencies of all the beat notes arising from these sources? [*Ans.* 88; 88; 176 vib/s.]

3. A violinist playing in harmonics sounds his D and G strings simultaneously. If the frequencies of these two sounds are 297 and 198 vib/s, respectively, what is their beat frequency.

4. The following musical tetrad is sounded on the strings of a harp: 264, 330, 396, and 528 vib/s. Find the different frequencies of the beat notes produced. [*Ans.* 66; 132; 198; 264.]

5. The horn of a car is blown as the car approaches an intersection at 75 mi/hr. If the frequency heard by an observer standing at the intersection is 260 vib/s, what is the frequency of the horn? Assume a temperature of 75°F.

6. A train going 75 mi/hr sounds its whistle, pitched to a frequency of 400 vib/s. What frequency would be heard by an observer on the ground (a) ahead of the train, and (b) behind the train? Assume the speed of sound to be 1100 ft/s. [*Ans.* (a) 444 vib/s, (b) 364 vib/s.]

7. A car traveling 30 m/s on the highway, sounds its horn as it overtakes and passes another car traveling 20 m/s in the same direction. If the horn frequency is 550 vib/s, what is the frequency heard by the driver in the slower car (a) before passing, and (b) after passing? Assume the speed of sound to be 350 m/s.

8. The siren at a ranger station along the highway is sounded with a frequency of 800 vib/s. What frequency is heard by motorists traveling at 90 Km/hr along the highway if they are (a) approaching, and (b) receding from the station? Assume a temperature of 28°C. [*Ans.* 857 vib/s, 742 vib/s.]

9. To a person standing in front of a flight of steps, a sharp clap of the hands will produce a sound wave that is reflected back to the observer from each step. If the step treads are 35 cm deep, what frequency is heard by the observer? Assume a temperature of 32°C.

10. Two radio loud-speakers sounding the same frequency are placed 1.6 m apart as shown in Fig. 24H. A microphone is located 5 m away on the perpendicular bisector. As the box is slowly turned, the first maximum response is observed when the angle $\theta = 20°$ (see Fig. 24J). Find the wavelength of the sound waves. [*Ans.* 0.542 m.]

11. In performing the experiment shown in Fig. 24H, the distance between speakers is 1.8 m and the distance from the center point to the microphone is 3.5 m. As the sound box is turned away from its 90° position the first maximum response of the microphone is observed when $\theta = 42°$. Find the wavelength of the sound waves.

12. Two radio speakers in a hi-fi record player are located 2.0 m apart. A listener is located 3 m away from the center of the cabinet and at an angle of 20° with the perpendicular to the front of the cabinet. What frequencies between 0 and 5000 vib/s, sounded by both speakers, will not be heard? Assume the speed of sound to be 350 m/s. [*Ans.* 269, 807, 1345, 1883, 2421, 2959, 3497, 4035, 4573 vib/s.]

13. Two loud speakers in a hi-fi record player are located 2.0 m apart. An observer is located 4 m away from the center of the cabinet and at an angle of 30° with the perpendicular to the front of the cabinet. What frequencies, between 0 and 3000 vib/s, sounded by both speakers, will not be heard? Assume the speed of sound to be 350 m/s.

14. The motion of a vibrating source of waves is given by

$$y = 3 \text{ mm} \sin\left(\frac{\pi}{8}t + \frac{\pi}{4}\right).$$

If the velocity of the waves is 12 m/s, find (a) the amplitude, (b) the initial phase angle in degrees, (c) the phase angle at the end of 12 s, (d) the period of vibration, and (e) the wavelength. [*Ans.* (a) 3 mm, (b) 45°, (c) 315°, (d) 16 s, (e) 192 m.]

15. The motion of a vibrating source of waves is given by

$$y = 2.8 \text{ mm} \sin\left(\frac{\pi}{18}t + \frac{\pi}{12}\right).$$

If the speed of the waves is 20 m/s, find (a) the amplitude, (b) the initial phase angle in degrees, (c) the phase angle at the end of 6 min, (d) the period, and (e) the wavelength.

16. Two waves coming together at a given point are represented at that point by the equations

$$y_1 = 4 \text{ mm sin} \left(8\pi t + \frac{\pi}{6} \right)$$

and

$$y_2 = 3 \text{ mm sin} \left(8\pi t + \frac{\pi}{3} \right),$$

respectively. Find (a) the amplitude of each vibration, (b) the initial phase angles, (c) the resultant amplitude, (d) the initial phase angle of the resultant, and (e) the equation of the resultant vibration. [*Ans.* (a) 4 mm and 3 mm, (b) 30°

and 60°, (c) 6.77 mm, (d) 42.8° or 0.75 rad, and (e) $y = 6.77$ mm sin $(8\pi t + 0.75)$].

17. Two waves of the same frequency arriving at the same receiver are represented by the equations

$$y_1 = 3 \text{ mm sin} \left(10\pi t + \frac{\pi}{10} \right)$$

and

$$y_2 = 2 \text{ mm sin} \left(10\pi t + \frac{\pi}{5} \right),$$

respectively. Find (a) the amplitude of each vibration, (b) the initial phase angles, (c) the resultant amplitude, (d) the initial phase angle of the resultant, and (e) the equation of the resultant vibration.

SOURCES OF
MUSICAL SOUNDS

From the subjective point of view, music is based upon the relative pitch and timbre, or quality, of sound waves produced by the voice and musical instruments. From the scientific point of view the pitch of a note depends upon the vibration frequency of the source, and the timbre or quality depends upon the complexity of the vibration mode.

The frequencies of notes are usually chosen so that they produce the greatest amount of melody or harmony. Two or more notes are said to be harmonious or concordant if they are pleasing to the ear. If they are not pleasant to hear, they are discordant.*

Musical instruments are often classified under one of the following heads: *strings*, *winds*, and *percussions*. These terms apply to the material part of the instruments set into vibration when the instrument is played, or to the method by which it is set into vibration. It is the purpose of this chapter to consider these sources and the various factors governing the frequencies of their musical notes.

25.1. Stringed Instruments. There are two principal reasons why stringed instruments of different kinds do not sound alike as regards *tone*

---

* The essential difference between *melody* and *harmony* is quite generally recognized by everyone. Melody consists of a succession of notes and conveys the idea of motion that should go on and on, while harmony consists of the simultaneous and often sustained sounding of several notes like a chord, followed by other similar combinations of notes. The latter seems to stand still, each chord of notes being more or less complete in itself.

quality—first, the design of the instrument, and second, the method by which the strings are set into vibration. The violin and cello are bowed with long strands of tightly stretched horsehair, the harp and guitar are plucked with the fingers or picks, and the piano is hammered with light felt mallets.

Under very special conditions a string may be made to vibrate with nodes at either end as shown in Fig. 25A. In this state of motion the string

Fig. 25A *Single string vibrating with its fundamental frequency.*

gives rise to its lowest possible note, and it is said to be vibrating with its *fundamental frequency*.

Every musician knows that a thick heavy string has a lower natural pitch than a thin one, that a short strong string has a higher pitch than a long one, and that the tighter a string is stretched the higher is its pitch. The G string of a violin, for example, is thicker and heavier than the high-pitched E string, and the *bass* strings of the piano are longer and heavier than the strings of the *treble*.

25.2. Harmonics and Overtones. When a professional violinist plays "in harmonics" he touches the strings lightly at various points and sets each one vibrating in two or more segments, as shown in Fig. 25B. If a string is touched at the center, a node is formed at that point and the vibration frequency becomes double that of the fundamental. If the string is touched lightly at a

at the same time. This is accomplished by plucking or bowing the string vigorously. As an illustration a diagram of an ideal string vibrating with two normal modes at the same time is

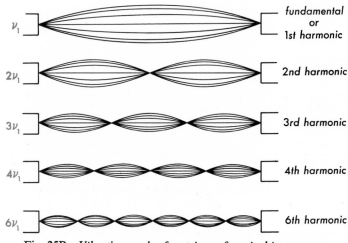

ν_1 — fundamental or 1st harmonic

$2\nu_1$ — 2nd harmonic

$3\nu_1$ — 3rd harmonic

$4\nu_1$ — 4th harmonic

$6\nu_1$ — 6th harmonic

Fig. 25B   *Vibration modes for strings of musical instruments.*

point one-third the distance from the end, it will vibrate in three sections and have a frequency three times that of the fundamental.

In the elementary theory of string instruments, it is assumed that each string is thin, uniform, and highly flexible, and that it vibrates with small amplitude between unyielding supports. For such an ideal string, the above vibration modes have frequencies exactly equal to whole number multiples of the fundamental frequency ν_1, and are called *harmonics*.

The frequencies ν of all harmonics of a given string are given by the relation

$$\nu = n\nu_1 \qquad (25a)$$

where

$$n = 1, 2, 3, 4, \ldots.$$

To show how closely a real string meets these ideal conditions, the measured frequencies of a piano string whose fundamental frequency is 32.70 vib/s are given in the following table.*

It is not difficult to set a string vibrating with its fundamental and several of its higher modes

* See R. W. Young, *Am. J. Phys.*, **20**, 177 (1952).

TABLE 25A. HARMONIC FREQUENCIES OF A PIANO STRING

Mode number	Meas. freq.	Harmonic freq.	Ratio
1	32.70	32.70	1.000
2	65.52	65.40	2.003
3	98.39	98.10	3.008
4	131.4	130.8	4.018
5	164.7	163.5	5.038
6	198.4	196.2	6.066
7	232.4	228.9	7.106
8	266.8	261.6	8.159

shown in Fig. 25C. As the string vibrates in two loops with a frequency $2\nu_1$, it also moves up and

Fig. 25C   *String vibrating with its first and second harmonics simultaneously.*

down as a single loop with the fundamental frequency ν_1.

The sound wave sent out by such a vibrating

string, as shown in Fig. 25D, is composed of two frequencies, the fundamental or first har-

arc lamp is focused on the central section of a stretched steel string, which, except for a small

Fig. 25D *Sound wave vibrations from a string vibrating with its fundamental and the second harmonic.*

monic of frequency ν_1, diagram (a), and the second harmonic or first partial with the frequency $2\nu_1$, diagram (b). The sound waves combine as they travel through the air, and upon

vertical slot, is masked by a screen. An image of the slot and the string section seen through it is focused on a screen by a second lens, after reflection from a rotating mirror. As the string

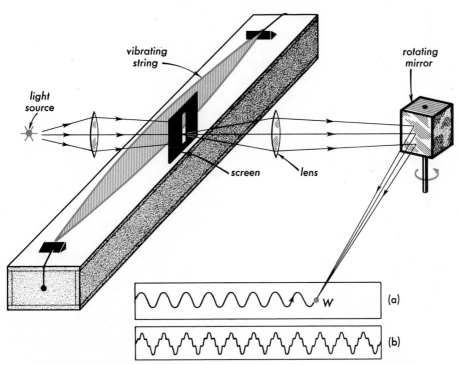

Fig. 25E *Experiment for observing the detailed vibrations of a stretched string.*

their arrival at the ear, set the eardrum vibrating as shown in diagram (c).

An interesting experiment with a vibrating string is diagramed in Fig. 25E. Light from an

vibrates up and down, only a blurred image of the short section of string is seen, but when the mirror is rotated the wire section draws out a clearly visible curve W.

If the string is plucked gently near the center, a smooth wave form (a) is drawn out on the screen, but, if it is plucked hard near the end to produce a harsh-sounding note, the wave form is more complex as shown in (b). In the first case, the string is vibrating only with its fundamental mode, while in the second case various harmonics, called *overtones* or *partials*, are also present.

As a string vibrates with *transverse waves*, it strikes air molecules all around it, sending periodic impulses through the air as *longitudinal waves*.

25.3. The Theory of Vibrating Strings. A string set into vibration with nodes and loops is but an example of standing waves (see Fig. 22L). A disturbance produced at one end, as in the plucking or bowing of a string, sends a wave or train of waves along the string to be reflected back and forth from end to end. When traveling in one direction the wave is on top and, upon reflection, it flips to the under side. Because the wave is always on top when moving to the right, and on the bottom when moving to the left, a flipping up and down of the string results.

Since the fundamental frequency of vibration is equal to the number of times per second that the wave arrives at the same end, the pitch will depend upon the velocity of the waves and the distance they have to travel.

The velocity of transverse waves along a rope or string under tension is given by

$$V = \sqrt{F/m} \qquad (25b)$$

where F is the tension and m is the mass per unit length of string. When standing waves are produced, the distance L between any two consecutive nodes is just equal to half a wavelength, $\frac{1}{2}\lambda$. Accordingly,

$$\lambda = 2L$$

To obtain an equation for the fundamental frequency of a vibrating string, the general wave equation $V = \nu\lambda$ is used [see Eq.(22g)]. If we solve this equation for ν, and then substitute the above values for V and λ, we obtain

$$\nu = \frac{1}{2L}\sqrt{F/m} \qquad (25c)$$

Accurate measurements with vibrating strings and musical instruments confirm this equation.

Example 1. A piano string that sounds three octaves below middle C is 1.10 m long. Calculate the tension on the string when, in proper tune, its frequency is 33 vib/s. Assume the mass of the string to be 160 g.
Solution. The *mass per unit length* of string is $m = 0.16$ Kg/1.1 m $= 0.145$ Kg/m. Solve Eq.(25c) for F and the frequency equation becomes $F = 4\nu^2L^2m$. By direct substitution,

$$F = 4 \times (33)^2 \times (1.10)^2 \times 0.145 = 764 \text{ N}$$

Since 1 N = 0.225 lb,

$$F = 172 \text{ lb}$$

The vibration of a string brought about by bowing is associated with friction. Because starting friction is greater than sliding friction, the resinous bow periodically engages the string, pushing or pulling it to one side. During one-half the vibration the string clings to the bow and is carried along by it. When the tension becomes too great and exceeds starting friction, the string slips back to the opposite side of its vibration. There it stops and upon reversal in direction is grabbed again by the bow.

25.4. Wind Instruments. Musical instruments, often classified as "wind instruments," are usually divided into two subclasses, "wood winds" and "brasses." Under the heading of wood winds, we find such instruments as the *flute, piccolo, clarinet, bass clarinet, saxophone, bassoon,* and *contra bassoon;* and under the brasses such instruments as the *French horn, cornet, trumpet, tenor trombone, bass trombone,* and *tuba* (or *bombardon*).

The fundamental principles involved in the vibration of an air column are demonstrated by means of an experiment shown in Fig. 25F. A vibrating tuning fork which acts as a source of sound waves is held over the open end of a long hollow tube containing water. Traveling down the tube with the velocity of sound in air, each train of sound waves is reflected from the water surface back toward the top. If the water is raised or lowered to the proper level, standing waves will be set up and the air column will resonate to the frequency of the tuning fork.

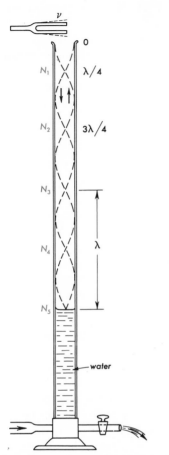

Fig. 25F *Sound waves from tuning fork set up standing waves in an air column which has been adjusted to the proper length.*

The first resonance occurs at N_1 when the water level is only a short distance from the top. The second resonance occurs at N_2, three times the distance of N_1 below the top, and the third N_3 at five times the distance, etc. The reason for these odd fractions is that only a *node* can form at the closed end of the pipe, i.e., at the water surface, and an *antinode* at the open end.

Standing waves in air are longitudinal in character, and they are difficult to represent in any drawing (see Fig. 22M). For convenience only, it is quite customary to indicate the positions of nodes and loops as if they were transverse standing waves (dotted lines in the diagram).

If the frequency of the tuning fork used in the above experiment is known, the velocity of sound in air can be calculated. The distance between consecutive nodes is equal to $\lambda/2$, so that λ is equal to the length of two segments $N_3 - N_1$, $N_4 - N_2$, or $N_5 - N_3$, as shown in the diagram. In an actual experiment when the temperature is 27°C, and a tuning fork is sounding 512 vib/s, the nodes are 13.37 in. apart. Substitution of these values in the general wave equation, Eq. (22g) gives

$$V = \nu\lambda = 512 \times 26.74 = 13690 \text{ in./s}$$

Dividing by 12, we get $V = 1141$ ft/s.

25.5. Vibrating Air Columns. The various modes in which air columns may vibrate in open or closed pipes are shown in Fig. 25G. Starting at the left, a pipe open at both ends may vibrate with (1) a single node at the middle and an antinode at both ends, (2) two nodes and three antinodes, or (3) with three nodes and four antinodes, etc. On the other hand, a pipe closed at one end and open at the other may vibrate with (1) one node and one antinode, (2) two nodes and two antinodes, or (3) three nodes and three antinodes, etc. *In all vibrating air columns, an antinode always forms at an open end and a node at a closed end.*

The various possible frequencies to which a pipe may resonate are definite and fixed in value, and depend only upon the length of the pipe and the velocity of sound in air. If, for example, the pipes in Fig. 25G are all 2 ft long and the velocity of sound in air is 1120 ft/s, $V = \nu\lambda$ shows that they will vibrate with the following respective frequencies:

ν	2ν	3ν	ν'	$3\nu'$	$5\nu'$
280	560	840	140	420	700

With an open pipe, the lowest possible vibration frequency is called the *fundamental;* the others, with whole-numbered multiples of the fundamental frequency, 2ν, 3ν, 4ν, etc., are called *harmonics*. With closed pipes, the lowest frequency is again the fundamental and the others with odd integral multiples, $3\nu'$, $5\nu'$, $7\nu'$, etc., are harmonics.

All these vibration modes are referred to as natural modes and their corresponding frequencies as natural frequencies. *The fundamental is*

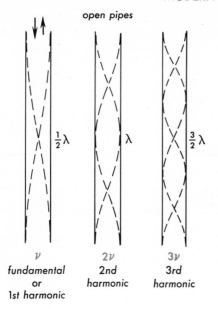

open pipes

$\frac{1}{2}\lambda$ λ $\frac{3}{2}\lambda$

ν 2ν 3ν
fundamental   2nd   3rd
or   harmonic   harmonic
1st harmonic

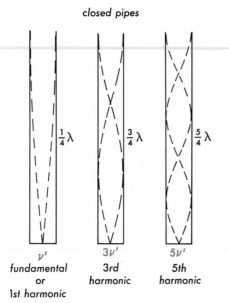

closed pipes

$\frac{1}{4}\lambda$ $\frac{3}{4}\lambda$ $\frac{5}{4}\lambda$

ν' $3\nu'$ $5\nu'$
fundamental   3rd   5th
or   harmonic   harmonic
1st harmonic

Fig. 25G   *Air columns in open and closed pipes have definite frequencies of vibration.*

also called the first harmonic. It should be noted that with one end of a pipe closed, all even-numbered harmonics cannot be sounded.

The existence of standing waves in a resonating air column may be demonstrated by a long hollow tube filled with illuminating gas as shown in Fig. 25H. Entering through an adjustable plunger at the left, the gas escapes through tiny holes spaced at regular intervals in a row along the top. Sound waves from an organ pipe enter the gas column by setting into vibration a thin paper sheet, stretched over the right-hand end.

When resonance is attained by sliding the plunger to the correct position, the small gas flames will appear as shown. Where the nodes occur in the vibrating gas column, the molecules are not moving [see Fig. 22M(b)]; at these points the pressure is high and the flames are tallest. Halfway between are the antinodes—regions where the molecules vibrate back and forth with large amplitudes, and the flames are low. Bernoulli's principle is chiefly responsible for the pressure differences (see Sec. 18.9), for, where the velocity of the molecules is high the pressure is low, and where the velocity is low the pressure is high.

In many of the wind instruments of the orchestra, the vibrating air columns are not entirely uniform and the far open end is considerably flared. Because of this nonuniformity, the nodes are not equally spaced nor are the possible frequencies exactly harmonics of the fundamental. As an example of how nearly the various normal modes come to being harmonics of a fundamental, the following measured frequencies of the *open notes* of a B♭ cornet are given in the table below: ($\nu_1 = 116.7$ vib/s).

TABLE 25B. HARMONIC FREQUENCIES
OF A B♭ CORNET

Mode number	Meas. freq.	Harmonic freq.	Ratio
1	116.7	116.7	1.000
2	233.4	233.4	2.000
3	349.8	350.1	2.998
4	467.5	466.8	4.007
5	587.7	583.5	5.037
6	706.2	700.2	6.058
8*	948.6	933.6	8.130

*The seventh harmonic was not sounded.

Open notes are those for which all valves are open and the entire air column is vibrating.

Fig. 25H   *Standing waves in a long tube containing illuminating gas.*

25.6. Theory of Vibrating Air Columns.
The various notes produced by most wind instruments are brought out by varying the length of the vibrating air column. This is illustrated by the organ pipes in Fig. 25I. The longer the pipe,

Fig. 25I   *Organ pipes arranged in a musical scale. The longer the pipe, the lower is its fundamental frequency and pitch. The vibrating air column of the flute is terminated at various points by openings along the tube.*

the lower the fundamental frequency or pitch of the note. In a regular concert organ, the pipes vary in length from about 6 in. for the highest note to almost 16 ft for the lowest. For the middle octave of the musical scale, the open-ended pipes vary from 2 ft for middle C to 1 ft for C^1, one octave higher. In the wood winds, like the flute, the length of the column is varied by openings in the side of the instrument; and in many of the brasses, like the trumpet, by means of valves. A valve is a piston which, on being pressed down, throws in an additional length of tube.

Since a vibrating air column is a condition of standing waves, the frequency of vibration will depend upon two factors, the length of the pipe and the velocity of waves through it. The velocity of longitudinal waves in a gas is given by Newton's formula as modified by Laplace,

$$V = \sqrt{K\frac{P}{\rho}} \qquad (25d)$$

where K is a number representing the compressibility of a gas, P is the gas pressure in N/m², and ρ its density in Kg/m³. For monatomic gases, $K = 1.67$; for diatomic gases, $K = 1.40$; and for triatomic gases, $K = 1.33$, and V is in m/s.

For all standing waves, the distance L between any two consecutive nodes, that is, the length of one segment, is just equal to half a wavelength, $\lambda/2$. Accordingly,

$$\lambda = 2L$$

By substituting this relation and the velocity above in the general wave equation, Eq.(22g), we get the general formula

$$\nu = \frac{1}{2L}\sqrt{K\frac{P}{\rho}} \qquad (25e)$$

Measurements with resonating pipes confirm this relation.

The effect of the density of a gas on the pitch of a note may be demonstrated by a very interesting experiment with the human voice. Voice sounds originate in the vibrations of the vocal cords in the larynx (see Fig. 25J). This source of vibration, which determines the fundamental pitch of the speaking or singing voice, is controlled by muscular tension on the cords. The quality of the voice is determined by the size and shape of the throat, the mouth, and the nasal cavities.

Fig. 25J *Cross-section diagram showing the vocal chords in the larynx. (A) Soft palate, (B) pharynx, (C) nasal cavity, (D) hard palate, (F) tongue, (G) epiglottis, and (J) windpipe.*

If a gas lighter than air is breathed into the lungs, the above equation shows that the voice quality should change. The demonstration can be best and safely performed by exhaling completely, and then filling the lungs with helium gas (hydrogen is unsafe). Upon speaking, the experimenter will be observed to have a very peculiar high-pitched voice, which must be heard to be appreciated. The peculiarities arise from the fact that the fundamental pitch, due to the vocal-cord frequency, remains practically normal, while the harmonics from the resonating mouth, throat, and nasal cavities are raised by about $2\frac{1}{2}$ octaves.

Example 2. A straight piece of pipe 2 m long and open at both ends, is filled with carbon dioxide gas at standard temperature and pressure. Find (a) the speed of sound in carbon dioxide, and (b) the fundamental frequency of the pipe.

Solution. To find the speed use Eq.(25d). Since CO_2 is a triatomic molecule, $K = 1.33$. From Table 18A, the density of CO_2 gas is 1.98 Kg/m³. By direct substitution in Eq.(25d), we obtain

$$V = \sqrt{\frac{1.33 \times 1.013 \times 10^5 \text{ N/m}^2}{1.98 \text{ Kg/m}^3}}$$

$$V = \sqrt{6.80 \times 10^4 \text{ m}^2/\text{s}^2}$$

$$V = 261 \text{ m/s}$$

(b) To find the fundamental frequency, use Eq. (22g). Since an antinode forms at the open end of a pipe, the pipe length is equal to $\frac{1}{2}\lambda$, and this is equal to L, the length of one loop. By substitution in Eq. (22g), we obtain,

$$\nu = \frac{1}{2 \times 2 \text{ m}} 261 \frac{\text{m}}{\text{s}}$$

$$\nu = 65.2 \frac{\text{vib}}{\text{s}}$$

25.7. Edge Tones. Although the pitch of the note sounded by any wind instrument is determined by the vibration of an air column according to principles of resonance, the method by which the air is set into vibration varies widely among instruments. In instruments like the saxophone, clarinet, oboe and bassoon, air is blown against a thin strip of wood called a reed, setting it into vibration. In most of the brasses the musician's lips are made to vibrate with certain required frequencies, while in certain wood winds, like the flute and piccolo and in organs and whistles, air is blown across the sharp edge of an opening near one end of the instrument, setting the air into vibration. A brief discussion of these source vibrations is therefore important here.

When wind or a blast of air encounters a small obstacle, little whirlwinds are formed in the air stream behind the obstacle. This is illustrated by the cross section of a flue organ pipe shown in Fig. 25K. Whether the obstacle is long, or a small round object, the whirlwinds are formed alternately on the two sides as shown (see Fig. 8H). The air stream at B waves back and forth, sending a pulse of air first up one side and then the other. Although the wind blows through the opening A as a continuous stream, the separate whirlwinds going up each side of the obstacle become periodic shocks to the surrounding air. Coming at perfectly regular intervals, these pulses give rise to musical notes often described as "edge tones."

The number of whirlwinds formed per second, and therefore the pitch of the edge tone, increases with the wind velocity. When the wind howls through the trees, the pitch of the note rises and falls, its frequency at any time denoting the velocity of the wind. For a given wind velocity,

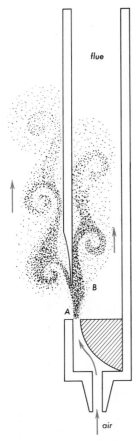

flap periodically in the breeze, while the waving of the flag at the top of a pole shows the whirlwinds that follow each other along each side.

The air column in an organ pipe, flute, or piccolo, has its own natural frequency of vibration which may or may not coincide with the frequency of an edge tone. If it does coincide, resonance will occur, the air column will vibrate with a large amplitude, and returning pulses of air down the tube with each vibration will force the air stream out at just the right moment, thus aiding in building up the natural frequency of the pipe. If the edge tone has a frequency different from the fundamental of the string, or air column, vibrations will be set up but not as intensely as before. If the frequency of the edge tone of an organ pipe, for example, comes close to double that of the fundamental, and this can be obtained by a stronger blast of air, the pipe will resonate to double its fundamental frequency and give out a strong note one octave higher.

By blowing more sharply against the opening in a piccolo or flute, the entire scale of notes can be raised one octave above normal playing range of the instrument. In all instruments like those mentioned above where air is blown across the sharp edge of an opening to make it sing, as in the organ pipe of Fig. 25K, an antinode is formed at that end. Whether an antinode or node forms at the other end depends upon whether it is open or closed, respectively.

25.8. Percussion Instruments. Vibrating Rods.

If a number of small sticks are dropped upon the floor, the sound that is heard is described as a noise. If one stick alone is dropped, one would also describe the sound as a noise, unless, of course, a set of sticks of varying lengths were arranged in order of length and each one dropped in its order. If this is done, one notices that each stick gives rise to a rather definite musical note and that the set of sticks could be cut to the proper length to form a musical scale. The use of vibrating rods in a musical instrument is found in the *xylophone*, the *marimba*, and the *triangle*. Standing waves in a rod, like those in a stretched string, may be any one of three different kinds —transverse, longitudinal, and torsional. Only

Fig. 25K   *A steady stream of air blown across the lip of an organ pipe sets up whirlwinds along both sides of the partition.*

smaller objects give rise to higher-pitched notes than large objects.

A fine-stretched wire or rubber band, when placed in an open window or in the wind, will be set into vibration and will give out a musical note. Each whirlwind shock to the air reacts on the obstacle (the wire or rubber band), pushing it first to one side and then the other. These are the pushes that cause the rope of a flagpole to the first two of these modes of vibration will be treated here.

Transverse waves in a rod are usually set up by supporting the rod at points near each end and striking it a blow at or near the center. As illustrated in Fig. 25L(a), the center and ends of

cymbal plate is in general due to the high intensity of certain characteristic overtones. These overtones in turn are due to the very complicated modes of vibration of the source.

Cymbals consist of two thin metal disks with handles at the centers. Upon being struck to-

Fig. 25L   *The bars of the marimba or xylophone vibrate transversely with nodes near each end.*

the rod move up and down, forming nodes at the two supports. Like a stretched string of a musical instrument, the shorter the rod the higher is its pitch; and the longer and heavier the rod, the lower is its frequency of vibration and pitch.

The xylophone is a musical instrument based upon the *transverse vibrations* of wooden rods of different lengths. Mounted as shown for the marimba in Fig. 25L(b), the longer rods produce the low notes and the shorter ones the higher notes. The marimba is essentially a xylophone with a long straight hollow tube suspended vertically under each rod. Each tube is cut to such a length that the enclosed air column will resonate to the sound waves sent out by the rod directly above. Each resonator tube, being open at both ends, forms a node at its center.

The tuning fork depends for its pitch upon the transverse vibrations of a bar. Sounding its fundamental as shown in Fig. 25M, an antinode forms at both ends. Due to the bend in the center, the two nodes are closer together than in a straight bar, and the antinode at the center transmits forceful vibrations of small amplitude through the shaft to any surface on which it is rested.

25.9. Vibrating Plates. Although the drum or the cymbals should hardly be called musical instruments, they are classified as such and are used in nearly all large orchestras and bands. The sound given out by a vibrating drumhead or

gether, their edges are set into vibration with a clang. A drumhead, on the other hand, is a stretched membrane of leather held tight at the periphery, and is set into vibration by being struck a blow at or near the center.

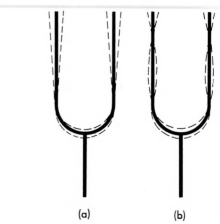

Fig. 25M   *Vibration nodes of a tuning fork show (a) fundamental and (b) first overtone.*

To illustrate the complexity of the vibrations of thin metal plates, ten typical sand patterns are shown in Fig. 25N. The sand-pattern method of studying the motions of plates was invented in the eighteenth century by Chladni, a German physicist. A thin square or circular metal plate is clamped at the center C and sand is sprinkled over the top surface. Then, while touching the

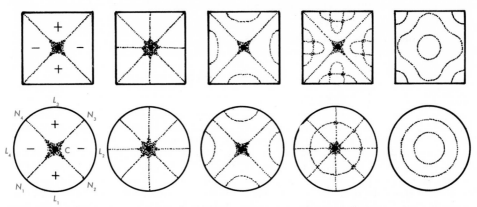

Fig. 25N *Chladni's sand figures showing the nodes and loops of vibrating plates; all but the last two on the right are clamped at the center; the last two are clamped at the periphery.*

rim of the plate at two separated points N_1 and N_2, a cello bow is drawn down over the edge at a point L. Nodes are formed at the stationary points N_1 and N_2, and antinodes in the regions of L_1 and L_2. The grains of sand bounce away from the loops and into the nodes, the regions of no motion. At one instant the regions marked with a $(+)$ sign all move up, while the regions marked with a $(-)$ sign all move down. Half a vibration later, the $+$ regions are moving down and the $-$ regions up. Such diagrams are called *Chladni's sand figures.*

With cymbal plates held tightly at the center by means of handles, a node is always formed there, and antinodes are always formed at the periphery. With a drumhead, on the other hand, the periphery is always a node and the center is sometimes, but not always, an antinode.

Such vibrations constitute *two dimensional standing waves.*

25.10. Bells. In some respects a bell is like a cymbal plate, for when it is struck a blow by the clapper, the rim in particular is set vibrating with nodes and loops distributed in a symmetrical pattern over the whole surface. The vibration of the rim is illustrated by a diagram in Fig. 25O(a) and by an experiment in diagram (b). Small cork balls are suspended by threads around, and just touching, the outside rim of a large glass bowl. A violin bow drawn across the edge of the bowl will set the rim into vibration with nodes at some points and loops at others. The nodes are always even in number just as they are in cymbal plates and drumheads, and alternate loops move in while the others move out.

Strictly speaking, a bell is not a very musical

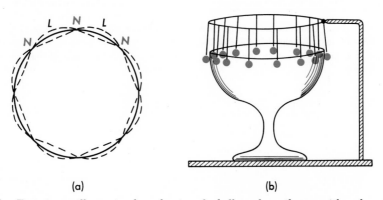

(a)   (b)

Fig. 25O *Experiment illustrating how the rim of a bell or glass vibrates with nodes and loops.*

instrument. This is due to the very complex vibrations of the bell surface which give rise to so many loud overtones. Some of these overtones harmonize with the fundamental, while others do not.

PROBLEMS

1. Find the mass of a piano string 55 cm long if, under a tension of 600 N, it has a frequency of 300 vib/s.

2. The A string of a violin is 35 cm long and has a mass of 2 g. Find the tension in newtons when properly tuned to a frequency of 440 vib/s. [*Ans.* 542 N.]

3. A piano string 90 cm long has a frequency of 132 vib/s, and a mass of 15 g. Find the tension in newtons.

4. The G string of a violin is 35 cm long and has a frequency of 198 vib/s. If the mass of this length of string is 15 g, what is the tension in the string? [*Ans.* 823 N.]

5. The E string of a violin has a fundamental frequency of 660 vib/s. Find the wavelength of the 4th and 6th harmonics of the sound waves it produces if the speed of sound is 350 m/s.

6. A harp string with a length of 75 cm is tuned to a frequency of 440 vib/s. What is the wavelength of the fourth harmonic (a) on the string, and (b) in the air? Assume the speed of sound to be 350 m/s. [*Ans.* (a) 37.5 cm, (b) 0.199 m.]

7. A steel wire 1.5 m long has a mass of 45 g. If this wire is fastened at both ends and then put under a tension of 1000 N, what will be the frequency of its third harmonic?

8. A rope 100 m long has a mass 1 Kg. Find the speed with which waves will travel along this string if it is put under a tension of 500 N. [*Ans.* 224 m/s.]

9. What is the shortest length of pipe, open at both ends, that will resonate to a tuning fork of frequency 66 vib/s? Assume a temperature of 30°C.

10. A tuning fork with a frequency of 264 vib/s is used in the experiment shown in Fig. 25F. Find the distance between consecutive nodes if the temperature is 30°C. [*Ans.* 66.1 cm.]

11. The lowest-pitched note from a bugle has a frequency of 66 vib/s. What are the frequencies of the next five harmonics?

12. A piece of water pipe 2 m long is open at both ends. What is the frequency of the eighth harmonic of the enclosed air column. Assume the speed of sound to be 345 m/s. [*Ans.* 690 vib/s.]

13. Find the frequency of (a) the fundamental, and (b) the sixth harmonic of a 5-m-long organ pipe, closed at one end and open at the other. Assume the speed of sound to be 360 m/s.

14. An organ pipe 1 m long, with both ends open, is used to produce the sound waves in the experiment shown in Fig. 25H. If the speed of sound in air is 348 m/s, and in the illuminating gas is 300 m/s, what is the distance between consecutive points where the flames are a maximum? [*Ans.* 0.862 m.]

15. A whistle has a fundamental frequency of 5000 vib/s at a temperature of 30°C. If antinodes are formed at both ends, find the length of the air column.

16. An organ pipe open at both ends and filled with air at 30°C has a fundamental frequency of 132 vib/s. What would be its fundamental frequency if the air were replaced by CO_2? The speed of sound in CO_2 is 272 m/s. [*Ans.* 102.8 vib/s.]

17. An organ pipe with one end closed has a fundamental frequency of 220 vib/s when the temperature is 40°C. Find its frequency when the temperature drops to 0°C.

18. Calculate the speed of sound in carbon monoxide at normal temperature and pressure. Assume the density of CO to be 1.25 Kg/m³. [*Ans.* 336 m/s.]

19. Calculate the speed of sound in chlorine gas at normal temperature and pressure. Assume the density of the gas to be 3.21 Kg/m³. Chlorine is diatomic.

20. Calculate the speed of sound in nitrous oxide gas at normal temperature and pressure. Assume the density of N_2O to be 1.978 Kg/m³. [*Ans.* 261 m/s.]

21. A pipe 60 cm long, open at both ends is filled with sulphur dioxide gas at normal temperature and pressure. Find (a) the speed of sound in sulphur dioxide, and (b) the fundamental frequency to which this pipe will respond. Assume SO_2 to have a density of 2.927 Kg/m³.

22. Make free-hand drawings of the figures shown in Fig. 25N. Label all areas with appropriate + and − signs to show the relative phases of the antinodes, as in the first two figures.

ELECTRICITY AT REST

It is impossible to say when electricity was first discovered. Records show that as early as 600 B.C. the attractive properties of amber were known. Thales of Miletus (640–546 B.C.), one of the "seven wise men" of ancient Greece, is credited with having observed the attraction of amber for small fibrous materials and bits of straw. Amber was used by these people, even as it is now, for ornamental purposes. Just as the precious metals had their names of gold and silver, so amber had its name "electron."

Although the electrification of amber by friction was handed down from one writer to another, nothing new about the phenomenon was discovered for more than 2000 years. It was not until the beginning of the 17th century that Sir William Gilbert* announced the discovery that many substances could be electrified by friction. Gilbert named this effect "electric" after the word "electron." It is now well established that all bodies when rubbed together become electri-

---

* Sir William Gilbert (1540–1603), court physician to Queen Elizabeth and a noted philosopher and experimental physicist. In 1600 he published a book on magnetism, *De Magnete*. This book was full of valuable facts and experiments on electricity and magnetism, and among other things contained many criticisms of his contemporaries, predecessors, and the early philosophers. In his preface he wrote: "Why should I submit this new philosophy to the judgment of men who have taken oaths to follow the opinions of others, to the most senseless corrupters of the arts, to lettered clowns, grammatists, sophists, spouters, and the wrong-headed rabble. To you alone true philosophers, ingenious minds, who not only in books but in things themselves look for knowledge, have I dedicated these foundations of magnetic science." So strongly does he advocate here, and carry out, himself, the experimental method, that he is to be classed as a scientist with his contemporary Galileo, "the father of modern physics."

fied and that amber is just one of a number of substances which show the effect most strongly.

26.1. Electrostatic Attraction. The word "electrostatic" means electricity at rest, and the word "attraction" refers to the force exerted by one body upon another at a distance. To demonstrate electrostatic attraction, one can use a rubber or amber rod and rub it with a piece of flannel or fur. This electrifies the rod, so that, when the rod is held close to some small bits of paper, they jump up to the rod and hold fast.

The attraction of an electrified rubber rod for wood is illustrated in Fig. 26A. A small arrow cut from a piece of dry wood is mounted so that it is free to turn as shown. When the electrified rubber rod is brought near the pointed end of the arrow it attracts the wood, turning the arrow until it points toward the rod. Brought near the opposite end, the wood is again attracted, turning the arrow to point away from the rubber rod.

An ordinary hard-rubber comb when drawn through the hair becomes charged with electricity and will attract light objects in the same way. Sometimes the electrical charges produced in a comb are so great that tiny sparks can be seen to jump between the comb and hair. This is particularly noticeable in a darkened room. These sparks are the reason for the crackling noise so often heard when hair is being combed.

A spectacular effect is produced by bringing a charged rubber rod close to one side of a smoothly running stream of water from a faucet. As shown in Fig. 26B, the stream is diverted to one side and even into the horizontal before it falls again.

An ordinary sheet of writing paper, placed on

Fig. 26A   *A rubber rod, electrified by rubbing against a piece of fur, attracts wood, as shown by the turning of the arrow.*

the panel of a door or other similar flat surface and rubbed, will hold fast and remain there for some little time without falling down.

26.2. Electricity + and −. When two different substances are rubbed together and then sepa-

Fig. 26B   *A thin stream of water is easily deflected by an electrified rod or comb.*

rated, both are found to be electrified, one with one kind of electricity and the other with another. To illustrate this, one end of a rubber rod is charged by rubbing with fur and is then sus-

pended in a small wire stirrup, as shown in Fig. 26C.

When the electrified end of a similarly charged rod is brought close by, as shown in diagram (a), the suspended rod turns away, showing repulsion. If the fur is brought close by, in place of the rubber, the suspended rod is attracted and turns toward the fur. When a glass rod, previously rubbed with silk, is brought close by, as in diagram (b), there is attraction, and when the silk is brought up there is repulsion.

Since the fur, as well as the glass, attracts the electrified rubber rod, they each have the same kind of electrification: they are said to be *positively charged*. By similar notation the rubber and silk by their actions are said to be *negatively charged*. Positive charges are designated by a (+) sign and negative charges by a (−) sign.

Not only do the above experiments indicate the existence of two kinds of electrification, but they also demonstrate a rule concerning the action of one kind of electrification on another. Diagram (a), illustrating a negatively charged rubber rod repelling a similar rod, shows that two negative charges repel each other. Diagram (b) shows that positive and negative charges attract each other, and diagram (c) that two positive charges repel each other. The general law can therefore be stated that:

Like charges repel and unlike charges attract.

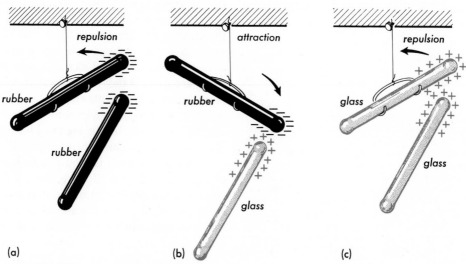

Fig. 26C   *Like charges of electricity repel each other and unlike charges attract.*

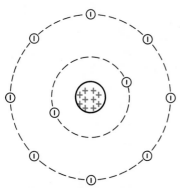

Fig. 26D *Schematic diagram of a neon atom showing its nucleus at the center with ten positive charges (called protons) surrounded on the outside by ten negative charges (called electrons).*

26.3. Theory of Electrification. Historically there have been two outstanding theories of electrification: the one-fluid theory of Benjamin Franklin* and the two-fluid theory of Charles Du Fay. According to the two-fluid theory, all objects contain equal amounts of two fluids. When two different substances are rubbed together, one kind of fluid (positive) is spread over one object and the other kind of fluid (negative) over the other.

According to the one-fluid theory of Franklin, all bodies contain a certain specified amount of an "electric fire" or fluid to keep them in an uncharged or neutral state. When two objects are rubbed together, one accumulates an excess of fluid and becomes positively charged while the other loses fluid and becomes negatively charged. To Franklin we owe the terms "plus" and "minus," "positive" and "negative" electricity.

Both of these theories are in part correct, for now we know the mechanism by which bodies become electrified by friction. The modern theory is based upon the principle already put forward

—that all substances are made of atoms and molecules. Each atom contains a nucleus having a known amount of positive charge (see Fig. 26D). This positive charge is due to the presence in the nucleus of a certain number of *protons*. All protons are alike and have the same mass and positive charge. Around every atomic nucleus there are a number of negatively charged particles, called *electrons*.

Normally each atom of a substance is electrically neutral; in other words, it has equal amounts of negative and positive charge. Since each electron has the same amount of charge as every other electron, and the same amount as every proton but of opposite sign, there are just as many protons in every nucleus as there are electrons around the outside.

While protons are much smaller than electrons in size, they contain the bulk of the mass of every atom. One proton, for example, weighs nearly two thousand times as much as an electron. The electrons therefore are light particles or objects around a small but relatively heavy nucleus.

Individual atoms or large groups of atoms and molecules have an *affinity*, an *attraction*, for additional electrons over and above the exact number which will just neutralize the positive charges of the nuclei. This attraction of the atoms for more than a sufficient number of electrons varies considerably from atom to atom and substance to substance. When, therefore, two different substances are brought into contact, the substance with greater electron affinity seizes nearby electrons from the other, and thus acquires a net negative charge. Such is the case, for example, with rubber and amber when rubbed with fur. Having a strong affinity for electrons, both of these solids become strongly negative, whereas the fur becomes deficient of electrons and thereby positively charged.

26.4. The Electroscope. An electroscope is an instrument for measuring the electrical potential of a charged body. A thin strip of gold leaf is fastened to the side of a long narrow rod of metal and mounted in a metal and glass box (see Fig. 26E). The gold-leaf support, which will here be called the "stem," is insulated from the box with amber. When the metal knob N is touched

Fig. 26E   *Diagram of an electroscope showing how such an instrument may be given a negative charge.*

by a charged rubber rod, some of the charge flows onto and distributes itself over the gold leaf and support. Since like charges repel each other, the gold leaf is pushed out as shown in the diagram. When the source of charge is taken away the electroscope retains its acquired charge, which, distributing itself more or less uniformly over the stem, causes the leaf, as shown in diagram (b), to stand out at a somewhat smaller angle. The more charge given the electroscope, the higher the gold leaf is repelled.

If an electroscope is first charged negatively as shown in Fig. 26E(b), and then a negatively charged body is brought close to but not touching the knob, as shown in Fig. 26F(a), the gold leaf will rise as indicated. This happens because the electrons are repelled away from the knob to the far end of the stem, causing the gold leaf to

rise still higher. As long as the two bodies do not touch each other, allowing more negatives to go to the electroscope, the gold leaf will fall back to its original angle when the negatively charged rod is taken away.

If a positively charged body is brought up as shown in Fig. 26F(b), negatives from the stem and gold leaf are attracted to the knob, causing the gold leaf to fall. *Thus, with a negatively charged electroscope, a positive charge brought nearby causes the gold leaf to drop, and a negatively charged body causes it to rise.* If the electroscope is positively charged, the reverse action will take place: a positive charge causes it to rise and a negative causes it to fall.

26.5. Conductors and Insulators. Not all substances are good conductors of electricity. As a general rule, metals are good conductors whereas nonmetals are poor conductors. The poorest of conductors are commonly called *insulators*, or *nonconductors*. Several examples of conductors and nonconductors are listed in Table 26A.

The property of electrical conduction is illustrated by an experiment in Fig. 26G. One end of a long thin copper wire is connected to an electroscope and the other end to a small brass knob mounted on a glass pedestal. When a charged rubber rod is touched to the knob as shown, the gold leaf of the distant electroscope rises immediately. Electrons have been conducted along the wire. If a positively charged rod con-

Fig. 26F   *Brought near a negatively charged electroscope, (a) a negatively charged body causes the gold leaf to rise, and (b) a positively charged body causes the gold leaf to fall.*

TABLE 26A. EXAMPLES OF SUBSTANCES THAT ARE
GOOD ELECTRICAL CONDUCTORS AND OTHERS
THAT ARE NONCONDUCTORS OR INSULATORS

Conductors	Nonconductors
Aluminum	Amber
Copper	Glass
Gold	Mica
Iron	Paper
Mercury	Porcelain
Nickel	Rubber
Platinum	Silk
Silver	Sulfur

tacts the knob, electrons flow away from the
electroscope, leaving the gold leaf with a positive
charge.

If the copper wire in the above experiment is
replaced by a nonconductor, like a silk thread,
the electroscope cannot be charged by the rod

conductor, it repels nearby free electrons in the
conductor, causing them to move. They in turn
repel free electrons in front of them, thus giving
rise to a flow of electrons all along the conductor.
Hence in Fig. 26G it is not necessarily the electrons from the charged rubber rod that actually
reach the electroscope leaf, but rather the electrons from the end of the wire where it touches
the electroscope knob.

There are a large number of substances that
are neither good conductors of electricity nor
good insulators. These substances are called
semi-conductors. In them, electrons are capable
of being moved only with some difficulty, i.e.,
with considerable force.

26.6. The Law of Electrostatic Force. It has
already been demonstrated that like charges
repel and unlike charges attract. Nothing that
has thus far been said, however, has indicated

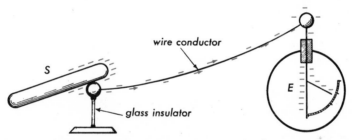

Fig. 26G   *Experiment illustrating an electric current as the flow of electrons along a wire
conductor.*

contacting the distant knob. Poor conductors,
such as glass and amber, are used to support
metal parts of electrical apparatuses for the purpose of insulating them from unnecessary losses
of electricity. An electroscope, for example, will
retain its electric charge well if the gold leaf and
stem are insulated from the electroscope case
with amber, as shown in Fig. 26E.

The difference between a conductor and an
insulator, or dielectric, is that in a conductor
there are free electrons, whereas in an insulator
all of the electrons are tightly bound to their
respective atoms. In an uncharged body, there
are an equal number of positive and negative
charges. In metals a few of the electrons are free
to move from atom to atom, so that when a
negatively charged rod is brought to the end of a

just how strong the repulsion or attraction might
be, nor how it depends on the magnitude of the
charges and the distance between them.

The first quantitative measurements of the
force between two charged bodies were made
by Coulomb a French scientist and engineer,
in 1780. He proved experimentally that:

*The force acting between two charges is directly
proportional to the product of the two charges and
inversely proportional to the square of the distance
between them.*

Symbolically, this law is usually written as an
algebraic equation,

$$F = k\frac{QQ'}{d^2} \qquad (26a)$$

where F is the force, Q and Q' are the charges, and d is the distance between them (see Fig. 26H). The constant of proportionality k has a value that depends upon the units chosen.

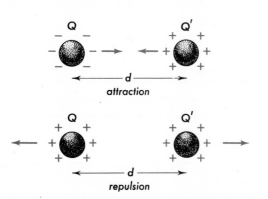

attraction

repulsion

Fig. 26H *Coulomb's law. Two like charges repel each other, or two unlike charges attract each other, with a force proportional to the product of their charges and inversely proportional to the square of the distance between them.*

In the mks system of units, *force* is given in newtons, *distance* in meters, *charge* in coulombs, and

$$k = 9 \times 10^9 \frac{\text{newton meters}^2}{\text{coulombs}^2} \qquad (26b)$$

It is customary to define the coulomb (C) in terms of the *ampere* the practical unit of electric current. Along with the kilogram, meter, and second, the ampere is to be considered as the fourth fundamental unit, defined later in Sec. 27.2, and all other electrical units are derived units.

The coulomb is defined as that quantity of electrical charge which passes by any point in a wire each second when a current of one ampere is flowing.

$$1 \text{ coulomb} = 1 \text{ ampere second}$$

or $$1 \text{ ampere} = 1 \frac{\text{coulomb}}{\text{second}}$$

From here on we will use almost exclusively the mksa system of units.

Since the unit of charge in the mksa system is measured in terms of electric currents, the numerical value of k in Eq.(26a) must be deter-

mined experimentally. The best value to date is $k = 8.9878 \times 10^9$. For most practical purposes, however, the approximation $k = 9 \times 10^9$ is used. In abbreviated symbols

$$k = 9 \times 10^9 \frac{\text{N m}^2}{\text{C}^2}$$

Experiments described in later chapters show that electrons are all alike and that each carries a charge

$$\boxed{e = 1.6019 \times 10^{-19} \text{ coulomb}} \qquad (26c)$$

This means that, when a body has a unit negative charge of one coulomb, it has an excess of 6.24×10^{18} electrons and that a body charged positively with one coulomb has a deficiency of 6.24×10^{18} electrons.

$$1 \text{ coulomb} = 6.24 \times 10^{18} \text{ electrons} \qquad (26d)$$

To simplify some of the equations that are derived from Coulomb's law, it is convenient to introduce a new constant, ϵ_0, in place of k.

$$k = \frac{1}{4\pi\epsilon_0} \qquad (26e)$$

and write Coulomb's law

$$F = \frac{1}{4\pi\epsilon_0} \cdot \frac{QQ'}{d^2} \qquad (26f)$$

Using the numerical value of k from Eq.(26b) it follows that

$$\epsilon_0 = \frac{1}{4\pi \times 9 \times 10^9}$$

$$= 8.85 \times 10^{-12} \frac{\text{C}^2}{\text{Nm}^2}.$$

This is the so-called rationalized mksa system of units.*

Example 1. A charge of $+25 \times 10^{-9}$ C is located 6 cm from a charge of -72×10^{-9} C. Calculate the force between them.

Solution. The given quantities are $Q = 25 \times 10^{-9}$ C and $Q' = -72 \times 10^{-9}$ C, $d = 0.06$ m. Substitution in Eq.(26a) gives

* Some books define ϵ_0 by the equation $\epsilon_0 = 1/k$ instead of $1/4\pi k$. Coulomb's law then becomes $F = QQ'/\epsilon_0 d^2$, where $\epsilon_0 = 1.11 \times 10^{-10}$. This is the so-called non-rationalized mska system. One must be careful in reading other texts to determine which system is being used.

$$F = 9 \times 10^9 \frac{(25 \times 10^{-9})(-72 \times 10^{-9})}{(0.06)^2 \text{ m}^2}$$

$$F = -4.50 \times 10^{-3} \text{ N}$$

The minus sign indicates attraction.

In the cgs system of units, force is measured in *dynes*, distance in *centimeters*, and *unit charge* is chosen so that $k = 1$. Coulomb's law with $k = 1$ then defines unit charge, called the *electrostatic unit* or the *statcoulomb*. One electrostatic unit, or one statcoulomb, is defined as that charge which when placed one centimeter from an equivalent charge exerts upon it a force of one dyne.

Experimental measurements give as the best probable value: 1 coulomb = 2.9979×10^9 statcoulombs. For most practical uses it is assumed that

$$1 \text{ coulomb} = 3 \times 10^9 \text{ statcoulombs}$$

26.7. Attraction of Neutral Bodies. An interesting demonstration of electrostatic attraction is shown in Fig. 26I. A tiny ball cut from the pithy

(a)   (b)

Fig. 26I   (a) A metallic-coated pith ball is attracted by a charged rod. (b) After contact, the pith ball is repelled.

core of a corn cob is coated with tin foil or metallic paint and suspended by a silk thread. When a charged rod is brought nearby as in (a), the pith ball is attracted to the rod and upon contact bounces away. As the rod is now moved toward the ball, it avoids the rod and keeps as far away as possible.

To explain this result, assume the rod to be negatively charged in the position shown in (a). Free electrons on the sphere are repelled to the opposite side, leaving an equal number of posi-

tives on the near side unneutralized. Attraction now takes place, because the positive charges are closest and the attractive force acting on them is greater than the repelling force on the negatives. When contact is made, negatives on the rod neutralize all the positives and the ball, with its negative charges, moves away by mutual repulsion.

26.8. Charging by Induction. To charge a body by induction is to give it a charge without touching it. One method of inducing a charge is illustrated in Fig. 26J. Two metal spheres A and B,

Fig. 26J   *Experiment showing how bodies may be charged by induction.*

insulated by glass standards, are touching each other when a charged rubber rod is brought close to one of them. If sphere B is now moved away, and then the rod is removed from the vicinity, both spheres are found to be charged, sphere A positively and sphere B negatively.

The explanation is similar to that of the pith ball in the preceding section, the close proximity of the charged rod repels free electrons from sphere A to the far side of sphere B leaving unneutralized positives behind. Separated under these conditions, both spheres are left with their respective charges. This is called *charging by induction*.

26.9. Faraday Ice-Pail Experiment. The distribution of charge over a metallic conductor can in part be demonstrated by an experiment first performed by Michael Faraday in 1810. This demonstration, known as *Faraday's ice-pail experiment*, involves a small metal ball, a hollow metal container like a tin pail, and an electroscope, as shown in Fig. 26K.

If the ball is charged from another source and

then lowered into the pail, the leaf of the electroscope rises. Upon moving the ball around inside the pail, and even touching the inside surface with it, no change in the potential is shown by

Fig. 26K *Diagram illustrating Faraday's ice-pail experiment.*

the electroscope leaf. After the ball has been removed, the inner surface of the pail and the ball are found to be completely free of charge.

To explain what happens, let the ball be charged negatively and lowered to the position shown. Free electrons in the metal pail are repelled to the outer surface and to the connecting electroscope, leaving positives on the inside unneutralized. When the ball touches the pail, all negatives leave the ball and neutralize an equal number of positives. The fact that the electroscope leaf remains fixed when the ball is removed shows (1) that there is no redistribution of the negative charges on the outer pail surface, and (2) that the number of induced positives within the pail was equal to the number of negatives on the ball.

When static charges are acquired by a nonconductor like hard rubber, glass, or amber, they remain where they were first located. When a conductor like copper, silver, or gold acquires a charge, however, the charge quickly spreads over the entire surface. With a metallic sphere, whether solid or hollow, the charge spreads uniformly over the surface as shown in Fig. 26L. On other shaped conductors the charge distributes itself according to surface curvature, concentrating more at points and less where the walls are more nearly straight.

Fig. 26L *Charge density on conductors is greatest in regions of greatest curvature.*

PROBLEMS

1. Two charges of -6×10^{-7} C each are located 3 cm apart. What is the repelling force on each in N?

2. Two unlike charges of 8×10^{-8} C each are located 16 cm apart. What is the force on each in N? [*Ans.* 2.25×10^{-3} N.]

3. Two equal charges are located 9 cm apart, and repel each other with a force of 0.45 N. Find the magnitude of each charge in C.

4. Two small spheres 18 cm apart, and having equal negative charges, repel each other with a force of 6×10^{-3} N. Find the total charge on the two bodies in C. [*Ans.* 2.93×10^{-7} C.]

5. A positive charge of $+12 \times 10^{-8}$ C is located 6 cm from a negative charge -8×10^{-8} C. Calculate the force in N exerted by either charge upon the other.

6. A charge of -10×10^{-7} C is located 12 cm from another charge of -10×10^{-7} C. Calculate the force in N exerted by one charge upon the other. [Ans. 0.625 N.]

7. What charge Q placed 6 cm from a charge of $+50 \times 10^{-8}$ C will produce a force of 0.24 N?

8. Four equal charges of $+6 \times 10^{-8}$ C each are located at the corners of a square 3 cm on a side. Calculate the resultant force on each charge and show its direction on a diagram drawn to scale. [Ans. 6.89×10^{-2} N.]

9. Two positive charges $+12 \times 10^{-7}$ C each, are located diagonally opposite each other on the corners of a square 9 cm on a side. Two negative charges of the same magnitude are located at the other two corners. Calculate the resultant force on each charge, and show this resultant on a diagram drawn to scale.

10. Three equal charges of 10×10^{-8} C, respectively, are each located at the corners of a right triangle whose sides are 15 cm, 20 cm, and 25 cm, respectively. Find the force exerted on the charge located at the 90° angle. [Ans. 4.59×10^{-3} N.]

11. Four equal charges of $+8 \times 10^{-6}$ C each are located at the corners of a square 6 cm on a side. Calculate the magnitude of the force on each charge, and show its direction on a diagram drawn to scale.

12. Two positive charges $+15 \times 10^{-7}$ C each, are located at diagonally opposite corners of a square 5 cm on a side. Two negative charges -15×10^{-7} C each are located at the other corners, respectively. Calculate the resultant force on each charge, and show this resultant on a diagram drawn to scale. [Ans. 7.40 N inward along each diagonal.]

13. Three equal charges of $+6 \times 10^{-6}$ C each are located at the corners of an equilateral triangle whose sides are 12 cm long. Calculate the resultant force on each charge.

ELECTRICITY IN MOTION

When an electric charge is at rest it is spoken of as *static electricity*, but when it is in motion it is referred to as an *electric current*. In most cases, an electric current is described as a flow of electric charge along a conductor. Such is the case, for example, in the experiment of charging an electroscope from a distant point by means of a long copper wire and a charged rubber rod (see Fig. 26G). This experiment is explained by stating that electrons already in the wire are pushed along toward the electroscope by the repulsion of electrons from behind. No sooner does this current start, however, than the negative charge of the rod is dissipated and the current stops flowing.

27.1. Electron Current. To make an electron current flow continuously along a wire, a continuous supply of electrons must be available at one end and a continuous supply of positive charges at the other (see Fig. 27A). This is like

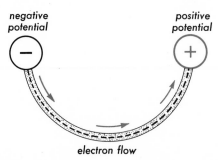

electron flow

Fig. 27A *Two terminals at different potentials and connected by a conductor give rise to an electron current.*

the flow of water through a pipe: to obtain a continuous flow, a continuous supply of water must be provided at one end and an opening for

its escape into some receptacle at the other. The continuous supply of positive charge at the one end of a wire offers a means of escape for the electrons. If this is not provided, electrons will accumulate at the end of the wire and their repulsion back along the wire will stop the current flow.

Many years ago, before it was known which of the electric charges, (+) or (−), moved through a wire, there seemed to be some evidence that it was the positive charge and not the negative. This notion became so thoroughly entrenched in the minds of those interested in electrical phenomena that in later years, when it was discovered that the negatives move in solid conductors and not the positives, it became difficult to change.

The convention that electric current flows from plus to minus is still to be found in many books and is used by some electrical engineers in designing electrical machines and appliances. The rapid growth and the importance of radio engineering and electronics, however, is bringing about a change in this practice, and we shall hereafter in this text speak of current as one of electron flow from (−) to (+) and call it electron current.

There are two general methods by which a continuous supply of electrical charge is obtained: one is by means of *a battery* and the other by means of *an electric generator*. The battery is a device by which chemical energy is transformed into electrical energy; the generator is a device by which mechanical energy is transformed into electrical energy.

27.2. The Ampere. We have seen in the preceding chapter that electron current is measured in units called *amperes*. The ampere, named in honor of the French physicist Ampère,* is one of the four fundamental units in the *mksa rationalized system*, and was used in Sec. 26.6 to define the unit of electric charge called the *coulomb*. Although the ampere will be defined precisely in Sec. 32.8, its meaning may be described as follows: one coulomb of electric charge flowing past any given point in a conductor in one second constitutes a current of one ampere.

$$1 \text{ ampere} = \frac{1 \text{ coulomb}}{1 \text{ second}}$$

$$1 \text{ A} = \frac{1 \text{ C}}{1 \text{ s}}$$

If two coulombs pass by in one second, the current is 2 A. Thus electron current is analogous to the rate of flow of water through a pipe.

$$\text{current} = \frac{\text{quantity of charge}}{\text{time}}$$

$$I = \frac{Q}{t} \qquad (27a)$$

As stated in Sec. 26.6,

$$1 \text{ coulomb} = 6.24 \times 10^{18} \text{ electrons}$$

so that a current of 1 A means a flow of 6.24×10^{18} electrons per second past any given point. This enormous number does not mean that the electrons are flowing with high speed through the conductor. In a good conductor like copper, for example, there are approximately 1×10^{23} electrons per cubic centimeter free to move as an electric current. This means that for a current of 1 A flowing through a wire 1 mm² in diameter (18-gauge wire), the average drift velocity of the electrons is approximately 4 m/hr.

When we picture a solid conductor as a crystal lattice, similar to that shown in Fig. 47G, the electrons are thought of as moving through the intervening spaces. This movement is quite random, however, since it is influenced by the repul-

sion and attraction of like and unlike charges.

27.3. Batteries. Batteries as continuous sources of electrical energy are the result of a long series of experiments which started with the discoveries of Alessandro Volta† more than one hundred years ago. Today battery cells are manufactured in two common forms: (1) dry cells, as used in flashlights, portable radios, etc., and (2) wet cells, as used in automobiles, airplanes, boats, etc.

The voltaic cell, as shown in Fig. 27B, is composed of three parts, a pair of dissimilar metal

terminals

electrodes

electrolyte

cell

Fig. 27B *Diagram of a voltaic cell.*

plates called *electrodes*, a dilute acid solution called the *electrolyte*, and a nonconducting liquid container called the *cell*. While many different combinations of materials have been tried and used in such cells, zinc and carbon as electrodes, dilute sulfuric acid as the electrolyte, and a glass or hard rubber container as the cell, are quite common.

27.4. The Cell Electromotive Force. When zinc and carbon electrodes are immersed in an electrolyte as shown in Fig. 27C, each one acquires

---

* André M. Ampère (1775–1836), French physicist and mathematician. Ampère began his career as professor of physics and chemistry at Bourg at the early age of 26. He later established the relation between electricity and magnetism, and helped to develop the subject he called electrodynamics. His only son, Jean J. Ampère, also became famous; he was a philologist, lecturer, and historian.

† Alessandro Volta (1745–1827), Italian scientist, and for more than 20 years was professor of physics at Pavia. Traveling considerably throughout Europe, he became acquainted with many celebrities. In 1801 he was awarded the Copley medal of the Royal Society of London, and then was called to Paris and awarded a medal by Napoleon. In 1815 the Emperor of Austria made him director of the philosophical faculty of the University of Padua. A statue now stands in his memory at Como, his birthplace.

its appropriate charge. The positive electrode, called the *anode*, acquires a positive potential; and the negative electrode, called the *cathode*, acquires a negative potential.

Fig. 27C   *The emf of a voltaic cell is measured with a voltmeter.*

When a voltmeter is connected to the two terminals of the cell, the pointer indicates the *difference of potential* in volts, and this we call the *electromotive force* (emf). The *volt* is the unit of potential difference in the mksa system, and is defined in Sec. 33.2. Volt is abbreviated V.

27.5. The Dry Cell. Probably the most common form of battery used today is composed of dry cells. While these cells are manufactured in different shapes and vary in size from $\frac{1}{8}$ in. to many inches, they all produce the same emf of about 1.5 V between their two terminals.

One common form of dry cell is shown in Fig. 27D. The negative electrode is a zinc-coated metal container in which all chemical ingredients are sealed, and the positive electrode is a round carbon rod. In place of a liquid electrolyte we have a paste containing ammonium chloride, zinc chloride, and a little water. Surrounding

Fig. 27D   *Cross-section diagram of a dry cell or "flashlight" battery, showing the essential elements.*

the anode is a thin layer of powdered carbon and manganese dioxide.

When current is being supplied by the dry cell, zinc ions forms at the cathode, while ammonium ions gain electrons at the carbon rod, forming hydrogen and ammonia gas. The hydrogen reacts chemically with the manganese dioxide, and the ammonia gas with the zinc chloride. While the emf of all dry cells is 1.5 V, the larger the cell, the greater is the current and the total electrical energy that it can supply.

27.6. Storage Batteries. When the electrical energy contained in a battery composed of dry cells has been exhausted, it is thrown away. A storage battery, on the other hand, is composed of what are called *wet cells;* when exhausted of its stored-up energy, such a battery can be rejuvenated or *recharged*.

The negative electrode of a storage cell, as shown in Fig. 27E, is composed of a set of

Fig. 27E   *The cell of a storage battery has a number of plates.*

parallel lead grills filled with *spongy lead* (Pb), while the positive electrode is another set of lead grills filled with porous *lead dioxide* (PbO$_2$).

Regardless of the size, each such cell develops an emf of 2.0 V. While many other kinds of storage cells have been developed, the lead battery is the most widely used in the United States.

The source of electrical energy in any battery cell is chemical by nature, and the process by which this energy is converted into electricity belongs to that branch of science called physical chemistry. For this reason the detailed chemical activity taking place in batteries when they are charging or discharging will not be taken up here.

27.7. The Battery. If two or more cells are connected together as shown in Fig. 27F, they

The common flashlight contains several dry cells connected in series as shown in Fig. 27G.

Fig. 27G   *Cross section of a 3-cell flashlight.*

When new cells are inserted, they are all turned in the same direction so that the (+) terminal at the center of each cell makes good contact with the (−) case of the next cell. The closing of the switch shown in the figure applies the end terminal voltage of 4.5 V to the light bulb.

The storage battery commonly used in automobiles contains six wet cells of 2 V each, connected in series as shown in Fig. 27H. Note how

Fig. 27F   *Four dry cells connected in series form a 6-volt battery.*

Fig. 27H   *Series connections for a 12-volt storage battery.*

form what is called a battery. In this diagram the battery is composed of four dry cells connected *in series*. By series connections it is meant that the (+) terminal of one cell is connected to the (−) terminal of the next.

The purpose in connecting two or more cells in series is to obtain a higher emf than that available with one cell alone. The potential difference between the extreme end terminals A and E of any battery is just the sum of those for the individual cells.

Each dry cell produces an emf of 1.5 V, so that if the voltmeter is connected to two points, it will indicate 1.5 V between A and B, 3.0 V between A and C, 4.5 V between A and D, and 6 V between A and E.

the heavy crossbars connect the (−) terminal of any one cell with the (+) terminal of the next. With six cells in series the end terminals produce a resultant of 12 V, hence its name of *twelve-volt battery*.

It is customary in circuit diagrams to represent battery cells as shown in Fig. 27I. The (+) and

Fig. 27I   *Circuit diagrams indicating the cells of a battery.*

(—) terminals of each cell are indicated by long and short lines, respectively. The first four diagrams shown represent one, two, three, and four cells, respectively, connected in series. If many cells are to be represented, four or five can be drawn and the over-all terminal voltage written beneath it as shown by $V = 45$ V.

27.8. Resistance. Every material object offers some resistance to the flow of an electron current through it. Good conductors like the metals, copper, silver, and aluminum, offer very little resistance, while nonconductors such as glass, wood, and paper offer a very high resistance.

The unit by which resistance is measured is called the *ohm*, in honor of the German physicist G. S. Ohm.*

An iron wire 1 mm² in cross section and 7 m long has a resistance of 1.05 ohms.

In the mksa system of units the ohm is defined as the resistance of a conductor which carries a steady current of 1 ampere when a steady potential difference of 1 volt is impressed across its terminals. The ohm is abbreviated Ω.

There are several factors that determine the electric resistance of any wire: (1) the material of which it is composed, (2) the size of the wire, and (3) its temperature. If the length of a wire is doubled, its resistance is likewise doubled; if the cross-sectional area is doubled and resistance is halved. In more general terms, the resistance of a wire is proportional to its length and inversely proportional to its cross-sectional area. Symbolically,

$$R = \rho \frac{L}{A} \qquad (27b)$$

where R is the resistance, L the length, A the

* George Simon Ohm (1787–1854), German physicist, was born at Erlavgen and educated at the university there. After teaching mathematics in Cologne for 16 years, and in Nuremberg for 16 more, he became professor of experimental physics in the high school at Munich. His writings were numerous and, but for one exception, were not of the first order. This single exception consists of a pamphlet on electric currents, the most important part of which is summarized in what is now called "Ohm's law." For this work he was awarded the Copley Medal of the Royal Society of London in 1841 and made a foreign member of the society one year later.

cross-sectional area, and ρ the resistivity of the material in question. Resistivity is defined as the resistance of a wire 1 m long and 1 m² in cross section. Values of this constant are given for several common metals in Table 27A. The smaller the constant ρ, the better is the substance as a conductor.

TABLE 27A. RESISTIVITY OF METALS, ρ, IN OHM METERS

Aluminum	$\rho = 3.2 \times 10^{-8}$
Bismuth	$\rho = 119 \times 10^{-8}$
Copper	$\rho = 1.72 \times 10^{-8}$
Iron	$\rho = 15 \times 10^{-8}$
Mercury	$\rho = 94.1 \times 10^{-8}$
Silver	$\rho = 1.05 \times 10^{-8}$
Tungsten	$\rho = 5.5 \times 10^{-8}$
Platinum	$\rho = 11 \times 10^{-8}$

To find the resistance of any size of wire made of one of these metals, the value of ρ is inserted in Eq.(27b) along with the length and cross-sectional area, and the value of R is calculated. To illustrate the method, consider the following:

Example 1. Find the resistance of a copper wire 1 mm² in cross section and 300 m long.

Solution. If we use Eq.(27b) and remember that there are 1000 mm in 1 m, we find that

$$R = 1.72 \times 10^{-8} \frac{300 \text{ m}}{1 \times 10^{-6} \text{ m}^2} = 5.16 \,\Omega \quad (27c)$$

The greater the resistivity of a wire, the poorer it is as an electrical conductor. Because of this, a term called the *conductivity* is sometimes used to specify the current-carrying ability of a material; it is defined as the reciprocal of the resistivity:

$$\sigma = 1/\rho. \qquad (27d)$$

What makes a material a good electrical conductor or not depends upon the number of free electrons within, and upon how easily these can move between the atoms from place to place. The free electrons in a metal behave a little like the molecules in a gas; they move about at random, with velocities that have a relatively high average value. In the mksa system of units, resistance in ohms has the units m²Kg/s³a².

27.9. Ohm's Law. This is the well-known and fundamental law in electricity which makes it possible to determine the current flowing through a conductor when the resistance of the conductor and the potential difference applied to it are known. What Ohm discovered was that the ratio of the potential difference between the ends of a metallic conductor and the current flowing through the metallic conductor is a constant. The proportionality constant is called the electrical *resistance*.

$$\text{resistance} = \frac{\text{potential difference}}{\text{current}}$$

Symbolically, Ohm's law is often written

$$R = \frac{V}{I} \qquad (27e)$$

In electrical units,

$$1 \text{ ohm} = \frac{1 \text{ volt}}{1 \text{ ampere}}$$

Transforming this equation, one obtains two other useful forms of the same basic law.

$$I = \frac{V}{R} \qquad (27f)$$

$$V = IR \qquad (27g)$$

The law is of great importance because of its very general application to so many electrical phenomena. One of its simplest applications is illustrated in Fig. 27J. A dry cell is directly connected by wires to a small light bulb. The battery maintains a potential difference of 1.5 V across the lamp. If the electron current flowing through the lamp is 0.5 A, the resistance of the lamp is

$$R = \frac{1.5 \text{ V}}{0.5 \text{ A}} = 3 \ \Omega$$

Although the resistance as found here is assumed to be the resistance of the light bulb, it really includes the resistance of the connecting wires. In practice one usually uses wires of such low resistance that they can be neglected in most calculations. If they are not small, they cannot be neglected and must be added in as part of the R in Ohm's law.

Consider the illustration shown in Fig. 27K, where a battery of many cells maintains a poten-

Fig. 27K   *Circuit diagram of a resistor R connected to a 60-volt battery.*

tial difference of 60 V across a conductor and a current of 5 A through it. By Ohm's law the resistance of the conductor is given by Eq.(27e) as

$$R = \frac{V}{I} = \frac{60 \text{ V}}{5 \text{ A}} = 12 \ \Omega$$

Resistance in circuit diagrams is represented by a saw-toothed line as shown.

To determine the resistance of any electrical circuit it is common practice to use a voltmeter and an ammeter. The voltmeter is applied across the resistance to measure the potential difference, and the ammeter is connected in series to measure the current.

Figure 27L represents a connector board arranged for measurements of this kind. An appliance, or unknown resistor R, is connected between two terminals at the top, so the current

Fig. 27J   *A dry cell connected to a small light bulb.*

Fig. 27L   *Connector board for determining electrical resistance.*

supplied by the battery below must pass through it as well as the ammeter. The voltmeter is connected across R to measure the potential difference between its ends.

Suppose that three heating elements, commonly used as replacement elements for electrical kitchen utensils, are connected in turn to the two terminals at the top of the board and a 6-V storage battery is applied to the terminals below. The voltage V and the current I from a sample set of measurements give the following results.

TABLE 27B. RECORDED DATA

Element	V	A
Toaster	6.3	2.3
Waffle iron	6.2	1.6
Iron	6.1	1.8

By Ohm's law, Eq.(27e), the resistance of each element can be calculated. This will be left as an exercise for the student.

When a switch is first closed to complete an electric circuit, there are essentially three velocities involved in the flow of an electron current: first, there is the electric impulse that travels along the wire with essentially the speed of light; second, the average random velocity of the electrons; and third, the *average drift velocity* of the electrons in the direction of the current, and this is relatively slow.

27.10. Resistors in Series. When several elec-

trical devices are connected in series, the resistance R of the combination is equal to the sum of the resistances of the individuals. Symbolically,

$$R = R_1 + R_2 + R_3 + R_4 + \text{etc.} \qquad (27h)$$

This, *the law of series resistances*, is illustrated by an application of Ohm's law to the external electric circuit in Fig. 27M. Three resistors $R_1 =$

Fig. 27M   *The same electron current flows through all resistors when connected in series.*

$5 \ \Omega$, $R_2 = 1 \ \Omega$, and $R_3 = 3 \ \Omega$ are connected in series with a battery capable of supplying a terminal voltage of 18 V.

To calculate the current supplied by the battery, we first find the equivalent resistance of the entire series circuit. By Eq.(27h)

$$R = 5 + 1 + 3 = 9 \ \Omega$$

In other words, if the three resistors R_1, R_2, and R_3, are replaced by a single resistor R of $9 \ \Omega$, the electron current supplied by the battery will be the same. To find this current we note that the potential difference maintained by the battery $V = 18$ V. Applying Ohm's law in the form of Eq.(27f), the electron current flowing through the circuit is

$$I = \frac{18 \text{ V}}{9 \ \Omega} = 2 \text{ A}$$

This electron current of 2 A flows through the high resistance as well as the low. Like water flowing through pipes of different sizes connected one after the other, just as much water passes through one pipe per second of time as through any other, and none can accumulate at any point.

A circuit diagram showing how an ammeter and a voltmeter are connected to a series circuit to measure current and voltage is given in Fig. 27N.

If the two leads of the voltmeter are connected to the two points J and K, the potential difference

Fig. 27N *Circuit diagram of three resistors in series.*

across R_1 is measured. Knowing the resistance of R_1 and the current I through it, one can calculate this potential difference by using Eq.(27g).

$$V_1 = I_1 R_1$$
$$V_1 = 2 \text{ A} \times 5\,\Omega = 10 \text{ V}$$

Because the potential differs by 10 V, from one side of the resistor to the other, this potential difference is commonly called the *IR drop*. In a similar way the *IR* drop across R_2 or R_3 can be measured by connecting the voltmeter to K and L, or L and M, or computed by means of Eq. (27G):

$$V_2 = 2 \text{ A} \times 1\,\Omega = 2 \text{ V}$$
$$V_3 = 2 \text{ A} \times 3\,\Omega = 6 \text{ V}$$

If we find the sum of all the *IR* drops around the circuit, we obtain

$$10 + 2 + 6 = 18 \text{ V}$$

This is known as Kirchhoff's law and is written in the general form

$$\boxed{V = V_1 + V_2 + V_3 + \ldots} \qquad (27i)$$

PROBLEMS

1. A 12-V battery supplies a current of 60 A when the starter in a car is turned on. What is the resistance of the starter motor?

2. A storage battery of 12 V supplies a current of 75 A when the starter of a car is turned on. Find the resistance of the circuit. [*Ans.* 0.160 Ω.]

3. A battery of three dry cells is used in a flashlight with a bulb of 20 Ω. What current does it draw?

4. A storage battery of 12 cells is used in a boat. If the battery maintains its full voltage across each of the two running lights of resistance 4.8 Ω, find the current supplied to each bulb. [*Ans.* 5.5 A.]

5. A reading lamp connected to a house lighting circuit of 120 V draws a current of 0.36 A. Find (a) the resistance, and (b) the number of electrons per second passing by any given point in the wire each second.

6. A copper wire is 3 mm in diameter and 8 Km long. What is its resistance? [*Ans.* 19.5 Ω.]

7. The heater wire in an electric hotplate is made of ribbon wire, 0.04 cm by 0.10 cm in cross section. Calculate its resistance if it is made of iron and is 1.5 m long.

8. A fine platinum wire 0.5 mm in diameter is 2 m long. Find the resistance. [*Ans.* 1.12 Ω.]

9. A battery of 6 dry cells is used to run a small electric motor having a resistance of 21 Ω. Find the electron current when the motor is turned on.

10. A battery of 4 dry cells is used for ringing a doorbell in a mountain cabin. If the resistance is 18 Ω, what current does the bell draw? [*Ans.* 0.333 A.]

11. A storage battery of 6 cells is used in a small truck. Each of the two headlights has a resistance of 2.4 Ω. Find the total current supplied by the battery.

12. Three resistors $R_1 = 5$ Ω, $R_2 = 12$ Ω, and $R_3 = 9$ Ω, are connected in series, and to a battery of 15 dry cells. Calculate the current flowing in the circuit. [*Ans.* 0.865 A.]

13. Three resistors $R_1 = 8$ Ω, $R_2 = 12$ Ω, and $R_3 = 24$ Ω, are connected in series, and then to a battery of 30 dry cells. Find the current flowing in the circuit.

14. Three resistors $R_1 = 5$ Ω, $R_2 = 10$ Ω, and $R_3 = 25$ Ω, are connected in series, and then the combination connected to the 120-V lighting circuit. Calculate (a) the current through the circuit, and (b) the *IR* drop across each resistor. [*Ans.* (a) 3 A, (b) 15 V, 30 V, 75 V.]

15. Three resistors $R_1 = 12$ Ω, $R_2 = 30$ Ω, and $R_3 = 48$ Ω, are connected in series, and then to a battery of 20 dry cells. Find (a) the current supplied by the battery, and (b) the *IR* drop across each resistor.

16. Four resistors of 4, 6, 12, and 26 Ω, respectively, are connected in series with a house lighting circuit of 120 V. Find (a) the current flowing through each resistor, and (b) the voltage across each resistor. [*Ans.* (a) 2.5 A, (b) 10 V, 15 V, 30 V, 65 V.]

17. Five resistors of 2, 5, 8, 15, and 20 Ω, respectively, are connected in series with a storage battery containing 60 cells. Find (a) the current flowing through the circuit, and (b) the voltage across each resistor.

KIRCHHOFF'S LAWS
AND ELECTRICAL CIRCUITS

The construction and operation of any electrical device, whether it is simple or complex, should always be preceded by a certain amount of planning and calculation. The procedure involves a knowledge of the properties of the various electrical components required to accomplish the objective, the drawing of a circuit diagram, and the calculation of the currents that will flow through various parts of the circuit.

In this chapter we will be concerned with circuits involving steady-state currents and voltages; conditions generally referred to as *direct currents*, or dc.

28.1. Parallel Circuits. A circuit diagram showing three resistors R_1, R_2, and R_3 connected in parallel is shown in Fig. 28A. The electron

Fig. 28A *Parallel circuit for three resistors R_1, R_2, and R_3.*

current I, leaving the battery at the lower left, divides at the first junction; part I_1 goes through R_1, and the remainder goes on to the next junction. Part of this current I_2 goes through R_2, and the remainder goes on and through R_3. These three currents recombine at the top junctions and form, finally, the same total electron current I returning to the battery.

It is clear from this explanation that for any number of resistors in parallel

$$I = I_1 + I_2 + I_3 + \text{etc.} \qquad (28a)$$

where I is the total current and I_1, I_2, I_3, etc., are the separate currents through the resistors. Equation (28a) is the second of Kirchhoff's laws. For Kirchhoff's first law, see Eq.(27i).

An excellent demonstration of the second law is shown in Fig. 28B, where four ordinary tung-

Fig. 28B *Parallel circuit of four light bulbs.*

sten-filament light bulbs are connected in parallel to a house lighting circuit of 120 V. The lamps used in this experiment are all different and are rated as 25, 50, 75, and 100 W, respectively. We begin the experiment with all of the lamps sufficiently loose in their screw bases to be disconnected. Each lamp in turn is tightened in its socket, the ammeter current is read and recorded, and then that lamp loosened again to disconnect it. The recorded currents are those shown at the left in Table 28A.

TABLE 28A. RECORDED DATA

$I_1 = 0.24$ A	$I_1 = 0.24$ A
$I_2 = 0.44$ A	$I_1 + I_2 = 0.68$ A
$I_3 = 0.65$ A	$I_1 + I_2 + I_3 = 1.33$ A
$I_4 = 0.85$ A	$I_1 + I_2 + I_3 + I_4 = 2.18$ A

Fig. 28C *Three resistors in parallel, illustrating Kirchhoff's law.*

As the second step, each lamp in turn is tightened in its socket without loosening any, and as each new lamp comes on, the current is recorded. This second set of recorded currents is shown at the right in Table 28A.

A careful examination of the current sums in the second set of observations will be seen to confirm Kirchhoff's law, as given by Eq.(28a).

Another type of diagram frequently drawn for parallel circuits is shown in Fig. 28C. Three resistors R_1, R_2, and R_3 are connected in parallel to a 90-V battery. To find the total current through such a circuit, we proceed to find a single resistance R which, when substituted for the parallel combination of R_1, R_2, and R_3, will result in the same current. This equivalent resistance is given by *the law of parallel resistances* as

$$\boxed{\frac{1}{R} = \frac{1}{R_1} + \frac{1}{R_2} + \frac{1}{R_3} + \text{etc.}} \qquad (28b)$$

To illustrate its use, let $R_1 = 8\ \Omega$, $R_2 = 12\ \Omega$, and $R_3 = 24\ \Omega$, as shown in Fig. 28C. By direct substitution in Eq.(28b)

$$\frac{1}{R} = \frac{1}{8} + \frac{1}{12} + \frac{1}{24}$$

Since the common denominator is 24,

$$\frac{1}{R} = \frac{3}{24} + \frac{2}{24} + \frac{1}{24} = \frac{6}{24}$$

from which

$$R = \frac{24}{6} = 4\ \Omega$$

If we now imagine the parallel combination of three resistors replaced by a single resistor $R = 4\ \Omega$, the circuit will have the general form as Fig. 27K, and the current I will be given by Ohm's law as follows:

$$I = \frac{V}{R} = \frac{90\text{ V}}{4\ \Omega} = 22.5\text{ A}$$

This is the total current I supplied by the battery to the parallel circuit of Fig. 28C.

To find how this current divides at A into three parts I_1, I_2, and I_3, we note that the full 90 V are directly applied to each resistor. Therefore, Ohm's law can be applied to each resistor separately as follows:

$$I_1 = \frac{90\text{ V}}{8\ \Omega} = 11.25\text{ A}$$

$$I_2 = \frac{90\text{ V}}{12\ \Omega} = 7.50\text{ A}$$

$$I_3 = \frac{90\text{ V}}{24\ \Omega} = 3.75\text{ A}$$

If we now apply Kirchhoff's law, Eq.(28a), we find

$$I = 11.25 + 7.50 + 3.75 = 22.5\text{ A}$$

and this is a check upon the previous total current. Note that the largest of the three currents, $I_1 = 11.25$ A, flows through the smallest resistance, and the smallest current I_3 flows through the highest resistance.

Kirchhoff's law of currents is frequently stated as follows:

The sum of all the currents flowing into any junction point is equal to the sum of all the currents flowing out.

An inspection of junction A or junction B in Fig. 28C will show how this definition gives us Eq.(28a).

Example 1. A battery supplies a potential difference of 180 V to the ends of a circuit containing four resistors of 5, 6, 8, and 20 Ω as shown in Fig. 28D. Calculate (a) the equivalent resistance of the 5- and 20-Ω parallel combination, (b) the electron current supplied by the battery, and (c) the electron current through each resistor.

Solution. (a) Apply the law of parallel resistances, Eq.(28b).

$$\frac{1}{R} = \frac{1}{5} + \frac{1}{20} = \frac{4}{20} + \frac{1}{20} = \frac{5}{20}$$

from which, by inverting, we obtain

$$R = 20/5 = 4 \, \Omega$$

(b) Since the parallel combination of 5 and 20 Ω is equivalent to 4 Ω, and it is in series with the other

Fig. 28D   *Series and parallel resistances in the same circuit.*

two of 6 and 8 Ω, respectively, the three are added by the law of series resistance, Eq.(27h),

$$R = 6 + 4 + 8 = 18 \, \Omega$$

Apply Ohm's law, Eq.(27f).

$$I = \frac{V}{R} = \frac{180 \text{ V}}{18 \, \Omega} = 10 \text{ A}$$

(c) The electron current of 10 A flows through the 6-Ω resistor and divides at B of the parallel circuit. Combining again at C, the total electron current flows through the 8-Ω resistor. To find how the current divides in the parallel circuit, the *IR* drop across that circuit is found.

$$IR = 10 \text{ A} \times 4 \, \Omega = 40 \text{ V}$$

This value of 40 V is the potential difference between B and C. If we apply Ohm's law to each of the two resistors separately, we obtain

$$I = \frac{40 \text{ V}}{5 \, \Omega} = 8 \text{ A} \quad \text{and} \quad I = \frac{40 \text{ V}}{20 \, \Omega} = 2 \text{ A}$$

Hence 8 A flows through the 5-Ω resistor, and 2 A through the 20-Ω resistor. Note that these currents are in inverse ratio to their resistances.

28.2. Internal Resistance. Although the terms *electromotive force* and *potential difference*, as applied to electrical circuits in general, are both

measured in *volts*, there is a recognized distinction between them. This difference may be illustrated by a demonstration experiment shown by circuit diagram in Fig. 28E.

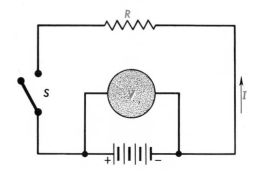

Fig. 28E   *The measured voltage V changes when the switch is closed.*

A battery of four dry cells is connected to a resistor R of about 3 Ω. When the switch S is open, no current will flow around the circuit. The voltmeter, however, with its very high resistance of several thousand ohms will draw a negligibly small current from the battery, yet one that will indicate the electromotive force E. For the four dry cells it would read 6.0 V.

When the switch S is closed to complete the electric circuit, a current I of about 2 A will flow around and through R, and the voltmeter will show a potential difference V between the battery terminals of about 5.4 V.

The drop in battery voltage from 6.0 V on open circuit to 5.4 V on closed circuit is due to the *internal resistance* of battery cells. This internal resistance behaves as though it were in series with the battery and may be illustrated circuitwise as shown in Fig. 28F. The total re-

Fig. 28F   *Batteries have an internal resistance R_i.*

sistance of this circuit is composed of the external resistance R in series with the battery's internal resistance R_i. When the switch is closed, the current I flowing through the circuit is given by Ohm's law as,

$$I = \frac{E}{R} \qquad (28c)$$

where

$$R = R + R_i \qquad (28d)$$

and E is the internal electromotive force of the battery ($E = 6.0$ V).

If the internal resistance $R_i = 0.3\ \Omega$, and $R = 2.7\ \Omega$, the total resistance $R = 3.0\ \Omega$, and a current of 2 A will flow through the circuit. The IR drop across R_i will be $2 \times 0.3 = 0.6$ V, and the voltmeter will indicate $V = 5.4$ V instead of the 6.0 V it indicates on open circuit.

The emf E may be thought of as the driving force of the battery acting on the electrons in the circuit conductors. A voltmeter always measures the potential difference between the two points to which it is connected. This is true whether they are battery terminals or two points anywhere in the circuit. We see therefore that the effective V across a battery will depend upon the battery emf, the current being drawn from that battery, and the internal resistance.

Instead of applying Eq.(28c) to a circuit, it is customary to measure or specify V, the terminal voltage, on closed circuit and then apply Ohm's law in the form

$$I = \frac{V}{R} \qquad (28e)$$

where R is the external resistance only.

28.3. The Wheatstone Bridge. An accurate method commonly employed for measuring resistance is known as the *Wheatstone bridge*. As shown in Fig. 28G, this device consists of an electrical network of four resistors R_1, R_2, R_3, and X; a galvanometer G; and a battery V. By sliding the contact D along the straight resistance wire AB, a point is located where the galvanometer current is zero. Under these conditions the electron current I_1 must go on through R_1 and X, the current I_2 must go on through R_2 and R_3, and points C and D must be at the same potential. From the latter it is seen that the potential difference across R_1 must be the same as that across R_2, and the difference across X must be the same as that across R_3. Hence we can write

$$I_1 R_1 = I_2 R_2 \qquad \text{and} \qquad I_1 X = I_2 R_3$$

Dividing the second equation by the first, we obtain

$$\frac{I_1 X}{I_1 R_1} = \frac{I_2 R_3}{I_2 R_2} \qquad \text{or} \qquad X = R_1 \frac{R_3}{R_2} \quad (28f)$$

Since the resistors R_2 and R_3 are proportional to the wire lengths p and q, their ratio q/p can be substituted for R_3/R_2. Knowing the value of R_1 and measuring the lengths of p and q, we can calculate the unknown resistance X. In some arrangements the slide wire AB is done away with, and three adjustable resistance boxes are used for R_1, R_2, and R_3 as shown in Fig. 28H.

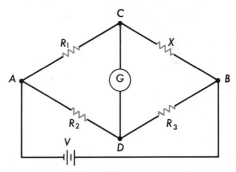

Fig. 28H   *Wheatstone bridge.*

28.4. The Potential Divider. A potential divider is an electrical circuit constructed around a variable resistor or rheostat with one sliding contact. Connected to a battery as shown schematically in Fig. 28I, its purpose is to supply any desired potential difference from zero up to the full voltage of the battery.

Suppose, as an illustration, that a battery supplies 20 V to the extreme ends of a resistance

Fig. 28G   *Slide-wire Wheatstone bridge.*

wire AB and that a voltmeter V is connected to one end A and the sliding contact C. When

Fig. 28I *Potential-divider circuit for obtaining variable voltage.*

the slider C is at A the voltmeter will read zero, but as it moves down toward B the reading will

steadily rise. One-quarter of the way along, the voltmeter will read 5 V; halfway along, 10 V; three-quarters of the way, 15 V; and finally at B it will read 20 V. As a general rule the potential difference is directly proportional to the length of the resistance wire between A and C.

As a sample calculation, let the total resistance A to B in Fig. 28I be 100 Ω. By Ohm's law the current through AB will be

$$I = \frac{20 \text{ V}}{100 \text{ Ω}} = 0.2 \text{ A}$$

Let C be located three-quarters of the way along toward B so that the resistance A to C is $100 \times \frac{3}{4}$, or 75 Ω. The *IR* drop across this portion is, therefore,

$$IR = 0.2 \times 75 = 15 \text{ V}$$

as read by the voltmeter.

PROBLEMS

1. Three resistors of 12, 24, and 36 Ω, respectively, are connected in parallel. Calculate the resistance of the combination.

2. Three resistors, $R_1 = 9 \text{ Ω}, R_2 = 12 \text{ Ω},$ and $R_3 = 36 \text{ Ω},$ are connected in parallel. Find the equivalent resistance. [*Ans.* 4.50 Ω.]

3. Two resistors of 8 Ω, and 24 Ω, respectively, are connected in parallel to a battery supplying a potential difference of 48 V. Find (a) the equivalent resistance of the parallel circuit, (b) the total current, and (c) the current through each resistor.

4. Two resistors of 20 Ω and 60 Ω, respectively, are connected in parallel and to a 90-V battery. Find (a) the equivalent resistance of the parallel circuit, (b) the total battery current, and (c) the current through each resistor. [*Ans.* (a) 15 Ω, (b) 6 A, (c) 4.5 A and 1.5 A.]

5. Three electrical appliances having resistances of 9, 27, and 54 Ω, respectively, are connected in parallel to a 120-V battery. Find (a) the equivalent resistance of the parallel resistance circuit, (b) the total electron current supplied by the battery, and (c) the electron current through each appliance.

6. A battery has an emf of 16 V and an internal resistance of 0.8 Ω. (a) Find the current supplied when the battery is connected to a 4-Ω appliance. (b) What is the *IR* drop within the battery? (c) What is the potential difference across the battery? [*Ans.* (a) 3.33 A, (b) 2.67 V, (c) 13.33 V.]

7. A battery has an emf of 28 V and an internal resistance of 1 Ω. What is the potential difference between the battery terminals when connected to a 6-Ω appliance?

8. A battery has an emf of 60 V and an internal resistance of 1.2 Ω. (a) What current is supplied when it is connected to a 12-Ω appliance. (b) What is the potential difference across the battery? (c) What is the *IR* drop across the resistor? [*Ans.* (a) 4.54 A. (b) 54.5 V, (c) 54.5 V.]

9. Three electrical fixtures of 4, 5, and 20 Ω, respectively, are connected in parallel to a 110-V battery whose internal resistance is 0.5 Ω. Find (a) the resistance of the parallel circuit, (b) the total current, and (c) the current through each fixture.

10. Four appliances of 5, 6, 10, and 30 Ω, respectively, are connected in parallel to a battery with an emf of 120 V and internal resistance of 0.5 Ω. Find (a) the equivalent resistance of the parallel circuit, (b) the total current supplied by the battery, and (c) the current through each appliance. [*Ans.* (a) 2 Ω, (b) 48 A, (c) 19.2, 16.0, 9.6, and 3.2 V.]

11. Two resistors of 4 Ω and 12 Ω are connected in parallel. This parallel circuit is connected in series with 5 Ω, and the entire circuit is connected to a battery with an emf of 36 V and internal resistance of 1 Ω. Find (a) the equivalent resistance of the circuit, (b) the current supplied by the battery, and (c) the current through each resistor.

12. Two resistors, $R_1 = 8 \text{ Ω},$ and $R_2 = 24 \text{ Ω},$ are connected in parallel. This combination is connected in series with a resistor $R_3 = 5 \text{ Ω},$ and battery with an emf of 90 V and an internal resistance of 1 Ω. Find (a) the equivalent resistance of the parallel circuit, (b) the current supplied by the battery, and (c) the current through each resistor. [*Ans.* (a) 6 Ω, (b) 7.5 A, (c) 5.62 A for $R_1,$ 1.88 A for $R_2,$ and 7.5 A for $R_3.$]

13. Three resistors, 4, 6, and 12 Ω, respectively, are

connected in parallel. This combination is connected in series with two other resistors of 5 and 7 Ω, respectively, and a battery with an internal resistance of 1 Ω and an emf of 45 V. Find (a) the resistance of the entire circuit, (b) the current supplied by the battery, and (c) the current through the 6-Ω resistor.

14. An unknown resistor is connected to a Wheatstone bridge and the variable resistors are adjusted until the galvanometer shows no current. The resistances are $R_1 = 65$ Ω, $R_2 = 82$ Ω, $R_3 = 145$ Ω. Find the unknown resistance. [Ans. 115 Ω.]

15. Two resistors of 4 Ω and 12 Ω are connected in parallel, and two other resistors of 18 Ω and 36 Ω are connected in parallel. The two combination pairs are connected in series with a resistor of 4 Ω, and a battery with an internal resistance of 1 Ω, and an emf of 75 V. Find (a) the resistance of the external circuit, (b) the current supplied by the battery, and (c) the voltage across each of the two parallel circuits.

ELECTRIC FIELDS,
POTENTIAL, AND CAPACITANCE

In the space around every charged body is an invisible something we call an *electric field*. This field is just another way of describing the action of one charge upon another at a distance.

We have seen in Sec. 26.6 that the basic law concerning the forces between charged bodies is known as Coulomb's law.

The force acting between two charges is directly proportional to the product of the two charges, and inversely proportional to the square of the distance between them. As an equation,

$$F = k \frac{Qq}{r^2} \qquad (29a)$$

In the mksa system of units, we have seen that F is in newtons, Q and q are the charges in coulombs, r is the distance between them in meters, and k is a proportionality constant,

$$k = 9 \times 10^9 \frac{\text{Nm}^2}{\text{C}^2} \qquad (29b)$$

29.1. The Electric Field. The electric field around isolated charged bodies is shown diagramatically in Fig. 29A(a) and (b).

The intensity of the electric field at any point in the region around a charged body is equal to the force per unit charge exerted on any charge placed at that point:

$$\varepsilon = \frac{F}{q} \qquad (29c)$$

This concept is analogous to gravitational-field intensity as given by Eq.(14c) in Sec. 14.1. Since force is a vector quantity, an electric field has magnitude and direction. The field about a positive charge is described as radially outward as

shown in diagram (a) of Fig. 29A. The direction is an arbitrary assignment and is based upon the custom of finding the direction in which a force would act upon a positive test charge $+q$.

Fig. 29A *Diagrams of the electric field around charged bodies.*

By a similar reasoning the field about a negative charge is radially inward as shown in diagram (b). These lines are sometimes called *electric lines of force*. It is to be noted that as many lines as desired can be drawn and that no two lines ever cross. Furthermore, the lines are imaginary and do not actually exist. They were first introduced by Michael Faraday about 1820 as an aid to the understanding of various electrical phenomena.

Since ε, the electric field intensity, is defined as the force per unit charge for any charge placed there, Eq.(29c), Coulomb's law may be used to obtain a formula for the field intensity at any point near a body having a charge Q. Dividing both sides of Eq.(29a) by q gives

$$\frac{F}{q} = k \frac{Q}{r^2}$$

or

$$\mathcal{E} = k \frac{Q}{r^2} \qquad (29d)$$

If the charge Q is in coulombs, and the distance r is in meters, the field intensity $\mathcal{E}$ is in newtons per coulomb. Since F represents the force on any charge q placed at that point,

$$F = q\mathcal{E} \qquad (29e)$$

$$1 \text{ newton} = 1 \text{ coulomb} \times 1 \frac{\text{newton}}{\text{coulomb}}$$

Example 1. Alpha rays are atomic particles each having a mass of 6.6×10^{-27} Kg and a positive charge of $+3.20 \times 10^{-19}$ C. Calculate the force on an alpha particle in an electric field $\mathcal{E}$ having an intensity of 8000 N/C.

Solution. By direct substitution in Eq.(29e)

$$F = 3.2 \times 10^{-19} \text{ C} \times 8000 \frac{\text{N}}{\text{C}}$$

$$F = 2.56 \times 10^{-15} \text{ N}$$

29.2. Electric Potential. If the connection of a charged body to the ground by a metallic conductor would cause electrons to flow to that body from the ground, the body is at a positive potential [see Fig. 29B(a)]. Conversely, if the

positive potential   *negative potential*

electrons   electrons

ground
zero potential

(a)   (b)

Fig. 29B *Showing the direction of the flow of electrons when a positively or negatively charged body is connected to the ground by a wire conductor.*

connection of a body to the ground would cause electrons to flow from that body into the ground, the body is at a negative potential [see diagram (b) of Fig. 29B].

In these definitions it is assumed that the earth is at zero potential. The bodies therefore have positive and negative potentials, respectively, before they are grounded, because after they are grounded, the flow of electrons to or from the ground will bring them to zero potential.

Electrical potential is analogous to gravitational potential in mechanics [see Sec. 14.3 and Eq.(14r)]. The electrical potential V of a body is equal to the amount of work done W, or potential energy stored E_p, per unit positive charge in carrying any charge q from the ground up to the body (see Fig. 29C).

$$V = \frac{E_p}{q} \qquad (29f)$$

In the mksa system of units, E_p is in joules, q is in coulombs, and V is in volts:

$$1 \text{ volt} = 1 \frac{\text{joule}}{\text{coulomb}} \qquad (29g)$$

If Q is positive, energy is stored in carrying a positive charge q up to the body, and the poten-

Fig. 29C *Diagram illustrating the expenditure of energy in transporting a positive charge q from the ground to a positively charged body Q.*

tial V is positive. If Q is negative, energy is liberated in carrying a positive charge q to the body, and the potential is negative. It must be pointed out that potential as here defined applies to the body of charge Q before the small test charge q arrives at the surface; the instant that contact is made, the total charge Q has been altered by an amount q.

The difference of potential V between two bodies having potentials V_1 and V_2, respectively, is defined as the energy expended per unit positive charge in carrying any charge from one body to the other:

$$V = V_2 - V_1 \qquad (29h)$$

For example, the difference of potential between the two terminals of a car storage battery is 12 V. This means that the energy expended per unit positive charge in carrying a charge q from one terminal to the other is 12 J/C.

Solving Eq.(29f) for E_p, which is equivalent to the work done, we obtain

$$W = qV \qquad (29i)$$

If we connect the negative terminal of a 12-V battery to the ground, this brings that terminal to zero potential, and the positive terminal to $+12$ V. If the positive terminal is grounded, that terminal will come to zero potential and the negative terminal to -12 V. The difference of potential between the two terminals will be the same in either case: it is 12 V.

Consider an example in which a 12-V battery is connected to two metal plates V_1 and V_2 as shown in Fig. 29D. The grounding of V_1 main-

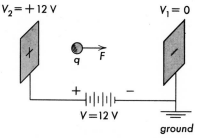

Fig. 29D *Energy is expended or liberated when a charge q is transported through a difference of potential V.*

tains that plate at zero potential and the battery maintains V_2 at $+12$ V. If we now carry a negative charge $-q$ from V_2 to V_1, an amount of energy $W = Vq$ is consumed, but in carrying it back again from V_1 to V_2 the same amount of energy is liberated.

In carrying a charge $+q$ from V_2 to V_1 an amount of energy Vq is liberated, but in carrying it from V_1 to V_2 the same amount is consumed. If V_1 and V_2 are connected by a metallic conductor, electrons will flow toward V_2 and the liberated energy will be converted into heat.

The volt is defined as the steady potential difference across a conductor which carries a current of 1 ampere and which dissipates thermal energy at the rate of 1 watt. The volt has been the legal standard of potential difference since 1950. In the mksa system the volt has the dimensions m^2 Kg/s² A.

Just as every point in the space around a mass M has a gravitational potential P, so every point in the space around a charge Q has an electrical potential V (see Fig. 14F). The electrical potential at any point in an electric field may be defined as the work done W, or potential energy stored E_p, per unit positive charge in carrying any charge from infinity up to that point (see Fig. 29E).

$$V = \frac{E_p}{q} \qquad (29j)$$

Following the same procedure used in Sec. 14.3 to derive an equation for the gravitational

Fig. 29E *The electrical potential at a point A at a distance r from the center of charge Q is given by* kQ/r.

potential at a point in space, it can be shown that the stored electrical energy under the analogous electrical conditions is given by [see Eq.(14q)]

$$E_p = k \frac{Qq}{r} \qquad (29k)$$

For a mass m in a gravitational field the force is one of attraction and the equation carries a minus sign, while for like charges the force is one of repulsion and the equation carries a plus sign.

From the concept of electrical potential as given by Eq.(29j), we can divide both sides of Eq.(29k) by q, and obtain

$$V = k \frac{Q}{r} \qquad (29l)$$

If q is close to the charge Q, the distance r is small and the magnitude of V is large. For positive Q, V is positive; for negative Q, V is negative. Note that by definition of electrical potential the charge q is positive. As r gets larger and approaches infinity, the potential V approaches zero.

Mathematically then, the ground, referred to in the preceding section as having zero potential, is the same as the potential of a point infinitely far away.

If the charge Q is located on a spherical conductor of radius R, the potential at all points outside the sphere is the same as though the charge Q were concentrated at the geometrical center. At the surface where $r = R$ the potential will be

$$V = k \frac{Q}{R}$$

while inside the sphere it will remain the same as at the surface.

29.3. Uniform Electric Field. In many experimental studies of atomic structure, a great deal of knowledge can be obtained by observing the behavior of charged atomic particles traversing a uniform electric field. To obtain such a field, that is, a field constant in magnitude and direction over a specified volume of space, two flat metal plates are set up parallel to each other as shown in Fig. 29F.

Fig. 29F *The electric field between two parallel charged plates is uniform.*

When the terminals of a battery are connected to these plates as indicated in the diagram, a uniform electric field ε is produced between the plates. Outside the plates and near the ends, the field is not uniform.

In mechanics, work done is given by force times distance, $W = F \times d$. The electrical equivalent of this equation can now be obtained by using Eq.(29i) for the energy W, and Eq.(29e) for the applied force F:

$$Vq = q\varepsilon \times d$$

$$\boxed{\varepsilon = \frac{V}{d}} \qquad (29m)$$

between parallel plates

If V is in volts and d is in meters, ε is in volts/meter:

$$1 \frac{\text{volt}}{\text{meter}} = 1 \frac{\text{newton}}{\text{coulomb}} \qquad (29n)$$

Example 2. Two flat metal plates 2 cm apart are connected to a 1000-V battery. A proton with a positive charge of 1.6×10^{-19} C is located between these plates. Find (a) the electric field intensity between the plates and (b) the force on the proton in newtons.

Solution. By direct substitution of given quantities in Eq.(29m) we obtain for (a)

$$\varepsilon = \frac{1000 \text{ V}}{0.02 \text{ m}} = 50,000 \frac{\text{V}}{\text{m}}$$

By direct substitution in Eq.(29e), we obtain for (b)

$$F = 50,000 \frac{\text{V}}{\text{m}} \times 1.6 \times 10^{-19} \text{ C}$$

$$F = 8.0 \times 10^{-15} \text{ N}$$

Just as the path of a mass m moving in a uniform gravitational field is a parabola, so the trajectory of a charge q moving in a uniform electric field is a parabola. This behavior is considered in detail in Chapter 48.

29.4. Total Energy. Consider the illustration in Fig. 29G of a small charge $-q$ moving in a

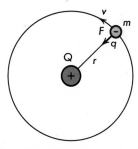

Fig. 29G *A mass m of charge −q is shown moving in a stable orbit in the radial electric field of the fixed body of charge +Q.*

circular orbit of radius r around a fixed charge $+Q$. The motion of this charge $-q$, moving in the radial electric field of Q, is analogous to the motion of a satellite of mass m moving in the radial gravitational field of a planet (see Fig. 14D).

The total energy E_t of the moving charge $-q$

is composed of two parts: the kinetic energy of the mass m, given by $\frac{1}{2}mv^2$, and the electrical potential energy $-k\frac{Qq}{r}$ given by Eq.(29k). Adding these two energies

$$E_t = \frac{1}{2}mv^2 - k\frac{Qq}{r} \qquad (29o)$$

If the orbit is mechanically and electrically stable, the centripetal force $m\frac{v^2}{r}$ keeping the mass m in its orbit is the same as the electrostatic force of attraction given by Coulomb's law. We can therefore write

$$m\frac{v^2}{r} = k\frac{Qq}{r^2} \qquad (29p)$$

Multiplying both sides by r, we obtain

$$mv^2 = k\frac{Qq}{r}$$

The term $k\frac{Qq}{r}$ can be substituted for mv^2 in Eq.(29o), and we obtain

$$E_t = \frac{1}{2}k\frac{Qq}{r} - k\frac{Qq}{r}$$

which simplifies to

$$E_t = -\frac{1}{2}k\frac{Qq}{r} \qquad (29q)$$

29.5. The Capacitor. A capacitor is an electrical device for storing quantities of electricity in much the same way that a reservoir is a container for storing water or a steel tank is a container for storing gas. The general form of a capacitor is that of two parallel conducting plates as shown in Fig. 29H.

Such plates are of relatively large area, close together, and contain between them a nonconducting medium called the *dielectric*. Common dielectrics are *air*, *glass*, *mica*, *oil*, and *waxed paper*.

Quantitatively, the capacitance of a capacitor is a measure of its ability to store-up electricity. To increase the capacitance of a capacitor, one or more of the following changes can be made: first, the area of the plates can be increased; second, the plates can be brought closer together; and third, a more suitable dielectric can be inserted between the plates. If the plates of a capacitor are small in area and at the same time relatively far apart, the capacitance is small. If the area is large and the plates close together, the capacitance is large.

The principles of the capacitor are illustrated in Fig. 29I. One plate of this capacitor is

Fig. 29I   *Demonstration of the principles of a capacitor.*

grounded, and the other is insulated but connected to an electroscope or electrometer. If the right-hand plate is now given a negative charge as shown, electrons in the other plate are repelled into the ground, leaving that plate positively charged. If the insulated plate is given a positive charge (not shown), electrons from the ground are attracted to the other plate and it acquires a negative charge.

In either case the grounded plate is, by definition, at *ground potential*, or *zero potential*. The right-hand plate is at negative potential, since, if connected to the ground, its electrons would escape into the ground. As shown in the diagram, however, the capacitor is charged.

Fig. 29H   *Diagram of the principal elements of a capacitor.*

If, while in the charged condition, the two plates of a capacitor are suddenly connected by a conductor, the negatives can flow through the conductor to the positives, thus neutralizing the charges. The capacitor has thus been discharged.

During the time a capacitor is being charged, the plates acquire a greater and greater difference of potential. If in Fig. 29I more electrons are added to the right-hand plate, the potential difference is increased. The amount of charge stored up in this way is limited only by the breakdown of the dielectric between the two plates. When the charge becomes too great, a spark will jump between the plates, thus discharging the capacitor.

Capacitance is not determined by the amount of charge a capacitor will hold before sparking occurs; it is defined as the amount of charge Q on one plate necessary to raise the potential V of that plate 1 V above the other. Symbolically,

$$C = \frac{Q}{V} \qquad (29r)$$

The unit of capacitance, the *farad*, named in honor of Michael Faraday, is defined as the capacitance of a capacitor of such dimensions that *a charge of one coulomb on each plate will give the plates a difference of potential of one volt.*

$$1 \text{ farad} = \frac{1 \text{ coulomb}}{1 \text{ volt}} \qquad (29s)$$

Whether one plate of a 1-farad capacitor is grounded or not, the potential difference between the plates will be 1 V when one plate has a positive charge of 1 coulomb and the other plate has a negative charge of 1 coulomb. Grounding simply brings that plate to zero potential without changing its charge. The charge stays with the grounded plate because of its strong attraction from the oppositely charged plate.

A capacitance of 1 farad, abbreviated F, is very large and for practical purposes is seldom used. The *microfarad* is more convenient. The smaller unit is one-millionth of the farad and is abbreviated μF. In other words, 1,000,000 microfarads are equivalent to 1 farad. A still smaller unit, the *micromicrofarad*, or *picofarad*, is some-

times used. One picofarad is one-millionth of 1 microfarad and is abbreviated $\mu\mu$F, or pF

$$1 \ \mu\text{F} = 10^{-6} \text{ F} \qquad (29t)$$

$$1 \ \text{pF} = 10^{-12} \text{ F} \qquad (29u)$$

The charging of a capacitor until the difference of potential is 1 V is analogous to raising the level of water in a tank to 1 ft, whereas the charging of the same capacitor to the point where it sparks over is like filling a tank until water runs over the top. A large capacitance is like a tank of large cross-sectional area, and a small capacitance is like a tank of small area. It takes more charge to raise the potential of a large capacitance 1 V, and it takes more water to raise the level in a large tank 1 ft.

Capacitors in common use today are of various kinds, sizes, and shapes. Perhaps the most common is the so-called "paper capacitor," used commonly in radios and the ignition system of automobiles. Two long strips of tin foil are glued to the two faces of a strip of thin paper. This paper is then soaked in paraffin or oil and rolled up with another paraffin-soaked strip of paper into a small compact unit. Each sheet of tin foil becomes one plate of the capacitor, and the paper becomes the dielectric separating them.

Another type of capacitor is the variable capacitor commonly used in tuning radios (see Fig. 29J). The capacitance of such a device can be

Fig. 29J *Variable capacitor commonly used in radio sets.* (Courtesy, Hammarlund Manufacturing Co.)

varied in amount at will by the turning of a knob. The turning of a knob moves one set of plates between the other set, thus increasing or decreasing the effective plate area, and hence, the capacitance. The capacitance of such variable air capacitors is from zero to about 4000 $\mu\mu$F.

29.6. Calculation of Capacitance. A general formula for calculating the capacitance of a parallel-plate capacitor is the following:

$$C = \epsilon \frac{A}{d} \qquad (29v)$$

where, as shown in Fig. 29H, A is the area of either of the parallel plates in m², d is the distance between them in m, ϵ a constant of the separating medium, and C is the capacitance in farads.

The constant ϵ, called the *permittivity*, is the product of the constant

$$\epsilon_0 = 8.85 \times 10^{-12} \text{ C/m}$$

and K the *dielectric constant*, or *dielectric coefficient*.

$$\epsilon = \epsilon_0 K \qquad (29w)$$

Values of the dielectric constant of a few substances are given in Table 29A.

TABLE 29A. DIELECTRIC CONSTANTS

Dielectric	K
Vacuum	1.0000
Air	1.0006
Glass	5–10
Rubber	3–35
Mica	3–6
Glycerine	56
Petroleum	2
Water	81

In the mksa system, permittivity has the units of A² s⁴/Kg m³ or, what is the equivalent, C²/Nm².

Example 3. Two rectangular sheets of tinfoil 20 cm × 25 cm are stuck to opposite sides of a thin sheet of mica 0.1 mm thick. Calculate the capacitance if the dielectric constant is 5.

Solution. The given quantities are $K = 5$, $d = 1 \times 10^{-4}$ m, and $A = 0.20 \times 0.25 = 0.05$ m². By substituting in Eqs. (29v) and (29w), we obtain

$$C = 5 \times 8.85 \times 10^{-12} \frac{0.05}{1 \times 10^{-4}}$$

$$= 221 \times 10^{-10} \text{ farad} = 0.0221 \ \mu\text{F}$$

When capacitors are connected in parallel, as shown in Fig. 29K, their combined capacitance is

parallel capacitors

Fig. 29K *Circuit diagram of parallel capacitors.*

just the arithmetic sum of the individual capacities.

$$C = C_1 + C_2 + C_3 + \text{etc.} \qquad (29x)$$

parallel capacitors

When capacitors are connected in series, as shown

series capacitors

Fig. 29L *Circuit diagram of capacitors connected in series.*

in Fig. 29L, the combined capacitance is given by the reciprocal of the sum of the reciprocals.

$$\frac{1}{C} = \frac{1}{C_1} + \frac{1}{C_2} + \frac{1}{C_3} + \text{etc.} \qquad (29y)$$

series capacitors

The first formula is derived from the principle that capacitors in a parallel combination each have the same potential difference V given by $V = Q/C$, while $Q = Q_1 + Q_2 + Q_3 + \text{etc.}$ The second of these formulas is derived from the principle that capacitors in a series combination acquire the same charge Q given by $Q = CV$, while $V = V_1 + V_2 + V_3 + \text{etc.}$

It should be noted with care that these two formulas are just the reverse of those for series and parallel resistors.

PROBLEMS

1. A metal sphere with a charge of 6×10^{-8} C is supported on the end of a glass rod. What is (a) the electric-field intensity, and (b) the potential of a point 30 cm from the center of the sphere?

2. A hollow metal ball 5 cm in diameter is given a charge of -8×10^{-8} C. What is (a) the electric-field intensity, and (b) the electric potential at a point 20 cm from the center of the ball? [Ans. (a) -1.8×10^4 N/C, (b) -3.6×10^3 V.]

3. A charge of 5×10^{-7} C is carried from a distant point up to a charged body. What is the electrical potential of that body if the work done is 7.5×10^{-3} J?

4. A spherical conductor 1 m in diameter has a charge of 5×10^{-7} C. Calculate the potential of (a) the spherical conductor and (b) a point 1 m from the center. [Ans. (a) 9×10^3 V, (b) 4.5×10^3 V.]

5. Two flat metal plates 2 cm apart are connected to a 2000-V battery. An atomic particle with a charge of 3.2×10^{-19} C passes between the plates. Find (a) the electric-field intensity between the plates and (b) the force on the particle.

6. A 5000-V battery is connected to two parallel metal plates 5 cm apart. A small oil drop with a charge of 9.6×10^{-19} C is falling between the plates. Find (a) the electric-field intensity between the plates, in N/C, and (b) the force on the oil drop. [Ans. (a) 1.0×10^5 N/C, (b) 9.6×10^{-14} N.]

7. Two metal spheres 1 m apart each have a positive charge of $+5 \times 10^{-7}$ C. Calculate (a) the electric-field intensity, and (b) the potential at a point 0.8 m from the center of each sphere.

8. Two insulated spheres 1 m apart each have a charge of -5×10^{-7} C. Calculate (a) the field intensity, and (b) the potential at a point on a straight line through the centers of the spheres, and 1 m beyond one of the spheres. [Ans. (a) -5.62×10^3 N/C, (b) -6.75×10^3 V.]

9. Two metal spheres 4 m apart have charges of $+8 \times 10^{-5}$ C and -8×10^{-5} C, respectively. Calculate (a) the field intensity and (b) the potential at a point on a straight line through the centers of the spheres, and 4 m beyond the negatively charged sphere.

10. A metal sphere 10 cm in diameter has a charge of $+2 \times 10^{-8}$ C. What is the electric-field intensity at a distance from the center of (a) 30 cm, (b) 20 cm, (c) 10 cm, (d) 5 cm? (e) Plot a graph of the field intensity $\mathcal{E}$ vs the distance r. Show the curve from $r = 0$ to $r = 40$ cm. [Ans. (a) 2×10^3, (b) 4.5×10^3, (c) 1.8×10^4, (d) 7.2×10^4 N/C.]

11. Two flat metal plates 2.5 cm apart are connected to a 1200-V battery. A small charged body of 8×10^{-9} C is located between the plates. Find (a) the electric-field intensity between the plates, and (b) the force on the charged body.

12. A battery of 5000 V is applied to two metal plates

4 cm apart. What is the force on an electron of charge 1.6×10^{-19} C when it passes through the uniform electric field between the plates? [Ans. 2.0×10^{-14} N.]

13. A 600-V battery is connected to a 50-μF capacitor. What is the charge on each plate?

14. A 10,000-V potential difference is applied to a 5-μF capacitor. What is the charge on each plate? [Ans. 5×10^{-2} C.]

15. Two flat metal plates 0.5 m $\times$ 0.8 m are mounted parallel to each other and 1 mm apart. Find the capacitance when they are immersed in oil having a dielectric constant of 2.3.

16. Two sheets of tin foil 10 cm $\times$ 5 m are glued to opposite faces of wax paper 0.05 mm thick. Find its capacitance if the dielectric constant of the waxed paper is 2.8. [Ans. 2.48×10^{-7} F, or 0.248 μF.]

17. Three capacitors 3, 9, and 18 μF, respectively, are connected in series. Find the capacitance of this combination.

18. Three capacitors 8, 10, and 40 μF, respectively, are connected in series. Find the capacitance of the combination. [Ans. 4.0 μF.]

19. Three capacitors 4, 6, and 12 μF, respectively, are connected in series to a 500-V battery. Find (a) the equivalent capacitance, (b) the charge on each capacitor plate, and (c) the voltage across each capacitor.

20. Three capacitors, 12, 15, and 60 μF, respectively, are connected in series to a 250-V battery. Find (a) the equivalent capacitance, (b) the charge on each capacitor, and (c) the voltage across each capacitor. [Ans. (a) 6.0 μF, (b) 1.5×10^{-3} C on each, (c) 125 V, 100 V, and 25 V.]

21. A variable air capacitor is made of 13 semicircular aluminum plates 4 cm in diameter. Find its maximum capacitance in $\mu\mu$F if alternate plates are connected together for the rotor, and the remaining plates for the stator. Assume the air gap between the plates to be 0.3 mm.

22. Two capacitors $C_1 = 4$ μF and $C_2 = 12$ μF, are connected in parallel. This combination is connected in series with a capacitor $C_3 = 8$ μF, and a battery of 200 V. Find (a) the capacitance of the circuit, (b) the charge on each plate of C_3, (c) the voltage across C_3, (d) the voltage across the parallel circuit, and (e) the charge on C_1 and C_2. [Ans. (a) 5.33 μF, (b) 1.067×10^{-3} C, (c) 133.3 V, (d) 66.7 V, (e) 2.67×10^{-4} C, and 8.0×10^{-4} C.]

23. Find all capacitance values that can be obtained with the following capacitors: 4, 5, and 20 μF, respectively.

24. Starting with the formula $Q = CV$, and Fig. 29K, derive the formula for the capacitance of capacitors connected in parallel.

25. Starting with the formula $Q = CV$, and Fig. 29L, derive the formula for the capacitance of capacitors connected in series.

MAGNETISM

Magnetism was known to the early Greek philosophers. According to one story Magnes, a shepherd, when on Mt. Ida on the island of Crete, was so strongly attracted to the ground by the tip of his staff and the nails in his shoes that he had difficulty in getting away. Upon digging into the ground to find the cause, he discovered a stone with the most amazing properties of attracting iron. This stone is now called lodestone or magnetite.

The idea that a lodestone can be used as a compass is a very old one. There is some evidence that the Chinese knew this as far back as A.D. 121. At any rate, a Chinese author, writing as early as the beginning of the 12th century, explains that a needle, when rubbed with lodestone and suspended free to turn, will point toward the south. This appears to be the first evidence that a piece of iron could be magnetized by a lodestone and used as a compass. The action of a lodestone or a bar magnet when suspended free to turn about a vertical axis is illustrated in Fig. 30A.

Fig. 30A *Magnetized bodies, when free to turn, come to rest in a north-south direction.*

A compass as it is often made for demonstration purposes usually consists of a straight steel needle which has been magnetized and mounted free to turn on a sharp pointed rod as shown in Fig. 30B. In the early days of the mariner's compass, it was common to float several small magnetic needles on water by mounting them on a

Fig. 30B *A compass needle is a magnet.*

block of wood or other light material. In more recent designs a compass needle with a jewel in its center is set upon the sharp point of a hard metal rod, much shorter than that shown in Fig. 30B, and placed in a small brass box with a glass top. Such compasses are familiar in appearance to everyone.

30.1. Magnets. Until recent years, magnets have been made of hardened steel and molded or rolled into many shapes. Perhaps the most common of these is the horseshoe magnet shown in Fig. 30C, or the straight bar magnet shown in Fig. 30D. The strongest magnets are now made of an alloy containing aluminum, cobalt, nickel, and iron. Small magnets of this alloy are strong enough to lift hundreds of times their own weight.

Pure iron (sometimes called soft iron), when magnetized, will not retain its magnetism and is

Fig. 30C *The attraction of a magnet for iron acts through all substances.*

therefore useless in making what are called permanent magnets. Soft iron is used, however, in the construction of electromagnets. These devices will be discussed and demonstrated in another chapter. Of the many practical applications of permanent magnets, the compass, the telephone receiver, and the radio loud-speaker are perhaps the most common.

Fig. 30D *The attraction of iron filings by a straight bar magnet shows greater attraction near the ends. These regions of greatest attraction are called* magnetic poles.

30.2. The Power of Attraction. Nearly everyone has at sometime or another played with a small horseshoe magnet and discovered for himself that it attracted only things containing iron. Upon drawing the same magnet through the dry sand or dirt, you probably discovered that it will pick up small grains of iron ore.

If more extensive experiments are carried out, a magnet can be shown to attract magnetic sub-

stances at a distance even though matter lies in the intervening space. In other words, magnetic attraction acts right through matter of all kinds. This can be demonstrated as shown in Fig. 30C by picking up iron filings on one side of a thin wooden board by holding a magnet close to the other side. If a sheet of copper, or brass, or, as a matter of fact, any substance, is placed over the magnet, the power of attraction is not destroyed. A small region of space can be partially shielded from magnetic fields if it is entirely surrounded by layers of soft iron.

While a few metals are known to be feebly attracted by a magnet, most substances like aluminum, copper, silver, gold, wood, glass, paper, etc., do not exhibit any noticeable effect. Of those weakly affected, nickel and cobalt are the most important. These two metals, as mentioned above, when alloyed together with other metals in the proper proportions, are found to exhibit stronger magnetic susceptibility than the best grades of iron or steel. As a pure element, however, iron is by far the most strongly magnetic.

30.3. Magnetic Poles. When an ordinary straight bar magnet is dipped into a box of iron filings, the tiny bits of iron are observed to cling to the ends as shown in Fig. 30D. These preferred regions of attraction are called *magnetic poles*. If this same magnet is suspended by a thread as shown in Fig. 30A, it will come to rest in a position close to the north–south direction. The end toward the north is therefore called the N or *north-seeking pole*, and the other end the S or *south-seeking pole*.

That the N and S poles of a magnet are different may be shown by bringing the magnet close to a compass needle. Such an experiment is illustrated in Fig. 30E. When the S pole of the magnet is brought close to the S pole of the compass needle as in diagram (a), there is a force of repulsion acting, and the compass needle turns away as shown. A similar repulsion occurs between the two N poles as shown in diagram (b). If the N and S poles are brought near to each other, however, a very strong attraction arises and the compass needle turns toward the other, as shown in diagrams (c) and (d). These experiments show, therefore, that *two kinds of magnetic*

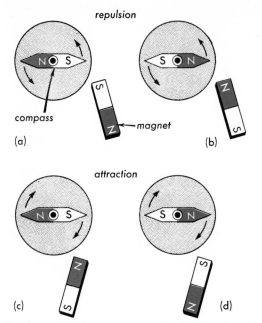

Fig. 30E *When the pole of one magnet is brought close to the pole of another magnet, like poles are found to repel each other and unlike poles to attract.*

poles exist and that *like poles repel and unlike poles attract.*

Permanent magnets can now be made so strong that one magnet can be lifted by the repulsion of another. This is illustrated in Fig. 30F.

Fig. 30F *One magnet may be suspended in mia-air by the strong repulsion of like poles of another magnet.*

Unless guide rods of glass or some other substance are used, however, the floating bar will move to one side and then fall. In other words, the forces of repulsion are such that the upper bar is not in stable equilibrium. If the floating magnet is turned end for end, opposite poles become adjacent and the two magnets attract each other. Although the forces may be great enough, no one has ever succeeded in floating a magnet in mid-air by means of permanent mag-

nets, against the pull of gravity, without guide rods.

It should be pointed out that each magnetic pole in a magnetized body is not confined to a single point but extends over a finite region. From a distance, however, each polar region acts as though it were concentrated at a point, similar to that of the center of mass in mechanics.

30.4. Poles Exist in Pairs. If a magnet is broken in the middle in an attempt to separate the poles, one finds new poles formed at the broken ends. If one of these pieces is again broken, each piece is again found to contain two poles of opposite kind. As long as this process is repeated, the same result is obtained—a magnetic pole of one kind is always accompanied by a pole of opposite polarity. This is conveniently illustrated by magnetizing a hack-saw blade and breaking it successively into smaller and smaller pieces as shown in Fig. 30G. Each time a piece

Fig. 30G *The poles of a magnet cannot exist alone. When a bar magnet is broken, poles appear on either side of the break, such that each piece has two opposite poles.*

is broken, each fragment, upon being tested with a compass, is found to have an N pole on one side and an S pole on the other. A hack-saw blade is readily magnetized by stroking it from one end to the other with one of the poles of a magnet.

It is possible to magnetize a bar of steel so that it has three or more polar regions. This is illustrated in Fig. 30H where a hack-saw blade

Fig. 30H *Diagram of a bar magnet with iron filings showing three polar regions.*

has been magnetized with an N pole at each end and an S polar region in the center. The combined strength of the N poles is seen by the quantity of iron filings to be equal to the S pole strength in the center. We might say, therefore, that the magnet has four poles: an N pole at either end and two S poles at the center.

30.5. The Magnetic Field. In the space surrounding every magnet, there exists what is called a magnetic field. Although this field cannot be seen, it can be demonstrated and mapped out in the following way.

If a very small compass is placed at some point near the N pole of a straight bar magnet, and then moved always in the direction the compass is pointing, the center of the compass will trace out a smooth line called a magnetic line of force. Starting at various points, many such lines may be drawn as shown in Fig. 30I. Each line starts

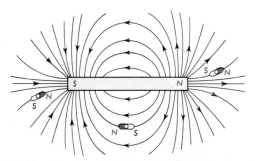

Fig. 30I   *Diagram of the magnetic field and magnetic lines of force about a straight bar magnet, as obtained with a small compass needle.*

at some point near the N pole and ends at a corresponding point near the S pole.

These magnetic *lines of force*, as they are called, do not really exist; they are but useful devices that may be used in describing the many different magnetic phenomena to be taken up in later chapters. It should be noted that, where the magnet exerts its strongest attraction near the poles, the lines are closest together and that each line points away from the N pole and toward the S pole. This latter is an arbitrary assignment, being the direction indicated by the N pole of the compass.

A close examination of the iron filings that cling to a magnet (Figs. 30D and 30H) shows that each tiny needle-like piece of iron lines up in the direction of the magnetic lines of force.

The reason for this is that each filing has become magnetized by the magnet, and having its own N and S poles, acts like a compass. An excellent demonstration of the field and its direction can be performed by laying a plate of glass or a sheet of paper over a magnet and then sprinkling iron filings over the top. By gently tapping the glass or paper, the filings turn and line up as shown in the photographic reproduction given in Fig. 30J.

Fig. 30J   *Photograph of the iron filings lined up by the magnetic field of a permanent straight bar magnet.*

30.6. The Field about Separated Magnets. When two magnets are brought close together as shown in Fig. 30K, the mutual action of the two is such as to produce a complicated magnetic field. This is illustrated by compass-made drawings at the top and by photographic reproductions of the iron-filing method of observation at the bottom.

A simplified explanation of many electric and magnetic phenomena can be given by assuming that these imaginary *lines of force* are endowed with certain real but simple properties. *Lengthwise along the lines they act as though they were stretched rubber bands under constant tension, whereas sideways they act as if they repelled each other.* Both of these properties are illustrated in Fig. 30K. When the two poles are of different polarity as in diagram (a), the lines of force acting like stretched rubber bands tend to pull the poles together. In diagram (b) where the poles are alike, the lines repel each other, pushing the poles apart.

30.7. The Earth's Magnetic Field. To Sir William Gilbert we owe the view that the earth is a great magnet. To prove his theory, Gilbert shaped a lodestone into a sphere and demonstrated that a small compass placed at any spot

Fig. 30K *Diagrams and photographs illustrating the magnetic fields around pairs of magnetic poles.*

of the globe always pointed, as it does on the earth, toward the North Pole.

The earth, therefore, has been schematically pictured in Fig. 30L as a large magnetized sphere

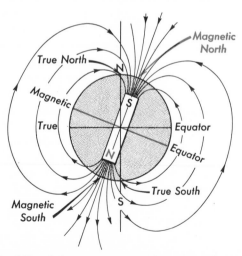

Fig. 30L *Schematic diagram illustrating the earth as a huge magnet surrounded by a magnetic field extending far out into space.*

of iron, or as though it contained a huge permanent magnet. Since the magnetic axis is at an angle with the polar axis, the earth's magnetic

poles are not at the *true North* and *true South Poles*. The true North and true South Poles are points located on the earth's rotational axis.

The *North Magnetic Pole* is located in far northern Canada, while the *South Magnetic Pole* is located almost diametrically opposite in the Southern Hemisphere. As for polarity, the North Magnetic Pole is an S pole and the South Magnetic Pole is an N pole. This becomes apparent from the magnetic lines of force which always start from an N pole and are directed toward, and end, at an S pole.

Although the cause for the earth's magnetism is not completely understood, several reasonable theories have been proposed. The earth is known to contain large iron ore deposits, some of these deposits being almost pure iron. One theory proposes that, during the ages past, all these iron deposits gradually became magnetized, in very nearly the same direction, and that together they act like one huge permanent magnet. Another theory, and a very plausible one, is that the magnetism is due to large electric currents which are known to be flowing around the earth, not only in the earth's crust but also in the air above. These earth currents seem to be connected in some direct way with the earth's rotation. This

Fig. 30M A magnetic map of the United States for the year 1954 showing the declination of a compass from true north and the angle of dip of a dip needle. Such maps are drawn from data assembled by the U.S. Coast and Geodetic Survey.

appears to be corroborated by the fact that the earth is magnetized in a direction almost parallel to the earth's polar axis.

30.8. Magnetic Declination. Since the earth's magnetic and polar axes do not coincide, a compass needle does not in general point toward True North. Because of the influence of the irregular iron deposits near the earth's surface, the magnetic field is not as regular as it is pictured in Fig. 30L and a compass needle may deviate considerably from magnetic north. The angle that a compass needle deviates from True North is called the *angle of declination*.

A map showing the angle of declination for the United States during the year 1954 is shown in Fig. 30M. The more or less vertical set of irregular lines are lines of equal declination and are called *isogonic lines*. At every point along the line marked 20°E, for example, a compass needle actually points 20° east of True North. In the region of San Francisco the declination is seen to be about 18°E, while in the region of New York it is about 11°W. The line through points where a compass points True North, 0°, is named the *agonic line*.

30.9. Magnetic Dip. If a compass needle is mounted free to turn about a horizontal axis as shown in Fig. 30N, it will not come to rest in a

Fig. 30N   *A magnetic dip needle.*

horizontal position but will dip down at some angle with the horizontal as shown. This direction, called the *dip*, is the angle the earth's field makes with the earth's surface at the point in

question. Referring to Fig. 30L it is seen that in the far north and south the angle of dip is quite large, whereas near the equator it is quite small. Figure 30O indicates the approximate dip at

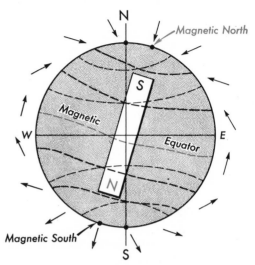

Fig. 30O   *Arrows show the direction a dip needle takes at different parts of the earth's surface.*

different latitudes for one cross section of the entire globe.

At a region on the Boothia Peninsula just north of Hudson Bay and 20° from True North, a dip needle points straight down, perpendicular to the earth's surface, and locates the North Magnetic Pole. At a region about 18° from the true South Pole a dip needle points straight up, at 90° from the horizontal, and locates the South Magnetic Pole.

On maps of terrestrial magnetism, all points that have equal dip angles are connected by a line called an *isoclinic* line. Such lines for different angles from a set of nearly parallel lines as shown on the map of the United States in Fig. 30M.

Careful and accurate measurements of the *declination* and *dip* show that the earth's magnetic field is continually changing. Although these changes are extremely small, they are somewhat periodic and at times quite erratic.

30.10. Magnetization. When a strong magnet is brought close to a piece of soft iron, the iron takes on all the properties of a new but somewhat weaker magnet. This phenomenon, called *magnetization*, is illustrated in Fig. 30P(a). As

permanent magnets

(a)   (b)

Fig. 30P *Soft iron may be magnetized by induction at a distance or by contact.*

long as the permanent magnet is held close to the soft iron bar, the iron filings cling to the end as shown. When the permanent magnet is removed, however, the soft iron immediately loses its magnetism and the iron filings drop off.

When a piece of iron is magnetized, a pole of opposite sign is created at the points of closest approach as shown in the diagrams. If a common iron nail is brought up to the N pole of a permanent magnet, it will become magnetized with an S pole at the point of contact and an N pole at the other end, as shown in diagram (b). Having two poles, the nail is thus magnetized and will attract another nail and magnetize it in the same way. With a good strong magnet this process can be repeated by adding one nail after the other.

It is now clear how iron filings line up with the lines of force of a magnet. Each filing becomes magnetized and, like a small compass, turns parallel to the field in which it is located.

30.11. Coulomb's Law for Magnetic Poles. For a study of the law of force between magnetic poles, specially designed magnets have been used.

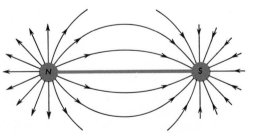

Fig. 30Q *Map of the magnetic field around a special type of permanent magnet.*

The necessity for this is realized when it is remembered that single magnetic poles cannot be isolated by breaking a magnet in two. The special magnets consist of thin steel rods about 18 in. long, with a small steel ball on either end. When magnetized the N and S poles become concentrated in the steel balls as shown in Fig. 30Q.

As used in the Hibbert balance* shown in Fig. 30R, one magnet is balanced on a special

Fig. 30R *Diagram of the Hibbert magnetic balance for measuring the force between two magnetic poles.*

set of scales and another is held tightly in an adjustable clamp stand. If the two adjacent poles, when they are brought together, are alike, the repulsion will throw the one magnet off balance. The weight that must then be added to the left-hand side to restore balance again is a direct measure of the force of repulsion. Carrying out experiments of a similar nature, Coulomb was the first to find that *the force acting between two magnetic poles is inversely proportional to the square of the distance between them.* Having discovered this relation, he compared the pole strengths of different magnets with each other and found that *the force between two poles is proportional to the product of the pole strengths.* Combining these two relations, Coulomb proposed as a general law for magnetic poles,

$$F = \kappa \frac{mm'}{d^2}$$ (30a)

for magnetic poles

where F is the force m and m' are the strengths of the poles, and d is the distance between them. In the rationalized mksa system used in this text, F is in *newtons,* m and m' are in *ampere meters,* and κ, the proportionality constant, is

* Magnetic balance made by W. G. Pye & Co., Cambridge, England.

$$\kappa = 10^{-7} \frac{newton}{amperes^2}$$

$$\kappa = 10^{-7} \frac{N}{A^2} \qquad (30b)$$

When two magnets are arranged in the configuration shown in Fig. 30S, the two poles near-

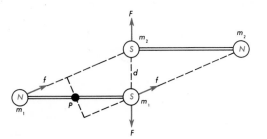

Fig. 30S   *Geometry of the forces and torques involved in the Hibbert balance.*

est each other will exert by far the strongest forces on each other. These forces, represented by *F* in the diagram, are an *action* and *reaction pair.*

To measure the force *F* exerted on the lower S pole, the lower magnet is initially balanced carefully on a pivot P at its center of mass. Under these conditions the two attractive forces *f*, due to the poles of the upper magnet, will cancel out since they exert equal and opposite torques.

If the magnets are long and the distance *d* relatively small, the force of repulsion between the extreme end poles will be exceedingly small. To a first approximation, this force and the torque it exerts can be neglected.

30.12. Magnetic Induction B. It is quite common practice to refer to the strength or the intensity of a magnetic field as the *magnetic induction.*

The magnetic induction B at any point in space may be defined as the force per unit N pole acting on any pole placed at that point.

Algebraically,

$$B = \frac{F}{m'} \qquad (30c)$$

Suppose, for example, that when a unit pole of *1 ampere meter* is placed at a given point in space it experiences a force of *5 newtons*. The

magnetic induction *B* at that point is then said to have a magnitude of *5 newtons/ampere meter* (N/Am). If a pole with a strength of *m″* ampere meters is placed at this same point where the magnetic induction is known to be *B* newtons/ampere meter, the force acting on the pole in newtons is

$$F = m''B \qquad (30d)$$

From the above definition that $B = F/m'$, and Coulomb's law, a relation for the magnetic induction at any point near a single pole of strength *m* may be obtained. When Eq.(30a) is solved for F/m', we obtain

$$\frac{F}{m'} = \kappa \frac{m}{d^2}$$

or

$$B = \kappa \frac{m}{d^2} \qquad (30e)$$

where *d* is the distance from the field producing pole *m* to the point in question.

While the magnetic induction, as given by either Eq.(30c) or Eq.(30e), is in N/Am, it is customary to express *B* in webers/meter². In other words

$$1 \frac{newton}{ampere\ meter} = 1 \frac{weber}{meter^2}$$

$$1 \frac{N}{Am} = 1 \frac{Wb}{m^2} \qquad (30f)$$

This means that the constant κ can be expressed in fundamental units as

$$\kappa = 10^{-7} \ Kg\ m/s^2\ A^2 \qquad (30g)$$

or in derived units as

$$\kappa = 10^{-7} \ Wb/Am \qquad (30h)$$

The direction of the magnetic field at any point is the direction of the force acting on an N pole placed at that point. This is another way of determining or plotting magnetic lines of force. As illustrated in Fig. 30T, an N pole placed in a position (a), equidistant from the two poles of the magnet, is repelled by the N pole with the same force that it is attracted by the S pole. The resultant of these two forces is the horizontal force to the right and parallel to the magnet. If an S pole were located at the same point, the resultant force would be just oppositely directed.

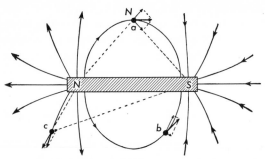

Fig. 30T *The force acting on a unit N pole placed in a magnetic field gives the magnitude and direction of the magnetic field at that point.*

It is therefore clear why a compass placed at (a) turns parallel to the magnet, and why at other points like (b) it turns in another direction. Forces acting on each pole of the compass needle turn it into the equilibrium positions found and plotted as the magnetic field in Fig. 30I.

In San Francisco the earth's magnetic induction B is 5.4×10^{-5} Wb/m², or 0.54 gauss [see Eq.(32l)] and the angle of dip about 62°. This gives a horizontal component of 0.25×10^{-4} Wb/m² or 0.25 gauss.

Example 1. Calculate the magnetic induction B at a point 8 cm from an N pole of 48 Am.

Solution. By making direct substitutions of the given quantities into Eq.(30e), we obtain

$$B = 10^{-7} \frac{\text{Wb}}{\text{Am}} \times \frac{48 \text{ Am}}{64 \times 10^{-4} \text{ m}^2} = 7.5 \times 10^{-4} \frac{\text{Wb}}{\text{m}^2}$$

The direction of B is outward, away from N.

30.13. Molecular Theory of Magnetism. The modern theory of magnetism, which is now quite firmly established as being correct, is that a piece of iron consists of myriads of tiny elementary magnets. These tiny ultramicroscopic magnets consist of individual atoms. How single atoms can act as magnets will be explained later.

Before a piece of iron or steel has been magnetized, these elementary magnets may be thought of as being oriented more or less at random throughout the metal as shown in Fig. 30U(a).

During the time a piece of iron is being magnetized, the elementary magnets are turned around and lined up parallel to each other and to the magnetizing field. This is shown by the schematic representation in diagram (b). Lined up in this way, the small N and S poles are adjacent to each other and cancel each other's effect on external objects. At one end there are many free N poles, and at the opposite end an equal number of free S poles.

When a magnet is broken at any point, *free S poles* are exposed at one side of the break and *free N poles* at the other. It is therefore clear why poles always exist in pairs and that, no

(a)

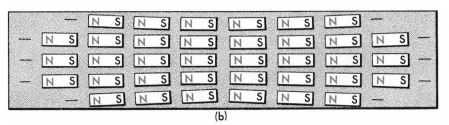

(b)

Fig. 30U *Schematic diagrams of the elementary magnets within a piece of iron: (a) unmagnetized, and (b) magnetized.*

matter how many times a magnet is broken, each piece will contain an N at one end and an S pole at the other.

When soft iron is magnetized by induction and the permanent magnet is taken away, the elementary magnets return to their original random orientations, but, when hardened steel becomes magnetized, they remain lined up after the magnetizing field is taken away.

PROBLEMS

1. Two S poles of separate magnets are located 6 cm apart as shown in Fig. 30S. If the poles of each magnet have a strength of 10 Am and are 8 cm apart, find (a) the force exerted by one S pole on the other, (b) the force of one N pole on the S pole of the other magnet, and (c) the force of one N pole on the other.

2. Two magnetic S poles are located 10 cm apart as shown in Fig. 30S. If the poles of each magnet have a strength of 8 Am, and are 20 cm apart, find (a) the force exerted by one S pole on the other, (b) the force of one N pole on the S pole of the other magnet, and (c) the force of one N pole on the other. [Ans. (a) 64.0×10^{-5} N, (b) 12.8×10^{-5} N, (c) 3.76×10^{-5} N.]

3. Two magnets of the type shown in Fig. 30Q, are arranged with their pole centers at the four corners of a 20-cm square. If each pole has a strength of 5 Am, and like poles are diagonally opposite each other, find the force on each pole.

4. Two magnets of the type shown in Fig. 30Q have poles 10 cm apart and each with a strength of 20 Am. If the poles are located at the four corners of a tetrahedron, find the direction and magnitude of the force on each pole. Neglect the force between the two poles of the same magnet. [Ans. 4.0×10^{-3} N parallel to axis of other magnet.]

5. The two poles of a bar magnet have a strength of 15 Am each and are 5 cm apart. Find the magnitude of the magnetic induction at a point in line with the two poles, (a) 5 cm beyond the S pole, and (b) 10 cm beyond the N pole.

6. A straight bar magnet has two poles of 25 Am each, spaced 10 cm apart. Find the magnetic induction at a point in line with the poles, (a) 5 cm from the N pole, (b) 10 cm from the N pole, and (c) 20 cm from the N pole. [Ans. (a) 8.89×10^{-4} Wb/m², (b) 1.87×10^{-4} Wb/m², (c) 0.347×10^{-4} Wb/m², outward.]

7. A magnet of the type shown in Fig. 30Q has poles of 10 Am and located 10 cm apart. Find the magnitude of the magnetic induction at a point in line with the poles and at a distance beyond the N pole of (a) 5 cm, (b) 10 cm, (c) 15 cm, (d) 20 cm, and (e) 25 cm. (f) Plot a graph of B vs x, where x is the distance from the N pole of the magnet.

8. A magnet of the type shown in Fig. 30Q has poles of strength 10 Am and located 10 cm apart. Find the magnetic induction along a line through the center of the magnet perpendicular to the magnet axis and at distances from the center of (a) 5 cm, (b) 10 cm, (c) 15 cm, (d) 20 cm, and (e) 25 cm. (f) Plot a graph of B vs x, where x is the distance from the center of the magnet. [Ans. (a) 28.3×10^{-5}, (b) 7.15×10^{-5}, (c) 2.53×10^{-5}, (d) 1.14×10^{-5}, (e) 0.604×10^{-5}.]

9. A bar magnet with two poles, each with a strength of 12 Am, is located in a magnetic field of 1.5 Wb/m². Find the magnitude of the force acting on each pole.

10. When an N pole of 25 Am is placed 10 cm from another pole of unknown strength, it experiences a repulsive force of 4×10^{-4} N. Find (a) the magnetic induction at the point, and (b) the unknown pole strength. [Ans. (a) 1.6×10^{-5} Wb/m², (b) 1.6 Am.]

11. A small magnet of the kind shown in Fig. 30Q, has two poles 10 cm apart and each of 16 Am. If this magnet is located in a uniform magnetic field of 1.5 Wb/m², with its axis at right angles with B, find (a) the force on each pole, and (b) the torque acting on the magnet.

12. A compass needle has poles 3 cm apart and each pole a strength of 0.4 Am. (a) Find the force on each pole when the compass is located in the earth's magnetic field of 5.4×10^{-5} Wb/m². (b) What is the torque on the needle when its axis is at right angles to B.? [Ans. (a) 2.16×10^{-5} N, (b) 6.48×10^{-7} N m.]

EFFECTS OF ELECTRIC CURRENTS

Everyone is more or less familiar with the electrical appliances of the modern household: the electric lights, electric toaster, iron, refrigerator, vacuum cleaner, washing machine, etc. All of these devices depend for their operation upon one or more of five general effects produced by electric currents; these are

heating effect
magnetic effect
mechanical effect
chemical effect
lighting effect

It is the purpose of this chapter to consider the first three of these different effects and to take up in some detail the important principles involved.

31.1. Electric Energy. When the householder pays his monthly electricity bill, he pays according to the amount of electric energy consumed. To calculate electric energy, a general formula involving *current*, *voltage*, and *time* is usually employed. A battery or generator, in supplying current to any electric system, maintains a constant difference of potential between two ends of the circuit.

Consider the two terminals of a battery as shown in Fig. 31A and the mechanical work that would be required to move a negative charge from the (+) terminal to the (−) terminal. *The amount of work done per unit charge in carrying any charge Q from one terminal to the other is called the difference of potential.* Symbolically,

$$V = \frac{W}{Q} \tag{31a}$$

where V is in volts, W in joules, and Q in coulombs.

If, instead of carrying a charge from one terminal to the other and thereby doing work, we

Fig. 31A *The work done per unit charge in carrying any charge Q from one terminal to the other is called the difference of potential V.*

connect the two terminals with a conductor, a current I will flow and the battery will be doing work for us in creating heat. *The current I is given by the amount of charge Q flowing per second of time.*

$$I = \frac{Q}{t} \tag{31b}$$

If we solve this equation for Q,

$$Q = It$$

and substitute It for Q in Eq.(31a), we obtain

$$V = \frac{W}{It}$$

Upon solving for W, we find

$$\boxed{W = VIt} \tag{31c}$$

joules = volts × amperes × seconds

If V is in volts, I is in amperes, and t is in seconds, the energy W is in joules. Since by

Ohm's law, $I = V/R$, direct substitution for I or for V gives two other useful forms of the same equation.

$$W = I^2Rt \qquad W = \frac{V^2}{R} t \qquad (31d)$$

31.2. Electric Power. Power is defined in mechanics, as well as in electricity, as the rate at which energy is developed or expended. $P = W/t$. Dividing each of the above energy equations by t, we find that

$$P = I^2R \qquad P = V^2/R$$

and

$$\boxed{P = VI} \qquad (31e)$$

where P is in watts. These are practical equations since with most electrical equipment the *voltage*, *current*, and *resistance* are usually known from voltmeter and ammeter readings. The last equation is well worth memorizing: "*Power in watts is equal to potential difference in volts times current in amperes.*" The other two follow by a direct substitution from Ohm's law.

The *watt* is abbreviated W. One thousand watts is called the *kilowatt*, and is abbreviated KW.

$$1000 \text{ W} = 1 \text{ KW}$$

Energy as expressed in Eq.(31c) is power VI multiplied by the time t. *Power in kilowatts multiplied by the time in hours gives the energy in kilowatt-hours.* The kilowatt-hour is the unit of electric energy by which all electric energy is calculated for payment.

The watt-hour meter placed on the premises of every consumer is a slowly revolving motor, having a low resistance winding which is in series with the line and which therefore conducts the current in the line, and a high resistance winding which is across the line and which therefore conducts a small current proportional to V. The time factor t is accounted for by the automatic recording of the total number of rotations of the armature by a small clocklike mechanism with dials and pointers.

Example 1. Two resistors of 3 Ω and 5 Ω, respectively, are connected in series with a battery of 20-V terminal voltage (see Fig. 31B). Calculate (a) the

electron current through the circuit, (b) the potential difference across each resistor, (c) the power consumed by each resistor, (d) the total energy consumed in 2 hr of operation, and (e) the total cost of operation for 40 hr at 3 cents per KW-hr.

Fig. 31B *The power consumed by any resistance is given by the voltage across it multiplied by the current.*

Solution. Connected in series, the two resistors $R_1 = 3$ Ω and $R_2 = 5$ Ω have a total resistance of $R = 8$ Ω.

(a) If we apply Ohm's law, the electron current through the circuit is found to be

$$I = V/R = 20/8 = 2.5 \text{ A}$$

(b) The drop in potential across any resistor is given by IR.

$$V_1 = I_1R_1 = 2.5 \times 3 = 7.5 \text{ V}$$
$$V_2 = I_2R_2 = 2.5 \times 5 = 12.5 \text{ V}$$

(c) The power consumed is given by VI, the potential drop across each resistor multiplied by the electron current through it.

$$P_1 = V_1I = 7.5 \times 2.5 = 18.75 \text{ W}$$
$$P_2 = V_2I = 12.5 \times 2.5 = 31.25 \text{ W}$$

(d) The power supplied by the battery is VI, the voltage across its terminals multiplied by the total electron current in amperes.

$$P = VI = 20 \times 2.5 = 50 \text{ W}$$

in agreement with the sum of the two values in (c). To find the energy, multiply by the time in seconds.

$$W = 50 \text{ W} \times 7200 \text{ s} = 360,000 \text{ J}$$

(e) The power 50 W should next be expressed in KW and multiplied by the time in hours, to give

$$W = 0.05 \text{ KW} \times 40 \text{ hr} = 2 \text{ KW-hr}$$

At 3 cents per KW-hr, the total cost will be 6 cents.

31.3. The Heating Effect of an Electric Current. When an electron current is sent through a wire, heat is generated and the temperature of the wire rises. If the current is increased, the rate at which heat is generated increases rapidly until the wire itself glows a deep red. A still further increase in current will heat the wire to a yellow or white heat. Beyond this point, if it has not already done so, the wire will reach a temperature where it will melt and become a liquid.

Whether a wire is only warmed by an electron current or heated to incandescence depends upon a number of factors, the two principal ones being the current and the resistance. Experiment shows that the energy expended in a wire is given by Eq.(31c).

$$W = VIt$$

where V is in volts, I is in amperes, and t is in seconds. Electrical energy, like mechanical energy, is measured in joules. Heat energy is measured in kilocalories.

By the law of conservation of energy, each kilocalorie of heat produced will require the expenditure of a definite amount of electrical energy. As an equation we can therefore write

$$W \propto H$$

or

$$W = JH \qquad (31f)$$

where J is a proportionality constant and, as in mechanics, is found to have the value

$$J = 4.179 \times 10^3 \, \frac{\text{joules}}{\text{kilocalorie}} \qquad (31g)$$

If we solve Eq.(31f) for H, we obtain

$$H = \frac{1}{J} W$$

and substituting W from Eq.(31c),

$$H = \frac{1}{J} VIt$$

or

$$H = 2.39 \times 10^{-4} \, VIt$$

If Ohm's law is introduced in the form $V = IR$, we can substitute IR for V and obtain

$$\boxed{H = 2.39 \times 10^{-4} \, I^2 Rt} \qquad (31h)$$

This is known as *Joule's law*.

Example 2. If the heating element of an electric toaster has a resistance of 22 Ω and is connected to an ordinary house lighting circuit of 110 V, how much heat will be generated in 1 min?

Solution. From Ohm's law, $I = V/R$, the electron current is first calculated.

$$I = 110/22 = 5 \text{ A}$$

We can now make use of Joule's law by substituting in Eq.(31h).

$$\text{heat} = 2.39 \times 10^{-4} \times (5)^2 \times 22 \times 60 = 7.89 \text{ Kcal}$$

For some electric appliances, heating is a desired effect, while in others it is a source of trouble and even danger. In an electric iron, hot plate or toaster, for example, heat is the main objective of the device. In such appliances a relatively large current of several amperes is sent through a coil or element of special wire having a resistance of several ohms. As a rule the wire is of some alloy, such as nichrome, and of such a size that the heat developed will not raise the temperature higher than red hot. Diagrams of typical heating elements used in three different household appliances are shown in Fig. 31C.

Fig. 31C *Diagrams of the heating elements of various electrical appliances found in many modern homes: (a) electric iron, (b) electric stove, and (c) electric toaster.*

31.4. Magnetic Effect, Oersted's Experiment. The first discovery of any connection between electricity and magnetism was made by Oersted*

* Hans Christian Oersted (1777–1851), Danish scientist. Born the son of an apothecary, Oersted spent part of his boyhood teaching himself arithmetic. At the age of 12, he assisted his father in his shop and there became interested in chemistry. Passing the entrance examinations at the University of Copenhagen at the age of 17, he entered the medical school, and graduated six years later with his doctorate in medicine. At age 29 he returned to

in 1820. Often, during his lectures at the University of Copenhagen, Oersted had demonstrated the nonexistence of a connection between electricity and magnetism. His usual procedure was to place a current-carrying wire at right angles to, and directly over, a compass needle to show that there was no effect of one on the other. On one occasion, at the end of his lecture, when several members of the audience came up to meet him at the lecture room desk, he placed the wire parallel to the compass needle and, not the least expecting it, saw the needle move to one side (see Fig. 31D). Upon his reversing the cur-

mapped by means of a small compass or by iron filings. If a wire is mounted vertically through a hole in a plate of glass or other suitable nonconductor, and then iron filings are sprinkled on the plate, there will be a lining-up of the filings parallel to the magnetic field. The result shows that the magnetic lines of force or *lines of induction* are concentric circles whose planes are at right angles to the current. This is illustrated by the circles in Fig. 31E.

Fig. 31D *Diagram of Oersted's experiment illustrating the effect of an electron current upon a compass needle.*

Fig. 31E *Experiment demonstrating the magnetic field about a straight wire carrying an electron current.*

rent in the wire, the needle, to his amazement and perplexity, deviated in the opposite direction. Thus this great discovery was made quite by accident, but, as Lagrange once said of Newton on a similar occasion, "such accidents come only to those who deserve them."

31.5. The Left-Hand Rule. Oersted's experiment is interpreted as demonstrating that *around every wire carrying an electric current there is a magnetic field.* The direction of this field at every point, like that around a bar magnet, can be

The left-hand rule used in electromagnetism can always be relied upon to give the direction of the magnetic field due to an electron current in a wire. Derived from experiment, the rule states:

If the current-carrying wire were to be grasped with the left hand, the thumb pointing in the direction of the electron current, $(-)$ to $(+)$, the fingers will point in the direction of the magnetic induction.

In other books, using the older convention that current in a wire is from $+$ to $-$, the *right-hand rule* is used to give the magnetic field the same direction that it has here.

31.6. Magnetic Properties of a Solenoid. Not long after the announcement of Oersted's discovery of the magnetic effect of a current-carrying wire, Ampère found that a loop or coil of wire acted as a magnet. This is illustrated by a single loop of wire in Fig. 31F, and by a coil of several turns of wire in Fig. 31G. A coil of wire of this kind is sometimes referred to as a *solenoid,*

the university, this time as professor of physics. It was at one of his demonstration lectures on chemistry and metaphysics that he discovered the magnetic effect bearing his name. The discovery not only brought him many endowments and prizes, but also made him one of the most eminent personalities in his own country.

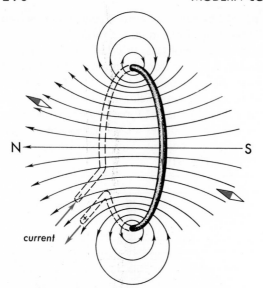

current

Fig. 31F   *Diagram of the magnetic field through and around a single loop of wire carrying an electron current.*

or as a *helix*. In either case, the magnetic lines of force are such that one side or end of the coil acts like a N magnetic pole and the other side or end like an S magnetic pole.

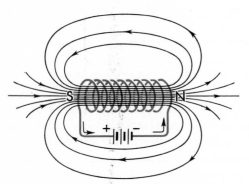

Fig. 31G   *Diagram of the magnetic field around a solenoid carrying an electron current.*

At all points in the region around a coil of wire carrying a current, the direction of the magnetic field, as shown by a compass, can be predicted by the left-hand rule. Inside each loop or turn of wire, the lines point in one direction, whereas outside they are oppositely directed.

Outside the coil, the lines go from N to S in quite the same way they do about a permanent

bar magnet, whereas inside they go from S to N.

Not only does one coil of wire act like a magnet but two coils may be used to demonstrate the repulsion and attraction of like and unlike poles.

Another left-hand rule which must not be confused with the one in the preceding section, but which follows directly from it, is the following: *If the solenoid were to be grasped with the fingers pointing in the direction of the electron current, around the coil from* $(-)$ *to* $(+)$, *the thumb would point in the direction of the internal field as well as the N pole.*

31.7. The Electromagnet. Five years after Oersted's discovery and Ampère's demonstration of the magnetic properties of a solenoid, William Sturgeon filled the center of a coil of wire with soft iron and thereby produced a powerful magnet. This is illustrated in Fig. 31H. As long as the

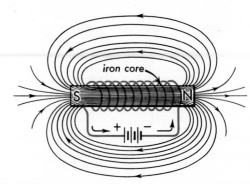

Fig. 31H   *Diagram of an electromagnet and the field surrounding it when a current flows through the coil.*

electron current continues to flow, the addition of the iron core produces a magnet hundreds of times stronger than does the solenoid alone. A nearby compass needle, if set oscillating, will demonstrate this effect by vibrating quickly with the iron core in place, and slowly with it removed.

Again, with the iron core in the solenoid, a nearby rod of soft iron, magnetized by induction as shown in Fig. 30P, will attract iron filings much more strongly than when the iron core is removed.

31.8. Mechanical Effects of Electric Currents. In 1821, Michael Faraday discovered that, when a wire carrying a current is placed in the field of a magnet, a mechanical force is exerted on the wire. This is the principle upon which the modern electric motor is based.

A demonstration of Faraday's discovery is shown in Fig. 31I, where a flexible copper wire

Fig. 31I *Demonstration of the mechanical effect of an electron current in a magnetic field.*

about one meter long is suspended from a support. A U-shaped magnet straddles the wire somewhere near the middle.

Upon closing the switch K, an electron current flows up through the wire and the wire moves to the left. If the battery connections are reversed, thereby reversing the electron current, the deflection of the wire will be to the right.

If the magnet is turned over, thereby interchanging N and S poles, the deflection of the wire will again reverse. In other words, the reversing of either the magnetic field or the direction of the electron current will reverse the direction of the force acting on the wire. The reversal of both will make it the same.

The existence of a mechanical force may be demonstrated by another simple experiment as shown in Fig. 31J. Two parallel brass bars fastened to a board are placed over the N pole of a

Fig. 31J *An experimental arrangement for demonstrating that a wire carrying a current in a magnetic field experiences a force tending to move it across the field at right angles to the current, and at right angles to the field.*

magnet and then connected to a battery. When a round metal rod is laid across the bars, thus allowing an electron current to flow in the direction shown, the rod experiences a force and rolls to the left. A reversal of either the electron current or the polarity of the magnet will cause the rod to roll to the right. A reversal of both will cause it to roll to the left.

It should be emphasized here that this force is exerted on the electrons, the moving charges in the wire, and that they, being confined to the wire, cause it to move. An electron at rest in a magnetic field experiences no force from the magnet. An electron moving across magnetic lines of force experiences a force at right angles to both the field and the direction of motion.

31.9. Interaction Between Magnetic Fields. To gain some understanding of this mysterious invisible force acting on a current-carrying wire in a magnetic field, consider the diagrams in Fig. 31K.

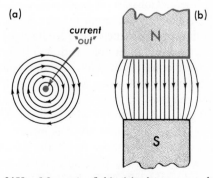

Fig. 31K *Magnetic fields (a) due to an electron current and (b) due to magnetic poles.*

The circles in diagram (a) represent the circular magnetic lines of force around a straight wire carrying a current. The directions of the arrows are given by the left-hand rule, shown here for an electron current up and out of the page.

The lines of force in diagram (b) represent the magnetic field between two opposite poles of a magnet.

If we now place the current-carrying wire between the poles of the magnet, the two fields interact on each other. The interaction is such that a newly formed field like that shown at the right in Fig. 31L is obtained. Imagining that the

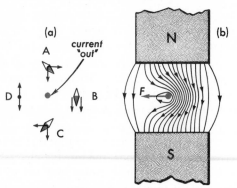

Fig. 31L *Diagrams of two interacting magnetic fields.*

magnetic lines of force act like stretched rubber bands, one can predict from this diagram that the wire should experience a force F to the left.

To understand how such a field can arise out of two interacting symmetrical fields, it should be remembered that the field direction at any point is that taken by a small magnetic dipole placed there. Consider as examples the points A, B, C, and D of diagram (a). At A the field due to the current in the wire is to the right, and that due to the magnet poles is down. If the two fields exert equal torques on the tiny compass needle, it will point along a direction half-way between the two.

At B the field due to the wire is down, and so is the field due to the magnet. A compass at this point would point down. At C the fields are again at right angles, and the compass points down and to the left. At D the fields are oppositely directed and, if they are equal in magni-

tude, cancel each other's effect. This process repeated for many other points will lead to the field shown in diagram (b).

It is important to note that the direction of the current I in the wire, the direction of the magnetic field B at the wire due to the magnet, and the direction of the force F acting on the wire are all at right angles to each other. Furthermore, the direction of the force F can be quickly ascertained by applying the left-hand rule to the electron current in the wire. If the wire were to be grasped with the left hand, the thumb pointing in the direction of the electron current ($-$ to $+$), the force is toward the weakened field, that is, toward the region where the fingers are oppositely directed to the field of the magnet.

31.10. The Electric Motor. An electric motor is a device by which electrical energy in the form of an electron current is transformed into mechanical energy. The principle of the motor is illustrated in Fig. 31M. A wire carrying an elec-

Fig. 31M *Principal elements for demonstrating the principles of an electric motor.*

tron current is bent into a loop and placed between two magnetic poles as shown in Fig. 31N. In this horizontal position, the resultant magnetic field is warped, which forces one wire down and the other up. Mounted free to turn about an axis, the loop rotates until it is in a vertical plane. At this point, the current in the loop is reversed in direction by means of *sliding contacts* and a *split-ring commutator*. The reversal of the electron current reverses the forces so that the side of the loop which was previously pushed up is now pushed down, and the side

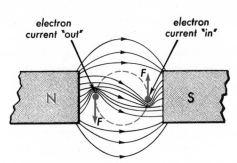

Fig. 31N   *Magnetic field lines in an electric motor with two poles.*

Fig. 31O   *Diagram of the essential parts of an ammeter or voltmeter.*

previously pushed down is now pushed up. The loop therefore rotates through half a turn more, where the current again reverses. A repetition of this reversing process at each half turn gives rise to a continuous rotation, the left side of the coil or loop always moving down and the right side always moving up.

31.11. Ammeters and Voltmeters. Electrical instruments designed to measure an electric current are called *ammeters*, and those designed to measure potential difference are called *voltmeters*. The principle upon which both of these devices operate is essentially the same as that of the electric motor as shown in Fig. 31M. They differ from the motor, however, in the delicateness of their construction and the restrained motion of the rotating armature.

A coil of fine copper wire is so mounted between the two poles of a permanent magnet that its rotation, as shown in Fig. 31O, is restrained by a hairspring. The farther the coil is turned from its equilibrium or zero position, the greater is the restoring force. To this coil is fastened a long pointer, at the end of which is a fixed scale reading amperes if it is an ammeter, or volts if it is a voltmeter. Upon increasing the current through the moving coil of an ammeter or voltmeter, the resultant magnetic field between the coil and the magnet is distorted more and more. The resulting increase in force therefore turns the coil through a greater and greater angle, reaching a point where it is just balanced by the restoring force of the hairspring.

Photographs of two small panel instruments are shown in Fig. 31P. The two connections

Fig. 31P   *Photographs of the front face of a typical voltmeter and ammeter. The two electrical connections to each of these instruments are on the back and are not shown. (Courtesy, General Electric Co.)*

necessary in each instrument are on the back and are not shown. On each instrument they lead to the moving coil by means of flexible connections near or through the armature pivots.

Whenever an ammeter or voltmeter is connected to a circuit to measure electron current or potential difference, the ammeter must be connected in series and the voltmeter in parallel. As illustrated in Fig. 31Q, the ammeter is so connected that all of the electron current passes through it. To prevent a change in the electron current when such an insertion is made, all ammeters must have a low resistance. Most ammeters therefore have a low-resistance wire, called a *shunt*, connected across the armature coil.

A voltmeter, on the other hand, is connected across that part of the circuit for which a measurement of the potential difference is required.

Fig. 31Q *Circuit diagram showing the connections for an ammeter and voltmeter.*

If the potential difference between the ends of the resistance R_1 is wanted, the voltmeter is con-

nected as shown. If the potential difference across R_2 is desired, the voltmeter connections are made at C and D, whereas, if the potential difference maintained by the battery is desired, the connections are made at A and D. In order that the connection of a voltmeter to a circuit does not change the electron current in the circuit, the voltmeter must have a high resistance. If the armature coil does not have a large resistance of its own, additional resistance is added in series.

Very delicate ammeters are often used for measuring very small currents. A meter whose scale is calibrated to read thousandths of an ampere is called a *milliammeter*. One whose scale is calibrated in millionths of an ampere is called a *microammeter* or *galvanometer*.

PROBLEMS

1. Two resistors of 5 Ω and 7 Ω, respectively, are connected in series to a 120 V outlet. Calculate (a) the electron current through the circuit, (b) the power consumed by each resistor, (c) the energy consumed by each resistor in 1 min, and (d) the cost of operating for 1 hr at 2.4 cents per KW-hr.

2. Two resistors of 6 Ω and 9 Ω, respectively, are connected in series to a house lighting circuit of 120 V. Calculate (a) the electron current through the circuit, (b) the power consumed by each resistor, (c) the energy consumed by each resistor per min, and (d) the total cost of operating for 1 hr at 2.8 cents per KW-hr. [*Ans.* (a) 8 A, (b) 384,576 W, (c) 23,000 J, 34,600 J, (d) 2.69 cents.]

3. Three resistors of 3 Ω, 4 Ω, and 12 Ω, respectively, are connected in parallel to a 120-V source. Find (a) the electron current through each resistor, (b) the power consumed by each resistor, (c) the energy consumed by each resistor per hr, and (d) the total cost of operating for 1 hr at 2.5 cents per KW-hr.

4. A coffee pot, when plugged into a 120-V outlet, draws an electron current of 2.5 A. How many Kcal of heat are produced per min.? [*Ans.* 4.32 Kcal.]

5. When an electric hotplate is plugged into a 120-V outlet, it draws an electron current of 3.8 A. How much heat is produced per min?

6. When an electric coffee pot is plugged into a 120-V outlet, it draws an electron current of 3.2 A. If the pot contains 2 Kg of water, and 75% of the heat goes into the water, how long will it take to raise the temperature of the water from 25°C to 100°C? [*Ans.* 36.3 min.]

7. A pan containing 3 Kg of water is placed on an electric hotplate. When plugged into a house lighting circuit of 120 V, the hotplate draws an electron current of 6 A. If 60% of the heat developed goes into the water, how long will it take to raise the temperature from 20°C to 100°C?

8. An electric toaster with a resistance of 30 Ω draws an electron current of 4 A when connected to a house lighting circuit. If it takes 1.5 min to make dark toast, how many Kcal were developed? [*Ans.* 10.3 Kcal.]

9. The heating element of an electric stove connected to a 220-V line draws an electron current of 4.5 A. Find the amount of heat produced in 15 min.

10. An electric iron having a resistance of 20 Ω is connected to a 120-V line. Find the heat developed in 15 min. [*Ans.* 155 Kcal.]

11. Calculate the heat developed by an electric iron in 5 min if it draws 2.8 A from a 120-V line.

12. A teakettle containing 4 Kg of water at a temperature of 20°C is heated on an electric stove. If the heating coil draws an electron current of 5 A from a 220-V line, and one-half of the heat generated goes to heat the water, how long will it take for the water to reach the boiling point? [*Ans.* 40.6 min.]

13. An electric iron having a resistance of 22 Ω is connected to a 115-V line. Find the heat developed in 5 min.

14. Calculate the heat developed by a 150-W electric soldering iron in 1 hr. [*Ans.* 129 Kcal.]

15. A boiler containing 20 Kg of water at a temper-

ature of 27°C is heated on an electric stove. If the heating element draws an electron current of 8 A from a 208-V line, and 75% of the heat generated goes into the water, how long will it take to reach the boiling point?

16. An electric coffee maker containing 12 Kg of water at 25°C is connected to a 220-V outlet. If the electron current drawn is 13.6 A and 70% of the heat developed goes into the water, how hot will the water be in 10 min? [Ans. 50°C.]

17. An electric heater connected to the house lighting circuit of 120 V is rated at 1 KW. (a) How much current does it draw, and (b) how much heat is given off per hour?

18. An electric heater is designed for operation on a 120-V line. If it is rated as 1200 W, find (a) the current drawn, and (b) the total heat produced per hour. [Ans. (a) 10 A, (b) 1032 Kcal.]

19. A voltmeter with a resistance of 150 Ω shows a full-scale reading when 5 V is applied to its terminals. What resistance connected to this instrument will give it a full-scale deflection when connected to 600 V?

20. A voltmeter with a resistance of 180 Ω shows a full-scale reading when 5 V are applied to its terminals. What resistance connected to this instrument will give it a full-scale reading when 25 V are applied? [Ans. 720 Ω in series.]

21. A voltmeter with a resistance of 2000 Ω shows a full-scale reading at 150 V. What resistance should be connected to this instrument to give it a full-scale reading of 2500 V?

22. A voltmeter having a resistance of 2000 Ω shows a full-scale reading when an electron current of 200 mA flows through it. What shunt resistance across this instrument will enable it to be used as an ammeter with 2 A as a full-scale reading? [Ans. 222 Ω.]

23. A voltmeter having a resistance of 800 Ω shows a full-scale reading when an electron current of 200 mA flows through it. What shunt resistance across this instrument will enable it to be used as an ammeter with 5 A as a full-scale deflection?

MAGNETIC INDUCTION

We have seen in the preceding lessons how an electron current gives rise to a magnetic field surrounding the conductor, and also how a current-carrying wire placed in a magnetic field experiences an unbalanced force tending to move it across the field. The mathematical formulation of the principles involved in these magnetic and mechanical effects depends primarily upon a quantitative account of the magnetic field strength.

The strength of the magnetic field at any point in and around any electrical equipment is represented by the letter B and is called the *magnetic induction*. As a simple illustration, the magnetic induction around a long, straight wire is everywhere perpendicular to the wire, and the magnetic lines of force representing B are drawn as concentric circles as shown in Fig. 32A. While the direction of B, as represented by the arrow-

heads, is given by the left-hand rule, the magnitude of B at any point is given by *Ampère's theorem*, a fundamental principle connecting electric currents with the magnetic fields they produce.

32.1. Ampère's Theorem. Consider a wire of any shape carrying an electron current. The current in each small part of the wire contributes to the magnetic induction at all points around the wire. In Fig. 32B, for example, the small element of wire of length l_1 at a distance r_1 from

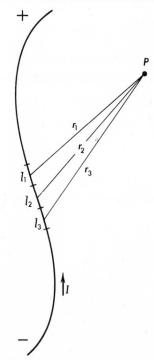

Fig. 32A *The magnetic field around a long, straight conductor.*

Fig. 32B *The magnetic induction at a point P is due to all current elements of the conductor.*

any chosen point P produces its own magnetic induction contribution at P which, by the left-hand rule for electron currents, is "out" from the page. Similarly, the small element of wire l_2, at a distance r_2 from the same point P, produces another contribution at P which is out from the page. The resultant magnetic induction at P is, therefore, the vector sum of the contributions from all elements of the wire.

The magnitude of the magnetic induction due to a small current element was first proposed by Biot and Savart in 1820, and later formulated by Ampère, to be given by

$$B = \kappa \frac{Il \sin \theta}{r^2} \qquad (32a)$$

where, as shown in Fig. 32C, B is the magnetic

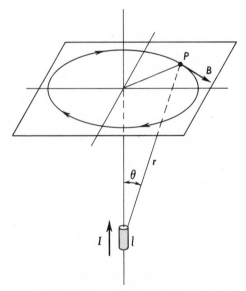

Fig. 32C   *Ampère's theorem.*

induction at a point P, l is the length of a current element of the wire, r is the distance from l to P, θ is the angle between r and l, and κ is a proportionality constant.

$$\kappa = 10^{-7} \frac{\text{webers}}{\text{ampere meter}}$$

Equation(32a) is called *Ampère's theorem.*

The magnitude of the constant κ, like the constant κ in Coulomb's law, depends on the choice of units for the other factors.

In applying Ampère's theorem to straight wires and circular coils of various kinds, the factor 4π enters so frequently into the formulas that it is convenient to express κ in terms of another constant μ_0, as follows,

$$\kappa = \frac{\mu_0}{4\pi} \qquad (32b)$$

This is analogous to replacing k in Coulomb's law for electric charges by $\dfrac{1}{4\pi\epsilon_0}$. See Eq.(30f).

Ampère's theorem, therefore, becomes

$$B = \frac{\mu_0}{4\pi} \cdot \frac{Il \sin \theta}{r^2} \qquad (32c)$$

If I is in amperes, and r and l are in meters, B is in webers/meter^2 and the constant

$$\mu_0 = 4\pi\kappa$$
$$\mu_0 = 12.57 \times 10^{-7} \frac{\text{Wb}}{\text{Am}} \qquad (32d)$$

From a study of Eq.(32a) and Fig. 32C, it seems reasonable that doubling the electron current I, or doubling the length of the element l, would double the magnetic induction. It is also reasonable by comparison with the field around magnetic poles, and Coulomb's law, that the magnetic induction should vary inversely as the square of the distance r. That the magnetic induction varies as $\sin \theta$, however, was first proved experimentally by Ampère.

To obtain the resultant value of B at any specified point near a current-carrying wire, the contributions from all small elements l of the entire circuit must be added together. To do this, a summation process, the *integral calculus*, is usually required. With the calculus, many different calculations are readily carried out, but without it they are, except for the following simple case, difficult.

32.2. The Magnetic Induction at the Center of a Circular Turn. Consider a circular loop of wire, as shown in Fig. 32D, where each small element l of the wire is perpendicular to the radial distance r, and equidistant from the center P. Since $\theta = 90°$, and $\sin \theta = 1$, Eq.(32c) becomes the same for each element l.

$$B_1 = \frac{\mu_0}{4\pi} \cdot \frac{Il_1}{r_1{}^2},$$

$$B_2 = \frac{\mu_0}{4\pi} \cdot \frac{Il_2}{r_2{}^2}$$

$$B_3 = \frac{\mu_0}{4\pi} \cdot \frac{Il_3}{r_3{}^2}, \text{ etc.}$$

If we sum up the mutually parallel contribu-

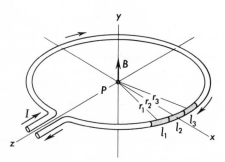

Fig. 32D   *Ampere's theorem applied to a single loop of wire.*

tions from all elements of the wire, the resultant magnitude of B becomes

$$B = \frac{\mu_0}{4\pi}\left(\frac{Il_1}{r^2} + \frac{Il_2}{r^2} + \frac{Il_3}{r^2} + \dots\right)$$

or

$$B = \frac{\mu_0 I}{4\pi r^2}(l_1 + l_2 + l_3 + \dots)$$

Since the sum $l_1 + l_2 + l_3 + \dots$ must equal the circumference of the wire loop, the above parenthesis can be replaced by $2\pi r$. When this is done we obtain,

$$\boxed{B = \mu_0 \frac{I}{2r}} \qquad (32e)$$

for single turn

where I is in amperes, r is in meters, and B is in webers/meter². Note that B is the magnetic induction at the center only and that its direction is perpendicular to the plane of the loop. For the general shape of the field, see Fig. 31E.

For a wire conductor that is wound in the form of a flat circular coil having a number of turns N, and a radius r, the magnetic field in and around the coil is greatly increased over that produced by a single turn (see Fig. 32F).

Along the axis of the coil the magnetic induction B is perpendicular to the plane of the coil and its magnitude is given by

$$B_x = \mu_0 \frac{NIr^2}{2d^3} \qquad (32f)$$

where N is the number of turns, r is their radius in meters, I is the current in amperes, and

$$d = \sqrt{r^2 + x^2}$$

Here x is the distance from the coil center to the axial point where B_x is to be calculated.

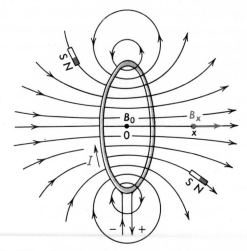

Fig. 32E   *Diagram of the magnetic field through and around a flat circular coil carrying an electron current I.*

At the coil center, where $x = 0$, $d = r$, and Eq.(32f) simplifies to

$$\boxed{B_0 = \mu_0 \frac{NI}{2r}} \qquad (32g)$$

center of a flat coil

32.3. Uniform Magnetic Fields. While there are numerous ways of producing uniform magnetic fields, the methods commonly employed in the research laboratory are few in number. One of these, shown in Fig. 32F, consists of sending a

Fig. 32F   *A solenoid of N turns of wire.*

current through a long straight solenoid. As indicated by the lines of induction drawn in the figure, the number of lines per square meter of cross section, i.e., webers/meter², is fairly constant over a considerable volume of space at the center.

The magnetic induction at the center of such a solenoid is given by

$$B = \mu_0 \frac{NI}{l} \qquad (32h)$$

long solenoid

where N is the number of turns, I is the current in amperes, and l is the length of the coil in meters.

A second experimental arrangement frequently employed to produce uniform magnetic fields is shown in Fig. 32G. Two identical flat coils of

electron current

Fig. 32G *Diagram of the magnetic field around Helmholtz coils, showing the uniformity of field over the large central volume of space.*

radius r, placed a distance r apart, form what are called *Helmholtz coils.*

The magnetic induction B at the geometrical center of this arrangement, and over a considerable volume of space around this center, is given by

$$B = 1.43\mu_0 \frac{NI}{2r} \qquad (32i)$$

Helmholtz coils

where N is the number of turns in one of the two identical coils.

This equation is derived from Eq.(32f) by setting $x = r/2$ and doubling the result, since the two coils contribute equal amounts to the field at the center.

When uniform fields of great strength are required, electromagnets are commonly employed (see Fig. 32H). As in any electromagnet, the soft

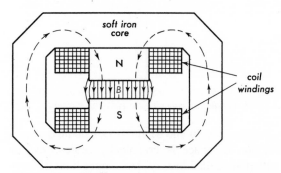

Fig. 32H *Diagram of an electromagnet for producing strong uniform magnetic fields.*

iron core increases the magnetic induction to several thousand times that produced by the coils alone.

Fields up to approximately 1.5 Wb/m² are produced by this means. Since the resultant field strengths thus produced depend a great deal upon the nature of the iron core itself, the magnitude of B between the poles is usually measured by experimental methods.

32.4. Field near a Straight Conductor. The magnetic induction around a straight wire is shown in Fig. 31E to be everywhere perpendicular to the wire, and the lines of force to be concentric circles. The magnitude of the induction at any point P, close to a long, straight wire, is found from Ampère's theorem to be given by

$$B = \frac{\mu_0}{4\pi} \cdot \frac{2I}{r} \qquad (32j)$$

for straight wire

where, as shown in Fig. 32I, r is the perpendicular distance to the point P in meters, and I is the electron current in amperes.

32.5. Total Magnetic Flux and Flux Density.

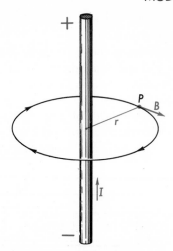

Fig. 32I   *Magnetic induction B around a straight conductor carrying an electron current.*

In Chapters 30 and 31 the magnetic field over a region of space is graphically represented by what are called *lines of force*. Since lines of force are frequently used as graphical representations of the variations in the magnetic induction from point to point, they are also called *lines of induction*.

The direction of the magnetic induction B at any point is tangent to the line of induction passing through that point, and its magnitude is given by the number of lines per unit area. The unit area is so chosen that it includes the point in question and is everywhere perpendicular to all lines passing through it.

In the mksa system of units, a line of induction is called a *weber*. The total number of lines of induction passing through a surface is called the magnetic flux and is represented by ϕ. In a region where the field is uniform and the surface area A is normal to the lines of induction,

$$\phi = BA \qquad (32k)$$

In the cgs system of units, each line of induction is called a *maxwell*, and B is given in *maxwells/cm²*, or *gauss* (G). For convenience of comparison with some of the older books, note that

1 maxwell/centimeter² = 1 gauss

and that

1 weber/meter² = 10,000 gauss   (32l)

32.6. Force on a Moving Charge. In Sec. 31.9 it was shown how a current-carrying wire, when placed in a magnetic field, experiences a mechanical force tending to move it across the field. This mechanical force is due directly to the force exerted by the magnetic induction upon the individual moving electrons within the conductor (see Fig. 32J).

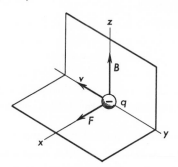

Fig. 32J   *Force on a negative charge moving across a magnetic field.*

A charge q, moving with a velocity v, through a magnetic field at right angles to B, experiences a force F given by

$$F = Bqv \qquad (32m)$$

In the mksa system, F is in *newtons*, B is in *webers/meter²*, v is in *meters/second*, and q is in *coulombs*. The vectors B, v, and F are all mutually perpendicular to each other.

If the velocity vector v makes an angle θ with B, as indicated in Fig. 32K, the magnitude of the

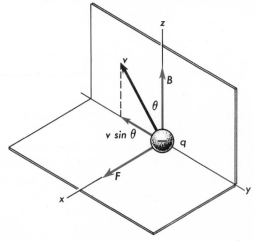

Fig. 32K   *Force on a negative charge moving at an angle to a magnetic field.*

force F is proportional to the component of the velocity perpendicular to B.

$$F = Bqv \sin \theta \qquad (32n)$$

If the charge q in Fig. 32K is positive, the force F is opposite in direction to the one shown. When a charged particle moves parallel to the field, that is, along the magnetic lines, $\sin \theta = 0$, there is no force.

32.7. Force on a Current-Carrying Wire. To find the force on a current-carrying wire in a magnetic field, we make use of the above Eq.(32n), $F = Bqv$ (see Fig. 32L). A single mov-

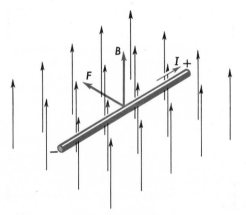

Fig. 32L *The force on a current-carrying wire in a magnetic field.*

ing charge q constitutes a current $I = q/t$. Moving with a velocity v it will, in a time t, travel a distance $l = vt$. Substituting It for q and l/t for v in Eq.(32n), we obtain

$$F = B \times It \times \frac{l}{t} \quad \text{or} \quad F = BIl \quad (32o)$$

In the mksa system, F is in *newtons*, B is in *webers/meter*^{2}, I is in *amperes*, and l is in *meters*. In the *cgs* system, F is in *dynes*, B is in *maxwells/cm*^{2}, I is in *abamperes*, and l is in *cm*. 1 *abampere = 10 amperes*, and *1 maxwell/cm*^{2} = 1 *gauss*.

Like a moving charge in Fig. 32K, a current-carrying wire that makes an angle θ with the field experiences a force proportional to $\sin \theta$.

$$F = BIl \sin \theta \qquad (32p)$$

Example 1. A wire 40 cm long and carrying an electron current of 2.5 A is located in a uniform magnetic field in which $B = 10^{-2}$ Wb/m^2. Calculate the force on the wire when it makes an angle of 60° with the field direction.

Solution. Since θ is measured from the direction of B, $\theta = 60°$, substitution in Eq.(32p) gives

$$F = 10^{-2} \times 2.5 \times 0.40 \times 0.866 = 8.66 \times 10^{-3} \text{ N}$$

32.8. Forces on Parallel Current-Carrying Wires. When two long parallel wires are each carrying a current, each gives rise to a magnetic field, and the interaction of the fields gives rise to mechanical forces acting on both wires. If the currents are in the same direction, the wires attract each other, as shown in Fig. 32M. If the

Fig. 32M *Parallel wires carrying currents exert forces on each other. This arrangement is used to define the ampere.*

two currents are oppositely directed, the wires repel each other.

The magnetic induction B_a at the point D, due to the current I_a is given by the left-hand rule as "up." The magnitude of B_a is given by Eq.(32j) as

$$B_a = \frac{\mu_0}{4\pi} \frac{2I_a}{r} \qquad (32q)$$

Since all points along the wire (b) lie in a field of this same intensity and direction, and wire (b) is carrying a current I_b, each length of the wire l will experience a force given by

$$F_b = B_a I_b l \qquad (32r)$$

By direct substitution of Eq.(32q) for B_a in Eq.(32r), we obtain

$$F_b = \frac{\mu_0}{4\pi} \frac{2I_a I_b l}{r}$$

Dividing both sides of this equation by l, we obtain the force per unit length of either wire on the other

$$\frac{F}{l} = \frac{\mu_0}{4\pi} \frac{2I_a I_b}{r}$$

or

$$\frac{F}{l} = 2 \times 10^{-7} \frac{I_a I_b}{r} \frac{\text{newton}}{\text{meter}} \qquad (32s)$$

This force of attraction between long parallel wires has been used since 1950, by international agreement, to define the fundamental unit of current, the *ampere*.

The ampere is defined as that current which, when flowing in two very long straight parallel wires, 1 meter apart in free space, will produce a force of 2.000 × 10⁻⁷ newtons per unit length on each wire.

One virtue of the rationalized mksa system of units is that nearly all electrical quantities expressed in it, such as the volt, the ampere, the ohm, the farad, and the henry, are natural units around which all practical electrical measuring instruments have been designed and used since the turn of this century.

PROBLEMS

1. Calculate the magnetic induction at a distance of 2 cm from a long straight wire carrying an electron current of 10 A.

2. Two long straight parallel wires 5 cm apart each carry an electron current of 25 A. Calculate the magnetic induction at a point between the wires, 2 cm from one and 3 cm from the other, when the currents are (a) in the same direction, and (b) in opposite directions. [*Ans.* (a) 0.833 × 10⁻⁴ Wb/m², (b) 4.17 × 10⁻⁴ Wb/m².]

3. A wire 30 m long is wound into a flat coil 4 cm in diameter. If an electron current of 8 A flows through the coil, what is the magnetic induction at the center?

4. A wire 25 m long is wound into a flat coil 8 cm in diameter. If an electron current of 6 A flows through the coil, what is the magnetic induction at the center? [*Ans.* 9.38 × 10⁻³ Wb/m².]

5. Two long straight parallel wires 8 cm apart carry an electron current of 50 A. Calculate the magnetic induction at a point between the wires, 3 cm from one and 5 cm from the other, when the currents are (a) in the same direction, and (b) when they are oppositely directed.

6. A flat coil of 35 turns has a diameter of 8 cm and carries an electron current of 12 A. Find the magnetic induction at a point (a) on the axis 8 cm from the center, and (b) at the center. [*Ans.* (a) 5.91 × 10⁻⁴ Wb/m², (b) 6.60 × 10⁻³ Wb/m².]

7. A flat coil of 75 turns has a diameter of 24 cm and carries an electron current of 5 A. Find the magnetic induction at (a) the center and (b) at a point on the axis 20 cm from the center.

8. A pair of Helmholtz coils, each 20 cm in diameter and of 25 turns, carrying a current of 2 A, are placed 10 cm apart. Find the magnetic induction at a point on the common axis, (a) half-way between the coils, and (b) at the center of either coil. [*Ans.* (a) 4.49 × 10⁻⁴ Wb/m², (b) 4.25 × 10⁻⁴ Wb/m².]

9. A pair of Helmholtz coils, each containing 20 turns, 30 cm in diameter, and carrying an electron current of 2.5 A, are located 15 cm apart. Find the magnetic induction at a point on the axis (a) halfway between the coils, and (b) at the center of either coil.

10. If the magnetic induction at the center of a solenoid 50 cm long is to be 4 × 10⁻² Wb/m² when an electron current of 8 A is flowing through it, how many turns must it have? [*Ans.* 1990 turns.]

11. If the magnetic induction at the center of a solenoid 80 cm long is to be 3 × 10⁻² Wb/m² when an electron current of 5 A is flowing through it, how many turns must it have?

12. A straight wire 20 cm long and carrying an electron current of 15 A is placed in a field where the magnetic induction is 0.5 Wb/m². If the wire and field are perpendicular to each other, find the force on the wire. [*Ans.* 1.5 N.]

13. A straight wire 30 cm long and carrying an electron current of 5 A is located in a uniform magnetic field where the magnetic induction is 0.25 Wb/m². If the wire and the field are perpendicular to each other, find the force on the wire.

14. A coil 80 cm long carries an electron current of 6 A. How many turns are required if the magnetic induction at the center is to be 100 G? [*Ans.* 1060 turns.]

15. A copper wire 80 m long is wound into a solenoid 10 cm in diameter and 1 m long. What is the magnetic induction at the center if an electron current of 1.2 A flows through the wire?

16. Two long straight wires and carrying a current of 5 A, are placed parallel to each other 5 cm apart. Find the force each wire exerts on the other. [*Ans.* 1 × 10⁻⁴ N/m.]

17. Two long straight wires are placed parallel to each

other and 10 cm apart. If each carries a current of 6 A, what will be the force each wire exerts on the other?

18. An electron with a charge of 1.60×10^{-19} C moves with $\frac{1}{20}$ the speed of light across a magnetic field of 0.05 Wb/m². Find the magnitude of the mechanical force acting on the electron (see Appendix I). [*Ans.* 1.2×10^{-13} N.]

19. An electron with its charge of 1.60×10^{-19} C, moves with $\frac{1}{30}$ the speed of light across a magnetic field of 0.5 Wb/m². (a) What is the force acting on the electron, and (b) what is the radius of its circular path (see Appendix I)?

20. Helmholtz coils placed 10 cm apart have a diameter of 20 cm, with 50 turns each, and carry a current of 1.5 A. A beam of electrons is made to enter the magnetic field near the center where B is most uniform. (a) Find the magnetic induction at the center of the coils. (b) Find the speed of the electrons if they move in a circle of 5-cm radius. [*Ans.* (a) 6.74×10^{-4} Wb/m², (b) 5.93×10^6 m/s.]

INDUCED ELECTRIC
CURRENTS

33.1. Induced Electric Currents. The discovery of induced electric currents goes back more than one hundred years to 1831 and the well-planned experiments of Michael Faraday.* A straight bar magnet plunged into a coil of wire was found to produce an electric current. The experiment is illustrated in Fig. 33A. As the N pole of the magnet is plunged into the coil, a galvanometer needle deflects to the *right;* when it is withdrawn, the needle deflects to the *left*, indicating a current

---

* Michael Faraday (1791–1867), English experimental physicist. Born the son of a blacksmith, Faraday's early life was spent earning his living as a bookbinder's apprentice. Taking time from his work to read some of the books passing through his hands, Faraday became intensely interested in science and developed a passionate desire to make science his life work. His chance finally came when he was made a valet and assistant to the great English scientist Sir Humphrey Davy of the Royal Institute. As a young man he openly proclaimed that women were nothing in his life, and even wrote and published a poem in criticism of falling in love. At the age of twenty-nine, he saw, fell desperately in love with, and married Sarah Barnhard who became a devoted and inspiring companion for the nearly fifty remaining years of his life. Four months after his marriage, he made the famous discovery of the motion of a wire carrying a current in the field of a magnet. Since a current-carrying wire would move in a magnetic field, should not the reverse be true and a magnet be made to produce current in a wire? For days he experimented with magnets and coils of wire until, in desperation, he plunged a magnet down into a coil and observed that a current was generated in the coil. Why had he not discovered this before? The motion was the connecting link he had failed to realize. For this discovery the whole scientific world sought to honor him. So many universities gave him honorary degrees that he soon had to turn down such honors. He refused the presidency of both the Royal Institute and the Royal Society of London, and also refused to be knighted. Like all great scientists, he loved his work more than these honors.

in the opposite direction. If the S pole is moved down into the coil, the needle deflects to the *left;* as it is withdrawn, the deflection is to the *right*.

Fig. 33A   *Diagram of Faraday's experimental discovery of induced electric currents.*

The relative motion of the coil and magnet is what produces the current; and it makes no difference whether the coil alone moves, whether the magnet alone moves, or whether they both move. In each case, when the relative motion ceases, the current stops. A somewhat "old-fashioned" way of describing the action is to say that only when a wire is cutting the lines of force is there an induced emf. A somewhat more acceptable statement at the present time is that only when the total magnetic flux linking a closed electrical circuit is changing is there an induced emf. To demonstrate this concept, a simple experiment like that shown in Fig. 33B may be performed.

Fig. 33B *Experimental arrangement for demonstrating induced electron currents.*

A flexible wire connected to an ammeter, and held in the hands, is moved in various ways across the pole of a magnet. When a straight section of the wire is held over the N pole and moved to the right, an electron current flows in the direction shown by the arrows. If the wire is moved in the opposite direction, the induced emf and current reverses direction. If the wire is moved vertically upward or downward, parallel to the magnetic induction, no current flows. In other words, *there is an induced emf only when the total number of lines of induction through the closed circuit is changing.*

The fact that a current is produced means that electrical energy has been created. It has been created at the expense of mechanical work, for, in moving the wire across the field, a force F had to be exerted for a distance l. The faster the wire moves, and the stronger the field through which it moves, the greater is the required force and the greater is the induced emf and the resultant electron current. If the wire stops moving in mid-field, the emf drops to zero. These are the essential principles of the electric generator.

The *left-hand rule* may be used to predict the direction of the induced emf in any section of wire. Imagine grasping the wire in the left hand, with the fingers pointing in the direction of the magnetic induction immediately in front of the wire. Then, as the wire moves through the mag-

netic field, the thumb will point in the direction of the induced emf, i.e., the direction of the flow of electrons.

33.2. Induced Electromotive Force. It was shown in Sec. 32.5 how an electric charge q, moving with a constant velocity v through a magnetic field where the flux density is B, experiences a force F upon it, given by

$$F = Bqv \qquad (33a)$$

where F, B, and v are all mutually perpendicular to each other.

When a single wire is made to cross magnetic lines of induction, as shown in Fig. 33C, every

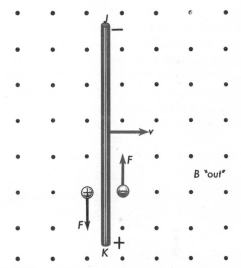

Fig. 33C *Forces on the charges in a conductor moving through a magnetic field.*

atomic charge within the metal experiences a force upon it, parallel to the conductor. The direction of the force on the + charges is from J to K, while the force on the − charges is from K to J. Since only the electrons are free to move in a metallic conductor, the negative charges migrate along the wire, building up a negative potential at one end and a positive potential at the other.

Consider the straight conductor sliding along a U-shaped conductor to form a closed circuit as shown in Fig. 33D. The potential difference, created between the ends, forces electrons through and around the circuit in the direction indicated.

Fig. 33D   *A current is induced by the motion of a conductor.*

In other words, the moving conductor becomes the source of an *electromotive force.*

The electromotive force developed within a moving conductor of length *l* is defined as the work per unit charge done in carrying any charge from one end to the other. From mechanics, we draw upon the principle that work done *W* is equal to *force times distance* moved. With the force given by Eq.(33a) and the distance moved by *l*, the work done on a charge *q* is

$$W = Bqvl$$

If we now divide both sides of the equation by *q*, the work per unit charge becomes

$$E = Bvl \qquad (33b)$$

where *E* is the emf, or work per unit charge done on the charges in this section of the moving conductor. [Potential difference *V* is given by *W/q*. See Eq.(29i).]

In the mksa system, *B* is in webers/meter², *v* is in meters/second, *l* is in meters, and *E* is in volts. It should be pointed out that it makes no difference in the above treatment whether the wire moves through a stationary magnetic field or whether the field moves across a stationary conductor. It is the relative motion giving rise to the crossing of lines of induction that produces the emf.

33.3. Faraday's Law. Faraday's law states that *the electromotive force generated in a conductor is equal to the rate of change of magnetic flux through the circuit.* For example, as the magnet

in Fig. 33A is plunged down into the coil, the number of lines of induction threading through the coil increases, and an induced electron current results. When the magnet is removed, the total flux linking the coil decreases, and again an electron current flows.

Consider again a U-shaped conductor with a slide wire moving with a velocity *v* across a uniform magnetic field *B*, as shown in Fig. 33E.

Fig. 33E   *The change of magnetic flux through a circuit.*

At one instant, the total flux ϕ_1 linking the circuit JKON is BA_1 [see Eq.(32n)]. In time *t*, the wire reaches the position ML where the total flux ϕ_2 linking the circuit MLON has increased to BA_2. The change in flux, therefore, is $\phi_2 - \phi_1 = B(A_2 - A_1)$, where the change in area, $A_2 - A_1 = l \times x$. Hence $\phi_2 - \phi_1 = xBl$. Dividing both sides by *t*, we obtain

$$\frac{\phi_2 - \phi_1}{t} = \frac{x}{t} Bl = Bvl = E \qquad (33c)$$

Hence, the electromotive force *E* is given by

$$E = \frac{\phi_2 - \phi_1}{t} \qquad (33d)$$

Here we have derived Faraday's law from Eq. (32n), for the particular case in which there is relative motion between a conductor and a magnetic field. However, the law is equally valid for the case in which the change in flux, $\phi_2 - \phi_1$, is due to a change in the strength of the magnetic field without any relative motion between conductor and flux. If it were not equally valid for this second case, the law of conservation of energy would be violated.

Since Eq.(33d) represents the flux change in a

single turn of wire of area A, then an equal flux change in a coil of N turns of wire will induce an over-all emf N times as great. In the mksa system, ϕ_2 and ϕ_1 are in webers, t is in seconds, and E is in volts. [Note: Eq.(33d) gives the *average* emf.]

33.4. The Electric Generator. An electric generator is constructed in the same way as an electric motor, with a rotating armature containing coils of wire, pole pieces, field windings, brushes, and a commutator. Instead of supplying an electron current to obtain mechanical rotation, mechanical work is done to turn the armature, thus producing an electron current.

If, in the construction of a generator, two solid rings are used as a commutator, as shown in Fig. 33F, the current delivered to the brushes flows

Fig. 33F *Illustration of the principles of the electric generator.*

first in one direction, then in the other. The reversal of current with each half-turn of the armature is due to the fact that each wire moves up across the field at one instant and down at the next. At one instant, the one terminal is positive and the other negative; at the next instant the first terminal is negative and the second positive. This periodically reversing emf produces what is called an *alternating* emf.

If a direct current is desired, the commutator of the generator must be of the split-ring type illustrated in Fig. 33G. It can be seen with this arrangement that one brush is at all times in contact with wires moving up across the field, while the other is in contact with wires moving down across the field. This produces a uni-direc-

Fig. 33G *Split-ring commutator for a direct-current generator.*

tional electron current and the whole machine is called a *direct-current* (dc) *generator.*

It is important to note that a generator does not make electricity. The electricity, or electric charge, is always in the wire, and a generator sets it into motion. A generator produces an electron current.

33.5. Direct and Alternating Currents. The difference between a direct and an alternating current is that a direct current always flows in one direction, while an alternating current reverses its direction periodically. To send a direct current through an electric circuit, a source capable of developing a constant electromotive force is necessary. For this purpose, a battery or direct-current generator is used.

To send an alternating current through a circuit, on the other hand, a source capable of reversing its emf is required. To do this, an alternating-current generator is generally used.

Graphical representations of both direct and alternating currents are given in Figs. 33H and 33I for purposes of comparison. The lower curves in each figure permit a comparison of the *electron currents* through a circuit while the upper curves permit a comparison of the *emf*, or *voltage*, of the source. The horizontal scale on all diagrams represents the *time*.

Within the short time of one second, the generators in most power plants reverse the emf many times. For example, the power supplied to private

Fig. 33H *Graphs of 110-volt direct voltage and current.*

homes and public buildings in nearly all cities in the United States is in the form of alternating current at 25, 50, or 60 cycles per second, and 110 or 220 volts.

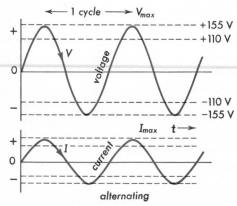

Fig. 33I *Graphs of 110-volt alternating voltage and current.*

A 60-cycle, 110-volt alternating emf, for example, is one in which the potential difference reverses direction 120 times per second. The rating of 110 volts specifies an effective voltage called the *root-mean-square* emf and not the so-called *peak* emf of 155 volts.

The magnitude of the emf induced in a coil rotating at uniform speed, as shown in Fig. 33F, may be computed either from the vertical velocities of the wires forming the sides of the coil or by the rate of change of flux through the coil. In either case,

$$E = NBA\omega \sin \omega t \qquad (33e)$$

where N is the number of turns in the coil, B is the magnetic induction in *webers/meter²*, A is the coil area in *meters²*, ω is the angular speed in *radians/second*, and t is the time in *seconds*. If f represents the *frequency of rotation,*

$$\omega = 2\pi f \qquad (33f)$$

The top curve in Fig. 33I represents the electromotive force E, or the output emf V, at any instant, where V_{max} and I_{max} are constants and represent the amplitude or *peak emf* and *peak current,* respectively. From Eq.(33e), the emf is a maximum when the plane of the coil is parallel to the field and zero when it is perpendicular to the field. In the parallel position the coil sides are cutting across the lines of induction, while in the perpendicular position they are moving along the lines of induction. Equation (33e) is a maximum when sin $\omega t = 1$. This gives

$$\boxed{E_{max} = NBA\omega} \qquad (33g)$$

Example 1. A rectangular coil of wire having 60 turns with dimensions of 10 cm × 20 cm is set rotating at a constant speed of 1800 rpm in a uniform magnetic field of flux density $B = 0.5$ Wb/m². The axis of the coil is perpendicular to the field. Find the maximum emf produced.

Solution. Since ω is $2\pi f$, $\omega = 2\pi \times 1800/60 = 188.5$ rad/s. Direct substitution in Eq.(33g) gives

$E_{max} = 60 \times 0.5$ Wb/m² $\times 0.10$ m
$\qquad\qquad \times 0.20$ m $\times 188.5$ rad/s

$$E_{max} = 113 \text{ Wb/s} = 113 \text{ V}$$

Since the power dissipated as heat in any resistor at any instant is I^2R, where I is the magnitude of the current at that instant, the average power dissipated when an alternating current flows through the resistor is the average of I^2R (not the square of the average I) over each cycle. Since the average of sin² ωt, as ωt varies from 0 to 2π, is $\frac{1}{2}$ (see Fig. 33J), the average value of I^2

Fig. 33J *The average value of sin² θ is $\frac{1}{2}$.*

is $\frac{1}{2}(I_{max})^2$. Calling the square root of this average I_{rms},

$$I_{rms} = 0.707\ I_{max} \qquad (33h)$$

In a similar averaging process the *root mean square emf* is given by

$$V_{rms} = 0.707\ V_{max} \qquad (33i)$$

For an rms value of 110 volts, the maximum is 155 volts.

If an alternating current is applied to circuits containing inductance and capacitance, Ohm's law, as it is used with resistance and direct current, does not apply. In such instances, the current and voltage are not in phase with each other, that is, they do not rise to a maximum at the same time or fall to zero at the same time, and more complicated formulas must be used. Such circuits will be treated in Chapter 35.

Alternating-current circuits for which the direct-current relations of Ohm's law do hold true are those in which all of the circuit elements are pure resistances. Most electric lights and many heating units are of this class. In applying Ohm's law to pure resistance circuits, it is common practice to use the rms voltage V_{rms} and calculate the rms current I_{rms}. These values can be used in Eqs.(31c), (31d), and (31e) to calculate energy or power.

PROBLEMS

1. A wire 0.40 m long moves with a speed of 50 m/s through a uniform magnetic field where the magnetic induction is 0.3 Wb/m². If the wire, field, and motion are all mutually perpendicular, what emf is produced in the wire?

2. A wire 5 m long is located in the wing of an airplane making 720 Km/hr. If the magnetic induction due to the earth's field has a value of 5×10^{-4} Wb/m², what is the maximum possible induced emf? [*Ans.* 0.5 V.]

3. A wire 2 m long moves with a speed of 18 m/s through a uniform magnetic field where the flux density is 0.05 Wb/m². If the wire, field, and motion are all mutually perpendicular to each other, what emf is induced in the wire?

4. A wire 12 m long is located in the wing of an airplane flying at 1800 Km/hr. If the magnetic induction of the earth's field has a value of 5.4×10^{-5} Wb/m² and makes an angle of 90° with the airplane's direction of motion, find the emf. Assume the wire to be perpendicular to the Bv plane. [*Ans.* 0.324 V.]

5. A wire 1 m long moves with a speed of 24 m/s through a uniform magnetic field where the flux density B is 0.2 Wb/m². If the wire, field, and motion are all perpendicular to each other, what emf is produced in the wire?

6. A wire 60 cm long is moved with a speed of 8 m/s through a uniform magnetic field where the magnetic induction B is 0.16 Wb/m². Find the emf produced in the wire. [*Ans.* 0.768 V.]

7. A U-shaped conductor 15 cm wide (see Fig. 33E) is located in a uniform magnetic field where the magnetic induction is 6×10^{-3} Wb/m². If a straight rod across the loop moves with a speed of 4 m/s, find (a) the magnitude of the emf, and (b) the rate of change of the flux linking the circuit.

8. A U-shaped conductor 18 cm wide (see Fig. 33E) is located in a uniform magnetic field where the magnetic induction is 4000 G. Find (a) the magnitude of the emf induced in a rod sliding along the loop at 6 m/s, and (b) the rate of change of flux. [*Ans.* (a) 0.432 V, (b) 0.432 Wb/s.]

9. A flat rectangular loop of wire, 12 cm by 24 cm, is located in a uniform magnetic field where the magnetic induction is 6×10^{-2} Wb/m² with its plane perpendicular to the flux lines. If the loop is turned to a position where its plane is parallel to the field in 0.01 s, what average emf is induced in the loop? Use Eq.(33d).

10. A flat rectangular coil, 9 cm by 20 cm, contains 40 turns of wire. Located in the earth's magnetic field where the magnetic induction is 5.4×10^{-4} Wb/m², the coil is turned from a position where its plane is parallel to the field where it is perpendicular to the field, in 0.05 s. What average emf is induced? Use Eq.(33d). [*Ans.* 7.78×10^{-3} V.]

11. A flat rectangular coil, 20 cm by 30 cm, and containing 60 turns of wire, is rotating at the constant speed of 1800 rpm in a magnetic field where the magnetic induction is 0.5 Wb/m². Calculate (a) the maximum emf produced and (b) the root-mean-square voltage.

12. A flat circular coil 16 cm in diameter, containing 120 turns of wire, is rotating at 900 rpm in a magnetic field where the magnetic induction is 0.40 Wb/m². Find (a) the maximum emf developed, and (b) the root-mean-square voltage. [*Ans.* (a) 91.0 V, (b) 64.3 V.]

13. A flat rectangular coil, 16 cm by 24 cm, and containing 80 turns of wire, is rotating at the constant speed of 3600 rpm in a magnetic field where the magnetic induction is 0.2 Wb/m². Calculate (a) the maximum voltage, and (b) the root-mean-square voltage.

14. A flat circular coil 30 cm in diameter and containing 110 turns of wire is rotating at 1800 rpm in a magnetic field where $B = 0.25$ Wb/m². Find (a) the maximum emf produced, and (b) the root-mean-square voltage. [*Ans.* (a) 366 V, (b) 259 V.]

15. A rectangular coil of 90 turns is 16 cm wide and 36 cm long. What is the speed at which this coil should rotate in the earth's magnetic field ($B = 5 \times 10^{-4}$ Wb/m^2) to produce a peak emf of 1.5 V?

16. A flat circular coil of 75 turns is 32 cm in diameter. If this coil is to be rotated in a uniform magnetic field to produce a root-mean-square voltage of 120 V at 2000 rpm, what must be the value of the magnetic induction? [*Ans.* 0.134 Wb/m^2.]

17. An ac generator whose terminal root-mean-square emf is 120 V is connected to a resistance of 30 Ω. If the internal resistance of the generator is 4 Ω, what is the peak electron current?

18. A resistance of 10 Ω is connected to an ac generator whose internal resistance is 1 Ω. If the rms current in the circuit is 6.4 A, find the peak emf of the generator on open circuit. [*Ans.* 99.6 V.]

19. An electric toaster with a resistance of 16 Ω is connected to a 208-V ac line. Find (a) the peak voltage, and (b) the peak electron current.

20. An electric iron with a resistance of 18 Ω is connected to a 208-V ac line. Find (a) the peak voltage,

and (b) the peak electron current. [*Ans.* (a) 294 V, (b) 16.3 A.]

21. Two resistances of 4 Ω and 12 Ω, respectively, are connected in parallel, and the combination in series with a resistance of 9 Ω. The ends of this circuit are connected to a generator supplying an rms emf of 120-V ac at its terminals. Find (a) the peak voltage across the 9 Ω resistance, and (b) the peak electron current through each resistance.

22. A rectangular coil of 500 turns is 15 cm wide and 30 cm long. What is the minimum speed at which this coil can be rotated in the earth's field to generate a peak voltage of 8.00 V? Assume the magnetic induction to be 5.0×10^{-5} Wb/m^2. [*Ans.* 1132 c/s.]

23. A flat circular coil of 25 turns is 24 cm in diameter. If this coil is located in a uniform magnetic field where $B = 0.5$ Wb/m^2, how fast must it rotate about a diameter to generate an rms emf of 50 V?

24. A flat circular coil of 50 turns is 18 cm in diameter. If a rms voltage of 120 V at 1000 c/s are to be obtained by rotating this coil in a uniform magnetic field, what must be the value of the magnetic induction? [*Ans.* 2.12×10^{-2} Wb/m^2.]

DIPOLE MOMENTS
AND MAGNETISM

In order to obtain a better understanding of the principles of electricity and magnetism, we will consider in this chapter the principles of electric and magnetic dipoles. We will then see how magnetic dipoles are used to explain the phenomena of ferromagnetism, paramagnetism, and diamagnetism, and in later chapters how these concepts are carried over to atomic and nuclear structure.

34.1. Electric Dipoles. An electric dipole may be described as two electric charges with their centers separated by a finite distance. Figure 29A shows the electric field around a dipole of like charges on the right, and unlike charges on the left.

Imagine two small metallic spheres with equal but opposite charges, $+q$ and $-q$, held a fixed distance apart by a nonconducting rod as shown in Fig. 34A. If the distance between the charge centers is l, and the dipole is free to move in an electric field of intensity ε, forces will be exerted on the charges tending to turn the dipole counter-clockwise about the center as shown. If the charges are equal and of the same sign, the two forces will be in the same direction and the system will not turn but move bodily in the direction of the forces.

For the dipole shown in Fig. 34A, the force on each charge is given by Eq.(29e). For each charge q we obtain for the force

$$F = q\varepsilon$$

where q is in coulombs, and ε is in volts per meter. For the negative charge the force is *down*, and for the positive charge the force is *up*.

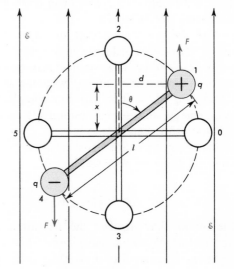

Fig. 34A   *An electric dipole in a uniform electric field experiences a torque, and work must be done to turn it against this torque.*

To find the torque exerted by each charge, we multiply each force F by the perpendicular lever arm d, and add.

$$L = d \times q\varepsilon + d \times q\varepsilon$$

Since $d = \frac{1}{2}l \sin \theta$, we substitute and obtain

$$L = lq\varepsilon \sin \theta$$

The product lq is called the *electric dipole moment* of the doublet, and is a quantity frequently designated by δ.

$$\boxed{\delta = lq} \qquad (34a)$$

electric dipole moment

Making this substitution, we may write for the torque

$$L = \delta\mathcal{E} \sin\theta \qquad (34b)$$

electric dipole torque

where θ is the angle between the dipole axis and the field $\mathcal{E}$, and the torque axis is at right angles to both.

If the dipole is free, the torque will cause it to turn and line up with its axis parallel to the field, with $+q$ in position (2), and $-q$ in position (3). To turn the dipole away from this equilibrium position will require work, and in so doing potential energy will be stored.

To find the potential energy of an electric dipole in an electric field we may select any angle for zero energy. If we assume zero energy when the dipole axis is at 90° with the field direction, $+q$ in position (2) corresponds to negative energy, and $+q$ in position (3) corresponds to positive energy.

To move the $+q$ charge from position (0) to position (1), the *work done* will be

$$W = F \times x$$
$$W = -q\mathcal{E} \times \tfrac{1}{2}l \cos\theta$$

The minus sign signifies the liberation of energy in turning counterclockwise. Since the same energy is required to move the $-q$ charge to the corresponding position (4), the potential energy is given by

$$E_p = -q\mathcal{E}l \cos\theta$$

or

$$E_p = -\delta\mathcal{E} \cos\theta \qquad (34c)$$

electric dipole energy

Note that in position (0), $\theta = 90°$, $\cos 90° = 0$, and $E_p = 0$. This establishes the zero potential-energy position at (0).

Example 1. An electric dipole is composed of two charges $+5 \times 10^{-8}$ C, and -5×10^{-8} C, 10 cm apart. If this dipole is placed in a uniform electric field of 100,000 V/m, find the potential energy in its equilibrium position.

Solution. Since the angle θ in the equilibrium position (2) is 0°, the cos 0° = 1, and direct substitution of all given quantities in Eq.(34c) gives

$$E_p = -5 \times 10^{-8}\,\text{C} \times 0.1\,\text{m} \times 10^5\,\text{V/m}$$
$$E_p = -5 \times 10^{-4}\,\text{C V}$$

By Eq.(29n), coulomb × volts = newton × meters, and from mechanics, newton × meters = joules. Therefore,

$$E_p = -5 \times 10^{-4}\,\text{J}.$$

34.2. Magnetic Dipoles. When a straight bar magnet is located in a uniform magnetic field as shown in Fig. 34B, it is acted upon by a torque

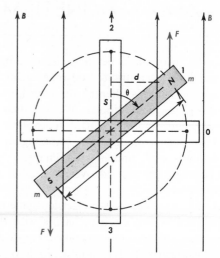

Fig. 34B *A magnetic dipole in a uniform magnetic field experiences a torque, and work must be done to turn it against this torque.*

which tends to line it up with the field. The force acting on each pole is given by Eq.(30d) as

$$F = mB$$

where m is the strength of either pole in ampere meters, and B is the strength of the field in which it is located, in webers/meter². Assuming the distance between pole centers to be l, each of these oppositely directed forces has a lever arm

$$d = \tfrac{1}{2}l \sin\theta$$

The total torque, therefore, is given by the sum of the two separate torques.

$$L = mB \times \tfrac{1}{2}l \sin\theta + mB \times \tfrac{1}{2}l \sin\theta$$

which simplified becomes

$$L = mlB \sin\theta$$

The product ml is a property of the magnet alone, and by analogy with *mass moment* and *force moment* in mechanics, and electric dipole moment in electricity, is called the *magnetic dipole moment*.

$$\mu = ml \qquad \text{(34d)}$$

magnetic dipole moment

The torque may therefore be written as

$$L = \mu B \sin \theta \qquad \text{(34e)}$$

magnetic dipole torque

By analogy with the derivation of Eq.(34c), from Eq.(34b) we can derive the equation for the energy of a magnetic dipole in a magnetic field. Such a derivation gives

$$E_p = -\mu B \cos \theta \qquad \text{(34f)}$$

magnetic dipole energy

34.3. Magnetic Moment of a Current Loop. We have seen in Sec. 33.10 that a current-carrying loop, or coil, located in a uniform magnetic field experiences a mechanical torque (see Fig. 31N).

This torque is in such a direction as to line up the magnetic field of the loop with the applied external magnetic field B. The loop comes to rest when the field along its central axis, created by the loop current, is parallel to the external field. To turn the loop away from this equilibrium position will also require a torque, and hence work to be done.

Since the behavior of a current-carrying loop in a magnetic field is similar to that of a bar magnet, acting as though it had an N pole on one side and an S pole on the other, we can explain the action by ascribing to the loop a *magnetic dipole moment*.

By applying the current-force equation Eq. (32o) to a current-carrying loop, located in a uniform magnetic field B, as shown in Fig. 34C, the torque acting upon the wire is found to be given by

$$L = IAB \sin \theta \qquad \text{(34g)}$$

where L is the torque in newton-meters, I is the current in amperes, A is the loop area in meters², B is the external field strength in webers/meter²,

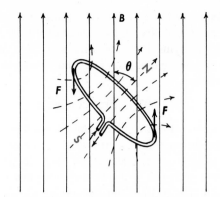

Fig. 34C *A current-carrying loop of wire in a magnetic field is acted upon by a torque.*

and θ is the angle between the axial field direction of the loop and the direction of B.

By comparing Eq.(34g) with Eq.(34e), we observe that the product IA is analogous to the dipole moment of a bar magnet and that we can define the magnetic dipole moment of a loop by the relation

$$\mu = IA \qquad \text{(34h)}$$

With this definition we may then use Eq.(34e) to determine torque, and Eq.(34f) to find the interaction, i.e., the stored energy E_p, for any current-carrying loop in a uniform magnetic field B. Since the dipole moment depends on the area, a loop may have any shape. It may be round, square, oval, rectangular, elliptical, etc.

If a flat coil of N turns is located in a magnetic field, each turn experiences a torque given by Eq.(34h) and the total torque will be just N times greater.

$$L = NIAB \sin \theta \qquad \text{(34i)}$$

and the magnetic moment by

$$\mu = NIA \qquad \text{(34j)}$$

34.4. The Origin of Magnetic Moments. The magnetic properties of all substances, whether in the solid, liquid, or gaseous state, are due entirely to the motions of electrons within the atoms, and magnets of all kinds are the result of the lining up of electron loops and spinning electrons.

According to the classical theory set forward by H. A. Lorentz in 1897, the electrons in all matter move in circular orbits. Since every electron has a negative charge, these orbits are like current-carrying loops of wire and have magnetic dipole moments. The charge on every electron is

$$e = 1.602 \times 10^{-19} \text{ coulombs}$$

It is now known that electrons also spin around an axis through their center of mass and behave as a tiny gyroscope. Because of their charge the spin too gives rise to a *spin magnetic moment*.

According to the Bohr theory, which will be taken up in detail in Chapter 51, the single electron in every normal hydrogen atom moves in a circular orbit of radius $r = 5.28 \times 10^{-11}$ m, with a velocity of $v = 2.188 \times 10^6$ m/s (see Fig. 34D).

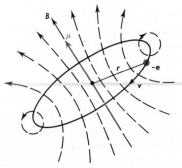

Fig. 34D *An electron of charge* $-e$ *moving in a circular orbit produces a magnetic field B, and a magnetic dipole moment* μ.

To find the magnetic moment of each such orbit, we can use Eq.(34h). While the area of the orbit is calculated from the radius,

$$A = \pi r^2 \qquad (34k)$$

the current equivalent of the orbiting electron is determined from the relation $I = Q/t$ as given by Eq.(27a). In words, the current is equal to the charge in coulombs passing any given point per second.

The frequency of revolution n will therefore give the number of times per second the charge e passes a given point. The frequency is given by the velocity v, divided by the circumference $2\pi r$, and when multiplied by the charge e will give the current in amperes.

$$I = \frac{v}{2\pi r} e \qquad (34l)$$

Combining Eqs.(34l) and (34k) gives

$$\mu = IA = \frac{v}{2\pi r} e \times \pi r^2 = \frac{ver}{2} \qquad (34m)$$

By direct substitution of the known values given above, we obtain

$$\mu = \tfrac{1}{2}(2.188 \times 10^6 \times 1.602 \times 10^{-19} \times 5.28 \times 10^{-11})$$

$$\mu = 9.27 \times 10^{-24} \text{ ampere meters}^2 \qquad (34n)$$

As we will see in Chapter 52, this is also the value of the magnetic moment of a spinning electron, and is called the *Bohr magneton*.

The magnetic dipole moment of a bar magnet, a coil of wire, or a charge moving in a circular path, is a vector quantity. The magnitude of the vector is given by the value of μ, and the direction is taken to be that of the axial field it produces.

34.5. Diamagnetism. Diamagnetism was discovered by Michael Faraday in 1846 when he placed a small piece of bismuth metal near the pole of a magnet and found it was repelled instead of being attracted. Such a behavior is so unlike a substance like common iron, which is strongly attracted, that he called the phenomenon *diamagnetic*.

Diamagnetism is a weak response to magnetism, yet, with but few exceptions, is common to most elements and their alloys and compounds. According to the Lorentz theory of matter we may visualize all the electrons in a substance as though they were moving in circular orbits as described in the preceding section. Each electron has a charge $-e$, and a magnetic moment μ. In most substances these orbits are randomly oriented so that there is no net magnetic effect (see Fig. 34E). With billions of magnetic dipoles, just as many will point in one direction as any other.

Suppose we now move such a diamagnetic specimen into a magnetic field. Although each dipole will experience a torque tending to line it up with the magnetic field, all of them are rigidly bound in their positions in the crystal lattice.

As the number of magnetic lines through each orbit increases, however, the induced current

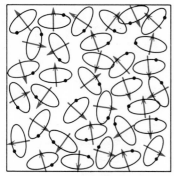

Fig. 34E *Schematic diagram showing the random orientation of electron orbits and their magnetic dipole moments in a diamagnetic substance like bismuth.*

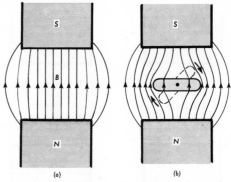

(a)   (b)

Fig. 34F *Diagram of the magnetic field between two magnet poles, (a) before a specimen is inserted, and (b) after a diamagnetic specimen is inserted. The diamagnetic rod comes to rest with its axis at right angles to original field B.*

effect, treated in Chapter 33, gives rise to a force on each electron [see Eq.(33a)]. This force, which in a loop of wire causes electrons to flow around the loop, is in such a direction as to increase the speeds of electrons rotating in one direction and reduce the speeds of others rotating in the opposite direction.

It can be shown from basic principles of electricity that the size of the orbits remains unchanged, with the result that for electrons that are speeded up the magnetic moment increases, while for those that are slowed down the magnetic moment decreases. The net effect is to produce a resultant magnetic moment for the entire specimen. In other words the specimen behaves as though it had a north and a south pole.

When we employ the left-hand rule for induced electron currents, the induced magnetic moment is found to be opposite in direction to the applied magnetic field *B*. This means that if a small rod is placed in a strong magnetic field, as shown in Fig. 34F, the net induced magnetic moment points opposite to *B*. Thus the end of the rod closest to the magnet N pole acts like an N pole and is repelled by the magnet. Similarly the end nearest the magnet S pole acts like an S pole and is repelled. The repelling forces cause the rod to turn and come to rest at right angles to the field.

This behavior is just opposite to that of a bar of iron which when placed in a similar field experiences strong forces lining it up parallel to *B* (see Fig. 34G).

34.6. Paramagnetism. According to modern theory of atomic structure, the orbits and spins of the electrons in most atoms are such that the magnetic moments cancel each other. For an electron moving in one direction around an orbit, another will be moving in a similar orbit in the opposite direction, and for one spinning one way, the other will have opposite spin.

In some substances, however, the magnetic moments of the electrons do not all cancel out so that the atom as a whole has a magnetic moment μ. This is the case for several of the transition elements in the periodic table like manganese, the rare earths and actinide elements, as well as for their alloys and compounds.

If a bar specimen of such material is placed free to move in a magnetic field, it will turn and line up with its axis parallel to the external field *B* (see Fig. 34G). The bar behaves like a permanent magnet with an N pole at one end and an S pole at the other.

In the field *B* each elementary atomic dipole tends to line up with the field. Perfect alignment, however, is hindered by the temperature vibrations of the atoms so that a partial alignment produces a small but net magnetic moment. The degree of alignment is specified by what is called the *magnetization*. The magnetization *M* of any specimen is defined as the magnetic moment per unit volume.

$$M = \frac{\mu}{V} \qquad (34o)$$

Fig. 34H   *Toroidal solenoid, or "Rowland ring."*

Fig. 34G   *Diagram of the magnetic field between two magnet poles, (a) before a specimen is inserted, and (b) after a paramagnetic specimen is inserted. Paramagnetic rod comes to equilibrium when its axis is parallel to the original field B.*

In 1895 Pierre Curie discovered experimentally that the magnetization of a paramagnetic substance is proportional to the external field strength B, and inversely proportional to the absolute temperature T.

$$M = C \frac{B}{T} \qquad (34p)$$

where C is called the *Curie constant*. This relation is known as *Curie's law*. Increasing B provides stronger forces tending to align the elementary magnets, while increasing the temperature increases the thermal vibrations to interfere with the alignment.

Experimentally Curie's law is found to hold true as long as B does not become too large. As B increases and alignment increases, there comes a time when nearly all dipoles have aligned themselves with the field, and the specimen approaches saturation.

34.7. Ferromagnetism. For a few of the chemical elements such as iron, cobalt, and nickel, and for some of their alloys and compounds, a very strong magnetic alignment of the elementary atomic dipoles is found to exist. The abnormally large effect these elements exhibit, called *ferromagnetism*, is attributed to a strong coupling between adjacent atoms.

Consider a long solenoid, with or without a core, bent into a ring as shown in Fig. 34H. Such a coil with a uniform and closely spaced winding

is called a Rowland ring, named after H. A. Rowland who first made use of it in his work on electricity and magnetism.

Assume, to start with, that the core is absent and that a vacuum prevails inside and outside the solenoid. When an electron current is sent through the winding, the magnetic lines of induction B are continuous, and confined entirely within the space enclosed by the winding. If l is the circumference of the ring, the magnetic induction inside is given by Eq.(32h),

$$B_0 = \mu_0 \frac{NI}{l} \qquad (34q)$$

for a vacuum

where μ_0 is the permeability of free space, and is given by

$$\mu_0 = 12.57 \times 10^{-7} \text{ Wb/Am}$$

This constant is not to be mistaken for μ used in this chapter to represent magnet dipole moment.

If the solenoid is now assumed to contain a uniform core of material, and a steady current is flowing in the winding, the field within the coil is increased or decreased. This change in B, over and above the field there previously, is to be ascribed to the field set up by the thousands of tiny magnetic dipoles that turn part way or all the way around to line up with or against the magnetizing field B_0. For para- and diamagnetic materials the induced magnetic induction B_M is proportional to the magnetizing field, and we can write

$$B_M = \chi \frac{NI}{l} \qquad (34r)$$

where the proportionality constant χ is positive in value and is called the *magnetic susceptibility*. For diamagnetic substances χ is negative, while for paramagnetic substances it is positive. Adding Eqs. (34q) and (34r) we find the total magnetic induction inside the core is given by

$$B = B_0 + B_M \qquad (34s)$$

or

$$B = \mu_0 \frac{NI}{l} + \chi \frac{NI}{l}$$

The quantity NI/l is called the *magnetic intensity* and is designated by H.

$$H = \frac{NI}{l} \qquad (34t)$$

By direct substitution, we obtain

$$B = \mu_0 H + \chi H \qquad (34u)$$
or
$$B = (\mu_0 + \chi)H \qquad (34v)$$

If the core of the solenoid is composed of a ferromagnetic material, the magnetic susceptibility χ is not constant. It not only varies with different specimens and with the magnetic intensity H, but it has very large positive values.

For iron, χ may go as high as 7×10^{-3} Wb/Am, and permalloy (Ni 78.5%, Fe 21.5%) as high as 7×10^{-2} Wb/Am.

Figure 34I shows a typical magnetization curve for silicon steel, a relatively common material used in motors, transformers, and other electrical equipment. As characteristic of all magnetic substances, the curve rises slowly at first (a to b), then rapidly and uniformly (b to c), and finally turns and flattens out (d to e). The flattened section represents a saturation condition in which B rises very little as H increases. In other words, when the tiny elementary magnets are all lined up, B increases only by the amount H contributes by the electron current in the winding.

Values of the important magnetic properties of silicon steel are given in Table 34A.

It can be seen from the graph, as well as the values in the table, that when H is small, between 0 and 200 A/m, χ is very large, and practically all of the field is due to the magnetization of the iron. Beyond $H = 160$ A/m, χ decreases and levels off to decrease very slowly beyond H = 1000.

Since χ varies widely with H, it is customary to write Eq.(34r) in the form

$$B_M = \kappa \mu_0 H \qquad (34w)$$

where κ is the permeability number. Values of this constant are given in the fourth column of Table 34A. For air or a vacuum $\kappa = 1.00$.

Since the quantity χH, as given by Eq.(34u), is a direct measure of the magnetic dipole alignment within the core, it can be shown that

$$\chi H = \mu_0 M \qquad (34x)$$

where M, as given by Eq.(34o), is the *magnetic moment per unit volume*, and is called the *magnet-*

Fig. 34I *Typical magnetization and permeability curves (for silicon steel).*

TABLE 34A. MAGNETIC CONSTANTS OF SILICON STEEL

H $\left(\dfrac{A}{m}\right)$	$\mu_0 H$ $\left(\dfrac{Wb}{m^2}\right)$	χ $\left(\dfrac{Wb}{Am}\right)$	κ —	χH $\left(\dfrac{Wb}{m^2}\right)$	B $\left(\dfrac{Wb}{m^2}\right)$
0	0	0.310×10^{-3}	248	0	0
50	6.3×10^{-5}	0.860×10^{-3}	685	0.043	0.043
100	12.6×10^{-5}	6.700×10^{-3}	5330	0.670	0.670
200	25.2×10^{-5}	6.000×10^{-3}	4770	1.200	1.200
500	62.8×10^{-5}	2.880×10^{-3}	2290	1.440	1.440
1,000	125.7×10^{-5}	1.580×10^{-3}	1260	1.580	1.580
10,000	1257.0×10^{-5}	0.170×10^{-3}	136	1.720	1.720

ization. The above equations and values of B, given in Table 34A for a Rowland ring, also hold approximately for the field inside, as well as very close to the end outside, of a long thin electromagnet like that shown in Fig. 31H.

Example 2. A silicon steel rod 5 cm in diameter and 50 cm long is wound with a single layer of copper wire. If the solenoid contains 125 turns, and a current of 0.80 A is sent through it, find (a) the magnetic intensity H, (b) the value of χ from Table 34A, (c) the magnetic induction B, (d) the permeability number, and (e) the magnetization.

Solution. (a) By direct substitution in Eq.(34t), we obtain

$$H = \frac{125 \times 0.8}{0.5} = 200 \text{ A/m}$$

(b) From Table 34A, $H = 200$ A/m gives $\chi = 6.0 \times 10^{-3}$ Wb/Am.

(c) By direct substitution in Eq.(34v),

$$B = (12.57 \times 10^{-7} + 6.0 \times 10^{-3})200$$
$$B = 1.20 \text{ Wb/m}^2$$

(d) By solving Eq.(34w) for κ, and substituting, we obtain

$$\kappa = \frac{B}{\mu_0 H} = \frac{1.20}{12.57 \times 10^{-7} \times 200} = 4770$$

(e) By solving Eq.(34x) for M, and substituting, we obtain,

$$M = \frac{\chi H}{\mu_0} = \frac{6.0 \times 10^{-3} \times 200}{12.57 \times 10^{-7}}$$
$$M = 9.55 \times 10^5 \text{ A/m.}$$

The most modern theory of ferromagnetism, and the explanation of a magnetization curve like that shown in Fig. 34I, is based upon magnetic domains. This theory assumes that a solid

specimen like iron is composed of tiny crystal-like regions, odd in shape and microscopic in size, that fit together as in a mosaic [see Fig. 34J and Fig. 55E(d)].

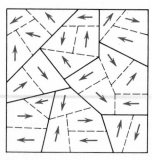

Fig. 34J *Cross-section diagram of the irregular-shaped crystals and magnetic domains in an unmagnetized ferromagnetic material. Thick lines represent crystal boundaries, dotted lines within each crystal represent domain boundaries.*

Within each crystal there are one or more domains, and within each domain there is essentially perfect alignment of the elementary magnetic moments. Each arrow in the diagram represents the net magnetic moment of that domain, and the random orientation of the arrows represents conditions existing in an unmagnetized ferromagnetic material like iron.

Within each domain strong exchange forces between atoms bind adjacent magnetic dipole moments together. Because they are all parallel, that is, saturated, they provide a large net magnetic moment.

When a piece of iron is subjected to an increasing field, two changes are found experimentally to take place. First, the orientation of the tiny atomic dipoles within a domain may suddenly swing around to line up with the external field, or an already aligned domain may grow in size at the expense of an adjacent domain adversely oriented. In other words, a common boundary between two adjacent domains in the same crystal will move.

As the field grows stronger, more and more domains flip around suddenly to line up, while others grow in size, until all domains are aligned.

If the temperature of a ferromagnetic specimen is heated above a certain temperature, called its *Curie point*, the exchange coupling disappears and the specimen becomes paramagnetic.

The contribution of each elementary magnetic dipole to the total dipole moment of a given specimen is given by the projection of each dipole moment on the magnetizing field direction H. The total dipole moment of the specimen is then seen to be given by the sum of all the components within it. This total dipole moment, divided by the volume, is the magnetization M.

The dipole moment of an iron atom in a solid is approximately one Bohr magneton [see Eq. (34n)]. When a soft iron specimen is fully magnetized, all of these dipoles are aligned with the field H, and the iron is said to be saturated. This condition corresponds in Fig. 34I to regions to the right of point e.

H	magnetic intensity
B	magnetic induction
B_M	induced magnetic induction
χ	magnetic susceptibility
μ_0	permeability of free space
M	magnetization
κ	permeability number
μ	magnetic dipole moment

34.8. Special Demonstrations. The sudden flipping over of the magnetization of domains in a ferromagnetic material, as the magnetic field is increasing or decreasing, was discovered by H. Barkhausen in 1919. The following experiment is an effective demonstration of the phenomenon.

A plastic tube about 15 cm long is slipped over a soft iron rod about 20 cm long and 5 to 10 mm diameter. Several hundred turns of fine insulated

copper wire are wrapped in one or more layers around the tube, and the ends connected to an audio amplifier or public address system (see Fig. 34K).

Fig. 34K   *Diagram of experimental arrangement for demonstrating the Barkhausen effect.*

When a permanent magnet is held near the coil, a hissing noise will be heard from the speaker only when the magnet is in motion. As the magnet moves quickly along, the flipping over of the magnetization of each domain induces an emf in the coil and these very small pulses to the amplifier are heard as a noise.

Another demonstration, developed recently by C. H. Harvey, involves the equilibrium suspension of a diamagnetic solid in a paramagnetic liquid, placed between the like poles of two permanent magnets. A solid plastic sphere of polystyrene about 5 cm in diameter is placed in a glass jar containing a solution of ferric chloride, $FeCl_3$.

The concentration of the solution is varied until the sphere has a slightly greater density and slowly sinks to the bottom. (If the solution becomes too dark, a few drops of hydrochloric acid, HCl, will improve the visibility.)

The jar is then placed between the N poles of two strong alnico magnets as shown in Fig. 34L. The left-hand diagram shows the shape of the field without the diamagnetic sphere, and the right-hand diagram the field when the sphere is centrally located.

When the jar is first placed between the poles, the sphere is at the bottom and close to the lower N pole. In this strong divergent field the net magnetic force on the sphere is up, toward the weaker field. If the pole of a third magnet is

Fig. 34L *Diagram of the equilibrium suspension of diamagnetic sphere in a paramagnetic liquid.*

brought in on one side of the jar, the sphere will move to one side. When this third magnet is removed the sphere will move back to the center where it is in stable equilibrium.

The net force from strong to weak field is readily understood by employing the principle presented earlier that magnetic lines of force act like stretched rubber bands and at the same time repel each other laterally. Furthermore, magnetic lines prefer to follow paramagnetic materials rather than free space or a diamagnetic material. Figuratively speaking, ferromagnetic and paramagnetic materials act like better conductors of magnetic lines of force than do diamagnetic materials.

PROBLEMS

1. An electric dipole is composed of two charges, $+4.8 \times 10^{-12}$ C, and -4.8×10^{-12} C, spaced 3×10^{-4} cm apart. If this dipole is located in a uniform electric field of 5×10^5 V/m, find (a) the electric dipole moment, (b) the potential energy in its equilibrium position, and (c) the energy required to rotate the dipole through $180°$ from its equilibrium position.

2. Two charges, $+3.2 \times 10^{-19}$ C, and -3.2×10^{-19} C, are located 2.4×10^{-10} m apart. If this permanent dipole is located in a uniform electric field of 4.0×10^5 V/m, find (a) the electric dipole moment, (b) the potential energy in its eqilibrium position, and (c) the energy required to rotate the dipole through $180°$. [*Ans.* (a) 7.68×10^{-29} mC, (b) 3.07×10^{-23} J, (c) 6.14×10^{-23} J.]

3. A bar magnet having two poles, each with a strength of 5 Am, and 10 cm apart, is located in a uniform magnetic field where $B = 6 \times 10^{-2}$ Wb/m². Find (a) the magnetic dipole moment, (b) the torque on the magnet when it is at $90°$ with the field direction, and (c) the energy required to turn the magnet from its equilibrium position to where its axis is $180°$ with the field direction.

4. A bar magnet having two poles with a strength of 8 Am, and 12 cm apart, is located in a magnetic field $B = 5 \times 10^{-3}$ Wb/m². Find (a) the magnetic dipole moment, (b) the torque on the magnet when its axis is at $90°$ with the field, and (c) the energy required to turn it from this position to its equilibrium position. [*Ans.* (a) 0.96 Am², (b) 4.80×10^{-3} Nm, (c) -4.80×10^{-3} J.]

5. A flat coil with a diameter of 16 cm, containing 25 turns of wire and carrying a current of 5 A, is located in a uniform magnetic field $B = 5 \times 10^{-2}$ Wb/m². Find (a) the magnetic dipole moment of the coil, (b) the maximum torque exerted on the coil, and (c) the energy

required to turn the coil from its equilibrium position through $180°$.

6. A flat coil with a diameter of 6 cm, containing 20 turns of wire, and carrying a current of 2 A, is located in a uniform field where $B = 0.5$ Wb/m². Find (a) the magnetic dipole moment of the coil, (b) the maximum torque exerted on the coil, and (c) the energy required to turn the coil from its equilibrium position through $180°$. [*Ans.* (a) 0.113 Am², (b) 0.0565 Nm, (c) 0.113 J.]

7. A flat rectangular coil 10 cm by 20 cm, containing 25 turns of wire and carrying a current of 5 A, is placed in a uniform magnetic field $B = 8 \times 10^{-2}$ Wb/m². Find (a) the magnetic dipole moment of the coil, (b) the maximum torque that can be exerted on the coil, and (c) the energy required to turn the coil from its equilibrium position through $180°$.

8. A Rowland ring like the one shown in Fig. 34H has a circumference of 60 cm, and contains 240 turns of wire. If an electron current of 2.5 A is sent through the coil, find (a) the magnetic intensity, (b) the magnetic susceptibility from Table 34A, (c) the magnetic induction, (d) the permeability number, and (e) the magnetization. [*Ans.* (a) 1000 A/m, (b) 1.58×10^{-3} Wb/Am, (c) 1.58 Wb/m², (d) 1.26×10^3, (e) 1.26×10^6 A/m.]

9. A silicon steel rod 1 m long is bent into a ring and wound with a single layer of insulated copper wire to form a Rowland ring. If the winding contains 500 turns and carries an electron current of 1 A, find (a) the magnetic intensity, (b) the magnetic susceptibility, (c) the total magnetic induction, (d) the permeability constant, and (e) the magnetization.

10. A permalloy steel rod 80 cm long is wound end to end with 400 turns of wire. If an electron current of 2.5 A through the winding produces a magnetic induction of

1.80 Wb/m², find (a) the magnetic intensity, (b) the permeability number, (c) the magnetic susceptibility, and (d) the magnetization. [Ans. (a) 1250 A/m, (b) 1146, (c) 1.440 × 10⁻³ Wb/Am, (d) 1.432 × 10⁶ A/m.]

11. A soft iron rod 1 m long is wound from end to end with 200 turns of copper wire. If an electron current of ˙4.0 A in the coil produces a magnetic induction of 1.48 Wb/m², find (a) the magnetic intensity, (b) the permeability number, (c) the magnetic susceptibility, and (d) the magnetization.

12. A steady current in the winding of a long solenoid gives rise to a magnetic intensity of 10,000 A/m, and a magnetic induction of 1.7 Wb/m². Find (a) the permeability number, (b) the magnetic susceptibility, and (c) the magnetization. If the iron in the core has a density of 7.9 g/cm³, and each iron atom has a mass of 9.6 × 10⁻²³ g, find (d) the number of atoms in 1 m³ of iron. If the magnetic moment of each atom is equivalent to one Bohr magneton [see Eq.(38n)], and these are all aligned with H, what is (e) the total magnetic moment per cubic meter? Compare this value with M. [Ans. (a) 135, (b) 1.71 × 10⁻⁴, (c) 1.36 × 10⁶, (d) 8.23 × 10²⁸ atoms, (e) 7.63 × 10⁵ A/m.]

13. Two identical bar magnets, each with a pole strength of 10 Am, and a length of 10 cm, are placed in a uniform magnetic field where $B = 0.05$ Wb/m². Find (a) the dipole moment of each magnet, and (b) the maximum torque that can be exerted on each. If the two magnets are fastened end to end with opposite poles adjacent, find (c) the maximum torque, and (d) the resultant dipole moment.

14. Three identical bar magnets, each with a pole strength of 10 Am, and a length of 10 cm, are placed in a uniform magnetic field where $B = 0.05$ Wb/m². Find (a) the dipole moment of each magnet, and (b) the maximum torque that can be exerted on each. If the three magnets are fastened end to end with opposite poles touching each other, find (c) the maximum torque, and (d) the resultant dipole moment. [Ans. (a) 1.00 Am², (b) 5 × 10⁻² Nm, (c) 15 × 10⁻² Nm, (d) 3.00 Am².]

TRANSFORMERS

Because of the widespread use of transformers in long-distance power transmission as well as in telephones, radio transmitters and receivers, television, etc., it is of interest to consider the elementary principles upon which these instruments operate. A transformer is an electrical device by which the *electromotive force* of a source of alternating current may be increased or decreased.

35.1. The Primary Circuit. To study the actions and principles of a transformer, we must return to the *solenoid*, or *electromagnet*, treated in Sec. 32.7. Before an electron current is started through the coil of an electromagnet, no magnetic field whatever exists. This is illustrated by diagram (a) in Fig. 35A. When the switch S is first closed, completing the electric circuit, the electron current does not rise immediately to its full value but requires a certain amount of time to "build up" (see Fig. 35B). Starting at zero at the time the switch is closed, the current increases rapidly at first, then more slowly, and finally reaches its full value, the value given by Ohm's law.

During the time the electron current is increasing, the magnetic induction B, in and around the solenoid, is increasing as shown in diagram (b) of Fig. 35A. This field continues to grow in strength until the current reaches its maximum value, whereupon both the current and the field become constant. In most circuits, this whole process requires but a small fraction of a second. A constant current is indicative, therefore, of a constant unchanging magnetic field as shown in diagram (c).

When the switch is opened, the current will not stop instantly, nor will the surrounding field vanish instantly. The current will decrease with time, as shown in the graph of Fig. 35B, and the magnetic induction will decrease accordingly as shown in Fig. 35A(d). When the current reaches zero, the field will once more vanish simultaneously as in diagram (a). Thus, by opening and closing a switch, a magnetic field of increasing and decreasing strength is produced.

35.2. The Secondary Circuit. If a loop of wire is placed around an electromagnet, as shown in Fig. 35C, and the switch in the circuit is closed and opened as described in the preceding section, an electromotive force, and hence an electron current, will be induced in the loop. Immediately after the switch has been closed and the current and magnetic induction begin to rise, the total flux through the loop increases so that we obtain an induced emf. An induced emf means that, if the loop ends are connected together or to something else to form a closed circuit, a current will flow in the loop as shown by the arrows in the diagram.

When the electromagnet current reaches a steady state, the field becomes constant. This means that the total flux through the loop is no longer changing and the loop current has dropped to zero.

If the switch S is opened at this time, allowing the electromagnet current to decrease, the magnetic induction will decrease, and the total flux through the loop will fall. This decreasing flux, linking the loop circuit, induces an electron current opposite in direction to that shown in the diagram. When the current in the electromagnet winding drops to zero, the field vanishes and so does the induced emf. The properly timed closing

Fig. 35B *Current–time graph for an electromagnet as illustrated in Fig. 35A.*

To increase the emf in the outside circuit, many loops of wire are usually employed. Such an arrangement is similar to that shown in Fig. 35D and is called an *open-core transformer*. The inside

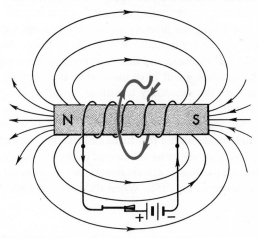

Fig. 35C *Diagram illustrating an electron current induced in a loop of wire placed in the changing field of an electromagnet.*

winding is called the *primary* and the outside winding is called the *secondary*. As the magnetic induction increases, the total flux through each loop of the secondary increases, and approxi-

Fig. 35A *Schematic diagrams of the changing magnetic field around an electromagnet when the current is increasing, constant, and decreasing.*

and opening of a switch can, therefore, induce in a loop of wire one complete cycle of an alternating current

Fig. 35D *Diagram of an open-core transformer.*

mately the same emf is induced in each turn of the coil. Since the turns are all in series with each other, the total emf between the outside ends is the sum of the individual emf's for each turn.

It is customary for both the primary and secondary windings of a transformer to be wound with well-insulated copper wire and for both windings to be electrically insulated from each other.

35.3. The Induction Coil. When the primary terminals of an open-core transformer are connected to a battery as a source of emf, a current in the secondary is induced only at the instant the circuit is closed and again when it is opened. To derive an alternating current from the secondary winding, the primary circuit must be opened and closed continually. When this is done, the field will increase and decrease periodically and the secondary will have induced in it, to deliver through the secondary terminals, an alternating current.

An induction coil is an open-core type of transformer with a few turns of large wire in the primary, many turns of fine wire in the secondary, and an automatic circuit *interrupter*, or *vibrator*, as shown in Fig. 35E. When the switch is closed

and a current is started through the primary winding PP, the iron core becomes magnetized and attracts the iron knob B. Mounted on a strip of spring steel L, the vibrator bends to the left, breaking the primary circuit at the point C. When the current stops and the core loses its magnetism, the vibrator springs back to the right, making contact again. Proper adjustment of the thumbscrew T will cause the iron knob B to vibrate back and forth periodically, making and breaking the electric circuit. Each time the circuit is made the magnetic field grows, inducing a current in the secondary winding in one direction; and each time it is broken the field falls, inducing an oppositely directed current. Since each vibration of the knob B completes one cycle of an alternating current, the frequency of the vibrator determines the frequency of the alternating current delivered at the secondary terminals.

If, as is usually the case, the number of turns of wire in the secondary greatly exceeds the number of turns in the primary, the average voltage of the secondary will be many times higher than the direct-current voltage impressed on the primary, and a spark will jump across the gap GG.

Fig. 35E   *Cross-section diagram of a laboratory induction coil capable of producing high-voltage sparks at the expense of a small battery.*

Perhaps the best example of a *vibrator type of induction coil* being used today is the automobile radio. Here a very small induction coil about 1 in. in diameter and 3 in. long is employed. The function of the coil is to take current from the 6- or 12-V storage battery, with which every car is equipped, and to deliver at the secondary terminals an alternating emf of from 200 to 300 V. This alternating current is then changed into direct current by a single radio tube, called *a rectifier*, and a system of coils and condensers called *a filter system*. Thus the constant high voltage necessary for the proper operation of the radio receiver is obtained in the roundabout way of first transforming constant low voltage into high voltage alternating emf and then rectifying it to a constant high voltage.

A similar induction coil without a vibrator, called *a spark-coil* or *auto-transformer*, is used in the ignition system of an automobile. Generally, such coils are about 2 in. in diameter and 4 in. long, and are wound on an open core as shown in Fig. 35D. The primary winding of such coils contains about 100 turns of heavy copper wire, and the secondary winding several thousand. The primary is connected to the 6- or 12-V storage battery by wires through the timing system, the purpose of which is to open and close the circuit periodically with the motion of each cylinder of the motor. Each time the circuit is closed and opened a high voltage induced in the secondary winding is connected to and is discharged as a spark across the terminals of one of the motor's spark plugs. The term "autotransformer" applies to a transformer in which one end of the primary winding is connected by a wire directly to one end of the secondary. This common junction has little effect upon the normal operation of the coil, and is usually connected to the ground. On an automobile, the ground connection is made to the metal frame of the car.

35.4. The Closed-Core Transformer. A transformer, like an induction coil, has *a primary winding*, *a secondary winding*, and *an iron core*. The principal difference between the two is that a transformer does not have a vibrator and it operates on an alternating-current supply.

Historically, the first closed-core transformer was made by Michael Faraday in 1831. Two coils of wire, one acting as a primary and the other as a secondary, were wound around opposite sides of an iron ring as shown in Fig. 35F. When a

Fig. 35F *Diagram of the first closed-core transformer. (Designed by Michael Faraday.)*

current is started in the primary winding, the magnetic field set up is confined almost entirely to the iron core. In other words, the lines of induction that develop in the primary, as a result of the growing primary current, also thread through the secondary, inducing an electromotive force and current. The iron acts like a good conductor of magnetic lines of induction, guiding them through the secondary winding.

When an alternating current is connected to the primary of a transformer, no vibrator is required to start and stop the current; the current rises and falls periodically, satisfying the conditions for a changing magnetic field and induced currents.

Most modern transformers are of the closed-core type, as illustrated in Figs. 35G and 35H.

35.5. Step-Up and Step-Down Transformer. Nearly all transformers come under one of the two following classes: (a) *step-up*, or (b) *step-down transformers*. As shown in Fig. 35G, the step-up transformer is one in which the secondary winding has more turns of wire than in the primary. In the step-down transformer the reverse is true. The importance of this distinction is based upon the general and well-established principle that the ratio of the number of turns of wire in the primary and secondary windings is the same as the ratio of the respective voltages in each. This may be stated as an equation.

$$\frac{\text{number of primary turns}}{\text{number of secondary turns}} = \frac{\text{primary voltage}}{\text{secondary voltage}}$$

$$(35a)$$

Thus, if a transformer has 100 turns in the primary and 100,000 turns in the secondary, the

secondary

primary

step-up transformer

Fig. 35G   *A step-up transformer with a closed core.*

voltage delivered at the secondary terminals will be 1000 times the voltage impressed upon the primary. If this same transformer were connected to the ordinary house lighting circuit of 110 volts ac, the voltage at the secondary terminals would be 110,000 volts ac.

The step-down transformer is just the reverse of this: the secondary voltage is lower than the primary voltage. As an illustration, suppose the primary of a transformer has 2000 turns of fine wire and the secondary has 100 turns. Having a turn-ratio of 20:1, this transformer when connected to the 110-volt ac line will deliver at its secondary a difference of potential of $\frac{1}{20}$ of 110 volts, or 5.5 volts. Such transformers are used in electric welding, for the ringing of doorbells, for the operation of toy electric trains, for lighting the filaments in radio tubes, etc.

Another type of transformer in common use has a tapped secondary. A tapped secondary is one in which different secondary voltages can be obtained by making connections to different

numbers of secondary turns as shown in Fig. 35H. If secondary connections are made to S_0

primary   secondary

P_2 S_5
                                                   S_4
                                                   S_3
                                                   S_2
                                                   S_1
P_1
                                                   S_0

Fig. 35H   *Transformer with a tapped secondary.*

and S_1, a relatively low voltage is obtained. If the upper connection is shifted to S_2, S_3, etc., more and more secondary turns are included, and the secondary voltage is proportionally larger. The effect is similar in many ways to the potential divider.

A type of transformer in widespread use today has two or more independent secondary windings (see Fig. 35I). Electrically insulated from each

P_2 S_4

                                                   secondaries

primary S_3
                                                   S_2

P_1 S_1

Fig. 35I   *Transformer with two secondaries.*

other, these secondaries produce their own voltage as given by Eq.(35a).

Transformers used in the construction of modern radio and television receivers and transmitters are of the shell type shown in Fig. 35J.

35.6. Autotransformers. This device employs a single winding of insulated copper wire that serves as both a primary and secondary. In principle it is similar to the *voltage divider* frequently used with direct-current sources and shown in Fig. 28I. A circuit diagram of an autotransformer is shown in Fig. 35K. One end of the winding A is common to primary and secondary, while two other contacts B and C form the other terminals, respectively.

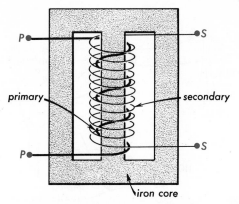

Fig. 35J   *Shell-type transformer.*

If A to C contains more turns than A to B, the device serves as a step-up transformer. Conversely if C is moved to the left of B, so that A to C has fewer turns than A to B, it serves as a step-down transformer.

Fig. 35K   *Circuit diagram for an autotransformer.*

There are many uses for a continuously variable voltage autotransformer of the type shown in Fig. 35L. In such devices the iron core is made in the shape of a ring, and a sliding contact C is moved along the winding by the turn of a knob

Fig. 35L   *Variable autotransformer for obtaining variable ac voltages.*

K. The insulation on the wire is removed on the very top of the winding and a small block of graphite G, under spring pressure, serves as the sliding contact.

With such transformers the voltage across the secondary terminals A to C is read directly from the pointer and scale.

35.7. Power. The increase in voltage of an alternating current by means of a step-up transformer appears at first sight to be a violation of the law of conservation of energy, i.e., it appears as though a large amount of energy could be obtained at the expenditure of a smaller amount. This is really not the case, for, when the voltage is increased, the current is simultaneously decreased by the same proportion.

When, for example, a transformer is used to step up the voltage to 100 times that supplied to the primary, the current in the secondary becomes only $\frac{1}{100}$ of the current in the primary. Therefore the power (V_pI_p) supplied at the primary is just equal to that delivered at the secondary (V_sI_s). In general, when the voltage is stepped up by a transformer, the current is stepped down by the same proportion.

In practice this is not exactly true, because a transformer is not quite 100% efficient. A small amount of electrical energy is continually expended, principally in the form of heat. In a well-designed transformer, such losses do not exceed 2 or 3%, so that a transformer is often considered to be almost 100% efficient.

35.8. Power Transmission. In the transmission of electrical energy over wires for long distances, transformers are practically indispensable. At the power house in the distant mountains, for example, electric current is generated by huge alternating-current generators at the relatively low voltage of several thousand volts. If an attempt were made to transmit this electrical energy, as a voltage of say 2200 V, over many miles of wire cable to a distant city, the current would be so large that nearly all of the energy would be consumed in heating the power line. The heat generated, it should be remembered [see Eq.(31h)], is proportional to the square of the current (heat = $0.24I^2Rt$).

To avoid large heat losses, transformers at the

Fig. 35M   *Illustration of the use of transformers in the transmission of electrical energy from the power house in the mountains to the consumer in the distant city.*

power house (see Fig. 35M) step the voltage up to some 220,000 V before switching the current onto the power line. Since the voltage in the case cited is increased one-hundred fold, the current drops by the same proportion to one-hundredth. Since the square of $\frac{1}{100}$ is $\frac{1}{10,000}$, the heat loss along the transmission line is only one ten thousandth of what it would have been had the transformer not been used.

At the city end of the power line, a transformer substation steps the voltage down to something like its original value of 2200 volts. From there, branch lines distribute the power to various sections of the city where smaller transformers, one

near each group of several houses, steps it down again to the relatively safe voltage of 110 to 220 volts.

An experimental transformer for studying the relations between primary and secondary voltages, power input and power output, etc., is shown in Fig. 35N. It consists of a closed-core transformer with one side of the core removable and a set of several coils with different numbers of turns.

Although coils with any desired number of turns may be used, typical ones for a laboratory

Fig. 35N   *Experimental transformer with changeable coils.*

Fig. 35O   *Electrical circuit diagram showing connections for transformer experiment.*

experiment would have 350, 250, 250, 200, 150, 100, and 50 turns, respectively. In addition to these, a special coil of 100 turns with taps at every twentieth turn, and a tube with two separate windings of 200 turns and 20 turns, respectively, would be useful. The auxiliary equipment needed is shown in Fig. 35O, and consists of an ac voltmeter reading up to 150 V, a potential divider of several hundred ohms, a double-pole-single-throw switch, and a double-pole-double-throw switch.

PROBLEMS

1. The secondary of a step-down transformer has 32 turns of wire, and the primary is connected to a 120-V ac line. If the secondary is to deliver 5 V at its output terminals, how many turns should the primary have?

2. The primary of a step-down transformer has 256 turns and is connected to a 120-V ac line. If the secondary is to supply 6 V at its terminals and an electron current of 100 mA, find (a) the number of turns in the secondary, and (b) the electron current in the primary. [Ans. (a) 12.8 turns, (b) 5.0 mA.]

3. A step-up transformer with 220 turns in the primary is connected to a 120-V ac line. The secondary delivers 12 KV at its terminals and a current of 40 mA. (a) How many turns are in the secondary? (b) What is the current in the primary? (c) What power is drawn from the line?

4. The primary of a step-up transformer is connected to a 120-V ac line. The secondary with 7200 turns delivers 10,000 V and a current of 30 mA. Calculate (a) the number of turns in the primary, and (b) the current drawn from the line. [Ans. (a) 86.4 turns, (b) 2.50 A.]

5. One end of a transmission line of 8 Ω is connected to a 220-V ac source, and the other end to a load resistance of 12 Ω. Find the power consumed by (a) the line, and (b) the load. Each of the two wires has a resistance of 4 Ω.

6. A variable autotransformer has a winding containing 250 turns. How many turns should be included in the primary if the secondary is to supply 0 to 180 V? Assume the primary voltage to be 115 V. [Ans. 159 turns.]

7. A step-up transformer has 160 turns in the primary and 25,000 turns in the secondary. If the primary is connected to a 218-V ac line, find the voltage delivered at the secondary terminals.

8. The primary of a step-up transformer having 320 turns is connected to a house lighting circuit of 115-V ac. If the secondary is to deliver 3000 V to a neon sign, how many turns must it have? [Ans. 8348.]

9. The secondary of a step-down transformer has 130 turns of copper wire, and the primary is connected to a 208-V ac line. If the secondary is to deliver 6 V at its output terminals, how many turns should the primary have?

10. The primary of a step-down transformer has 280 turns and is connected to a 120-V ac line. If the secondary is to supply 1.5-V ac at its terminals and an electron current of 150 A, find (a) the number of turns in the secondary, and (b) the electron current in the primary. [Ans. (a) 3.5 turns, (b) 1.87 A.]

11. A step-up transformer with 210 turns in the primary is connected to a 120-V ac line. The secondary delivers 12,500-V ac at its terminals and an electron current of 30 mA. (a) How many turns are in the secondary? (b) What is the current in the primary? (c) What power is drawn from the line?

12. The primary of a step-up transformer is connected to a 208-V ac line. The secondary with 9000 turns delivers 15 KV and a current of 25 mA. Calculate (a) the number of turns in the primary, and (b) the electron current drawn from the line. (c) What is the power? [Ans. (a) 125, (b) 1.80 A, (c) 375 W.]

13. A transformer with 600 turns in the primary is connected to a 120-V ac line. If the transformer is to have three separate secondaries to give 2.5, 6.0, and 450-V ac, respectively, how many turns should each have?

14. A radio transformer with 450 turns in the primary, is connected to a 120-V ac line. If the transformer is to have three separate secondaries to give 2.5, 7.5, and 500 V, respectively, how many turns should each have? [Ans. (a) 9.37, (b) 28.1, (c) 1875.]

15. An autotransformer with 306 turns is connected to a 120-V ac generator. If the primary terminals include 166 turns of the winding, what is the maximum voltage obtainable from the secondary?

16. An autotransformer with 220 turns is connected to a 120-V ac line. To what two points of the winding should the primary terminals be connected if the secondary range should be 0 to 175-V ac? [Ans. To include 151 turns.]

ALTERNATING CURRENTS

When a battery is first connected to the ends of a long straight copper wire, the electron current rises quickly to the value given by Ohm's law. When the same wire is wound into a coil or solenoid, however, the current rises more slowly as shown by curve (b) in Fig. 36A. If an iron core

Fig. 36A *Current–time graph for a long copper wire in the form of (a) a straight wire, (b) a coil, and (c) a coil with an iron core.*

is inserted to make the solenoid an electromagnet, the current rises much more slowly, as shown in curve (c).

The cause of this lagging of the current is an emf induced in the wire which is opposed in direction to the rising current. This *back emf*, as it is sometimes called, is extremely small if the wire is straight, is large if it is a coil, and still larger if a soft-iron core is inserted. To explain the existence of a back emf, consider a small section of one turn of wire in a solenoid of many turns. As the current rises in this section, the growing magnetic induction which develops around it threads through the neighboring loops of wire, inducing in them an emf. These induced emf's and their corresponding currents run counter to the impressed emf and current. This property is called *self-induction*.

36.1. Self-Induction. The unit by which one

measures the self-induction of a coil is called the *henry* in honor of the American scientist, Joseph Henry.*

A coil having an inductance of one henry is one in which a change in the current of one ampere per second produces a back emf of one volt.

A coil with a large number of turns is one that has a large inductance L, whereas one with only a few turns has a small inductance. The higher the inductance, the more slowly does the current rise or fall within the coil.

The establishment of a steady current in an inductance requires work, since the back emf must be overcome. Not all of the electrical energy expended in reaching the steady current state is lost. Some is stored up in the form of a magnetic field. When the source emf is disconnected from the circuit, the magnetic induction decreases, thereby inducing an oppositely directed emf and corresponding electron current.

Two experiments demonstrating the property of self-induction are illustrated in Fig. 36B. In diagram (a), a solenoid of many turns of wire is

* Joseph Henry (1797–1878), American physicist and scientific administrator, was born in Albany, New York, in 1797. He attended a country school, but quit at the age of thirteen. Later he attended the Albany Academy. Becoming interested in electricity and magnetism, he invented the magnetic telegraph and the electric relay, and discovered the phenomenon of self-induction. In 1832 he became professor of natural philosophy at Princeton, and in 1842 was elected by Congress as first secretary of the Smithsonian Institution in Washington, D.C. In this capacity, he founded the U. S. Weather Bureau and inaugurated the idea of distributing scientific publications to libraries and scientific bodies all over the world. He was the principal figure in the organization of the National Academy of Sciences, of which he was the second president. By general consent, Henry was the foremost American physicist of his time.

Fig. 36B *Two experiments illustrating the self-induction of a coil of wire. The circuit (b) is commonly used as a dimmer for electric lights.*

connected in parallel with an electric light to a 120-V battery. When the switch S is closed, the light flashes bright for an instant and then becomes dim. When the switch is opened, the light again flashes bright for a moment and then goes out. When the switch is closed, the back emf in the inductance prevents the current from building up rapidly through the inductance. The inductance therefore acts as though it had a very high resistance so that practically all of the current goes through C. When the current becomes steady, there is no back emf in L, and part of the current flows through C and part through L. When the switch is opened, the magnetic field falls off, inducing a current in L. This current flowing through the lamp C causes it to light up momentarily to full brightness.

The second experiment, as illustrated in diagram (b), demonstrates an increase in the self-induction of a coil due to a soft-iron core. Connected to an alternating emf, the light is bright when the iron core is out and dim when it is in place inside the solenoid. When the iron is inside, the back emf induced in the coil at each rise and fall of the current is very much greater than before, since the waxing and waning magnetic field is strengthened by its presence. The increased inductance therefore prevents the current's reaching a very high value before the current stops again and reverses its direction. The effect on the

brightness of the lamp is the same as if the inductance were replaced by a variable resistance whose value is greatest when the iron core is inside the solenoid.

When a current is started in an electromagnet, the tiny elementary magnets within the iron core (these are the elementary magnets referred to in Sec. 34.7) turn around from their random orientations and line up with each other to make a single magnet of the entire core. In turning around, the field of each elementary magnet threads through the coil windings, inducing an emf opposing the rising current. This is another way of accounting for the back emf of self-induction.

36.2. Calculation of Inductance. In many instances, the inductance of a solenoid can be calculated from its geometry. For a long solenoid of uniform cross section, or a Rowland ring as shown in Fig. 34H, the inductance L, in *henries*, is given by

$$L = \kappa\mu_0 \frac{N^2 A}{l} \qquad (36a)$$

where N is the number of turns of wire, A is the cross-sectional area of the core in *square meters*, κ is the permeability number for the core, μ_0 is the permeability of free space in *webers/ampere-meter*, and l is the length of the coil in meters [see Eq.(34w)].

Example 1. A round bar 4 cm in diameter and 20 cm long is wrapped with one layer of copper wire to form a solenoid. The coil has 200 turns, and the permeability number of the iron is 1590. Find the inductance.

Solution. The given quantities are just those occurring on the right in Eq.(36a). $N = 200$, $\mu_0 = 12.57 \times 10^{-7}$ Wb/Am, $l = 0.20$ m, and $A = \pi r^2 = 0.00126$ m^2.

$$L = \frac{1590 \times 12.57 \times 10^{-7} \times (200)^2 \times 0.00126}{0.2}$$

$$= 0.504 \text{ henry}$$

Without the iron core, the solenoid above would have a very much smaller inductance. For an air core, μ would be equal to $\mu_0 = 12.57 \times 10^{-7}$, and the inductance would be only 0.316 millihenry. *The millihenry* (mH) *is a smaller unit of inductance and is equal to one-thousandth of a henry; while a still smaller unit, the microhenry* (μH), *is equal to one-millionth of a henry.*

It should be noted that, if the core is air or a vacuum, L is a constant independent of the electron current and magnetizing field H. If the core is a ferromagnetic material, however, L will vary because the permeability varies.

36.3. Time Constants. When a capacitance C is connected in series with a resistance R and a battery emf V (see Fig. 36C), an electron current

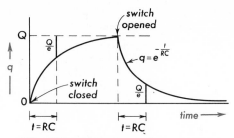

Fig. 36D   *Capacitance time constant.*

capacitor will discharge, and again an electron current will flow through R.

The time taken for the charge on the capacitor to reach within $1/e$th of its full charge Q while charging, and the time taken to drop to $1/e$th of its full charge while discharging, is called the circuit *time constant.*

$$\text{time constant} = RC \qquad (36b)$$

The constant e equals 2.718 ($1/e = 0.369$), and is the base of natural logarithms. The greater the resistance and the larger the capacitance, the greater is the time required to charge or discharge a capacitor.

When an inductance L is connected in series with a resistance R and a battery of emf V (see Fig. 36E), it takes time for the electron current I

Fig. 36C   *Series circuit containing capacitance and resistance.*

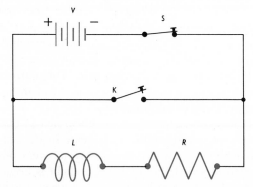

Fig. 36E   *Series circuit containing inductance and resistance.*

flows for a short period of time because it takes time for the plates of the capacitor to acquire their full charge Q. The rate at which a capacitor charges up is shown graphically in Fig. 36D. If now the switch S is opened, disconnecting the battery, and then the switch K is closed, the

and the accompanying magnetic field to build up to a steady state. When the switch S is opened and the switch K closed, the field decreases and the electron current falls, approaching zero as t approaches infinity. The time constant of the circuit, that is, the time for the electron current to rise within $1/e$th of its final value (see Fig. 36F), is given by

$$\text{time constant} = \frac{L}{R} \qquad (36c)$$

36.4. Stored Electrical Energy. When a capacitor like that shown in Fig. 36C is fully charged,

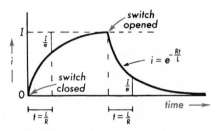

Fig. 36F *Inductance time constant.*

electrical energy is stored in the form of an electric field. If W represents the stored energy in *joules*,

$$\boxed{W = \tfrac{1}{2}CV^2} \qquad (36d)$$

where C is in farads and V is in volts.

Similarly, when a steady electron current is maintained in an inductance L, as shown in Fig. 36E, electrical energy is stored up in the surrounding magnetic field to the amount,

$$\boxed{W = \tfrac{1}{2}LI^2} \qquad (36e)$$

where L is in *henries*, I is in *amperes*, and W is in *joules*.

36.5. Inductive and Capacitive Reactance. All electrical devices connected to a source of alternating emf contain a certain amount of *resistance*, *inductance*, and *capacitance*. If the total inductance and capacitance of the circuit are small compared with the resistance, Ohm's law can be applied to find the current in the various parts.

If the inductance and capacitance are not relatively small, they will introduce phase differences, or time lags, between current and voltage, so that Ohm's law will not apply in the ordinary way. Such a circuit is shown schematically in Fig. 36G.

Since an emf suddenly applied to an inductance requires a certain time for the electron current to build up to a fixed value (see Fig. 36A), the application of an *alternating* emf finds the

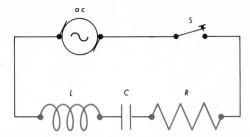

Fig. 36G *Series circuit containing inductance, capacitance, and resistance.*

current lagging behind the voltage in its rapid changes and reversals. Furthermore, if the frequency is very high there is not enough time for the electron current to rise very far from zero toward its Ohm's law value.

Because the inductance effect reduces the electron current, it may be thought of as something analogous to a resistance. The measure of this effect is called *inductive reactance*, to distinguish it from a true resistance where electrical energy is converted into heat.

$$X_L = 2\pi f L \qquad (36f)$$
inductive reactance

where f is the frequency or cycles per second.

When a capacitor is inserted into a *dc circuit*, the plates charge up, and the electron current drops to zero. The capacitor thereafter acts as though it were an infinite resistance. Connected to an alternating emf, however, it may act quite differently. As the frequency f rises in an *ac circuit*, the resistive effect of a capacitor decreases. The reversing of the emf reverses the flow of electrons to and from the plates of the capacitor, and the alternating flow of charge constitutes an *alternating current*. Because a capacitor differs from a pure resistance, in that it stores electrostatic energy, its resistive effect is called *capacitive reactance*.

$$X_C = \frac{1}{2\pi f C} \qquad (36g)$$
capacitive reactance

36.6. AC Series Circuit. When an inductance L, capacitance C, and a resistance R, are connected in series to an ac generator as shown in Fig. 36G, the electron current in the circuit can be determined by the following equation

$$I = \frac{V}{\sqrt{R^2 + (X_{\mathrm{L}} - X_{\mathrm{C}})^2}} \qquad (36h)$$

where I and V are the electron current and voltage, respectively. The quantity $X_{\mathrm{L}} - X_{\mathrm{C}}$ in this equation is often called the *reactance* and is represented by X,

$$X = X_{\mathrm{L}} - X_{\mathrm{C}}, \qquad \text{so that} \qquad I = \frac{V}{\sqrt{R^2 + X^2}}$$

The whole denominator is called the *impedance* and is represented by Z.

$$Z = \sqrt{R^2 + (X_{\mathrm{L}} - X_{\mathrm{C}})^2}$$

and

$$I = \frac{V}{Z} \qquad (36i)$$

Note the identical form of this last equation to Ohm's law for direct currents. The resistance R in Ohm's law has here been replaced by the impedance Z.

The relations between R, X_{L}, and X_{C} and the resultant impedance Z of a series circuit containing them may be represented graphically by treating all quantities as vectors. As shown in Fig. 36H, the resistance R is represented by a

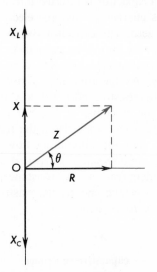

Fig. 36H   *Impedance diagram for ac circuit.*

vector along the x axis, the reactances X_{L} and X_{C} by vectors up and down on the y axis, and the impedance Z as the vector resultant of X and R.

In practice, R includes the resistance of the inductance winding as well as all the connecting wires of the circuit.

36.7. Phase Relations Between I and V. The effect of an inductance and a capacitance on an *ac series circuit* is such as to alter the phase of the electron current I with respect to the applied alternating emf or voltage. If the inductive reactance X_{L} is greater than the capacitive reactance X_{C}, the electron current will lag behind the impressed voltage; while if X_{C} is greater than X_{L}, the electron current will lead the impressed voltage.

The amount the electron current lags or leads is given by the phase angle θ, where θ is given by

$$\tan \theta = \frac{X}{R} \qquad (36j)$$

In Fig. 36H, θ is seen to be the angle between Z and R. In one complete cycle of either the current or voltage, the phase angle has changed by 2π rad, so that a phase lag of 45° means that the electron current is $\frac{1}{8}$ of a cycle behind the voltage. A graphical representation of this example is given in Fig. 36I.

Fig. 36I   *Graph showing current lagging 45° behind voltage.*

36.8. Power Factor. With direct-current circuits, the power is given by the product $V \times I$, and is measured in *volt-amperes*, or *watts*. In alternating-current circuits, the instantaneous rate at which energy is supplied is equal to the product of the instantaneous voltage and the instantaneous current. Since both of these are sometimes zero, it is clear that the power consumption varies over each cycle and that some sort of average power must be taken.

The average power supplied to any ac circuit is

equal to the rms voltage times the rms electron current multiplied by the cosine of the angle of lag.

$$P = VI \cos \theta \qquad (36k)$$

The quantity $\cos \theta$ is called the *power factor*. A low power factor in *ac circuits* is to be avoided, since, for a given supply voltage V, a large current would be needed to transmit appreciable electrical energy. The I^2R heat losses in the lines should be held to a minimum by making the power factor as near unity as possible. This means that θ should be as near zero as possible, thus allowing the smallest current for the power delivered.

Examination of the impedance diagram, Fig. 36H, will show that a circuit containing a relatively large inductive reactance should contain an equally large capacitive reactance to make $\theta = 0$, and the power factor $\cos \theta = 1$.

Example 2. A 60-Ω resistor is connected in series with a 0.25-H inductor, a 50-μF capacitor, and an ac generator delivering 110 V (rms) at 60 cycles. Find (a) the reactance, (b) the impedance, (c) the electron current in the circuit, (d) the power factor, and (e) the power.

Solution. By direct substitution in Eqs.(36f), (36g), (36h), and (36i),

$$X_L = 2\pi fL = 2\pi \times 60 \times 0.25 = 94.25 \ \Omega$$
$$X_C = 1(2\pi fC) = 1/(2\pi \times 60 \times 50 \times 10^{-6})$$
$$= 53.05 \ \Omega$$

(a) $X = X_L - X_C = 94.25 - 53.05 = 41.20 \ \Omega$
     $Z = \sqrt{R^2 + X^2} = \sqrt{(60)^2 + (41.2)^2} = 72.8 \ \Omega$
(c) $I = V/Z = 110/72.8 = 1.51$ A

Figure 36H is drawn to scale as a graphical solution for part of this problem. By direct substitution in Eq. (36j),

(d) $\tan \theta = \dfrac{X}{R} = \dfrac{41.2}{60} = 0.687$ or $\theta = 34.5°$

$\cos \theta = 0.824 =$ power factor

By Eq. (36k),

(e) $P = VI \cos \theta = 110 \times 1.51 \times 0.824 = 137$ W

The power expended in a circuit containing inductance and capacitance cannot be measured with a voltmeter and ammeter. To measure power, one uses a *wattmeter*. Such an instrument takes the emf, current, and power factor into account and reads the power directly. By reading a wattmeter, an ammeter, and a voltmeter, the power factor of a circuit can be determined by Eq.(36k).

$$\text{power factor} = \cos \theta = \frac{P}{VI} \qquad (36l)$$

36.9. Lenz's Law. When a conductor moves through a magnetic field, the induced current in the wire is in such a direction that its own magnetic field generated by that current acts on the original magnetic field in a way opposing the motion. Stated for the first time by H. Lenz in 1833, this is known as Lenz's law. The action of the two magnetic fields upon each other is always such as to oppose the motion or any change in conditions already existing, for if they assisted the change we would have perpetual motion and a violation of the law of conservation of energy.

If the N pole of a straight bar magnet is approaching a solenoid (see Fig. 33A), the induced electron current in the coil is in such a direction as to produce an N pole at the nearest face of the coil. The two N poles therefore repel each other, tending to stop the motion. To keep the current flowing, a force F must continually be supplied to the moving magnet. It is this force F, moving through a given distance, that determines the amount of mechanical work done in producing a given current. If now the N pole is withdrawn from the solenoid, the induced current in the coil reverses in direction and produces an S pole at the nearest face. The opposite poles therefore attract each other, tending to stop the motion. Again, to keep the current flowing, a force F must be continually supplied; thus work is done.

There are numerous ways of demonstrating Lenz's law. One common experiment is to move a flat copper or aluminum plate rapidly through a strong magnetic field as shown in Fig. 36J. As each part of the plate enters the field, a strong opposing force tends to stop it. What happens electrically is that strong eddy currents of electricity are produced in the metal as shown in Fig. 36K. The magnetic field arising from these eddy currents opposes the field through which it is moving. If the plate is held in the hand, the

Fig. 36J *Induced currents in the copper-disk pendulum quickly stop it from swinging through.*

Fig. 36L *Slotted copper disks for the demonstration of induced eddy currents.*

sensation is that of movement through thick molasses.

If the solid disk is replaced by a slotted disk, as shown in Fig. 36L(a), strong currents are induced in the vertical bars as they enter the field, and the disk stops quickly. If the slots are open at one end as in diagram (b), each bar is an open circuit and no large induced currents can be produced. Consequently, the disk is not strongly retarded but swings through the magnetic field rather freely.

Another interesting demonstration is illustrated in Fig. 36M. A coil of wire with an extra long iron core is set on end, and a solid metal ring or band slipped over the top as shown. At the instant an alternating emf is applied to the coil,

the metal ring is thrown upward several feet into the air. The explanation is not difficult since the arrangement is quite the same as a *step-down transformer;* the solenoid acts as a primary of many turns and the ring acts as a secondary of only one turn. As the current first starts to flow in one direction in the primary, the expanding magnetic field induces an oppositely directed current in the ring. The field set up by the ring

Fig. 36M *A metal ring is flipped up in the air by means of induced currents. A demonstration of Lenz's law.*

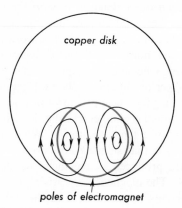

Fig. 36K *Eddy currents in a moving plate conductor.*

current therefore opposes the field of the primary, and the repulsion of like poles pushes the ring upward. When the primary current reverses, the secondary current also reverses, and again there is a repulsion. To demonstrate the existence of a large current, the ring, if held down over the core, will soon become hot.

36.10. Levitation. The phenomenon known as "levitation" is another illustration of Lenz's law.

(a)

(b)

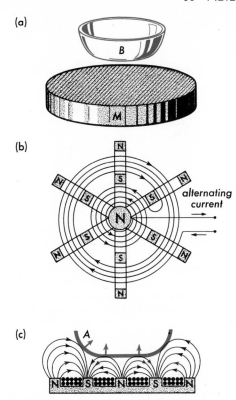

alternating current

(c)

Fig. 36N   *A metal bowl is suspended in mid-air.*

A metal bowl B, as in Fig. 36N(a), is supported in stable equilibrium in mid-air just above an electromagnet M of special design. Top and side views of the iron core and coil windings are shown in diagrams (b) and (c). Excited by an alternating current, the raised iron knobs, labeled N and S, reverse their polarity periodically with the current. As the electron current builds up in the direction indicated in diagram (b), the magnetic induction grows. With the aluminum bowl in place as in diagram (c), the growing field induces strong eddy currents in the aluminum conductor. These currents in turn give rise to opposing fields. Since the primary field being created by an alternating current increases and decreases rapidly, the bowl always experiences an upward force.

Should the bowl move to one side, as for example to the left in diagram (c), the changing field at A will induce stronger electron currents on that side of the bowl and give rise to an increased repulsion, pushing the bowl back toward

the center as indicated. The strong induced currents give rise to so much heat that the bowl soon becomes hot.

Because the coil windings of a levitator have a relatively large inductive reactance, a fairly large capacitance must be inserted in the ac circuit to raise the power factor close to unity, and thereby keep the current in the levitator coils at a maximum and the current supplied by the source at a minimum.

36.11. Hysteresis. In Sec. 34.7, it was shown how a rising electron current in a coil containing iron gives rise to a magnetization curve as shown in Fig. 34I. When an alternating current is applied to such an inductance, thereby reversing the magnetizing field H with each half cycle, the magnetization B lags behind as shown in Fig. 36O. As the elementary magnets within the iron try to line up with H, first one way and then the other, the tendency to turn around gives rise to mechanical stresses in the iron; these in turn produce heating. This wasted energy due to the cyclic magnetization is given by the area within the *hysteresis loop* in Fig. 36O and is called *hysteresis loss*.

Hysteresis losses are not to be confused with other losses due to eddy currents set up in the iron core (see Fig. 36K). To reduce these eddy currents to a minimum, thereby reducing heat losses, the iron core is laminated, that is, built up of layers of thin iron sheets.

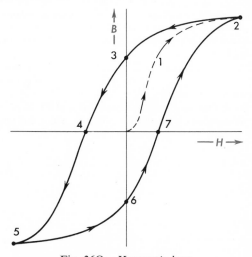

Fig. 36O   *Hysteresis loop.*

PROBLEMS

1. An electron current of 2 A flows through an inductance of 4 μH. How much energy is stored in the surrounding magnetic field?

2. What steady electron current will store up 5 J of energy in an inductance of 40 mH? [Ans. 15.8 A.]

3. An inductance of 25 μH is connected to a 60 c/s ac line. Calculate the inductive reactance.

4. A capacitance of 60 μF is connected to a 60 c/s ac line. Find the capacitive reactance. [Ans. 44.2 Ω.]

5. A capacitor of 12 μF is connected in series with an 80,000 Ω resistor. Calculate the time constant of this combination.

6. What resistance connected in series with a capacitance of 16 μF will give the combination a time constant of 15 s? [Ans. 9.37 $\times$ 10^5 Ω.]

7. What resistance connected in series with an inductance of 5 mH will give the combination a time constant of 0.5 s?

8. An inductance of 25 μH is connected in series with a 320-Ω resistor. Find the time constant. [Ans. 7.81 $\times$ 10^{-8} s.]

9. An oscillator coil is wound on a paper tube 8 cm in diameter and 40 cm long. How many turns of copper wire must it have to provide an inductance of 200 μH?

10. A round iron bar 4 cm in diameter and 20 cm long is wound with copper wire to form a solenoid. If the iron has a permeability of 10 $\times$ 10^{-4} Wb/Am, and the inductance is 0.20 H, how many turns does it have? [Ans. 179 turns.]

11. A solenoid 4 cm in diameter and 40 cm long has 500 turns of wire. Find its inductance when it has (a) an air core, and (b) an iron core of permeability 3.5 $\times$ 10^{-3} Wb/Am.

12. A solenoid 4 cm in diameter and 60 cm long has 1000 turns of fine copper wire. Calculate its inductance when it has (a) an air core and (b) an iron core of permeability 4.2 $\times$ 10^{-3} Wb/Am. [Ans. (a) 2.63 mH, (b) 8.80 H.]

13. A capacitance of 4 μF is connected to a dc voltage supply of 12 KV. Find (a) the stored charge, and (b) the stored electrical energy.

14. A capacitance of 20 μF has a charge of 2.5 $\times$ 10^{-2} C. Calculate (a) the potential difference across the ter-minals, and (b) the stored electrical energy. [Ans. (a) 1250 V, (b) 15.6 J.]

15. An inductance of 10 μH is connected to a 1000 c/s ac line. Calculate the inductive reactance.

16. A capacitance of 180 μF is connected to a 500 c/s ac line. Find the capacitive reactance. [Ans. 1.77 Ω.]

17. A 50-Ω resistor is connected in series with a 0.20-H inductor, a 40 μF capacitor, and an ac generator delivering 120 V (rms) at 60 c/s. Find (a) the inductive reactance, (b) the capacitive reactance, (c) the total reactance, (d) the impedance, (e) the electron current, (f) the power factor, and (g) the power.

18. An inductance of 200 mH is connected in series with a resistance of 20 Ω, a capacitance of 40 μF, and a generator delivering a 60 c/s rms voltage of 120 V at its terminals. Find (a) the inductive reactance, (b) the capacitive reactance, (c) the total reactance, (d) the impedance, (e) the rms current, (f) the phase angle, (g) the power factor, and (h) the power developed. [Ans. (a) 75.4 Ω, (b) 66.3 Ω, (c) 9.1 Ω, (d) 22.0 Ω, (e) 5.45 A, (f) 24.5°, (g) 0.910, (h) 595 W.]

19. A capacitance of 1.2 μF is connected in series with an inductance of 250 mH, and a generator supplying a 300 c/s rms voltage of 208 V at its terminals. If a resistance of 200 Ω is added to the circuit, find (a) the capacitive reactance, (b) the inductive reactance, (c) the total reactance, (d) the impedance, (e) the phase angle θ, (f) the rms current, (g) the power factor, and (h) the power.

20. A resistance of 180 Ω, a capacitor of 0.60 μF, an inductor of 120 mH, are connected in series to a generator delivering an rms voltage of 120 V at 500 c/s. Find (a) the capacitive reactance, (b) the inductive reactance, (c) the total reactance, (d) the impedance, (e) the rms electron current, (f) the phase angle θ, (g) the power factor, and (h) the power. [Ans. (a) 530 Ω, (b) 377 Ω, (c) 153 Ω, (d) 237 Ω, (e) 0.508 A, (f) 40.2°, (g) 0.762, (h) 46.4 W.]

21. A capacitance of 0.2 μF, an inductance of 100 mH, and a resistor of 600 Ω, are connected in series with a generator delivering a rms voltage of 500 V at a frequency of 1000 c/s. Calculate (a) the inductive reactance, (b) the capacitive reactance, (c) the total reactance, (d) the impedance, (e) the rms current, (f) the phase angle, (g) the power factor, and (h) the power.

PROPERTIES OF LIGHT

Light and its various phenomena present some of the most interesting studies in the whole realm of physics. They are interesting because the results of many experiments are revealed through the sense of vision as color phenomena. Equally important and every bit as interesting is the historical development and discovery of the various principles, concepts, and properties of light which give rise to these phenomena.

All of the various known properties of light are conveniently described in terms of the experiments by which they were discovered and the many and varied experiments by which they are now continually demonstrated. Numerous as they are, these experiments may be grouped together and classified under one of the three following heads: (1) *geometrical optics*, (2) *physical optics*, and (3) *quantum optics*. Each of these may be subdivided as follows:

Geometrical Optics

    rectilinear propagation
    finite velocity
    reflection
    refraction

Physical Optics

    diffraction
    interference
    polarization
    double refraction

Quantum Optics

    photoelectric effect
    Compton effect
    atomic excitation
    pair production

The first group, geometrical optics, treated in this chapter and the following chapter, deals with those optical phenomena that are most easily described with straight lines and plane geometry. The second group, physical optics, dealing with the wave nature of light, is treated in Chapters 43 and 44, whereas the third group, dealing with the quantum aspects of light, is treated in Chapters 45, 50, 53, and 61 to 69.

37.1. The Rectilinear Propagation of Light. The rectilinear propagation of light is another way of saying that "light travels in straight lines." The fact that objects may be made to cast fairly sharp shadows is an experimental demonstration of this principle. Another illustration is the image formation of an object produced by light passing through a small opening, as diagramed in Fig. 37A. In this figure, the object is an ordi-

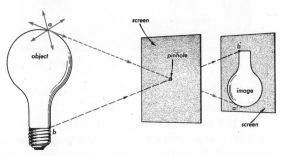

Fig. 37A   *An illustration of the principle that light travels in straight lines.*

nary incandescent light bulb. In order to see how an image is formed, consider the rays of light emanating from a single point a near the top of the bulb. Of the many rays of light radiating in all directions, the ray that travels in the direction of the hole passes through to the point a′ near the bottom of the image screen. Similarly, a ray leaving b near the bottom of the bulb and passing through the hole will arrive at b′ near the top of the image screen. Thus it may be seen that an inverted image is formed.

If the image screen is moved closer to the pinhole screen, the image will be proportionately smaller, whereas if it is moved farther away the image will be proportionately larger. The same thing happens when either the object or the pinhole is moved. Excellent photographs can be made with this arrangement by making a pinhole in one end of a small box and placing a photographic film or plate at the other. Such an arrangement is called a pinhole camera. For good, sharp photographs the hole must be very small, because its size determines the amount of blurring produced. The photograph shown in Fig. 37B was

Fig. 37B *Photograph taken with a pinhole camera.*

taken with such a camera. Note the undistorted perspective lines of the building.

37.2. Candela (Candle power). For many years the luminous intensity of all light sources was expressed in *standard candles*, or *candle power*. The standard candle, or international candle, was defined as the quantity of light given out by the flame of a certain make of candle, the constituents of which were specified by international agreement. The specification of a 50-candlepower tungsten-filament lamp, for example, was one that gave out an amount of light equivalent to 50 standard candle flames. Not many years ago,

the candle was considered to be unsatisfactory, and as the result of an extensive research program was replaced by an incandescent platinum metal surface. Platinum metal at its freezing temperature of 2033°K is "white hot" and each square centimeter of its surface emits an amount of light equal to approximately 60 standard candles.

Today the unit of luminous intensity is called the *candela* (cd). The name candela was adopted in 1946 by the International Committee on Weights and Measures as the unit of luminous intensity of $1/60$ cm² of a blackbody at the temperature of freezing platinum. The name and definition was adopted in the United States by an Act of Congress (PL 88-165, signed November 4, 1963). The Illuminating Engineering Society of the U.S. has been using candela since 1959.*

Ordinary tungsten-filament light bulbs used in general house lighting give a little more than one candela per watt of electrical power used. A 50-W lamp, for example, has a luminous intensity I of about 55 cd and a 100-W lamp a luminous intensity of about 125 cd, etc. (see Table 37A).

TABLE 37A. EFFICIENCY OF GAS-FILLED TUNGSTEN-FILAMENT LIGHT BULBS

Input (watts)	Output (candelas)	Output (lumens)
25	20.7	260
50	55.0	695
100	125	1,580
200	290	3,640
500	800	10,050
1000	1640	20,700

Luminescent tubes, on the other hand, have a considerably higher efficiency and yield about 4 cd/W.

37.3. The Inverse Square Law. Light sources are of many kinds, sizes, and shapes. It is convenient when specifying the illumination they provide on a screen or surface to distinguish between a *point source* and an *extended source*. A point source of light is one in which the dimensions are negligibly small (for practical purposes

* See J. Opt. Soc. Am., **54**, 850 (1964).

less than 10%) compared with the distance between the source and the receptor. A tungsten-filament lamp, with a 3-in. diameter frosted glass bulb, for example, would be considered a point source for a receiver of light 30 in. or more away.

An extended source is one in which the size of the light is comparable to, or larger than, the distance to a point or screen where illumination is to be measured.

The electromagnetic radiation streaming outward from a source is called *radiant flux*. The *luminous flux* on the other hand is the term used to specify only that part of the radiant flux that is visible to the unaided eye.

Light sources in general do not radiate the same in all directions. When, for example, the radiant flux emitted by a tungsten-filament lamp is measured, it is found to vary considerably with the direction. In the direction of the lamp base the radiant flux is zero. Because of such variations it has become common practice among illumination engineers to specify the total luminous flux given out by a source in *lumens*. The lumen is equal to the luminous flux falling on a surface of one square meter, all points of which are one meter from a uniform point source of one candela. Since the area of a sphere of one meter radius is 4π m², the luminous flux emitted by a point source of one candela is 4π lumens. The total output of a source in lumens is therefore determined by multiplying the output in candelas by 12.57.

The *illumination* of a surface is defined as the amount of luminous flux falling on a unit area. If a screen is placed 1 m from a 1-candela point source, the illumination on the screen is said to be 1 lux. One meter from a point source of 25 candelas, the illumination will be 25 lux, etc. The lux is the unit of illumination in the mksa system.

If a screen is placed 1 ft from a point source of 1 candela, the illumination on the screen is said to be 1 foot-candle. One foot from a source of 50 candelas, the illumination will be 50 foot-candles.

When the top surface of a table is illuminated by a single point source of light directly above it and then the light raised to twice the height, the illumination on the surface will only be $\frac{1}{4}$ as great. If it is raised to three times the first height the illumination will only be $\frac{1}{9}$ as great, etc. In other words, *illumination is proportional to the luminous intensity of the light source and is inversely proportional to the square of the distance.* This, the inverse square law, is illustrated in Fig. 37C by the three shaded patches of equal area.

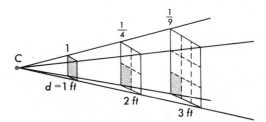

Fig. 37C *Illustration of the inverse square law.*

If the letter I represents the luminous intensity of a light source and d the distance to the illuminated surface, the illumination E is given by:

$$E = \frac{I}{d^2} \qquad (37a)$$

If I is in candelas and d is in meters, E is in lux

$$1 \frac{candela}{meter^2} = 1 \text{ lux}$$

If I is in candelas and d is in feet, E is in foot-candles (ft-c)

$$1 \frac{candela}{foot^2} = 1 \text{ foot-candle}$$

To illustrate the use of Eq.(37a), consider the following examples.

Example 1. A street lamp with a luminous intensity of 300 candelas is located 5 m above the pavement. Find the value of the illumination on the pavement.
Solution. By direct substitution in Eq.(37a) we obtain

$$E = \frac{300 \text{ cd}}{(5\text{m})^2} = 12 \frac{cd}{m^2}$$

$$E = 12 \text{ lux}$$

Example 2. A tungsten-filament lamp with a luminous intensity of 135 candelas is located 3 ft above the center of a table top. Find the value of the illumination.

Solution. By direct substitution in Eq.(37a), we obtain,

$$E = \frac{135 \text{ cd}}{(3 \text{ ft})^2} = 15 \frac{\text{cd}}{\text{ft}^2}$$

$$E = 15 \text{ foot-candles}$$
$$E = 15 \text{ ft-c}$$

Since 1 m = 3.281 ft, and 1 m² = 10.76 ft²,

$$1 \text{ foot-candle} = 10.76 \text{ lux}$$

37.4. Foot-Candle Meter. Many different kinds of direct-reading instruments for measuring the illuminance on a surface have been devised and manufactured. Most of these employ a *photo-electric cell* of one kind or another, and are classified as *illuminometers*. One such instrument using a special kind of photoelectric cell that requires no batteries is shown in Fig. 37D.

Fig. 37D   *Weston type of foot-candle meter.* (Courtesy, Weston Instruments Co.)

Light falling on the photo cell in the upper half of the instrument gives rise to an electric current, which in turn activates a highly senstive ammeter and pointer shown in the lower half. If the scale under the pointer is calibrated in foot candles as in the photograph, the instrument is called a *foot-candle meter*, but if it is calibrated with an arbitrary number scale it may be labeled an *exposure meter* of the kind used by photographers. The useful range of such instruments can be greatly extended by placing a screen with holes of a known size over the sensitive photocell area.

When using a foot-candle meter to measure the illuminance on a desk top, the face of the photocell should be placed parallel to the surface. If it is turned at an angle, the amount of light intercepted by the sensitive area may be quite different. The change in illuminance produced by a change in the direction of the incident light is shown diagrammatically in Fig. 37E. A maxi-

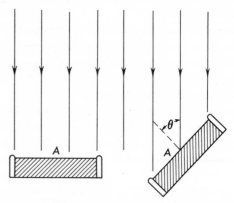

Fig. 37E   *Illumination is usually measured normal to the incident light rays.*

mum amount of light is intercepted by a given plane area *A* when it is perpendicular to the incident light rays, as shown at the left. When it is turned at an angle θ, the effective area is smaller and given by $A \cos \theta$. If, therefore, the inverse square law, as given in Eq.(37a), is to be applied to general problems, the factor $\cos \theta$ should be included.

$$E = \frac{I}{d^2} \cos \theta \qquad (37b)$$

Example 3. The top of a drafting table, inclined at an angle of 30° with the horizontal, is illuminated by a single 250-cp lamp suspended 4 ft directly above the center. Calculate the illuminance on the table top directly beneath the lamp.

Solution. The given quantities in this problem are $I = 250$ cp, $d = 4$ ft, and $\theta = 30°$. By direct substitution in Eq.(37b), we obtain

$$E = \frac{250}{16} 0.866 = 13.5 \text{ ft-c}$$

or $$E = 13.5 \times 10.76 = 145 \text{ lux}$$

37.5. The Law of Reflection. Experiment shows that, whenever a ray of light is reflected from a

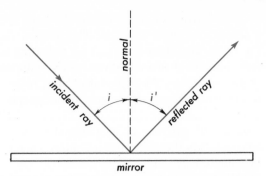

Fig. 37F   *Diagram illustrating the law of reflection from a plane surface.*

plane surface, the nature of the reflected light can be described in terms of a number of simple and well-defined laws. The simplest of these is the one known as the law of reflection. According to this law, the angle at which a ray of light strikes the reflecting surface is exactly equal to the angle the reflected ray makes with the same surface. Instead of measuring the angle of incidence and the angle of reflection from the mirror surface, however, it is customary to measure both from a line perpendicular to the plane of the

mirror. This line as shown in Fig. 37F is called the *normal*. As the angle i increases, the angle i' increases by exactly the same amount so that, for all angles of incidence,

$$\text{angle } i = \text{angle } i' \qquad (37c)$$

A second part of this law stipulates that the reflected ray lies in the plane of incidence, the plane of incidence being defined as the plane containing the incident ray and the normal. In other words, *the incident ray, the normal, and the reflected ray all lie in the same plane.*

In speaking of a mirror surface, one does not necessarily mean a silvered plate of glass; a mirror is any surface smooth enough to produce regular reflection as it has just been described.

37.6. Image in a Plane Mirror. The image of one's self seen in a mirror is formed by rays of light traveling in straight lines which are reflected according to the law of reflection. All objects seen in a plane mirror are images formed by reflection. This can be demonstrated by the experiment shown in Fig. 37G. A lighted candle O is placed on the table near a plate of glass MN.

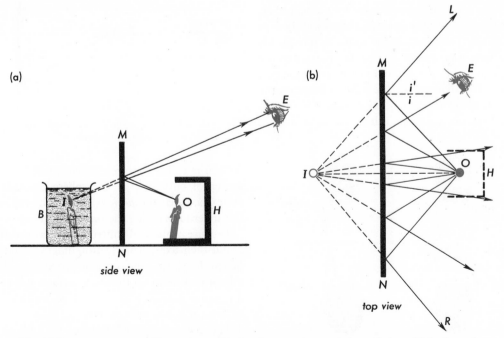

Fig. 37G   *An experiment illustrating reflection from a mirror or plate of glass. Light from the candle flame at O appears to come from I.*

With the candle itself hidden in the box H, the observer at E sees only the reflected image at I. If a glass of water is placed at B, this image appears as a real candle burning under water.

As shown in the top view, all rays of light leaving the source O are reflected according to the law of reflection. To an observer anywhere between L and R on the right side of the mirror, all light appears to come from the same point I. This image point is just as far behind the mirror as the object O is in front of it, and the two lie on the same perpendicular to the mirror.

The image one sees in a plane mirror is not a real image but a virtual image. A virtual image is one from which rays seem to radiate but actually do not. In the figure the rays do not come from I, they come from O and by reflection reach the observer.

This experiment illustrates a trick commonly used to make ghostlike figures appear to move about a room or stage. Light from real persons or objects, located below or above the stage, is reflected from a large sheet of plate glass at the front of the stage. With proper drapes and a darkened room, the illusion is very effective.

If one looks at his own face in a plane mirror, the image observed is technically described as *perverted*. The image is the same as though the face were reproduced as a rubber mask and the mask turned inside out and viewed from the new front. The right ear of the subject becomes the left ear of the image, and vice versa.

To see one's face as others see it, two front silvered mirrors should be placed 90° apart and touching each other along one edge as shown in Fig. 37H. The observer's right ear will then be seen, because of two reflections, as the right ear of his image, etc. This experiment must be performed to be appreciated, since many people's faces are, unknowingly, slightly unsymmetrical. Seen in 90° mirrors, all such irregularities are reversed; they therefore appear double in magnitude and are very noticeable.

37.7. Concave Mirrors. The concave mirror is an optical device which may by pure reflection form images on a screen. Such mirrors are often used in optical instruments in place of a lens. There are several very good reasons for this, one of them being that the concave mirror does not exhibit chromatic aberration, and another that there is only one curved surface to prepare and polish instead of two or more.

A spherical mirror has the form of a circular section of a hollow sphere as shown in cross section in Fig. 37I. The center point A of the

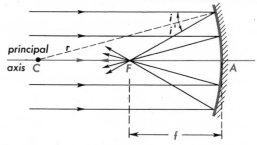

Fig. 37I   *The focal point F and focal length f of a concave mirror.*

section is called the *vertex*, and a line from the center of curvature of the sphere through the vertex is called the *principal axis*. The radius of the sphere r is called the *radius of the mirror*.

Because spherical mirrors are symmetrical about their axes, cross-section diagrams are sufficient to show their optical properties. If the mirror is silvered on the inner surface, it is called a *concave mirror*, while if silvered on the outer surface, it is a *convex mirror*.

The cross-section diagram of Fig. 37I shows how a beam of parallel light is reflected by a concave mirror. Each ray striking the mirror

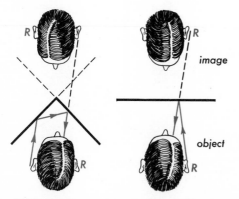

Fig. 37H   *One's own image seen in 90° mirrors is normal, that seen in a plane mirror is perverted.*

obeys the law of reflection, namely, that the angle of incidence *i* equals the angle of reflection *i'*.

The point F where the rays cross the principal axis is called the *principal* focus, and the distance A to F is called the *focal length f*.

If the mirror is silvered on the outer surface as in Fig. 37J, it becomes a convex mirror, and

Fig. 37J   *The focal point F and focal length f of a convex mirror.*

parallel incident light rays are reflected as if they came from a point F on the axis. The different rays, each obeying the law of reflection, diverge after reflection and never come to a focus.

Nevertheless, the distance A to F is called the *focal length* of the convex mirror.

37.8. Image Formation. If an illuminated object O is located in front of a concave mirror as shown in Fig. 37K, a real image I can be formed

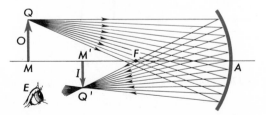

Fig. 37K   *A concave mirror forms a real image.*

nearby. All rays emitted by the object point Q and reflected by the mirror come to a focus at Q'. All rays emitted by the object point M would upon reflection come to a focus at M'. For every

object point in QM emitting rays, there will be a corresponding image point in Q'M' where focus is produced.

If the eye is located at E, the illuminated object will appear at Q'M', but inverted. If a screen is located at Q'M', a sharply defined image will be observed there. Because the image can be formed on a screen, it is called a *real image*.

The geometry of the reflection from a concave or convex mirror is such that the focal length AF is always equal to $\frac{1}{2}$ the radius of curvature *r*, where *r* = AC, and C is the center of curvature. As an equation,

$$AF = \tfrac{1}{2}AC \qquad \text{or} \qquad f = -\frac{r}{2} \qquad (37d)$$

It is common practice in optical diagrams involving a concave or convex mirror to show incident light rays moving from left to right.

(1) When an incident ray encounters a convex surface the radius *r* is positive.

(2) When an incident ray encounters a concave surface the radius *r* is negative.

As an illustration of the image-forming properties of a concave spherical mirror, consider the graphical construction in Fig. 37L. An object O

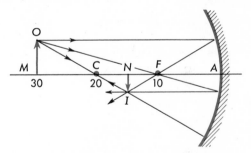

Fig. 37L   *Graphical construction for locating the image formed by a concave mirror.*

is located 30 cm from a concave mirror of radius *r* = −20 cm, center at C. By Eq.(37d) F must be halfway between A and C, giving *f* = +10 cm.

A light ray from O parallel to the principal axis is reflected, by definition of the focal point, through F. By the reversibility of light rays, another ray from O passing through F is reflected parallel to the principal axis. Where these two rays cross at I, the image is formed. A third ray from O through the center of curvature C strikes

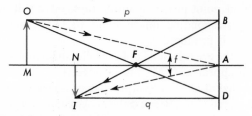

Fig. 37M *Geometrical diagram for the derivation of the object–image distance formula. Eq. (41e).*

the mirror normally and is reflected back on itself where it passes through I. Any two of these three rays are sufficient to locate the image. The third ray is then a check upon the other two.

We can derive a simple relation between *object distance*, *image distance*, and *focal length* of a spherical mirror by redrawing the rays in Fig. 37L, to form the simplified diagram shown in Fig. 37M, and then applying the principles of elementary geometry. From similar triangles BID and DFA, we can write proportionalities for corresponding sides as follows,

$$\frac{BD}{q} = \frac{BA}{f}$$

From similar triangles DOB and DFA, we can also write,

$$\frac{BD}{p} = \frac{AD}{f}$$

Adding equals to equals, we obtain,

$$\frac{BD}{p} + \frac{BD}{q} = \frac{BA}{f} + \frac{AD}{f}$$

or

$$\frac{BD}{p} + \frac{BD}{q} = \frac{BD}{f}$$

giving

$$\boxed{\frac{1}{p} + \frac{1}{q} = \frac{1}{f}} \qquad (37e)$$

To find the image distance for the illustration in Fig. 37L, Eq.(37e) can be applied directly. Given are the quantities, $p = 30$ cm, $f = +10$ cm. By substitution

$$\frac{1}{30} + \frac{1}{q} = \frac{1}{10}$$

$$\frac{1}{q} = \frac{1}{10} - \frac{1}{30}$$

$$\frac{1}{q} = \frac{3}{30} - \frac{1}{30}$$

from which

$$\frac{1}{q} = \frac{2}{30}$$

and

$$q = \frac{30}{2} = 15 \text{ cm}$$

An interesting experiment can be performed with a large concave mirror under the conditions illustrated in Fig. 37N. A flower hanging upside

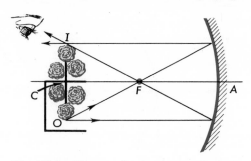

Fig. 37N *Diagram for the phantom bouquet.*

down in a box and placed just below the center of curvature will form a real and erect image at O directly above. An observer to the left cannot see the flower directly but can see the real image. So real is this image that it cannot be distinguished from a real object; the rays of light as shown in the diagram diverge from I, the same as they would if the object were located there.

In Fig. 37O an object is placed inside the focal

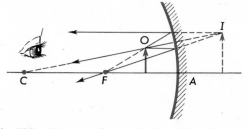

Fig. 37O *Diagram showing the formation of a virtual image.*

point; the rays after reflection diverge as if they had come from the point I. To the eye of an observer at E, a virtual image is seen magnified and right side up at I. As a problem, let the object distance $p = 10$ cm, the focal length $f = +20$ cm. Substitution of these in Eq.(37e) gives

$$\frac{1}{10} + \frac{1}{q} = \frac{1}{20}$$

$$\frac{1}{q} = \frac{1}{20} - \frac{1}{10}$$

$$\frac{1}{q} = \frac{1}{20} - \frac{2}{20}$$

from which

$$\frac{1}{q} = -\frac{1}{20}$$

or

$$q = -20 \text{ cm}$$

The image is located 20 cm from the mirror, the minus sign indicating that it is virtual and on the opposite side of the mirror from the object.

No matter where a real object is located in front of a convex mirror, the image is virtual and cannot be formed on a screen. When in using Eq.(37e) the focal length of a convex mirror is known, its value is substituted with a minus sign.

Convenient sign conventions for all spherical mirror problems, solved by the use of Eq.(37e), are the following:

(1) *Numerical values of real object distances are positive.*
(2) *Numerical values of real image distances are positive.*
(3) *Numerical values of focal lengths of concave mirrors are positive, while those of convex mirrors are negative.*

A formula for the size of the image formed by spherical mirrors may be derived from the geometry shown in Fig. 37M. The dashed lines representing a ray from O to A is shown reflected at an equal angle to pass through the image point I. These lines form similar triangles OAM and IAN. Since corresponding sides are proportional, we may write

$$\frac{-\text{IN}}{\text{OM}} = \frac{q}{p}$$

Calling OM the object height O, and IN the image height I, we may write

$$\frac{I}{O} = -\frac{q}{p} \tag{37f}$$

The minus sign has been inserted to account for the image inversion. The sign convention to be used here is that erect objects and images are positive, while inverted objects and images are negative. The ratio I/O is commonly called the *magnification*, and may be written,

$$M = -\frac{q}{p} \tag{37g}$$

In actual practice spherical mirrors are capable of forming reasonably sharp images if their apertures are small compared with their focal lengths. If the mirror sizes are large, however, the rays reflected from the outer edges cross the axis at different distances as shown at the left in Fig. 37P. This focusing defect gives rise to what is called *spherical aberration*.

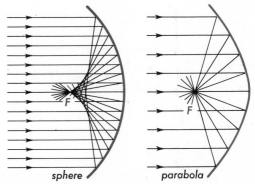

Fig. 37P *Diagrams showing the caustic curve obtained with a spherical mirror and the point focus with a paraboloidal mirror.*

A parabolic mirror on the other hand brings all rays to a focus at one point, as shown at the right. A small source of light located at the focal point of a parabolic reflector becomes a parallel beam after reflection, a principle used in spotlights, searchlights, and automobile headlights.

PROBLEMS

1. A 100-cp light bulb is located 4 ft above a dining room table. What additional light bulb at the same distance will bring the illuminance up to 25 ft-c?

2. A 75-W tungsten-filament light bulb has an efficiency of 1.10 c/W. How far above the table top should this bulb be placed to produce an illuminance of 20 ft-c? [*Ans.* 2.03 ft.]

3. Five tungsten-filament lamps of 150 W each are

located 4 ft above a table top. How many additional lamps of the same size, located 4 ft above the same table will bring the total illuminance to 100 ft-c? Assume an efficiency of 1.20 c/W.

4. How many 500-W tungsten-filament lamps located 4 ft above an operating table are required to produce an illuminance of 750 ft-c? Assume an efficiency of 1.20 c/W. [Ans. 20.]

5. A table top is illuminated by two 75-W lamps spaced 4 ft apart and 3 ft above the top. Calculate the illuminance in ft-c on the top (a) at a point directly under one lamp, and (b) at a point halfway between them. Assume an efficiency of 1.2 c/W.

6. A book lying on a table is illuminated by three 100-W lamps placed in a line, spaced 3 ft apart, and 4 ft above the top. Calculate the illuminance in ft-c on the book if it lies directly under the center lamp. Assume a lamp efficiency of 1.2 c/W. [Ans. 15.2 ft-c.]

7. A book lying on a table is illuminated by three 100-W lamps placed in a line, spaced 4 ft apart, and 3 ft above the top. Calculate the illuminance in ft-c on the book if it lies directly under the center lamp. Assume a lamp efficiency of 1.2 c/W.

8. An object 2 cm high is located 12 cm in front of a concave mirror with $r = -16$ cm. Find graphically and by formula (a) the position, and (b) the size of the image. [Ans. (a) +24 cm, (b) −4 cm.]

9. An object 4 cm high is located on the axis and 15 cm from a concave mirror of radius $r = -12$ cm. Find graphically and by formula (a) the position, and (b) the size of the image.

10. An object 2.5 cm high is located 15 cm in front of a concave mirror of radius −20 cm. Find the position

and size of the image (a) graphically, and (b) by formula. [Ans. (a) +30 cm, (b) −5.0 cm.]

11. An object 1.5 cm high is located 6 cm in front of a concave mirror having a −30-cm radius. Find the image position (a) graphically, and (b) by formula. (c) Find the image height.

12. An object 2 cm high is located 6 cm in front of a spherical mirror having a radius of −36 cm. Find (a) the image position, and (b) the image size. Verify your calculated answers by graphical methods. [Ans. (a) −9.0 cm, (b) +3 cm.]

13. An object 4 cm high is located 25 cm in front of a spherical mirror with a radius of +30 cm. Find the position and size of the image (a) graphically, and (b) by calculation.

14. An object 3 cm high is located 30 cm in front of a spherical mirror whose radius of curvature is +20 cm. Find (a) the position, and (b) the size of the image, graphically and by calculation. [Ans. (a) −7.5 cm, (b) 0.75 cm.]

15. A concave mirror has a radius of −24 cm. Where should an object be placed if the image distance is to be three times the object distance. Assume a real image.

16. A concave mirror with a radius of 20 cm is set up to form a real image that is 4 times the size of the object. Find the object and image distances. [Ans. 12.5 cm, and 50 cm.]

17. Two concave mirrors are located 10 cm apart with their concave surfaces facing each other and their principal axes on the same straight line. If they both have a radius of −4.8 cm, and an object of 0.5 cm high is located on the axis 4.0 cm from one mirror, find the image formed by the closest mirror. (b) With this real image as an object for the other mirror, find its image. (c) Will this second image serve as an object for the first mirror again?

REFRACTION

History tells us that Galileo once tried to measure the speed of light, but without success. Galileo stationed himself on one hilltop with one lamp and an assistant on another hilltop with a similar lamp. Galileo would first uncover his lamp for an instant, sending a short flash of light to the assistant. As soon as the assistant saw this light he uncovered his own lamp, sending a flash back to Galileo, who noted the total time elapsed. After numerous repetitions of this experiment at greater and greater distances between observers, Galileo came to the conclusion that they could not uncover their lamps fast enough and that light probably travels with an infinite speed. Knowing as we do now that light travels with the amazing speed of 186,300 mi/s, it is easy to see why Galileo's experiment failed.

38.1. The Speed of Light. The first terrestrial method of measuring the speed of light was devised by Fizeau in 1849.* His experimental ar-

* H. L. Fizeau (1819–1896). Born of a wealthy French family, he was financially independent and free to pursue his hobby—the measuring of the velocity of light. His experiments were carried out in Paris, the light traveling between Montmartre and Suresnes.

rangement is shown in Fig. 38A. Light from an intense source S was reflected from a semitransparent mirror G and then brought to a focus at the point O by means of a lens L_1. After being made into a parallel beam by a second lens L_2, the light traveled a distance of 5.39 mi to a hilltop, where a mirror M and lens L_3 reflected the light back again. Returning by the same path, some of the light passed through the mirror G and entered the eye of the observer at E.

The purpose of the rotating toothed wheel was to chop the light beam into short flashes and to measure the time it takes each of these signals to travel over to the far mirror and back. With the wheel at rest and in such a position that the light passes through an opening between two teeth at O, the observer at E will see an image of the light source S. If the wheel is now set rotating with slowly increasing speed, a condition will soon be reached in which the light passing through 0 will return just in time to be stopped by a, that passing through opening 1 will return just in time to be stopped by b, etc. Under these conditions the image will be completely eclipsed from the ob-

Fig. 38A *Experimental arrangement used by Fizeau in determining the speed of light.*

server. By further increasing the speed, the light will reappear, increasing in intensity until a maximum is reached. This will occur when the flashes sent out through the openings 0, 1, 2, 3, etc., return just in time to get through the openings 1, 2, 3, 4, etc., respectively. With a wheel containing 720 teeth, Fizeau observed this maximum at a speed of 25 rps. The time required for the light to travel over and back can therefore be calculated as 1/25 times 1/720, or 1/18,000th of a second. This, from the measured distance over and back of 10.78 mi, gave a speed of 194,000 mi/s, or 313,000 Km/s.

38.2. Michelson's Measurements of the Speed of Light.

In the years that followed these earliest experiments, several investigators improved upon Fizeau's apparatus and methods of observation, and obtained more accurate values for the speed of light. Of these, Michelson's* contributions and improvements stand out above the rest. Replacing the toothed wheel by a small eight-sided mirror and increasing the light path to about 44 mi, Michelson in 1926 obtained a value of 299,796 Km/s.

A recent, extensive and critical study of the values of the speed of light measured by all observers has been made by R. T. Birge. He concludes that the most probable value at the present time is as follows:

$$c = 299{,}790 \text{ Km/s}$$
or
$$c = 186{,}280 \text{ mi/s} \tag{38a}$$

For practical purposes where calculations are to be made, the speed of light in air or in a vacuum may be assumed to be

$$c = 3.0 \times 10^8 \text{ m/s}$$

One is justified in using this round-number value since it differs from the more accurate value in Eq.(38a) by less than $\frac{1}{10}$th of 1%.

* Albert A. Michelson (1852–1931). Distinguished American physicist, celebrated for the invention and development of the interferometer, an optical instrument, now named the Michelson stellar interferometer in his honor. This instrument is used to establish the length of the standard meter in terms of the wavelength of light, to make ether drift experiments (see Chapter 58 on Relativity), to determine the rigidity of the earth, to measure the distances and the diameters of giant stars, and to measure the speed of light. He was the first American scientist to be awarded the Nobel Prize (1907).

38.3. The Speed of Light in Stationary Matter.

In 1850, Foucault completed and published the results of an experiment in which he had measured the speed of light in water. This was a crucial experiment, for it settled a long existing controversy concerning the nature of light. According to Newton and his followers, light was believed to be made up of small particles or corpuscles emanating from a source. Huygens, on the other hand, regarded light as being composed of waves, similar in nature perhaps to water waves or sound waves. Now, Newton's corpuscular theory required light to travel faster in a dense medium like water than it did in a less-dense medium like air, whereas Huygens' wave theory required it to travel slower. By sending light back and forth through a long tube of water, Foucault found its speed to be less than that in air. This was a strong confirmation of Huygens' wave theory.

Years later, Michelson also measured the speed of light in water and found a value of 225,000 Km/s. This is just $\frac{3}{4}$ the speed in a vacuum. In common glass, the speed is still lower, being about $\frac{2}{3}$ the speed in vacuo, or 200,000 Km/s. In air, the speed is very little less than the speed in a vacuum, differing only by about 70 Km/s at sea level and less at higher altitudes where the air is less dense. For most practical cases this difference can be neglected, and the speed in air can be said to be the same as in a vacuum.

38.4. The Refractive Index.

The ratio between the speed of light in a vacuum and the speed in a medium is called the *refractive index*, or the *index of refraction* of the medium.

$$\frac{\text{Speed in vacuo}}{\text{Speed in a medium}} = \text{refractive index}$$

Symbolically, we write

$$\boxed{\frac{c}{v} = \mu} \tag{38b}$$

The Greek letter μ (mu) is frequently used to represent this ratio. Substituting the velocities given in the preceding section, we may calculate the following refractive indices:

for water, $\mu = 1.333$
for glass, $\mu = 1.520$ (38c)
for air, $\mu = 1.000$

Very exact measurements of the refractive index of air give a value 1.00029.

Various kinds of glass have different refractive indices. For most common glasses they range from 1.50 to 1.70. See Table 39A in next chapter.

38.5. Refraction at a Boundary. When light falls upon the smooth surface of a transparent substance like water or glass, part of it is reflected according to the law of reflection and the rest is refracted into the medium (see Fig. 38B). This

Fig. 38C   *Illustration of the graphical method of determining the angle of refraction.*

Fig. 38B   *Reflection and refraction of light at the boundary of a glass surface.*

bending is due to the change in the velocity of the light upon entering the second medium. The direction of the refracted ray, like the incident and reflected rays, is always measured by the angle it makes with the normal.

The angle of refraction, r, is found by experiment to depend upon two factors: (1) *the angle of incidence i* and (2) *the index of refraction μ.* As defined, by Eq.(38b), *the index of refraction is the ratio of the speed of light in vacuo to the speed of light in the medium.*

To determine the angle of refraction from these two factors, we perform the following graphical construction (see Fig. 38C). A parallel beam of light of width PQ is incident at an angle i on the surface of water. From the point A where the beam first strikes the surface, a line is drawn perpendicular to the beam intersecting QC at B.

Assuming a refractive index of $\mu = 1.333$ for

water, the line BC is divided into four equal parts. With a radius of three of these units and a center at A, the arc of a circle is scribed as shown. From the point C a tangent is drawn intersecting the arc at D. The refracted ray ADR is then drawn in and the other edge of the ray CS drawn parallel to it.

The law of refraction may now be stated in terms of the lines BC and AD as follows:

$$\frac{BC}{AD} = \mu \qquad (38d)$$

It was the Dutch astronomer and mathematician, Willebrord Snell, who first discovered from experiment that the ratio of these two lines for a given substance is the same for all angles of incidence. In other words, μ is a constant. The relation as given by Eq.(38d) is therefore called Snell's law.* The reason for the constancy of this ratio is that, while the light travels from B to C in air, it travels the corresponding lesser distance AD in water. The ratio $4/3 = 1.333 = \mu$. For common glass with a refractive index $\mu = 1.5$, the same two lines should be divided into 3 and 2 parts, respectively.

* Willebrord Snell (1591–1626), Dutch astronomer and mathematician, was born at Leyden in 1591. At the age of twenty-two he succeeded his father as professor of mathematics at the University of Leyden. In 1617, he determined the size of the earth from measurements of its curvature between Alkmaar and Bergen-op-Zoom. In 1621, he discovered the law of refraction which now carries his name.

38.6. Snell's Law of Refraction. It is customary, in treating the refraction of light, to express Snell's law in trigonometric terms. Referring to Fig. 38C, triangles ABC and ACD are right triangles. Since line PA is $\perp$ to AB and line MA is $\perp$ to AC, angle i = angle BAC. By similar relations, angle r = angle ACD. From triangles ABC and ACD,

$$BC = AC \sin i, \quad \text{and} \quad AD = AC \sin r$$

Substitution for BC and AD in Eq.(38d) gives

$$\frac{BC}{AD} = \frac{AC \sin i}{AC \sin r} = \frac{\sin i}{\sin r} = \mu \qquad (38e)$$

or

$$\boxed{\mu = \frac{\sin i}{\sin r}} \qquad (38f)$$

This latter form is the most useful form of Snell's law. For any given transparent substance, the ratio of the sine of the angle of incidence to the sine of the angle of refraction is the same for all angles of incidence and is equal to the refraction index, μ. Since μ is the ratio of the speeds of light in the two media, Snell's law may also be written

$$\frac{\sin i}{\sin r} = \frac{v_1}{v_2} = \mu \qquad (38g)$$

where v_1 represents the speed in the first medium and v_2 the speed in the second medium.

Example 1. Light, in air, is incident at an angle of 45° on the surface of a glass plate for which the refractive index is 1.52. Through what angle is the light deviated upon refraction at the top surface?

Solution. First find the angle of refraction r by use of Eq.(38f). By transposing and substituting the given quantities, we obtain

$$\sin r = \frac{\sin i}{\mu} = \frac{\sin 45°}{1.52} = \frac{0.707}{1.52} = 0.465$$

If we look up 0.465 in a table of natural sines, we find that angle r = 27.7°. Since the deviation of the light is the difference between angle i and angle r (45° − 27.7°),

$$\text{deviation} = 17.3°$$

38.7. Displacement in a Parallel Plate. One very useful principle concerning the behavior of light is *the reversibility of light rays. If, in any of the experiments or illustrations already described, the light rays could be reversed in direction, they would be found to retrace their paths exactly.*

If a beam of light, on being refracted into a denser medium like glass, is bent toward the normal, the light passing through and out of this denser medium into the air should be bent away from the normal. This can be demonstrated by sending light through a plane-parallel plate of glass as illustrated in Fig. 38D. In (c) the light is incident on the first surface at an angle i and is refracted at an angle r. This internal ray is now incident on the second surface at the same angle r and is refracted into the air at the same angle i. The light thus emerges in a direction parallel to the original beam, but displaced from it laterally.

This lateral displacement is zero for normal incidence as in diagram (a) and increases with the angle i as shown in diagrams (b), (c), and (d), respectively. If the parallel plate is very thin, as in the case of an ordinary windowpane, the displacement is quite small and for most practical purposes can be neglected.

A detailed drawing showing the geometry of the refraction of light at both boundaries of a thick parallel plate will enable the reader to apply

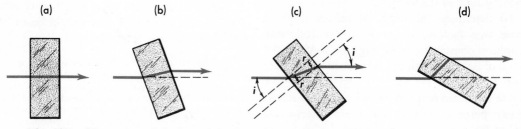

(a)　　　　　　(b)　　　　　　(c)　　　　　　(d)

Fig. 38D　*Illustration of the lateral displacement of a beam of light as it passes through a parallel plate of glass.*

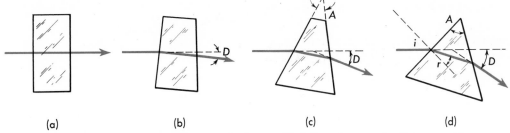

(a)   (b)   (c)   (d)

Fig. 38E   *Illustration of the bending of a beam of light by prisms made of the same glass.*

Snell's law, and the simple elements of trigo-nometry to derive the following equation

$$d = t \sin i \left(1 - \frac{\cos i}{\mu \cos r}\right) \qquad (38h)$$

where d is the lateral displacement between the incident and transmitted rays, t is the plate thickness, i is the angle of incidence, r is the angle of refraction, and μ is the refractive index.

38.8. Refraction by a Prism. When light passes through a prism, it is refracted at two surfaces, once on the way in and once on the way out. If the two sides involved are parallel, as they are in Fig. 38E, diagram (a), the emergent ray is always parallel to the incident ray. If the sides are not parallel, as in diagrams (b), (c), and (d), the emergent ray has a different direction. The larger the angle A between the two refracting surfaces, the larger is the angle of deviation D. Upon entering the prism at the first surface [see diagram (d)], the light is bent toward the normal. Emerging into the air from the second surface, the light is bent away from the normal. Note in Fig. 38E that neither the apex nor the base of the prism has any effect on the deviation of the light.

In verifying these results by experiment, light of only one color should be used, because white light will spread out into a spectrum of colors. Light of one color only is readily obtained by inserting a piece of red or green colored glass into a beam of white light.

A relatively simple graphical method of tracing a given ray of light through a prism is shown in Fig. 38F. Here we have a ray of light VP incident at an angle i on the first face of a prism of angle A and refractive index μ. In this diagram $A = 60°$. $\mu = 1.5$, and $i = 60°$.

Starting at one side, a line EF is first drawn parallel to the incident ray VP. With a center at any point O, and with radii, in this particular case, of 1.0 unit and 1.5 units, arcs CS and BR

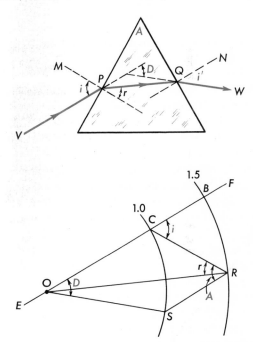

Fig. 38F   *Graphical construction for refraction by a prism.*

are drawn of indefinite length. From the intersection C a line is now drawn parallel to the normal M, intersecting the second arc at R. The line OR is drawn next, and from the point P of the prism a parallel line is drawn intersecting the second face at Q. Starting at R, a line is next drawn parallel to the normal N, intersecting the first arc at S. Finally the line OS is drawn in, and from the point Q on the second prism face a parallel line QW is drawn as the emergent ray.

In triangle OCR the length of side OC is 1.00, the length of side OR is 1.5 or μ, and the angle opposite side OR is $180° - i$. If we now apply the laws of sines to this triangle, we can write

$$\frac{\sin (180° - i)}{\mu} = \frac{\sin r}{1}$$

The sine of any angle i is always equal to the sine of 180° minus that same angle. Therefore,

$$\frac{\sin i}{\mu} = \frac{\sin r}{1}$$

from which we obtain

$$\frac{\sin i}{\sin r} = \mu$$

The same derivation can be applied to the triangle ORS.

Since the above construction obeys Snell's law, the accuracy of the graphical results depends upon the sharpness of the pencil used and the care with which the diagram is made. Furthermore, the lower diagram as well as the prism diagram includes all of the angles involved in the prism, including the angle of deviation D.

38.9. Minimum Deviation. If, during the time a beam of light is refracted by a prism, the prism is rotated continuously in one direction about an axis parallel to the refracting edge A, the angle of deviation will be observed to decrease, reach a minimum, and then increase again as shown in Fig. 38G. The smallest deviation angle is called the *angle of minimum deviation*, and occurs at that particular angle of incidence where the refracted ray inside the prism makes equal angles with the prism faces P and Q.

To derive a formula from which the angle of minimum deviation D_m can be calculated, reference is made to Fig. 38H. To start with, $i = i'$, and $r = r'$. To prove these angles equal, assume i does not equal i' when minimum deviation occurs. Reversal of the direction of the light rays will give the same angle of minimum deviation, yet the incident angle is now different from what it was before. This would mean that there are two different angles of incidence capable of giving minimum deviation. Since by experiment

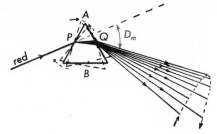

Fig. 38G   *Light refracted by a prism has a minimum angle of deviation D_m.*

there is only one, the two angles, i and i', must be equal.

By geometrical construction,

$$\angle i = \angle i' \qquad \angle r = \angle r' \qquad \text{and} \qquad \angle x = \angle x'$$

Since two of the angles in the four-sided figure APSQ are right angles, the sum of the other

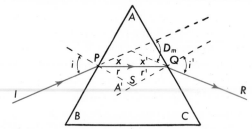

Fig. 38H   *Geometrical relations for minimum deviation in a prism.*

two angles, $A + S = 180°$. Furthermore, for a straight angle, $A' + S = 180°$. Therefore,

$$\angle A = \angle A'$$

In the isosceles triangle PQS, the exterior angle A' equals the sum of the interior angles, $r + r'$. Similarly, the exterior angle D_m equals the sum of the interior angles $x + x'$.

Consequently,

$$A = 2r \qquad D_m = 2x \qquad \text{and} \qquad i = r + x$$

If we solve these three equations for angle i and angle r,

$$r = \tfrac{1}{2}A \qquad i = \tfrac{1}{2}A + \tfrac{1}{2}D_m$$

or

$$i = \tfrac{1}{2}(A + D_m)$$

Since, by Snell's law, $\mu = \sin i / \sin r$,

$$\mu = \frac{\sin \tfrac{1}{2}(A + D_m)}{\sin \tfrac{1}{2}A} \qquad (38i)$$

This is the formula we set out to derive.

When, in the manufacture of optical glass, the refractive index of a given melt must be determined, a small prism is made from a sample of the glass and angles A and D_m are determined experimentally. The measured values are then substituted in Eq.(38i), and μ is calculated. Almost without exception, the light used for such measurements is the yellow light from a sodium lamp.

Example 2. Glass of known refractive index $\mu = 1.52$ is ground and polished into a prism having a refracting angle $A = 60°$. Calculate the angle of minimum deviation.

Solution. Since D_m is the unknown quantity, Eq. (38i) is solved for $\sin \frac{1}{2}(A + D)$, and the known values A and μ are substituted as follows:

$$\sin \tfrac{1}{2}(A + D_m) = \mu \sin \tfrac{1}{2}A = 1.52 \sin \tfrac{1}{2}60°$$
$$= 1.52 \times 0.50$$

$$\sin \tfrac{1}{2}(A + D_m) = 0.760$$

Looking up the angle whose sine is 0.760, we find

$$\tfrac{1}{2}(A + D_m) = 49.5°$$
and
$$A + D_m = 99°$$

which, on substituting $A = 60°$, gives

$$D_m = 99 - 60 = 39°$$

38.10. Critical Angle. When light passes from a medium, such as air, into a more dense medium, like glass or water, the angle of refraction is always less than the angle of incidence. As a

result of this decrease in angle, there exists a range of angles for which no refracted light is possible. To see what this range of angles is, consider the diagram in Fig. 38I, where for several angles of incidence the corresponding angles of refraction are shown. It is to be noted that, in the limiting case where the incident rays approach the angle of 90°, i.e., where they graze along the surface, the refracted rays approach a certain angle C, beyond which no refracted light is possible. In any medium this limiting angle, called *the critical angle,* depends for its value upon the index of refraction.

To calculate the critical angle of refraction, one takes the angle of incidence $i = 90°$ and angle r = angle C. Since $\sin 90° = 1$, Snell's law becomes

$$\mu = \frac{1}{\sin C} \quad \text{or} \quad \sin C = \frac{1}{\mu} \quad (38j)$$

For the most common of crown glass $\mu = 1.515$, substitution in this formula gives $C = 41.3°$. For water of index $\mu = 1.33$, it gives $C = 49°$. It should be noted in particular that the critical angle is measured from the normal, and not from the refracting surface.

38.11. Total Reflection. Another experiment illustrating the reversibility of light rays is shown in the diagram of Fig. 38J. A beam of light is

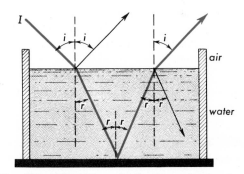

Fig. 38J   *Illustration of reflection and refraction.*

refracted at an angle r into a tank of water. From there it is reflected from a silvered mirror at the bottom of the tank, illustrating the law of reflection in a medium other than air. The reflected ray arriving at the upper surface at the same angle r is refracted into the air at the incident angle i. At

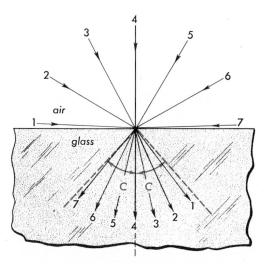

Fig. 38I   *Diagram illustrating the critical angle.*

each refraction at the air–water boundary, a small amount of the incident light is reflected, as indicated by the fine-lined arrows.

When a beam of light within a medium like water or glass approaches the surface at an angle greater than the critical angle, all of the light is reflected back into the medium. In other words, a water-to-air or glass-to-air surface acts under these conditions like a perfect reflector. This phenomenon is called *total internal reflection*. Since no light can be refracted into the water at such an angle (see Fig. 38I), none inside the water at large angles of incidence can be refracted out. The experiment is illustrated with a tank of water as shown in Fig. 38K. If light is sent into the

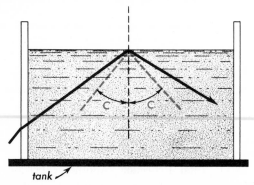

Fig. 38K   *Illustration of total reflection and the critical angle C.*

water through a glass plate in one end, the light approaches the upper surface at an angle greater than *C*, there to be totally reflected back into the water as shown.

An interesting demonstration can be performed with a clear glass or plastic rod bent into almost any form as shown in Fig. 38L. Light, on

Fig. 38L   *Light follows a bent rod by total reflection.*

entering one end, reflects from wall to wall by total reflection, causing it to follow the rod to the

end and emerge as a divergent beam. Various instruments used by physicians and surgeons employ this principle for internal body observations.

A whole new field of optics known as *fiber optics* has developed out of this principle in the last few years. Thousands of long thin glass fibers are bundled together to form a stranded cable. Each end of this cable is securely clamped in a ring and the two ends are ground and polished flat. A lens is then used to focus a sharply defined image on one end. The light entering each fiber then travels along to the other end, where the same orderly array of fiber ends reproduces the image.

Another demonstration consists of placing a lighted tungsten lamp in the bottom of a pitcher of water and pouring the water slowly into a larger vessel. The light follows the stream of water and produces an interesting display of light where it splashes into the other vessel. (Care should be taken to avoid electrical shock from this experiment.)

Total reflection is also employed in optical instruments such as telescopes, microscopes, prism binoculars, spectroscopes, etc. The optical parts employing this principle are known as *total-reflection prisms*. Such prisms are usually made of common glass with one angle a right angle and the other two 45° angles. As illustrated in Fig. 38M there are three ways in which these

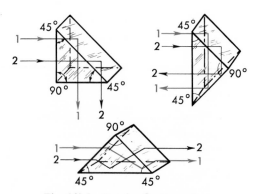

Fig. 38M   *Total-reflection prisms.*

prisms may be used. Incident normally upon the first surface, as in (a), the light enters the prism without deviation. Arriving at the second surface at an angle of 45°, just 3° greater than the critical angle, the light is totally reflected according to the law of reflection. Having thus been deviated through 90°, the light passes normally through the third surface without further deviation. The prism has therefore acted like a plane mirror with its reflecting surface at 45°.

In diagram (b), the light enters normally near one end of the long diagonal face of the prism. When it arrives at the second surface at 45°, total reflection takes place exactly as in diagram (a). A second reflection occurs at the third surface, sending the light out near the bottom of,

and normal to, the first surface. The light has thus been reversed in direction. Used in this way, the prism performs the function of two prisms, each used as in diagram (a).

In diagram (c) the light enters the first prism face at an angle. After refraction, the light is totally reflected from the second face and then refracted out of the third surface to be parallel to the original beam. Used in this way the prism is called an *erecting prism*. The incident ray, 1, which is on top, reverses its position and emerges from the prism at the bottom.

PROBLEMS

1. Find the speed of light in benzene if the refractive index is 1.385.

2. Find the speed of light in diamond if the refractive index is 2.426. [*Ans.* 123,600 Km/s.]

3. The average distance of the earth from the sun is 93×10^6 mi. How long does it take light from the sun to reach the earth?

4. Sirius, the "dog star," is approximately 4 light years from the earth. Calculate its distance in meters. [*Ans.* 3.78×10^{16} m.]

5. If the distance to one of the distant stars is 5×10^{21} m, how many years does it take its light to reach the earth?

6. If Fizeau's speed of light experiment were performed with a distant mirror 20 Km away, and he used a wheel having 360 teeth, how fast would the wheel have to turn for each pulse of light returning through the first succeeding opening to be seen? [*Ans.* 20.8 rps.]

7. Light is incident at 70° on the surface of water whose refractive index is 1.333. Use the graphical method shown in Fig. 38C to find the angle of refraction. Check this result by using Snell's law.

8. Light is incident at 75° on the surface of a plastic whose refractive index is 1.456. Find the angle of refraction (a) by using Snell's law, and (b) by the graphical method shown in Fig. 38C. [*Ans.* 41.4°.]

9. A parallel plate of glass 5 cm thick has a refractive index of 1.500. A ray of light incident on one side at 60° passes through and out the other side. Using Snell's law find the lateral displacement.

10. A parallel plate of flint glass 5 cm thick has a refractive index of 1.750. A ray of light is incident on one side at an angle of 70°. What is the lateral displacement of the ray emerging from the other side. [*Ans.* 3.61 cm.]

11. A rectangular aquarium with glass sides and filled with water is 25 cm thick. Find the lateral displacement of a beam of light incident on one of the sides at 45°. Neglect the thickness of the glass.

12. A 50° flint-glass prism has a refractive index of 1.68. Find the angle of deviation for a ray incident on the first surface at an angle of 60°. Solve both graphically and by calculation. [*Ans.* 43.2°.]

13. A dense flint-glass prism has a refracting angle of 50° and a refractive index of 1.72. Find the angle of deviation for a ray incident on one surface at an angle of 50°. Solve graphically and by calculation.

14. A 60° glass prism exhibits an angle of minimum deviation of 42°. Calculate the refractive index. [*Ans.* 1.554.]

15. A 55° prism exhibits an angle of minimum deviation of 44.5°. Calculate the refractive index.

16. A 52° glass prism has a refractive index of 1.64. Find the angle of minimum deviation (a) by calculation, and (b) by graphical method. [*Ans.* (a) 39.9°.]

17. A 65° plastic prism has a refractive index of 1.42. Find the angle of minimum deviation (a) graphically, and (b) by formula.

18. Find the critical angle for a plastic having an index of 1.42. [*Ans.* 44.8°.]

19. Find the critical angle for a dense flint glass with a refractive index of 1.78.

20. If the critical angle for a piece of plastic is 45.5°, what is its refractive index? [*Ans.* 1.402.]

21. Make a diagram of the passage of a ray of light through a parallel plate of transparent material showing angles of incidence and refraction at both surfaces. Using Snell's law derive Eq.(38h).

DISPERSION

It was known to the ancients that sunlight, on passing through transparent crystals and jewels of various kinds, would produce brilliant colors of light. The early philosophers, attempting to explain the phenomenon, attributed the origin of the colors to the crystal itself. It was Newton who first demonstrated with prisms that the colors were already present in the white sunlight and that the function of the prism was to separate the colors by refracting them in different directions.

39.1. Dispersion. We have already seen how light of one color is refracted at the boundary of a medium like glass or water, and how it is deviated by a prism. It may be seen in Fig. 39A

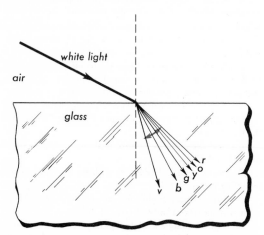

Fig. 39A   *Refraction of white sunlight into its spectrum colors.*

how, *with white light, each color is refracted by a different amount* to produce its own angle of deviation. *Red light is refracted least and violet*

light is refracted most. The angular spread of all the colors produced by sending white light through a prism is called the *dispersion* and the band of color so produced is called *a spectrum* (see Fig. 39B).

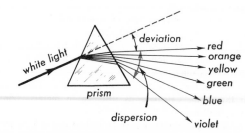

Fig. 39B   *Refraction at both surfaces of a prism produces higher dispersion.*

If white light is sent through a group of similar prisms made of different substances, each prism will be found to have a different dispersion. This can be demonstrated for solids by *flint* and *crown-glass prisms*, and for liquids by *kerosene*, *carbon bisulfide*, and *water*. It will be noted that the two glass prisms in Fig. 39C, one of flint glass and the other of crown glass, produce quite different dispersions. The liquid prisms, produced by filling thin-walled glass troughs with liquid, also disperse light by different amounts.

Since different colors are refracted by different amounts, the index of refraction is different for each color. In a vacuum all colors travel with the same speed, 186,300 mi/s, but in a transparent medium, like glass or water, they travel considerably slower and at different speeds. Among the spectrum colors, red travels the fastest and violet the slowest, with the speeds of all other

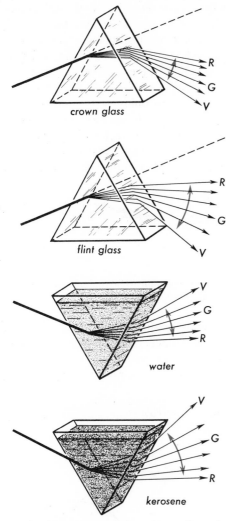

crown glass

flint glass

water

kerosene

Fig. 39C   *Illustration of the relative dispersions of solid as well as liquid prisms.*

colors somewhere in between. In air there is very little dispersion and in a vacuum there is absolutely none. This latter statement is proved by the fact that, when the dark star of an eclipsing binary passes in front of its brighter companion, all colors disappear and reappear simultaneously. If one color were to travel slightly faster than another, the dip in stellar intensity for that color would have plenty of time in its many years of travel to the earth to get ahead.

The refractive indices for a number of transparent solids are given in Table 39A. It will be noted that, although the values for any one substance do not vary greatly between colors, the values for blue and violet are the largest and those for orange and red are the smallest. Note the relatively high values for diamond and strontium titanate and the relatively low values for ice.

The wavelengths of the different colors of light are given in angstrom units.

$$1 \text{ Å} = 10^{-10} \text{ m}$$

or

$$10^{10} \text{ Å} = 1 \text{ m}$$

In the physics laboratory the index of refraction is determined with a prism, usually one having an angle of 60°. The prism is placed on a spectrometer where the spectrum of white light is observed in a small telescope, and the angle of minimum deviation is measured for each color separately. As the prism is slowly turned, the spectrum widens or narrows continuously and each color goes through its own angle of minimum deviation just as the rays of that same color make equal angles with the two prism faces.

TABLE 39A. REFRACTIVE INDEX FOR SEVERAL TRANSPARENT SOLIDS

Substance	Color wavelength λ in Angstroms					
	Violet 4100 Å	Blue 4700 Å	Green 5300 Å	Yellow 5900 A	Orange 6100 A	Red 6700 Å
Crown glass	1.5380	1.5310	1.5260	1.5225	1.5216	1.5200
Light flint	1.6040	1.5960	1.5910	1.5875	1.5867	1.5850
Dense flint	1.6980	1.6836	1.6738	1.6670	1.6650	1.6620
Quartz	1.5570	1.5510	1.5468	1.5438	1.5432	1.5420
Diamond	2.4580	2.4439	2.4260	2.4172	2.4150	2.4100
Ice	1.3170	1.3136	1.3110	1.3087	1.3080	1.3060
Strontium titanate	2.6320	2.5130	2.4460	2.4060	2.3980	2.3730

39.2. Prism Combinations. While substances that produce large deviations also produce large dispersions, the two properties are by no means proportional to each other. If a flint-glass prism, for example, produces twice the dispersion of a crown-glass prism, it is not true that the deviation of each color by the flint prism is twice that of the crown-glass prism. Useful devices illustrating this fact can be demonstrated by combining two prisms in opposition as shown in Fig. 39D.

times the fainter secondary bow, with colors reversed, are seen as the arcs of circles. From a high vantage point or an airplane, these bows may form complete circles whose common center lies in the direction of the observer's shadow.

The elementary theory of the rainbow was first given by Antonius de Demini in the year 1611 and later developed more exactly by Descartes. The general characteristics of the *primary* and *secondary bows* are satisfactorily accounted for by considering only the reflection and refrac-

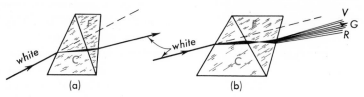

Fig. 39D   *Prism combinations: (a) achromatic prism giving deviation without dispersion, (b) direct-vision prism giving dispersion without deviation.*

For the achromatic combination in (a), the angles of both prisms are so selected that each prism alone will produce the same total dispersion. Since flint glass has the higher dispersive power, the flint prism will have a smaller angle as shown. Placed in opposition, the crown glass spreads the colors out and the flint prism bends them back parallel to each other again. Since the deviation produced by the two prisms is not the same, light will emerge as white light but in a different direction from that in which it first entered.

For the direct-vision combination in (b), the angles of the prisms are so selected that each prism alone will produce the same deviation for green light. For two such matched prisms the flint prism will produce the greater dispersion. Combined in opposition, the green light comes out on the far side, parallel to the incident white light on the left and the other spectrum colors on either side as shown.

39.3. The Rainbow. The rainbow is nature's most spectacular display of the spectrum of white light. The required conditions for the appearance of the phenomenon are that the sun be shining in one part of the sky and the rain be falling in the opposite part of the sky. Turning one's back to the sun, the bright primary bow and some-

tion of light by spherical raindrops. To understand how the phenomenon arises, we first confine our attention to an individual raindrop as shown in Fig. 39E. A ray of sunlight is shown

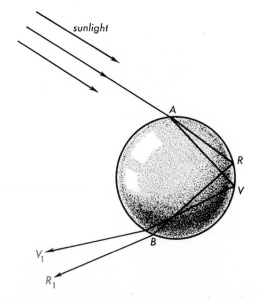

Fig. 39E   *Dispersion of sunlight by a single raindrop. (Primary rainbow.)*

entering a single raindrop at a point A near the top. At this point some of the light is reflected (not shown), and the remainder is refracted into the liquid sphere. At this first refraction the light is dispersed into its spectrum colors, violet being deviated the most and red the least.

Arriving at the opposite side of the drop, each color is partly refracted out into the air (not shown) and partly reflected back into the liquid. Reaching the surface at the lower boundary, each color is again reflected (not shown) and refracted. This second refraction is quite similar to that of a prism shown in Fig. 39B, where refraction at the second surface increases the dispersion already produced at the first. This is the path of the light in thousands of drops giving rise to the bright primary rainbow.

In Fig. 39F, a ray of sunlight, coming from

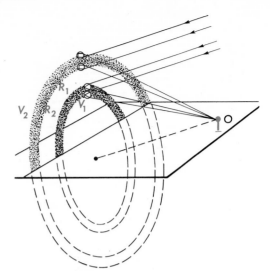

Fig. 39G   *The primary and secondary rainbows as seen by an observer at O.*

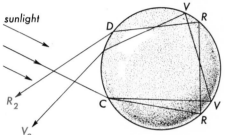

Fig. 39F   *Dispersion of sunlight by a single raindrop. (Secondary rainbow.)*

the same direction as in Fig. 39E, is shown entering a single raindrop at a point C near the bottom. After one refraction and two internal reflections the light is again refracted and dispersed, this time in a direction not greatly different from that in Fig. 39E. This is the path of the light in thousands of drops giving rise to the fainter secondary rainbow with its colors reversed.

Of all the sun's rays falling on one face of each individual drop, only a small part of them are responsible for the main features of both rainbows. The reasons for excluding the others will be explained in later paragraphs. Assuming for the present that the two rays shown are the only rays to be considered, let us see why the bows appear as they do in the sky.

As shown in Fig. 39G, the primary bow appears inside the secondary bow and arises from sunlight entering the tops of drops properly located. Those in a region R_1 refract red light

toward the observer's eye at O, and the violet and other colors over his head. Drops in the region of V_1 refract violet light to the observer's eye at O, and the red and other colors toward his feet. In other words, the light seen from any one drop is only one color, all drops giving this color lying on the arc of a circle. The reason they lie on the arc of a circle is that the angle between the incident sunlight and the refracted light of any one color is of necessity the same for each drop. In the primary bow, this angle is 42° for the red light and 40° for the violet.

The secondary bow is formed by similar reasoning and appears at higher angles of elevation, and with the colors reversed. The angles subtended by the secondary bow are 50° for the red and 54° for the violet.

39.4. The Theory of the Rainbow. The complete theory of the rainbow was first proposed by Thomas Young, and later worked out in detail by Potter and Airy. To understand why the particular rays shown in Fig. 39E are responsible for the rainbow, and that other rays which certainly enter the drop can be neglected, see Fig. 39H. Here, in the parallel beam of sunlight entering a single drop, our attention is confined to the rays of only one color. By this simplification, the phenomenon of dispersion is dispensed with and we consider only the reflection and refraction

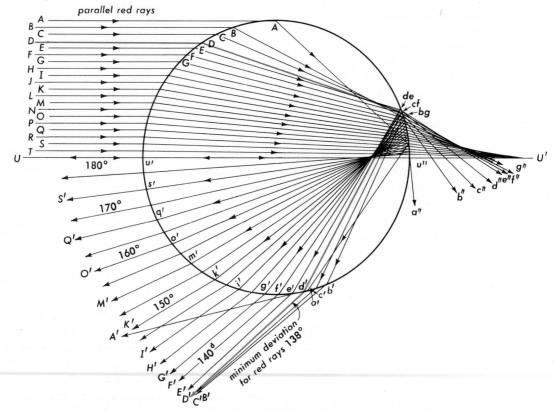

Fig. 39H   *Illustration of the refraction and reflection of light by a single raindrop and the minimum deviation of certain rays that produce the primary rainbow.*

of red light. As each of the parallel red rays A, B, C, etc., from the sun enter the drop, they are deviated according to the law of refraction. At the opposite side of the drop, in the region d to u″, these rays are partly reflected to the lower left boundary at a′, b′, c′, etc., where, by refraction, they pass out into the air in the directions of A′, B′, C′, etc., respectively, and are partly refracted in the direction of a″, b″, c″, etc., respectively.

From the diagram it will be noted that a ray like A, entering at the very edge of the drop, is deviated through an angle close to 180°, that is, it emerges in almost the opposite direction to that in which it entered. The same is true of a ray like Q nearer the center of the drop. Ray U is exactly reversed in direction and therefore deviated exactly 180°. Ray D, on the other hand, is seen to be deviated least of all and is therefore referred to as the ray at minimum deviation. In

going from A to U with the incident light, the emergent light is deviated less and less until it reaches a minimum for D′ and then increases again, reaching 180° with the axial ray UU′. The net result of this behavior is seen to be a slight crowding together of a considerable number of nearly parallel rays at minimum deviation where the light emerges as an intense and nearly parallel beam B′ to G′.

It should be noted that raindrops are spheres and not circles, as represented in the figures, and that the refracted rays emerge as cones of light. If Fig. 39H is rotated about the axial ray UU′, the emerging rays A′, B′, C′, etc., are confined to a cone bounded at the edges by the rays that have suffered the least deviation. In the direction of D′, the edge of the cone, the radiation is very intense, and inside the cone the rays are divergent and the radiation feeble. Outside the cone there is no light. Thus the selected ray A of the incident light in Fig. 39E is the ray D in Fig. 39H.

Similar diagrams for other colors lead to angles of minimum deviation and cones of light whose angles decrease in the order of the spectral colors red, orange, yellow, green, blue, and violet. An experimental demonstration of this can be made by sending a beam of parallel light from a carbon arc through a round glass bulb filled with water. The refracted cones of light falling on a screen in back of the arc source forms a complete primary rainbow. Outside this primary bow, and with colors reversed, is the fainter secondary bow.

To understand the secondary rainbow, additional rays must be added to Fig. 39H. Internally reflected rays from the points a', b', c', etc., are drawn up to where they again strike the surface of the drop and are there refracted out into the air. Out of these rays, a given set of rays, like those for the primary bow, will have a preferred direction in which the light is most intense. When the figure is rotated about the axial line UU', the rays form a secondary cone of light, the inner edge of which is sharply defined.

It is interesting to point out that no light emerges in the region between the primary and secondary cones of light. This agrees with the observations that the region between the two rainbows is quite dark, whereas outside the secondary bow and inside the primary bow a considerable amount of light is visible.

Theoretically three, four, and five reflections within raindrops should give rise to other rainbows. The third and fourth bows are located between the observer and the sun and, because the direct sunlight is so bright compared with the faint bows, the phenomenon has probably never been observed. The fifth bow, however, occurs in the same part of the sky as the primary and secondary bows, and would be seen except for the faintness of the light.

On occasions when the primary and secondary rainbows are particularly bright, a third bow just inside the primary, and a fourth bow just outside the secondary bow, may be seen. These are called supernumerary bows, and are due to peculiar interference effects of light. This interference occurs between pairs of rays that are parallel to each other on emergence, but which have traveled different paths within the drop. Such pairs of rays, for example, are D' and E', C', and F', B' and G', and A' and Q'. The two rays in each of these pairs are just those that cross each other at the reflecting surface d to u''; they are therefore symmetrical with the corresponding incident pairs of rays.

39.5. Coronas and Lunar Bows. Lunar bows may be seen under favorable conditions. When the full moon appears in one part of the sky and rain is falling in another part of the sky, an observer with his back to the moon may observe a barely visible rainbow. As a rule only the brighter colors, red and yellow, are visible.

At times when the sun or moon shines through a thin veil of fog, we observe a circular colored bow with the sun or moon at the geometrical center. Such a corona, as it is technically called, is due to the diffraction of light around the tiny fog particles. Popularly called a ring around the sun or a ring around the moon, a corona appears close to the luminary with red on the outside. It should not be confused with the larger rings or halos with red on the inside.

39.6. Halos. Halos are commonly observed as faint rainbow-like rings around the sun or moon, and are due to tiny ice crystals floating in the upper atmosphere. Such crystals are hexagonal in shape and, acting like prisms, refract and disperse white light into a spectrum. Two halos are frequently observed, the brighter one making an angle of 22° with the luminary and the fainter one an angle of 46°. Both exhibit confused spectrum colors with a decided red tint on the inside.

Crystals, like prisms, have an angle of minimum deviation for each color of light and, because they are oriented at random in space, millions of them appear to each observer to concentrate the light in a circle with the luminary at the center. As shown in Fig. 39I, the angle of minimum deviation for light entering and leaving different faces of either plate-like or rod-like crystals is 22° and 46°. The 22° angle arises from rays like (3) where the two refracting surfaces are alternate faces that make an angle of 60° with each other. The 46° angle arises from rays

Fig. 39I   *Typical forms of ice crystals showing reflected and refracted rays of sunlight that give rise to halos and "mock suns."*

like (4) where the two refracting surfaces make an angle of 90°. (The refractive index of ice for red light is 1.3060.)

A demonstration of such color effects can be produced as shown in Fig. 39J by means of an

regions, it is occasionally observed at low latitudes and at a time of day when the sun is not far from the horizon (see Fig. 39K).

This display too is caused by myriads of tiny ice crystals in the upper atmosphere, reflecting and refracting the light according to the well-established laws of optics. As shown in Fig. 39K, there are, in addition to the two rainbow-like halos at 22° and 46°, four radial streaks of white light, two vertical and two horizontal. Where these streaks of white light cross the halos, the colors appear intensified and form what are called *mock suns* or *sundogs*.

The explanation of the halos is the same as explained above, while the white streaks are due to reflection from all crystal faces. The plate-like crystals, falling freely under gravity, flutter slowly downward like leaves from a tree. Wobbling

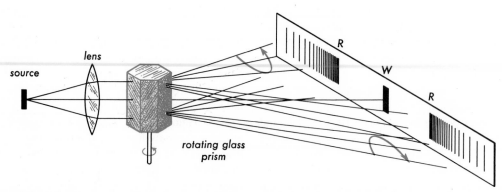

Fig. 39J   *Experiment demonstrating colors produced at minimum deviation by a single rotating prism.*

hexagonal or octagonal glass prism rotated rapidly about its axis in a strong beam of white light. Dispersed light refracted by alternate faces sweeps in from either side of the screen, slows down and stops at minimum deviation, and then retreats again. The blurred patches of light on the screen are brightest at the minimum deviation angles *R*.

39.7. "Mock Suns" or "Sundogs." Another natural phenomenon of great interest, and one one which is quite spectacular, is the formation of "mock suns" or "sundogs." Although the phenomenon is most commonly seen in the polar

slightly about a horizontal plane, they present vertical and horizontal faces from which light is reflected. At positions close in line between the sun and observer, the light reflected toward the observer is incident at a grazing angle, an angle where the reflecting power for all transparent solids is high.

39.8. Mirages and Flying Saucers. When walking across the desert sands or driving along a straight and level highway on a hot day, one notices that the sand or the dark asphalt in the distance seems to be covered with water. The water, of course, is just a reflected image of the

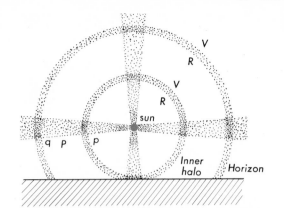

Fig. 39K   *Halos and "mock suns" or "sundogs" as seen frequently in polar regions, and occasionally at lower latitudes. P, parhelic circle, p, mock suns or parhelia; q, paranthelia.*

sky, and a distant object above the horizon will appear upside down below the horizon. The air in contact with the ground has been heated to a high temperature and, because its refractive index is lowered due to expansion, light rays are reflected as if from a plane mirror.

Oftentimes at night, when the air at the ground is cooler than the air above, the bending of light rays will occur in the opposite direction, and distant objects, like a row of bright city street lights, can be seen against the sky. This and similar phenomena, explain the "flying saucer" observations,* first observed centuries ago and reported so frequently in the last two decades.

* See D. H. Menzel, *Flying Saucers* (Harvard University Press, Cambridge, Massachusetts).

PROBLEMS

(*Note*. Use five-place trigonometry tables for the following problems.)

1. White light is incident at an angle of 80° on the smooth surface of a strontium titanate crystal. Calculate the dispersion produced by one surface, that is, the angle between the red and violet rays.

2. White light is incident at 89° on one face of a diamond crystal. Calculate the dispersion produced by this one surface, that is, the angle between the red and violet rays. [*Ans.* 31′.]

3. White light is incident at an angle of 60° on a dense-flint-glass prism. If the prism angle is 50°, find the angle between the red and violet rays emerging from the other side of the prism.

4. White light is incident at an angle of 35° on one surface of a crown-glass prism. If the prism angle is 60°, find the dispersion of the emergent light, that is, the angle between the red and violet rays. [*Ans.* 2° 50′.]

5. A six-sided prism is rotated in a beam of white light like that shown in Fig. 39J. If the prism is made of plastic of index 1.42, what will be the angle between the two minimum-deviation positions *RR*?

6. A six-sided prism is rotated in a parallel beam of white light as shown in Fig. 39J. If the prism is made of plastic with a refractive index of 1.38, what will be the angle between the two minimum-deviation positions? [*Ans.* 54° 32′.]

7. A parallel beam of red light is incident on a spherical drop of water as shown in Fig. 39H. Calculate the angle of deviation for a ray like I, at a distance $\frac{3}{5}$ of the way up from the center line toward the edge. Assume a refractive index of 1.3320.

8. A parallel beam of violet light is incident on a spherical raindrop as shown in Fig. 39H. Find the angle of deviation for a ray like D, at a distance $\frac{17}{20}$ of the way up from the center line toward the edge. Assume a refractive index 1.3340. [*Ans.* 148° 4′.]

LENSES

The primary function of a lens is to form images of real objects. Although most lenses are made of common glass, a few special lenses are made of other transparent materials like fused and crystal *quartz*, plastics, and crystal *fluorite*. To understand the principles upon which a lens functions, imagine a set of several matched prisms and blocks of glass arranged in the order shown in Fig. 40A. In the first arrangement, the

prisms are made so as to refract the incoming parallel light rays and to converge them to a focus at F. In the second arrangement, the parallel rays are made to diverge as if they had come from a common point F. In each system the greatest deviation occurs at the outermost prisms, for they have the greatest angle between the two refracting surfaces. No deviation occurs for the central rays, for at that point the glass faces are parallel to each other.

A real lens is not made of prisms, as indicated in Fig. 40A, but of a solid piece of glass with surfaces ground to the form of a sphere. Cross sections of several standard forms are shown in Fig. 40B. The first three lenses, which are thicker

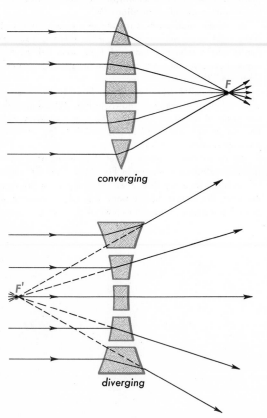

Fig. 40A *Matched sets of prisms illustrating lens-like action.*

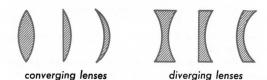

converging lenses   diverging lenses

Fig. 40B *Cross sections of standard forms of common lenses.*

in the center, are called *converging* or *positive lenses*, while the last three, which are thinner in the center, are called *diverging* or *negative lenses*. Special names attached to each of the six lens types shown are: (1) *double convex*, (2) *plano–convex*, (3) *convex miniscus*, (4) *double concave*, (5) *plano–concave*, and (6) *concave miniscus*.

There are two good reasons why lenses have spherical surfaces: first, with this shape they form reasonably good images; and second, a spherical form is by far the most practical shape to which smooth polished surfaces can be ground.

Diagrams showing the refraction of light by

converging and diverging lenses are given in Fig. 40C. The principal axis in each case is a straight line passing through the center of a lens perpendicular to the two faces at the points of

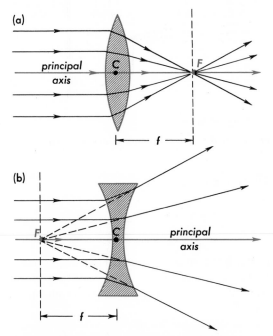

(a)

principal axis

C

F

f

(b)

F

C

principal axis

f

Fig. 40C *Converging and diverging lenses.*

intersection. The principal focus F lies on the principal axis; it is defined for a converging lens as the point where light rays parallel to the principal axis are brought together, and for a negative lens as a point from which light rays parallel to the principal axis appear to originate. *By symmetry every lens has two principal foci, one on each side of the lens and at the same distance from the center of the lens.* The distance from the focal point to the center of the lens is called the focal length.

CF = focal length = f

A plane perpendicular to the principal axis which passes through either principal focus is called the *focal plane.* Parallel light rays entering the lens from any other direction than shown in the diagrams will come to a focus at some point on the focal plane. This point is readily located by remembering that a ray through the center of the lens does not change in direction.

The greater the curvature of the two surfaces of a lens, the shorter is its focal length. The reason for this, as can be seen from the diagrams, is that the greater the curvature the greater is the deviation of the light rays passing through, near the edges of the lens.

One important principle concerning lenses is the reversibility of light rays. If a point source of light is placed at F in Fig. 40C(a), the rays of light that strike the lens will be refracted into a parallel beam of light moving to the left. Similarly, in Fig. 40C(b), if light rays are converging toward the focal point F they will be refracted by the lens into a parallel beam.

40.1. Image Formation. When an object is placed on one side of a converging lens beyond the principal focus, a real image will be formed on the opposite side of the lens. This is illustrated in Fig. 40D. If the object is moved closer to the focal point, the image will be formed farther away from the lens and will be bigger, that is, magnified. As the object is moved farther away from the lens, the image is formed closer to the focal point and is smaller in size.

In general there are two ways of accurately determining the position of an image: one is by graphical construction and the other is by use of the lens formula.

$$\frac{1}{p} + \frac{1}{q} = \frac{1}{f}$$ (40a)

where *p is the object distance, q the image distance,* and *f the focal length.*

The graphical method is illustrated in Fig. 40E. Consider the light emitted by some one particular point like O in the object. Of the rays going out from this point in all directions, the ray OA traveling parallel to the principal axis will be refracted to pass through the focal point F [see Fig. 40C(a)]. The ray OC arriving at the center of the lens where the faces are parallel will pass straight through, meeting the other ray at some point I. These two rays locate the tip of the image at I. All other rays from the point O which strike the lens will be brought to a focus at this same point. To check this, note that the ray OF, which passes from O through the left-hand focal

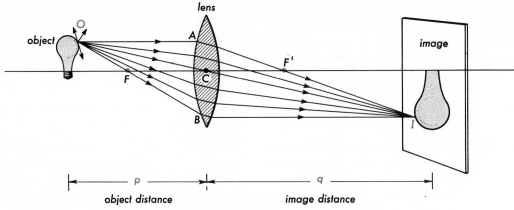

Fig. 40D *Ray diagram illustrating the formation of a real image by means of a single converging lens.*

point, by the principle of the reversibility of light rays, will be refracted parallel to the principal axis, crossing the other ray at I, as shown.

The use of the lens formula can be illustrated by the following example. Let an object be placed 60 cm in front of a lens of focal length 20 cm. If we solve Eq.(40a) for q, we obtain the expression:

$$q = \frac{p \times f}{p - f} \qquad (40b)$$

Then substituting the known quantities, we obtain

$$q = \frac{60 \times 20}{60 - 20} = 30 \text{ cm}$$

The image is formed 30 cm from the lens or 10 cm from F.

The size of the image can be calculated from the following simple relation:

$$\frac{\text{size of image}}{\text{size of object}} = \frac{\text{image distance}}{\text{object distance}}$$

This is the image formula,

$$\boxed{\frac{I}{O} = -\frac{q}{p}} \qquad (40c)$$

in which the ratio I/O is called the *magnification.* If we substitute known values of O, p, and q from the above problem, as an example, we obtain

$$m = \frac{I}{O} = -\frac{30}{60} \qquad I = -\tfrac{1}{2}O$$

The answer shows that the image is half the size of the object and that the magnification is $\tfrac{1}{2}$. The minus sign means that the image is inverted.

If a centimeter rule is used to construct this problem graphically, the resultant diagram will be similar to Fig. 40E. Each line is drawn in its proper position and size, and when the image is located by rays (1), (2), and (3) its position and size are measured by the same scale. Drawn care-

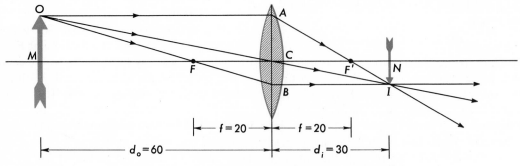

Fig. 40E *Graphical determination of image position and size.*

fully, the graphical results will agree in every detail with those calculated by the above formulas.

40.2. Virtual Images. The images formed by the lenses in Figs. 40D and 40E are *real*. *Real images* are defined as those that can be formed on a screen and are characterized by the fact that rays of light are actually brought together to a focus there. *Virtual images* are not real, they cannot be formed on a screen, and the rays from different points on the object do not pass through corresponding points in the image. Virtual images may be observed with a converging lens by placing an object close to the lens and inside the focal point, or by a diverging lens with the object at any point. These two examples are illustrated in Fig. 40F.

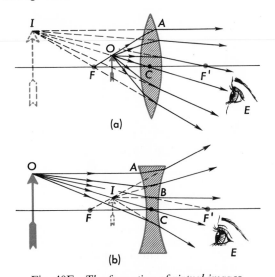

(a)

(b)

Fig. 40F   *The formation of virtual images.*

In the first case the lens is used as a magnifier, or reading glass. Rays of light radiating from the point of the object at O are refracted in the proper direction, but are not sufficiently deviated to come to a focus. To the observer's eye at E, these rays appear to be coming from a point I back of the lens. This is a *virtual image, right side up and magnified.* To find this image graphically, we observe that the ray FOA must be refracted parallel to the principal axis. The ray OC through the center of the lens goes on undeviated. These two refracted rays extended back-

ward intersect at I. If the lens formula, Eq.(40b), is used to find the image in such a case, the image distance q will come out as a negative quantity, showing it to be a virtual image on the same side of the lens as the object.

In the case of a negative lens the image is always virtual, closer to the lens, and smaller in size than the object. As shown in Fig. 40F(b), light rays diverging from the object point O are made more divergent by the lens. To the observer's eye at E, these rays appear to be coming from the point I back of, but close to, the lens. To find this image we observe that the ray OA parallel to the principal axis must be refracted in such a direction that it appears to come from F. The ray OC through the center goes on undeviated. Since these two directions intersect at I, the image is formed there.

In applying the lens formula to a diverging lens, the focal length f is always *negative* in sign. To illustrate this, consider the following example.

Example 1. An object is placed 30 cm in front of a diverging lens of focal length of 15 cm. Locate the image position.

Solution. Direct substitution in Eq.(40b) gives

$$q = \frac{30 \times (-15)}{30 - (-15)} \quad \text{or} \quad q = \frac{-450}{45}$$

From which

$$q = -10 \text{ cm}$$

The image is found at 10 cm from the lens, the negative sign indicating that it is virtual and, therefore, on the same side of the lens as the object.

A convenient sign convention for all lens problems solved with Eq.(40b) is the following:

(1) *Numerical values of real object distances are always positive.*

(2) *Numerical values of real image distances are positive; numerical values of virtual image distances are negative.*

(3) *Numerical values of focal lengths of convergent lenses are positive, of divergent lenses are negative.*

40.3. Conjugate Foci. Since the lens equation, Eq. (40a), is symmetrical in p and q, it follows that a real image and the object from which it was formed may be interchanged. For example, in Figs. 40D and 40E, if the object is located at I, the image would be located at O. The distances p and q are called *conjugate distances*, O and I *conjugate points*, and the intersections of the optic axis with the object and image planes *conjugate foci*.

In demonstrating conjugate distances with a lens and screen, the object and the image can be interchanged in position, or the lens can be moved. If, for example, an object distance $p = 30$ cm and an image distance $q = 50$ cm, the lens may be moved to a new position $p = 50$ cm. The image will be formed at $q = 30$ cm. In other words, for a fixed distance between object and image screen, there are two lens positions of good image formation (see Fig. 40G). Because

The sign convention for r_1 and r_2 is based upon the following rules:

(1) *Light rays entering and passing through a lens are always drawn from left to right.*

(2) *When such a ray encounters a convex surface, the radius r is positive.*

(3) *When a light ray encounters a concave surface, the radius r is negative.*

To illustrate the use of the lens maker's formula, consider the following example.

Example 2. A plano–convex lens having a focal length of 50 cm is to be made of glass of refractive index 1.52. Calculate the radius of curvature of the grinding and polishing tools that must be used to make this lens.

Solution. Since a plano–convex lens has one flat

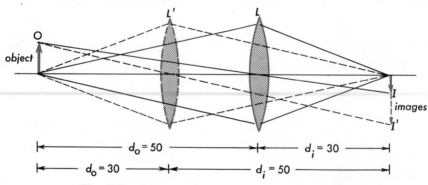

Fig. 40G　*Conjugate foci for a single converging lens.*

of the image–object relation, Eq.(40c), the two images will differ in size, the one being smaller than the object by the ratio $3:5$ as shown by the solid arrow, and the other larger by the ratio $5:3$ as shown by the dotted arrow.

40.4. The Lens Maker's Formula. To grind and polish a lens to some predetermined focal length, the refractive index of the glass should be known. Usually the refractive index is specified for the particular wavelength of yellow light emitted by a sodium lamp. With the index known, the radii of curvature of the two spherical surfaces can be calculated from the equation:

$$\frac{1}{f} = (\mu - 1)\left(\frac{1}{r_1} - \frac{1}{r_2}\right) \qquad (40d)$$

surface, the radius of curvature for that surface is infinite, and r_1 in Eq.(40d) is replaced by ∞. r_2 is the unknown. Direct substitution of all known quantities in the formula gives

$$\frac{1}{50} = (1.52 - 1)\left(\frac{1}{\infty} - \frac{1}{r_2}\right) \qquad (40e)$$

Solving for r_2,

$$\frac{1}{50} = (0.52)\left(0 - \frac{1}{r_2}\right), \qquad \frac{1}{50} = -\frac{0.52}{r_2}$$

which gives

$$r_2 = -50 \times 0.52 = -26.0 \text{ cm}$$

40.5. Defects of the Image. Although a simple converging lens may be made to form a relatively clear image of almost any object, there is present in every image a number of common defects tending to blur it. These defects are known as *spherical aberration, chromatic aberration, curvature of field, astigmatism, distortion,* and *coma.* Although some of these *aberrations,* as they are called, can be partly or almost entirely corrected by one means or another, they cannot all be eliminated entirely. These corrections are refinements that are usually considered in the design of lenses and are of some importance in the understanding of the principal action of a lens. We will be content to consider briefly the first two defects mentioned above—namely, spherical aberration, and chromatic aberration.

40.6. Spherical Aberration. Spherical aberration is an undesirable defect in the focusing properties of single glass lenses and is attributed to the fact that spherical surfaces are not exactly the correct surfaces to which a lens should be ground and polished. The reason they are not correct is shown for a double convex lens in Fig. 40H. Rays of light parallel to the principal axis

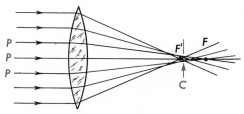

Fig. 40H *Spherical aberration of a lens. P, paraxial rays; C, circle of least confusion.*

which pass through the outer parts of the lens are not brought to exactly the same focus as those rays passing through the central portion. The result is that nowhere can a sharply defined image of a distant object be formed on a screen.

When a screen is placed between F and F′ and a blurred image is obtained, it is not difficult to find a position where the least blurring occurs. This point, C in the diagram, is called the *circle of least confusion.*

There are various ways in which spherical aberration in a lens may be reduced. Some of these are easily carried out, while others require expert lens design.

(1) The easiest way to reduce spherical aberra-

tion is to place a circular diaphragm in front of the lens and allow only the central bundle of rays to pass through. Such a procedure reduces the size of the circle of least confusion and thereby produces sharper images. This is one of the functions of the *iris diaphragm* in the lens cell of a camera. The smaller the effective diameter of a lens, the more sharply defined are its image-focusing properties. Reduced aperture, however, reduces the light-gathering power and for some purposes is not desirable.

Rays passing through or near the center of a lens, and at the same time making relatively small angles with the principal axis, are called *paraxial rays.* It is for such rays only that reasonably sharp focus is obtained and the equations used in the preceding sections can be applied.

(2) Because peripheral rays are deviated through too great an angle (see Fig. 40H), any method that will bring about lesser deviation from the outer edges of a lens will result in better focusing. The principle of minimum deviation offers one such method, because by carefully selecting the radii of curvature for the two lens faces, the peripheral rays can be brought to much more nearly the same focal point as the paraxial rays (see Fig. 40I). In diagram (a), parallel rays entering normal to the flat surface of a plano-convex lens are refracted at the second surface only, the outer rays being deviated through too great an angle. In (b), the outer rays, because they enter one face and leave the other at nearly the same angle, are near minimum deviation and cross the axis farther out. If, for any given object distance and image distance, the radii of curvature r_1 and r_2 are so chosen that *the peripheral rays pass through the lens at minimum deviation,* the lens will have a minimum of spherical aberration.

(3) To correct for spherical aberration, the two lens surfaces are sometimes ground and polished to other than a spherical form. Such a process, called *aspherizing,* is not only tedious and difficult, but any lens so made is good for only one pair of object and image distances.

(4) A fourth method of correcting spherical aberration is to combine a positive crown-glass

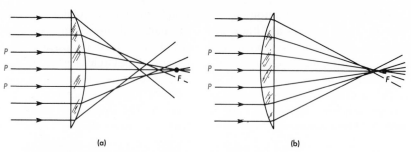

(a)   (b)

Fig. 40I *Spherical aberration for parallel rays is different on the two sides of a plane–convex lens. P, paraxial rays.*

lens with a negative flint-glass lens. Although both lenses have spherical surfaces, the curvatures of the two can be so chosen that the errors of one practically cancel those of the other.

40.7. Chromatic Aberration. When white light passes through a lens close to the edge, it is dispersed in much the same way that it is when passing through a large-angle prism (see Fig. 40J). The violet light, being deviated the most,

Fig. 40K, whereby the dispersion in one lens is compensated for by the opposite dispersion in the other, and yet the light is deviated to bring all colors to a common focus. Such a combination is called an *achromatic lens*. All first-class optical instruments use achromatic lenses. By the proper selection of surface curvatures, spherical aberration as well as chromatic aberration can be minimized with two lenses. The two ex-

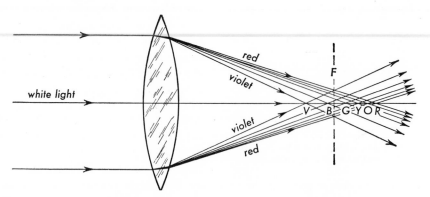

Fig. 40J *Ray diagram illustrating chromatic aberration with a single converging lens.*

comes to a focus nearer the lens than the red. The ray passing through the center of the lens and along the principal axis is not dispersed. For white light a single lens, therefore, cannot possibly form a sharply defined image.

To correct a lens for chromatic aberration, use is made of the principle of the achromatic prism [see Fig. 39D]. Two prisms, one of crown glass, the other of flint glass, are so chosen that when placed in opposition they produce deviation without dispersion.

A similar combination can be constructed of flint- and crown-glass lenses, as illustrated in

posed surfaces are chosen to give minimum deviation, and the two inner surfaces adjusted to correct chromatic aberration.

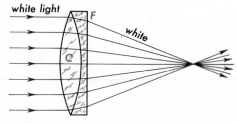

Fig. 40K *Achromatic lens combination.*

40.8. Two-Lens Combination.

Optical instruments often employ more than one lens to form an image of an object. Consider, for example, two converging lenses spaced some distance apart as shown in Fig. 40L. In the lower diagram

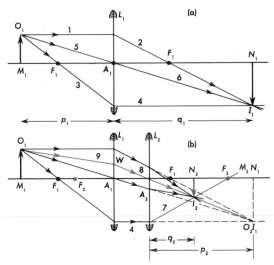

Fig. 40L *Illustration of the parallel-ray method for graphically locating the final image formed by two lenses.*

an object O_1M_1 is located at a given distance p_1 in front of the first lens, and an image I_2N_2 is formed a distance q_2 from the second lens. We will first apply graphical methods to find this image and then see how to apply the thin-lens formula to obtain the same result.

The first step is to disregard the second lens and find the image formed by the first lens as shown in diagram (a). In the diagram, the parallel-ray method is applied to the object O_1M_1, and the image I_1N_1 is obtained as a *real* and *inverted image*. Any two of the three incident rays 1, 3, and 5 are sufficient for the purpose.

We now insert the second lens in its proper position, as shown in diagram (b), and locate its focal points F_2, equal distance on each side of A_2. It will now be noted that ray 4 from the first lens is parallel to the axis and by the definition of focal length, must pass through F_2 as ray 7. To find the path of a second ray from L_2 we note that once we have found the image I_1N_1 in diagram (a), all the rays leaving O_1 would be re-

fracted to intersect at I_1. Making use of this fact, we now construct a ray by drawing line 8 back from I_1 through A_2 to W at the first lens. Line 9 is then drawn in connecting W and O_1.

Since ray 9, as refracted by lens L_1, passes through the center of lens L_2, it goes on undeviated and crosses ray 7 at the point I_2. Once this point has been located we can draw in the image I_2N_2. All rays refracted by lens L_1 toward I_1 will upon passing through L_2 be refracted toward I_2.

As a check on the graphical solution, we can calculate the image position by using the single-lens formula.'

Example 3. Two thin lenses with focal lengths of $+12$ cm and $+16$ cm, respectively, are located 8 cm apart. An object is located 20 cm in front of the first lens. Find the position of the final image.

Solution. Begin by applying Eq.(40b) to the first lens alone. The given quantities to be substituted are: $p_1 = +20$ cm, and $f_1 = +12$ cm.

$$q_1 = \frac{p_1 \times f_1}{p_1 - f_1}$$

$$q_1 = \frac{(+20) \times (+12)}{(+20) - (+12)}$$

$$q_1 = +30 \text{ cm}$$

This image formed by the first lens alone is therefore *real*, and 30 cm to the right of A_1. This image becomes the object for the second lens, and since it is 22 cm from A_2, the object distance becomes -22 cm. The minus sign is necessary and results from the fact that the object distance is measured to the right of the lens. Since the rays approaching the second lens are converging toward O_2, this object is *virtual* and its distance therefore has a negative sign.

Applying the lens formula Eq.(40b) to the second lens, we have $p_2 = -22$ cm, and $f_2 = +16$ cm.

$$q_2 = \frac{p_2 \times f_2}{p_2 - f_2}$$

$$q_2 = \frac{(-22) \times (+16)}{(-22) - (+16)}$$

$$q_2 = +9.26 \text{ cm}$$

The final image is 9.26 cm to the right of the second lens and is real. The magnification of the system is the ratio of the final image size I_2 divided by the original object size O_1, and is given by the product of the magnification of the first lens and the magnification of the first lens and the magnification of the second.

$$M = M_1 \times M_2$$

$$M = \left(\frac{I_1}{O_1}\right) \times \left(\frac{I_2}{O_2}\right) \qquad (40f)$$

When two *thin lenses* are placed in contact, the combination behaves as a single lens with a focal length of its own. If f_1 and f_2 represent the focal lengths of the two lenses, respectively, the equivalent focal length f of the combination is given by

$$\frac{1}{f} = \frac{1}{f_1} + \frac{1}{f_2} \qquad (40g)$$

Example 4. An achromatic lens is composed of two lenses: a converging crown-glass lens with a focal length of 8 in. and a diverging flint-glass lens with a focal length of 12 in. Find the equivalent focal length.

Solution. The two focal lengths given are $f_1 = +8$ in., and $f_2 = -12$ in. Substitution in Eq.(40g) gives

$$\frac{1}{f} = \frac{1}{8} - \frac{1}{12} \qquad \frac{1}{f} = \frac{3}{24} - \frac{2}{24} \qquad \frac{1}{f} = \frac{1}{24}$$

from which $f = 24$ in.

For a more complete account of geometrical optics, see F. A. Jenkins and H. E. White, *Fundamentals of Optics* (McGraw-Hill Book Co., Inc., New York, 1957), 3rd ed.

PROBLEMS

1. A lens with a focal length of of $+8$ cm is located 12 cm from an object 2.5 cm high. Find the image (a) position, and (b) size. Solve both by formula and graphically.

2. A lens with a focal length of $+6$ cm is located 9 cm from an object 2 cm high. Find graphically and by formula (a) the position, and (b) the size of the image. [*Ans.* (a) $+18$ cm, (b) -4 cm.]

3. A lens has a focal length of $+6$ cm. An object 1.5 cm high is located 8 cm away from the lens. Find (a) the position, and (b) the size of the image, graphically and by formula.

4. A lens has a focal length of $+4$ cm. An object 3 cm high is located 20 cm away from the lens. Find (a) the position, and (b) the size of the image, graphically and by formula. [*Ans.* (a) $+5$ cm, (b) -0.75 cm.]

5. A lens has a focal length of $+4$ cm. An object 1 cm high is located on the principal axis 3 cm from the lens. Find (a) the position and (b) the size of the image, graphically and by formula.

6. A lens has a focal length of $+9$ cm. An object 1.5 cm high is located on the principal axis 6 cm from the lens. Find (a) the position and (b) the size of the image, graphically and by formula. [*Ans.* (a) -18 cm, (b) $+4.5$ cm.]

7. An object 3 cm high is located on the principal axis and 12 cm from a lens with a focal length of -6 cm. Find (a) the position, and (b) the size of the image. Solve graphically and by formula.

8. An object 3 in. high is located 20 in. from a lens with a focal length of -30 in. Find the (a) position, and (b) the size of the image. [*Ans.* (a) -12 in., (b) $+1.8$ in.]

9. A lens with an index of 1.6 has the following radii: $r_1 = +18$ cm, and $r_2 = -12$ cm. Find its focal length.

10. A glass lens of index 1.68 has the following radii; $r_1 = +8$ cm, and $r_2 = -12$ cm. Find its focal length. [*Ans.* $+7.06$ cm.]

11. A plastic lens is made with radii $r_1 = +15$ cm and $r_2 = -25$ cm. Find its focal length if the refractive index is 1.45.

12. A miniscus lens with radii $r_1 = +12$ cm and $r_2 = +20$ cm, has a refractive index of 1.65. Find its focal length. [*Ans.* $+46.1$ cm.]

13. A lens with radii $r_1 = +5$ cm and $r_2 = +15$ cm, has a refractive index of 1.53. Find its focal length.

14. A lens with a focal length of $+20$ cm is used to form a real image on a screen 1.44 m from an object. How far from the object should the lens be placed? [*Ans.* $+24$ cm or 120 cm.]

15. An object is located 2 m from a screen. Find the focal length of a lens that will form a real image on the screen with a magnification of -4.

16. An object 4 in. tall is located 45 ft from a screen. A single lens is to be used to obtain a real image of this object on the screen 12 ft high. Find (a) the object distance, and (b) the focal length of the lens. [*Ans.* (a) 1.216 ft, or 14.6 in., (b) 1.183 ft, or 14.2 in.]

17. An object 3 cm high is located 15 cm in front of a lens of focal length $+10$ cm. A second lens of focal length $+24$ cm is located 6 cm beyond the first lens. Where is the final image located? Solve graphically and by formula.

18. An object 2 cm high is located 30 cm in front of a lens of focal length $+12$ cm. A second lens of focal length -30 cm is located 10 cm beyond the first lens. Where is the final image located, and what is its nature? [*Ans.* $+15$ cm from the second lens, real, inverted, and 2 cm high.]

19. An equi-convex lens of crown glass with an index of 1.52, and a plano-concave flint-glass lens of index 1.67, are placed in contact to form an achromatic lens. If all curved surfaces have radii of 20 cm, find the focal length of lens.

20. A crown-glass lens with radii $r_1 = +12$ cm and $r_2 = -6$ cm, and index 1.50, is combined with a flint-glass lens with radii $r_1 = -6$ cm and $r_2 = -24$ cm, and index 1.80, to form an achromatic lens. Find the focal length of (a) the crown-glass lens, (b) the flint-glass lens, and (c) the combination. [*Ans.* (a) $+8$ cm, (b) -10 cm, (c) $+40$ cm.]

OPTICAL INSTRUMENTS

The design of efficient optical instruments is the ultimate purpose of geometrical optics. The principles governing the formation of images by a single lens, and occasionally by simple combinations of lenses, have been set forth in the previous chapter. These principles find a wide variety of applications in the many practical combinations of lenses, frequently including also mirrors or prisms, which fall in the category of optical instruments. This subject is one of such large scope, and has developed so many ramifications, that in a book devoted to the fundamentals of physics it is only possible to describe the principles involved in a few standard types of instruments. In this chapter a description will be given of the more important features of cameras, spectacles, telescopes, binoculars, and microscopes. These will serve to illustrate some applications of the basic ideas already discussed and will, it is hoped, be of interest to the student who has used, or expects to use, some of these instruments.

41.1. The Camera. Since the photographic camera employs only a single lens unit, it may be considered as one of the simplest of all optical instruments. As illustrated by the roll-film camera in Fig. 41A, a converging lens forms a *real* and *inverted image* on the film. If the object is far away, the light rays approaching the lens are nearly parallel and the image is formed at the focal plane. If the object is close up, the image will be formed beyond the focal plane as shown in the diagram. To permit distant landscapes or "close ups" to be taken with the same camera, a bellows is used, allowing the lens distance to be varied at will. Motion of the lens to the proper image distance is called *focusing*.

Only a simple converging lens is used in the cheapest of cameras, which means that all of the common defects of images are present to give rise to a slightly blurred or diffuse image. In more expensive cameras, however, the most objectionable defects are fairly well corrected by a compound lens made of several individual lenses. As a rule, a good camera lens will contain from three to five lens elements and will partially correct for *chromatic aberration*, *spherical aberration*, *astigmatism*, and *curvature of field*.

Four typical high-quality camera lenses containing several lens elements are shown in Fig. 41B. Each lens contains an adjustable diaphragm or stop, shown in color.

The purpose of an iris diaphragm is to decrease the effective aperture of a lens and hence increase its *f*-number. Such practice is desirable in photographing still objects because the smaller the lens opening, the sharper will be the focus of near and far as well as central and peripheral objects.

The f-number of a lens is equal to its focal length divided by its diameter.

$$f\text{-number} = \frac{F}{D} \qquad (41a)$$

41.2. The Eye. Some aspects of this most remarkable optical instrument, the human eye,

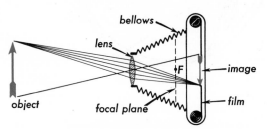

Fig. 41A *Diagram of the image formation by a camera.*

have been presented in Chapter 1. There it was pointed out that a single eye is in principle an exceptionally fine camera, with an elaborate lens system on one side and a sensitive screen or photographic film called the *retina* on the other.

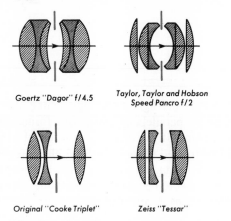

Goertz "Dagor" f/4.5

Taylor, Taylor and Hobson
Speed Pancro f/2

Original "Cooke Triplet"

Zeiss "Tessar"

Fig. 41B *Symmetrical and unsymmetrical camera lenses.*

When light from a distant object passes through the lens system of the eye, it is refracted and brought to a focus on the retina. There a real but inverted image of the object is formed. It is a most amazing fact that, while all retinal images are inverted, as shown in Fig. 41C, they are interpreted as being erect.

Accommodation is the ability to focus the eyes on near and far objects. In a camera the focusing of a picture on the photographic film or plate is accomplished by moving the lens toward or away from the film. In the human eye, however, *focusing is brought about by changing the shape of the crystalline lens.* This is accomplished by a rather complicated system of ligaments and muscles. Due to a tension which exists in the lens capsule, the crystalline lens, if completely free, would tend to become spherical in shape (see Fig. 1B).

The edge of the lens is surrounded by the *ciliary muscle* which, by contracting, causes the lens to bulge out. This reduces the focal length of the lens, bringing nearby objects to focus on the retina. When the ciliary muscle relaxes, the suspensory ligaments, being under tension, pull at the edges of the lens, thus tending to flatten it. Under these conditions the focal length increases, bringing distant objects to focus on the retina. This is the accommodation process.

The normal eye is most relaxed when it is focused for parallel light, i.e., for objects far away. To study the detail of an object, however,

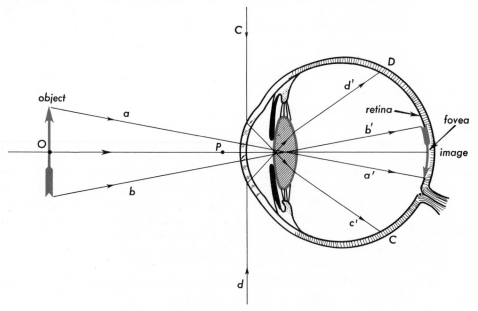

Fig. 41C *The human eye is similar to a camera. All retinal images are inverted.*

(a)

(b)

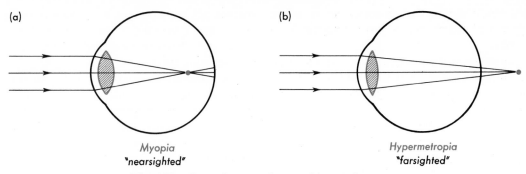

Myopia
"nearsighted"

Hypermetropia
"farsighted"

Fig. 41D   *Typical eye conditions of certain humans.*

the object should be brought close to the eye. The reason for this is that the closer the object is to the eye, the larger is the image formed on the retina. A distance of about 10 in. is found to be the distance of most distinct vision. Prolonged observation at distances of 10 in. or less will result in a considerable amount of fatigue and eyestrain.

41.3. Eye Correction with Spectacle Lenses.

rays converge to a point behind the retina, as in diagram (b), the person is farsighted and is said to have *hypermetropia*.

To correct these defects a diverging spectacle lens of the proper focal length is placed in front of the myopic eye and a converging lens of the proper focal length in front of the hypermetropic eye. The function of such lenses is shown in Fig. 41E. For the nearsighted eye, rays from a

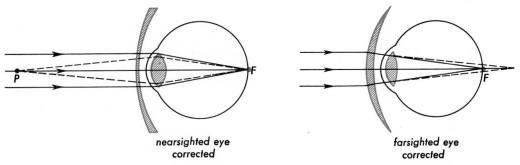

nearsighted eye
corrected

farsighted eye
corrected

Fig. 41E   *Nearsighted and farsighted eyes can be corrected by the proper selection of spectacle lenses.*

As the average person grows older the crystalline lens of the eye tends to harden and the muscles that control it to grow weaker, thus making accommodation more and more difficult. The existence of these conditions is referred to as *presbyopia*. The speed of the hardening varies among individuals. If the length of the eyeball is such that parallel incident rays converge to a point in front of the retina, the person is nearsighted and is said by the eye specialist to have *myopia* [see Fig. 41D(a)]. If parallel incident

nearby object at some point P will, in the absence of spectacles, come to focus on the fovea F. Insertion of the proper diverging lens will now diverge parallel rays as if they came from P and thus bring a distant object to focus at F.

For the farsighted eye, a converging lens adds some convergence to the incoming rays before they meet the eye lens and thus enables distant objects to be seen in good focus. To see close at hand, this same eye requires the use of a converging lens of still greater power. In other words this person should wear bi-focals, lenses whose upper and lower halves have different focal lengths.

It is customary in optometry and ophthalmology to express the focal length of any lens in *diopters* and to speak of the power of a lens in such terms.

The power of a lens in diopters is given by the reciprocal of the focal length in meters.

$$\frac{1\ \text{meter}}{\text{focal length in meters}} = \text{diopters}$$

$$\frac{1}{f} = P \qquad (41b)$$

A lens with a focal length of $+50$ cm, for example, has a power of $+2$ diopters (D), $P = +2$ D, whereas one of $+20$ cm focal length has a power of $+5$ D, $P = +5$ D, etc. Converging lenses have a plus power while diverging lenses have a minus power. Spectacle lenses are made to the nearest quarter of a diopter, thereby reducing the number of grinding and polishing tools required in the optical shops. Furthermore, the sides next to the eyes are always concave to permit free movement of the eyelashes and yet keep the lens as close to the eye as possible as they turn one way and then another.

When, with age, practically all accommodation has been lost, even the normal eye will require a lens of about $+3$ D to obtain good vision of objects at a normal reading distance. As illustrated by the dotted lines in Fig. 41F(a), parallel rays entering the unaided eye are brought to a good focus on the retina R. For an object close by, however, the power of the eye lens is not great enough and the rays converge toward a point S beyond the retina. With an object P

located $33\frac{1}{3}$ cm away and a $+3$ D lens in front of the eye, diagram (b), parallel rays enter the eye from the lens and are brought to a good focus on the retina R.

The principal advantage of the diopter system of measuring lens action is that, when two or more thin lenses are placed in contact, their combined power is just the sum of their separate powers. From Eq.(40g), and the use of Eq.(41b) for power,

$$\frac{1}{f} = \frac{1}{f_1} + \frac{1}{f_2}$$

$$\text{or} \qquad P = P_1 + P_2 \qquad (41c)$$

The power P of a combination of two thin lenses is equal to the sum of the powers of the two separately. As an illustration, two lenses of $+2\frac{1}{4}$ D and $+3\frac{1}{2}$ D, respectively, give in combination a power of $+5\frac{3}{4}$ D; and two lenses of $+3\frac{1}{2}$ D and $-2\frac{1}{4}$ D, respectively, give a power of $+1\frac{1}{4}$ D.

Example 1. A person with hypermetropia requires a $+1\frac{1}{4}$ D spectacle lens to see objects clearly at a great distance [see Figs. 41C and 41E(b)]. What power spectacles will this person require to see objects at 20 in. (or 50 cm)?

Solution. Since lens powers are additive, a lens can be added to the one already present, and of such a power that it will take the rays from any point on an object 50 cm away and make them parallel. A lens of focal length 50 cm will do just this, and by Eq.(41b) corresponds to a power of $+2$ D. Combining a $+2$ D lens with the $+1\frac{1}{4}$ D already required

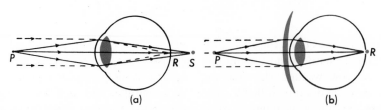

(a)   (b)

Fig. 41F   *The normal eye, having lost accommodation because of age, sees distant objects in good focus. To see nearby objects in focus requires spectacle lenses.*

rays entering the unaided eye are brought to a good focus on the retina R. For an object close by, however, the power of the eye lens is not great enough and the rays converge toward a point S beyond the retina. With an object P

gives an equivalent power of $3\frac{1}{4}$ D. Therefore, spectacle lenses with a power of $+3\frac{1}{4}$ D should be worn.

It frequently happens that the cornea acquires a greater curvature in one plane than in another. Such irregularities are called *astigma-*

tism. Whether accommodation by the crystalline lens has been lost or not, such eyes require astigmatic spectacle lenses, that is, lenses that have more curvature in one direction than at right angles. The surfaces of such lenses are not spherical and are a little more difficult to grind and polish.

41.4. Magnifiers. The magnifier is a positive lens whose function it is to increase the size of the retinal image over and above that which is formed with the unaided eye. The apparent size

image subtending a larger angle θ' will be formed on the retina. What the positive lens has done is to form a virtual image I of the close up object O, and the eye is able to focus upon this virtual image. Any lens used in this manner is called a *magnifier.* If the object O is located a short distance inside of F, the focal point of the magnifier, the virtual image I will be formed at the distance of most distinct vision and a greater magnification will be obtained.

The angular magnification M is defined as the

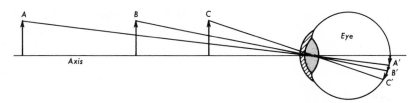

Fig. 41G *The angle subtended by the object determines the size of the retinal image.*

of any object as seen with the unaided eye depends on the angle subtended by the object (see Fig. 41G). As the object is brought closer to the eye, from A to B to C in the diagram, accommodation permits the eye to change its power and to form a larger and larger retinal image. There is a limit to how close an object may come to the eye if the latter is still to have sufficient accommodation to produce a sharp image. Although the nearest point varies widely between individuals, 25 cm is taken to be the standard *near point,* or as it is sometimes called the *distance of most distinct vision.* At this distance, as shown in Fig. 41H, the angle subtended by the object O will be called θ.

If a positive lens is now placed before the eye in the position shown in Fig. 41H the object O may be brought much closer to the eye and an

ratio of the angle θ' subtended by the image to the angle θ subtended by the object.

$$M = \frac{\theta'}{\theta} \qquad (41d)$$

Several common forms of magnifiers are shown in Fig. 41I.

From Fig. 41H, and the lens formula we find for the object distance p,

$$\frac{1}{p} + \frac{1}{-25} = \frac{1}{f}$$

or

$$p = \frac{25 \times f}{25 + f} \qquad (41e)$$

From the two right triangles in the diagram we can write

$$\tan \theta' = \frac{I}{25} = \frac{O}{p} \qquad (41f)$$

Fig. 41H *Illustrating the angle subtended at the naked eye by an object at the near point, and the angle subtended by the virtual image of an object located inside the near point.*

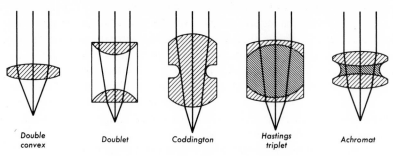

Fig. 41I *Common types of magnifiers.*

and
$$\tan \theta = \frac{O}{25}$$

Substituting the value of p from Eq.(41e), we can write for Eq.(41f),

$$\tan \theta' = O \frac{25+f}{25 \times f}$$

For small angles of θ and θ' the tangents can be replaced by the angles themselves, and we can write

$$\theta = \frac{O}{25} \quad \text{and} \quad \theta' = \frac{O(25+f)}{25 \times f}$$

which, when substituted in Eq.(41d), gives for the magnification

$$M = \frac{O(25+f)}{25 \times f} \frac{25}{O}$$

or
$$M = \frac{25}{f} + 1 \tag{41g}$$

41.5. The Telescope. History informs us that the first telescope was probably constructed in Holland in 1608 by an obscure spectacle lens grinder, Hans Lippershey. A few months later Galileo, upon hearing that objects at a distance may be made to appear close at hand by means of two lenses, designed and made with his own hands the first authentic telescope. The elements of this telescope are still in existence and may be seen on exhibit in Florence, Italy.

Astronomical telescopes today are practically the same in principle as they were in the earliest days of their development. A diagram of a small telescope is shown in Fig. 41J. Light rays from a single point of a far distant object are shown entering the objective lens as a parallel beam. These rays are brought to a focus and form a point image at I. In a similar manner, parallel sets of rays from other points of the same object

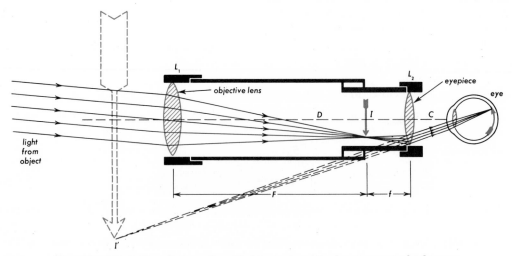

Fig. 41J *Illustration of the paths of light rays in a simple astronomical telescope.*

(not shown) will form point images in the focal plane of the objective. Assuming that the distant object is an arrow pointing upward, the image, as shown in the diagram by a green arrow, is *real* and *inverted*.

The function of the second lens in a telescope is to magnify the image formed by the objective. For this purpose a converging lens of short focus, called the *eyepiece*, is usually used. If the eyepiece is moved to a position where the image I is just inside its focal plane, a magnified image I′ will be seen by the eye. For normal observation, the image I and the focal planes of both lenses are in conjunction, and the light emerging from the eyepiece is parallel. The image I′ under these conditions appears to be far off to the left of L₁, "at infinity," and is of approximately the same angular size as shown in the diagram. Actually, of course, the final image is the one formed on the retina by rays that appear to have come from I′.

The magnifying power of a telescope is defined as the ratio between the angle subtended at the eye by the final image I′ and the angle subtended at the eye by the object itself. In other words, it is the number of times larger an object appears to be when viewed with the telescope. When plane geometry is applied to a simple light-ray diagram of a telescope, it is found that the magnifying power is equal to the ratio of the focal lengths of the two lenses.

$$\text{magnifying power} = -\frac{F}{f} \qquad (41h)$$

where F is the focal length of the objective, and f is the focal length of the eyepiece.

As an illustration, suppose the objective lens of a small telescope has a focal length of one yard and that it is used with an eyepiece having a focal length of 1 in.; the magnifying power would be 36/1 or 36. Distant objects viewed through this telescope would appear to be 36 times as tall and 36 times as wide as when viewed with the unaided eye. If an eyepiece with a focal length of only half an inch is used with the same objective, the magnification will be twice as great, or 72.

This would seem to indicate that the magnification of a telescope can be increased indefinitely, but this is not the case. There are a number of factors that set a practical upper limit, the chief one of which for small telescopes is the diameter of the objective lens.

If a telescope is to be used for astronomical purposes only, an inverted image is of no consequence to the observer, but if it is to be used to observe objects on the earth the magnified images should be right-side up. Instruments that give erect images are called *terrestrial telescopes*. To right the inverted image in a telescope, any one of several methods may be employed: one is to use a third lens, and another is to insert an erecting prism just in front of the eyepiece in place of the converging lens. A third method is the arrangement devised by Galileo in his first telescopes, and now commonly used in *field* and *opera glasses* (see Fig. 41K).

Fig. 41K *Lens and ray diagram of an opera glass, or Galilean telescope.*

41.6. Prism Binoculars. Prism binoculars are in reality a pair of twin telescopes mounted side by side, one for each of the two eyes. The objective lenses in front and the eyepieces at the rear are converging lenses as in the astronomical telescope, but each pair of total reflecting prisms inverts the rays to give erect images (see Fig. 41L). The doubling-back of the light rays has the advantage of enabling long-focus objective lenses to be used in short tubes, thus giving higher magnification. In addition to good achromatic lenses and accurately ground prisms, there are three features that go to make up good binoculars: these are (1) *magnification*, (2) *field of view*, and (3) *light-gathering power*.

Fig. 41L *Cutaway of a prism binocular showing the lenses and reflecting prisms.* (Courtesy, Bausch & Lomb Optical Company.)

For hand-held use, binoculars with a 6-, 7-, or 8-power magnification are most generally useful. Glasses with powers above 8 are desirable but require a tripod mount to hold them steady. For powers less than 4, lens aberrations usually offset the magnification and the average person can usually see better with the unaided eyes.

The field of view is determined principally by the eyepiece aperture and should be as large as is practical. For 7-power binoculars, a 6° field taken in by the objective is considered large since, in the eyepiece, the same field is spread over an angle of 7 × 6 or 42°.

The diameter of each objective lens determines the light-gathering power, and is important at night only when there is so little light available.

Binoculars with the specification of 6 × 30 have a magnification of 6 and objective lenses with an effective diameter of 30 mm. The specification 7 × 50 means a magnification of 7 and objective lenses 50 mm in diameter. Although glasses with the latter specifications are excellent day or night, they are considerably larger and more cumbersom than daytime glasses specified as 6 × 30's or 8 × 30's. For general use, the latter two types are by far the most useful.

41.7. The Reflection Telescope. Nearly all of the very large astronomical telescopes in the world today employ concave mirrors instead of lenses. There are several advantages to this: first, a concave mirror does not exhibit chromatic aberration, thereby requiring only one piece of

glass and one surface to be ground; and second, greater stability of the telescope is attained by having the large and heaviest optical part at the bottom of the instrument.

A diagram of the great 100-in. reflecting telescope of the Mt. Wilson Observatory is shown in Fig. 41M. Parallel light rays entering the tele-

Fig. 41M *Diagram of the 100-in. reflecting telescope of the Mt. Wilson Observatory.*

scope tube are brought to a focus at F. Instead of viewing or photographing images at this point, a small mirror m reflects the convergent rays to a focus at F'. Here, out of the path of the incoming light, the star images can be observed and photographed. While the small mirror m casts a shadow on the objective mirror M, the shadow area is relatively small so that only a small percent of the light is lost.

The 200-in. telescope now in operation on Palomar Mountain in Southern California is of the same optical design. The objective mirror is a little over 16 ft in diameter and has a hole 40 in. in diameter through its center. This hole cuts out only 4% of the mirror's total area. For various kinds of observations, photographic instruments and cameras of one kind or another are located in an observing booth 40 in. in diameter and located at the focal plane, F, in Fig. 41M. On other occasions a 40-in. convex mirror is placed at m, and the light is reflected back down the telescope tube through the hole in the big objective where it is brought to a focus below the telescope.

41.8. The Microscope. The simplest of microscopes is just a single converging lens of short focus used as a magnifier as shown in Fig.

40F(a). Since the shortest focal-length lenses produce the greatest magnification, it is not surprising that small glass beads in the form of perfect spheres were the first really successful microscopes. Lenses of this description were used by the famous Dutch microscopist, Van Leeuwenhoek, when in 1674 he discovered and gave an accurate account of the red corpuscles in blood.

The compound microscope, which now exceeds by far the magnifying power of a simple microscope, was invented by Galileo in 1610. Like a telescope, these instruments consist of an optical train of two lenses, one called the objective and the other the eyepiece. The objective of the microscope differs from the telescope, however, in that, instead of having a long focus, it has a short focus and it is placed close to the object as shown in Fig. 41N. This lens forms a real and magnified image at a point I just in front of the eyepiece. Since the eyepiece is another short-focus lens, it is used as a simple microscope or magnifying glass to produce a magnified virtual image at I'.

Early forms of the compound microscope displayed so much chromatic aberration that only low magnifying powers were attained. High-powered microscopes of today overcome this and other defects by using an objective containing as many as eight or ten lenses and an eyepiece containing two or more.

A high-quality microscope is usually equipped with a turret nose carrying three objectives, each of a different magnifying power. By turning the turret, any one of the three objectives may be rotated into proper alignment with the eyepiece. Diagrams of two typical objectives are shown in Fig. 41O.

Under suitable illumination, magnifying powers of a little more than 2000 diameters are commonly attained. Although this is not an upper limit to the magnification for optical microscopes of the future, we know from the wave nature of light that the ultimate limit is not many times that which has already been attained. This is not a pessimistic attitude but a scientific truth based upon our present knowledge of diffraction.

The electron microscope, capable of magnifications 50 to 100 times that of the best optical microscope, is described in Sec. 59.8.

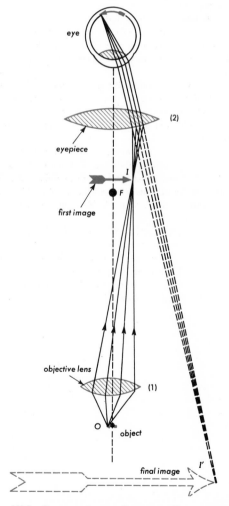

Fig. 41N *Lens and ray diagram of a compound microscope.*

Fig. 41O *Microscopic objectives (a) medium power, and (b) high power, oil immersion.*

PROBLEMS

1. A camera lens has a focal length of 50 mm. Calculate image distances for the following object distances: (a) infinity, (b) 4 m, (c) 1 m, (d) 0.5 m.

2. A portrait camera lens has an aperture of 3 cm, and an f-number of 3.5. What is its focal length? [Ans. +10.5 cm.]

3. The lens of a camera has a diameter of 28 mm and a focal length of 126 mm. What is its f-number?

4. A telephoto lens of a camera has a focal length of 250 mm. Calculate image distances for the following object distances: (a) infinity, (b) 5 m, (c) 1 m, (d) 0.5 m. [Ans. (a) 250 mm, (b) 263 mm, (c) 333 mm, (d) 500 mm.]

5. A boy with hypermetropia requires +1.75 spectacle lenses to see clearly at a distance. What power lenses should he have to read a book located 40 cm away?

6. A man with presbyopia sees distant objects clearly without glasses. Calculate the power of the spectacle lenses he should wear to see objects (a) 75 cm away, and (b) 33 cm away. [Ans. (a) +1.33 D, (b) +3.0 D.]

7. A near-sighted person sees objects clearly at a distance of 15 cm. Having lost his accommodation, what power spectacle lenses should he wear that will enable him to see distant objects clearly?

8. To an observer on the earth, the moon subtends an angle of approximately 0.5 degree of arc. If a telescope objective lens with a focal length of 2 m is used to photograph the moon, what will be the diameter of the image formed at the focal plane of the lens? [Ans. 1.74 cm.]

9. The lens of a camera has a focal length of 135 mm. and a diameter of 30.0 mm. Find its f-number.

10. The objective lens of a telescope has a focal length of 150 cm. What should be the focal length of an eyepiece if the observer wishes to obtain a magnification of 25? [Ans. 6.0 cm.]

11. The objective lens of a telescope has a focal length of 120 cm, and a diameter of 10.0 cm. The eyepiece has a focal length of 2.5 cm. Find (a) the magnification, (b) the position of the image of the objective as formed by the eyepiece.

12. The objective lens of a telescope has a focal length of 90 cm, and a diameter of 7.5 cm. (a) What focal length eyepiece should be used to obtain a magnification of 25? (b) What is the size of the image of the objective lens formed by the eyepiece, and (c) what is the distance of this image from the eyepiece? [Ans. (a) 3.6 cm, (b) 3.0 mm, (c) 3.74 cm.]

13. A pair of Navy type binoculars have the designation 12 × 85. If the eyepieces have a focal length of 2.2 cm (a) what are the diameters, and (b) the focal lengths of the objective lenses?

14. A lens with a focal length of 2.5 cm is to be used by an amateur astronomer for his reflecting telescope. If his objective is a concave mirror with a radius of curvature of 240 cm, what is the magnifying power he obtains? [Ans. 48.]

15. A pair of prism binoculars has a designation 5 × 18. If the objective lenses have a focal length of 10 cm, (a) what are the diameters of the objective lenses, (b) the focal lengths of the eyepieces, and (c) the magnifying power?

16. An amateur astronomer grinds his own telescope mirror for a reflecting telescope. The mirror has a focal length of 155 cm. What focal length eyepieces should he buy if he wishes to obtain magnifications of (a) 25, (b) 50, (c) 75, and (d) 100? [Ans. (a) 6.2 cm, (b) 3.1 cm, (c) 2.07 cm, (d) 1.55 cm.]

17. A Coddington magnifier has a focal length of 1.8 cm. Find its magnifying power.

18. An achromatic magnifying lens has a focal length of 2.8 cm. What is its magnifying power? [Ans. 9.93.]

19. A Hastings triplet lens has a focal length of 1.6 cm. What is its magnifying power?

THE SCIENCE OF COLOR

Color vision is perhaps man's most valued gift of nature. While color is for the most part a physiological phenomenon, its origin is considered by some to belong to the realm of physics. There is, on the one hand, the theory of *color mixing* and, on the other, the theory of *color vision*. The first of these theories deals with the action of matter on light before it reaches the eye, and the second with the visual functions of the eye. The science of color mixing has been made possible through the discovery that all colors can be completely analyzed by spreading them out into a prismatic spectrum. The science of color vision, on the other hand, involving the optics of the eye as well as the physiological functions of the entire vision mechanism, is not completely understood. Both of these subjects will be treated in this chapter on the science of color.

42.1. Effect of Illumination on Color. To see a body in its true color, that body must be illuminated by light of the same color. If a red rose, as an illustration, is placed in the different colors of a prismatic spectrum it will appear a brilliant red in red light and grey or black in all the others.

Another experiment is illustrated in Fig. 42A where yellow light from a sodium arc lamp is shown illuminating a row of colored skeins of yarn. When the lamp is turned on, only the yellow yarn appears with its true color; the white yarn is yellow and the others are black or grey. If the same set of colored yarns is illuminated with red light, only the red yarn will appear in its true color; the white yarn will now be red, and the others will be grey or black. In other words, unless the source emits the proper colors, the body cannot be seen in its true color. Sunlight will show each yarn in its true color, for sunlight contains all colors of the spectrum.

42.2. Surface Color. The above experiments demonstrate what is called *surface color.* When sunlight falls on a red rose, red yarn, red paint, or red glass, all of the colors except red are absorbed and do not get through or out again. The red, as it passes through, is reflected and refracted by the fine grains of pigment and comes out in all directions as shown in Fig. 42B.

Not all of the other colors are completely absorbed, for a small amount of each color is reflected from the first surface the white light

white red yellow green blue violet brown

colored yarns

sodium lamp
or flame

Fig. 42A *Experiment with colored skeins of yarn showing that, to see an object in its true surface color, it must be illuminated by the proper light.*

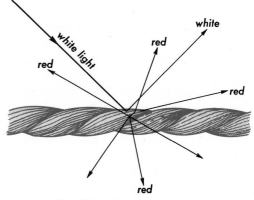

Fig. 42B *Illustration of color.*

strikes. This may be illustrated by a polished sheet of red glass. Although the glass appears red from both sides, a small amount of white light is reflected from the top surface, obeying the law of reflection. The red, on the other hand, is reflected and refracted in the usual way at each surface.

The three aspects of surface color are *hue*, *brightness*, and *saturation*. Hue refers to the *name* of a color, brightness to the relative *magnitude* of the sensory response, and saturation to the color *strength*. Hue is qualitative and is the most distinctive aspect of color, for without hue there is no color. Hue cannot be defined but only exemplified: red, yellow, green, blue, violet, purple, and various intermediaries between these are hues. *Brightness* is a subjective intensity and may exist alone, as in white light. White is devoid of hue and hence is devoid of color. Hue cannot exist alone, for if we have hue it has a certain brightness and saturation. Illustrations of these three concepts are shown in Fig. 42H.

Colors that do not contain any trace of white light are said to be *saturated*. The more white they contain, the less saturated they become. Pink is not a saturated color since it is a mixture of red and white. This may be demonstrated by mixing a small amount of red pigment with white paint, or, what is still more striking, by pulverizing a piece of red glass. As the glass is ground finer and finer the amount of white light reflected is increased by the increasing surface area, until the powder becomes almost white. Although the red light is still present, the white light by comparison is much stronger. A similar effect is produced by transparent substances like crystals and window glass; when powdered they become white. *The smaller the amount of white light mixed in with a color, the greater is the saturation.*

42.3. Metallic Color. Some substances appear to be one color by reflected light and a different color by transmitted light. This is particularly true of metals and of certain aniline dyes. Gold, for example, is always yellow-orange by reflected light but, if thin enough, is blue-green by transmitted light (see Fig. 42C).

White light, composed of the spectrum colors, red, orange, yellow, green, blue, and violet, is

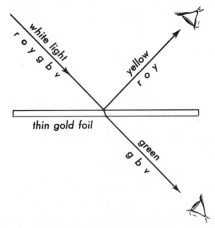

Fig. 42C　*A thin gold foil appears yellow-orange by reflected light and blue-green by transmitted light.*

incident on the thin film of gold. Although all of these colors are partially reflected and partially transmitted, the predominant colors in the transmitted light are green, blue, and violet, while those in the reflected light are red, orange, and yellow. To the eye the mixture of reflected colors appears yellow, and the mixture of transmitted colors appears green.

Graphs of the reflecting power of copper, silver, and gold are reproduced in Fig. 42D. Copper, it will be noted, reflects about 80% of all red light incident upon it and only 40% of the violet. Curiously enough, all metals are good absorbers of colors they best reflect, so that white light incident on a thin copper foil is partly robbed of red, orange, and yellow by having some of each of these colors reflected and some absorbed. Since smaller amounts of the green, blue, and violet are reflected and absorbed, these colors will predominate in the transmitted light, giving it, like gold, a blue-green or cyan appearance. If the metal is too thick, it becomes opaque to all colors. In a rough way the curves in Fig. 42D represent the absorption of light by metals as well as the reflecting power. Silver, like so many other metals, is a good reflector of all colors and therefore is nearly white.

42.4. Mixing Spectrum Colors. Over a period of many years, different color charts and color theories have been proposed, some of them good and some of them bad. Because the most success-

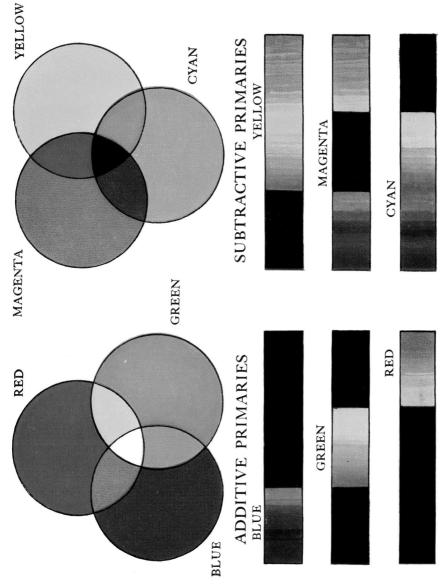

Fig. 42F   *Primary colors showing their combinations and component spectral colors.*

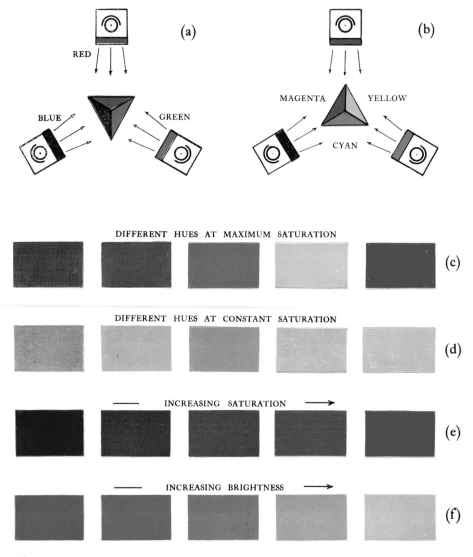

Fig. 42H   (a) *Additive primaries.* (b) *equal mixing of primary pairs.* (c) *Different hues at their maximum saturation values.* (d) *Different hues at constant saturation and equal brightness.* (e) *The same hue at constant brightness but increasing saturation.* (f) *The same hue at constant saturation but increasing brightness.*

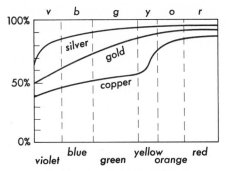

Fig. 42D *Graphs showing the reflecting power of metals for different colors of the spectrum.*

ful theories have, of necessity, been detailed and complicated, some simplification of their concepts and an explanation of their common principles will be given here.

As a starting point, consider the experiment shown in Fig. 42E in which a narrow beam of

in Fig. 42F, and to call these parts the *additive primaries*. When red and orange are allowed to mix, the rod appears a bright red; when yellow and green are mixed the rod appears bright green, and when blue and violet are mixed it appears blue-violet. As colors these additive primaries, red, green, and blue, appear like the three large circular areas at the upper left in Fig. 42F.

The next step is to mix the *primary colors* two at a time and to observe their resultant color mixture. When primary red and primary green mix at the glass rod, they produce yellow; red and blue produce magenta; and green and blue produce cyan, a light blue-green. These, the so-called *subtractive primaries*, are shown by the three large circles at the upper right in Fig. 42F, and the overlapping areas at the upper left. The pure spectrum colors that go to make up each

Fig. 42E *Experimental arrangement for mixing pure spectrum colors to form all primary colors.*

white light from a carbon arc and lens falls on a glass prism and is spread out into a complete spectrum. With the prism located near the center of curvature of a large concave mirror, all colors after reflection are brought to a focus on a translucent glass rod where, combined again, they produce white. A large white card is next held in front of the mirror to act as a screen to control the colors that are permitted to mix at the rod. By screening off violet, blue and green, for example, the remaining colors, red, orange, and yellow, come together and the rod appears orange.

We now proceed to divide the spectrum up into three equal parts, as shown at the lower left

subtractive primary are shown at the lower right.

42.5. The Color Triangle. The color triangle, as illustrated in Fig. 42G, is a triangular arrangement of the additive and subtractive primaries with white at the center. Red, green, and blue are located at the corners, while magenta, yellow, and cyan are located at the sides. The order of the colors is such that the sum of any two additive primaries at the corners gives the subtractive primary between them on the sides, and the sum of all three primaries gives white at the center.

Colors opposite each other on the color triangle are *complementary*.

Two colors are said to be complementary if

when added together they produce white. Magenta and green are complementary, for when added together, as can be seen from their spectral distributions in Fig. 42F, they contain all of the spectrum colors of white light. Similarly red and cyan, as well as yellow and blue, are complementary.

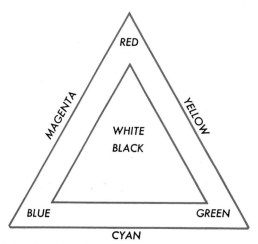

Fig. 42G *Diagram of the color triangle, with the additive primaries at the corners and the subtractive primaries at the sides.*

42.6. Additive Method of Color Mixing. The mixing of colored lights described in the two preceding sections is called the additive method of color mixing and differs greatly from the subtractive method to be described in the following section. An interesting experiment for demonstrating the additive method is shown in Fig. 42H. Three boxes containing white lights are arranged to illuminate separately the three sides of a white pyramid. A matched set of glass filters, one for each of the additive primary hues, red, green, and blue, respectively, are placed in front of each box opening, thereby illuminating the pyramid faces as shown in the left-hand diagram.

Upon rotating the pyramid slowly a point is reached, as shown in the right-hand diagram, where pairs of lights mix in equal amounts on each of the three faces. These mixtures are the subtractive primaries, magenta, yellow, and cyan. As the pyramid turns from position (a) to position (b), all variations of two colors are seen on the pyramid faces. Television in full color is produced by the additive method of color mixing.

42.7. Subtractive Method of Color Mixing. This is the method most familiar to everyone, the method used in the mixing of pigments to produce various colored paints. For this purpose the subtractive primaries, *magenta, yellow,* and *cyan,* often referred to by artists as *red, yellow,* and *blue,* are the most useful. The mixing in equal amounts of any two subtractive primaries will produce the additive primary lying between them on the color triangle. When cyan and yellow paints are mixed, the result is green.

At first it seems strange that yellow and cyan, neither one of which has the appearance of an additive primary, should produce green when mixed together. A spectrum analysis of these two colors, as shown at the lower right in Fig. 42F, shows that green and yellow are spectrum colors common to both.

Mixing by the subtractive method is demonstrated with prisms and filters in Fig. 42I. To see what happens to each spectral hue in each filter, the white light is first spread out into its complete spectrum. To illustrate, the yellow filter alone in diagram (h) absorbs blue and violet, and the cyan filter alone in (f) absorbs red and orange. When both are inserted as in diagram (d), only green and yellow are transmitted. To the eye this mixture appears bright green. The other two pairs of filters in diagrams (e) and (i) give the other two primaries, red and blue.

To carry these experimental demonstrations to the mixing of paint, each little grain of pigment is like a piece of colored glass (see Fig. 42J). Assuming the oil in which the yellow pigment is imbedded to be transparent, white light entering the paint is reflected and refracted as shown. Wherever blue or violet rays pass through pigment grains, they are absorbed. After many reflections and refractions the red, orange, yellow, and green can still escape. Together these four colors (see Fig. 42F) appear as yellow.

When yellow and cyan pigments are mixed together as illustrated by the detailed diagram in Fig. 42K, only green and yellow light is transmitted by both pigments.

The essential difference between the additive method and subtractive method of color mixing

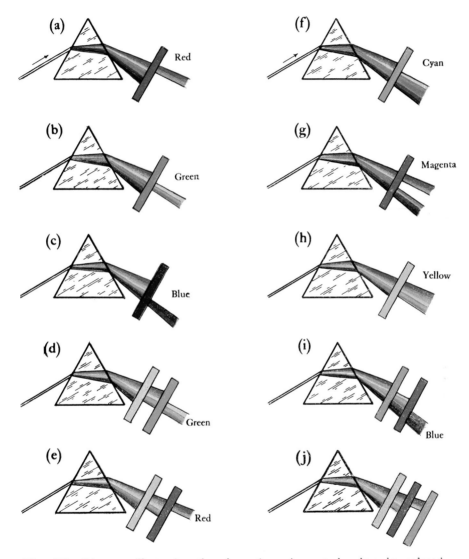

(a) Red

(b) Green

(c) Blue

(d) Green

(e) Red

(f) Cyan

(g) Magenta

(h) Yellow

(i) Blue

(j)

Fig. 42I   *Diagram illustrating the absorption of spectral colors by colored filters and the subtractive method of color mixing.*

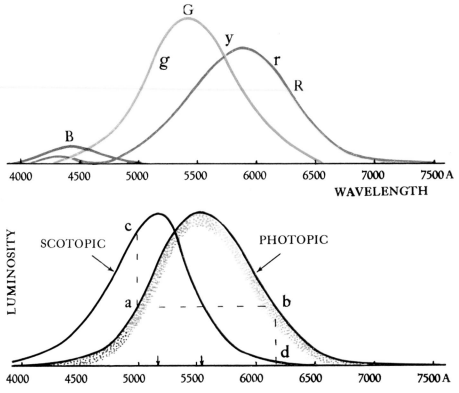

Fig. 42L (a) *Standard luminosity and relative brightness curves for the visible spectrum,* (b) *Tri-stimulus curves for the red, green, and blue sensitive cones of the retina,* (c) *Photopic and scotopic curves comparing cone vision by day with rod vision by night.*

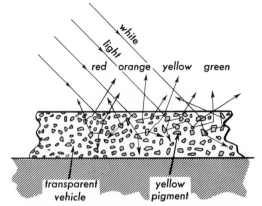

Fig. 42J *Illustration of the absorption of blue and violet light by yellow paint and the emission of red, orange, yellow, and green.*

is just that suggested by the name; in the additive method the resultant color is just the *sum* of the two constituents used to produce it, and in the subtractive method it is just the *difference* between the two. Addition always produces a brighter color, and subtraction produces a darker color. Just as the additive mixing of red, green, and blue produces white, so the subtractive mixing of magenta, yellow, and cyan produces black. Similarly, two complementary colors, when mixed additively, produce white, and when mixed subtractively, produce black.

42.8. Color Vision. When radiant energy at different wavelengths of the spectrum falls upon the retina of the normal human being, the visual

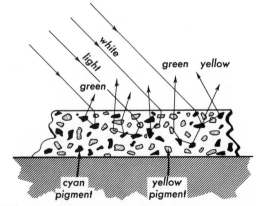

Fig. 42K *When blue and yellow paints are mixed together, green and yellow are the only pure spectral colors transmitted by both pigments.*

sensations vary as shown at the top in Fig. 42L. The maximum, which occurs in the green at $\lambda = 5550$Å, is assigned the arbitrary value of 1000. On either side of this maximum the response falls off smoothly toward the violet at one end and the red at the other (for Å see p. 408).

The *standard luminosity curve* is experimentally determined by matching the brightness of one color against that of another for each part of the spectrum and then measuring the relative amounts of energy in each of the two color fields. In comparing green and red, for example, much less intensity is required to give green light a brightness apparently equal to that of a red light. The solid curve is therefore a plot of *photometric energy magnitudes* and not relative brightness.

Brightness is a *sensory magnitude* in light just as loudness is a sensory magnitude in sound. Both vary over a wide range of values as the logarithm of the energy. To double the brightness of a surface, its emission must increase many fold. A plot of the logarithms of the luminosity gives the *relative brightness* curve for an equal-energy spectrum. In other words, the dotted curve represents the relative brightness of the colors of a constant-energy spectrum and clearly indicates the rather abrupt cutoff at either end.

During the past century, many attempts to formulate a scientific theory of color vision have been made. While some of these theories have met with considerable success, none of them has been able to explain every known phenomenon. The most successful theory was first advanced by the English scientist, Thomas Young, and later improved by the German scientist, Von Helmholtz. According to the Young–Helmholtz theory, the tiny cones in the retina of the eye (see Fig. 1B) are of three kinds.

One set of cones produces the visual sensation of red, the second set gives the sensation of green, and the third set the sensation of blue. A set of sensation graphs for each of these color-sensitive cones is given by the center curves in Fig. 42L. The R curve shows that to stimulate the red-response cones any wavelength from spectral violet to red is satisfactory, but wavelength 6000Å will produce the maximum response. Similarly the B and G cones are seen to be stimulated by a whole range of different wavelengths.

When pure spectrum yellow enters the eye, as represented by y in the diagram, both the R and G cones respond equally and the sensation is yellow. If pure spectral red and pure spectral green are permitted to enter the eye (like r and g in the diagram), both the R and G cones again respond equally and the sensation produced is yellow. Because of the stimulus equality, the brain is unable to tell the difference from the y stimulus, and the mixture has neither *redness* nor *greenness*. It is therefore possible to obtain a yellow hue with no spectral yellow present. A similar behavior occurs near wavelength 5000Å where the B and G cones are stimulated equally to produce a *cyan hue*.

If the eye is subjected to faint light of wavelength 4500Å, the visual sensation is *blue*, but when the intensity is raised the hue turns to violet or purple, indicating a noticeable stimulation of the R cones. This is the evidence for the small "bump" in the R curve in Fig. 42L. White is produced by the presence of all wavelengths in equal amounts, but it can also be produced by as few as three wavelengths.

By the additive process of three primary responses, red, green, and blue, all of the thousands of recognized hues can be produced. The power of the eye and the brain to synthesize colors is to be compared with the reverse process by which the ear and brain are able to analyze musical tones into components.

42.9. Color Deficiency and Color Blindness. About 8% of males and 1% of females are color deficient or color blind, that is, do not have normal color vision. Although there are many forms and degrees of this defect, the two most common types are called *protanopia* and *deuteranopia*.* Numerous tests and experiments indicate that protanopia is due to the absence of

---

* Both of these forms of *dichromacy* are hereditary, recessive, and sex linked. Theoretically, one woman in seven is a genetic carrier who does not herself exhibit color deficiency but transmits it *through* half of her daughters and *to* half of her sons. If one of these dichromatic males marries a normal woman, all of their children will be normal but the daughters will all be carriers.

R cones in the retina [see Fig. 42L(b)], whereas deuteranopia arises wherever the G cones have the same spectral response as the normal R cones.

The true *protanope* is characterized by his observation that the long-wavelength end of the spectrum is green and stops at about 6800Å, instead of the normal 7600Å. Although he is able to match colors reasonably well, the number of hues seen by this individual is only a small fraction of those seen by the normal person. With only two primary colors, blue and green, at his disposal, he sees only those hues produced by their mixture in all possible proportions.

To the *deuteranope*, the spectrum is not shortened at the ends, but, since the G and R cones are equally stimulated with all the longer wavelengths, he sees only yellow from about 5700Å on. With only red and blue primaries, only hues described by the normal as yellow, blue, or white are produced. Although various methods have been devised for detecting color deficiencies, the most sensitive and accurate determinations are made with an optical instrument known as the *anomaloscope*.

Color vision with only two primaries, as in protanopia and deuteranopia, is called *dichromacy*, whereas vision with only a partial deficiency of one of the three cone types is called *anomalous trichromacy*. In the *anomalous trichromat*, there is a reduction in the brightness of either red, green, or less commonly blue, but the number of possible hues is greater than with the *dichromat* and, in many cases, approaches the *normal* individual who is a *trichromat*.

42.10. Photopic and Scotopic Vision. In a well-lighted room or in bright sunlight, the peak sensitivity of the eye is in the yellow-green part of the visible spectrum. When the light is extremely faint, however, the maximum shifts to the blue-green region and practically all color discrimination disappears. Two brightness sensitivity curves, one for high-level illumination and the other for very low illumination are shown in Fig. 42L. Although the peaks are drawn to the same height, the vertical scales for the two are different. The P curve is actually thousands of times higher than the S curve.

Under daytime illumination, normal vision is

acquired by what is called *photopic vision*, a condition whereby the color-sensitive cones in the retina of the eye are responsible for visual sensations. On dark nights, however, when the illumination is very low, the highly sensitive rods account for what little vision is attained, and we have what is called *scotopic vision. Photopic vision is cone vision; scotopic vision is rod vision.* The normal eye contains about 7 million cones and 130 million rods.

An interesting demonstration may be performed with an ordinary projection lantern, a slide that is half red and half blue, and an iris diaphragm located in front of the projection lens. The red and blue glass of the slide should be matched for equal brightness under normal projection on a white screen. As the iris diaphragm is narrowed down, the red field will appear to fade more rapidly than the blue, and finally to disappear altogether. The persistence of the blue is more strikingly observed by directing the eyes to one side of the two colored fields. If the original matching of red and blue corresponds to equal brightness points like (a) and (b) in Fig. 42L, the reduced illumination corresponds to the unequal brightness points (c) and (d). This observed phenomenon is called the *Purkinje effect*.

42.11. The ICI Chromaticity Diagram. Well-planned steps toward a quantitative measurement of color were taken by the International Commission on Illumination in 1931. At that time three additive primaries, red, green, and blue, were adopted, in which the visible spectrum was divided into three overlapping spectral-response curves somewhat similar to those in Fig. 42L. Although a treatment of this standard

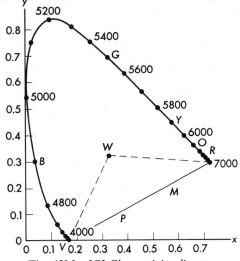

Fig. 42M   *ICI Chromaticity diagram.*

ICI system* must be left for more advanced studies, it should be mentioned here that any given color sample can be measured with a spectroscope in terms of the three adopted primaries, and the results of the measurements can be expressed by two numbers. These two numbers can then be plotted on a graph.

When the pure spectrum colors ROYGBV are matched against a mixture of the standard primaries, a smooth curve as shown in Fig. 42M is obtained. With white at the center, the complete gamut of all possible color mixtures lies within the enclosed area RGBVW, with the purples P and magentas M confined to the region RWV between the two ends of the spectrum.

* For a treatment of the ICI color system, see F. W. Sears, *Principles of Physics* (Addison-Wesley Publishing Co., Inc., Reading, Massachusetts), Chap. 13.

PROBLEMS

1. The following pairs of colors are mixed additively. What is their resultant color? (a) red and green, (b) red and blue, (c) blue and green, (c) blue and yellow, and (e) red and cyan.

2. The following pairs of colors are mixed subtractively. What is their resultant color? (a) yellow and cyan, (b) magenta and cyan, (c) magenta and yellow, (d) magneta and green, and (e) red and cyan.

3. Make charts showing the various parts of the pure spectrum colors belonging to each of the additive and subtractive primaries.

4. Diagram the color triangle from memory.

5. Draw scotopic and photopic curves for day and night vision, and briefly explain the Purkinje effect.

6. Yellow and magenta are mixed (a) additively, and (b) subtractively. What are the resultant colors in each case?

7. (a) What color added to red will give white? (b) What color subtracted from red will give black?

8. What colors are complementary to each of the following: (a) red, (b) yellow, (c) green, (d) cyan, (e) blue, (f) magenta, (g) white, and (h) black?

9. How can it be shown that the actual colors of the spectrum combine to form the colors shown on the color triangle? Describe the experiment.

10. What are complementary colors? When two complementary colors are added together, what spectrum colors would be present? If they are mixed subtractively, what spectrum colors would be present?

11. Which of the two methods of color mixing produces brighter colors as the result of mixing?

12. What color added to red will give (a) white, (b) magenta, and (c) yellow?

13. What color mixed subtractively with yellow will produce (a) green, (b) red, and (c) black?

14. Make a diagram and briefly explain how yellow and cyan pigments when (a) mixed as paints can produce green. (b) Do the pigment particles themselves become green?

DIFFRACTION
AND INTERFERENCE OF LIGHT

When light passes close to the edge of any object, it is bent in its path and travels on in a new direction. This bending of light around corners is called *diffraction*.

To observe the phenomenon of diffraction, the following simple experiment may be performed in a darkened room. A box containing a light bulb and a pinhole is placed on one side of the room and a ground-glass observing screen or photographic film is placed on the other. Objects of various kinds are then placed about halfway between the source and the screen as shown in Fig. 43A. This is the arrangement used in ob-

Fig. 43A *The shadow cast by the light from a small source is not sharp at the edges, but exhibits a banded structure.*

taining the photograph reproduced in Fig. 43B. Notice that the edges of the shadows are not sharp but are bounded at the edges by narrow bands or fringes. At the center of two figures the fringes form sets of concentric rings.

43.1. Huygens' Principle. The phenomenon of diffraction was explained in the time of Newton by assuming that light is composed of small particles or corpuscles obeying the ordinary laws of

mechanical motion. And so it was that Newton and his followers held for many years to the idea that a source of light is a source of high-speed particles radiated in all directions.

Although such a viewpoint was accepted for many years, it was later abandoned in favor of a wave theory of light, according to which a beam of light is made up of many waves of extremely short wavelengths. By adopting the wave hypothesis, a complete and adequate account of the phenomena of reflection, refraction, diffraction, interference, and polarization was finally formulated on a mathematical basis at the beginning of the nineteenth century by Augustin Fresnel, a French physicist. The wave theory of light was first proposed by the English physicist Robert Hooke in 1665 and improved 20 years later by the Dutch scientist and mathematician, Christian Huygens.*

Everyone has at some time or another dropped a stone in a still pond of water and watched the waves spread slowly outward in ever-widening concentric circles. In the analogous case of a

---

* Christian Huygens (1629–1695), famous Dutch physicist and contemporary of Isaac Newton. Born at The Hague in 1629, young Christian got his first ideas about waves and their propagation by watching the ripples on the canals about his home. Although his chief title-deed to immortality is his development of the wave theory of light, he made many and valuable contributions to mathematics and astronomy. He improved upon the method of grinding telescope lenses and discovered the Orion nebula, part of which is now known by his name. He was elected to the Royal Society of London in 1663, and delivered before that august body the first clear statement of the laws governing the collision of elastic bodies. He died a confirmed bachelor at The Hague in 1695.

Fig. 43B *Photographs of the shadows cast by small objects. The narrow bands are due to the diffraction of light.*

point source of light, the spreading waves form concentric spheres moving outward with the extremely high speed of 186,300 mi/s. This is represented diagramatically in Fig. 43C. Each circle

Fig. 43C *Diagram of waves spreading out from a point source. The secondary wavelets and new wavefronts illustrate Huygens' principle.*

represents the crest of a wave so that the distance between consecutive circles is one wavelength.

According to Huygens' principle, every point on any wavefront may be regarded as a new point source of waves. Regarding each of any

number of points like a, b, c, etc., as point sources like S, secondary wavelets spread out simultaneously as shown. The envelope of these an instant later is the new wavefront A, B, C, etc., and still later the wavefront L, M, N, etc. Although Huygens' principle at first glance might seem to be a useless play with circles, it has quite general application to many optical phenomena.

A direct experimental demonstration of Huygens' principle is illustrated in Fig. 43D. Plane waves approaching a barrier AB from the left are reflected or absorbed at every point except at

Fig. 43D *Diagram of the diffraction of waves at a small opening. Huygens' principle.*

Fig. 43E *The behavior of light waves as they pass through a converging lens.*

S, where they are allowed to pass on through. When the experiment is carried out with water, one can see the waves spreading out in all directions as if S were a point source.

If AB is an opaque screen and S is a pinhole small in comparison to the wavelength of light, the light waves will spread out in hemispheres with S at their center. If S is a long narrow slit (perpendicular to the page), the waves spread out with cylindrical wavefronts. Cross sections of all of these cases are represented by the semicircles, the light traveling in the direction of the arrows.

The action of a converging lens on light waves is illustrated in Fig. 43E. If a point source of light is placed at the focal point, as in diagram (a), the expanding waves pass through the lens and come out as plane waves, i.e., as parallel light. In diagram (b), incident plane waves are shown emerging from the lens as converging waves which come to a focus at F. The change brought about by the lens can be explained by the fact that light travels faster in air than it does in glass.

It is important to note that the time taken for light rays leaving the point source and arriving at the point image is the same for all paths.

43.2. Interference. When two stones are dropped simultaneously into a still pond of water, two sets of waves will spread outward as shown in Fig. 43F. As these waves cross each other, they act one upon the other, producing what is called an *interference pattern*. Where the crests of two waves come together at the dotted intersections, they are in step, or in phase, and the amplitude of the water surface is increased. Where the crest of one wave and the trough of another come together, they are out of step, or

out of phase, and the amplitude of the water surface is reduced.

The in-phase regions of the waves move outward along the dotted lines, such as x, y, and z,

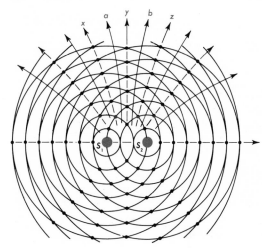

Fig. 43F *Concentric waves traveling outward from a double source, producing what is called an interference pattern.*

and we have what is called *constructive interference*. The out-of-phase regions move outward along the solid lines, such as a and b, and we have what is called *destructive interference*.

An instantaneous photograph of such a wave pattern is shown in Fig. 43G. Note how clearly the interference regions of the waves stand out. Photographs of this kind, as well as direct observations of such wave patterns, are readily made as follows. A glass tray for maintaining a shallow water layer can be made from a piece of window glass and a wooden frame. A thin metal strip, clamped at one end and set vibrating up and down over the water, is used as a source. A piece of wire, fastened to the vibrating end of this strip, should have one wire end dipping into the water for a single-wave source, and both ends dipping into the water for a double source. Intermittent viewing of the waves through a slotted disk or illumination by means of a stroboscopic light source makes the wave pattern appear to stand still or to progress in slow motion.

Fig. 43G *Ripple-tank photograph of the interference of water waves from two sources.* (Courtesy, Physical Sciences Study Committee Project.)

43.3. Coherence. Coherence is a condition that must exist between two or more waves if a steady state of interference is to be observed, and is a condition involving the relative phases of waves wherever they are brought together.

If two wave sources are set up to emit identical frequencies, and the sources are made to vibrate in step, out of step, or to maintain a constant phase difference between them, the waves they emit are said to be *coherent*.

In the case of the water waves as demonstrated in Fig. 43G, the two sources are made to vibrate in phase with each other by mounting the two prongs on one vibrating metal strip. When two separately mounted metal strips are used, each

with a single prong dipping in the water, each may be set vibrating with any random phase. As long as they have the same vibration frequency the sources will maintain the same phase difference, the waves will be coherent, and a steady interference pattern will be produced. With different phase angles between the sources, however, the direction lines, x, a, y, b, and z, as shown in Fig. 43F, will be different.

In order to obtain interference patterns with light waves, two or more coherent sets of waves are derived from the same light source. We find by experiment that it is impossible to obtain interference from two separate sources, such as two lamp filaments set side by side. This failure is caused by the fact that the light from any one source is not an infinite train of waves. On the contrary, emission is random and there are sudden changes in phase occurring in very short intervals of time (of the order of 10^{-8} s).

Thus, although interference patterns may exist for a short time interval, they will shift in position and shape each time there is a phase change, and no interference fringes will be seen. To produce a steady prolonged interference pattern, the difference in phase between any pair of points in the two sources must remain constant. It is characteristic of any interference experiment that the sources must have a point-to-point phase relation, and sources that have this relation are called coherent sources.

43.4. Young's Double-Source Experiment. Young's double-source experiment, first performed with sunlight and pinholes in 1801, served as a crucial test deciding between Newton's corpuscular theory of light and Huygens' wave theory. This is represented schematically in Fig. 43H. Sunlight from a pinhole S was allowed to fall on a distant screen containing two pinholes, S_1 and S_2. The two sets of spherical waves emerging from the two holes interfered with each other in such a way as to form a symmetrical pattern of bands on another screen MN.

For convenience it is now customary to perform Young's experiment with narrow slits in place of pinholes. If S, S_1, and S_2 in Fig. 43H represent the cross sections of three narrow slits,

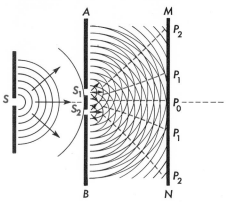

Fig. 43H *Diagram of Young's double-slit experiment illustrating the interference of light waves.*

the light falling on the farther screen MN has the appearance of equidistant bands or fringes, as shown by the photograph in Fig. 43I. The bright fringes correspond to the points P_0, P_1, P_2,

Fig. 43I *Interference fringes produced by a double slit as in Young's experiment.*

etc., and the dark fringes to the points halfway between.

As the waves travel outward from each slit S_1

and S_2, they cross each other only at points that lie along the dotted lines shown in the diagram. These lines represent the areas where the crests of two waves come together and produce a maximum brightness. About halfway between these dotted lines lie other areas where the crest of one wave and the trough of another cancel each other and produce darkness. This is the same interference phenomenon as is illustrated by water waves in Fig. 43G. With light waves, where the bright fringes are formed there is constructive interference, and where the dark fringes appear there is destructive interference.

This experiment is frequently performed in the elementary physics laboratory, and from measurements of fringe and slit spacings, as well as double-slit to screen distance, the wavelengths of different colors of light are calculated.

A formula for the wavelength of light can be derived from the geometry of Fig. 43J. Let P be the position of any bright fringe on the screen, and d the distance between slit centers. P_0 is located on the perpendicular bisector of the double slit S_1 and S_2.

The two rays emerging from S_1 and S_2 parallel to CP are brought to a focus at P. Line S_2A, drawn perpendicular to the two rays, forms a right triangle S_1AS_2. By this construction the short side S_1A becomes the extra distance that light must travel from the upper slit to arrive at the screen MN.

To produce a bright fringe at P, the interval S_1A must be equal to one whole wavelength, two

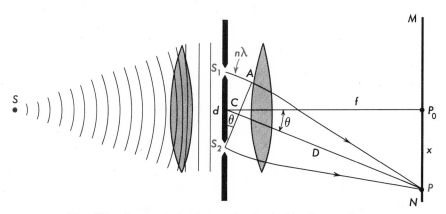

Fig. 43J *Geometrical relations for the double-slit experiment.*

whole wavelengths, three whole wavelengths, etc., for only then will waves from S_1 and S_2 arrive at P in phase. From the right triangle S_1AS_2, we can write

$$\frac{n\lambda}{d} = \sin\theta \qquad (43a)$$

where

$$n = 1, 2, 3, 4, \ldots$$

Since line CP_0 is perpendicular to MN and S_2A is perpendicular to CP, angle S_1S_2A equals angle P_0CP, and we can write

$$\frac{x}{D} = \sin\theta \qquad (43b)$$

Since the fringes are so close together, and the focal length f is long by comparison, D and f are so nearly equal we can write

$$\frac{x}{f} = \sin\theta \qquad (43c)$$

Combining left-hand sides of Eqs. (43a) and (43c), we obtain

$$\frac{n\lambda}{d} = \frac{x}{f} \qquad (43d)$$

from which

$$x = \frac{n\lambda f}{d} \qquad (43e)$$

This formula shows that on increasing the slit spacing d, the fringe spacing decreases. On increasing the wavelength λ, the bands are farther apart.

By measuring the fringe spacing x, the distance between slit centers, and f, the wavelength of different colors of light can be calculated. Repeated experiments, carefully performed, give the following results.

Violet, $\lambda = 4.1 \times 10^{-7}$ m
Blue, $\lambda = 4.7 \times 10^{-7}$ m
Green, $\lambda = 5.5 \times 10^{-7}$ m
Yellow, $\lambda = 5.8 \times 10^{-7}$ m
Orange, $\lambda = 6.1 \times 10^{-7}$ m
Red, $\lambda = 6.6 \times 10^{-7}$ m

As illustrated by the drawing of waves in Fig. 43K, red light has the longest waves.

These wavelengths, measured by the double-slit experiment, are therefore average values,

Fig. 43K *Diagram showing the relative wavelengths of light.*

since each color corresponds to a range of different wavelengths.

If the wavelengths are given in angstrom units,* we would list the spectrum colors as follows:

Violet, $\lambda = 4100$Å
Blue, $\lambda = 4700$Å
Green, $\lambda = 5500$Å
Yellow, $\lambda = 5800$Å
Orange, $\lambda = 6100$Å
Red, $\lambda = 6600$Å

43.5. Diffraction by a Single Slit. If a beam of parallel light is allowed to pass through a single narrow slit, the emerging light is spread out and forms a pattern of bands on a distant screen.

An experimental arrangement for observing such a diffraction pattern is shown in Fig. 43L. A single slit is a rectangular aperture, long in comparison to its width. An adjustable slit S is set up with its long dimension horizontal, and illuminated by parallel light of one wavelength. This beam of monochromatic light is obtained by the use of a source of light with a filter, a very narrow slit S′, and two lenses L_0 and L_1.

An actual photograph of the light falling on a screen such as the one at the right is reproduced in Fig. 43M. The photograph shows a wide central band and narrow bands symmetrically located on either side. For this photograph the

* For a definition of the angstrom unit (Å) see Sec. 45.7.

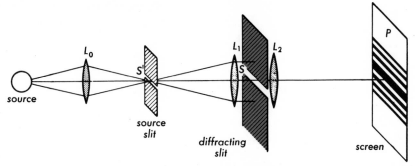

Fig. 43L *Experimental arrangement for obtaining the diffraction pattern of a single slit. Fraunhofer diffraction.*

distance S'L₁ was 25 cm, and L₂P was 100 cm. The width of slit S' was 0.10 mm and S was 0.090 mm. When S' was widened to more than 0.33 mm, the details of the pattern began to disap-

Fig. 43M *Photographs of the single-slit diffraction pattern.*

pear. On the original photograph the total width of the central band was 9.68 mm. The light source was a small mercury arc and a violet glass filter transmitting only the mercury violet light, $\lambda = 4358 \times 10^{-10}$ m.

This diffraction pattern can be observed directly by ruling a groove on an unused photographic plate with a penknife, holding it in front of the eye, and then looking directly at the light coming through another such slit several feet away.

The explanation of the single-slit pattern lies in the interference of many waves and is similar in principle to the interference of two waves described in Sec. 43.2. The many waves to be considered here can be thought of as sent out from

every point on a wave crest at the instant that it crosses the plane of the slit.

The cross-section diagram of Fig. 43N shows a slit AB, of width *d*, with parallel wave crests

Fig. 43N *Geometry for the single-slit diffraction experiment.*

approaching from the left. The wave crest at the slit is shown divided into 12 imaginary segments of equal width. Each of these segments may be thought of as a new source for a secondary wavelet. Let us now choose a point P₁ on the distant screen where the light intensity is observed to be zero, corresponding to the point P₁ in Fig. 43M. This is a point in Fig. 43N where the length of the light path BCP₁ is one whole wavelength λ greater than the light path AP₁. In other words the path BC = 1λ.

To see why this is just the right condition for no light on the screen, consider the wave diagram in Fig. 43O. The points marked a, b, c, etc., correspond to the relative phases of the wavelets arriving at P₁ at the same instant from

Fig. 43O *Graph of the single-slit wavelet contributions for the first dark band, point P_1 of Fig. 43N.*

all 12 of the slit elements. The heights of the vertical lines give the relative displacements of the instantaneous light contributions at P_1 due to the different slit elements. Note that the wave from a has a small upward displacement, while the wavelet from u has an equal downward displacement. One cancels the other to produce darkness. At this same instant the wavelet from b has a larger upward displacement while the wavelet from v has an equal downward displacement; thus they cancel each other. Similarly the elements c and w may be paired off with opposite displacements, and the process continued across the slit. Each pair of displacements is seen to cancel out and to produce destructive interference, or darkness, at P_1.

Suppose we now consider a point higher up on the screen corresponding to the center of the next dark band, P_2 of Fig. 43M. For this point the light path BC in Fig. 43N will be two whole wavelengths. If the slit is again divided into an equal number of small segments, the phases of the light wavelets arriving at P_2 will again be found to cancel in pairs.

When this treatment is applied to the point P_0 at the center of the screen, all the paths are the same, all wavelets arrive in phase, and we obtain the bright band center.

If the above treatment of pairing-off light contributions from small elements of a single aperture is carried out over all angles of θ, complete cancellation will be found to occur only when the path difference BC is exactly a whole-number multiple of one wavelength, i.e., BC = 1λ, 2λ, 3λ, 4λ, etc. For the dark bands, then, we can write BC = $n\lambda$, where $n = 0, 1, 2, 3$, etc. Since line AC is perpendicular to EP_1 and line AB is perpendicular to EP_0, the two triangles can be

assumed to be similar, and the following proportions between corresponding sides can be written:

$$\frac{n\lambda}{d} = \frac{x}{D} \qquad (43f)$$

But $x/D = \sin \theta$, and we may write

$$\frac{n\lambda}{d} = \sin \theta \qquad (43g)$$

from which we can write

$$n\lambda = d \sin \theta \qquad (43h)$$
dark bands

This formula shows that by widening the slit the diffraction bands become narrower, and vice versa. By increasing the wavelength the bands become wider.

If the path difference BC in Fig. 43N is not equal to a whole number of wavelengths λ, the wavelet contributions to those points on the screen will not cancel out, and this accounts for the bright bands.

A more detailed theory than that given above shows that the light intensity on the screen should have a distribution like that graphed in Fig. 43P. If we call the central intensity 100%, the maximum intensity of the side bands reaches the relatively low values of 4.7%, 1.6%, 0.83%, etc. Note carefully that the dark points P_0, P_1, P_2, etc., are equally spaced but that the maxima do not come exactly halfway between.

To find the distance from the center point P_0 to the first dark band, we place $n = 1$ in Eq.(43f), and transpose D to obtain

$$x_1 = \frac{\lambda D}{d} \qquad (43i)$$

The value of x_1 gives directly the width of all side bands, as well as the halfwidth of the central bright band.

Example 1. A parallel beam of monochromatic light falls on a single slit 1 mm wide. When the diffraction pattern is observed on a screen 2 m away, the central band is found to have a width of 2.5 mm. Find the wavelength of the light.

Solution. The given quantities in this problem are $D = 2.0$ m, $d = 0.10$ cm, $n = 1$, and $2x = 0.25$ cm. Upon substitution in Eq.(43f), we obtain

$$\frac{1\lambda}{1 \times 10^{-3} \, \text{m}} = \frac{1.25 \times 10^{-3} \, \text{m}}{2 \, \text{m}}$$

from which

$$\lambda = \frac{1 \times 10^{-3} \times 1.25 \times 10^{-3} \text{ m}}{2.0 \text{ m}} = 6.25 \times 10^{-7} \text{ m}$$

The light, $\lambda = 6.25 \times 10^{-7}$ m, is red in color.

43.6. Diffraction by a Circular Aperture. The diffraction pattern formed by light passing

scope objective are diffraction patterns of this kind.

We can see from this why the magnification by a telescope or microscope is limited, and cannot exceed certain values. If the eyepiece of an instrument has too high a magnifying power, each point in the object is observed as a disk, and

Fig. 43P   *Single-aperture diffraction pattern.*

through a circular aperture is of considerable importance, as it applies to the resolving power of telescopes and other optical instruments. The resolving power refers to the ability of an instrument to reveal fine detail in the object being viewed.

Owing to the diffraction of light waves as explained in the preceding section, light through a circular aperture produces a diffraction pattern having the same general intensity variations as given by Fig. 43P. Being circular, however, the parallel bands of light from a slit aperture are replaced by concentric circles with a bright disk at the center. It is as if the graph of Fig. 43P were rotated around the center line.

A lens acts as a circular aperture for light passing through it, and the image it forms for every bright spot in any object is a tiny diffraction pattern. The photograph in Fig. 43Q shows that, with pinholes in a screen as objects, the images formed by a single lens are composed of tiny disks surrounded by faint concentric rings of light. The larger the lens aperture, the smaller the diffraction patterns. The distant stars act as point objects, and their images formed by a tele-

the image appears blurred. The mathematical treatment of diffraction by a circular aperture requires Bessel functions and leads to the same

Fig. 43Q   *Photographs of diffraction images of one point source taken with a circular aperture, two points close together, and two point sources farther apart. Top: Short exposure. Bottom: Longer exposure.*

formula as Eq.(43i) but with the factor 1.22 introduced in place of $n = 1$ in Eq.(43f):

$$x = 1.22 \frac{\lambda D}{d} \qquad (43j)$$

where d is the diameter of the circular aperture and x is the radius of the disk of the diffraction pattern. Transposing D to the other side of the equation, and noting that D is usually hundreds of times greater than x, the quantity x/D can be replaced by θ_1, and we obtain

$$\theta_1 = \frac{1.22\lambda}{d} \qquad (43k)$$

where the angle θ_1 is in radians.

Sound waves from the circular aperture of a radio loud-speaker will form diffraction patterns of the same kind. Such behavior gives rise to marked changes in sound quality at different points around a room. The microwaves from a radar reflector radiate outward as a single-aperture diffraction pattern, with a central maximum radiated straight forward.

The *lobe* patterns shown for three different wavelengths in Fig. 43R, are polar graphs of the

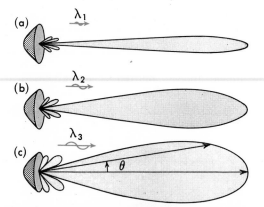

Fig. 43R   *Polar diagrams of the diffraction patterns for waves of different wavelength from the same parabolic reflector.*

intensity contour shown in Fig. 43P. In such polar graphs the intensity in any direction making an angle θ with the central line is plotted from the center out. The length of any arrow drawn at any angle θ is therefore proportional to the intensity radiated in that direction.

The shorter the wavelength and the greater the diameter of the circular aperture emitting the waves, the narrower the lobe pattern. Light waves from a point source at the focus of a parabolic mirror will produce a very narrow beam as shown in diagram (a), while radar and microwaves, with their much longer wavelengths,

will produce much wider beams as shown in diagrams (b) and (c).

43.7. The Diffraction Grating. The diffraction grating is an optical device widely used in place of a prism for studying the spectrum and measuring the wavelengths of light. Gratings are made by ruling fine grooves with a diamond point either on a glass plate to produce a transmission grating or on a polished metal mirror to produce a reflecting grating. As illustrated in Fig. 43S

Fig. 43S   *Schematic diagram of the grooves or rulings on a diffraction grating.*

the rulings are all parallel and equally spaced. The best gratings are several inches in width and contain from 5000 to 30,000 lines/in.

The transmission grating and its effect on light is idealized by the cross-section diagrams in Fig. 43T. The heavy green lines represent the lines which permit no light to get through and the open intervals between them represent the undisturbed parts of the glass which transmit the light and act like the parallel slits in Young's double-slit experiment. In diagram (a) parallel light is shown arriving at the grating surface as a succession of plane waves. The light then passing through the openings spreads out as Huygens' wavelets and forms new wavefronts parallel to the grating face. These wavefronts, parallel to the original waves, constitute a beam of light W traveling on in the same direction as the original beam.

These are not the only wavefronts, however, for other beams of parallel light are to be found traveling away from the grating in other directions. Two other such wavefronts are illustrated in diagrams (b) and (c). In (b), a dotted line is

Fig. 43T *Diagrams showing the formation of wavefronts forming the various orders of interference observed with a diffraction grating.*

drawn tangent to the seventh wave from opening 1, the eighth wave from opening 2, the ninth wave from opening 3, etc., to form what is called a wavefront of the first order of interference. In (c), a line is drawn tangent to the fourth wave from opening 1, the sixth wave from opening 2, the eighth wave from opening 3, etc., to form what is called a wavefront of the second order of interference. Similarly, by taking every third wave or every fourth wave from consecutive slits, other parallel wavefronts corresponding to the third or fourth orders are found moving off at greater angles. By symmetry all of the orders found on one side of the zeroth order are also found at the same angle on the other side.

Experimentally there are two methods of observing the various orders of interference from a small diffraction grating; one is to place the grating directly in front of the eye and the other

is to place it in the parallel beam of light between two lenses as shown in Fig. 43U. In the latter case the second lens is shown converging the various wavefronts of the different orders to a focus on a distant screen. If the source is a slit as shown at the left, and a colored glass filter is used to let through light of any one color, say violet, the light falling on the screen will appear as shown in the top photograph in Fig. 43V. Each vertical line is an image of the slit source and is violet in color.

If the three diagrams in Fig. 43T are redrawn for light of a longer wavelength, i.e., a greater distance between waves, the central beam of light W would travel on in the same direction as before, but the various *orders of interference* would be diffracted out at greater angles. Should green light of one wavelength be used, the slit images formed on the screen would be farther

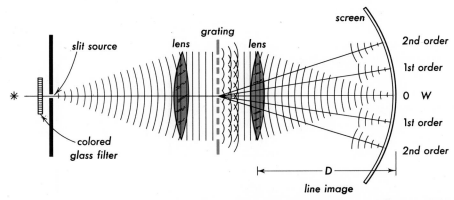

Fig. 43U *How the wavefronts of the various orders of interference from a diffraction grating are brought to a focus by the same lens.*

4th 3rd 2nd 1st　0　1st 2nd 3rd 4th order

V_3　V_2　V_1　V_0　V_1　V_2　V_3
G_3　G_2　G_1　G_0　G_1　G_2　G_3

Fig. 43V　*Photographs of the different orders of interference of violet and green light obtained with a diffraction grating as shown in Fig. 43U.*

apart than for violet light, as illustrated by the images marked G in Fig. 43V. This lower photograph was taken with both violet and green light from a mercury arc passing through the grating. These line images are called spectrum lines.

It will be noted that the separation of the

For this reason only the first and second orders of the spectrum from any grating are generally used in practice.

The general appearance of a spectrum, produced by a diffraction-grating spectrograph, can be seen in the photographs reproduced in Chapter 46.

43.8. Mathematical Theory of the Diffraction Grating. The theory of the diffraction grating is similar to that of the double slit and is shown in its simplest form in Fig. 43X. These diagrams derive their construction from Fig. 43T. The wavefronts for the first order emerge at such an angle θ that the difference in path between the rays from any two consecutive openings, like 1 and 2, is just one wavelength. Since any tangent drawn to any circle is always perpendicular to the radius drawn through the point of contact,

Fig. 43W　*Diagram of the first several orders of the continuous spectrum as displayed by a diffraction grating.*

spectrum lines V and G in the *third order* is three times as great as in the *first order*. In other words, any two spectrum lines are separated by an amount that is proportional to the order of interference.

If white light is sent through a grating, all of the different wavelengths, corresponding to the different colors, form their own characteristic wavefronts and produce a complete and continuous spectrum in each order of interference. This is illustrated by a diagram in Fig. 43W. Since the zeroth order for all colors comes to the same point, the central image is white. Because the width of each spectrum is proportional to the order, the higher orders overlap one another more and more. The violet of the third order, V_3 for example, falls on the red of second order, R_2.

triangle ABD is a right triangle, and $\sin \theta = \lambda/d$. Transposing, we obtain

$$\lambda = d \sin \theta \qquad (43l)$$

where λ is the wavelength of the light, d is the grating spacing, and θ is the angle that the emer-

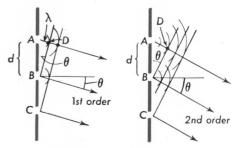

Fig. 43X　*Geometry for the wave theory of the diffraction grating.*

gent light of the first order makes with the grating normal.

By similar reasoning, and by the use of diagrams like the one shown for the second order, it will be seen that spectra of the second, third, fourth, etc., order are formed at such angles θ that the difference in path between consecutive slits is 2λ, 3λ, 4λ, etc. In general, the side AD of the right triangle ABD must be equal to $n\lambda$, where $n = 1, 2, 3, 4$, etc., and $\sin \theta = n\lambda/d$. If we transpose as before, we obtain the general formula

$$\boxed{n\lambda = d \sin \theta} \qquad (43m)$$

In this general grating formula, n is the spectrum order.

Example 2. Red light of one particular wavelength falls normally on a grating having 4000 lines per cm.

If the second-order spectrum makes an angle of 36° with the grating normal, what is the wavelength of the light?

Solution. Since the grating has 4000 lines per cm, the spacing between the lines is 1/4000, or $d = 0.00025$ cm. The other given quantities are $\theta = 36°$ and $n = 2$. Substituting in Eq.(43m), and solving for λ, we get

$$\lambda = \frac{2.5 \times 10^{-6} \text{ m} \times \sin 36°}{2}$$

$$= \frac{2.5 \times 10^{-6} \text{ m} \times 0.588}{2} = 7.35 \times 10^{-7} \text{ m}$$

or $\lambda = 7350$ Å

For a detailed treatment of interference and diffraction phenomena, see F. W. Jenkins and H. E. White, *Fundamentals of Optics* (McGraw-Hill Book Co., Inc., New York, 1957).

PROBLEMS

1. Red light of wavelength 6.5×10^{-7} m is used in observing the interference fringes produced by a double slit. If the centers of the two slit openings are 0.3 mm apart and the distance to the observing screen is 1.2 m, what is the fringe spacing?

2. Blue light of wavelength 4.3×10^{-7} m falls on a double slit; 2 m away, on a white screen, interference fringes are formed 3.5 mm apart. Calculate the double-slit separation. (*Ans.* 0.245 mm.)

3. Monochromatic light falls upon a double slit. The distance between the slit centers is 0.5 mm, and the distance between consecutive fringes on a screen 3 m away is 0.4 cm. What is the wavelength and the color of the light?

4. A beam of parallel light, $\lambda = 5 \times 10^{-7}$ m, falls normally on a grating, and the third order is diffracted at an angle of 35° with the grating normal. How many lines per cm are on the grating? (*Ans.* .3827.)

5. Parallel yellow light of wavelength 5.8×10^{-7} m falls normally on one side of a diffraction grating having 4000 lines per cm. Calculate the angle between the first-order spectrum on opposite sides of the grating normal.

6. A diffraction grating with 5000 lines per cm is used with two lenses, each of 1.50-m focal length, as shown in Fig. 43U. Find the width of the first-order spectrum of white light as it is formed on the screen. Assume that

$\lambda = 4 \times 10^{-7}$ m and $\lambda = 7 \times 10^{-7}$ m for the shortest and longest wavelengths and a curved screen of radius 1.50 m. (*Ans.* 23.5 cm.)

7. A grating having 5000 lines per cm is set up with 2 m focal-length lenses as shown in Fig. 43U. (a) What fourth-order wavelength will be diffracted at the same angle as the third-order of $\lambda = 5 \times 10^{-7}$ m? (b) What is the angle?

8. Green light of wavelength 5.5×10^{-7} m from a narrow slit falls on a double slit of separation 0.032 cm. If the interference pattern is formed on a screen 2.0 m away, what will be the linear separation between fringes on the screen? (*Ans.* 0.343 cm.)

9. Red light of wavelength 6300×10^{-10} m is incident on a double slit of separation 0.15 mm. If the interference pattern is formed on a screen 1.2 m away, what will be the linear separation between fringes?

10. Yellow light of wavelength 5800×10^{-10} m is incident on a double slit. If the over-all separation of 10 fringes on a screen 2.0 m away is 1.6 cm, find the double-slit separation. (*Ans.* 0.0725 cm.)

11. Blue light of wavelength 4.5×10^{-7} m falls as a parallel beam on a diffraction grating containing 9000 lines per cm. At what angle will the second-order spectrum be located?

THE POLARIZATION
OF LIGHT

The experiments described in the preceding chapter illustrating the *diffraction* and *interference* of light are generally regarded as proof that *light is a wave motion*. Although such experiments enable the experimentalist to measure accurately the wavelengths of light, they give no information of the kinds of waves involved. The reason for this is that all types of waves, under the proper conditions, will exhibit diffraction and interference. The desired information in the case of light waves is found in another group of phenomena known as *polarized light*. Some of the phenomena, which will be described in this chapter, are considered to be a proof that *light is a transverse wave motion* in contrast with the longitudinal wave motion in sound.

In the case of longitudinal waves the vibrations are always parallel to the direction of propagation, so that in a plane at right angles to the direction of travel there is no motion and hence there is perfect symmetry. If light is a transverse wave motion, the vibrations of a beam of light are all at right angles to the direction of propagation and there may or may not be perfect symmetry around the direction of travel. If perfect symmetry does not exist for a beam of light the beam is said to be *polarized*.

The experimental methods by which light may be polarized are classified under one of the following heads:

> *reflection*
> *double refraction*
> *selective absorption*
> *scattering*

44.1. Plane-Polarized Light. A better understanding of the experiments to be described in this chapter can best be attained by first presenting the graphical methods of representing transverse waves. We assume at the outset that each light wave is a transverse wave whose vibrations are along straight lines at right angles to the direction of propagation. Furthermore, we assume that a beam of ordinary light consists of millions of such waves, each with its own plane of vibration, and that there are waves vibrating in all planes with equal probability. Looking at such a beam end-on as in Fig. 44A, there should

Fig. 44A   *End-on view of a beam of unpolarized light illustrating schematically the equal probability of all planes of vibration.*

be just as many waves vibrating in one plane as there are vibrating in any other. This then can be referred to as perfect symmetry.

If, by some means or other, all the waves in a beam of light are made to vibrate in planes parallel to each other, the light is said to be plane polarized. Diagrams illustrating such light are shown in Fig. 44B. The top diagram (a)

Fig. 44B   *Diagrams illustrating plane-polarized rays of light.*

represents plane-polarized light waves traveling to the right and vibrating in a vertical plane, while the second diagram (b) represents a ray of plane-polarized light vibrating in a horizontal plane. The dotted line indicating waves in diagram (a) is usually omitted.

It can be shown that a beam of ordinary unpolarized light, vibrating in all planes, may be regarded as being made up of two kinds of vibrations only, half of the waves vibrating in a vertical plane as in diagram (a) and the other half vibrating perpendicular to it as in diagram (b). The reason for this is that waves not vibrating in either of these two planes can be resolved into two components, one component vibrating in a vertical plane and the other vibrating in a horizontal plane. Although these two components may not be equal to each other, the similarly

resolved components from all waves will average out to be equal. Diagram (c) is regarded therefore as being equivalent to ordinary unpolarized light.

44.2. Polarization by Reflection. When ordinary unpolarized light is incident at an angle of about 57° on the polished surface of a plate of glass, the reflected light is plane polarized. This fact was first discovered by Etienne Malus, a French physicist, in 1808. The experiment usually performed to demonstrate his discovery is illustrated in Fig. 44C.

A beam of unpolarized light AB is incident at an angle of 57° on the first glass surface at B. This light is again reflected at the same angle by a second glass plate C placed parallel to the first, as in diagram (a). If now the lower plate is rotated about the line BC by slowly turning the pedestal on which it is mounted, the intensity of

Fig. 44C   *Common experiment performed to demonstrate the polarization of light by reflection from a smooth glass surface.*

the reflected beam CD is found to decrease slowly and vanish completely at an angle of 90°. With further rotation the reflected beam CD appears again, reaching a maximum at an angle of 180° as shown in diagram (c). Continued rotation causes the intensity to decrease to zero again at 270°, and to reappear and reach a maximum at 360°, the starting point as in diagram (a). During this one complete rotation the angle of incidence on the lower plate, as well as the upper, has remained at 57°.

If the angle of incidence on either the upper or lower plate is not 57°, the beam CD will go through maxima and minima every 90° as before, but the minima will not go to zero. In other words, there will always be a reflected beam CD.

A complete mathematical theory of the polarization of light by reflection was first given by Fresnel in 1820. The remarkable confirmation of this theory, in every detail, by experimental observations on the behavior of light and measurements, establishes Fresnel as the greatest contributor to the whole field of optics.

The expansion of the above experiment is made clearer by a detailed study of what happens to ordinary light when it is reflected at the polarizing angle of 57° from glass. As illustrated in Fig. 44D, 8% of the light is reflected as plane-

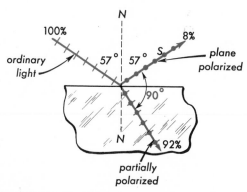

Fig. 44D *Light reflected from glass at an angle of 57° is plane-polarized, while the refracted light is only partially plane-polarized.*

polarized light vibrating in the plane at right angles to the plane of incidence, and the other 92% is refracted as partially plane-polarized light, 42% vibrating perpendicular to the plane of inci-

dence and 50% vibrating parallel to the plane of incidence. The plane of incidence is defined as the plane passing through the incident ray and the ray normal NN. In nearly all diagrams the plane of the page is the plane of incidence.

If in Fig. 44D the angle of incidence is changed to some other value than 57°, the reflected beam will not be plane polarized but will contain a certain amount of light vibrating parallel to the plane of incidence. In general, the light reflected from a transparent medium like glass or water is only partially plane polarized; only at a certain angle, called the *polarizing angle*, is it plane polarized. It was Sir David Brewster, a Scottish physicist, who first discovered that *at the polarizing angle the reflected and refracted rays are 90° apart.* This is now known as *Brewster's law.* The polarizing angle for water is 53°, for at this angle the reflected and refracted rays make an angle of 90° with each other.

Because these two rays make 90° with each other, the angle of incidence i and the angle of refraction r are complements of each other and $\sin r$ in *Snell's law* ($\sin i / \sin r = \mu$) can be replaced by $\cos i$, giving

$$\frac{\sin i}{\cos i} = \mu \quad \text{or} \quad \boxed{\tan i = \mu} \quad (44a)$$

This formula is useful in calculating the angle of polarization. For example, with water, $\mu = 1.33$, angle $i = 53°$; whereas for glass with $\mu = 1.52$, angle $i = 57°$.

Returning to the experiment demonstrated in Fig. 44C, we observe that the reflected light from the first mirror is plane polarized as shown, and that the refracted light goes into the glass plate where it is absorbed by the black paint on the back face. The second mirror acts as a testing device or analyzer for polarized light. A certain fraction of the incident waves is reflected when the vibrations are perpendicular to the plane of incidence, and all are refracted (to be absorbed) when the vibrations are parallel to the plane of incidence.

44.3. Polarization by Double Refraction. The double refraction of light by Iceland spar (calcite) was first observed by a Swedish physician, Erasmus Bartholinus, in 1669, and later studied

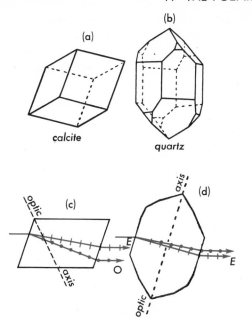

Fig. 44E   *Diagrams and cross sections of calcite and quartz crystals showing double refraction and polarization.*

Each face of every calcite crystal is a parallelogram whose angles are 78° and 102°. Chemically, calcite is a hydrated calcium carbonate, $CaCO_3$; and quartz is silicon dioxide, SiO_2.

Not only is light doubly refracted by calcite and quartz, but both rays are found to be plane polarized. One ray, called the *ordinary ray*, is polarized with its vibrations in one plane, and the other ray, called the *extraordinary ray*, is polarized with its vibrations in a plane at right angles to the first. This polarization is illustrated in diagrams (c) and (d) by *dots* and *lines* and can be proved by a glass plate rotated as plate C in Fig. 44C, or with some other analyzing device like a *Nicol prism* or a *polarizing film*. These devices will be described in the next two sections.

Since the two opposite faces of a calcite crystal are always parallel to each other, the two refracted rays always energe parallel to the incident light and are therefore parallel to each other. If the incident light falls perpendicularly upon the surface of the crystal, as in Fig. 44F, the extraordinary ray will be refracted away from the normal and will come out parallel to, but displaced from, the incident beam. The ordinary ray will pass straight through without deviation.

In general, the O ray obeys the ordinary laws of refraction, and in this way the crystal acts like glass or water, whereas the E ray obeys no such simple law and behaves quite abnormally.

In other words, the O ray travels with the same velocity regardless of its direction through the crystal, whereas the velocity of the E ray is different in different regions. This is the origin of the designations ordinary and extraordinary.

in detail by Huygens and Newton. Nearly all crystalline substances are now known to exhibit the phenomenon. The following are but a few samples of crystals that show this effect: *calcite, quartz, miča, sugar, topaz, selenite, aragonite,* and *ice.* Calcite and quartz are of particular importance because they are used extensively in the manufacture of special optical instruments.

Calcite, as found in nature, always has the characteristic shape shown in Fig. 44E(a), whereas quartz has many different forms, the most complicated of which is illustrated in diagram (b).

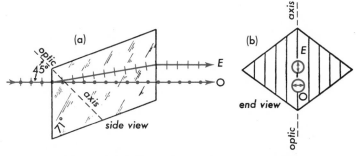

Fig. 44F   *Double refraction in calcite. At normal incidence the O ray travels straight through and the E ray is refracted to one side.*

One important property of calcite and quartz is that there is one and only one direction through either crystal in which there is no double refraction. This particular direction, called the *optic axis*, is shown by the dashed lines in Fig. 44E. The optic axis, it should be noted, is not a single line through a crystal, but a direction.

A plane passing through the crystal parallel to the optic axis and perpendicular to one face of the crystal is called a *principal section*. The plane of the page in Fig. 44F(a) is but one of any number of principal sections which, from the end view in diagram (b), appears as a vertical line. A useful rule always to be remembered is that the vibrations of the O ray are always perpendicular to the optic axis.

44.4. The Nicol Prism. The Nicol prism is an optical device made from a calcite crystal and used in many optical instruments for producing and analyzing polarized light. Such a prism, as illustrated in Fig. 44G, is made by cutting a

Fig. 44G *Cross section and end view of a Nicol prism showing the elimination of the O ray by total reflection.*

crystal along a diagonal and cementing it back together again with a special cement called *Canada balsam*. Canada balsam is used because it is a clear transparent substance whose reflective index is midway between that of the calcite for the O and E *rays*.

Optically the Canada balsam is more dense than calcite for the E ray and less dense for the O ray. There exists, therefore, a critical angle of refraction for the one O ray but not for the E ray. After both rays are refracted at the first crystal surface, the O ray is *totally reflected* by the first Canada balsam surface, as illustrated in the diagram, while the E ray passes on through to emerge parallel to the incident light. Starting with ordinary unpolarized light, a Nicol prism thus transmits plane-polarized light only.

If two Nicols are lined up one behind the other as in Fig. 44H, they form an optical system frequently used in specially constructed microscopes for studying the optical properties of other crys-

Fig. 44H *Two Nicol prisms mounted as polarizer and analyzer. (a) Parallel Nicols. (b) Crossed Nicols.*

tals. The first Nicol which is used to produce plane-polarized light is called the *polarizer*, and the second which is used to test the light is called the *analyzer*.

In the parallel position, diagram (a), the polarized light from the polarizer passes on through the analyzer. Upon rotating the analyzer through 90°, as in diagram (b), no light is transmitted. For the same reason that the O vibrations in the original beam were totally reflected in the polarizer, the E vibrations are totally reflected as O vibrations in the analyzer.

Rotated another 90°, the light again gets through the analyzer just as in the parallel position in diagram (a). Still another 90° finds the Nicols crossed again, with no light passing through.

44.5. Polarization by Selective Absorption. When ordinary light enters a crystal of tourmaline, double refraction takes place in much the same way that it does in calcite, but with this difference: one ray, the so-called O ray, is entirely absorbed by the crystal, while the other ray, the E ray, passes on through. This phenomenon is called "selective absorption" because the crystal absorbs light waves vibrating in one plane and not those vibrating in the other.

Tourmaline crystals are therefore like Nicol prisms, for they take in ordinary light, dispose of the O vibrations, and transmit plane-polarized light as illustrated in Fig. 44I(a). When two such crystals are lined up parallel, with one behind the other, the plane-polarized light from the first crystal passes through the second with little loss in intensity. If either crystal is turned at 90° to the other, i.e., in the *cross position*, the light is completely absorbed and none passes through.

Fig. 44I *Diagrams illustrating the polarization of light by (a) tourmaline crystals, and (b) polarizing films.*

The behavior of tourmaline and similar optical substances is due to the molecular structure of the crystal. To draw an analogy, the regularly spaced molecules of a single crystal are like the regularly spaced trees in an orchard or grove. If one tries to run between the rows of trees carrying a very long pole held at right angles to the direction of motion, the pole must be held in a vertical position. If it is held in the horizontal plane, the runner will be stopped.

The reason tourmaline is not used in optical instruments in place of Nicol prisms is that the crystals are yellow in color and do not transmit white light.

A more satisfactory substance for this purpose, which does transmit white light, is a relatively new manufactured material known as "Polaroid." This material is made in the form of very thin films, which have the general appearance of the more common substance "Cellophane," and is made from small needle-shaped crystals of an organic compound *iodosulphate of quinine.* Lined up parallel to each other and embedded in a *nitrocellulose mastic,* these crystals act like tourmaline be absorbing one component of polarization and transmitting the other. Two such films

mounted separately in rings between thin glass plates are shown schematically in Fig. 44I(b). In the crossed position no light can pass through both films, whereas in the parallel position white light vibrating in the plane indicated by the parallel lines is transmitted. Many practical applications are being found for polarizing films of this kind, particularly wherever glaring light is not desired. The glaring light reflected at an angle from a table top, a book, a window pane, the water, or the road ahead when one is driving a car, is polarized and can be partly eliminated by polarizing films.

44.6. Dispersion by a Calcite Prism. In Fig. 44J a prism is shown cut from a calcite crystal

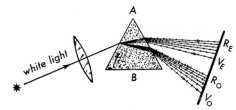

Fig. 44J *Refraction of white light by a prism cut from a calcite crystal.*

with the optic axis parallel to the refracting edge A. The optic axis, being perpendicular to the page, is represented by dots. (For the direction of the optic axis in calcite, see Fig. 44E.)

When white light is incident on one side of this prism, two completely separated spectra emerge from the other side. Not only is each spectrum complete in all its colors from red to violet but the light in each is plane polarized. This can be demonstrated with an analyzing device like a Nicol prism, or polarizing film. By inserting the analyzer anywhere in the light beam and rotating it, one spectrum disappears first; then, 90° from it, the other fades and disappears while the first returns to full intensity.

The vibrations of all colors in the lower spectrum in Fig. 44J are perpendicular to the optic axis and are O vibrations. The upper spectrum with all vibrations parallel to the optic axis consists of E vibrations. If a prism is cut so that the refracted light as it travels through the crystal is parallel to the optic axis, only one spectrum is produced.

44.7. Scattering and the Blue Sky. The blue of the sky and the red of the sunset are due to a phenomenon called "scattering." When sunlight passes through the earth's atmosphere, much of the light is picked up by the air molecules and given out again in some other direction. The effect is quite similar to the action of water waves on floating objects. If, for example, the ripples from a stone dropped in a still pond of water encounter a small cork floating on the surface, the cork is set bobbing up and down with the frequency of the passing waves.

Light is pictured as acting in the same way on air molecules and fine dust particles. Once set into vibration by a light wave, a molecule or particle can send out the absorbed light again, sometimes in the same direction but generally in almost any other direction. This is illustrated schematically in Fig. 44K. Waves of light are

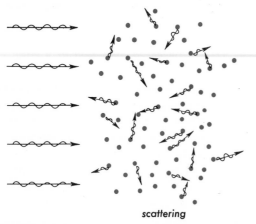

scattering

Fig. 44K   *Light waves are scattered by air molecules.*

shown being scattered at random in all directions.

Experiments show, in agreement with the theory of scattering, that the shortest waves are scattered more readily than longer waves. To be more specific, the scattering is inversely proportional to the fourth power of the wavelength:

$$\text{scattering} \propto \frac{1}{\lambda^4} \qquad (44b)$$

According to this law the short waves of violet

light are scattered about ten times as readily as the longer waves of red light. The other colors are scattered by intermediate amounts. Thus when sunlight enters the earth's atmosphere, *violet* and *blue light* are scattered the most, followed by *green, yellow, orange,* and *red,* in the order named. For every ten violet waves ($\lambda = 4 \times 10^{-7}$ m) scattered from a beam, there is only one red wave ($\lambda = 7 \times 10^{-7}$ m).

violet	blue	green	yellow	orange	red
10	7	5	3	2	1

At noon on a clear day when the sun is directly overhead, as illustrated by an observer at A in Fig. 44L, the whole sky appears *light blue.* This is

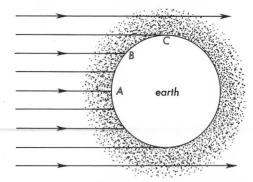

Fig. 44L   *Schematic diagram showing the scattering of light by the air molecules of the earth's atmosphere.*

the composite color of the mixture of colors scattered most effectively by the air molecules. It can be demonstrated that light blue is obtained by the added mixture of *violet, blue, green,* and *yellow.*

44.8. The Red Sunset. The occasional observation of an orange-red sunset is attributed to the *scattering of light* by fine dust and smoke particles near the earth's surface. This is illustrated in Fig. 44M. To an observer at A, it is noonday and the direct sunlight from overhead, seen only by looking directly at the sun itself, travels through a relatively short dust path. As a result, very little violet and blue are scattered away and the sun appears white.

As sunset approaches, however, the direct sunlight has to travel through an ever-increasing dust path. The result is that an hour or so before

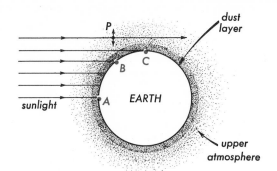

Fig. 44M *The scattering of light by a layer of dust near the earth's surface causes the sun to turn yellow, then orange, and finally red at sunset.*

sundown, when the observer is at B, practically all of the blue and violet have been scattered out and, owing to the remaining colors, red,

direct rays must travel through so many miles of dust particles that all but red are completely scattered out and the sun appears red. At this same time the sky overhead is still light blue. If the dust blanket is too dense, even the red will be scattered appreciably from the direct sunlight and the deepening red sun will become lost from view before it reaches the horizon.

An excellent demonstration of scattering by fine particles is illustrated in Fig. 44N. A parallel beam of white light from a carbon arc and lens L_1 is sent through a water trough with glass sides. After passing through an iris diaphragm at the other end, a second lens L_2 forms an image of the circular opening on the screen. To produce the fine particles for scattering, about 40 g of photographic fixing powder (hyposulfite of soda) are

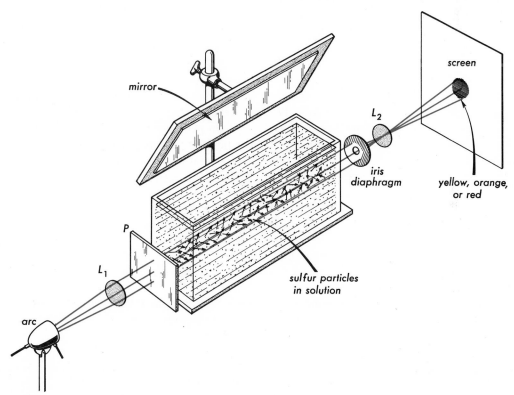

Fig. 44N *The sunset experiment. Demonstration of the scattering and polarization of light by small particles.*

orange, yellow, and a little green, the sun appears yellow. At sunset, when the observer is at C, the

first dissolved in about 2 gal of water. Next, about 1 to 2 cm³ of concentrated sulfuric acid is added and the contents thoroughly mixed in the trough.*

As the microscopic sulfur particles begin to form, scattered blue light will outline the parallel beam through the trough. A little later, when more particles have formed, the entire body of water will appear light blue, due principally to multiple scattering. Light scattered out of the central beam of light is scattered again and again before emerging from the trough. At first the transmitted light which falls on the screen appears white. Later, as more scattering takes out the shorter wavelengths, this image representing the sun turns yellow, then orange, and finally red.

44.9. Polarization by Scattering. If the blue of the sky is observed through a piece of polaroid, the light is found to be partially plane-polarized. This polarization can also be seen in the scattering experiment described above. Observed through a polaroid film, the beam in the tank appears bright at one orientation of the polaroid and disappears with a 90° rotation.

Scattering is not a practical means of polarizing light because the polarization is usually incomplete and the intensity is quite low. The polarization of the blue light of the sky, however, is direct evidence of the transverse character of light waves.

In Fig. 44O, let P represent any of the millions of air molecules or tiny dust particles high overhead on a clear sunny day. Unpolarized sunlight is incident from just above the horizon on the left. Suppose an incident wave, vibrating in the *xy* plane, is absorbed and sets a particle at P vibrating in the *y* direction. Upon giving up this light the wave can be emitted in almost any direction except along the *y* axis. To emit a wave in the *y* direction the wave would have to be longitudinal. Since light waves are not longi-

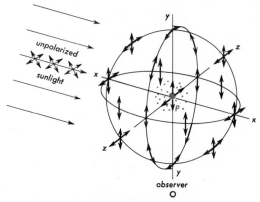

Fig. 44O   *Diagram showing the polarization of light by scattering from fine particles.*

tudinal, but are transverse, the *y* direction is forbidden.

If the incident wave is vibrating in the *xz* plane the particle at P will be set vibrating along the *z* axis. Emission by this particle is now allowed in all directions except along the *z* axis. Hence an observer looking at the blue sky, in a direction at right angles to the incident sunlight, will find the light plane-polarized with its vibrations perpendicular to the *xy* plane.

Note that no particles at P can be set vibrating along the *x* axis, since this would require an incident light wave to be longitudinal.

It is well known that light is composed of electromagnetic waves, and that such waves have two vibration components. Each wave has an *electric* component vibrating in one plane and a *magnetic* component vibrating in a plane at right angles (see Fig. 54G). Numerous experiments show, however, that the electric vibrations are the only ones responsible for all the known optical effects.

* The correct amount of acid to produce the best results is determined by trial. The first visible precipitate should appear after 2 or 3 min.

For a more complete account of polarized light, see F. W. Jenkins and H. E. White, *Fundamentals of Optics* (McGraw-Hill Book Co., Inc., New York, 1957).

PROBLEMS

1. Find the polarizing angle for yellow light reflected from diamond, with its refractive index of 2.4172.

2. If the polarizing angle of a transparent plastic is found to be 59°, what is the refractive index? [*Ans.* 1.6643.]

3. The polarizing angle for yellow light incident on a

clear transparent solid is 61°. Calculate the refractive index.

4. Find the polarizing angle for a clear plastic with a refractive index of 1.380 for green light. [*Ans.* 54.1°.]

5. What is the polarizing angle for a dense flint glass having a refractive index of 1.674?

6. What is the polarizing angle for water, with its refractive index of 1.333? [*Ans.* 53.2°.]

7. Calculate the polarizing angle for red light incident on crown glass. Assume a refractive index of 1.520.

8. The polarizing angle for red light incident on a clear transparent material is 62.5°. Calculate the refractive index. [*Ans.* $\mu = 1.921$.]

9. What is the refractive index of flint glass if the polarizing angle is 62°?

10. If the refractive index for a plastic is 1.25, what is the angle of refraction for a ray of light incident at the polarizing angle? [*Ans.* 38.7°.]

11. The polarizing angle of a piece of glass, for green light, is 60°. Find the angle of minimum deviation * for a 60° prism made of the same glass.

12. If the polarizing angle of a piece of clear plastic is 61.5°, find the angle of minimum deviation for a 60° prism made of the same plastic. [*Ans.* 74.0°.]

13. If the critical angle of a clear crystal for blue light is 48°, calculate the polarizing angle. For the critical angle r, $\mu = 1/\sin r$.

14. The critical angle for violet light incident on a piece of glass is 35°. (a) Find the refractive index and (b)

* For a minimum deviation $\mu = \sin \frac{1}{2}(A + \delta)/\sin \frac{1}{2}A$, where A is the prism angle, and δ is the angle of minimum deviation.

calculate its corresponding polarizing angle. For the critical angle r, $\mu = 1/\sin r$. [*Ans.* (a) 1.743, (b) 60.2°.]

15. Find the polarizing angle for the boundary separating water of index 1.33 from glass of index 1.52. Assume the incident ray to be in water.

16. Find the amount of light, relative to yellow light, scattered by each of the following wavelengths of light: ultraviolet light 2.0×10^{-7} m, violet light 4.0×10^{-7} m, yellow light 5.8×10^{-7} m, red light 7.0×10^{-7} m, and infrared light 10×10^{-7} m. [*Ans.* 70, 4.4, 1.0, 0.47, and 0.11 times, respectively.]

17. Strontium titanate deposited on a glass surface is a clear transparent material having a refractive index of 2.44. Calculate the polarizing angle for this medium.

18. A 50° calcite prism is cut with its faces parallel to the optic axis. Calculate the angle of minimum deviation for yellow light for each of the two polarized rays. The refractive index for calcite for the O ray is 1.658, and for the E ray, 1.486. [*Ans.* 39.0° and 27.8°.]

19. What is the ratio of the scattering of light waves between yellow light of wavelength 6.5×10^{-7} m and violet light of wavelength 4.0×10^{-7} m?

20. For every 200 waves of red light scattered by the air, how many waves of violet light will be scattered? Assume the wavelengths to be 7.0×10^{-7} m and 4.0×10^{-7} m, respectively. [*Ans.* 1875.]

21. Calculate the ratio of the numbers of light rays scattered by the air for violet light ($\lambda = 4 \times 10^{-7}$ m) and green light ($\lambda = 5.5 \times 10^{-7}$ m).

22. Find the ratio of light waves scattered by fine particles between blue light ($\lambda = 4.3 \times 10^{-7}$ m) and orange light ($\lambda = 6.2 \times 10^{-7}$ m). [*Ans.* 4.33.]

LIGHT SOURCES AND SPECTROGRAPHS

When a block of metal like iron or copper is heated slowly to incandescence, the first noticeable change in its appearance occurs at a temperature of about 1000°K. At this temperature, the metal has a dull red glow. As the temperature continues to rise, the color changes slowly to orange, then to yellow, and finally to white.

If the metal, as it is slowly being heated, is observed through a prism, the first appearance of visible light will be found at the extreme red end of the spectrum. As the temperature rises, the light spreads slowly out across the spectrum until, at white heat, the entire band of visible colors from red to violet is seen. At the orange stage where the temperature is about 1500°K, the pure spectrum colors contain red, orange, and yellow; when the yellow stage is reached

where the temperature is about 2000°K, the spectral green is included. When the white stage is reached at about 3000°K, and the spectrum is complete, a further rise in temperature continues to increase the intensity of each color without a noticeable change in color.

What the prism has done in such an experiment is to separate all of the light waves according to their wavelengths, the longest waves of red light at the one side, the shortest waves of violet light at the other, and the intermediate waves at their proper places in between. The fact that the color is continuous from red through violet is characteristic of the spectrum of all solids and liquids; this means that there is a continuous set of different wavelengths present.

45.1. The Spectrum. To demonstrate the exist-

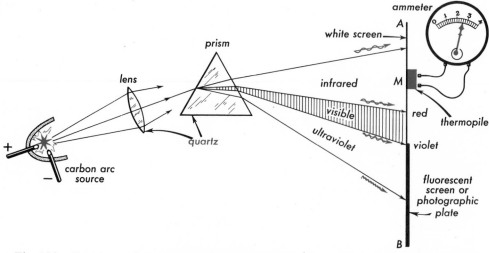

Fig. 45A *Experiment demonstrating the existence of the ultraviolet and infrared rays beyond the visible spectrum.*

ence of an ultraviolet and infrared spectrum, an experiment of the type illustrated in Fig. 45A may be performed. The visible light from a carbon-arc lamp is made to pass through a of the screen at A. A graph of the energy from the carbon arc source, for the different parts along the screen, is shown by the 3000°K curve in Fig. 45B.

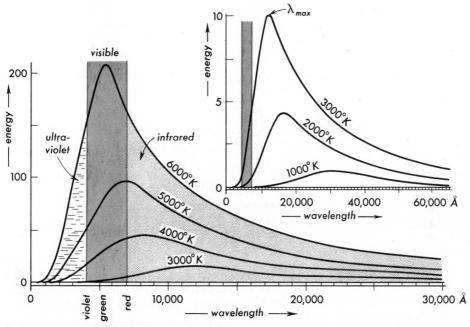

Fig. 45B *Distribution of the energy emitted by a hot solid at different temperatures.*

quartz lens and prism to be focused on a nearby screen.

If at the violet end of the spectrum the screen is painted with luminous paint, a bright fluorescence will be observed for a short distance beyond the visible violet. When the screen is replaced by a photographic plate, the exposed and developed picture will again show the extension of the spectrum into the ultraviolet.

To detect the presence of the infrared radiations, a thermopile is conveniently used, as shown at the top of the screen. Connected to an ammeter, a thermopile measures the amount of light energy falling upon its front face. If the thermopile is first placed to receive violet light, and then slowly moved across the visible spectrum out into the infrared region beyond, the ammeter will show a steady rise in current. The current will continue to rise until a maximum is reached at a point in the region of M, and then it will drop off slowly as the thermopile approaches the end

Each curve represents the amount of energy given out over the entire spectrum by a solid at different temperatures. Studying these curves, one will observe that at low temperatures very little light is emitted in the visible spectrum. At 1000°K, only the visible red is seen and even that is very faint. At 2000°K, not only does the brightness of the red increase, but the other colors, orange, yellow, and green, appear. At 3000°K, the temperature of a low-current carbon arc or tungsten-filament light, all of the visible spectrum is emitted, but the maximum radiation is in the infrared. At 6000°K, the temperature of the surface of the sun, the maximum energy is radiated in the green of the visible spectrum, with an appreciable amount of ultraviolet light on the one side and the infrared on the other. Thus the visible spectrum, as seen by the human eye, is but a small band out of all the waves emitted by a body as hot as the sun.

45.2. Wien's Displacement Law. It is an inter-

esting fact that the maximum energy radiated by
a hot body shifts to shorter and shorter waves as
the temperature rises (see Fig. 45B). To be more
exact, if the temperature of a body is doubled,
the radiated energy maximum, λ_{max}, shifts to $\frac{1}{2}$
the wavelength. If the temperature is tripled, the
energy maximum shifts to $\frac{1}{3}$ the wavelength, etc.
This is known as Wien's* displacement law, and
is written as an algebraic equation

$$\lambda_{max} T = C \qquad (45a)$$

where C is a constant, found by experiment to
have a value of 2.897×10^{-3} meter degrees, T is
the absolute temperature, and λ_{max} the wavelength in meters at which the maximum energy
is radiated. By substituting the value of the constant C in Eq.(45a), the wavelength maximum
radiated by a hot body can be calculated for any
temperature.

45.3. Emission and Absorption. The rate at
which a body radiates or absorbs heat depends
not only upon the absolute temperature, but
upon the nature of the exposed surfaces as well.
Objects that are good emitters of heat are also
good absorbers of the same kind of radiation.
This is known as *Kirchhoff's law of radiation.* A
body whose surface is blackened is an excellent
emitter as well as an excellent absorber. If the
same body is chromium plated it becomes a poor
emitter and a poor absorber.

If the outside surface of a hot coffee cup were
painted a dull black, the rate of cooling would
be more rapid than if it were chromium plated.
A highly polished surface, as in the Dewar flask,
would help by reflection to keep radiant heat
from crossing the boundary.

Black clothes should not be worn on a hot day
since black is a good absorber of the sun's radiant
heat. While black is also a good emitter, the external temperature is higher than the body temperature and the exchange rate is therefore such

as to heat the body. White clothes are worn in
hot climates because white is a good reflector
and therefore a poor absorber.

45.4. Black-Body Radiation. The relation between the total radiant heat energy E emitted by
a body and its temperature was first made through
the extensive laboratory experiments of Josef
Stefan. The same law was later derived from
theoretical considerations by Ludwig Boltzmann,
and is now known as the *Stefan-Boltzmann law*:

$$E = kT^4 \qquad (45b)$$

Here E represents the energy radiated per
second by a body at an absolute temperature T,
and k is a proportionality constant. The law
applies only to so-called "black bodies."

*A black body is defined as one that absorbs all
of the radiant heat that falls upon it.*

Such a perfect absorber would also be a perfect
emitter.

If E represents the heat in kilocalories radiated
per second per square meter of a black body, then
$k = 1.36 \times 10^{-11}$. If E is measured in J/sm^2,
then $k = 5.67 \times 10^{-8}$.

The best laboratory approach to a black body
is a hole in a blackened box. Practically all heat
entering such a hole would be absorbed inside.
Black velvet cloth or a surface painted dull with
lampblack will absorb about 97% of the radiant
heat falling on it, and may for many purposes be
considered a black body. Polished metal surfaces,
however, are far from black bodies; they absorb
only about 6% of the incident energy and reflect
the remainder. Most other substances have absorption ratios between these two extremes.

45.5. The Quantum Theory. The first successful attempt to explain the shape of the black-
body radiation curves as shown in Fig. 45B was

* Wilhelm Wien (1864–1928), German physicist, chiefly
known for important discoveries with cathode rays, canal
rays, and the radiation of light. He was awarded the
Nobel Prize in physics in 1911 for his discovery of the
displacement law of heat radiation named in his honor.

* Ludwig Boltzmann (1844–1906), Austrian theoretical
physicist, was educated at Linz and Vienna. At 23 he was
appointed assistant at the physical institute in Vienna.
Later he became professor at Graz, then at Munich, and
finally back at Vienna. His first publication was on the
second law of thermodynamics, and was followed by
numerous papers on molecular motion, on viscosity and
diffusion of gases, on Maxwell's electromagnetic theory,
on Hertz's electrical experiments, and on Stefan's law for
black-body radiation.

made by Max Planck* in 1900. Planck's theoretical considerations led him to the conclusion that matter is composed of a large number of oscillating particles and that all conceivable vibration frequencies of these particles are possible. Although the frequency of any one particle according to classical theory could have any value, he assumed that the vibration energy must be given by

$$E = nh\nu \qquad (45c)$$

where ν is the frequency of vibration, h is a constant, and n is a whole number,

$$n = 1, 2, 3, 4, 5, \ldots \qquad (45d)$$

When an oscillator emits radiant energy, it does so in the form of electromagnetic waves and only in "chunks" given by Eq.(45c).

The whole number n is called a *quantum number*, h is called *Planck's constant*, and $h\nu$ is called a *quantum* of energy. Today we know that all quanta of radiation have an energy $h\nu$ and all quanta of the same frequency have the same energy. Quanta of high frequency, such as gamma rays, have a large amount of energy,

From his theory Planck derived a radiant-energy formula for which the rate of emission of a black body is a maximum at the value given by Wien's displacement law, Eq.(45a), and falls off at higher and lower wavelengths as shown in Fig. 45B. Planck's formula for the radiated energy E is

$$E_\lambda \, \Delta\lambda = \frac{hc^3 \, \Delta\lambda}{\lambda^5(e^{hc/\lambda kT} - 1)} \qquad (45e)$$

where E_λ = joules per second per square meter of surface in the wavelength band between λ and $\lambda + \Delta\lambda$, c is the velocity of light, λ is the wavelength, T is the absolute temperature, e is the base of the Naperian logarithms, k is the so-called *Boltzmann constant* determined from the general gas laws, and h is Planck's constant:

$$h = 6.6238 \times 10^{-34} \text{ J s}$$
$$k = 1.3805 \times 10^{-23} \text{ J/°Abs.}$$
$$c = 3 \times 10^8 \text{ m/s}$$
$$e = 2.7183$$

45.6. The Complete Spectrum. *Visible*, *ultraviolet*, and *infrared* light waves do not represent all of the known kinds of electromagnetic radi-

Fig. 45C   *Complete wavelength and frequency chart of the electromagnetic spectrum as it is now known.*

while those of low frequency, such as radio waves, have a small amount of energy.

* Max Planck (1858–1947), German theoretical physicist, was born in Kiel, on April 23, 1858. He studied in Munich and Berlin and devoted much of his life to theoretical physics, particularly to thermodynamics. He published several books on this subject and is called the father of the quantum theory of radiation. For his contributions to the theory of black-body radiation he was awarded the Nobel Prize in physics for the year 1918.

ation. A complete chart of the known spectrum is shown in Fig. 45C. Beyond the visible and infrared toward longer wavelengths, we find the *heat waves* and the *wireless waves*, while beyond the ultraviolet toward shorter wavelengths we find the *X rays* and the *gamma rays*.

In spite of the tremendous expanse of wavelengths ranging all the way from the longest wireless waves several miles in length to γ-ray waves one-million-millionth of a centimeter in length, all electromagnetic waves travel with the same velocity in vacuum: 186,300 mi/s, or 3×10^8 m/s.

Although their velocities in a vacuum are all the same, the properties of the various waves differ considerably. One striking illustration of these differences is found in the response of the human eye. Of the entire spectrum, only one very narrow band of waves can be seen, all the rest being invisible. Another illustration is the passage of light waves through the atmosphere. With the exception of the band of waves known as the extreme ultraviolet, the air is fairly transparent to all electromagnetic waves. To waves of the extreme ultraviolet, the air is quite opaque. *Fog is opaque to all but the wireless waves.*

45.7. The Angstrom as a Unit of Length. Because the wavelengths of light are so very short, the physicist has adopted a smaller unit of

where, for the mksa system, ν is the frequency in vib/s and λ is the wavelength in meters. From this we see that the longer the wavelength, the lower the frequency; and the shorter the wavelength, the higher the frequency.

Here is a list of wavelengths of the approximate center of each color band.

Violet	$\lambda = 4100$ Å
Blue	$\lambda = 4700$ A
Green	$\lambda = 5500$ Å
Yellow	$\lambda = 5800$ Å
Orange	$\lambda = 6100$ Å
Red	$\lambda = 6600$ Å

In other units green light, for example, has a wavelength of 5.5×10^{-5} cm, 5.5×10^{-7} m, or $0.55\ \mu$.

45.8. Prism Spectrographs. One of the most common forms of prism spectrographs is shown in Fig. 45D. This *Littrow* type instrument, as it

Fig. 45D   *Littrow type of prism spectrograph showing dual use of a lens and prism.*

length than the meter, centimeter, or millimeter. This unit is called the *angstrom* (Å), after the Swedish scientist by that name. In 1868 Ångstrom published a map of the visible spectrum of the sun, and on this map he labeled the wavelengths in ten-millionths of a millimeter. Since that time, light waves have been specified in these units.

In one meter there are 10,000,000,000 angstroms:

$$1\text{ m} = 10^{10} \text{ Å} \qquad (45\text{f})$$

It is common practice among physicists to designate the wavelength of light waves by the Greek letter λ (lambda) and the frequency by the Greek letter ν (nu).

For all electromagnetic waves, visible or invisible, the velocity c in a vacuum is 3×10^8 m/s, and the following wave equation holds true:

$$c = \nu\lambda \qquad (45\text{g})$$

is called, employs a long-focus lens, a slit, a 30° glass prism silvered on the back surface, and a curved photographic plateholder.

In this instrument a single lens serves a dual function; it provides a parallel beam of light incident upon the prism face, and it brings the emergent light of different wavelengths to a focus at different points on the photographic plateholder. Since the light crosses the glass–air boundary twice, the dispersion of the colors is the same as for an unsilvered 60° prism.

When a glass-prism spectrograph is used to study a source of light, only a small part of the ultraviolet spectrum can be photographed. The reason for this is that glass absorbs ultraviolet light at wavelengths less than 3600 Å. To photograph the shorter waves, lenses and prisms made of quartz are frequently used. Quartz is transparent to ultraviolet light as far down in wavelength as 2000 Å. Beyond this point the waves are absorbed by air.

Glass-prism spectrographs are seldom used for the infrared spectrum since the dispersion for these wavelengths is so small.

45.9. Diffraction-Grating Spectrographs. The diffraction grating is an optical device widely used in place of a prism for studying the spectrum and measuring the wavelengths of light.

The basic principles of how a grating spreads light out into a spectrum by diffraction have been explained in Sec. 43.7. The principal advantage of the diffraction grating over the prism spectrograph is that it is capable of producing high dispersion for all regions of the spectrum and the light is distributed over a uniform wavelength scale. By comparison a prism instrument produces high dispersion at the violet end of the spectrum and crowds the longer red wavelengths into a shorter space.

Transmission gratings were first made by Fraunhofer, a German physicist, in 1819, and the first reflection gratings were made by H. A. Rowland,[*] an American physicist, in 1882. Although Rowland's first gratings were ruled on flat surfaces, his best ones were ruled upon the polished surfaces of concave mirrors.

One of the most useful of all spectrographs to be found in the research laboratory today is one whose design was originally devised by F. Paschen. A concave reflection grating with a radius of curvature of about 21 ft is mounted in one corner of a dark room. The slit and light source are located in another corner and a long plateholder directly opposite (see Fig. 45E).

Light from the source to be studied passes through the narrow slit and then falls on the grating to be diffracted. Note that the grating performs the double function of dispersing the light into a spectrum and of focusing it as well.

The slit, grating, and photographic plateholder are all located with high precision on the periphery of a circle whose diameter is equal to the

* Henry A. Rowland (1848–1901), American physicist, is noted principally for his ruling of the first high-quality diffraction gratings and his publication of a large and detailed photograph of the sun's spectrum. He was the recipient of many honors, including the Rumford Medal and the Draper Medal.

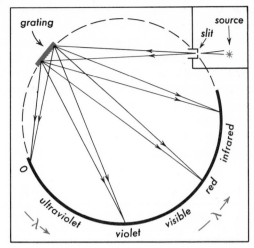

Fig. 45E *Diagram of a spectrograph employing a concave diffraction grating. The Paschen mounting.*

radius of curvature of the grating. Such an arrangement brings the different wavelengths to focus all along the plateholder. This circle is called the *Rowland circle* in honor of H. A. Rowland.

When a photograph of any part of the spectrum is desired, a strip of plate or film is placed in the proper place in the plateholder and exposed to the spectrum. The original photographs in Fig. 46L were made with a 21-ft Paschen spectrograph.

Another useful type of mounting for a concave reflection grating is shown in Fig. 45F. Different

Fig. 45F *Diagram of a spectrograph employing a concave reflection grating.*

wavelength regions of the spectrum are brought to focus on the photographic plate by turning and moving the grating and plateholder by fine adjusting screws (not shown). Adjustments are made so that the slit, grating, and plateholder lie on the Rowland circle.

Since the light at no point, from source to photographic plate, traverses glass elements, such a spectrograph can be mounted in a suitable housing and highly evacuated for the study of the ultraviolet and extreme ultraviolet spectrum of any source.

Oxygen and nitrogen gases absorb broad wavelength regions of the ultraviolet, from 1900 Å to approximately 50 A. Spectrum lines throughout this entire region are therefore to be photographed only by highly evacuated instruments of this kind. While ordinary clear dry air at and near sea level is transparent to ultraviolet light down to 1900 Å, the ozone high in the stratosphere absorbs strongly in the region 1900 Å to 3000 A, and sunlight in this band does not reach the earth's surface.

PROBLEMS

1. At what wavelength will the maximum energy be radiated by a solid piece of metal heated to a temperature of 2400°C?

2. Find the wavelength at which the maximum energy is radiated from a block of black carbon at a temperature of 327°C. What kind of light is it? [*Ans.* 4.83×10^4 Å. Infrared.]

3. The wavelength range of the light of the visible spectrum extends from 4000 Å in the violet to 7500 Å in the red. What are these same wavelength limits in (a) centimeters, (b) meters, and (c) microns?

4. X rays from a certain X-ray source have a wavelength of 0.056 Å. What is the wavelength in meters? [*Ans.* 5.6×10^{-12} m.]

5. Find the frequency of blue light of wavelength 4600 Å.

6. What is the frequency of X rays if the wavelength is 0.25 Å? [*Ans.* 12.0×10^{18} vib/s.]

7. Calculate the wavelength maximum for light radiated by a body at 5 million degrees absolute. To what kind of light is this equivalent?

8. A small copper ball 4 cm in diameter is coated with lampblack and heated to a temperature of 927°C. How much heat is radiated from this sphere in 1 min? [*Ans.* 0.850 Kcal.]

9. The rear wall of a brick fireplace has an effective open area of 0.750 m². Find the number of kilocalories radiated per minute if this area is maintained at 227°C. Assume the surface to be a black body.

10. A silver ball 8 cm in diameter is coated with lampblack and its temperature maintained at 327°C. (a) How much heat will this body radiate each second of time? (b) If the walls of the room are maintained at 27°C, how much heat will this ball absorb each second of time? Assume black-body surfaces. [*Ans.* (a) 0.0354 Kcal/s, (b) 0.002 Kcal/s.]

11. Why must the air be removed from a spectrograph that is used to observe spectrum lines in the region of 500 Å to 1000 Å?

12. Would a diffraction grating spectrograph have to be evacuated to photograph the spectral region 2500 Å to 3000 Å? Explain your answer.

Fig. 46A *Illustrations of continuous and line spectra.*

CLASSIFICATION
OF SPECTRA

A spectrum may be defined as a smooth and orderly array of light arranged in the order of wavelength. Such an array is usually photographed with a prism or diffraction-grating spectrograph of the kind described in the preceding chapter.

Different sources of light produce different wavelength displays and hence display different spectra. All spectra may be grouped into five main classes:

Continuous emission spectra
Line emission spectra
Continuous absorption spectra
Line absorption spectra
Band spectra

46.1. Continuous Emission Spectra. The continuous emission spectrum has already been treated in detail in Sec. 45.1. There it was demonstrated that, when light from a hot *solid* like the tungsten filament of an electric light, or the positive carbon of an arc, is sent through a prism, a continuous band of color from red to violet is observed (see color plate, Fig. 46A). The intensity of such a spectrum depends upon the temperature and upon the hot body itself. All hot solids raised to the same temperature give very nearly the same continuous emission spectrum.

46.2. Line Emission Spectra. When the slit of a spectrograph is illuminated by the light from a mercury arc, a sodium lamp, a helium or a neon discharge tube, a number of bright lines appear on the photographic plate in place of a continuous spectrum (see Figs. 46A and 46B).

It is important to realize that line spectra derive their name from the fact that a slit is used whose image constitutes a line. If a small circular opening were used in place of a slit, a disk image would appear in the place of each line.

Fig. 46B *Photographs of the line emission spectrum from four different elements in the gaseous state.*

The ability to distinguish between two or more wavelengths, differing only slightly from one another, is therefore increased by the use of a slit.

The most intense spectrum lines are obtained from metallic arcs and sparks. The flame of a carbon arc may be used for demonstration purposes by previously soaking the *positive carbon rod* in various chemicals. An experimental arrangement for projecting the spectrum on a large screen is shown in Fig. 46C. Common salt water (sodium chloride in solution) gives a brilliant yellow line characteristic of sodium. Solutions of strontium or calcium chloride will show other strong spectrum lines in the red, green, and blue.

While a continuous emission spectrum arises

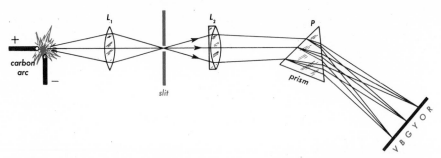

Fig. 46C *Experimental arrangement used in demonstrating spectrum lines in emission.*

from hot solids, a *line spectrum always arises from a gas at high temperatures and low pressures.* It is the gas flame of the carbon arc that gives rise to the line emission spectrum in Fig. 46C.

46.3. Continuous Absorption Spectra. Continuous absorption spectra are usually produced by passing the light of a continuous emission spectrum through matter in the solid or liquid state. Good demonstrations can be performed by allowing white light to pass through colored glass. When the light is later dispersed by a prism, the missing colors will in general cover a wide band of wavelengths. A red piece of glass, for example, will absorb all visible light but the red. A magenta-colored piece of glass will absorb the whole central part of the visible spectrum.

46.4. Line Absorption Spectra. Line spectra in absorption are produced by sending continuous white light through a gas. Experimentally, the gas or vapor is inserted in the path of the light as shown in Fig. 46D. Light from a carbon arc, after passing as a parallel beam through a glass tube containing sodium vapor, is brought to a focus at the slit C. From there the light passes

through a lens L_3 and a prism P to form a spectrum on the observing screen.

Sodium is chosen as an example for demonstration purposes because of its convenience. The vapor is produced by inserting a small amount of metallic sodium in a partially evacuated glass tube and heating it with a small gas burner. As the metal vaporizes, filling the tube with sodium vapor, a dark line will appear in the yellow region of the spectrum (see color plate, Fig. 46A).

If a photograph is taken of this absorption, and the photographic plate is long enough to extend into the ultraviolet, many absorption lines as shown in Fig. 46E are detected. A systematic array of absorption lines like this occurs with only a few elements, principally with the alkali metals, lithium, sodium, potassium, rubidium, and cesium. All elements in the gaseous state, however, give rise to a number of absorption lines, usually in the ultraviolet region of the spectrum. The absorption of yellow light by normal sodium atoms, for example, is a kind of resonance phenomenon. By virtue of their electronic structure, atoms have definite and discrete

Fig. 46D *Experimental arrangement for demonstrating the line absorption spectrum of sodium vapor.*

↑
limit

sodium series

Fig. 46E   *Absorption spectrum of sodium vapor. The principal series of Sodium.* (After F. A. Jenkins.)

natural frequencies to which they will vibrate in resonance. When light of one of these frequencies passes by, they respond to vibration and in so doing absorb the light energy.

46.5. The Sun's Spectrum. The solar spectrum, consisting of a bright colored continuous spectrum interspersed by thousands of dark lines,

In 1882, the American physicist H. A. Rowland photographed and published a 40-ft-long map of the sun's spectrum. Two small sections of Rowland's map are reproduced in Fig. 46G. These lines are explained as being due to the absorption of light by the solar atmosphere.

The surface of the sun at a temperature of

Fig. 46F   *Diagram of the solar spectrum indicating the most prominent lines labeled with the first letters of the alphabet as they first were by Fraunhofer.*

was first observed by Wollaston in 1802, and independently discovered and studied by Fraunhofer in 1817. Fraunhofer mapped out several hundred of these lines and labeled eight of the most prominent lines by the first letters of the alphabet. The strongest of these lines, now called Fraunhofer lines, are illustrated in Fig. 46F.

6000°K emits light of all wavelengths, i.e., a continuous emission spectrum. As this light passes out through the cooler gas layers of the solar atmosphere (see Fig. 46H), certain wavelengths are absorbed. Because the absorbing medium is in the gaseous state, the atoms and molecules there do not absorb all wavelengths

Fig. 46G   *Photographic reproductions of the solar spectrum taken from Rowland's original map.*

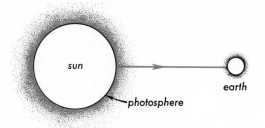

Fig. 46H   *Light from the sun must pass through the solar atmosphere and the earth's atmosphere before reaching an observer on the earth's surface.*

equally, but rather they absorb principally those wavelengths they would emit if heated to a high temperature. Thus the atoms of one chemical element with their own characteristic frequencies absorb certain wavelengths, whereas the atoms of other elements absorb certain other wavelengths.

Before the sunlight reaches the earth's surface where it can be examined by an observer with a spectrograph, it must again pass through absorbing gases, this time the earth's atmosphere. Here, too, certain wavelengths are partially absorbed, producing other dark lines.

That the missing wavelengths correspond to definite chemical elements is illustrated by diagram in Fig. 46I. The center strip (b) represents

an iron or calcium line, are due to other elements.

It has been possible by spectrum photographs of this kind to identify about two-thirds of the known chemical elements as existing on the sun. The reason why not all 90 or more elements are found is that some are too rare to produce absorption, whereas for other elements existing within the sun in large enough quantities the temperature is either too high or too low to bring out their lines.

Nine prominent Fraunhofer lines labeled in Fig. 46F have been identified as follows:

A, oxygen......... $\lambda = 7594$ Å
B, oxygen......... $\lambda = 6870$ Å
C, hydrogen....... $\lambda = 6562$ Å
D, sodium......... $\lambda = 5893$ Å
E, iron........... $\lambda = 5270$ Å
F, hydrogen....... $\lambda = 4861$ Å
G, iron........... $\lambda = 4308$ Å
H, calcium........ $\lambda = 3969$ Å
K, calcium........ $\lambda = 3935$ Å

46.6. The Doppler Effect and the Sun's Rotation. It is not difficult to determine which of the Fraunhofer lines are due to absorption by the sun's atmosphere and which are due to the earth's atmosphere. The sun, like the earth, is rotating about an axis, and this motion produces for an

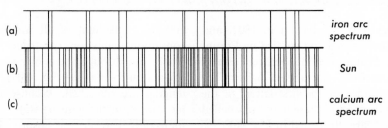

Fig. 46I   *Schematic diagram illustrating the comparison of laboratory spectra from different elements with the many-line spectrum of the sun.*

a small section of the visible spectrum as obtained with sunlight entering the slit of a spectrograph. The upper and lower strips, (a) and (c), represent the line spectrum observed when an iron arc and a calcium arc are successively placed in front of the same slit. Where each calcium line occurs in the laboratory source, an absorption line is found in the sun's spectrum. The same is true for each iron line. The remaining lines, not matched by

observer on the earth a slight change of wavelength of light. This change in wavelength is due to the well-known Doppler effect so often observed with sound.

On one side of the sun, the east limb, the surface emitting light and the absorbing gases are approaching the earth at a high speed, while on the other side, the west limb, the emitting surface and gases are receding from the earth.

On the Doppler principles the light waves emitted by the approaching side are crowded together to give a higher frequency, while those emitted by the receding side are lengthened out to give a lower frequency. Since the absorbing gases are also moving, the absorption lines due to these gases should be shifted in the solar spectrum.

The lines marked by arrows in Fig. 46J(a)

black, that is, devoid of all light; they are dark only in contrast with the far brighter colored background. Actually the sun's atmosphere is not cold but, as seen at the time of a total eclipse, is quite hot and emits light of its own. When this light is observed in a spectroscope, or photographed with a spectrograph, it consists of a bright-line spectrum called a *flash spectrum*.

The photograph of a flash spectrum repro-

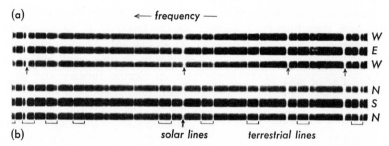

Fig. 46J *Photographs of the spectrum of different regions of the sun's disk. E and W were taken with the light from the east and west limbs of the sun. The lines marked by an arrow show a Doppler shift as evidence of the sun's rotation.*

show the Doppler shift. The lines marked by brackets, on the other hand, are produced by the earth's atmosphere which, because it is stationary with respect to an observer on the earth's surface, gives rise to unshifted lines. Remaining fixed, the unshifted lines serve as fiducial marks from which to observe and measure the shift in the solar lines.

The lower photograph (b) in Fig. 46J, shows that at the solar poles where there is relatively no motion toward or away from the earth, no Doppler shift is observed in the solar lines.

46.7. The Flash Spectrum. The Fraunhofer lines of the solar spectrum are not absolutely

duced in Fig. 46K was made in the following way. During a solar eclipse, at just the instant before the moon's disk blanks out all of the sun's disk, leaving only a narrow bright crescent of the sun to be seen on one side, the light is allowed to enter a spectrograph.

With the customary slit and collimator lens removed from the instrument, each spectral line becomes a crescent-shaped image of the sun as cast by light of that wavelength. Note the high intensity of the H and K lines due to ionized calcium, and the solar prominences that appear at the same points on each image. Note also the high intensity of the lines marked H_α, H_β, H_γ, H_δ,

Fig. 46K *Photograph of the flash spectrum of the sun taken at the time of a total eclipse. Note the prominences, called Halley's beads. (Courtesy of the Lick Observatory.)*

and H_ϵ, as well as the succeeding lines, indicating a long series of spectral wavelengths. These lines are due to hydrogen and are known as the *Balmer series*.

The spectra of many of the distant stars are composed almost exclusively of the lines of the Balmer series, while others like our own sun exhibit more complex arrays.

46.8. The Balmer Series of Hydrogen. The first successful attempt to obtain a formula that represents the hydrogen series was made by Balmer in 1885. Since that time, these lines have become known as the Balmer series of hydrogen. Balmer's formula is written

$$\lambda = B\left[\frac{n_2^2 \times n_1^2}{n_2^2 - n_1^2}\right] \tag{46a}$$

where λ = wavelength in angstroms.

$$B = 911.27 \text{ Å}$$
$$n_1 = 2$$
$$n_2 = 3, 4, 5, 6, 7, \dots$$

If the number 3 is substituted for n_2 in the above formula, the wavelength λ of the first line of the series is calculated. Likewise, if the number 4 is substituted in its place, the wavelength of the second line can be calculated, etc. When these calculations are carried out, the following wavelengths are obtained for the first four lines:

	CALCULATED	MEASURED
$H_\alpha = B\frac{3\,6}{5}$	= 6561.1 Å	6562.1 Å
$H_\beta = B\frac{6\,4}{1\,2}$	= 4860.8 Å	4860.7 Å
$H_\gamma = B\frac{1\,0\,0}{2\,1}$	= 4339.4 Å	4340.1 Å
$H_\delta = B\frac{1\,4\,4}{3\,2}$	= 4100.7 A	4101.3 Å

These wavelengths, as well as those calculated for other lines of the series, agree remarkably well with the measured values. Balmer did not derive his formula from any theory, but simply formulated it from the measured wavelength for each series line. The meaning of those whole numbers n_1 and n_2 is given in Sec. 51.2.

46.9. The Temperature Effect. The effect of raising the temperature of a source of light is to bring out new spectrum lines and cause others to disappear. This is illustrated by a small section of the spectrum of vanadium, element number 23, in Fig. 46L. The first three photographs were taken by heating small bits of vanadium metal in an electric furnace and photographing the light coming from the vapor just above the hot metal. The fourth photograph was made by placing a small piece of vanadium metal in the tip of the positive carbon of an arc, and the fifth by a high-voltage electric spark jumping between two vanadium metal rods.

Though the top spectrum taken at a temperature of 200°K appears to be quite different from the lower one taken at a temperature at least twice as high, all of the lines arise from vanadium atoms and are characteristic of that element alone.

It is a well-founded and general rule that as the temperature of a gas is increased, the maximum intensity shifts toward shorter wavelengths. At a low temperature, for example, the lines in the visible part of the spectrum of an element may be brightest, while at a higher temperature those in the ultraviolet become most intense.

Fig. 46L *Ultraviolet spectrum of vanadium, element 23. (a) 2000°K. (b) 2300°K. (c) 2600°K. (d) From a direct-current arc between vanadium metal electrodes. (e) High-voltage electric spark between vanadium metal electrodes. (After A. S. King.)*

46.10. Relation Between Emission and Absorption Spectra. When the line emission spectrum of an element is compared with the line absorption spectrum of the same element, the lines are found to coincide exactly. This is illustrated by a small section of the complex spectrum of iron in Fig. 46M. The strips (a) and (c), above and

the incident light waves from the beam. This is like the resonance of two tuning forks that may be demonstrated for sound. Only when the sound waves from the first fork have exactly the same frequency as the second fork does the second fork pick up the motions and vibrate.

In the event that white light is sent through

Fig. 46M   *Emission and absorption spectrum of iron.* (After Anderson and Smith.)

below, show the emission lines from the hot flame of an iron arc, while the middle strip (b) shows the absorption lines resulting from the passage of a continuous emission spectrum through cooler iron vapor.

To give a simple explanation of this we may picture the emission of light as due to the motions or vibrations of the electrons in the atoms of the source. These moving electric charges give rise to electromagnetic waves having the same frequencies as the electrons themselves. In any source of light only a small percent of the atoms have their electrons vibrating at any given time. These few, which we refer to as vibrating atoms, are called *excited atoms*, while those not vibrating are called *unexcited atoms*.

When yellow light from a sodium arc passes through sodium vapor, as in Fig. 46D, many individual atoms respond and become excited. In becoming excited the atoms have absorbed

sodium vapor, only those light waves having frequencies equal to the natural frequencies of the atoms are absorbed. This is the explanation of the series of absorption lines in Fig. 46E. Again, when white light passes through iron vapor, only those light waves having frequencies equal to the natural frequencies of iron atoms are absorbed.

Although the atoms which are set into vibration by absorbing light from the beam emit the light again a small fraction of a second later, their chance of emitting it in some one direction is equally probable for all directions. Very little of this re-radiated light is therefore given out in the forward direction, parallel with the incident light.

46.11. Band Spectra. All of the line spectra described thus far are known to arise from single free atoms in a heated gas. Molecules of two or more atoms also give rise to spectrum lines

Fig. 46N   *Band spectra taken with a large spectrograph.* (After Jenkins.)

grouped together into what are called bands. As shown by the reproductions in Fig. 46N, these bands have the appearance of flutings.

Each fluting in the spectrum of a diatomic molecule is not a continuous band but a set of regularly spaced lines. The third photograph in Fig. 46N is a very greatly enlarged picture of a single band taken in the second order of a 21-ft grating spectrograph of the type shown in Fig. 45E.

The left-hand edge of the band is called the band head and the right-hand side of the tail of the band. Note that one line near the band head is missing. The mystery of this missing line is now well understood, for it is the starting point of the band in place of the band head, and is called the band origin. The theory of band spectra and the present-day knowledge of how diatomic molecules emit so many frequencies will be taken up in another chapter.

PROBLEMS

1. Calculate to five figures the wavelength of the twelfth and twentieth lines of the Balmer series of hydrogen.

2. Calculate to five figures the wavelength of the tenth line of the Balmer series of hydrogen. [*Ans.* 3749.2 Å].

3. Briefly describe an experimental arrangement by which a line emission spectrum is produced.

4. Briefly describe an experimental arrangement by which a line absorption spectrum is produced.

5. Find the wavelength of the fifteenth line of the Balmer series of hydrogen.

6. Calculate the wavelength of the eighth line of the Balmer series of hydrogen. [*Ans.* 3796.9 Å].

7. Determine the wavelength of the series limit of the Balmer series of hydrogen. (Note $n_2 = \infty$.)

8. From what kind of source does one obtain the most intense line emission spectrum?

9. How can one produce a line absorption spectrum in the laboratory?

10. How is it possible to determine the elements existing in any given distant star?

11. A given piece of metal is composed of several elements. How could one determine spectroscopically whether it contains sodium?

THE ATOMIC STRUCTURE
OF MATTER

In dealing with the physical properties of matter it is convenient to divide substances into three forms or states: (1) *the solid state*, (2) *the liquid state*, and (3) *the gaseous state*. Most substances may be made to take on any of these three forms simply by altering the temperature.

The atomic theory of matter assumes that all matter in the universe is made up of ultra-microscopic bodies called atoms and that these are at all times in a rapid state of motion. The nature of this motion and its activity depends upon the temperature and the state of the matter in question, as well as upon the kinds of atoms of which it is composed.

47.1. Kinds of Atoms. Although there are thousands of different substances known to the scientific world, they are all, when broken down into small components, found to be composed of one or more kinds of atoms. A substance that contains atoms of one kind only is called an *element*, while those containing more than one kind are called *compounds* or *mixtures*. Iron, copper, aluminum, platinum, mercury, hydrogen, and helium are examples of elements; whereas water, salt, brass, wood, and air are examples of compounds and mixtures.

The technical names and chemical abbreviations of a few of the more commonly known elements are given in Table 47A. A complete table of the more than 100 known elements is given in the Appendix.

With each element it is customary to associate two numbers; one is called the *atomic number*, the other the *atomic weight*. The atomic number, given at the left in the tables, specifies the posi-

TABLE 47A. SOME OF THE CHEMICAL ELEMENTS ATOMIC WEIGHTS BASED ON CARBON-12 AS 12 EVEN

Atomic No.	Element	Symbol	Atomic Weight
1	hydrogen	H	1.0080
2	helium	He	4.0026
3	lithium	Li	6.9390
4	beryllium	Be	9.0122
6	carbon	C	12.0111
7	nitrogen	N	14.0067
8	oxygen	O	15.9994
10	neon	Ne	20.1830
13	aluminum	Al	26.9815
26	iron	Fe	55.847
29	copper	Cu	63.540
47	silver	Ag	107.870
50	tin	Sn	118.69
78	platinum	Pt	195.09
79	gold	Au	196.97
80	mercury	Hg	200.59
82	lead	Pb	207.19
88	radium	Ra	225.92
92	uranium	U	238.03
94	plutonium	Pu	239.16

tion that element always occupies with respect to all the others, while the atomic weight on the right gives the average weight of one atom of that element relative to the carbon-12 isotope as having a weight of 12.000000 (see Appendix VII). On this basis, the lightest known element, hydrogen, has an average weight of approximately unity.

To illustrate the minuteness of individual atoms, the actual masses in kilograms and approximate diameters in meters of the lightest element, hydrogen, and the very heavy element, plutonium, are as follows:

1. hydrogen $\begin{cases} \text{mass} = 1.66 \times 10^{-27} \text{ Kg} \\ \text{diameter} = 1 \times 10^{-10} \text{ m} \end{cases}$

94. plutonium $\begin{cases} \text{mass} = 3.9 \times 10^{-25} \text{ Kg} \\ \text{diameter} = 6 \times 10^{-10} \text{ m} \end{cases}$

The actual mass of any atom in kilograms can be obtained by multiplying the atomic weight of that element by the unit atomic mass 1.66×10^{-27} Kg.

Although the intricate structure of each atom plays an important part in its physical and chemical behavior, we will neglect this detailed structure for the time being and think only of each atom as being a tiny sphere-like particle with a very small mass. Later, in other chapters where it is pertinent to do so, the structure of individual atoms will be considered in detail.

47.2. Molecules. One of the most important properties of atoms is their ability to act upon one another at a distance. Some atoms, when they come close together attract each other, while others exhibit a force of repulsion. When, at the close approach of two or more atoms, attraction occurs, the atoms may combine to form a molecule. Once a molecule has formed, it will move about and behave as a unit particle under various physical conditions.

Molecules in general may contain almost any number of atoms. Those having only one atom are called *monatomic molecules*, those with two are called *diatomic molecules*, and those with three *triatomic molecules*. In the free state of a gas, some atoms, like helium, neon, and krypton, prefer to exist alone, whereas others like hydrogen, nitrogen, and oxygen prefer to combine and move about in pairs.

Examples of monatomic molecules are helium (He), neon (Ne), and krypton (Kr); of diatomic molecules are hydrogen (H_2), nitrogen (N_2), oxygen (O_2), and carbon monoxide (CO); and of triatomic molecules are ozone (O_3), carbon dioxide (CO_2), water (H_2O), and hydro-cyanic acid (HCN) (see Fig. 47A). Besides these simplest atomic aggregates, there are molecules known to contain many atoms. Along with triatomic molecules they are called *polyatomic molecules*.

It is clear from the diagrams in Fig. 47A that the atoms of a molecule may be of the same kind or may be different. The question as to why some atoms cling together in pairs and others do not is a subject involving the structure of the atoms themselves. If the individual atoms of a

Fig. 47A *Schematic diagrams of a few common molecules. First row: Helium, neon, hydrogen, nitrogen, oxygen, carbon monoxide, hydrochloric acid. Second row: Ozone, carbon dioxide, water, hydrocyanic acid. Third row: Methane, acetylene, benzene, methyl alcohol, ethyl alcohol.*

molecule are brought much closer together than their normal separation, they repel each other and are pushed apart. If they are pulled farther apart, the forces become attractive, pulling them together. In other words, they act as though they were connected by springs as shown in Fig. 47B.

Fig. 47B   *The forces between atoms in a molecule behave like springs.*

Pushed closer together or pulled farther apart, they tend to move back to some equilibrium distance. In terms of energy they occupy a position of *minimum potential energy*. To push them closer together or to separate them requires work.

At large distances, all atomic forces become very weak so that if by some means or other the atoms of a molecule are pulled far enough apart they become completely separated as free atoms.

A graph of the forces between atoms is shown in Fig. 47C. The horizontal scale giving the

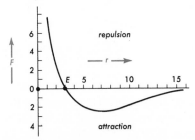

Fig. 47C   *Typical graph of the force between two atoms of a diatomic molecule.*

distance *r* between atoms will be slightly different for different atoms, but the equilibrium position E is approximately 3×10^{-10} m.

47.3. Molecular Weight. The molecular weight of a substance is defined as the sum of the atomic weights of the atoms which make up one mole-

cule of that substance. A carbon dioxide molecule, for example, has two oxygen atoms of weight 16 and one carbon atom of weight 12. The molecular weight of carbon dioxide is therefore $16 + 16 + 12 = 44$. Similarly, the molecular weight of nitrogen is 28, oxygen 32, and helium 4. To find the mass of a molecule in grams, its molecular weight should be multiplied by unit atomic mass 1.66×10^{-24} gm.

47.4. Three States of Matter. As already stated, matter may exist in three states: (1) the solid state, (2) the liquid state, and (3) the gaseous state. If a solid is heated sufficiently it can be made to melt or liquefy, and by continued heating it can be boiled or vaporized. As a vapor, it is in the gaseous state. If, on the other hand, a gas is cooled sufficiently, it will condense and become a liquid. The continued cooling of a liquid will cause it to solidify or freeze. In the case of water, nature performs all these changes of state: ice is melted to become water, and water is vaporized to become steam; water vapor or clouds condense to become rain, and rain freezes to become ice or hail. Although it may sometimes require extreme heat or extreme cold, all substances can be transformed from any one state to another.

47.5. The Gaseous State. When a substance is in the gaseous state, it is in an extremely rarefied condition. Most of the atoms are grouped together into molecules which, on the average, are very far apart. These molecules are not at rest but are moving about with extremely high speeds, bumping into each other and into the walls of the container. It is the bumping of many millions of molecules against the walls of the containing vessel that gives rise to what is called gas pressure.

A good example of gas pressure is to be found where air has been pumped into an automobile tire or into a toy balloon. Since there are so many more air molecules bombarding the rubber walls inside than outside, the walls are held out by greater bombardment. In addition to moving linearly, a gas molecule, made up of two or more atoms, also vibrates and rotates about its center of mass. As the temperature of the gas is raised, all of these motions increase in speed, causing an increase in pressure. As the temperature is decreased, the atomic motions slow down, decreasing the pressure.

Molecular motion can be illustrated by means of a mechanical model as shown in Fig. 47D.

Fig. 47D   *Mechanical model illustrating the random motion of molecules in a gas.*

Small steel marbles are placed between two parallel glass plates and set into motion by means of vibrating metal strips around the sides. Each strip V is mounted at the end of a short strip of spring steel and is set into vibration by means of small electromagnets S. As the steel balls bump into these strips, they are bounced off with high speed. On the average, the small steel marbles move considerably faster than the larger ones. This is characteristic of the different-sized molecules in a mixture of two different gases like helium and neon. By increasing the vibrations of the strips the steel marbles move faster. This is analogous to the heating of a gas to a higher temperature.

47.6. The Liquid State. When a gas is continually cooled, the molecular motion slows down until at a certain temperature the gas condenses into a much smaller volume and changes into a liquid. Although the molecules continue to move, they no longer move as rapidly as they did in the gaseous state. Being much closer together, however, they now attract each other with sufficiently strong forces to cause them to move in closely packed swarms.

The swarming of honeybees as they fly through the air is comparable to the molecules of a gas, while their subsequent collection on the branch of a tree corresponds to condensation into the liquid state.

47.7. Brownian Motion. Although no one has ever observed directly the random motions of molecules, it is possible to observe in a microscope the resultant recoils of larger particles under their continual bombardment. The effect was first discovered in 1827 by Robert Brown, a British botanist, who observed the irregular but lifelike motions of small particles suspended in a liquid. These microscopic particles appear to be continually agitated and make a succession of quick jumps first one way and then another. The path of a single particle is illustrated in Fig. 47E.

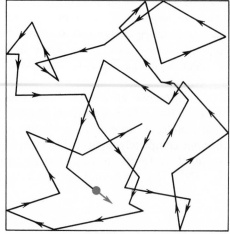

Fig. 47E   *Diagram of the random path of a single molecule.*

Such motions are called Brownian movements, after their discoverer. These curious Brownian movements were first explained by Sir William Ramsey in 1879 and may be observed in either liquids or gases. The invisibly small molecules of air or water, as the case may be, move at relatively high speeds and, bombarding the larger visible particles vigorously from all sides, make them dart here and there. The larger the particles, the slower their Brownian movement.

One method of observing Brownian motion in a gas is illustrated in Fig. 47F. Smoke from the tip of a match, just extinguished, is drawn into a

Fig. 47H   *Atomic model for ice (H_2O).*

Fig. 47F   *Experimental arrangement for observing the Brownian motion of smoke particles.*

small box by squeezing and releasing the rubber bulb. A strong beam of light from a carbon arc, entering the box through a glass lens in the side, illuminates the smoke particles, enabling them to be seen from above with a high-power microscope. The tiny smoke particles appear as bright starlike points darting first one way and then another.

To observe Brownian movement in a liquid, a small amount of powdered gamboge (an orange-yellow gum resin) is first put into some distilled water, and one drop of this solution put on a microscope slide. By illuminating the slide with a strong light, the microscopic gamboge particles will be seen to dance about as they are continually being hit by water molecules. If one remem-

bers that the gamboge particles are thousands of times heavier than the water molecules, it will be realized that the latter must be moving with very high speeds to cause such visible recoils.

47.8. The Solid State. As the temperature of a liquid is lowered, the molecular activity decreases. This permits the molecules to pack a little more closely together and accounts for the slight contraction of a liquid on cooling, and conversely for its expansion on heating. As the molecules come closer and closer together, the tendency of each molecule to wander through the liquid decreases. If the temperature is lowered still further a point is ultimately reached where the liquid freezes and becomes a solid.

In the solid state, each molecule is confined to a definite small space between neighboring molecules. This is illustrated in Figs. 47G, 47H, and 47I by atomic models of ultramicroscopic crystals. The model in Fig. 47G illustrates a cubic lattice, a simple type of structure in which the

Fig. 47G   *Atomic model for sodium chloride (NaCl is common table salt).*

Fig. 47I   *Atomic model for iceland spar, or calcite, $CaCO_3$.*

atoms take positions at the corners of cubes. Common table salt with its two kinds of atoms, sodium and chlorine, always forms such a cubic lattice, the individual atoms alternating in kind in each of the three directions, Na, Cl, Na, Cl, Na, etc.

The crystal model in Fig. 47H is of the hexagonal lattice form in which the principle structure presents parallel hexagonal "holes" through the crystal. Water, in freezing to form ice, or snowflakes, takes on this form (see Fig. 47J). Note that

Fig. 47J *Photographs of snow crystals exhibiting hexagonal structure.*

within the atomic lattice each oxygen atom is bound by connecting links between four hydrogen atoms, while each hydrogen atom is linked between two oxygen atoms. The silicon and oxygen atoms of *quartz*, chemically SiO_2, take on a somewhat similar structure, and in the natural state also exhibits its hexagonal structure (see Fig. 47K).

Fig. 47K *Natural crystals of quartz and calcite.*

The third model, Fig. 47I, shows the atomic structure for a crystal of calcite. Calcite, which chemically is calcium carbonate ($CaCO_3$), is a clear transparent crystal found in nature. Because of its particular structure it has interesting optical properties, which will be discussed in a later chapter on polarized light. Note how the calcium and carbon atoms form the corners of parallelograms, with each carbon atom surrounded by three oxygen atoms.

Although there are some twenty or more basic crystal structures known to exist, two of the simplest and most common forms, face-centered and body-centered cubic crystals, are shown in Fig. 47L. These show the least number of atoms

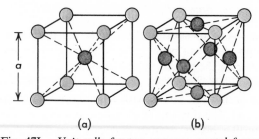

(a)   (b)

Fig. 47L *Unit cells for two common crystal forms: (a) a body-centered cube and (b) a face-centered cube.*

necessary to illustrate the general structure of any given class of crystals and are called *unit cells*.

A number of chemical elements that form face-centered or body-centered cubic structures are listed in Table 47B. The size of the structure is

TABLE 47B. SOME ELEMENTS AND THEIR CUBIC CRYSTAL STRUCTURES

Face-centered		Body-centered	
Element	a (Å)	Element	a (Å)
Aluminum	4.0493	Barium	5.0250
Copper	3.6149	α Iron	2.8665
Gold	4.0786	Rubidium	5.6300
γ Iron	3.5910	Sodium	4.2906
Lead	4.9505	Strontium	4.8500
Lithium	4.404	Titanium	3.3060
Nickel	3.5239	Tungsten	3.1147
Platinum	4.0862	Uranium	3.4740
Silver	4.0862	Zirconium	3.6200

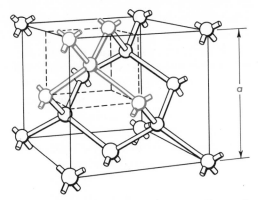

Fig. 47M *Diamond crystal structure. For carbon, silicon, and germanium a = 3.56, 5.43 and 5.66 Å, respectively. Nearest-neighbor spacing is $a\sqrt{3}/4$, and maintains tetragonal symmetry. (After Shockley.)*

Diamond, one of several known crystal forms of carbon atoms, is a closely packed crystal that has, until recently, defied laboratory reproduction. Small diamonds for use in the manufacturing of high-speed cutting tools are now produced in quantities by the General Electric Company. It was in the company's laboratories that the production of real diamonds was accomplished by applying extremely high temperatures and pressures to small graphite slugs.

The important features of the diamond structure are shown in Fig. 47M, and this is the characteristic structure for the elements C, Si, Ge, Sn, and Pb in the fourth column of the Periodic Table (see Appendix X). Note that while the outermost atoms form a large cube, all atoms are bound by chemical bonds to their four nearest neighbors. Furthermore, each set of four nearest neighbors lie at corners of a cube, with atoms diagonally opposite each other on the square sides.

For C, Si, and Ge, a = 3.56, 5.43, and 5.66 Å, respectively, while the nearest-neighbor spacing is $\frac{3}{4}a$.

While some crystal types present a more open structure than others, the actual size of each atom in the models shown above has been reduced in

specified in each case by the dimension a between cube corners, and is given in angstroms: 1 angstrom = 1×10^{-10} m.

While some elements or compounds always seem to form the same crystal pattern on solidifying, others are known to take on any one of a number of different forms. For example, two of the forms of iron are given in Table 47B. While most of the different forms of crystals known today have been found in nature, there are some that have been produced in the laboratory only.

(a)   (b)   (c)   (d)

Fig. 47N *Electron microscope photographs showing the crystalline-like structure of metals: (a) pure aluminum 5600X, (b) magnesium-aluminum alloy 13,000X, (c) polished steel 14,000X, and (d) polished copper 14,000X. (Courtesy, R. D. Heidenreich, Dow Chemical Co.)*

order to reveal the positions of others behind.

Actually, the atoms in most liquids begin to form localized crystal arrays before solidification takes place but, due to the rapid state of atomic vibration, each localized crystal region can move with respect to another. A liquid may therefore be looked upon as a transition state between the gas where individual molecules exist and the solid where individual atoms become part of a crystal structure and can no longer be associated with any particular molecule.

Metals in general, when they cool down from the molten state, solidify into thousands of ultra-microscopic crystals that pack closely together to form a three-dimensional mosaic. This is well illustrated by the electron-microscope photo-graphs reproduced in Fig. 47N. Note the clear-cut cubic structure of pure aluminum.

While each atom or molecule in a solid is confined to a definite space within the body lattice, it is in a state of vibration within that space. As the temperature decreases, this motion becomes slower and slower until at absolute zero, $-273°C$, all molecular motion ceases. By molecular motion is meant the motion of the molecule as a whole. At absolute zero, however, the atoms of certain solids are still vibrating. This residual energy of vibration is known to be an inherent property of some solids, which cannot be utilized or taken away.*

* An introductory book on crystal structure is Alan Holden and Phylis Singer, *Crystals and Crystal Growing* (Doubleday & Co., Garden City, New York).

QUESTIONS

1. What are the three states of matter? How do these states differ from each other? Which, in general, is the most compact?

2. How many known elements are there? What constitutes an element?

3. What is mean by (a) atomic number and (b) atomic weight?

4. Give an example of (a) a monatomic molecule, (b) a diatomic molecule, (c) a triatomic molecule, and (d) a polyatomic molecule.

5. What general treatment of most solids will change their state to the liquid or gas?

6. What is Brownian motion? How is it observed?

7. What can you say about the arrangement of atoms in a solid, like iron? In a solid like common table salt?

8. How could you set up an experiment to demonstrate the forces between the atoms of a linear triatomic molecule? If you were to push the outer atoms of a molecule toward each other and suddenly release them, what kind of motion do you think would ensue?

THE DISCOVERY OF
THE ELECTRON

Modern physics, dealing principally with atoms, molecules, and the structure of matter, has developed at such a tremendous rate within the past three-score years that it now occupies the center of attention of many leading scientists the world over. Recent discoveries in atomic physics have had, and will continue to have, a tremendous influence on the development of civilization. Because the subject of atomic physics is relatively new, it is logical to treat the subject matter associated with each major discovery in roughly chronological order.

48.1. Electrical Discharge Through a Gas. In 1853 an obscure French scientist by the name of Masson sent the first electric spark from a high-voltage induction coil through a partially evacuated glass vessel and discovered that, instead of the typical spark observed in air, the tube was filled with a bright glow. Several years later, Heinrich Geissler, a German glass blower in Tübingen, developed and began to manufacture gaseous discharge tubes. These tubes, made in diverse sizes, shapes, and colors of glass, and resembling the modern neon and argon signs used in advertising, attracted the attention of physicists in the leading scientific institutions and universities of the world. They purchased many of these "Geissler tubes" and used them for study and lecture demonstrations.

In 1869, W. Hittorf of Munster, with improved vacuum pumps, observed a dark region near one electrode of the electrical discharge that grew in size as the exhaustion was continued. This is but one of a number of phases of the study of electrical discharges through gases that were observed

and studied a few years later by Sir William Crookes.*

In Fig. 48A, a long glass tube about 4 cm in diameter and 150 cm long is shown connected to a mercury diffusion pump and a mechanical vacuum pump. The purpose of the pumps is to enable one to observe continuously the changes in the electrical discharge as the air is slowly removed from the tube. The purpose of the *trap* is to freeze out any mercury vapor and to prevent it from reaching the discharge. High voltage from an induction coil is shown connected to the two electrodes, one at either end of the tube.

Although an induction coil does not deliver direct current, its characteristics are such that the potentials are higher on half of the alternations than they are on the other, and the two electrodes act nearly the same as if a high-voltage direct current were used. The negative electrode under these circumstances is called the *cathode*, and the positive electrode the *anode*.

As the long tube is slowly pumped out, an emf of 10,000 to 15,000 V will produce the first discharge when the pressure has dropped to about $\frac{1}{100}$ of an atmosphere, i.e., at a barometric pressure of about 8 mm of mercury. This first discharge, as illustrated in diagram (a) of Fig. 48B, consists of long, thin streamers. As the gas pres-

* Sir William Crookes (1832–1919), English physicist and chemist. At the age of 22 he became an assistant at the Radcliffe Observatory in Oxford. He was knighted in 1897, received the Order of Merit in 1910, and was president of the Royal Society from 1913 to 1915. He invented and made the first focusing type of X-ray tube. His experiments with electrical discharges through rarefied gases led to his discovery of the dark space that now bears his name.

Fig. 48A *Diagram of a gaseous discharge tube, showing the electrical connections as well as the vacuum pumps and accessories.*

sure drops to about 5 mm of mercury, sometimes called a Geissler-tube vacuum, the discharge widens until it fills the whole tube as shown in diagram (b). At a still lower pressure of about

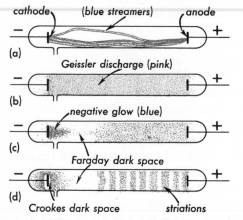

Fig. 48B *Sketches of the general appearance of a high-voltage electric discharge through rarefied air of various stages of evacuation.*

2 mm, a dark region called the *Faraday dark space* appears in the region of the cathode, which divides the bright discharge into two parts, a long pinkish section called the *positive column* and a short bluish section called the *negative glow*. As the pressure drops still further, the Faraday dark space grows in size and the negative glow moves away from the cathode, producing another dark

space between it and the cathode. With the appearance of the second dark region, called the *Crookes dark space*, the positive column divides into a number of equally spaced layers, called "striations."

As the pumping proceeds, the striations and the negative glow grow fainter, and the Crookes dark space widens, until finally, at a pressure of about 0.01 mm, it fills the whole tube. At this point a new feature appears: the whole glass tube itself glows with a faint greenish light.

48.2. Cathode Rays. The green glow in the final stage of the gaseous discharge just described was soon found to be a *fluorescence of the glass produced by invisible rays emanating from the cathode itself.* These *cathode rays*, as they are called, believed by Sir William Crookes to be an "ultra gaseous state" and by Johann W. Hittorf to be a "fourth state" of matter, were discovered to be tiny corpuscles which we now call *electrons*. In the relatively free space of a highly evacuated tube, cathode particles, torn loose from the atoms of the cathode, stream down the length of the tube and seldom collide with a gas molecule until they hit the glass walls.

The first important discovery concerning the nature of cathode rays was that they travel in straight lines. This was first revealed by Hittorf, in 1869, by casting shadows of objects placed inside the discharge tube. Hittorf's discovery is usually demonstrated by a tube of special design, as shown in Fig. 48C.

Fig. 48C *A Crookes discharge tube for demonstrating that cathode rays travel in straight lines.*

Where the rays strike the walls of the tube, the glass fluoresces green, while in the shadow it remains dark. Under continuous bombardment of the walls by cathode rays, the fluorescence grows fainter because of a fatigue effect of the glass. This effect is demonstrated by tipping the object down on its hinge, thus permitting the rays to strike the fresh glass surface. Where the shadow appeared previously, a bright green image of the object is clearly visible.

That *cathode rays have momentum and energy* was first demonstrated in 1870, by Crookes, who used a tube of special design as illustrated in Fig. 48D. Leaving the cathode and acquiring a high speed on their way toward the anode, the rays strike the mica vanes of a small pinwheel and

Fig. 48D *Experiment showing that cathode rays have momentum and energy. Cathode rays striking the vanes of a small pinwheel cause it to roll from one end of the tube to the other.*

exert a force, causing it to turn and thus roll along a double track toward the anode. When it reaches the end of the track, a reversal of the potential, making the right-hand electrode the cathode, will send it rolling back toward the anode, now at the left. From this experiment Crookes concluded that cathode particles have *momentum*, and that they therefore have *mass*, *velocity*, and *kinetic energy* $\frac{1}{2}mv^2$.

That *cathode rays are negatively charged particles* was first discovered in Paris in 1895 by Jean Perrin. A discharge tube of special design usually used to demonstrate this property is illustrated in Fig. 48E. A beam of cathode rays

Fig. 48E *The bending of a beam of cathode rays in the field of a magnet demonstrates that cathode rays are negatively charged particles.*

is narrowed down to a thin pencil or ribbon of rays by a narrow slit near the cathode. The path of the rays is made visible by allowing them to strike a long strip of metal painted with zinc sulfide, a fluorescent paint. By placing a horseshoe magnet over the outside of the tube, as illustrated, the path of the cathode rays is bent down. If the polarity of the magnet is reversed, the path is bent up. The bending shows that they are charged, and the direction of bending shows the kind of charge. Being charged, a stream of particles is like an electron current. From the direction of the magnetic field and the current, and by application of the left-hand rule (see Sec. 31.5), the charge is found to be *negative*. [Remember that the left-hand rule applies to a current from $(-)$ to $(+)$.]

The penetrating power of cathode rays was first demonstrated by Heinrich Hertz and his assistant, P. Lenard, by passing cathode rays through thin aluminum foils. Out in the air, the rays were found to retain sufficient power to cause fluorescence and phosphorescence.

48.3. J. J. Thomson's Experiments. When, in 1895, it was discovered that cathode rays were negatively charged particles, the question immediately arose whether they were all alike. It was clear from the beginning that two things would have to be done: (1) measure the amount of charge on the particles and (2) measure the mass of the particles.

Although the first attempts to measure the electronic charge and mass were not entirely successful, J. J. Thomson* did succeed, in 1897, in determining the velocity of the rays and in measuring the ratio between their charge and mass.

The discharge tube designed for these experiments is shown in Fig. 48F. Cathode rays, origi-

When the two metal plates P are connected to a source of high voltage, the particles experience a downward force, and their path curves to strike the screen at N. Without a charge on the plates, the beam passes straight through undeviated and strikes the screen at S.

When the magnetic field alone is applied, so that the magnetic lines are perpendicular to the plane of the page, the path of the rays curves upward to strike the fluorescent screen at some point M. If both the electric field and the magnetic field are applied simultaneously, a proper adjustment of the strength of either field can be made, so that the deflection downward by the one is exactly counteracted by the deflection upward of the other. When this condition is attained, a measurement of the magnetic induction B and the electric intensity ε permits a calculation of the velocity of cathode rays.

Fig. 48F *Diagram of discharge tube used by J. J. Thomson to measure the velocity of cathode rays.*

nating at the left-hand electrode and limited to a thin pencil of rays by pinholes in diaphragms DD, are made to pass between two parallel metal plates and the magnetic field of two external solenoids to a fluorescent screen at the far end.

* Sir Joseph John Thomson (1856–1940), English physicist, educated at Owens College, Manchester, and at Trinity College, Cambridge. He was appointed Cavendish professor at Cambridge in 1884, and professor of physics at the Royal Institution, London, in 1905. He was awarded the Nobel Prize in physics in 1906, was knighted in 1908, and elected to the presidency of the Royal Society in 1915. He became master of Trinity College in 1918 and helped to develop at Cambridge a great research laboratory attracting scientific workers from all over the world.

48.4. Deflection in an Electric Field. In Chapter 29, on the theory of electricity, it is shown that if e is the charge on a body located in an electric field of strength ε, the force exerted on the body is given by [see Eq.(29e)]

$$F_E = e\varepsilon \qquad (48a)$$

As a charged particle like an electron enters the electric field between two charged plates (shown in Fig. 48G), this force acts straight downward, parallel to the field lines at all points. The net result is that the particle traverses a parabolic path in much the same way that a

Fig. 48G *Electrons in a uniform electric field &
follow a parabolic path.*

projectile follows a parabolic path in the earth's
gravitational field.

48.5. Deflection in a Magnetic Field. In Sec.
33.2 it is shown that if e is the charge on a body
moving through a magnetic field B with a velocity v, the force acting upon it is given by

$$F_B = Bev \qquad (48b)$$

Since this force is always at right angles to
both the magnetic induction and the direction
of motion, the particle will traverse a circular
path (see Fig. 48H). By counterbalancing the

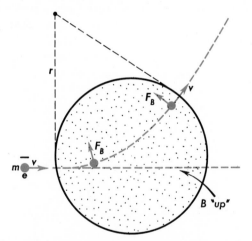

Fig. 48H *Electrons in a uniform magnetic field B
follow a circular path.*

two forces F_E and F_B, i.e., by making them equal
in magnitude and opposite in direction, the two
relations can be set equal to each other:

$$e\mathcal{E} = Bev \qquad (48c)$$

By canceling the charge e on both sides of this
equation, we obtain

$$\mathcal{E} = vB$$

from which

$$v = \frac{\mathcal{E}}{B} \qquad (48d)$$

where $\mathcal{E}$ is in volts per meter, B is in webers per
meter², and v is in meters per second. If we insert
the known values of $\mathcal{E}$ and B, the *velocity v can
be calculated.* The results show that cathode rays
generally travel with a speed of several thousand
miles per second, about $\frac{1}{5}$ *the velocity of light.*
Furthermore, the velocity is not always the same
but depends upon the voltage applied between
the anode and cathode. By increasing this voltage, the velocity of the rays is increased.

Tubes used for scanning and observing moving
pictures by modern television receivers are quite
similar in shape and principle to J. J. Thomson's
cathode-ray tube of Fig. 48F.

48.6. The Ratio of Charge to Mass, e/m. The
next step taken by Thomson was to measure the
deflection of the cathode beam produced by a
magnetic field alone and, from this, to calculate
the ratio between the charge e and the mass m
of the electron. To do this, he reasoned that, if
a charged particle moving through a uniform
magnetic field has a force exerted on it at right
angles to its direction of motion, causing it to
move in the arc of a circle, the force is of the
nature of a centripetal force Calling F_B a centripetal force,

$$F_B = m\frac{v^2}{r}$$

and from Eq.(48b), we obtain

$$Bev = m\frac{v^2}{r} \qquad (48e)$$

Solving for e/m, we obtain

$$\frac{e}{m} = \frac{v}{Br}$$

where r is the radius of the circular arc in meters
through which the particles are deviated; v is the
velocity of the particles in meters per second, as
measured in the last section; m is the particle
mass in kilograms; and B is the magnetic induction in webers per meter². With all of these
known, the value of e/m can be calculated. It is
found to be

$$e/m = 1.7589 \times 10^{11}\frac{C}{Kg} \qquad (48f)$$

Such a large number means that the mass of a
cathode ray particle in Kg is extremely small,

Fig. 48I *Schematic diagram of Millikan's oil-drop experiment. With this experiment the charge on the electron was determined.*

compared with the charge it carries in coulombs. If now it were possibly by some experiment to measure the charge e alone, the value could be substituted in Eq.(48f) and the mass m calculated.

48.7. Millikan's Oil-Drop Experiment. Millikan* began his experiments on the electronic charge e in 1906. His apparatus is illustrated by the simple diagram in Fig. 48I. Minute oil drops from an atomizer are sprayed into the region just over the top of one of two circular metal plates, V^+ and V^-. Shown in cross section, the upper plate is pierced with a tiny pinhole P through which an occasional oil drop from the cloud will fall. Once between the plates, such a drop, illuminated by an arc light from the side, is observed by means of a low-powered microscope.

With the switch S in the "up" position, the

* Robert Andrews Millikan (1868–1953), American physicist, educated at Oberlin College and Columbia University, for 25 years professor of physics at the University of Chicago and for 30 years president of the Norman Bridge Laboratory at the California Institute of Technology in Pasadena. He served during World War I in the research division of the Signal Corps with the rank of lieutenant colonel. His principal contributions to science were his measurement of the charge on the electron, his photoelectric determination of the energy in a light quantum, and his precision study of cosmic rays. He was the second American to be awarded the Nobel Prize in physics (1923). He was also awarded the Edison Medal, the Hughes Medal of the Royal Society, the Faraday Medal, and the Mattenci Medal.

capacitor plates are grounded so that they are not charged. Under these conditions, the oil drop falling under the pull of gravity has a constant velocity. This *terminal velocity*, as it is called, is reached by the drop before it enters the field of view and is of such a value that the downward pull of gravity, F_g, in Fig. 48J(a), is exactly

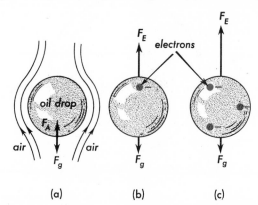

Fig. 48J *Diagrams of oil drop with extra electronic charges.*

equalized by the upward resisting force of the air. By measuring this velocity of fall, the force F_g can be calculated and from it the mass of the oil drop determined. The velocity of the drop can be determined by using a stop watch to measure the time required for the drop to fall the distance between the two cross hairs illustrated in Fig. 48K.

Fig. 48K   Microscope field of view showing oil drop.

As the drop nears the bottom plate, the switch S is thrown "down," charging the two parallel plates positive and negative. If now the drop has a negative charge, as illustrated in diagram (b), there will be an upward electrostatic force F_E, acting to propel the drop up across the field of view. The drop will move upward with a constant velocity if F_E is greater than the gravitational force F_g. Again using the stop watch, this time to measure the velocity of rise, we can calculate the upward force F_E. Knowing the force, and the voltage on the capacitor plates, we can compute the charge on the drop.

As the drop nears the top plate, the switch S is thrown "up" and the plates are again grounded. Under these conditions the drop falls again, under the pull of gravity alone. Upon nearing the bottom plate, the switch is again thrown "down" and the drop rises once more. When this process is repeated, a single drop may be made to move up and down many times across the field of view. Each time it falls, the velocity is measured and the mass computed, while each time it rises the velocity is measured and the charge computed.

Millikan found that, if X rays were allowed to pass through the apparatus while an oil drop was being observed, the charge on the drop could be increased or decreased almost at will. One time, on rising, the velocity would be low due to a small charge [see diagram (b) in Fig. 48J], while the next time the velocity would be high due to a larger charge, as in diagram (c). Regardless of the amount of charge, the rate of fall for a given drop will always be the same, because the total mass of a number of electrons is so small compared with the mass of the oil drop that their added mass is not perceptible.

Millikan, and numerous other experimenters who have repeated these experiments, have found that the charge on a drop is never less than a certain minimum value, and is always some integral multiple of this value. In other words, any one electron is like every other electron, each carrying this minimum charge called e:

$$e = -1.6019 \times 10^{-19} \, \text{C} \qquad (48g)$$

This is the most recent and probable value of the electronic charge.

48.8. The Mass of the Electron. From Millikan's determination of the charge on the electron and Thomson's measurement of e/m, the mass of the electron can be calculated by dividing one value by the other. Using the most accurately known values for both e and e/m, we obtain

$$m = \frac{e}{e/m} = \frac{1.6019 \times 10^{-19} \, \text{C}}{1.7589 \times 10^{11} \, \text{C/Kg}}$$

which gives

$$m = 9.1072 \times 10^{-31} \, \text{Kg} \qquad (48h)$$

This mass is unbelievably small; its value has been determined many times and by many experimenters, and yet it is always the same.*

* For a more complete and elementary treatment of these early experiments, see R. A. Millikan, *Electrons + and −* (the University of Chicago Press, Chicago).

PROBLEMS

1. Electrons with a velocity of $\frac{1}{25}$ the speed of light enter a uniform magnetic field at right angles to the magnetic induction. What will be the radius of their circular path if $B = 6.0 \times 10^{-3} \, \text{Wb/m}^2$?

2. Electrons entering a uniform magnetic field where $B = 50$ G, in a direction at right angles to the lines of induction, have a velocity of 4.8×10^9 cm/s. Calculate the radius of their circular path. [*Ans.* 5.46 cm.]

3. Two flat and parallel metal plates 25 cm long and 5 cm apart (see Fig. 48G) are connected to a 45-V battery. If electrons enter this field with a velocity of 2.0×10^9 cm/s, how far will they be deviated from their original

straight line path by the time they reach the other end?

4. In J. J. Thomson's experiment shown in Fig. 48F, a magnetic induction field of 2.4×10^{-3} Wb/m² is employed. If electrons entering this field have a velocity of 3.4×10^9 cm/s, what potential difference applied to the parallel plates will keep their path straight? Assume the plates to be 0.8 cm apart [see Eq.(29m)]. [*Ans.* 652.8 V.]

5. Electrons, moving in a uniform magnetic field where $B = 10$ G, follow a circular path of 5-cm radius. Calculate their velocity.

6. Electrons, moving in a uniform magnetic field $B = 6 \times 10^{-4}$ Wb/m², follow a circular path of 20-cm radius. Find the velocity. [*Ans.* 2.11×10^7 m/s.]

7. If $\frac{1}{2}$ g of free electrons could be bound together on the moon and another $\frac{1}{2}$ g of electrons on the earth, what would be their force of repulsion? Earth–moon distance is 239,000 mi.

8. Make a diagram and briefly explain the experiment by which J. J. Thomson measured the velocity of electrons.

9. Make several diagrams showing the main features of an electrical discharge through a gas-filled tube as the pressure is lowered.

10. Diagram and briefly explain the three experiments given in this chapter to demonstrate that cathode rays (a) travel in straight lines, (b) have momentum and energy, and (c) are negatively charged particles.

11. Explain and give a diagram of Millikan's oil-drop experiment. What conclusions were reached by Millikan in this experiment?

12. Electrons are injected with a speed of 2×10^7 m/s into a uniform magnetic field at right angles to the lines of force. If the magnetic induction is 2×10^{-3} Wb/m², find the diameter of the circular path. [*Ans.* 11.36 cm.]

13. If a beam of electrons, moving with a speed of 2×10^7 m/s, enters a uniform magnetic field at right angles to the lines of force and describes a circular path with a 30-cm radius, calculate the magnetic induction.

14. A 300-V battery is connected to two flat, parallel metal plates 8 cm long and 1.5 cm apart. If electrons enter this field from one end, moving with a constant velocity of 4×10^7 m/s, how far will they be deviated from their original straight-line path by the time they reach the other end? [*Ans.* 0.702 cm.]

15. Electrons are injected with a speed of 8×10^6 m/s into a uniform magnetic field at right angles to the lines of induction. If the magnetic induction B is 4×10^{-3} Wb/m², find the diameter of their circular path.

16. If a beam of electrons with a speed of 3×10^7 m/s enters a uniform magnetic field at right angles to B and describes a circular path of 10-cm radius, what is the value of B? [*Ans.* 1.70×10^{-3} Wb/m².]

ATOMS AND
THE PERIODIC TABLE

Although no one has ever seen individual atoms, there is no doubt that such particles really exist. To the physicists and chemists who have built up and established the present-day theories of the structure of matter, atoms are as real as any material objects large enough to be seen with the eyes or to be felt with the hands. Their reality is evidenced by hundreds of experiments that can be planned and executed in the research laboratory.

As the subject of atomic physics is developed in this and the following chapters, it will become more and more apparent that, although a physicist requires an extremely imaginative mind, the accumulated knowledge of atoms, their structure, and their behavior under a multitude of conditions is based upon exact results of experiments performed with the greatest of accuracy and precision.

49.1. The Discovery of Positive Rays. During the latter part of the nineteenth century, when many physicists were investigating the properties of cathode rays, Goldstein designed a special discharge tube; with it he discovered new rays called *canal rays*. The name "canal rays" is derived from the fact that the rays, traveling in straight lines through a vacuum tube in the opposite direction to cathode rays, pass through and energe from a canal or hole in the cathode. A tube designed to illustrate this is shown in Fig. 49A.

Shortly after the measurement of the ratio of the electronic charge of the electron to its mass by J. J. Thomson in 1896, W. Wien deflected a beam of canal rays in a magnetic field and came to the conclusion that the rays consisted of positively charged particles. Owing to this and other experiments, canal rays have become more commonly known as *positive rays*.

Since the time of Goldstein's discovery, posi-

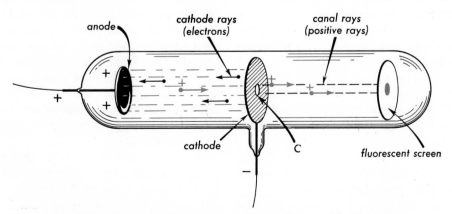

Fig. 49A *Experiment illustrating canal rays discovered by Goldstein.*

tive rays have been found to be charged atoms of different weights. The origin of the charge carried by such atoms is explained briefly as follows. As the electrons from the cathode stream down the tube toward the anode, they occasionally collide with the atoms and molecules of the small quantity of remaining gas, knocking electrons from them. This process, called *ionization*, is illustrated by a schematic diagram of a single oxygen atom in Fig. 49B. Before the collision, the atom

Fig. 49B　*Schematic diagram of an oxygen atom in the process of becoming ionized by a collision with a high-speed electron.*

as a whole, with its eight electrons and eight equal positive charges on the nucleus, has no net charge. After one of the electrons is removed by collision, it has only seven electrons and therefore a net positive charge equivalent in amount to the charge of one electron.

Since the atom is now positively charged, the anode repels and the cathode attracts such atoms, accelerating them toward the cathode. There exist, therefore, between the anode and cathode, two streams of particles: electrons moving toward the anode, and positively charged atoms or molecules moving toward the cathode.

Of the many particles striking the cathode in Fig. 49A, the ones moving toward the small opening C, constituting the observed canal rays, pass straight through to the fluorescent screen. As each atom or molecule strikes the screen, a tiny flash of light is produced. These tiny flashes, which can be seen individually in the field of view of a microscope, are called *scintillations*.

Any process by which an electron is removed from an atom or molecule is called *ionization*,

and the resulting charged particle is called a *positive ion*. The amount of charge carried by an electron is a unit called *the electronic charge*.

49.2. The Thomson Mass Spectrograph. Ever since the time canal rays were shown to be positively charged atoms or molecules of the gas contained within the discharged tube, physicists have tried to determine with ever-increasing accuracy the mass and charge of the individual ray particles. Although the charge and mass of every electron were known from Thomson's and Millikan's experiments to be the same as those for every other electron, it could be postulated that the mass of the positive rays should be different for the atoms of different chemical elements. The further postulation could be made that if each positive ion were produced by the removal of one electron from a neutral atom, all positive ions should have the same net charge. This, in part, is anticipating what is now known.

In 1911, J. J. Thomson developed a method of measuring the relative masses of different atoms and molecules by deflecting positive rays in a magnetic and an electric field. The apparatus he developed for doing this is shown schematically in Fig. 49C; it is called *Thomson's mass spectrograph*.

The entire spectrograph, enclosed in an airtight glass chamber, is first thoroughly evacuated; then a small quantity of the gas, the masses of whose atoms are to be measured, is admitted to the bulb at the left. When a high voltage is applied to this chamber, electrons from the cathode ionize the atoms and molecules in the region between the anode A and the cathode C. Traveling to the right, many of these positively charged particles pass through the narrow hole in the cathode, thus forming a very narrow pencil of rays. Leaving the cathode with a constant velocity, they then pass between the poles of an electromagnet and the parallel plates of a capacitor, and thence to a fluorescent screen at the far end of the chamber.

The two parallel plates, when charged, exert an upward force on the particles, deflecting them from the point O toward E. The magnetic field, on the other hand, with its magnetic lines vertically downward and in the plane of the page, exerts a force at right angles to this, deflecting the particles "into" the page from the point O toward H.

Suppose now that the apparatus contains a pure gas like helium, all of the atoms of which have exactly the same mass. Of these atoms, the

result is that the heavier particles form one parabolic curve like xy, and the lighter particles another curve like ac.

By substituting a photographic plate for the fluorescent screen and exposing it to the rays for several minutes, photographs like those repro-

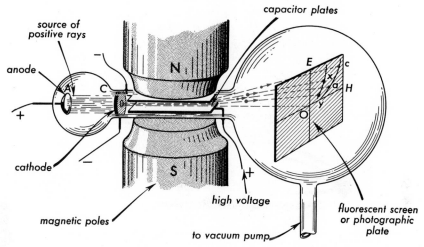

Fig. 49C   *Diagram of J. J. Thomson's mass spectrograph.*

ones that are ionized in a region near the cathode C cannot attain a very high speed before reaching the cathode. Since these atoms remain longer in the deflecting fields, their paths are bent considerably up and back to a point such as c on the screen. Particles ionized near the anode A, on the other hand, attain a high speed upon reaching the cathode and, being under the influence of the deflecting fields for a shorter time, have their paths bent only a little, to a point like a on the screen. Since the velocities of the particles vary considerably, a bright streak or line of fluorescence will appear on the screen. From a calculation of the forces exerted by both fields, it is found that the line on the screen should have the shape of a parabola.

If the gas in the apparatus is not pure but contains two kinds of atoms, the positive ions passing through the cathode will have two different masses. Although each ion will contain the same positive charge, and will therefore experience the same electric and magnetic forces when passing through the fields, the heavier particles will not be deflected as much as the lighter ones. The net

duced in Fig. 49D are obtained. The continual bombardment of the photographic plate by atoms and molecules has the same effect as does light, and images are produced upon development. The upper half of each picture is taken with the connections as shown in Fig. 49C, and the lower half by reversing the polarity of the electromagnet and exposing for an equal length of time.

When photograph (a) was taken, the spectrograph contained *hydrogen*, *oxygen*, and *mercury*, and the magnetic field was relatively weak. From the known strengths of both the electric and magnetic fields, and the assumption that each atom carries a unit positive charge, the mass of the atoms producing each parabola can be calculated. The results of these calculations show that the two largest parabolas are due to ionized hydrogen atoms (H^+) of mass 1, and ionized hydrogen molecules (H_2^+) of mass 2. The next three are due to ionized oxygen atoms (O^+) of mass 16, ionized oxygen molecules of mass 32, and ionized mercury atoms (Hg^+) with a mass of approximately 200.

When photograph (b) was taken, the mass spectrograph contained carbon monoxide gas and mercury vapor, and the magnetic field was relatively strong. Upon calculating the masses of the particles producing the different parabolas, the four intense lines were identified as due to

larger parabolas, because they undergo greater deflections.

The principal conclusion to be drawn from Thomson's experiments is: *Positive rays or canal rays are charged atoms or molecules of whatever gas is present in the apparatus.*

Fig. 49D   *Reproductions of the photographs of parabolas made with Thomson's mass spectrograph.*

ionized carbon atoms (C^+) of mass 12, ionized oxygen atoms (O^+) of mass 16, ionized carbon monoxide molecules (CO^+) of mass 28, and ionized mercury atoms (Hg^+) of mass about 200. The three faint parabolas which show in the original photograph but probably not in the reproduction, are due to doubly ionized atoms of *carbon*, *oxygen*, and *mercury*.

A doubly ionized atom or molecule is one that has lost two electrons rather than only one and, having a net positive charge of two units, is designated by two (+) signs as superscripts. Since the particles have double charges, the electric and magnetic forces exerted on them are double those for singly ionized atoms and they produce

It is significant to point out that, while Thomson found many atoms could be doubly and some even triply ionized, hydrogen could never be found more than singly ionized or helium more than doubly ionized. The reason for this, as will be seen later, is that neutral hydrogen atoms have only one electron and neutral helium atoms only two. All other elements have more than two electrons.

49.3. The Periodic Table of Elements. From present-day knowledge of physics, chemistry, and astronomy, it is quite certain that the entire universe is made up of 80 to 90 stable elements. By an element we mean a substance composed of atoms having identical chemical properties. All but two or three of these elements have been found in the earth's crust, some of them in much greater abundance than others. Silicon and iron are examples of abundant elements, whereas platinum is an example of a rare element.

Long before the Thomson mass spectrograph had been devised and used to measure the relative masses of atoms, the chemist had arranged all of the elements in a table according to their atomic weights. The most common form of this arrangement is given in Appendix X. Divided as they are into eight separate groups, all elements in the same column have similar chemical properties. In Group I, for example, the elements Li, Na, K, Rb, Cs, and Fr, known as the *alkali metals*, have one set of chemical properties, whereas the elements Be, Mg, Ca, Sr, Ba, and Ra in Group II, known as the *alkaline earths*, have another set of chemical properties. The largest group of elements having similar chemical properties are the fourteen rare earth elements listed by themselves starting with Ce, in the next to the last row at the bottom of the table.

The names of the elements are all indicated by one-letter and two-letter symbols. The full names are given in the second column of Appendix VII. The number in the first column before each abbreviation is the order number of that element and is called *the atomic number*. The average weight of atoms of that element called *the atomic weight*, is given in the last column (see Chap. 47).

The atomic weights of all elements are based upon the weight of carbon 12. This is purely an arbitrary selection of a unit of weight but one which has considerable significance when it is noted that the weights of the first 25 elements, with the exception of chlorine (Cl), atomic number 17, are very close to whole numbers. This suggests the possibility that the weights of all atoms are really whole number units of the unit of weight, the hydrogen atom, and that those weights of an element which differ considerably from whole numbers are incorrectly determined values. On the strength of this, Prout was the first to propose the hypothesis that all elements are made of hydrogen atoms as building stones. These suppositions, as will be seen later, are partly true.

49.4. Thomson's Discovery of Isotopes. In 1912, Thomson, in comparing the mass of the neon atom with the known masses of other elements, discovered two parabolas for neon in place of one. Upon computing the masses of the particles involved, the stronger of two parabolas was found to be due to particles of mass 20 and the other, a fainter parabola, to particles of mass 22.

Since the atomic weight of neon was then known to be 20.2, Thomson expressed the belief that neon is composed of two kinds of atoms, 90% of which have a mass of 20 and the other 10% a mass of 22. Because these two kinds of atoms exist as a mixture and cannot be separated chemically, their atomic weight, when measured by chemical methods, is found to be their average value, 20.2.

The discovery of two kinds of neon atoms, identical chemically but differing in atomic weight, suggested the possibility that all other elements whose atomic weights were not whole numbers might also be mixtures of atoms that do have whole number weights. Not only has this been confirmed by experiment, but a large majority of the elements have been found to be mixtures of from two to ten different kinds of atoms.

To all atoms of different weight belonging to the same element, Soddy gave the name *isotopes*. The external structures of all isotopes of a given element are identical. The two atoms, Ne-20 and Ne-22, shown in Fig. 49E, are neon isotopes. Each of these neutral atoms, before it is ionized to become a positive ray, has ten external electrons and ten positive charges on the nucleus. They differ only in the weight of the nucleus.

Fig. 49E *Schematic diagrams of two kinds of neon atoms, one of mass 20 and the other of mass 22. The external electron structures of two such isotopes are identical.*

Today it is known that there are three stable isotopes of neon. In addition to the two shown in Fig. 49E, there exists a rare isotope Ne-21 (see Appendix VII).

on the photographic plate, so that their masses could be more accurately measured.

An Aston mass spectrogram is reproduced in Fig. 49F(a). In taking this particular photograph,

Fig. 49F   *Reproductions of photographs taken with a mass spectrograph illustrating the linear shift of atoms differing by one unit of mass. (a) Carbon monoxide, sulfur, chlorine, and HCl lines. (b) Isotopes of tin. (c) Isotopes of mercury and lead.*

Atoms having different weights but belonging to the same chemical element have the same atomic number and are called isotopes.

49.5. Aston's Mass Measurements. Immediately following World War I, in 1919, F. W. Aston* developed a new and improved type of mass spectrograph, employing both the electric and magnetic fields. The chief improvement of this device over Thomson's mass spectrograph was the "focusing" of the rays of different velocities to the same point on the screen or photographic plate. This had two important effects: (1) it made it possible to observe rare isotopes which might otherwise escape detection, and (2) it produced sharper images of the different masses

* Francis William Aston (1877–1945), British scientist, born in Birmingham and educated at Malvern College and Cambridge University. He became assistant lecturer in physics at the Birmingham University in 1909, and received the Mackenzie Davidson Medal of the Röntgen Society in 1920. In 1922, he was awarded the Hughes Medal of the Royal Society and the coveted Nobel Prize in chemistry for his work on atomic mass measurements. He wrote an authoritative book entitled *Isotopes*, in which a full account of his work is given.

Aston had introduced into his apparatus, among other things, a little *hydrochloric acid* (HCl), *carbon monoxide* (CO), and *sulfur dioxide* (SO_2). Being close together in the periodic table, these elements furnish an excellent demonstration of the linear shift of atoms and molecules, differing in mass by one unit. It is found from this, and other photographs, that sulfur has three isotopes with masses 32, 33, and 34, and that chlorine has two isotopes of mass 35 and 37.

Since the atomic weight of chlorine is 35.453, then for every atom of mass 37 in a given quantity of chlorine gas there are four of mass 35. Mixed together in these proportions, they give an average mass of 35.4.

The photographic lines corresponding to masses 28, 36 and 38 are due to diatomic molecules CO and HCl each molecule having the combined weight of its constituent atoms. Since there are two relatively abundant chlorine isotopes, there are two kinds of HCl molecules. One type, H^1Cl^{35}, has a mass of 36; and the other type, H^1Cl^{37}, a mass of 38.

A CO molecule of the type producing the strong line at mass 28 in Fig. 49F(a) is shown schematically in Fig. 49G. Since the molecule is neutral, there are just as many electrons sur-

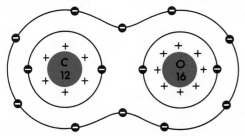

Fig. 49G *Schematic diagram of a diatomic molecule, carbon monoxide (CO).*

rounding the two bound atoms as there are positive charges on the nuclei (six on the carbon nucleus and eight on the oxygen nucleus). When the molecule becomes ionized and is moving through the apparatus as a positive ray, it contains one less electron than the number shown. Since the mass of the electrons is negligibly small, the mass of the molecule is 12 + 16 or 28 mass units.

So successful was Aston with his mass measurements and his determination of isotopes of different elements that he attempted an investigation of the entire periodic table. All of the known elements are listed in Appendix VII, with all of their observes stable isotopes. In each case, the most abundant isotope is indicated in heavy type, while the very rare isotopes, i.e., those present to less than 1%, are listed in parentheses. Where more than one isotope is set in heavy type, the isotopes occur with almost equal abundance. The masses printed in italics represent unstable atoms which are responsible for *radioactivity*, the subject of Chapter 62. Recent developments in mass spectroscopy have made it possible to detect exceptionally rare isotopes. In neon, for example, an isotope of mass number 21 has been found, making three in all, with relative abundances as follows:

Isotope..........	Ne-20	Ne-21	Ne-22
Abundance, %.....	90.92	0.26	8.82

In a pure carbon monoxide gas, all of the molecules are diatomic and alike in every respect except for mass. Since there are two carbon isotopes, 12 and 13, and three oxygen isotopes, 16, 17, and 18 (see Appendix VII), there are six different combinations of atoms to form molecules. These are $C^{12}O^{16}$, $C^{12}O^{17}$, $C^{12}O^{18}$, $C^{13}O^{16}$, $C^{13}O^{17}$, and $C^{13}O^{18}$. The relative abundances of all but the C^{12} and O^{16} isotopes are so small, however, that more than 90% of the molecules in a given quantity of gas are of the type $C^{12}O^{16}$, with a mass of 28.

49.6. Isobars. Another mass spectrograph of remarkably high precision was devised in 1933 by an American physicist, K. T. Bainbridge.

Two photographs taken with this instrument are shown in Fig. 49F. The middle picture (b) shows the many isotopes of tin, and the lower plate (c) the isotopes of mercury and lead. The rare lead isotope 204 falls on top of the strong mercury isotope 204. Such coincidences are called *isobars*.

Atoms having the same mass but belonging to different chemical elements are called isobars.

The first pair of isobars (see Appendix VII) occurs in argon and calcium. The principal isotope of argon, atomic number 18, has a mass of 40, as does also the principal isotope of calcium, atomic number 20. Other examples are Cr^{54} and Fe^{54}, Ge^{76} and Se^{76}, Rb^{87} and Sr^{87}, Zn^{92} and Mo^{92}. The isobars Hg^{204} and Pb^{204} are illustrated in Fig. 49F(c).

49.7. Unit Atomic Mass and the Hydrogen Atom. Until 1927, all oxygen atoms were thought to have the same mass and were arbitrarily chosen to be the standard by which all atomic masses were measured. At this time Giauque and Johnson discovered the existence of two rare oxygen isotopes with masses 17 and 18. So rare are these heavier particles that in every ten thousand oxygen atoms twenty of them have a mass of 18, and only four a mass of 17.

Retaining natural oxygen with its mixture of three isotopes as a standard, the chemists continued to use $\frac{1}{16}$ the weight of this mixture as *unit atomic weight*. The physicists, on the other hand, found it most convenient for their purposes to adopt a mass scale based upon the mass of the most abundant oxygen atom as exactly 16, and $\frac{1}{16}$ of this as *unit atomic mass*.

As isotope mass determinations (measured largely by research physicists) became more and more accurate, and mass differences became more important, the slight differences between the two scales became more and more of a problem.

In 1960 the International Union of Pure and Applied Physics (IUPAP), met in Ottawa and adopted the atomic mass scale based upon the carbon-12 isotope as having a mass of exactly 12. The same scale was adopted by the International Union of Pure and Applied Chemistry (IUPAC), at their Montreal meeting in 1961. While this new atomic weight scale differs ever so slightly from the older O = 16 scale, the accurate masses of isotopes show greater differences, as can be seen in Appendix VIII.

Standard unit atomic mass is now generally accepted to be $\frac{1}{12}$ of the mass of the carbon-12 isotope. On this basis very accurate measurements give for the mass of the hydrogen atom 1.0081456 atomic mass units (amu), a value nearly 1% higher than unity.

For many practical purposes it is convenient to know the masses of atoms in kilograms. For easy calculations the following value may be used:

$$M = 1.660 \times 10^{-27} \, Kg \qquad (49a)$$
unit atomic mass

This number multiplied by the atomic mass of any atom will give its mass in kilograms.

Compared with the mass of the electron, namely,

$$m = 9.1072 \times 10^{-31} \, Kg \qquad (49b)$$
electron mass

an atom of unit mass would be 1824 times as heavy. The hydrogen atom is slightly heavier than one unit mass and is about 1836 times as heavy as the electron. This latter number is convenient to remember, for it is often quoted to illustrate the enormous difference between the mass of the nucleus of a hydrogen atom and the mass of its one and only electron.

Atomic number is defined as the number ascribed to an element specifying its position in the periodic table of elements (see column 1, Appendix VII).

Mass number is defined as the whole number nearest the actual mass of an isotope measured in atomic mass units (see column 4, Appendix VII).

Atomic weight is defined as the average weight of all the isotopes of an element, weighted according to relative abundance and expressed in atomic mass units (see column 5, Appendix VII).

PROBLEMS

1. The atomic weight of cobalt is 58.9332. Find the mass in grams of one cobalt atom.

2. If the atomic weight of gold is 196.967, how many atoms are there in 1 g of gold metal? [*Ans.* 3.05×10^{21} atoms.]

3. The atomic weight of iodine is 126.9044. How many atoms are there in 1 g of iodine crystals?

4. If the atomic weights of silicon and oxygen are 28.086 and 15.9994, respectively, find the mass in grams of a silicon dioxide molecule, SiO_2. [*Ans.* 9.97×10^{-23} g.]

5. The atomic weights of hydrogen, carbon, and oxygen, are 1.00797, 12.01115, and 15.9994, respectively. How many ethyl alcohol molecules are there in 1 g of ethyl alcohol (C_2H_5OH)?

6. Define or briefly explain the meaning of the following: (a) *isotopes*, (b) *isobars*, (c) *positive rays*, (d) *atomic weight*, and (e) *unit atomic mass*.

7. Name five members of each of the following classifications: (a) alkali metals, and (b) alkaline earths (see Appendix X).

8. What chemical element has the greatest number of isotopes (see Appendix VII)?

9. Make a list of elements having (a) atoms of one mass only, and (b) only two isotopes (see Appendix VII).

10. Carbon has two isotopes, 12 and 13, while oxygen has three, 16, 17, and 18. Find to three figures only the mass in kilograms for each of the six possible CO molecules. [*Ans.* $C^{12}O^{16} = 4.65$, $C^{12}O^{17} = 4.81$, $C^{12}O^{18} = 4.98$, $C^{13}O^{16} = 4.81$, $C^{13}O^{17} = 4.98$, $C^{13}O^{18} = 5.15 \times 10^{-26}$ Kg.]

11. Gallium has two isotopes, 69 and 71. Calculate the mass in kilograms to three figures only for each of the three possible kinds of diatomic molecules.

12. The two stable isotopes of copper have masses of 63 and 65 atomic mass units. The normal mixture of these

atoms has an atomic weight of 63.54. What percentage of any given amount of the normal metal is composed of Cu^{63} atoms? [*Ans.* 73%.]

13. The forty-seventh element in the periodic table, silver, has two stable isotopes with masses of 107 and 109 atomic mass units, respectively. The normal mixture of these atoms has an atomic weight of 107.870. Calculate the percentage of any given amount of the normal silver composed of Ag^{109} atoms.

THE PHOTOELECTRIC EFFECT

The photoelectric effect was discovered by Heinrich Hertz in 1887 when he observed that ultraviolet light, falling on the electrodes of a spark gap, caused a high-voltage discharge to jump greater distances than when it was left in the dark. One year later, Hallwachs made the important observation that ultraviolet light falling on a negatively charged body caused it to lose its charge, whereas a positively charged body was not affected. Ten years later J. J. Thomson and P. Lenard showed independently that the action of the light was to cause the emission of free negative charges from the metal surface. Although these negative charges are no different from all other electrons, it is customary to refer to them as "photoelectrons."

50.1. Photoelectrons. The photoelectric effect, in its simplest form, is demonstrated in Fig. 50A. Light from a carbon arc is focused by means of a quartz lens onto a freshly polished plate of zinc metal. When the plate is charged negatively and the light is turned on, the gold leaf of the attached electroscope slowly falls. It falls because the electrons, under the action of the light, leave the zinc plate at the illuminated spot P. When the plate is positively charged, the gold leaf does not fall, showing that the plate retains its charge. The same result of no discharge is observed if the zinc plate is negatively charged and a sheet of glass is inserted, as shown in the figure. When the glass is removed, the gold leaf again falls. Since common glass transmits visible and infrared light, but not ultraviolet, we conclude from the latter result that electrons are liberated only by ultraviolet light. This is also generally true for nearly all of the known metals.

A few elements—the alkali metals, *lithium, sodium, potassium, rubidium,* and *cesium*—are

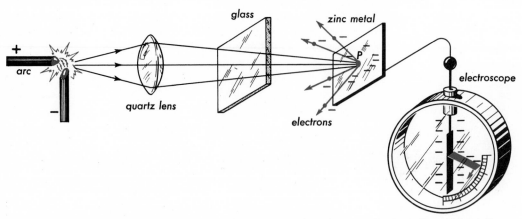

Fig. 50A *Experimental arrangement for demonstrating the photoelectric effect. When the glass plate is inserted, the effect stops.*

exceptions to this, for they will eject photo-electrons when visible light falls on them. For this reason the *alkali metals* are often used in the manufacture of photoelectric cells.

50.2. The Photoelectric Cell. Photoelectric cells are usually made by depositing a thin layer of an alkali metal on the inner surface of a small vacuum tube (see Fig. 50B). If the cell is to oper-

strikes the metal P, there is a flow of electrons to the collector C, thus causing a current to flow around the circuit. This current can be measured by means of an ammeter at A. If the intensity of the light increases, the number of photoelectrons increases and the current therefore rises. When the light is shut off, the photoelectric action ceases and the current stops. If the metal film

Fig. 50B   *Diagram of a photoelectric cell, showing the light beam and electrical connections necessary for its operation.*

ate in ultraviolet light, it is made of quartz, whereas if it is to be used in visible light it is made of common glass. The cell must be thoroughly evacuated, as the oxygen content of the air will combine chemically with the active metal layer, contaminating its surface and making it insensitive to visible light. A small section of the cell is always left clear to serve as a window for the incoming light. Photoelectrons, upon leaving the metal surface, are attracted and collected by the positively charged electrode C. The photosensitive surface, the cathode, and the collector, the anode, are maintained at a constant potential difference by the battery B.

A beam of light shining through the window of a photoelectric cell acts like a switch that completes an electric circuit. When the light

is positively charged, the cell becomes nonreactive to light, since electrons released from the plate are held back by electrostatic attraction. All of these factors are readily demonstrated by a simple electrical circuit arranged as shown in Fig. 50B.

50.3. Practical Applications. Talking motion pictures, television, and burglar alarms are but three of the hundreds of practical applications of the photoelectric cell. The simplest of these is the burglar alarm, in which a beam of infrared light (invisible to the eye) is projected across the room into a photoelectric cell connected as shown in Fig. 50B. When an intruder walks through the beam, thus interrupting the beam for an instant, the photoelectric current ceases momentarily. An electric relay in place of the ammeter at A in the circuit moves, causing another electric circuit to be completed and thereby ringing an electric bell.

During the filming of talking motion pictures, a sound track is produced photographically on the side of the master motion-picture film. Such sound tracks are shown in Fig. 50C. In strip (a),

Fig. 50C (a) Section of a moving-picture film showing the single variable-density sound track. (b) Enlarged section of sound track from (a). (c) Section of a unilateral variable area sound track. (d) Section of a bilateral variable area sound track.

which is just a sample of one of the several kinds of sound tracks, the sound vibrations on the stage are converted into electrical vibrations by the stage microphone and then carried over wires to the camera taking the pictures. There the electrical impulses are made to move one of the jaws of a narrow slit through which a beam of light passes to the edge of the film. Loud sounds open the slit wide with each vibration, allowing a large amount of light through.

When the film is developed and positives are made for distribution, the loud sounds show up as periodic bands with considerable contrast as at L in strip (b). The latter strip is an enlarged section of the *single variable-density* sound track seen on the right in photograph (a). Weaker sounds produce bands with less contrast as at S.

Strips (c) and (d) are enlarged sections of two other types of sound track used in other patented recording systems.

When a sound film is projected on the screen in the theater (see Fig. 50D), the film for the

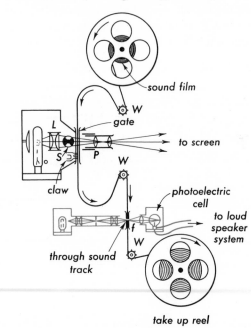

Fig. 50D Cross section of a motion-picture projector with sound attachment.

pictures themselves must of necessity move intermittently through the projection system P of the projection machine. As the film moves downward, each picture (frame) stops momentarily in front of the condensing lenses L and then moves on for the next frame. While the film is moving, the light is cut off by a rotating shutter S, and while it is at rest the light passes through to the screen. Thus the continuous motion seen on the screen is the result of a number of still pictures projected one after the other in rapid succession. To make this motion seem smooth and not jumpy, it is standard practice to project 24 frames each second.

To produce the sound, a small subsidiary beam of light, shown in detail in Fig. 50E, shines through the sound track at a point 25 frames farther along on the film where the motion is no longer intermittent, but smooth. As the sound track moves through the focus line f of the

Fig. 50E Detail of sound pickup system of a moving-picture projector showing the exciter lamp, sound track, and photoelectric cell.

subsidiary light at constant speed, the transmitted light falling on the photoelectric cell fluctuates exactly as the sound track interrupts it. The photoelectric cell then changes the fluctuating light beam into a fluctuating electric current with the same variations. When transmitted to the radio amplifier and loud-speaker, the fluctuating current is changed into sound vibrations. Thus, sound vibrations have been carried over a light beam from the photographic film to the photoelectric cell and then by means of a loud-speaker system reproduced as sound.

50.4. Sound over a Light Beam. The sending of voice and musical sounds for several miles over a light beam is readily accomplished with a suitable light source as transmitter and a photoelectric cell as a receiver. A convenient laboratory demonstration can be made by using a small $\frac{1}{4}$-W neon glow lamp as a source of light, as shown in Fig. 50F.

the light is changed back into a varying electric current. This faint signal is then amplified by a two-stage amplifier before it is delivered to the loud-speaker.

If the microphone is replaced by a phonograph pickup, records can be played at the transmitter end, and excellent reproduction can be obtained from the loud-speaker. The light beam can be made completely invisible by placing an infrared filter in the light beam at F. Talking several miles over a beam of invisible light was developed to quite a high state of perfection during World War II. One system employs the infrared light from a glow discharge tube containing cesium, while several others, modulated by mechanically vibrating mirrors, employ the infrared from a tungsten-filament lamp. Another system employs the invisible ultraviolet light from a glow discharge tube containing gallium.

50.5. Velocity of Photoelectrons. The first measurements of the velocity of photoelectrons led to the very startling discovery that the velocity does not increase as the intensity of the light increases. Increasing the intensity of the light increases the number of photoelectrons, but not their velocity. This discovery, as we shall see later, has had far-reaching implications in its result, for it has played an important role in the development of the quantum theory and our modern concepts of light and atomic structure.

Lenard's experiments, performed as far back as 1902, showed, that to increase the velocity of

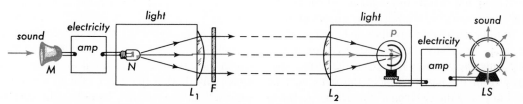

Fig. 50F Voice and musical sounds can be sent long distances over a beam of light.

Sound waves entering the microphone M produce electric-current fluctuations which, after being strengthened by a two-stage amplifier, cause the intensity of the neon glow lamp N to fluctuate accordingly. Made into a parallel beam by a lens L_1, the light travels across the room to a second lens L_2 and a photoelectric cell, where

photoelectrons one must increase the frequency of the light, i.e., use shorter wavelengths. The shorter the wavelength of the light used, the higher the velocities of the electrons.

50.6. Einstein's Photoelectric Equation. Following an earlier idea of Planck's that light waves consist of tiny bundles of energy called *photons* or *quanta,* Einstein proposed an explanation of the photoelectric effect as early as 1905. His ideas were expressed in one simple relation, an algebraic equation destined to become famous in the annals of physics. Two Nobel Prizes, one to Einstein in 1921 and one to Millikan in 1923, have been granted on this, the photoelectric equation,

$$hv = W + \tfrac{1}{2}mv^2 \qquad (50a)$$

The first term, hv, represents the total energy content of a single quantum of light incident on a metal surface, as shown in Fig. 50G. The letter

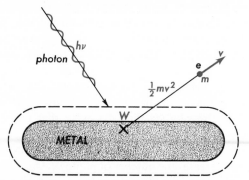

Fig. 50G *A light quantum (photon) of energy hv, incident on a metal surface, ejects an electron with a velocity v given by Einstein's equation.*

h is a constant, called *Planck's constant of action,* which has the same value for all light waves regardless of the frequency v. At or beneath the surface of the metal, this *light quantum,* better known as a *photon,* is completely absorbed and, in disappearing, imparts its total energy to a single electron. Part of this energy W is consumed in getting the electron free from the atoms and away from the metal surface; the remainder is used in giving the electron a kinetic energy $\tfrac{1}{2}mv^2$, and therefore a velocity. For some metals like platinum, the energy required to pull an electron away from the surface is large, whereas for other metals like the alkalies it is quite small. W is called the *work function* of the metal.

50.7. Millikan's Measurements of h. The letter h in Einstein's photoelectric equation is important because it is fundamental to the structure of all matter and is therefore *a universal constant.*

Having first been introduced by Planck in 1901, the name *Planck's constant* has become firmly attached to this symbol h. The first experimental confirmation of Einstein's photoelectric equation came in 1912 when A. L. Hughes, and independently O. W. Richardson and K. T. Crompton, observed that the energy of photoelectrons increased proportionately with the frequency. The constant of proportionality they found to be approximately equal to a constant, Planck's constant h.

Subsequently, Millikan carried out extensive experiments which established the photoelectric equation so accurately that his work is now regarded as giving one of the most trustworthy values for h.

To determine the value of h, it was necessary to measure the three factors, v, W, and $\tfrac{1}{2}mv^2$, and calculate h as the unknown quantity in Eq.(50a). A schematic diagram of part of Millikan's apparatus is shown in Fig. 50H. Light from

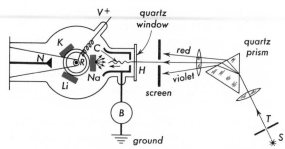

Fig. 50H *Diagram of apparatus used by Millikan in confirming Einstein's photoelectric equation.*

a source S through a slit T is dispersed by means of a prism, and the spectrum is focused on a screen as shown. With a small aperture in this screen any desired frequency of light v could be admitted to the vacuum chamber through the window H.

Photoelectrons from any one of the three alkali metals, Na, K, or Li, could be obtained at will by turning the wheel R into the required position.

Previous experiments on the photoelectric effect had shown that good results could be obtained only when the metal surfaces were clean. By ingenious magnetic devices, operated from outside the vacuum chamber, Millikan was able to prepare uncontaminated metal surfaces just prior to each set of measurements.

By rotating R, one of the metal blocks could be brought opposite the knife N and a thin shaving of metal removed from the alkali metal. The fresh surface was then rotated 180° into a position directly in line with the light entering the window.

For each different frequency of light admitted to the chamber the velocity or energy of the photoelectrons had to be measured. This was accomplished by collecting the electrons in the cylinder C and measuring the accumulated charge by means of a sensitive electroscope or electrometer B.

By applying a positive potential to the metal block at V^+ the electrons would arrive at C with lower speeds owing to the retarding action of the charges. The positive charge on the Na block, for example, attracts the fast ejected electrons, slowing them down.

The velocity with which the electrons leave the metal can therefore be determined by measuring the potential difference V which is just great enough to prevent the electrons from reaching C. This stopping potential, applied between V^+ and the ground, can be equated to the photoelectron's ejected energy, by use of Eq.(29i). Replacing q by the electronic charge e, and the energy W by $\frac{1}{2}mv^2$, we obtain

$$Ve = \tfrac{1}{2}mv^2 \qquad (50b)$$

In the mksa system, V is in volts, e is in coulombs, m is in kilograms, and v is in meters/second. As we shall see in succeeding chapters this is a very useful and important equation.

50.8. The Photoelectric Threshold. Having made the measurements described in the preceding section, Millikan calculated the photoelectron energies for different frequencies of light, and plotted the results on a graph as shown in Fig. 50I. The point at which the straight line intersects the bottom line determines the threshold frequency ν_0. The photoelectric threshold ν_0, is defined as the frequency of light which, falling on a surface, is just able to liberate elec-

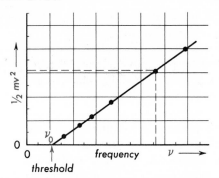

Fig. 50I *Graph showing the energy of photoelectrons ejected by light of different frequencies.*

trons without giving them any additional kinetic energy. For such a frequency, the kinetic energy $\frac{1}{2}mv^2$ in Einstein's equation is zero and the energy of the photon $h\nu_0 = W$. Equation(50a) can therefore be written in the form

$$h\nu = h\nu_0 + \tfrac{1}{2}mv^2 \qquad (50c)$$

The meaning of ν_0 in this new equation is quite clear: For frequencies lower than ν_0, electrons are not liberated, whereas for frequencies greater than ν_0 they are ejected with a determined velocity.

The photoelectric threshold for most metals lies in the ultraviolet where the frequencies are relatively high. For the alkali metals the threshold lies in the visible and near-infrared spectrum. In other words, it takes photons of less energy to free electrons from the alkali metals than it does to free them from most other metals.

Since every quantity in Eq.(50c), except h, is a measured quantity, the equation can be solved for h:

$$h = \frac{\tfrac{1}{2}mv^2}{\nu - \nu_0} \qquad (50d)$$

Upon substitution of all measured quantities Millikan obtained the value $h = 6.56 \times 10^{-34}$ joule second. The most recent value obtained for this universal constant is

$$h = 6.6238 \times 10^{-34} \text{ joule second}$$

Since the frequency of visible light is about 6×10^{14} vib/s, the energy in a single photon or quantum of visible light is the product of these two numbers, or 3.972×10^{-19} J. In other words, it would take about 2.5×10^{18} photons to do one joule of work.

It was for his outstanding experimental work in the determination of the value of Planck's constant h, as well as the value of the electronic charge e, that Millikan was awarded the Nobel Prize in physics in 1923.

The photon, in ejecting an electron from a metal surface as in the photoelectric effect, disappears completely, i.e., it is annihilated. This is exactly the reverse of the process of the production of X rays, where a high-speed electron, upon hitting a metal target and being suddenly stopped, creates and emits a photon of high frequency.

50.9. Secondary Electrons. When electrons strike the surface of a metal plate, they knock additional electrons free from the surface. These are called *secondary electrons* and the process is called *secondary emission* (see Fig. 50J). As the

Fig. 50J *The impact of a single electron liberates additional electrons from a metal surface.*

speed of a primary or incident electron increases from zero to a few hundred volts, the number of secondaries increases toward a definite maximum. For most metal surfaces, this maximum is in the neighborhood of two, while for certain alkali metal films it may be as great as eight or ten. In general, it is greatest for surfaces having a *low work function.*

50.10. Photomultiplier Tubes. The process of secondary electron emission is widely used in a special type of photoelectric cell used most effectively in detecting faint light. A cross-section

diagram of such a photomultiplier tube is given in Fig. 50K.

Fig. 50K *Photo-multiplier tube with six stages. Cesium oxide, silver-coated photo-cathode.*

The number of photoelectrons from the photocathode A is proportional to the intensity of the incident light. These are attracted toward the next plate B, more positive by 100 V, where upon impact additional electrons are liberated. Attracted to the next more-positive plate C, still more electrons are liberated. By the time the collector plate has been reached, a small avalanche of electrons has developed, and a correspondingly large charge and current are led off through that electrode to a suitable recording device.

If each electron on impact releases n secondaries, then, in a tube with k stages, the number arriving at the collector would be n^k. For example, if $n = 6$, and if $k = 5$, then $n^k = 7776$ electrons. This is an enormous gain over the signal obtained from a standard photo tube. Photomultiplier tubes have been used most successfully with faint light, not only visible but infrared and ultraviolet as well.

PROBLEMS

1. Find the energy equivalent to a light wave of wavelength 5×10^{-7} m. Such light is in the green region of the visible spectrum.

2. Calculate the energy in joules of ultraviolet light photons of wavelength 3×10^{-7} m. [*Ans.* 6.62×10^{-19} J.]

3. If X rays with a wavelength of 1.5×10^{-10} m fall on a metal plate, what would be the maximum velocity of the photoelectrons emitted? (Assume the work function to be negligibly small, $W = 0$.)

4. Assuming the work function of sodium to be negligibly small, what will be the velocity of photoelectrons emitted as the result of incident light of wavelength 3×10^{-8} m? This is ultraviolet light. [*Ans.* 3.81×10^6 m/s].

5. Find the energy equivalent to a γ ray whose wavelength is 0.20×10^{-3} Å.

6. Calculate the energy in joules of a visible light photon of wavelength 7500 Å. [*Ans.* 2.65×10^{-19} J.]

7. If the photoelectric threshold of metallic silver is at $\lambda = 3800$ Å, and ultraviolet light of wavelength 2600 Å falls on it, find (a) the maximum kinetic energy of the photoelectrons ejected, (b) the maximum velocity of the photoelectrons, and (c) the value of the work function in joules.

8. If light of wavelength 6000 Å falls on a metal surface and emits photoelectrons with a velocity of 4.0×10^5 cm/s, what is the wavelength of the photoelectric threshold? [*Ans.* 7690 Å.]

9. If X rays with a wavelength of 4.0 Å fall on a metal plate, what would be the maximum velocity of the photoelectrons emitted? The work function can be assumed to be negligibly small.

10. Find the over-all gain of a ten-stage photomultiplier tube if the average number of secondary electrons produced by each primary election is six. [*Ans.* 60.4×10^6.]

11. An eight-stage photomultiplier tube has an over-all gain of 64,000. Find the average number of secondary electrons produced by each primary electron.

12. Make a diagram showing how a photoelectric cell could be used to count the number of cars passing a given point on a highway in a single day.

13. When X rays with a wavelength of 12.0 Å fall on a copper plate, what will be the maximum velocity of the photoelectrons emitted? Assume the work function to be negligible.

THE STRUCTURE
OF ATOMS

Early in the twentieth century, while Einstein was working out his special theory of relativity, J. J. Thomson proposed a type of electron shell structure for all atoms. His model structures were worked out by mathematics from Coulomb's law for charged particles and soon became known as the "*plum-pudding atom.*"

51.1. The Thomson Atom. Thomson visualized all of the positive charge of an atom as being spread out uniformly throughout a sphere about 10^{-10} m in diameter, with the electrons as smaller particles distributed in shells somewhat as shown in Fig. 51A. While the net force exerted by the

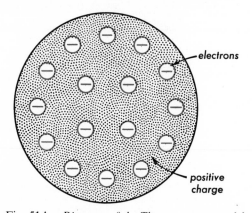

Fig. 51A   *Diagram of the Thomson atom model.*

positively charged sphere on each electron is toward the center of the sphere, the electrons mutually repel each other and form shells.

An excellent demonstration of the tendency to form rings for a two-dimensional model is shown in Fig. 51B. A glass dish 6 to 10 in. in diameter is wound with about 30 turns of No.

14 insulated copper wire. The most common steel sewing needles are then mounted in small corks (8 mm diameter and 8 mm long) as shown at the left, and magnetized by stroking from top to bottom with the N pole of a strong alnico magnet.

Fig. 51B   *Floating needles in a magnetic field demonstrating the electron shell structure of the Thomson atom.*

With water in the dish, and a current of 1 to 2 A through the coil, a single needle is placed upright in the water. Released, it will migrate to the center where the magnetic field is strongest. The addition of needles, one after another, near the edge of the dish, will result in the formation of geometrically symmetrical patterns and rings.

An increase or decrease in current will cause any given pattern to shrink or expand, corresponding to a greater or lesser positive charge. The stability of such ring patterns undoubtedly influenced the later extension by Bohr and Stoner of the quantized orbit model of the hydrogen atom to all atoms.

51.2. Bohr's Theory of the Hydrogen Atom. In 1913 Niels Bohr* proposed a theory of the hy-

---

* Niels Bohr (1885–1962), Danish physicist, was born at Copenhagen, the son of Christian Bohr, professor of physiology at the University of Copenhagen. After taking

drogen atom that marked the beginning of a new era in the history of physics. With his theory, Bohr gave not only a satisfactory explanation of the Balmer series of hydrogen but a model for the structure of all other atoms as well.

Starting with what should be the simplest of all atoms, Bohr assumed that a hydrogen atom, $Z = 1$, consists of a nucleus with one positive charge $+e$ and a single electron of charge $-e$ revolving around it in a circular orbit of radius r (see Fig. 51C). Because it is 1836 times heavier

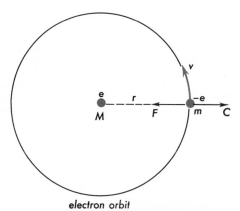

electron orbit

Fig. 51C   *Orbital diagram of the hydrogen atom according to the Bohr theory.*

than the electron, the nucleus could be assumed at rest.

To keep the electron in its orbit and prevent it from spiraling in toward the nucleus, or away from it to escape, Bohr next assumed that the inward centripetal force is due to, and therefore is, the inward electrostatic force F. From dynamics we know that the centripetal force is mv^2/r, and from Coulomb's law, Eq.(26a), the electrostatic force is kee/r^2. Equating these two, we obtain

_____

his Ph.D. degree at Copenhagen in 1911, he studied for one year under J. J. Thomson at Cambridge, and one year under Ernest Rutherford at Manchester. Returning to Copenhagen in 1913, with the results of the Rutherford scattering experiments fresh in his mind, he worked out and published his now famous theory of the hydrogen atom. In 1920 Bohr was appointed head of the institute for theoretical physics at the University of Copenhagen. In 1921 he was awarded the Hughes Medal of the Royal Society, and in 1922 the Nobel Prize in physics.

$$m\frac{v^2}{r} = k\frac{ee}{r^2} \qquad (51a)$$

In the mksa system of units,

 m is in kilogram
 v is in meter/second
 e is in coulombs
 r is in meters
 $k = 9 \times 10^9$ newton meter^2/coulomb^2

At this point Bohr introduced his second assumption, *the quantum hypothesis.* The electron, he assumed, cannot move in any sized orbit, stable under the conditions of the equation above, but in just certain *definite and discrete orbits.* The sizes of these orbits are governed by Eq.(51a) and the rule that the *angular momentum of the electron in its orbit is equal to an integer n times a constant h divided by 2π:*

$$mvr = n\frac{h}{2\pi} \qquad (51b)$$

$$n = 1, 2, 3, 4, 5, \ldots$$

In this equation, n is called the principal *quantum number* and, because it can take whole number values only, it fixes the sizes of the allowed orbits. To find the radii of these "Bohr circular orbits," Eq.(51b) is solved for v, then squared and substituted in Eq.(51a) to give

$$r = \frac{n^2h^2}{4\pi^2me^2k} \qquad (51c)$$

If we put into this equation the known values of the constants e, m, h, and k,

$$e = -1.60 \times 10^{-19} \text{ C}$$
$$m = 9.10 \times 10^{-31} \text{ Kg}$$
$$h = 6.62 \times 10^{-34} \text{ Js}$$
$$k = 9 \times 10^9 \text{ Nm}^2/\text{C}^2$$

the orbits shown in Fig. 51D are calculated. The innermost orbit, with $n = 1$, has a radius $r = 0.528 \times 10^{-10}$ m, or 0.528 Å, and a diameter of 1.056 Å.

$$r_1 = 0.528 \times 10^{-10} \text{ m}$$
$$1 \text{ meter} = 10^{10} \text{ angstroms}$$

The second orbit is four times larger, and the

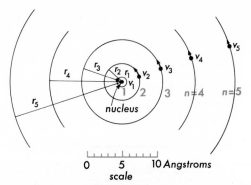

Fig. 51D   *Scale diagram of the Bohr circular orbits
of hydrogen.*

third is nine times, etc. The constant h is *Planck's
constant*.

The speed of the electron, when it is in any
one orbit, can be determined from Eqs.(51b) and
(51c). By substituting the value of r from Eq.(51c)
in Eq.(51b) and solving for the speed v, we obtain

$$v = k \frac{2\pi e^2}{nh} \qquad (51d)$$

In the innermost orbit, $n = 1$, the speed v is
$\frac{1}{137}$ the speed of light. In the second orbit the
speed is only $\frac{1}{2}$ as great, and in the third only $\frac{1}{3}$
as great, etc. With such small orbits and such
high speeds, the number of revolutions per second
becomes very high.

Since the circumference of any circular orbit
is $2\pi r$, the frequency with which an electron goes
around each orbit is given by

$$f = \frac{v}{2\pi r} \qquad (51e)$$

In the second Bohr circular orbit, the frequency is calculated to be 10^{15} rps. This, by comparison with the frequency of vibration of visible
light waves, is of the same order of magnitude.

It should be noted that the one and only electron in each hydrogen atom can occupy only one
orbit at any one time. If the electron changes its
orbit, it must move to one of the allowed orbits
and never stop in between.

51.3. Electron Jumps. Bohr's third and final
assumption regarding the hydrogen atom concerns the emission of light. Bohr postulated that
light is not emitted by an electron when it is

moving in one of its fixed orbits, but only when
the electron jumps from one orbit to another, as
illustrated in Fig. 51E. Bohr said that the frequency of this light is not determined by the

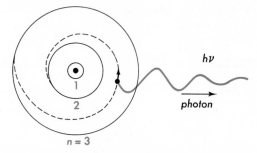

Fig. 51E   *Schematic diagram of Bohr's quantum hypothesis of the radiation of light from a hydrogen atom.*

frequency of revolution but by by the difference
in energy between the initial and final orbit,

$$\boxed{E_2 - E_1 = h\nu} \qquad (51f)$$

where E_2 is the energy of the *initial orbit*, E_1 the
energy of the *final orbit*, h is Planck's constant,
and ν is the frequency of the light.

To illustrate this, let E_1, E_2, E_3, E_4, etc., represent the total energy of the electron when it is in
the orbits $n = 1, 2, 3, 4$, etc., respectively. When,
for example, the electron is in orbit $n = 3$ where
its energy is E_3, and it jumps to orbit $n = 2$
where the energy is E_2 (see Fig. 51E), the energy
difference $E_3 - E_2$ is ejected from the atom in
the form of a light wave of energy $h\nu$ called a
photon. Here, then, is the origin of light waves
from within the atom.

51.4. Bohr's Success. The success of Bohr's
theory is not to be attributed so much to the
mechanical picture or model of the atom just
proposed, but rather to the development of an
equation that agrees exactly with experimental
observations.

By combining the equations presented in the
preceding section, Bohr derived an equation for
the frequency ν of the light waves emitted by
hydrogen atoms. This equation is

$$\nu = 3.28965 \times 10^{15} \left(\frac{1}{n_1^2} - \frac{1}{n_2^2} \right) \qquad (51g)$$

where n_1 and n_2 represent the *principal quantum numbers* of two orbits.

If we introduce the wave equation, valid for all waves,

$$c = \nu\lambda \qquad (51h)$$

and replace ν by c/λ in Eq.(51g) it can be written

$$\lambda = 911.27 \text{ Å} \left(\frac{n_2^2 \times n_1^2}{n_2^2 - n_1^2} \right) \qquad (51i)$$

where λ is the wavelength of the light in angstroms, n_2 is the quantum number of any orbit of the hydrogen atom in which an electron is confined, and n_1 is the quantum number of the orbit to which the electron jumps to emit light of wavelength λ.

Bohr found that, if in Eq.(51i) he placed $n_1 = 2$ and $n_2 = 3$, the calculated wavelength, $\lambda = 6564.7$ Å, is obtained, which is extremely close to the measured wavelength of the red spectrum line of hydrogen. If he placed $n_1 = 2$ and $n_2 = 4$, the calculated wavelength agreed exactly with the measured wavelength of the blue-green spectrum line of hydrogen.

In fact, the entire series of lines in the hydrogen spectrum are exactly represented by Eq.(51i), by setting $n_1 = 2$ and $n_2 = 3, 4, 5, 6$, etc. This series of lines, so prominently displayed by the sun and stars, as well as by any hydrogen discharge tube in the laboratory, is known as the *Balmer series* (see Sec. 46.8).

These quantum-number changes correspond, as shown in Fig. 51F, to an electron jumping from any outer orbit n to the next to the smallest orbit $n = 2$. In any high-voltage electrical discharge in a glass tube containing hydrogen gas, many thousands of atoms may each have their one and only electron jumping from orbit 3 to 2, while in many other atoms the electron may be jumping from other orbits to $n = 2$. Hence, upon observing the light through a spectroscope, one may observe the entire Balmer series of lines.

51.5. Bohr's Predicted Series. Bohr's orbital model of the hydrogen atom not only accounts for the Balmer series of hydrogen, but also for many other observed lines as well.

By substituting $n_1 = 1$ and $n_2 = 2, 3, 4$, etc., in Eq.(51i), one obtains a series of spectrum lines

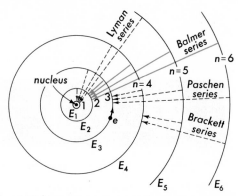

Fig. 51F   *Diagram of the Bohr circular orbits of hydrogen showing the various electron jumps that give rise to the emission of light waves of different frequency.*

in the ultraviolet region of the spectrum. These lines were first photographed by T. Lyman of Harvard University, and the wavelengths are found to check exactly with calculations. This series, now called the Lyman series, which can only be photographed in a vacuum spectrograph, is reproduced in Fig. 51G. On the orbital picture of Fig. 51F, the Lyman series of lines arises from electron jumps from any outer orbit directly to the innermost orbit, the *normal state*.

If, in Eq.(51i), n_1 is set equal to 3 and n_2 to 4, 5, 6, etc., the calculated frequencies predict spectrum lines in the infrared spectrum. These lines were first looked for and observed, exactly as predicted, by F. Paschen; the series is now known by his name. Another series of lines arising from electron jumps, ending on orbit $n = 4$, was predicted and observed in the far infrared by Brackett.

51.6. Normal and Excited Atoms. When the single electron of a hydrogen atom is in the innermost orbit, $n = 1$, the atom is said to be in its normal state. As the name implies, this is the condition of most free hydrogen atoms in a gas under normal room temperature and pressure. If an electrical discharge is sent through a vessel containing hydrogen gas, cathode rays (electrons) moving at high speed make frequent collisions with electrons, knocking some of them out of the atom completely and some of them into one of the outer allowed orbits, $n = 2, 3, 4$, etc.

When the electron is completely removed from

Lyman series of hydrogen

Fig. 51G   *Photograph of the extreme ultraviolet series of hydrogen, predicted by Bohr's theory and first observed by Lyman.*

the atom, the atom is said to be *ionized;* whereas when it is forced into an outer orbit, the atom is said to be *excited*. Once in an excited state, an atom will not remain that way long, for the electron under the attraction by the nucleus will jump to an inner orbit. By jumping to an inner orbit, the electron loses all or part of the energy it had gained.

When an electron is in an excited state, it does not necessarily return to the innermost orbit by a single jump, but may return by several jumps, thereby emitting several different light waves, or quanta.

51.7. Energy Levels. By combining Bohr's equations, Eq.(51a) and Eq.(51b), the energy of an electron in a circular orbit of the hydrogen atom can be calculated. The total energy is just the sum of the kinetic energy $\frac{1}{2}mv^2$, and the potential energy (see Sec. 29.4):

$$E_t = E_k + E_p \qquad (51j)$$

To find the potential energy of the electron in its orbit we use Eq.(29l). By this equation we see that the potential V, at any point at a distance r from the nuclear charge $+e$, is given by

$$V = k\frac{e}{r}$$

Since V is the work done per unit charge in carrying any charge from a distance r out to infinity, one must multiply by the electron's charge $-e$ to obtain as the stored potential energy, $-Ve$.

The two forms of stored energy are, therefore,

$$E_k = \frac{1}{2}mv^2$$

$$E_p = -k\frac{e^2}{r}$$

Substituting these values of E_k and E_p in Eq.(51j) and the value of r from Eq.(51c), we obtain, as Bohr did,

$$E_t = -\frac{2\pi^2 m e^4 k^2}{n^2 h^2} \qquad (51k)$$

The minus sign signifies that one must do work on the electron to remove it from the atom.

With the exception of the principal quantum number n, all quantities in this equation are the same for all orbits. We can therefore write

$$\boxed{E_t = -\frac{1}{n^2}R} \qquad (51l)$$

where R is constant and equal to

$$R = \frac{2\pi^2 m e^4 k^2}{h^2}$$

which, upon substitution of the known values of all the constants, gives

$$R = 2.1790 \times 10^{-18} \text{ joules} \qquad (51m)$$

Equation(51l) is an important equation in atomic structure, for it gives the energy of the electron when it occupies any one of the different orbits of the hydrogen atom. Instead of drawing orbits to the scale of their radius as in Fig. 51D, it is customary to draw horizontal lines to an energy scale, as shown in Fig. 51H. This is called an *energy-level diagram*. The various electron jumps between the allowed orbits of Fig. 51F

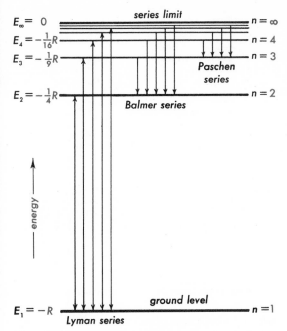

$E_\infty = 0$ — series limit — $n = \infty$

$E_4 = -\frac{1}{16}R$ — $n = 4$

$E_3 = -\frac{1}{9}R$ — $n = 3$

Paschen series

$E_2 = -\frac{1}{4}R$ — $n = 2$

Balmer series

energy

$E_1 = -R$ — ground level — $n = 1$

Lyman series

Fig. 51H *Energy-level diagram for the hydrogen atom. Vertical arrows represent electron jumps.*

now become vertical arrows between the energy levels.

The importance of this kind of diagram is to be attributed to Bohr's third relation, Eq.(51f), where the energy $h\nu$ of each radiated light wave is just equal to the difference between two energies. The energy of each radiated photon is, therefore, proportional to the length of its corresponding arrow.

The first line of the Balmer series $\lambda = 6561$ Å, the red line in Figs. 46A and 46K, corresponds to the short arrow, $n = 3$ to $n = 2$. The second line of the same series is the blue-green line $\lambda = 4861$ Å, and corresponds to the slightly longer arrow, $n = 4$ to $n = 2$, etc.

When an electrical discharge is sent through hydrogen gas, each atom, by collision with other atoms, has its only electron excited to an upper level, and then that electron jumps down again from one level to another, giving rise to the emission of light waves. If, as another experiment, a whole continuous spectrum of light waves is sent through a tube containing hydrogen gas, the hydrogen atoms will be in the ground level, $n = 1$, and by *resonance* may absorb frequencies

corresponding to any one of the Lyman series. In absorbing one of these frequencies, the electron of that atom will jump to an upper energy level. The arrowheads at the top of these vertical lines, correspond, therefore, to resonance absorption. Those same excited electrons can then return by downward jumps, emitting light, and stopping finally on the ground level.

Resonance absorption is the explanation of the dark lines of the sodium spectrum shown in Fig. 46E and the solar spectrum in Fig. 46G.

51.8. Bohr–Stoner Scheme of the Building-Up of Atoms. Bohr and Stoner proposed an extension of the orbital model of hydrogen to include all of the chemical elements. As shown by the examples in Fig. 51I, each atom is composed of a positively charged nucleus with a number of electrons around it.

Although the nucleus is a relatively small particle less than 10^{-14} m in diameter, it contains almost the entire mass of the atom, a mass equal in *atomic mass units* to the *atomic weight*.

The positive charge carried by the nucleus is equal numerically to the atomic number, and it determines the number of electrons located in orbits outside.

A helium atom, atomic number $Z = 2$, has two positive charges on the nucleus and two electrons outside. A lithium atom, atomic number $Z = 3$, contains three positive charges on the nucleus and three electrons outside. A mercury atom, atomic number 80, contains 80 positive charges on the nucleus and 80 electrons outside.

The orbits to which the electrons are confined are the Bohr orbits of hydrogen with $n = 1, 2, 3$, etc., and are called electron shells. Going from element to element in the atomic table, starting with hydrogen, electrons are added one after the other, filling one shell and then another. A shell is filled only when it contains a number of electrons given by $2n^2$. To illustrate this, the first shell $n = 1$ is filled when it has 2 electrons, the second shell $n = 2$ when it has 8 electrons, the third shell $n = 3$ when it has 18 electrons, etc. $2 \times 1^2 = 2$, $2 \times 2^2 = 8$, $2 \times 3^2 = 18$, etc.

quantum number	$n = 1$	$n = 2$	$n = 3$	$n = 4$
number of electrons	2	8	18	32

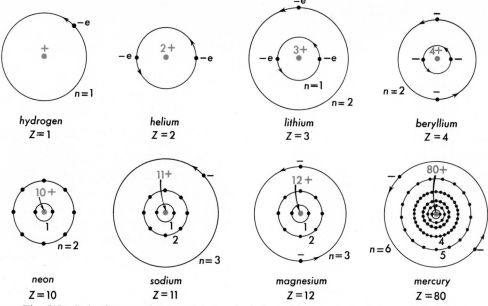

Fig. 51I   *Bohr–Stoner orbital models for the light and heavy atoms of the periodic table.*

Among the heavier elements there are several departures from the order in which the shells are filled. Although these departures are not important from the present standpoint, their nature is illustrated by the mercury atom, Fig. 51I. The four inner shells, $n = 1, 2, 3,$ and 4, are entirely filled with 2, 8, 18, and 32 electrons, respectively, while the fifth shell contains only 18 electrons and the sixth shell 2 electrons. The reasons for such departures are now well understood and are indicative of the chemical behavior of the heavy elements.

It is important to note that, as the nuclear charge increases and additional electrons are added in outer shells, the inner shells, under the stronger attraction of the nucleus, shrink in size. The net result of this shrinkage is that the heaviest elements in the periodic table are not much larger in diameter than the lighter elements. The schematic diagrams in Fig. 51I are drawn approximately to the same scale.

The experimental confirmation of these upper limits to the allowed number of electrons in each shell is now considered one of the most fundamental principles of nature. A sound theoretical explanation of this principle of atomic structure was first given by W. Pauli, in 1925, and is com-

monly referred to as the *Pauli exclusion principle.*

51.9. Elliptical Orbits. Within only a few months after Bohr (in Denmark) published a report telling of his phenomenal success in explaining the hydrogen spectrum with circular orbits, Sommerfeld (in Germany) extended the theory to include elliptical orbits as well. Because these orbits played such an important role in later developments in atomic structure, they deserve some attention here.

The net result of Sommerfeld's theory showed that the electron in any one of the allowed energy levels of a hydrogen atom may move in any one of a number of orbits. For each energy level $n = 1, n = 2, n = 3$, etc., as shown in Fig. 51H, there are n possible orbits.

Diagrams of the allowed orbits for the first three energy levels are shown in Fig. 51J. For $n = 3$, for example, there are three orbits, with designations $l = 2, l = 1,$ and $l = 0$. The diameter of the circular orbit is given by Bohr's theory, and this is just equal to the major axes of the two elliptical orbits. The minor axes are $\frac{2}{3}$ and $\frac{1}{3}$ of the major axis.

It is common practice to assign letters to the l values as follows.

$$l = 0 \quad l = 1 \quad l = 2 \quad l = 3 \quad l = 4$$
$$s \qquad p \qquad d \qquad f \qquad g$$

According to this system, the circular orbit with $n = 3$ and $l = 2$ is designated $3d$, while the elliptical orbit $n = 2$ and $l = 0$ is designated $2s$, etc. n is the *principal quantum number* and l is

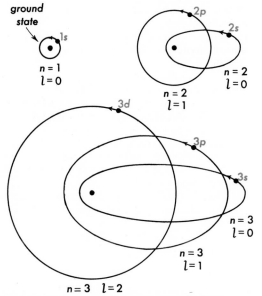

Fig. 51J *Electron orbitals for the hydrogen atom according to the Bohr–Sommerfeld theory.*

the *orbital quantum number*. All orbits having the same value of n have the same total energy, the energy given by Bohr's equation for circular orbits, Eq.(51l).

Each of the allowed orbits of the Bohr–Sommerfeld model of the hydrogen atom becomes a subshell into which electrons are added to build up the elements of the periodic table in the Bohr–Stoner scheme. These subshells are tabulated as follows:

subshells

n \ l	0	1	2	3	4
1	$1s$				
2	$2s$	$2p$			
shells 3	$3s$	$3p$	$3d$		
4	$4s$	$4p$	$4d$	$4f$	
5	$5s$	$5p$	$5d$	$5f$	$6g$

The maximum number of electrons allowed in any one subshell is given by the relation

$$2(2l + 1)$$

This is called the *Pauli exclusion principle*, each subshell being filled when it contains the following number of electrons.

$l = 0$	1	2	3	4
Subshell s	p	d	f	g
Number of electrons 2	6	10	14	18

An orbital diagram of an argon atom is given in Fig. 51K. The electron configuration is given

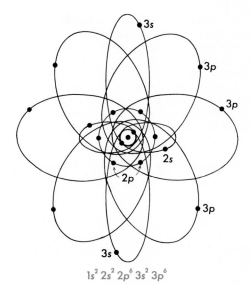

$$1s^2 \, 2s^2 \, 2p^6 \, 3s^2 \, 3p^6$$

Fig. 51K *Electron configuration for an argon atom: Z = 18.*

below, the exponents specifying the total number of electrons in that subshell. Because such elliptical orbits are not easily drawn, it is customary to group all subshells of the same n value together and show them in rings as in Fig. 51I.

A complete table of subshell buildup of all the known elements is given in Appendix XI. The rules for the filling of subshells, and ones that hold throughout the periodic table are the following:

1. *Subshells are grouped under like values of $n + l$.*
2. *Groups are filled in the order of increasing $n + l$.*
3. *Within each $n + l$ group, subshells are filled in the order of decreasing l values.*

PROBLEMS

1. Find the diameters of the 6th, 12th, and 36th circular orbits of hydrogen according to the Bohr theory.

2. What would be the approximate quantum number n for a circular orbit of hydrogen 0.0005 mm in diameter? This would be just big enough to see under a microscope. [Ans. n = 69.]

3. Calculate the wavelength of the tenth line of the Balmer series of hydrogen.

4. Find the wavelengths of the fourth and fifth lines of the Balmer series of hydrogen. [Ans. 4100.7 Å; 3969.1 Å.]

5. Compute the wavelengths of the 4th, 5th, and 6th lines of the Lyman series of hydrogen.

6. Find the wavelengths of the first three lines of the Paschen series of hydrogen. [Ans. 18,746 Å; 12,815 Å; 10,935 Å.]

7. Make a diagram of an iron atom (atomic number 26) according to the Bohr–Stoner scheme.

8. Make a diagram of a bromine atom (atomic number 35) according to the Bohr-Stoner scheme. [Ans. 2, 8, 18, 7.]

9. Calculate the wavelengths of the 10th and 20th spectrum lines of the Paschen series of hydrogen [see Eq.(51i)].

10. Calculate the wavelength of the second spectrum line of the Brackett series of hydrogen [see Eq.(51i)]. [Ans. 26,245 Å.]

11. Find the radius of the 100th orbit of the electron in a hydrogen atom.

12. Make a diagram of a copper atom according to the Bohr–Stoner scheme.

13. Make a diagram of a xenon atom, showing the number of electrons in each shell according to the Bohr–Stoner scheme.

14. Determine the wavelength of the fourth line of the Brackett series of hydrogen. [Ans. 19,440 Å.]

15. What would be the approximate quantum number n for a circular orbit of hydrogen 1 mm in diameter?

16. (a) Solve Eq.(51a) for r as the only unknown. (b) Solve Eq.(51b) for r as the only unknown.

17. Set the right-hand sides of the equations obtained in Problem 16 equal to each other, and solve for v as the unknown quantity.

18. Using Eq.(51d) for v and the known values of e, m, h, and k, calculate the electrons' speed in the first Bohr circular orbit. [Ans. 2.19×10^6 m/s.]

SPINNING ELECTRONS

With the development of the Bohr–Sommerfeld theory of the hydrogen atom in 1913, and its extension to the building-up of the electron structure of all atoms of the periodic table within only a few years, three new but important discoveries followed: (1) the discovery of the spinning electron, (2) the quantization of orbital electrons in a magnetic field, and (3) the direct experimental evidence for the existence of electron shells.

52.1. Orbital Mechanical Moment. The foundations of our present-day concepts of atomic structure were introduced into modern science when Bohr first proposed his theory of the hydrogen atom (see Chapter 51.) According to Bohr's theory, the hydrogen atom is composed of a proton as a nucleus with a single electron revolving around it in a circular orbit. The quantum theory was introduced when Bohr assumed, through Eq.(51l), that the total energy of a hydrogen atom is given by

$$E_t = -\frac{1}{n^2} R \qquad n = 1, 2, 3, 4, \ldots$$

where n is the *principal quantum number*, R is a constant,

$$R = \frac{2\pi^2 m e^4 k^2}{h^2}$$

and $\qquad h = 6.6238 \times 10^{-34}$ Js

With the introduction of elliptical orbits as allowed states for the electron, a new quantum number l was introduced. This new quantum number, too, has integral values only, and is assigned letters as follows:

$$l = 0 \quad 1 \quad 2 \quad 3 \quad 4 \quad 5 \quad 6 \quad 7 \ldots$$
$$s \quad p \quad d \quad f \quad g \quad h \quad i \quad j \ldots$$

In this newer notation, the orbital angular momentum is given by

$$p_l = l\frac{h}{2\pi} \tag{52a}$$

The angular momentum p_l is frequently called the *mechanical moment*, and unit angular momentum $h/2\pi$ is frequently abbreviated $\hbar$:

$$\hbar = \frac{h}{2\pi} \tag{52b}$$

where $\hbar = 1.054 \times 10^{-34}$ Js.

The mechanical moment of an s-electron orbit is 0; of a p-electron orbit, $1\hbar$; of a d-electron orbit, $2\hbar$, of an f-electron orbit, $3\hbar$, etc.

52.2. Orbital Magnetic Moment. Since an electron has a negative charge, its orbital motion, like that of an electron current in a loop of wire, sets up a magnetic field. The direction of this field, as shown in Fig. 52A, is given by the *left-hand rule*. Since angular momentum is a vector

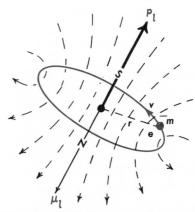

Fig. 52A *An orbital electron produces a magnetic field.*

(a)

ultraviolet   violet blue   green   red

series limit H_ϵ H_δ H_γ H_β H_α

(b)

Fig. 52B   (a) *Small section of the spectrum of titanium, Z = 22. (b) Photograph of the Balmer series of hydrogen, Z = 1.*

quantity p_l is shown pointing up along its axis of rotation. The direction of this mechanical moment is given by the *right-hand rule*.

The magnetic field produced by the orbital electron is quite similar to the field around a bar magnet, and is therefore specified as a magnetic dipole moment. This magnetic moment μ_l is related to the mechanical moment as follows:

$$\frac{\mu_l}{p_l} = \frac{e}{2m} \qquad (52c)$$

where e and m are the charge and mass of the electron. The left-hand term μ_l/p_l is called the *gyromagnetic ratio*. It is the ratio between the magnetic moment and the mechanical moment. By substituting p_l from Eq.(52a), we obtain

$$\boxed{\mu_l = l\hbar\,\frac{e}{2m}} \qquad (52d)$$

All symbols on the right, except l, are fixed atomic constants, and together they form a unit of magnetic moment called the *Bohr magneton*. The Bohr magneton is given by

$$\boxed{\mu_B = \hbar\,\frac{e}{2m}} \qquad (52e)$$

which evaluated is equal to

$$\mu_B = 9.273 \times 10^{-24}\,\text{Am}^2 \qquad (52f)$$

The magnetic moment for a p-electron orbit is one Bohr magneton, for d-electron orbit is two Bohr magnetons, etc. An s-electron orbit with

$l = 0$, has no mechanical moment and no magnetic moment.

52.3. Spectral Series. When the spectra of most of the elements in the periodic table are examined, they are found to be complex arrays of hundreds of lines spaced in what appear to be random patterns [see Fig. 52B(a)]. A few of the elements, however, give rise to a much simpler looking spectrum, with the lines arranged in series like those in Figs. 52B(b), 46E, and 46K. In addition to hydrogen, the elements revealing such simple spectral series are the elements in the first column of the periodic table (Appendix X).

	Li	Na	K	Rb	Cs	Fr
$Z =$	3	11	19	37	55	87

The spectrum arising from each of these, the alkali metals, is composed of several spectral series in different wavelength regions, but having the same general appearance as shown in Fig. 46E. If the wavelengths of any one of these series are measured, and the frequencies are calculated and plotted, one obtains a graph of the kind shown in Fig. 52C.

The first successful attempt to fit all such lines of a series into one general formula was made by Rydberg* in 1896. His formula is

$$\boxed{\nu_n = \nu_\infty - \frac{\Re}{(n+\mu)^2}} \qquad (52g)$$

* The Rydberg constant $\Re$ used here can be obtained by dividing the value of R given in Eq.(51m) by Planck's constant h and the speed of light c.

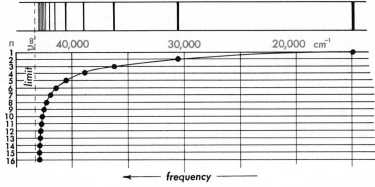

Fig. 52C *Frequency plot of the principal series in the spectrum of lithium, Z = 3.*

where ν_n is the frequency of the different lines n, and ν_∞ is the frequency of the series limit. For example, for the *principal series of lithium*, shown in Fig. 52C,

$$\Re = 109,722 \text{ cm}^{-1}$$
$$\nu_\infty = 43,488 \text{ cm}^{-1}$$
$$\mu = 0.9596$$
$$n = 1, 2, 3, 4, \ldots$$

By substituting $n = 1$ in Eq.(52g), one obtains the frequency of the first line of the lithium series, $\nu_n = 14,915 \text{ cm}^{-1}$, corresponding to $\lambda = 6705\text{Å}$. By substituting $n = 2$, one obtains the frequency of the second line of the series, etc.

The success of the Rydberg formula is remarkable because by changing the constants ν_∞ and μ it fits all series in all spectra. $\Re$ remains the same for all series in all elements. Because the actual frequencies of visible light waves are so extremely high, it is customary to divide them all by the speed of light ($c = 3 \times 10^{10} \text{ cm/s}$). Such frequencies are then called *wavenumbers*. The frequency of a spectrum line in wavenumbers is therefore just equal to the number of wavelengths in a distance of 1 cm, instead of the number in $3 \times 10^{10} \text{ cm}$. Frequencies, in wavenumbers, have the units of $1/\text{cm}$ (cm^{-1}).

52.4. The Spinning Electron. If the spectrum lines of hydrogen, lithium, sodium, potassium, etc., are observed under high magnification, each series member is found to be a double line (see Fig. 52D). These closely spaced doublets arise from the fact that all electrons are spinning. The single electron in the hydrogen atom, which is responsible for the observed spectrum, is spinning around its own axis as it moves in an orbit

Fig. 52D *Highly magnified photographs, showing the doublet structure of (a) the first member of the Balmer series of hydrogen (the red line), and (b) the first member of the principal series of sodium (the yellow line).*

around the nucleus. Similarly, the single-valence electron in all sodium atoms is spinning as shown in Fig. 52E.

Electrons in any completed (closed) subshell pair off with axes parallel but with opposite spin and orbit directions. Hence, in sodium, with $Z = 11$, the one outermost electron $3s$ is unpaired, and its spin constitutes the resultant spin of the entire electronic system. Furthermore, it is the jumping of this valence electron from one orbit to another that is responsible for the observed spectrum.

The outermost electrons in any atom are largely responsible for its ability to combine

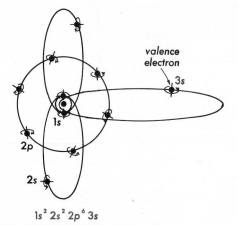

$1s^2 2s^2 2p^6 3s$

Fig. 52E *Atomic model of sodium showing the spinning of all electrons: Z = 11.*

chemically with other atoms to form molecules and are called *valence* electrons.

The spinning of electrons in atoms was first proposed by Goudsmit and Uhlenbeck, in 1925, to explain the double-line structure in the spectra of the alkali metals. Each electron, whether it is bound to an atom or a crystal, or is alone in free space, has an angular momentum. The spin angular momentum is given by

$$p_s = s\hbar \qquad (52h)$$

where s is the spin quantum number and has the value $\frac{1}{2}$:

$$s = \tfrac{1}{2} \text{ only} \qquad (52i)$$

Since an electron always has a negative charge, its spinning around its own mechanical axis generates a magnetic field like that shown in Fig. 52F. This field is similar to the field around a bar magnet and may be specified by its equivalent

Fig. 52F *A spinning electron has a mechanical moment p_s and a magnetic moment μ_s.*

magnetic moment. The magnetic moment μ_s of a spinning electron is given by

$$\frac{\mu_s}{p_s} = 2\,\frac{e}{2m} \qquad (52j)$$

and is oppositely directed to its mechanical moment. Note that the *gyromagnetic ratio* is twice that for an electron orbit [Eq.(52c)].

By substituting the value of p_s from Eq.(52h) in this formula, we obtain

$$\mu_s = \hbar\,\frac{e}{2m} \qquad (52k)$$

Since this is the same as Eq.(52e), we see that while *a spinning electron has a mechanical moment of $\frac{1}{2}\hbar$, it has a magnetic moment of one Bohr magneton.*

52.5. Electron Spin–Orbit Interaction. The fact that the spectrum lines in the Balmer series of hydrogen, and those in the series of the alkali metals, are doublets, is interpreted to mean that each of the energy levels of these atoms is double. (See Fig. 52G for the energy-level diagram of sodium.)

Fig. 52G *Energy-level diagram for the sodium atom, Z = 11.*

The doubling of energy levels in atoms having one valence electron is due to the interaction between the magnetic field of the electron orbit and the magnetic field of the electron spin. We have seen in Sec. 34.2 that a bar magnet located in a magnetic field has a torque exerted on it which tends to line it up parallel to the field. A spinning electron in a magnetic field behaves in exactly the same way; there is a torque acting upon it, trying to turn its axis parallel to the field. Owing to the mechanical properties of a revolving mass, the electron precesses around B in much the same way that a mechanical top precesses in a gravitational field.

A schematic diagram of the precession of a spinning electron is given in Fig. 52H. Such a

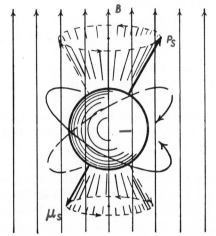

Fig. 52H *A spinning electron in a magnetic field precesses around an axis, parallel to the magnetic induction B.*

motion is called a *Larmor precession*, and its frequency f is given by

$$f = \frac{e}{4\pi m} B \tag{52I}$$

A good demonstration of this precession can be made by a gyroscope of the kind shown in Fig. 52I. A nonconducting sphere, mounted free to turn in ball-bearings, is mounted in double gimbal rings and placed directly over the center of an electromagnet as shown. When the ball is set spinning in the position shown, and the magnetic field is turned on, the ball will retain its inclination angle as it precesses around the vertical axis. By reversing the magnetic field the precession will reverse direction.

Owing to orbital motion, as well as the positive charge on the nucleus, every electron in an atom is subjected to a magnetic field. To see how this field comes about, consider the simple case

Fig. 52I *A spinning ball gyroscope will precess in a magnetic field. (Note: A small permanent bar magnet is mounted inside and on the axis of the ball.)*

of a hydrogen atom with its one electron in an orbit around a positive charge. If we imagine ourselves riding around with the electron, looking out at the nucleus, we see this positive charge as though it were moving in an orbit around us. This moving charge gives rise to a magnetic field at the electron of the form shown in Fig. 52J. In this field the electron carries out a Larmor precession.

Since an electron has a spin angular momentum sh, as well as an orbital angular momentum lh, the total angular momentum of the atom will be the vector sum of the two, and its magnitude

Fig. 52J   *The magnetic field at an electron in an atom is due to the positively charged nucleus that appears to be going around it in an orbit.*

will depend upon their relative orientations. If we represent $l\hbar$ and $s\hbar$ by vectors as shown in Fig. 52K, their vector sum $j\hbar$ will represent the total angular momentum. j is called the *total quantum number*.

Fig. 52K   *Angular momentum vectors for electron spin and orbital motions.*

The quantum theory requires that all possible vector sums for these two quantities differ from each other by $\hbar$. For each value of the orbital quantum number l, there are two possibilities,

either $j\hbar = l\hbar + s\hbar$
or $j\hbar = l\hbar - s\hbar$ (52m)

Since all angular momenta have the common factor $\hbar$, the quantum numbers l, s, and j, may be used as vectors, and we can write

$$j = l + s \quad \text{and} \quad j = l - s \quad (52n)$$

For a d electron, for example, $l = 2$ and $s = \frac{1}{2}$,

$$j = 2 + \tfrac{1}{2} = \tfrac{5}{2} \quad \text{and} \quad j = 2 - \tfrac{1}{2} = \tfrac{3}{2}$$

All values of l, except $l = 0$, will give two j values (see Fig. 52L), and these will always be half-integral. Since the total energy of the atom with l and s parallel will be different from when

Fig. 52L   *Angular momentum vectors for the two allowed states of an orbital electron.*

they are oppositely directed, all levels except s levels will be double.

52.6. Selection Rules. In doublet spectra arising from atomic systems containing only one valence electron, i.e., one electron in an incompleted subshell, the small letters s, p, d, f, g, etc., for the different electron orbits are replaced by the corresponding capitals ^2S, ^2P, ^2D, ^2F, ^2G, etc., for the energy levels. The small superscript 2 in front of each capital letter indicates that the level in question, including S levels, has doublet properties and belongs to a doublet system.

Although all S levels are single, their doublet nature will later be seen to reveal itself when the atom is placed in a magnetic field. In order to distinguish between two fine-structure levels having the same n and l values, the cumbersome but theoretically important half-integral subscripts are used.

Observation shows that, for the transition of an electron from one energy state to another, definite selection rules are in operation. This is illustrated in Fig. 52M by six different sets of transitions. From these diagrams, which are based upon experimental observations, selection rules for doublets may be summarized as follows: In an electron transition

l changes by $+1$ or -1 only

and is written $\Delta l = \pm 1$

j changes by 0, $+1$ or -1 only

and is written $\Delta j = 0, \pm 1$

with $0 \rightarrow 0$ forbidden.

The total quantum number n has no restrictions and may change by any integral amount.

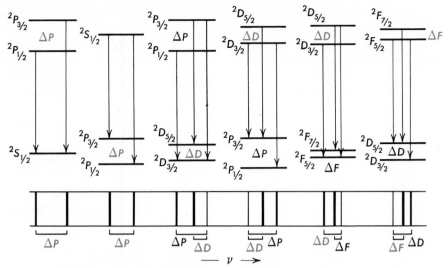

Fig. 52M   *Diagrams of selection rules for transitions between doublet energy levels, and the appearance of the corresponding spectrum lines.*

Note that transitions involving a change of l by 2, e.g., $^2D \rightarrow {}^2S$, are forbidden.

Note how the energy-level differences ΔP, ΔD, and ΔF show up as frequency differences between pairs of spectrum lines. This follows from the fact that energies of all emitted photons are given by $h\nu$.

The relative intensities of the observed spectrum lines are illustrated by the widths of the lines directly below each transition arrow at the bottom of the figure. Combinations between ^2P and ^2S always give rise to a doublet, whereas all other combinations give rise to two strong lines and one fainter line.

In designating any spectrum line like one of the yellow doublet in sodium, $\lambda = 5890\text{Å}$, the lower state is written first followed by the upper state thus, $3^2S_{1/2} - 3^2P_{3/2}$. The other line of the sodium doublet, $\lambda = 5896\text{Å}$, is written $3^2S_{1/2} - 3^2P_{1/2}$. Spectrum lines in absorption are written the same way, the lowest level first.

52.7. The Normal Order of Doublet Energy Levels. In the doublet energy levels of atomic systems containing one valence electron it is generally, but not always, observed that the energy level with $j = l - \frac{1}{2}$ lies deeper than the corresponding level $j = l + \frac{1}{2}$. For example, in the case of p and d electrons, $^2P_{1/2}$ lies deeper than $^2P_{3/2}$ and $^2D_{3/2}$ lies deeper than $^2D_{5/2}$.

As explained in Sec. 52.5 and shown in Fig. 52J, the orbital electron is subjected to a magnetic field arising from the positively charged nucleus. In this field the most stable state of a given doublet will be the one in which the spinning electron, thought of as a small magnet of moment μ_s, is parallel to the magnetic field. This is the state in which $j = l - \frac{1}{2}$. In the state $j = l + \frac{1}{2}$, the spin magnetic moment μ_s is opposite in direction to the field (see Fig. 52N).

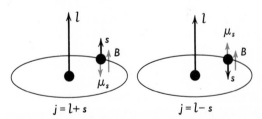

Fig. 52N   *Illustrating the mechanical and magnetic moments of the spinning electron for doublet energy levels $j = l + s$ and $j = l - s$.*

Of the two possible orientations of the electron, the one $j = l - \frac{1}{2}$ is classically the more stable and lies deeper on an energy-level diagram. To turn any magnet from a position where it lines up parallel to the field in which it is located to any position where it makes an angle with the field requires that work be done.

52.8. Space Quantization and the Zeeman

Effect. When hydrogen atoms are located in a magnetic field B, the quantum theory requires that their electrons take on certain specified directions. These directions are determined as follows: The projection of the total angular momentum jh on the field direction B (see Fig. 52O)

Fig. 52O   *Orientation diagram of an atom in an external magnetic field B.*

must take on half-integral values of $\hbar$, from the largest to the smallest possible, and all half-integral values in between. As an equation

$$jh \cos \theta = mh \qquad (52o)$$

where m is the *magnetic quantum number*, and is given by

$$m = \pm\tfrac{1}{2}, \pm\tfrac{3}{2}, \pm\tfrac{5}{2}, \ldots \pm j \qquad (52p)$$

If, for example, the total quantum number $j = \tfrac{5}{2}$, the allowed orientations of j are six in number, and are specified by

$$m = +\tfrac{5}{2}, +\tfrac{3}{2}, +\tfrac{1}{2}, -\tfrac{1}{2}, -\tfrac{3}{2}, -\tfrac{5}{2} \qquad (52q)$$

These six orientations are shown in Fig. 52P, and the process is referred to as *space quantization*. The minus values indicate only that the component of jh is opposite in direction to the field B.

A diagram of the precession of an atom in a magnetic field, when the electron is in a state $l = 2, s = \tfrac{1}{2}, j = \tfrac{5}{2}$, and $m = \tfrac{3}{2}$, is shown in Fig. 52Q. Because the energy of the atom differs slightly between the different orientations of the electron, energy levels as well as spectrum lines will be split into a number of equally spaced components. To observe this phenomenon, the

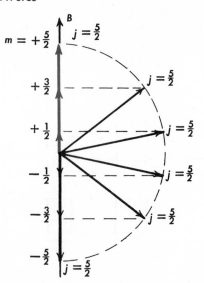

Fig. 52P   *Vector diagram representing space quantization of an atom in a magnetic field B.*

light source must be placed in a strong and uniform magnetic field, and the light observed with a spectrograph. The phenomenon, called the Zeeman effect, is observed in the spectra of all

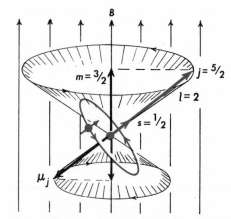

Fig. 52Q   *An electron spin and orbit precess together as a unit around the magnetic field direction B.*

elements. Some line patterns contain only a few lines, while others contain many. Typical Zeeman patterns, as seen under high magnification, are reproduced in Fig. 52R.

52.9. Pauli Exclusion Principle. We have now seen that four quantum numbers are required to specify the state of an electron in an atom. These are

Fig. 52R *Small section of the spectrum of rhodium, Z = 45.* (Upper) *Ordinary lines with no magnetic field.* (Lower) *Zeeman patterns when light source is in strong magnetic field of 7.0 Wb/m².* (After Harrison and Bitter.)

n	principal quantum number
l	orbital quantum number
j	total quantum number
m	magnetic quantum number

(52r)

According to the Pauli exclusion principle, no two electrons in the same atom can have all four quantum numbers alike. They may have three alike but at least one must be different.

Consider, for example, the number of electrons that can have $n = 3$ and $l = 2$. Such electrons are designated $3d$. The two j values possible are $j = l + s$ and $j = l - s$, i.e., $j = \frac{5}{2}$ and $j = \frac{3}{2}$ [see Eq.(52n)]. For $j = \frac{5}{2}$ there are six possible values of m, and for $j = \frac{3}{2}$ there are four possible values of m. Together, these are

$$j = \tfrac{5}{2}, m = +\tfrac{5}{2}, +\tfrac{3}{2}, +\tfrac{1}{2}, -\tfrac{1}{2}, -\tfrac{3}{2}, -\tfrac{5}{2}$$
$$j = \tfrac{3}{2}, m = \qquad +\tfrac{3}{2}, +\tfrac{1}{2}, -\tfrac{1}{2}, -\tfrac{3}{2}$$

(52s)

or ten possibilities in all. Note that this is just the number of electrons that fills an $l = 2$ subshell in the building up of elements in the periodic table. In a similar way, an s subshell can have two electrons, a p subshell 6, and an f subshell 14.

52.10. Elastic and Inelastic Impacts. When an electron collides with a neutral atom in a rarefied gas, the collision is either *elastic* or *inelastic*. An elastic collision is one in which the laws of conservation of momentum and conservation of mechanical energy are both upheld. In other words, the atomic particles behave as though they were perfectly elastic spheres; the total energy and total momentum before impact is equal to the total energy and total momentum after impact (see Fig. 52S).

An inelastic collision is one in which the impinging electron, in striking a neutral atom, hits one of the electrons and either knocks it into one of the outer orbits (energy levels), or knocks it completely out of the atom. In the first instance, we say the atom has been *excited*, and in the second case it has been *ionized*. In either case it is usually a valence electron that is involved.

Fig. 52S *Schematic diagrams showing elastic and inelastic impacts.*

To raise an electron from its normal state to an excited state, or to remove it from the atom, requires the expenditure of energy; this is supplied by the impinging electron. As a consequence, some of the total energy before collision is used for excitation or ionization, and what is left is divided between the two particles. Because the masses of atoms are thousands of times that of the electron, nearly all kinetic energy before impact, and after, is confined to the electron. The recoil velocity and kinetic energy of an atom that has been hit by a moving electron is relatively small.

52.11. Franck–Hertz Experiments. One of the most direct proofs of the existence of energy levels or electron shells within an atom is to be found in the Franck–Hertz experiments. These experiments make it possible to measure the energy necessary to raise an electron from the ground state in an atom to an outer orbit, or state, or to remove it from the atom entirely.

In the Franck and Hertz experiments, a vapor like sodium or mercury is bombarded with electrons of known velocity. A diagram of the apparatus in its simplest form is given in Fig. 52T.

Fig. 52T　*Diagram of the Franck and Hertz experiment.*

Electrons from a hot filament F are accelerated toward a grid G by applying a voltage V between them. An opposing voltage V', much smaller than V, is applied between the grid G and the plate P. If sodium atoms are to be used, the gas pressure is reduced until the mean distance between atomic collisions (the mean free path) is considerably smaller than the filament-to-grid distance, and somewhat greater than the grid-to-plate distance.

If an electron starts from rest at the filament and reaches the grid G without hitting a sodium atom, its velocity v is given by the equation

$$Ve = \tfrac{1}{2}mv^2 \qquad (52t)$$

where V is in volts, e is in coulombs, m is in Kg, and v is in m/s [see Eq.(50b)]. In order for an electron to collide inelastically with an atom, it must have sufficient kinetic energy $\tfrac{1}{2}mv^2$ to raise the valence electron from its ground level to the first excited level. To find how much energy this is, consider the example of sodium, $Z = 11$, in which the first energy state above the ground state is responsible for the yellow light we observe in any sodium arc light or lamp. This light arises from the jump of the valence electron from a $3p$ orbit, into the ground state, a $3s$ orbit (see

Fig. 52G). This light of wavelength $\lambda = 5893\text{Å}$ has a frequency $\nu = 5.091 \times 10^{14}$ vib/s, and each photon an energy $h\nu = 3.359 \times 10^{-19}$ J.

To find the voltage equivalent of this energy, we write

$$Ve = h\nu \qquad (52u)$$

and substituting the electronic charge $e = 1.601 \times 10^{-19}$ C and $h = 6.6238 \times 10^{-34}$ Js, we obtain

$$V = 2.1 \text{ volts}$$

This means that electrons accelerated by a potential difference of 2.1 V or more, upon collision with a normal sodium atom, can knock the single valence electron from its $3s$ orbit into the $3p$ orbit. In so doing the electron gives up kinetic energy equivalent to 2.1 electron volts and slows down accordingly.

The curve reproduced in Fig. 52U, showing the variation in plate current with the accelerating voltage V, is characteristic of the Franck and Hertz experiment with sodium. As V starts from zero and is slowly increased, the speed and number of electrons reaching the grid G increase and the plate current rises. When the velocity has increased sufficiently to excite sodium atoms, however, inelastic collisions occur.

With a further increase in V, more electrons reach the critical velocity, are stopped by inelastic collision, and, not being able to reach the plate P, cause a drop in the current. This drop in current continues until the critical speed is attained far enough in front of the grid to collide inelastically again and reach the plate. The current, therefore, rises again and continues to rise until the electrons, after one inelastic collision, attain the critical speed and make a second inelastic collision.

The double peaks in Fig. 52U show that not only have collisions occurred in which the valence electron has been excited, but also collisions in which the electron is completely removed from the atom. Complete ejection of the electron from sodium requires an electron velocity equivalent to $V = 5.1$ V. This then is the ionization potential of sodium, which in Fig. 52G is equivalent to raising the valence electron from its *ground state* to the *series limit*.

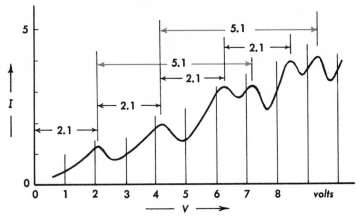

Fig. 52U *Critical potential curve for sodium atoms showing the excitation potential of 2.1 volts and the ionization potential of 5.1 volts.*

52.12. Ionization Potentials. The ionization potential of an element is defined as the energy in electron volts required to remove the most loosely bound electron from the normal atom. The *electron volt* is defined as the energy equivalent to the kinetic energy of an electron accelerated through a potential difference of 1 V. In other words an energy of 1 eV is 1.60×10^{-19} J.

A graph of the ionization potentials of the elements of the periodic table is given in Fig. 52V. It is clearly seen that the alkali metals, Li, Na, K, Rb, Cs, and Fa, have low values, about 5 V, while the inert gases, He, Ne, A, Kr, Xe, and Rn, have the highest values. The inert gases represent those atoms in which all the electron subshells are complete. The adding of one more

proton to the nucleus, and the addition of one more electron to the outer structure to make the next atom, an alkali metal, requires that electron to go into a new subshell, an outer orbit. Such an electron, being on the average farther away from the nucleus, requires less energy to remove it from the atom. As protons are added to the nucleus, and electrons are added in this same subshell, the binding of the electrons grows stronger and stronger.

A direct correlation between the low ionization potentials of the alkali metals and the beginning of new subshells, as shown by the arrows at the bottom of Fig. 52V, leads to the building-up of the periodic table as given in Appendix XI.

Fig. 52V *Ionization potentials of the elements.*

QUESTIONS AND PROBLEMS

1. What is the atomic unit of angular momentum? What is the unit of magnetic moment?

2. What is the Rydberg formula? What is Larmor precession?

3. What is a total quantum number? What is the Pauli exclusion principle? What are the four quantum numbers involved in the Pauli exclusion principle?

4. What is the Zeeman effect? What is space quantization?

5. What was the Franck–Hertz experiment?

6. What is an excitation potential? What is an ionization potential?

7. The Sharp Series of spectrum lines of lithium has a series limit at 28,573 cm^{-1}. If the series constant $\mu = 0.5884$, what is (a) the frequency, and (b) the wavelength, of the second, third, and fourth lines of the series?

8. Using the Rydberg formula, calculate (a) the frequency, and (b) the wavelength of the second member of the principal series of lithium. [*Ans.* (a) 30,952 cm^{-1}, (b) 3231 Å.]

9. Make a space quantization diagram for the electronic state, $l = 4$, $s = \frac{1}{2}$, $j = F$.

10. Calculate the excitation potential for the first line of the principal series of lithium.* (*Note:* The energy level diagram for lithium is quite similar to that for sodium, Fig. 52G. See Fig. 52C.) [*Ans.* 1.85 V.]

11. Calculate the ionization potential for lithium.†

---

* For a more complete account of atomic structure, see H. E. White, *Introduction to Atomic Spectra* (McGraw-Hill Book Co., Inc., New York).

† Frequency in wavenumbers (cm^{-1}) when multiplied by the speed of light, $c = 3 \times 10^{10}$ cm/s, gives the true frequency ν.

(*Note:* The limit of the principal series represents the valence electron at infinity. See Fig. 52C.)

12. (a) Plot an energy-level diagram for potassium, $Z = 19$, using the following values for the term values in wavenumbers.

Config.	Sym.	J	Term values
4s	^2S	$\frac{1}{2}$	35,005.9
4p	^2P	$\frac{1}{2}$	22,020.8
		$\frac{3}{2}$	21,963.1
5s	^2S	$\frac{1}{2}$	13,980.3
3d	^2D	$\frac{3}{2}$	13,470.3
		$\frac{5}{2}$	13,467.5
5p	^2P	$\frac{1}{2}$	10,304.4
		$\frac{3}{2}$	10,285.7
4d	^2D	$\frac{3}{2}, \frac{5}{2}$	7608.3
6s	^2S	$\frac{1}{2}$	7555.7
4f	^2F	$\frac{5}{2}, \frac{7}{2}$	6878.5
6p	^2P	$\frac{1}{2}, \frac{3}{2}$	6009.3
5d	^2D	$\frac{3}{2}, \frac{5}{2}$	4821.9

(b) Show all allowed transitions based upon the selection rules. (c) Calculate the frequencies in wavenumbers for the first members of the sharp, principal, diffuse, and fundamental series of spectrum lines. (d) Calculate the corresponding wavelengths to four significant figures. Make a table of your answers.

13. Calculate the excitation potential for the first line of the principal series of potassium. Use the energy-level values given in Problem 12.

14. Calculate the ionization potential for potassium. See Problem 12 for energy levels. [*Ans.* 4.76 V.]

15. Calculate the excitation potential for the second line of the principal series of potassium. Use Problem 12 for energy levels.

X RAYS

One of the most interesting episodes in the history of modern science began with the accidental discovery of X rays by Wilhelm Röntgen* in 1895. While studying the green fluorescent stage of an electrical discharge in a Crookes tube, Röntgen observed the bright fluorescence of some nearby crystals of barium platino-cyanide. Even though the discharge tube was in a darkened room, and entirely surrounded with black paper to prevent the escape of visible light, a distant screen covered with crystals would fluoresce brightly when the discharge was turned on. Röntgen reasoned, therefore, that some kind of invisible, yet penetrating, rays of an unknown kind were being given out by the discharge tube. These rays he called *X rays*, the letter *X* meaning, as it so often does in algebra, an unknown.

In the short series of experiments that followed his discovery, Röntgen found that the unknown rays were coming from the glass walls of the tube itself and, in particular, from the region where the most intense part of the cathode ray beam was striking the glass. So great was the importance of this discovery that, within only a few weeks of Röntgen's announcement, X rays

* Wilhelm Konrad von Röntgen (1845–1923). Born at Lennep on March 27, 1845, Röntgen received his education in Holland and Switzerland. His scientific career began at the age of 25 when he became an assistant in the physics laboratory at Würtzburg, Germany. After a teaching period extending over a period of 25 years, which carried him to the University of Strasbourg, then to Hohenheim, back to Strasbourg, then to Giessen, and finally to Würzburg again, he discovered X rays in his laboratory at Würzburg in 1895. For this discovery, he received the Rumford Medal of the Royal Society in 1896 and the first Nobel Prize in physics in 1901. Röntgen also conducted researches in light, heat, and elasticity, but none of these works compares in importance with his discovery of X rays.

were being used as an aid in surgical operations in Vienna. This, along with other practical applications and uses that can be made of this single scientific discovery, is a good example of the role played by modern science in the rapid advancement of civilization.

53.1. X-ray Tubes. The Crookes tube with which Röntgen made his discovery bears very little resemblance to the modern X-ray tube. In form it had somewhat the appearance of the tube shown in Fig. 48C. Within a short period of time after Röntgen's discovery, quite a number of noteworthy improvements upon tube design were made. The first important contribution in this direction came immediately after the discovery that it is the sudden stopping of electrons that gives rise to X rays.

In X-ray tubes of early design, the electrons from the cathode were not allowed to strike the glass walls, but were directed toward the anode as a target, as shown in Fig. 53A. By curving the

Fig. 53A   *Diagram of early form of X-ray tube.*

cathode like a concave mirror, it was found that it was possible to focus the electrons on one spot on the target, thus making of that spot a localized source of X rays. Radiating outward in all possible directions, these "Röntgen rays," as they are sometimes called, have no difficulty in passing through the glass walls of the tube.

The biggest improvement in X-ray tube design was made by Coolidge, an American physicist, in 1913. In the Coolidge tube, now a commercial product (see Fig. 53B), a tungsten-wire filament

Fig. 53B   *Diagram of a Coolidge X-ray tube employing a hot cathode.*

is placed at the center of the cathode and heated to incandescence by a storage battery or low-voltage transformer. This filament, being a copious source of electrons, gives rise at the target to a far more intense source of X rays than was previously possible with a cold cathode. Under the terrific bombardment of the target by so many electrons, most metals will melt. To overcome this difficulty, a metal with a high melting point, like tungsten or molybdenum, is imbedded in the face of a solid copper anode to become the target. Copper, being a good heat conductor, helps to dissipate the heat.

The early sources of high voltage applied to the anode and cathode of X-ray tubes were induction coils of various descriptions. Although some of these sources are still in use, they have been almost entirely supplanted by a more efficient high-voltage transformer. The emf generated by these transformers varies between 50,000 and 2,000,000 V. The normal emf used for surgical work is about 100,000 V, whereas for the treatment of diseases the higher emf's are employed. The high-voltage alternating emf supplied by a transformer is not applied directly to the X-ray tube, but is first changed into direct current by means of rectifier tubes.

53.2. Penetration of X Rays. Four useful and important properties of X rays are their ability (1) penetrate solid matter, (2) to cause certain chemical compounds to fluoresce, (3) to ionize atoms, and (4) to affect a photographic plate. The penetration of X rays depends upon two things: first, the voltage applied between the anode and cathode of the X-ray tube; and second, the density of the substance through which the rays must travel. The higher the voltage applied to the tube, the greater is the penetration. *X rays of great penetrating power are called hard X rays, whereas those having little penetrating power are called soft X rays.*

The relation between density and penetration may be illustrated in several ways. When X rays are sent through a block of wood containing nails, or a closed leather purse containing coins, a clear and well-defined image of the nails, or coins, can be formed and observed on a fluorescent screen. The experimental arrangement is the same as that shown in Fig. 53C. When X rays

Fig. 53C   *Arrangement for taking X-ray photographs of the bones of the hand.*

are sent through the hand or any part of the body to obtain photographs of the bones, it is the difference in penetration between the flesh and the bones that permits a picture to be made. Materials like paper, wood, flesh, etc., composed principally of light chemical elements like those at the beginning of the periodic table, are readily penetrated by X rays. In other words, they are poor absorbers of X rays. For materials like

Fig. 53D *X-ray photographs of the wrist bones of the hand.* Above, *with hand in water.* Below, *with lead oxide ointment spread on hand.* (Courtesy, Stamford Research Laboratories, American Cyanamid Co.)

brass, steel, bone, gold, etc., composed partly of heavy elements, like those farther along and near the end of the periodic table, the penetration of X rays is very poor. Hence, heavy elements, or dense substances, are good absorbers.

The bones of the body, which contain large amounts of calcium, are relatively good absorbers of X rays, whereas the soft tissue, composed principally of much lighter elements—hydrogen, oxygen, carbon, and nitrogen—are poor absorbers. This explains the general appearance of X-ray photographs. X-ray pictures like the ones in Fig. 53D are similar to shadows cast by the objects being photographed. The focus point on the X-ray target, being bombarded by high-speed electrons, acts as a point source of rays. These rays spread out in straight lines as shown in Fig. 53C. On passing through the hand to the photographic film, more X rays are absorbed by the bones than by the flesh. The shadow cast by the bones is therefore lacking in X rays, and the photographic film for these areas becomes transparent upon development.

Where only flesh is traversed, the X rays penetrate through to the photographic film, causing it to develop out black. The bones therefore appear white against a darker background. If this "negative film," as it is called, is printed on paper as in Fig. 53D, it becomes a "positive," the bones appearing black.

If the photographic film is placed farther away from the hand than shown in the diagram, the shadow picture will be larger and less distinct. The best pictures are obtained by placing the film as close in contact with the object to be photographed as is physically possible. Whenever a film is being exposed for an X-ray picture, it is mounted in a black paper envelope or thin aluminum box. This prevents visible light from reaching the film but allows the X rays to pass through.

53.3. Ionizing Power. As X rays pass through matter in the solid, liquid, or gaseous state, they are found to *ionize* atoms and molecules. This can be shown by charging a gold-leaf electroscope positively or negatively and placing it some 10 to 15 ft away from an X-ray tube. When the

X-ray tube is turned on (see Fig. 53E), the gold leaf falls, showing discharge.

The explanation of this experiment is as follows. X rays pass through the electroscope and

Fig. 53E   *X rays discharge an electroscope.*

ionize the air by removing electrons from many of the oxygen and nitrogen molecules. Leaving these particular molecules with a net positive charge, the freed electrons move about until they are picked up by other neutral molecules, which thus take on a net negative charge. The result is that the passage of X rays through matter produces both *positively charged* and *negatively charged* ions. If the electroscope is negatively charged, it attracts the positively charged ions to the gold leaf, neutralizing the charge and repelling the negatively charged ions to the "grounded" walls where they, too, become neutralized. If the electroscope is positively charged, it attracts the negative ions to it, again neutralizing the charge. The positive ions in this case are repelled to the walls. In either case, whether the electroscope is positively or negatively charged, the gold leaf falls, showing discharge.

It is the ionization of atoms and molecules in a substance that limits the penetrating power of X rays. Heavy elements contain more electrons than light elements, thus placing more electrons in the path of the X rays to stop them. The stopping power of a thin sheet of lead, for example, is equivalent to the stopping power of a sheet of aluminum several times thicker. Lead atoms each contain 82 electrons, whereas aluminum atoms each contain only 13.

53.4. Practical Applications. During the first few weeks following Röntgen's discovery of X rays, reports from all over the world were received by the editors of scientific journals telling how the new rays could be put to practical use. A few examples of the first applications were (1) the location of a bullet in a patient's leg, (2) the observation and photography of the healing of a broken bone, (3) the detection of contraband in baggage, (4) the distinction between artificial and real gems, (5) the detection of pearls in oysters, and (6) the examination of the contents in parcel post. In 1897 Dr. Morton exhibited in New York an X-ray picture of the entire skeleton of a living and fully clothed adult.

The biological effects became important when it was found that X rays killed off some forms of animal tissue more rapidly than others. This made them a possible means of cure for certain skin diseases. In particular, the application to the treatment of well-known forms of cancerous growths in animals and human beings has yielded amazing results, and oftentimes a cure. When an internal cancer is treated by sending a beam of X rays directly through the body, the cancerous tissue as well as the normal tissue is slowly killed off. It is principally because the normal tissue grows in again more rapidly than the cancerous tissue that it is possible to bring about a cure. Periodic radiation allows the normal tissue to build up in the intervals.

Although only certain diseases can be successfully treated by X rays, a great deal of research work is still being carried on with extremely high voltage X rays in the hope of discovering new and more effective medical aids. It is generally believed that the killing-off of cell tissue by X rays is due in part to ionization and in part to the formation of free radicals of the molecules within the individual cells.

The importance of X rays in some phases of the field of engineering cannot be overestimated. This can be appreciated when it is realized that metal castings or welded joints sometimes contain internal flaws or blowholes that otherwise escape detection. Because of the disastrous results that might occur by the insertion of defective castings or welded joints into a bridge or building, many such metal parts are examined by X rays before they are used.

53.5. X Rays Are Waves. Not long after Röntgen's discovery of X rays, there arose in scientific circles two schools of thought concerning the nature of these penetrating rays. One school held to the belief that X rays are high-speed particles like cathode rays, but more penetrating; and the other school held to the idea that they are electromagnetic waves of extremely high frequency. Although many experiments were performed to test these two hypotheses, several years passed before the wave theory was proven to be correct.

The crucial experiment came in 1912 when Von Laue* suggested to his associates, W. Friedrich and P. Knipping, that they try diffracting X rays by sending them through a thin crystal. Believing that the ultramicroscopic structure of a crystal is a three-dimensional array of regularly spaced atoms, Von Laue reasoned that the equally spaced layers of the atoms would act like a diffraction grating.

The experiment, as it was performed, is shown diagrammatically in Fig. 53F. X rays from a cold-cathode X-ray tube, and limited to a narrow pencil of rays by a pinhole in each of the two lead screens L_1 and L_2, are shown passing through a thin crystal to a photographic film or plate at P. In addition to the central beam, the major part of which goes straight through to produce a blackened spot at the center of the film, there are many other weaker beams emerging in different directions to produce other spots on the same film. The pattern of spots obtained

---

* Max von Laue (1879–1960). Born near Coblenz, Germany, in 1879, young Max was educated in the German universities of Strasbourg, Göttingen, and Munich. Following this, his teaching and research work carried him to the university at Munich, Zurich, Frankfurt on the Main, and finally Berlin. Since he was interested in theoretical physics, his early attentions were confined to various phases of Einstein's theory of relativity and to Bohr's quantum theory of atomic structure. His chief contribution to physics, however, was the instigation and supervision of experiments leading to the diffraction of X rays by crystals. For this work, which proved the wave nature of X rays, he was granted the Nobel Prize in 1914.

Fig. 53F *Experimental demonstration of the wave property of X rays. Diffracted by the atoms in a crystal, a Laue pattern is photographed.*

in this way is always quite symmetrical, and is referred to as a *Laue pattern.*

Photographs of two Laue patterns obtained with single crystals are reproduced in Fig. 53G.

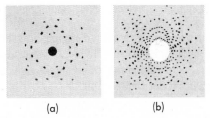

Fig. 53G *X-ray diffraction patterns from crystals: (a) Zinc sulfide crystal (face-centered cubic crystal). (b) Sugar crystal (a complex crystal structure).*

The small number of spots in (a) is indicative of a relatively simple crystal structure for zinc sulfide, ZnS, and the large number of spots signifies a relatively complex crystal structure for sugar, $C_{12}H_{22}O_{11}$. While the picture for sugar was being taken, the central beam was masked off by a small lead disk placed just in front of the film to prevent excessive blackening. Simple Laue patterns in general arise from simple crystal structures. Common salt is an example of a simple crystal, containing sodium ions $(Na)^+$ and chlorine ions $(Cl)^-$ in equal numbers arranged in a three-dimensional cubic lattice. Figure 53H is a cross section through such a crystal, showing the alternation of ions in two of the three directions. Here, in this two-dimensional array, the origin of the different spots on a Laue pattern is illustrated.

Each spot arises from the reflection of some of the incident X rays from one of the various sets of parallel crystal planes, three of which are shown by the sets of parallel lines. Always, the rays obey the law of reflection that the angle of incidence equals the angle of reflection. While

Fig. 53H *Illustration of the reflection of X rays from the various atomic planes in a cubic crystal lattice.*

the reflection planes shown in the diagram are all perpendicular to the plane of the page, there are many other planes in a three-dimensional lattice to reflect the rays off in other directions.

The success of the Laue experiment proves the correctness of two postulates: (1) that X rays are light rays of very short wavelength, and (2) that the ions of a crystal are arranged in a regular three-dimensional lattice. These are the results for which Von Laue was granted the Nobel Prize in physics in 1914. As a direct result of the Laue experiment, two new and important fields of experimental physics were opened up: (1) the study and measurement of X-ray wavelengths, and (2) the study of crystal structures by their action on X rays.

53.6. The X-Ray Spectrograph. No sooner had Von Laue, Friedrich, and Knipping announced the results of their experiments then many investigators began a study of the various phases of *X-ray diffraction* by crystals. The most outstanding of these experiments are those of W. H. Bragg* and his son, W. L. Bragg; they also

* Sir William Henry Bragg (1862–1942), British physicist and professor at the University of London. Bragg's researches on radioactive phenomena brought him early recognition from scientific societies at home and abroad. Joint work with his son, William Lawrence Bragg (1890–   ), on the arrangement of ions in crystals, and the development of the X-ray spectrograph are his

developed the X-ray spectrometer and spectrograph.

A diagram of an X-ray spectrograph is shown in Fig. 53I. Instead of having pinhole screens, as in Fig. 53F, and sending a narrow pencil of rays through a crystal, the early spectrographs used screens with narrow slits and reflected the rays from one face of a crystal. The crystal is not fixed tightly in place but can be turned back and forth about a pivot C at the center of the front face. As this rocking motion takes place, the crystal acts somewhat like a mirror and causes the reflected X-ray beam to sweep back and forth along the photographic film from one end to the other. After the photographic film has been exposed to the rays for some time, and then developed, it is found to have the general appearance of the reproduction in Fig. 53J. This unusually clear photograph was originally taken by De Broglie who used an X-ray tube containing a tungsten-metal anode target. Instead of a general blackening from end to end, the film shows *bands* and *lines*, indicating that at certain orientation angles of the crystal the reflected rays were unusually intense, while at others there were apparently none. The lines, which are particularly noticeable at points marked $K\alpha$, $L\alpha$, $L\beta$, and $L\gamma$, are called *X-ray spectrum lines*.

The origin and interpretation of these spectrum lines are illustrated by a detailed diagram in Fig. 53K. To reflect X rays of one given wavelength from a crystal, a certain relation must exist between the direction of the incident rays and the distance *d* between surface layers of the crystal. This relation, known as *the Bragg rule*, requires the waves to be incident on the crystal face, at such an angle θ that the crests of the waves reflected from adjacent atomic layers move off together. This occurs when the additional distance traveled by ray (2), AMB in the diagram, is exactly one whole wavelength greater than that traveled by the ray (1) next above it. When the angle is adjusted so that this is true, other rays like (3), belonging to the same wave train as (1) and (2), will be reflected from the

greatest scientific contributions. In 1915, father and son were jointly granted the Nobel Prize in physics, as well as the Barnard Gold Medal from Columbia University.

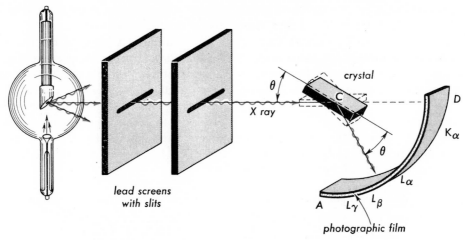

Fig. 53I *Schematic diagram of a Bragg X-ray crystal spectrograph.*

third crystal layer to be "in step" with the others.

Suppose now that the X-ray tube in Fig. 53I emits X rays of only one wavelength; then, as the crystal rocks back and forth, there will be

Fig. 53J *X-ray spectrogram taken with an X-ray tube containing a tungsten metal target. (After De Broglie.)*

no reflection except at one particular angle θ, and this will occur where the conditions of Bragg's rule are satisfied. At this particular position on the photographic plate, a single dark line will appear. If now the distance d between crystal layers is known, and the angle θ for the X-ray line measured, the wavelength of the X rays can be calculated. One wavelength, it will be noted in Fig. 53K, is equal to twice the length of the side AM of the right triangle AMC. Thus,

with one side and two angles of a triangle known, either of the other sides can be calculated. Bragg's rule therefore becomes

$$2d \sin \theta = \lambda \qquad (53a)$$

In the case of a sodium chloride crystal, NaCl, the atomic spacing is 2.81 Å, or 2.81×10^{-10} m.

Fig. 53K *Illustration of the Bragg rule of reflection for X rays from the surface layers of a crystal.*

Since several spectrum lines appear in the photograph in Fig. 53J, there are several different wavelengths emitted by the same X-ray tube. The two fluted-appearing bands between the K and L X-ray lines are not of interest here because they appear on all X-ray spectrograms; they are due to the strong absorption of X rays of many other wavelengths by the silver and bromine atoms in the photographic plate itself. Had the original photographic film been exposed for a much longer time, the spectrogram would have shown a general blackening over the whole plate. This blackening, illustrated by the shaded area in the curve above, is due to X rays of all different wavelengths being emitted by the X-ray tube; it is these which, although not very intense, strongly affect the photographic plate at the two bands, Ag and Br.

53.7. The Origin of X Rays. X rays, like visible light, originate from the jumping of an electron from one orbit to another. When high-speed electrons from the cathode of an X-ray tube strike the target, they ionize many of the atoms composing the surface layers of the metal.

Owing to their very high speeds (about $\frac{1}{10}$ the velocity of light), the electrons penetrate the atoms and remove an electron from the inner shells by collision. This is illustrated in Fig. 53L

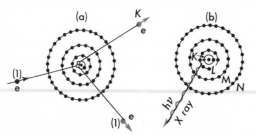

Fig. 53L *Schematic diagram illustrating (a) the ionization of an atom by a high-speed electron, and (b) the subsequent jumping of an inner electron with the simultaneous emission of an X ray.*

where an electron is knocked out of the K shell. The designations K, L, M, N, O, P, etc., for the various electron shells originated with the X-ray spectroscopist and are identical with the quantum numbers $n = 1, 2, 3, 4, 5, 6$, etc. When an electron is missing in the innermost K shell, a nearby electron from the next shell beyond jumps into the vacant space, simultaneously emitting a photon of energy $h\nu$. Such X rays, arising from millions of atoms, produce the K lines shown in Fig. 53J.

Since the L shell now has one less electron, and M electron can jump into the L shell vacancy, with the consequent emission of another but different X-ray frequency. These are the L lines in Fig. 53J. The jumping process continues until the outermost shell is reached, where an electron jumping in gives rise to visible light. Thus we see

how it is possible for a single atom to emit X rays of different wavelengths.

The continuous X-ray spectrum, illustrated by the shaded area under the curve in Fig. 53J, is due to another phenomenon often referred to as "Bremsstrahlung." These radiations are due to the slowing down of high-speed electrons as they pass close to the nuclei of the atoms within the target of the X-ray tube. The process is illustrated in Fig. 53M. As the electron passes

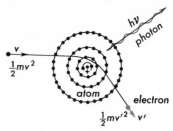

Fig. 53M *Diagram illustrating the production of a photon by a high-speed electron as it passes through an atom close to the nucleus ("Bremsstrahlung").*

through the atom, it is attracted by the positive charge of the nucleus and deflected in its path.

During the deflection of the electron in the strong electric field of the nucleus, a light wave of energy $h\nu$ is emitted. Since the law of conservation of momentum must hold for such a collision, the electron is deflected off to one side of the atom, and the photon off to the other. Since the law of conservation of energy must hold, some of the energy of the incoming electron $\frac{1}{2}mv^2$ is given up to the newly created photon $h\nu$, and the remainder $\frac{1}{2}mv'^2$ is retained by the electron. Thus the electron is slowed down to a velocity v' by the encounter. The closer the electron comes to the nucleus, the greater is its loss in velocity and energy, and the greater is the frequency and energy of the radiated photon. By the conservation of energy,

$$\frac{1}{2}mv^2 - \frac{1}{2}mv'^2 = h\nu \qquad (53b)$$

The highest frequency that is possible is one in which the electron is completely stopped by the atom. In this special case,

$$\frac{1}{2}mv^2 = h\nu_{max} \qquad (53c)$$

Since the kinetic energy of the electrons in the

beam striking the target is given by the voltage V applied to the tube, we may use Eq.(50b),

$$Ve = \tfrac{1}{2}mv^2 \qquad (53d)$$

and obtain

$$Ve = h\nu_{max} \qquad (53e)$$

While Eq.(53d) must be replaced by the rela-

tivistic equation, Eq.(59b), when voltages are greater than 20,000 V, Eq.(53e) holds true for all voltages.*

* For a more complete treatment of X rays, see A. H. Compton and S. K. Allison, *X-Rays in Theory and Experiment* (D. Van Nostrand Co., Inc., Princeton, New Jersey, 1935).

QUESTIONS AND PROBLEMS

1. What contribution did Coolidge make to the design and construction of X-ray tubes?

2. What are hard X rays? What are soft X rays? How is hardness or softness related to X-ray wavelengths?

3. How is X-ray absorption related to the periodic table of elements?

4. Which of the following materials is the best absorber of X rays: (a) beryllium, (b) magnesium, (c) calcium, (d) copper, (e) gold, (f) lead, or (g) uranium?

5. What is the process of ionization by X rays? What happens to the liberated free electrons?

6. Why does the skin show so clearly in the X-ray photograph in Fig. 53D(b)?

7. If a small child swallowed a safety pin, why would an X-ray photograph clearly show the location of the pin?

8. How is the penetrating power of X rays related to the voltage applied to the tube?

9. Briefly explain why an X-ray photograph of the hand shows the bones more clearly than the flesh surrounding them.

10. An X-ray photograph of a closed leather purse will easily show silver coins or other metal articles inside. Explain.

11. How and by whom where X rays discovered?

12. Diagram a modern X-ray tube of the type developed by Coolidge.

13. X rays sent through a Bragg crystal spectrometer using a rock salt crystal are reflected at an angle of 14°. What is the wavelength of the X rays?

14. X rays sent through a Bragg crystal spectrometer show three spectrum lines at 4.28°, 5.92°, and 7.56°, respectively. If the crystal used is rock salt, what are the wavelengths of the X rays? [*Ans.* 0.420 Å, 0.582 Å, 0.740 Å.]

15. X rays of wavelength 1.60×10^{-8} cm are diffracted by a Bragg crystal spectrograph at an angle of 12.8°. Find the effective spacing of the atomic layers in the crystal.

16. X rays having a wavelength of 0.36×10^{-8} cm are diffracted at an angle of 4.8° in a Bragg crystal spectrograph. Find the effective spacing of the atomic layers in the crystal. [*Ans.* 2.15 Å.]

17. When a nickel target is used in an X-ray tube, the two shortest wavelengths emitted are found with a Bragg crystal spectrograph to be diffracted at angles of 8.6° and 12.7°, respectively. Find their wavelengths. Assume a crystal spacing of 2.81×10^{-8} cm.

18. When a tungsten target is used in an X-ray tube, the two shortest wavelengths emitted are found with a Bragg crystal spectrograph to be diffracted at angles of 2° 47' and 3° 16', respectively. Find their wavelengths. Assume a crystal spacing of 2.81×10^{-8} cm. [*Ans.* 0.273 A and 0.320 A.]

ELECTROMAGNETIC WAVES
AND VACUUM TUBES

There is little doubt that *radio, radar,* and *television* are among the greatest miracles of modern science. Traveling with the speed of light, code signals, the human voice, and music can be heard around the world within the very second they are produced in the broadcasting studio. Through television, world events can be observed in full color at the same moment they occur hundreds and even thousands of miles away.

The more we learn of the fundamental principles of radio and its operation, the more amazing does their reality become. It is the purpose of this chapter to introduce some of the earlier fundamental principles of wireless telegraphy in the approximate chronological order in which they were discovered and developed, and in so doing to gain some familiarity with *electromagnetic waves.*

54.1. The Leyden Jar. A cross section of a "Leyden jar" of the type invented by the Dutch scientist Musschenbroek in 1746 is shown in Fig. 54A. Two metallic conductors forming the plates of a capacitor are separated by a glass bottle as a dielectric insulator. When such a capacitor is connected to a source of high potential, one plate will become positively charged and the other will be negative. If the source voltage is high enough, an electric spark will jump between the terminals indicating a sudden discharge of the capacitor, and an electron current will surge first one way and then the other around the circuit.

This oscillatory current was first postulated by Joseph Henry, then derived from theory by Lord Kelvin, and later proven experimentally by Fedderson. Fedderson, looking at a capacitor discharge with a rotating mirror, observed that each initial breakdown spark was followed by a succession of fainter sparks. The initial spark ionizes

Fig. 54A   *The discharge of a Leyden jar is oscillatory.*

the air, making of it a good conductor and, of the entire system ABCDEFGA, a complete electrical circuit.

54.2. The Oscillatory Circuit. The Leyden jar circuit in Fig. 54A contains, in addition to a *capacitance,* an *inductance* as well. The single loop FGABCD and E forms practically one turn of a coil. An inductance and capacitance, connected as shown in simplest schematic form in Fig. 54B, form the necessary elements of all oscillating circuits.

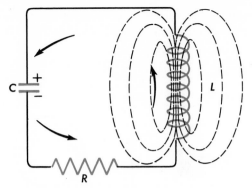

Fig. 54B *Schematic diagram of an oscillating circuit.*

If, initially, the capacitance is charged as indicated, the surplus electrons on the plate below cause a surge of negative charge counterclockwise around the circuit to neutralize the positives and, in so doing, set up a magnetic field in and around the inductance. When the positives become neutralized and the electron current tends to cease, the magnetic flux linking the circuit decreases and keeps the current flowing in the same direction. Once this field has vanished and the current has ceased, the capacitance is found to be in a charged condition, the upper plate negative and the lower plate positive.

Having reversed the charge on the capacitance, the above process will repeat itself, this time the electron current surging clockwise around the circuit. Thus the current rushes first in one direction, then the other, oscillating back and forth in an electrical way just as any spring pulled to

Fig. 54C *A vibrating spring is like an electrical oscillating circuit.*

one side and released vibrates in a mechanical way (see Fig. 54C).

When a straight spring is pulled to one side and released, the kinetic energy it gains upon straightening keeps the spring moving, and it bends to the other side. Just as the vibration amplitude of the spring slowly decreases because of *friction*, so also does the current in the electrical circuit decrease because of *electrical resistance*. A graph showing how current slowly dies out in an electric circuit is given in Fig. 54D.

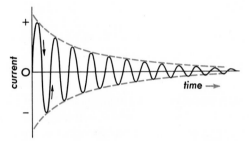

Fig. 54D *Graph of the damped oscillations of an electrical circuit.*

These are called *damped vibrations*, or *damped oscillations*. If the resistance of the circuit is high, the damping is high and the current quickly dies out after only a few oscillations. If the resistance is low, however, the damping is small the amplitude decreases slowly, and there are many oscillations.

To calculate the frequency of an oscillating circuit, either of the following formulas may be used:

$$T = 2\pi\sqrt{LC}$$

$$\nu = \frac{1}{2\pi\sqrt{LC}} \qquad (54a)$$

where L is the inductance in henries, C is the capacitance in farads, T is the time for one complete oscillation in seconds, and ν is the number of oscillations per second. T is the period and ν the frequency. The formula above is to be compared with the analogous formula for the period of a vibrating spring:

$$T = 2\pi\sqrt{m/k} \qquad (54b)$$

The mass m for the spring is analogous to the

inductance L for the circuit, and the stiffness $1/k$ is analogous to the capacitance C. An increase of the inductance L, or capacitance C, or both, increases the period and decreases the frequency of the oscillating circuit.

Example 1. A Leyden jar with a small capacitance of 0.01 μF is connected to a single turn of wire (about 6 in. in diameter) having an inductance of 1 μH. Calculate the natural frequency of the circuit.

Solution. Since 1 henry = 10^6 microhenries and 1 farad = 10^6 microfarads, direct substitution for L and C in Eq.(54a) gives

$$\nu = \frac{1}{2\pi\sqrt{LC}} = \frac{1}{2\pi\sqrt{1 \times 10^{-6}\,H \times 1 \times 10^{-8}\,F}}$$

$$= 1,590,000 \text{ c/s}$$
or
$$1.59 \text{ Mc/s}$$

54.3. Maxwell's Electromagnetic Wave Theory. In 1856 James Clerk Maxwell wrote his now famous theoretical paper on electromagnetic waves. In this scientific publication, he proposed the possible existence of electromagnetic waves and at the same time postulated that if such waves could ever be produced, they would travel through free space with the speed of light.

Light itself, said Maxwell, is propagated as an electromagnetic wave, and electrically produced waves should differ from light only in their wavelength and frequency. Because Maxwell gave no clues as to how such waves might be generated or detected, their real existence was not discovered until 32 years later when Heinrich Hertz made his important discovery.

54.4. Hertzian Waves. In 1888, a young German scientist, Heinrich Hertz,* began a series of experiments in which he not only produced and detected electromagnetic waves, but also demonstrated their properties of reflection, re-

* Heinrich Rudolf Hertz (1857–1894), German physicist born at Hamburg, February 22, 1857. He studied physics under Helmholtz in Berlin, at whose suggestion he first became interested in Maxwell's electromagnetic theory. His researches with electromagnetic waves which made his name famous were carried out at Karlsruhe Polytechnic between 1885 and 1889. As professor of physics at the University of Bonn, after 1889, he experimented with electrical discharges through gases and narrowly missed the discovery of X rays described by Röntgen a few years later. By his premature death, science lost one of its most promising disciples.

fraction, and interference. One of his experimental arrangements is diagramed in Fig. 54E.

Fig. 54E *Schematic diagram of the apparatus with which Hertz produced and detected the first radio waves.*

The transmitter consists of two spheres QQ' located near the ends of two straight rods MN separated by a spark gap S. With the two rods connected to an induction coil I, sparks jump across the gap S, giving rise to oscillating currents in MN. That such a generator is an oscillating circuit can be seen from the fact that the spheres QQ' form the plates of a capacitor and the rods form the inductance.

The receiver, or detector, consists of a single loop of wire with a tiny spark gap at R. This circuit, too, is an oscillating circuit with the spark gap as a capacitance and the loop as an inductance. Tuning the transmitter frequency to that of the receiver is accomplished by sliding the spheres QQ' along the rods MN, resonance being indicated by the appearance of sparks at R.

With apparatus of this general type, Hertz was able to transmit signals a distance of several hundred feet. He found that large metal plates would reflect the radiation, and that at normal incidence the reflected waves would interfere with those coming up to set up standing waves with nodes and loops. As the receiver was moved slowly away from the reflector, nodes and loops were located by the appearance of sparks only at equally spaced intervals.

With a large prism of paraffin he demonstrated refraction, and with a lens made of pitch he focused the waves as a glass lens focuses visible light.

54.5. Electromagnetic Waves. To visualize the production of waves by a Hertzian oscillator, consider the schematic diagram in Fig. 54F. Let

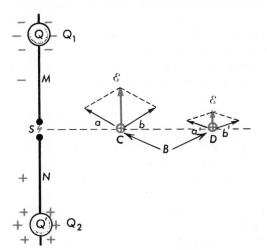

Fig. 54F   *A Hertzian dipole.*

the rods MN and spheres Q and Q' be charged initially as indicated, and consider the electrostatic action of the charges on a small charge C located some distance away. The negative charge Q_1 attracts C with a force a and the positive charge Q_2 repels it with a force b. Since by symmetry these two forces are of equal magnitude, their resultant Cε is parallel to MN. If the isolated charge is farther away as at D, the resultant force is also parallel to MN, but weaker. In other words, the electric field ε at points C and D is up and parallel to MN, decreasing in intensity as the distance from the transmitter increases.

Suppose that a spark jumps the gap S and oscillation sets in. One-half cycle after the condition shown in Fig. 54F, electrons have surged across the gap, charging Q positively and Q' negatively. With reversed charges the resultant force on C and D will be down instead of up. Thus it is seen how oscillations in the transmitter, which constitute a surging of electrons back and forth between M and N, give rise to a periodically reversing electric field at distant points.

In addition to an electric field at C and D, the surging electrons in MN give rise to a magnetic

field as well. When the electron current is down (using the conventional left-hand rule), the magnetic induction B at C or D is perpendicular to and into the plane of the page, and when the electron current is up the magnetic induction is out from the page. The surging of the charges therefore gives rise to a periodically reversing magnetic induction, the direction of which is at right angles to the electric intensity at the same points.

According to Maxwell's theory, the ε and B fields do not appear instantly at distant points; time is required for their propagation. The speed of propagation, according to Maxwell (and this has been confirmed by numerous experiments) is the same as the speed of light. The changing ε and B fields at C therefore lag behind the oscillating charges in MN, and those at D lag behind still farther.

Figure 54G is a graph of the instantaneous

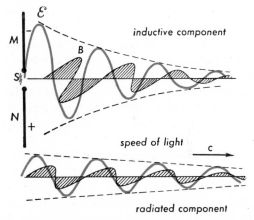

Fig. 54G   *Graph of the electromagnetic waves emitted by a Hertzian dipole.*

values of the electric and magnetic fields as they vary with distance from the transmitter. At certain points the fields are a maximum and at other points they are zero. As time goes on, these electric and magnetic waves move away from the transmitter with a speed of 186,300 mi/s.

The mathematical theory of electromagnetic radiations shows that, close to the transmitter, the ε and B fields, called the *inductive components*, are 90° out of phase and that their magnitudes fall off very rapidly with distance. Farther out, however, the two get in step with each other and their amplitudes fall off more slowly, as shown in the diagram. The latter are called the *radiated components* and are the ones detected at great distances.

Suppose now that a series of sparks is made to occur in the gap S of a transmitter as in Fig. 54H. Each spark will give rise to a damped oscil-

Fig. 54H *Damped electromagnetic waves from a Hertzian oscillator.*

lation in MN which in turn sends out a damped electromagnetic wave. The succession of sparks sends out a train of such waves which, as they leave the antenna, decrease rapidly in magnitude at first, then more slowly as they get farther away. Only the electric component of such waves is shown in the diagram.

If an electrical conductor is located at some distant point, the free electrons within it will, as such waves go by, experience up and down forces tending to set them in oscillation. If the conductor is an oscillating circuit whose natural frequency is that of the passing waves, resonance will occur and large currents will be set up.

54.6. Air-Core Inductances and Transformers. When a high-frequency alternating current is sent through a solenoid with an iron core or the primary of an iron-core transformer, the back emf is so large that the current as well as the magnetic induction cannot build up to any appreciable value before it reverses in direction. The result is that in one ten-thousandth of a second or less the current hardly gets started in one direction before it stops and reverses.

In an iron-core transformer the back emf in the primary winding so retards the building up of strong fields that little or no induced currents can be "drawn" from the secondary. To overcome this difficulty, the iron core is done away with, so that we have what is called an *air-core transformer*. In the absence of any iron, the current in the coil may rise to an appreciable value

each time it changes in direction. The rapidly increasing and diminishing flux that links both circuits induces a current in the secondary of exactly the same frequency.

Air-core transformers, consisting of nothing more than two coils of a few turns each, a primary winding and a secondary winding, are used extensively in radio, microwave, and television transmitters and receivers. In these instances the alternating currents with frequencies of thousands and even millions of cycles per second are usually referred to as *radiofrequencies*, and the transformers are referred to as *radiofrequency transformers*.

54.7. The Vacuum-Tube Rectifier. While the great American inventor Thomas A. Edison was striving by a process of trial and error to produce a satisfactory electric light bulb, he made an accidental discovery, the importance of which was first recognized and used successfully by Sir John Fleming. Now called a vacuum-tube rectifier or diode, the Fleming valve is used in nearly every radio and television transmitter and receiver to change alternating current into direct current.

The Fleming valve, as shown in Fig. 54I, consists of a highly evacuated glass bulb containing a wire filament that is heated electrically to in-

Fig. 54I *Diagram of a Fleming valve, or rectifier tube. Such tubes are now called diodes.*

candescence. Surrounding the filament and connected to the outside through the tube base and a prong P_1 is a cylindrical metal plate P. When the filament is heated to incandescence, it gives off large quantities of electrons in much the same way that water, when heated to the boiling point, gives off steam. The emission of electrons by a hot body is called *thermionic emission* and is due to the high temperature and not to the electric current. Heating a metal by any other means will produce the same effect. Electrons emitted from hot metal surfaces are called *thermoelectrons*.

The principal action of the *filament* F and *plate* P is explained by means of a typical electric circuit shown schematically in Fig. 54J. The circuit

Fig. 54J *Circuit diagram of a Fleming valve rectifier.*

consists of a *transformer* having *two secondary windings*, a *Fleming valve*, and a *load*. The latter, shown as a resistance, represents any electrical device requiring unidirectional current for its operation. With an alternating current of 110 V supplied to the primary, a high voltage, 240 V for example, is delivered by one secondary to the terminals ED and a low voltage of 6 V alternating current is delivered by the other secondary to

the terminals CH. The latter, called the *filament winding*, is for the purpose of heating the filament.

When for a fraction of a second the plate P of the tube is positively charged and the filament F is negatively charged, the electrons from F are attracted to the plate P and constitute a current flowing across the vacuum space PF and through the load from B to A. One-half cycle later, when the potential is reversed and P becomes negatively charged and F positively charged, the electrons from F are repelled by P and very little current flows.

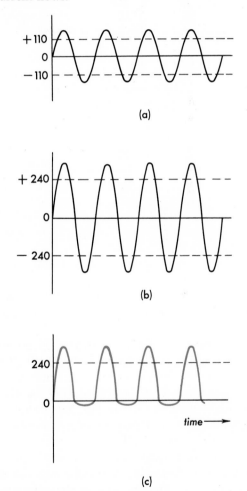

Fig. 54K *Alternating current as rectified by a Fleming valve or diode.*

The emf's in each part of the rectifier circuit are shown by graphs in Fig. 54K. The primary emf of 110 V is shown in (a), the secondary emf of 240 V in (b), and the *rectified* or *pulsating emf* through the load AB in (c).

54.8. Full-Wave Rectifier. A full-wave rectifier tube, sometimes called a *duo-diode*, is essentially a double Fleming valve with two plates and two filaments (see Fig. 54L). The two prongs F_1 and

Fig. 54L *Drawing of a full-wave rectifier tube.*

F_2 in the base are connected to both filaments in series, while the prongs P_1 and P_2 are connected one to each plate.

A schematic diagram of a rectifier circuit employing such a tube is shown in Fig. 54M. Here an iron-core transformer with one primary and two secondary windings is used, differing from the single-phase rectifier in Fig. 54J in that the center of each secondary winding is now connected to the load. CHJ is the filament winding and supplies current to both filaments (shown as one bent wire) while GED is the high-voltage winding. The latter supplies an alternating potential to the plates so that, when P_1 is $+$ and P_2 is $-$, electrons from the filament are attracted to P_1, and, when a moment later P_1 is $-$ and P_2 is $+$, electrons from the filament are attracted to P_2.

Fig. 54M *Diagram for a full-wave rectifier circuit.*

In the first instance a current flows around the circuit $F_1P_1GEABHJF_1$, and in the second it flows around the circuit $F_2P_2DEABHCF_2$. In each case the current has gone through the load AB in the same direction and has pulsating characteristics as shown in Fig. 54N.

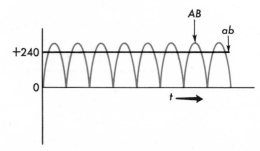

Fig. 54N *Rectified voltage from a full-wave rectifier circuit.*

If such a pulsating current were used to supply the direct current needed in every radio receiver, a loud objectionable hum with a frequency of 120 cycles would be heard. To make this current a steady smooth direct current, as illustrated by the straight line in the same graph, and thus eliminate the hum, a *filter circuit* as shown in

Fig. 54O is used. The terminals A and B are connected to, and replace, the load A and B in Fig. 54M. K is an iron-core inductance and C_1 and C are capacitors of large capacity.

Fig. 54O   *Electrical filter circuit for "smoothing out" pulsating direct current.*

As the current through AabB starts to flow, the capacitors become charged, as shown, and a magnetic field is created around K. This has a retarding action which prevents the current from reaching its otherwise peak value. When a moment later the filament-to-plate current drops to near zero, the capacitors discharge and the field around K collapses, thus sending a current through AB. This process is repeated with each pulse of electrons from either plate of the tube, and the current through ab remains steady. Large capacities and large self-inductances deliver more constant voltage.

54.9. Modern Vacuum Tubes. Every radio enthusiast today knows that there are hundreds of different kinds of radio tubes. Some contain two filaments and two plates, while others contain as many as three or four separate grids. Although a treatment of such complex tubes is out of place here, the fundamental principles of all of them are little different from De Forest's audion. One important difference, however, is illustrated in Fig. 54P, and that is the employment in most tubes of a cathode in place of a filament as a source of thermal electrons.

A fine tungsten-wire filament is threaded through two small holes running lengthwise through a porcelain-like insulating rod. Fitting snugly around this rod is the cathode, a metal cylinder coated on the outside with a thin layer of thorium, strontium, or cesium oxide. These particular oxides are copious emitters of elec-

Fig. 54P   *A modern radio tube with a cesium-coated cathode as a source of thermal electrons. The filament serves only to heat the cathode.*

trons when heated to a dull-red heat. Insulated from the cathode, the filament as a source of heat can be, and generally is, connected directly to an appropriate transformer winding.

54.10. Vacuum-Tube Oscillator. To broadcast the human voice by radio, a generator of alternating current of extremely high frequency and constant amplitude is required. In commercial broadcasting stations and amateur transmitters, this function is performed by a vacuum tube and circuit of relatively simple design.

One type of oscillator circuit is shown in Fig. 54Q. When the switch S is closed, connecting the B battery to the plate of the tube, an electron current from the cathode K to the plate P starts a current in the circuit $PRVL_3K$. This growing current in L_3 creates an expanding magnetic field, which, cutting across L_2, induces a current in the grid circuit in such a direction that the grid becomes negative. A negative charge on the grid, causes the plate current to decrease. This decreasing current causes the field about L_3 to col-

Fig. 54Q   *Vacuum-tube oscillator circuit for generating radio waves of constant amplitude.*

Fig. 54S   *Amplifier circuit with one vacuum tube.*

lapse, thus inducting a reversed current in the grid circuit and therefore a positive charge on the grid. Such a charge increases the plate current, and the above process is repeated.

If the two circuits, L_2C_2 and $PRVL_3$, are properly tuned by adjusting C_2, resonance will occur and energy from the B battery will be continuously supplied to keep the oscillations going with constant amplitude. The graph of the continuous oscillations shown in Fig. 54R represents

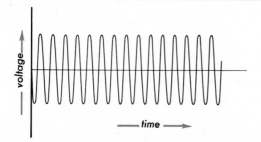

Fig. 54R   *Continuous oscillations in a vacuum-tube oscillator circuit like that shown in Fig. 54Q.*

the voltage across L_3 as it varies in time. The L_2C_2 circuit controls the frequency by controlling the grid potential while the large voltage and current fluctuations take place in the L_3 circuit.

54.11. Vacuum-Tube Amplifier. One of the most important functions of the vacuum tube is its use as an *amplifier* of radiofrequency or audiofrequency currents, as shown in Fig. 54S. The *input* resistor represents some part of any circuit in which a weak but varying current is flowing; the *output* resistor represents another circuit to which a stronger current of the same form is delivered. In some cases these are resistors as

shown, but in others they are the primary and secondary windings of separate transformers. The source of the additional energy is the B battery plate supply.

In amplifying any given signal current, a faithful reproduction of the *wave form* must be carried out, otherwise *distortion* will result; musical sounds from a radio will be harsh or pictures from a television receiver will be blurred. To amplify without distortion, a tube that has a long straight section in its *characteristic curve* must be used, and it should be operated at the center of this straight portion. Such an operation is shown by the graph in Fig. 54T.

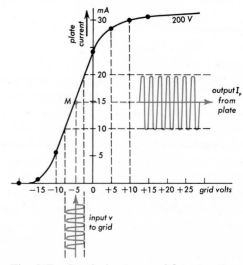

Fig. 54T   *Graph showing amplifier operation.*

To make the tube operate at M, a small battery, called a C battery or C bias, is inserted in the grid circuit to maintain the grid at a negative potential. For the curve and tube shown, this requires -5 V, while for other types of tubes it might well require greater or smaller potentials.

When no input signal potentials are imposed, the grid is held at -5 V and a steady current of 150 mA flows through the plate and output circuit. If now an alternating current like a radio frequency of constant amplitude is impressed across the input terminals, the grid potential will rise and fall in the same way, and an undistorted but amplified current will flow in the plate and output circuit. The time variations in grid potential are shown at the bottom in Fig. 54T,

and the corresponding plate current oscillations at the right. If the input radio frequency is voice-modulated, the amplified current will also be voice-modulated without distortion. It should be noted that if the impressed grid voltage variations are too large, say -20 to $+10$ V, the amplified currents will reach the curved portions of the curve above and below, and *distortion* of the *wave form* will result. As long as the tube is operated on the straight portion of the curve, the plate current is directly proportional to the impressed grid potential, and faithful amplification takes place.

QUESTIONS

1. What is an oscillatory circuit? What are its three principal elements?

2. Upon what does the natural frequency of a circuit depend? What is the formula for the frequency?

3. What is electrical resonance? Under what conditions does it arise?

4. What are Hertzian waves? What is a Hertzian dipole?

5. What are electromagnetic waves? What is their nature? With what speed do they travel?

6. What are damped oscillations? How can damping be reduced?

7. Draw from memory a schematic wiring diagram of a full-wave rectifier showing the vacuum tube, transformer, and load.

8. Make a schematic diagram of a full-wave rectifier and filter circuit consisting of a transformer, vacuum tube, inductance, two capacitors, and a load.

9. Diagram the circuit of a vacuum-tube oscillator for generating high radio frequencies of constant amplitude.

10. Draw from memory an amplifier circuit with one vacuum tube.

PROBLEMS

1. Calculate the frequency and period of an oscillating circuit containing one 4-μF capacitor and an inductance of 3.6 μH if both are connected in parallel.

2. What inductance connected to a capacitor of 0.05 μF will give the circuit a natural frequency of 6 Mc/s? [*Ans.* 0.0141 μH.]

3. What capacitance, if connected in parallel to an inductance of 8 μH, will give an oscillating circuit a frequency of 400 Kc/s?

4. Determine the frequency of an oscillating circuit composed of two capacitors and one inductor, all connected in parallel: $C_1 = 5$ μF, $C_2 = 25$ μF, and $L = 10$ μH. [*Ans.* 9.19 Kc/s.]

5. Two capacitors of 40 μF each are first connected in series and then the combination is connected across an inductor of 5 μH. Calculate the period of the oscillating circuit.

6. Calculate all of the possible frequencies that can be obtained by combining two or more of the following to form an oscillating circuit. $C_1 = 2$ μF, $C_2 = 4$ μF, $L = 8$ μH. [*Ans.* 39.8, 28.1, 23.0, 48.6 Kc/s.]

7. A 5 mH inductor is connected in parallel with a 12-μF capacitor. What is the natural frequency of this circuit?

8. A 60-μH inductor is connected across a 75-μF capacitor. What is the frequency of the fifth harmonic of the oscillating circuit thus formed? [*Ans.* 11.86 Kc/s.]

9. What capacitance connected in parallel to an inductance of 0.4 μH will produce an oscillating circuit with a fundamental frequency of 5 Mc/s?

10. What inductance connected in parallel to a capacitance of 20 μF will produce an oscillating circuit with a fundamental frequency of 30 Kc/s? [*Ans.* 1.41 μH.]

11. Calculate the frequency of an oscillating circuit composed of a 5-μF capacitor and a 5-μH inductor.

12. What capacitance in parallel with an inductance of 0.1 μH will have a frequency of 1 Mc/s? [*Ans.* 0.253 μF.]

13. A capacitance of 0.08 μF is connected to an inductance of 12×10^{-8} H. Find (a) the frequency and (b) the wavelength of the electromagnetic waves emitted.

14. What capacitance should be used with an inductance of 0.09 μH to produce electromagnetic waves having a wavelength of 10 cm? [*Ans.* 0.0313 $\mu\mu$F.]

15. What inductance should be used with a capacitance of 0.05 μF to produce electromagnetic waves of wavelength 40 cm?

THE SOLID STATE
AND SEMICONDUCTORS

One of the most active and important branches of science and technology today is called *solid state physics*. This is a field of research concerned with a study of the physical properties of solids, and includes such subjects as the detailed configurations of atoms in solids, the behavior of free and bound electrons in a crystal lattice, the electrical conductivity of pure substances and those containing impurities, the magnetic and mechanical properties of solids at low and high temperatures. Since solid state physics has grown to such huge proportions (and so has the number of people active in the field) only a small part of the subject will be given in this chapter.

55.1. Conductors and Nonconductors. The crystal structure of the common highly conducting metals, like copper, silver, gold, and platinum, is such that the outermost electrons are shared by all the atoms. The complete inner shells of electrons are bound to their individual nucleus, but the outermost electrons in uncompleted shells, the so-called *valence electrons*, are free to wander throughout the substance. This diffusion of electrons is similar to the random motion of molecules in a gas.

In contrast with *good conductors* there are *good insulators*, called *nonconductors*, which have practically no free electrons. In substances like quartz, mica, and sulfur, all of the electrons remain bound to their respective atoms. The resistivity of a good conductor is as low as 10^{-7} or 10^{-8} ohm-meters, compared to values as high as 10^{16} ohm-meters for an insulator like quartz.

55.2. Semiconductors. There are a large number of solids that are neither good conductors of electricity nor good insulators. Since the resistance range between these two groups of materials is about 10^{23}, a majority of known substances lie in between. These substances are called *semiconductors*. In them, electrons are capable of being moved only by the application of relatively strong electric fields of hundreds of thousands of volts per meter.

Of the large number of semiconductors known to science, certain ones are of considerable importance. Typical examples are the crystalline forms of the elements listed in the fourth column of the periodic table (see Appendix X). Two important ones are *silicon* and *germanium*.

Figure 55A is a diagram of a small germanium

Fig. 55A *Circuit diagram for demonstrating the photoconductivity of a semiconductor like germanium or silicon.*

crystal about 5 mm square and 2 cm long, connected to a battery and a milliammeter by wires, and completing an electric circuit. When light is allowed to fall on the crystal, its electrical resistance decreases and the current rises. This response to light is instantaneous and is called *photoconductivity*.

If the germanium crystal is heated, the current again rises, indicating a decrease in electrical resistance. This *heating effect* is not instantaneous, however, since it takes a long time for the current to return to its original value, that is, for the temperature of the crystal to return to room temperature. The resistance of metallic conductors behaves in just the opposite way; their resistance increases with a rise in temperature.

In order to explain the light and heat effects described above, we must refer to the crystal lattice of semiconductors. Silicon and germanium atoms each have what the chemists call four *valence electrons*, that is, four electrons that enter into the chemical binding in solids. The atomic pattern of atoms in both crystals is a tetrahedral structure, as shown in Fig. 47M. In Fig. 55B it will be seen that each atom shares

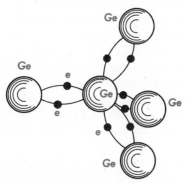

Fig. 55B *Each atom in a germanium crystal is bound at the center of a tetrahedron formed by its four nearest neighbors.*

one of its electrons with each neighbor, and the neighbor in turn shares one of its four with it. Such a sharing of electrons between two atoms is called a *covalent bond.*

Because of the difficulty of drawing a three-dimensional tetrahedral lattice structure, it is convenient to flatten the diagram out and represent the bonding as a square lattice, as shown in Fig. 55C.

At temperatures close to absolute zero, all electrons in a crystal are tied up strongly by these chemical bonds. When the crystal is raised to room temperature, however, the thermal vibra-

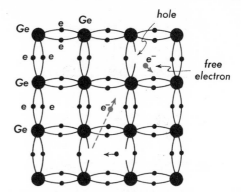

Fig. 55C *Schematic diagram of the covalent bonding of atoms in a germanium crystal. Thermal agitation breaks some bonds and liberates electrons.*

tions of the atoms are sufficient to break some of the bonds and free some of the electrons to wander throughout the crystal. Where an electron has broken free, as shown at the upper right and lower left in Fig. 55C, a hole has been created and the process is referred to as *dissociation.* Since that part of the crystal was neutral beforehand, it now lacks an electron, and the vacant hole is equivalent to a net positive charge.

Owing also to thermal agitation, a *bound* electron next to a hole can move across to fill the gap, the net motion of the negative charge from one bonded position to another being in effect equivalent to the motion of a hole in the opposite direction. The motion of a hole is, therefore, equivalent to the motion of a positive charge. This action is shown at the lower center in Fig. 55C.

55.3. N-Type and P-Type Crystals. The widespread use of semiconductors in such devices as solar cells and transistors has resulted from the technical development of pure semiconductor crystals impregnated with minute quantities of certain impurities. The crystals most commonly used for these purposes are those mentioned in the preceding section, *silicon* and *germanium.*

If crystals are formed with *arsenic* as an impurity, the arsenic atoms, with five valence electrons each, provide a crystal lattice with extra electrons. Such a crystal as shown in Fig. 55D is therefore one in which each arsenic atom donates one free electron to the system. With arsenic present in quantities of one to a million, *donor*

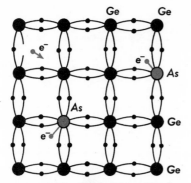

Fig. 55D   *N-type crystal lattice with arsenic atoms as an impurity.*

atoms are on the average about 100 atoms apart, or there are about 10^{17} arsenic atoms and 10^{17} free electrons per cubic centimeter. In a good conductor like copper there are approximately 10^{23} free electrons per cm³.

By thermal agitation a few bound electrons are also "shaken loose" and an equal number of holes thereby created. The ratio of the number of *donor electrons* to the number of unbound electrons or *holes* is approximately 10,000 to 1. Since by far the majority of free-to-move charge carriers are electrons, the lattice is called an *N-type crystal*.

If crystals are grown with *aluminum* as an impurity, the aluminum atoms, with only three valence electrons each, form a crystal lattice with an electron deficiency, that is, with holes (see Fig. 55E). Such a crystal is therefore one in which each aluminum atom provides one hole to the system that is free to accept an electron.

By thermal agitation a few bound electrons are

also shaken loose and an equal number of holes are produced. Since by far the majority of the charge carriers are holes, and these act like positive charges, this type of lattice is called a *P-type crystal.*

Since the donor electrons in an N-type crystal, and the holes in a P-type crystal, far outnumber the electrons or holes contributed by thermal agitation, the donor charges are called *majority carriers*, and those caused by dissociation are called *minority carriers.*

Neither of these crystals, by itself, has a net charge. The surplus of free negatives in an N-type crystal is compensated for by the positive charges on the arsenic nuclei, while the surplus of holes in the P-type crystal is compensated for by the deficiency in positive nuclear charge of the aluminum nuclei.

When light falls on a crystal as in Fig. 55A, the light is absorbed within a few atomic layers. The absorbed energy breaks some of the electron bonds and creates holes. This process is called *photoionization*. The potentials applied at the ends of the crystal cause the electrons to move to the left, and the holes to the right, This flow of charge constitutes a current.

When the light is shut off, free electrons fall at random into holes as the crystal cools. The falling of an electron into a hole is called *recombination*.

55.4. The PN Junction, or Diode. When two semiconductors of the P and N types are brought into contact, as shown in Fig. 55F, they form what is called a *PN junction*, or *diode*. In the

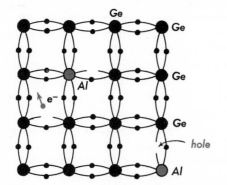

Fig. 55E   *P-type crystal lattice with aluminnm atoms as an impurity.*

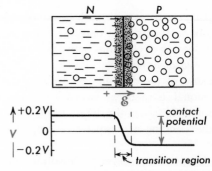

Fig. 55F   *When P and N crystals are brought into contact, a difference of potential called the contact potential is set up between them.*

region of contact, a cloud of free electrons in the N crystal diffuse across the boundary to the right, much the same as gas atoms diffuse through a porous ceramic material.

Since electrons leave the N crystal, that side of the junction acquires a positive potential, while the P crystal gains electrons and acquires a negative potential. As this diffusion of electrons continues, the potential difference between the two sides rises. The filling of holes in the P crystal gives rise to more holes developing in the N crystal, and this action is the same as though holes had diffused across the boundary to the left.

As the N crystal becomes more positive, and the P crystal more negative, electrons will be attracted back toward the left, and an equilibrium condition will develop in which equal numbers of electrons will be crossing the boundary in opposite directions.

The electrostatic potential of different points across the crystal boundary under equilibrium conditions, as just outlined, is shown graphically below the PN junction in Fig. 55F. Notice that the sudden drop of the potential in the region of the junction gives rise to a large electric field ε.

Although various methods for producing diodes have been developed commercially, some mixing of the two semiconductor materials is purposely brought about at the junction. This area of mixing, called the *transition region*, accounts for the smooth way in which the potential curve changes from point to point through this region.

For a typical PN junction the transition region is about 6×10^{-5} mm thick, and the potential difference, called the *contact potential*, may have any value from a small fraction of a volt to 1 or 2 V depending on the two materials in contact. These values indicate an electric field ε of several million volts per meter. This is called the *diffusion field* ε, shown in green at the center of the diagram.

If we now fuse metal plates to the ends of a PN junction and connect them to a milliammeter, the device becomes effective as a solar battery or cell (see Fig. 55G). When the entire crystal is maintained at a constant temperature in a darkened room, no current will be observed through the milliammeter. The reason for this is that

Fig. 55G (a) *PN junction used as a solar battery cell.* (b) *Potential graph when cell is in the dark, and* (c) *when it is in light.*

reverse contact potentials, due to electron diffusion, are set up between the crystal ends and the metallic electrodes, so that no potential difference exists between E and C [see diagram (b)].

If we now shine light on the PN junction, the light is absorbed, freeing additional electrons and creating holes. By virtue of the strong electric field ε in the transition region, electrons now move to the left and holes to the right, and we have a current. Such a current is readily measured by a milliammeter.

The drift of electrons to the left lowers its potential while available free holes move to the right and raise its potential. The lead connections have not changed their contact potentials; so we now have a net useful potential difference as shown in diagram (c). Acting as the terminals of a battery cell the end plates send an electron current I through the external circuit.

Since the useful ionization process arising from the absorption of light occurs only in the surface layers of atoms, solar batteries are made with very thin crystals deposited on some insulating material which serves as a rigid backing.

The electrostatic potential graphs in diagrams (b) and (c) are drawn assuming 0.15-V contact potentials at the ends. These are typical but their values will depend upon what metals are used.

55.5. PN-Junction, or Diode, Rectifier. When a PN junction is connected to a battery for the purpose of sending a current through it, there are two ways in which the voltage can be applied. If the P crystal is connected to the positive terminal of the battery as shown in Fig. 55H, elec-

Fig. 55H *Schematic diagram of a PN junction, or diode, with an applied voltage (forward bias). Graphs showing potentials across the junction at different voltages V_{CE}.*

trons will be pulled to the right and holes to the left. Both of these constitute a current. Note carefully that holes are being pulled from where there are lots of holes and electrons from where

there are lots of electrons, and we obtain a large current.

If we reverse the PN junction as in Fig. 55I, we will be trying to pull holes from where there are only a few holes, and electrons from where there are only a few electrons, and experimentally we obtain a relatively small current.

If we now apply different voltages, in turn, across a PN junction and measure the current for each value, we obtain a graph of the type shown in Fig. 55J. This so-called *characteristic*

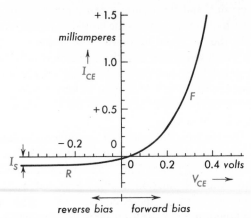

Fig. 55J *Typical characteristic curve for a PN-junction diode.*

curve shows that in one direction the current increases rapidly with small increases in voltage, whereas in the opposite direction the current is small and remains small even for relatively large values.

This is why a PN junction acts like a *rectifier* of alternating currents. When P is positive with respect to N, a large current flows and the junction has what is called a *forward bias*. When P is negative with respect to N, there is a small current and the junction is said to have a *reverse bias*.

With a small forward bias V_{CE} on the PN junction we are operating in the F region of the characteristic curve. Since this applied potential difference is in opposition to the diffusion field potential, the resultant drop in potential across the transition region is flattened out as shown in Fig. 55H(b). As the forward bias is increased, the current rises and the resultant potential curve flattens still more.

With a reverse bias V_{CE} on the PN junction,

we are operating in the R region of the characteristic curve and there is a small current through the transition region. Even though there is a high positive charge on the N-crystal side of the junction, there are so few electrons to pull across the boundary from the P crystal that saturation is produced by a relatively small reverse bias. Reverse-bias potentials of many volts cannot increase this current and it will remain constant.

55.6. Transistor Triode. A transistor is composed of three semiconductor elements, two of the N-type crystals and one of the P-type crystals (see Fig. 55K). This combination is referred to as an *NPN-type transistor*. We can also have a *PNP-type transistor*.

Suppose we now apply a potential difference V_{BE} across the first junction of the NPN transistor and a potential difference V_{CB} across the second junction as shown in the diagram. Because of the reduced electric field across the first junction, electrons from the emitter E move to the right, and the positive holes from the base B move to the left. Operating in the F region of Fig. 55J, a small voltage V_{BE} will give rise to a relatively large current across this junction. With a reverse bias on the second junction, electrons from the P crystal try to move to the right, and holes from the collector C to the left. Operating in the R region of the characteristic curve, little or no transport of charge takes place. Since there are few holes in the collector and few electrons in the base, then an increase of V_{CB} even to a large value will not produce an appreciable current. Because of this blocking action of the second junction a large current will flow between the emitter E and the base B.

Fig. 55K *Schematic diagram of an NPN transistor, or triode, showing typical forward and reverse bias voltages.*

By making the center element of the transistor very thin, as shown in Fig. 55L an important

Fig. 55L *Circuit diagram showing how a transistor or triode is used as a voltage amplifier.*

change takes place. The electrons diffusing across the first junction have little time to find a hole and be neutralized. Most of them are quickly attracted into the collector crystal by the high positive potential.

Because of the high resistance vertically along the thin P crystal, few electrons will get through to the base B. Hence the current across the two junctions is approximately the same.

Since a few electrons do recombine with holes in the center element, however, the current I_C is not quite as large as the current I_E, so that the ratio is slightly less than unity:

$$\frac{I_C}{I_E} = \alpha \qquad (55a)$$

A typical value of α, for a well-designed transistor, would be 0.98, or 98%.

55.7. Transistor Structure. Junction diodes and triodes consist of semiconductors having relatively thin regions of change from N-type material to P-type material. There is a deliberate attempt in the manufacturing process to produce nonuniform distributions of impurities.

The physical structure of one type of NPN transistor is shown in Fig. 55M. From the dimensions given it will first be observed how very small it is. Note secondly how very thin the base region is. In some transistors the base is no more than 10,000 Å thick while the transition region is not over 500 Å. Thin as transition regions are, there are many atomic layers, since interatomic distances are from 2 to 4 Å.

In some manufacturing processes the end crystals, with their metal electrodes already soldered

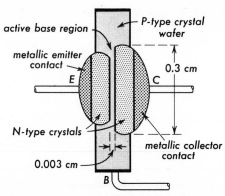

Fig. 55M *Cross-section diagram of an NPN transistor, or triode. The N crystals under pressure and temperature are fused into the P-type crystal wafer.*

or welded on, are heated and fused into the base wafer by pressure.

55.8. Single-Stage Transistor Amplifier. An amplifier circuit using a transistor in place of a vacuum tube is shown in Fig. 55L. Since the current I_C is very nearly equal to the current I_E, little electron current flows through BM. With the input resistance R_E small, and the output resistance R_C large, the nearly equal currents through them signify a small $I_E R_E$ drop across the input and a large $I_C R_C$ drop across the output. Hence, there is a voltage gain and a power gain.

The ratio of the output power $I_C^2 R_C$ to the input power $I_E^2 R_E$ is called the power gain:

$$A = \frac{I_C^2 R_C}{I_E^2 R_E} \qquad (55b)$$

A typical power gain would be $A = 40$. If we now apply a weak alternating current as an input power, the ac output power in the collector circuit could be 40 times larger.

Simple schematic diagrams of transistors, as used in circuit diagrams, are shown in Fig. 55N.

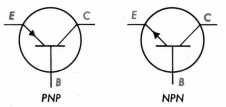

Fig. 55N *Schematic diagrams of transistors. Arrows are opposite to electron flow.*

The arrow is always shown on the emitter lead and its direction indicates the flow of positive current through the emitter material. The arrow therefore distinguishes between NPN and PNP transistors.

The basic principles of a transistor triode are analogous to those of a vacuum-tube triode, the base functioning very much as a control grid. A small alternating voltage is applied between B and E, and an amplified current I_C flows from the collector C.

As an example of the application of a single transistor as a voltage amplifier, consider the circuit diagram in Fig. 55O. This is a diagram of

Fig. 55O *Circuit diagram of a one-way call system employing one transistor.*

a *call system* in which by speaking into the first loud-speaker S_1 the amplified voice can be heard emerging from a distant loud-speaker S_2.

When the switch Sw is closed, an electron current flows from the battery (−), through the switch, up through the NPN transistor and through R_L to the battery (+). The function of R_B is to adjust the voltage across CE so that most of the potential difference is across CB, the collector, and a relatively small voltage is across BE, the emitter (see Fig. 55L). R_B is called the *biasing resistor* and is carefully selected so as to adjust the transistor for maximum amplification.

When the sound vibrations of the voice enter S_1, they set the cone vibrating. In some types of speakers a small coil is mounted on the apex of the cone, and as the coil vibrates back and forth in the strong magnetic field of an alnico permanent magnet, a minute "voice current" is generated. The speaker functions in this way as a microphone.

Since the generated voice current is an alternating current of varying amplitude and frequency, some of it passes through C_1 and is superimposed upon the input direct current to the emitter. Together these two currents constitute a varying dc as an input load.

The amplified signal from the collector circuit is also a varying dc. The dc portion of this current returns through R_L to the battery, while the ac portion passes through C_2 and the speaker where it is converted into sound. Notice that C_1 and C_2 prevent dc battery current from flowing through S_1 and S_2, respectively. R_L limits the amount of direct current through the transistor and is called the *load resistor*.

To understand the basic principles involved in transistor operation, typical characteristic curves for a transistor triode are given in Fig. 55P. The upper set of curves (A) applies to the *output* and

show how the collector current I_C varies with different voltages across CE. The lower curve (B) applies to the *input* and shows how the current I_B into the base varies with different emitter voltages across BE.

As a sample operation we select an NPN triode with the characteristics shown in Fig. 55P, and we choose a battery voltage $V_{CC} = 10$ V. To obtain good amplification it is then good practice to provide the appropriate load resistor R_L so that the voltage across CE is about $\frac{1}{2}V_{CC}$. In this example, therefore, we select $V_{CE} = 5$ V. These two points for V_{CC} and V_{CE} are shown on the horizontal voltage scale in diagram (A).

Upon drawing a vertical line at 5 V, an appropriate base current curve is selected, and the one chosen is $I_B = 0.20$ mA. A straight line is then drawn through P and V_{CC}, as the output current–voltage operating path, and a horizontal line extended from P to establish the corresponding collector current $I_C = 25$ mA.

We can now determine the value of the appropriate load resistor R_L, since the IR drop across it should be approximately 5 V. This leaves the other 5 V for the transistor. Applying Ohm's law, $V = IR$, we can write

$$5 \text{ V} = 25 \text{ mA} \times R_L$$

from which we obtain

$$R_L = 200 \ \Omega$$

A normal biasing resistor R_B of 50 K to 100 K Ω will alter this so little its effect is negligible (see R_2, R_4, and R_8 in Table 55A).

With the selection of $I_B = 0.2$ mA for the input to the base, a horizontal line can be drawn through this point, as shown in diagram (B) of Fig. 55P. Where this line intersects the curve at Q a vertical line is drawn to find $V_{BE} = 0.25$ V.

The values thus far determined are the dc operating voltages and current, and we now apply an alternating potential difference to BE through the capacitor C_1. Suppose this alternating potential has a maximum amplitude of 0.025 V as shown by the double arrow at the bottom in diagram (B). This produces a current swing of I_B from approximately 0.15 mA to 0.25 mA.

Referring these values to the output operating

Fig. 55P   *Characteristic curves for the operation of a typical transistor triode.*

path $\mathrm{P}V_{\mathrm{CC}}$ on the upper graphs, the output current I_{C} swings from 20 mA to 30 mA while V_{CE} swings from 4 V to 6 V.

The reason the output operates along the slanted line $\mathrm{P}V_{\mathrm{CC}}$ may be explained as follows. As an input voltage rises, V_{BE} diagram (B), the

These and internal power losses limit the *power amplification* to approximately 40, as stated by Eq.(55b).

55.9. Three-Stage Transistor Amplifier. A circuit diagram for a three-stage amplifier is shown in Fig. 55Q. This application is called an *inter-*

Fig. 55Q   *Complete circuit diagram of a two-way intercommunication circuit employing three transistors.* (Courtesy, General Electric Co.)

base current I_{B} rises. A rise in I_{B}, diagram (A), causes a rise in collector current I_{C}. This increased current through the load resistor R_{L} produces a bigger IR drop across R_{L} leaving less of the battery voltage V_{CC} across the resistor V_{CE}.

The voltage amplification of a transistor triode can be defined in several ways, but if we take as a definition *the ratio of the output voltage to the input voltage*, we obtain from Fig. 55P

$$A_V = \frac{v_{\mathrm{o}}}{v_{\mathrm{i}}} = \frac{1.0 \text{ V}}{0.025 \text{ V}} = 40$$

The current amplification may be defined as *the ratio of the output current to the input current*. Using the values from Fig. 55P as an example,

$$A_I = \frac{i_{\mathrm{o}}}{i_{\mathrm{i}}} = \frac{5 \text{ mA}}{0.05 \text{ mA}} = 100$$

The transistor is not a source of energy; it simply converts dc energy obtained from the battery to ac energy by the control signal applied at the base. These amplification values just illustrated are theoretical only and are not actually realized in practice. For one thing, the input capacitor C_1 and the output capacitor C_2 limit markedly the input and output frequencies.

communication system, in which each of two identical speakers is used as a microphone or as a loud-speaker. When the reversing switch Sw_2 is in the UP position, speaker S_1 is used as a microphone and S_2 as a loud-speaker, whereas with the switch in the DOWN position their functions are reversed.

The first transistor circuit forms the *input stage* in which the voice current is received from the speaker acting as a microphone. The second transistor circuit forms the *driver stage* because it receives the amplified signal current from the first stage. It is called the driver stage because it "drives" the third stage. This final transistor circuit is the *output stage* which powers the speaker acting now as a speaker.

Capacitor C_2 has a relatively small capacitance and shunts part of the ac away from the second stage. This is done in order to prevent the high-frequency portion of the sound signal from reaching the final stage of amplification and the loud-speaker. There are limits to the frequencies that a loud-speaker can handle without distortion. The lower ac signals with frequencies in the middle of the audible range are passed by the larger capacitance C_3 to EB, the input of the second stage.

The output of the second stage passes the amplified ac signal through C_4 to the final stage. Since the emitter of the PNP transistor is at the top, the amplified voice signal emerges via the collector C and passes through the switch Sw$_2$ to the remote speaker S$_2$. This speaker ignores the dc portion of the current and reacts to the variations as if they were ac.

Resistor R_8 limits the amount of dc current through PNP 3, while C_5 carries the ac output signal from the second stage to the emitter of

the third stage. If C_5 were not provided, part of the power needed for driving the remote speaker would be lost in R_8. Table 55A gives a list of appropriate resistor and capacitor values.

TABLE 55A. RESISTANCE AND CAPACITANCE VALUES
FOR A THREE-STAGE AMPLIFIER CIRCUIT

R_2	100 KΩ	C_1	0.22 μF
R_3	3.3 KΩ	C_2	0.05 μF
R_4	47 KΩ	C_3	0.22 μF
R_5	1.5 KΩ	C_4	6 μF (electrolytic)
R_6	470 Ω	C_5	50 μF (electrolytic)
R_7	1.5 KΩ	S_1	20 Ω
R_8	47 Ω	S_2	20 Ω

K = 1000

Figure 55R shows a simple oscillator circuit employing an NPN transistor. The oscillation frequency is determined by L and C in the collector circuit, and feedback of a weak oscillating signal to the emitter is accomplished by the small coil F which picks up induced voltages from L.

Fig. 55R   *Oscillator circuit using an NPN transistor.*

QUESTIONS AND PROBLEMS

1. (a) What is a semiconductor? (b) What is a P-type crystal? (c) What is a PN junction?

2. (a) What is a solar battery? (b) What are the principles of the solar battery?

3. (a) What is a transistor? (b) What is a PNP transistor?

4. Explain the photoconductivity of a semiconductor like germanium.

5. Since an N-type semiconductor crystal has more free electrons than holes, why is it electrically uncharged?

6. Since a P-type semiconductor crystal has more holes than free electrons, why is it electrically uncharged?

7. Make a circuit diagram of a transistor amplifier using a PNP transistor. Show the (+) and (−) terminals of any batteries.

8. Make a diagram showing what instruments you would connect to a PNP transistor to obtain readings for

plotting curves like those in Fig. 55P. How would you obtain different voltages and read the currents?

9. If each of the three stages of the circuit diagram in Fig. 55Q has an amplification factor of 12, what is the over-all amplification?

10. Make a circuit diagram of a two-stage intercommunication system using an NPN transistor for the first stage and a PNP transistor for the second.

11. Make a circuit diagram of a three-stage intercommunication system using three NPN transistors.

12. If a 12-V battery is used for a transistor circuit of the kind shown in Fig. 55O, and a base current $I_B = 0.25$ mA is selected for its operation, find (a) the desirable voltage across CE, (b) the corresponding collector current I_C, (c) the load resistance to be used, (d) the base voltage V_{BE}, (e) the theoretical voltage amplification, and (f) the theoretical current amplification. Use the graphs in Fig. 55P.

MOVING FRAMES
OF REFERENCE

As an introduction to Einstein's theory of relativity let us consider the relative motions of bodies as seen from different frames of reference. We begin with the motion of a body in a medium which is itself moving. The drift of an airplane in a wind or the drift of a boat on a moving body of water is a good example.

56.1. The Airplane Problem. The pilot of a plane wishes to fly to a city directly to the north. If the plane has a cruising speed of 100 mi/hr and a steady wind is blowing from the west with a velocity of 50 mi/hr, at what angle should the pilot head his plane into the wind [see Fig. 56A(a)]?

wind velocity known, draw the first vector toward the east, 50 units long [see diagram (b)]. Label it with the moving body, the wind W at the head, and the ground G to which the velocity is referred, at the tail. Since only the magnitude of the airplane velocity is known, draw a temporary arrow 100 units long, at an arbitrary angle, and label it with the moving body, the plane P, at the head, and the air or wind W, to which the velocity is referred, at the tail.

The next step is to combine the two vectors with their like labels W together, as follows. After drawing the vector GW, draw a perpendicular

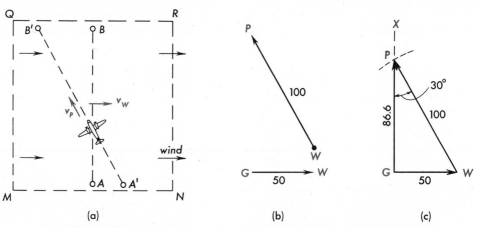

Fig. 56A *To fly a desired course, the wind velocity must be taken into account.*

Because this type of problem is often solved incorrectly, its correct solution should be noted with care. The procedure to be followed is appropriately called the *domino method of vector addition*.

With both the direction and magnitude of the

line GX upward. With a compass of radius 100 units and the center at W, draw a short arc intersecting the vertical line at P.

The vector WP is then completed, and the length of the side GP measured. The vector GP of 86.6 pointing north represents the velocity of the plane P with respect to the ground G, while the angle 30°, measured from the triangle, gives the direction in which the plane must be headed.

Diagram (a) in Fig. 56A shows how the plane, heading in a direction 30° west of north, and flying through the air with a velocity of 100 mi/hr, follows the northward land course from A to B with a *ground speed* of 86.6 mi/hr. In the air mass (MNRQ), which is a moving frame of reference, the plane flies from A′ to B′.

56.2. Relative Times for Two Planes. Because of its direct bearing upon Einstein's theory of relativity, the following problem should be of primary interest to every student. Suppose two pilots with identical planes are to fly to different cities equally far away. As shown in Fig. 56B

ground speed GP is the same each way, by the Pythagorean theorem for a right triangle, we find that

$$GP = \sqrt{c^2 - v^2}$$

Starting out for city X, the second pilot, with the same air cruising velocity c, sets his course due east. Since his plane is flying *with* the wind, the ground speed GP is just the arithmetic sum of the two speeds:

$$GP = c + v$$

To return to home base H, the pilot sets his course due west. Flying against the wind, the plane has a reduced ground speed equal to the arithmetic difference between the two speeds:

$$GP = c - v$$

Fig. 56B   *Comparisons of flight time for a plane flying downwind, upwind, and crosswind.*

one pilot flies north to city Y, at right angles to the wind, and returns, while the other flies east to city X, parallel to the wind, and returns. We now wish to find whether the two total flight times are different.

Let c represent the cruising speed of both planes, and v the velocity of the wind. Starting out for city Y, the first pilot, cruising at velocity c, sets his course west of north so that his flight path, with respect to the ground, is due north, as shown by the left-hand vector diagram. To return to home base H, he sets his course west of south so that his flight path is due south, as shown by the upper velocity triangle. Since his

To find the total flight time $t_\perp$ of the first plane, we divide the total distance 2L by the velocity $\sqrt{c^2 - v^2}$:

$$t_\perp = \frac{2L}{\sqrt{c^2 - v^2}} \tag{56a}$$

To find the total flight time $t_\parallel$ of the second plane, the two different velocities $c + v$ going, and $c - v$ returning must be used. Therefore, we have

$$t_\parallel = \frac{L}{c + v} + \frac{L}{c - v}$$

Placing these two terms over a common denominator, we obtain

$$t_{\parallel} = \frac{2Lc}{c^2 - v^2} \qquad (56b)$$

One way to compare these flight times is to divide the perpendicular flight time by the parallel flight time and obtain

$$\frac{t_{\perp}}{t_{\parallel}} = \frac{2L}{\sqrt{c^2 - v^2}} \div \frac{2Lc}{c^2 - v^2}$$

Inverting the divisor and multiplying we find

$$\frac{t_{\perp}}{t_{\parallel}} = \frac{2L}{\sqrt{c^2 - v^2}} \times \frac{c^2 - v^2}{2Lc} = \frac{\sqrt{c^2 - v^2}}{c}$$

from which we obtain the simplified result

$$\boxed{\frac{t_{\perp}}{t_{\parallel}} = \sqrt{1 - \frac{v^2}{c^2}}} \qquad (56c)$$

This equation shows that flying with no wind blowing $v = 0$, the ratio of the two flight times is unity, which means that they are equal, as one would expect. When the wind is blowing, however, the ratio is less than unity, and the plane flying parallel to the wind requires the greater time. If the wind velocity increases to nearly that of the cruising speed of the planes, the ratio tends toward zero. If the wind velocity exceeds the cruising speed of the planes, the ratio becomes imaginary: the first plane is blown off its course and the second plane cannot get back to home base.

It will be left as a problem for the student to show that the time of flight over both of these two courses is greater when the wind is blowing than when it is calm.

56.3. Frames of Reference. If two observers are moving with respect to one another, and both observers make measurements of any event, they could both be expected to come to the same conclusions as to what took place. In Fig. 56C we see two sets of rectangular, or *Cartesian*, coordinates called *frames of reference*. In the space common to these two frames is a single point marked A, and it is to this point that measurements are to be made. The first observer O' in the upper right-hand frame measures the distance to A and finds the coordinates of this distance to be x', y', and z'. The second observer O in the lower left-hand frame measures the

Fig. 56C *The coordinate distances of a point A measured in two different frames of reference (Cartesian coordinates).*

distance to A and finds coordinate distances x, y, and z.

Suppose that observer O' now wishes to make measurements from which he can determine x, y, and z as observed by O. To do this, he measures the distance from O' to O and finds the coordinates to be x_0, y_0, and z_0. He can now write down the following equalities:

$$\left. \begin{array}{l} x = x' + x_0 \\ y = y' + y_0 \\ z = z' + z_0 \end{array} \right\} \qquad (56d)$$

Suppose observer O wishes to make his own determinations of x', y', and z' as observed by O'. To do this, he measures his distance from O to O' and finds the coordinates to be x_0, y_0, and z_0. He then writes down the equations

$$\left. \begin{array}{l} x' = x - x_0 \\ y' = y - y_0 \\ z' = z - z_0 \end{array} \right\} \qquad (56e)$$

Note that the two sets of equations are the same and that they permit either observer to transform measurements made in his frame of reference to those made in the other. It is for this reason that such equations are called *transformation equations*.

56.4. Distance Measurements in Moving Frames of Reference. To transform measurements from one moving frame of reference to another, we will confine the motion to the line joining the two origins. It is along this straight line that x axes are set up for two frames, as shown in Fig. 56D. Here one observer O is located on a stationary platform C and the other observer O' on a flat car C' capable of moving freely along

mations, distances are said to be *invariant*, that is, they are the same.

We say, therefore, that in any Galilean–Newtonian system an object measured and found to

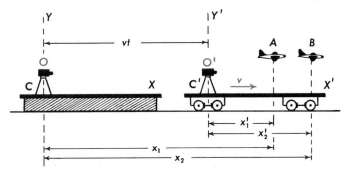

Fig. 56D   *Distance measurements of two airplanes, A and B, from two frames of reference.*

a track. Observer O and reference frame C will be assumed at rest, while observer O' and car C' will be assumed moving along together with constant velocity v.

Both observers start their stop clocks at the instant O' is opposite O. At some later time, both observers simultaneously note the time and snap pictures of two airplanes, A and B, directly over the track. From their stereophotographs, observer O finds the distances to be x_1 and x_2, while observer O' finds the distances to be x'_1 and x'_2. Each observer now decides to use the transformation equations to find the other observer's distance measurements. Observer O uses Eq.(56e) and writes

$$x'_1 = x_1 - vt \quad \text{and} \quad x'_2 = x_2 - vt \quad \text{(56f)}$$

and observer O' uses Eq.(56d) and writes

$$x_1 = x'_1 + vt \quad \text{and} \quad x_2 = x'_2 + vt$$

In each case they arrive at the same equations. Each observer finds that upon taking the difference between his own measured distances,

$$x_2 - x_1 = x'_2 - x'_1$$

Each observer concludes, therefore, that the distance between A and B is the same whether viewed from one frame or the other. The transformation of measurements from one moving frame of reference to another by means of the above equations is referred to as a *Galilean–Newtonian transformation*. Under such transfor-

have a length l in one reference frame will be found to have the same length l' when measured in any other reference frame:

$$l' = l \quad \text{(56g)}$$

Note that this equality of results does not depend upon the value of v or of t, but does depend upon all observations being made at the same instant, that is, *simultaneously*. In other words, anything happening in one frame at an instant t' is observed from the other frame as occurring at the same instant t:

$$t' = t \quad \text{(56h)}$$

56.5. Velocity Measurements in Moving Frames of Reference. We have seen in the preceding section that, under a Galilean–Newtonian transformation, the straight-line distance between two points is invariant. The question next arises whether the *velocity* of a moving body should be invariant, i.e., should the velocity be the same when observed from different frames which are themselves moving with different velocities? To find the answer to this question, we again make use of two observers, one stationary, and the other on a flatcar as shown in Fig. 56E.

Both observers start their stopclocks at the instant the moving observer O' is opposite the stationary observer O. At some later time, both observers simultaneously note the time t_1 as they snap stereo pictures of an airplane A_1 flying along and over the track. A short time later, both

Fig. 56E *Velocity measurements of an airplane as observed from two frames of reference.*

observers again note the time t_2 as they simultaneously snap pictures of the same plane at A_2. From their respective photographs each observer determines the plane's distance for each of the two times. Applying the transformation equations, Eq.(56f), they can write

$$x'_1 = x_1 - vt_1 \quad \text{and} \quad x'_2 = x_2 - vt_2$$

To find the average velocity of the plane, observer O' takes his measured distance it has traveled, $x'_2 - x'_1$, and divides by the elapsed time $t'_2 - t'_1$. Taking the difference, he obtains

$$x'_2 - x'_1 = (x_2 - x_1) - (vt_2 - vt_1)$$

and dividing each term by either of the two equal time differences, he finds

$$\frac{x'_2 - x'_1}{t'_2 - t'_1} = \frac{x_2 - x_1}{t_2 - t_1} - \frac{v(t_2 - t_1)}{t_2 - t_1}$$

The term on the left represents the average velocity u' of the plane as observed by O', while the middle term represents the average velocity u observed by O.

$$u' = \frac{x'_2 - x'_1}{t'_2 - t'_1} \quad \text{and} \quad u = \frac{x_2 - x_1}{t_2 - t_1}$$

Observer O' can therefore write

$$\boxed{u' = u - v} \qquad (56i)$$

Exactly the same equations can be written by observer O. Thus the two velocities measured by the two observers are not the same; they differ by the relative velocity of the two observers. We say that, *under a Galilean–Newtonian transformation, velocities are not invariant.*

56.6. An Accelerated Body Viewed from a Frame Moving with Constant Velocity. Suppose

that the plane in Fig. 56E is increasing its speed, and by appropriate means of observation observers O and O' determine its velocity when it passes point A_1, and again when it passes A_2. Using the transformation equation just derived for velocities, Eq.(56i), both observers can write down

$$u'_1 = u_1 - v \quad \text{and} \quad u'_2 = u_2 - v$$

Taking the difference between the two velocities u'_2 and u'_1, each would obtain

$$u'_2 - u'_1 = u_2 - u_1 \qquad (56j)$$

Since each observer measured the time t between positions A_1 and A_2, each can divide his velocity difference by t to obtain the acceleration

$$\frac{u'_2 - u'_1}{t} = \frac{u_2 - u_1}{t}$$

or

$$a' = a \qquad (56k)$$

In other words, the acceleration seen by both observers is exactly the same.

The conclusion to be drawn from this result is that *acceleration is invariant.* If we now assume the mass of a body is invariant, we can assume that the two observers could apply Newton's second law of motion, $F = ma$, and find the same force exerted by the plane's jet engines.

56.7. Falling Body Observed from a Constant-Velocity Frame. Suppose you as an observer O', riding in a train, plane, bus, or ship with constant velocity, hold out a coin in front of you and drop it. The coin will appear to fall straight downward with the acceleration $g = 9.8$ m/s^2.

If an observer outside on the ground were to observe the coin's motion, he would find it tra-

Fig. 56F *A falling-body experiment, showing the trajectory as viewed from a stationary frame and from a moving frame.*

verses a parabolic path. While the two observed paths would appear to be different, both observers would measure the same time of fall, and each could apply the transformation equations to determine what the other observer saw.

A simple demonstration of such an experiment is shown in Fig. 56F. A small car with a vertical stand is pulled along the table top at constant speed by means of an electric motor and drum. While the car is moving, an electric switch is opened; this deactivates an electromagnet and releases a steel marble for free fall. The ball falls in a small cup at the base of the stand, thus illustrating that to an observer O′ on the car the trajectory is straight downward.

To a stationary observer O the released ball has an initial horizontal velocity v, and traverses the parabolic path as a projectile. If we apply the transformation Eq.(56i) to this example, the horizontal velocity u of the ball, as seen by observer O, is equal to the velocity v of the car, so that $u = v$. This gives $u' = 0$ as observed by O′, and the ball falls vertically downward.

56.8. Falling Bodies Observed from an Accelerated Frame. Suppose you, as an observer O′ riding in an accelerated vehicle, drop an object and observe its free fall. To an observer on the ground outside the object will appear to follow a parabolic path, but to you it will appear to fall in a straight-line path making an angle with the vertical. It will behave as though in addition to a downward acceleration g it also has a backward horizontal acceleration a.

An informative experiment demonstrating these observations is shown in Fig. 56G. A small car with a vertical stand attached is accelerated along the table top by a cord passing over two pulleys to a large mass M. Shortly after the car starts, an electric switch is opened, deactivating an electromagnet, releasing a steel marble for free fall. The marble falls in a small cup at one side of the base of the stand.

To a stationary observer O, the released marble has an initial horizontal velocity v_1 (the velocity of the car at the instant of release), and it traverses the parabolic path as shown. To the

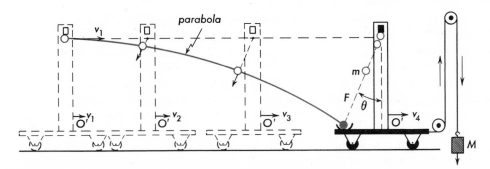

Fig. 56G *A falling-body experiment, showing the trajectory as viewed from a stationary frame and from an accelerated frame.*

accelerated observer O′ there appears to be a force F giving the marble an acceleration $a′$ along a straight-line path making an angle $θ$ with the vertical. This force is the vector resultant of the downward force of gravity F_1 and a horizontal force F_2. These forces, as well as their corresponding accelerations, g, a, and $a′$, are shown in Fig. 56H:

$$F_1 = mg, \qquad F_2 = ma, \qquad \text{and} \qquad F = ma′$$

Since there is no apparent reason for the horizontal force F_2 it is called a *fictitious force*. To the observer O this force does not exist and the marble obeys Newton's laws of motion.

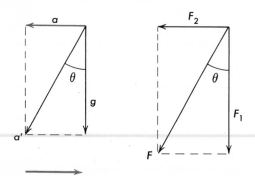

frame acceleration

Fig. 56H *A falling body in an accelerated frame of reference appears to have two simultaneous accelerations, one an acceleration g vertically downward due to gravity, and the other an acceleration a opposite in direction to that in which the frame is accelerated.*

56.9. Motion in a Rotating Frame. Imagine that you, as an observer O′, are on a merry-go-round and while it is turning with constant speed you place a marble on the floor at your feet. Since it is free to move, the marble will roll away from your feet and out along a curved path toward the periphery.

If a stone is fastened to a string and you hold the other end in your hand, it will not hang vertically but with the string making an angle with the vertical. At the center of rotation it will hang straight down, but at points away from the center the centrifugal component of force will increase the radius of its circular path.

If a large gun, fixed in position on the earth's surface, fires a shell at a distant ground target,

the projectile deflects to the right in the northern hemisphere and to the left in the southern. The explanation of this phenomenon, that it is due to the earth's rotation, was first given by the French scientist Coriolis about the middle of the last century.

Consider a demonstration in which a gun G, mounted on a turntable as shown in Fig. 56I, is

Fig. 56I *The projectile from the gun on the rotating table will miss both targets, because of the Coriolis force.*

aimed at targets T and P. The target P is off the table and in a stationary frame of reference, while target T is on the table and in a rotating frame of reference. If the table is not turning, the projectile leaving the gun with a velocity $v′$ will pass through T and hit the target P.

If the table is rotating with an angular velocity $ω$, and the gun is fired at the instant the two targets are in line, the projectile will pass to the right of T (shown dotted) and to the left of P.

Since the gun rotates with the table, the tip end of the gun barrel, at a distance r from the center of rotation C, will give the projectile an additional velocity v'' at right angles to v', and equal in magnitude to the product ωr:

$$v'' = \omega r$$

Since the projectile is given two simultaneous velocities v' and v'', with respect to the fixed frame of reference, a stationary observer will observe the mass m moving with a velocity v along the straight-line path GQ.

To an observer on the rotating table there appears to be a force F_c at right angles to v' deflecting the projectile to the right of the target T at which it is aimed. This apparent force, called the *Coriolis force*, is demonstrated in Fig. 56J.

Fig. 56J *Apparatus for demonstrating the curved path of a projectile and the Coriolis acceleration.*

A rotating table made of plywood with a diameter of 4 ft contains a small spring gun and two metal frame targets, T_1 and T_2. The push button B for a trigger is located on the axis, and thin paper is glued over the target frames. When the table is set rotating at a relatively low angular speed, the trigger B is depressed, firing the small wood or aluminum projectile. When the table is stopped, the gun muzzle and the holes in the paper targets clearly indicate the curved path.

A derivation of the formula for the Coriolis acceleration and Coriolis force follows from Fig. 56K. A mass m is given a velocity v in a direction which is radially outward from C toward the stationary observer O. When it passes the point Q the table has turned through an angle θ. To the rotating observer O', the projectile has moved away from the point P a distance s. From classical mechanics

$$x = \tfrac{1}{2}at^2$$

Since $x = r\theta$, and $\theta = \omega t$, we substitute and find

$$r\omega t = \tfrac{1}{2}at^2$$

from which

$$a = \frac{2r\omega}{t}$$

Since the velocity v is just r/t, we obtain

$$a = 2v\omega \tag{56l}$$

as the Coriolis acceleration. By Newton's second law of motion, $F = ma$, the Coriolis force becomes

$$F = 2mv\omega \tag{56m}$$

56.10. Classical Relativity; Newtonian Mechanics. From the treatment of the kinematics

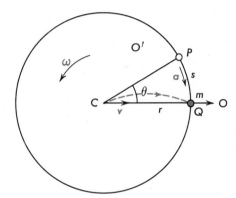

Fig. 56K *Geometry for the derivation of the Coriolis acceleration $a = 2v\omega$.*

of motion in this chapter, we have seen how an observer in one reference frame can make measurements of something happening in another reference frame and, by applying simple transformation equations, find the measurements that apply to the second frame.

We have seen that if the relative velocity of the two frames is constant, the distance between two points, or the length of an object measured from either frame, is found to be the same. If the *acceleration* of an object is measured from both frames, the two results again come out the same, but if the *velocity* is measured, the two values are different. In other words:

Distances and accelerations are invariant and do not depend upon any relative velocity of an observer, while velocities are variant.

Even though velocities may be different for two observers, the transformation equations make the two velocities compatible. If measurements of the motion of a body in one frame of reference are transformed to find the measurements that would apply in another frame, we say that we are applying the Newtonian transformation equations. These transformation equations are

$$
\begin{aligned}
x' &= x - vt \\
u' &= u - v \\
l' &= l \\
a' &= a \\
t' &= t
\end{aligned}
\tag{56n}
$$

A set of coordinates that is fixed relative to an observer is called the *observer's frame of reference*.

If a frame of reference is accelerated, a body initially at rest or moving in that frame appears to have a fictitious force acting upon it.

Since, therefore, Newton's laws of motion do not apply in an accelerated frame of reference, a frame that is not accelerated is called a *Galilean–Newtonian* or *inertial frame of reference*.

In setting up the Galilean–Newton transformation equations, it was assumed that all measurements were simultaneous, i.e., that the light with which one sees an object travels with an infinite speed. If the relative velocities of moving frames are small compared with the speed of light (186,00 mi/sec), the speed of light can be assumed to be infinite, and the principles developed in this and the preceding chapters are valid. Newtonian mechanics applies, therefore, to velocities that are low compared with the speed of light, while a modified system called *relativistic mechanics* will apply to velocities comparable to the speed of light (see Chapter 58).

PROBLEMS

1. A motorboat capable of 10 mi/hr is headed straight across a river. If the water flows at the rate of 2 mi/hr, what will be the velocity of the boat with respect to the starting point on the bank?

2. To an observer on a ship sailing east at 24 knots, it appears that a 16-knot wind is blowing from the northwest. Find the true wind velocity. [*Ans.* 37.1 knots at 17.7° south of east.]

3. A pilot with a plane having a cruising speed of 180 mi/hr leaves an airport and sets his course at 30° north of east. After flying for 1 hr, he discovers he is 120 mi directly east of his starting point. What is the average wind velocity that blew him off his course?

4. Two pilots flying identical aircraft with a cruising speed of 200 mi/hr fly to equally distant cities 400 mi away, and return to their home base. City X lies to the east and city Y lies to the north as shown in Fig. 56B. Aloft, there is a 70-mi/hr wind blowing from the west. Find (a) the time of flight going to each city, (b) the time of flight returning, (c) the difference in total times of flight, and (d) the ratio of the two total flight times. [*Ans.* (a) 1.48 hr to X, 2.14 hr to Y; (b) 3.08 hr from X, 2.14 hr from Y; (c) 0.28 hr or 16.8 min; (d) 1.067.]

5. Two swimmers, starting simultaneously from the same anchored marker in a river, swim to distant markers and return. One marker X is directly downstream 450 ft, and the other, Y, is directly across-stream 450 ft. If both swimmers can make 2 mi/hr in the water, and the river flows at 1 ft/s, (a) how long will it take each swimmer to reach his distant marker, (b) what is each swimmer's time to return, (c) what is the difference between their total

times, and (d) what is the ratio of these times as determined from Eq.(56c)?

6. Two pilots flying identical aircraft with a cruising speed of 280 mi/hr fly to equally distant cities 300 mi away, and return to their home base. City X lies to the west, and city Y lies to the south of home base. Aloft there is an 80-mi/hr wind blowing from the west. Find (a) the time of flight going to each city, (b) each time of flight returning, (c) the difference in total time of flight times, and (d) the ratio of total flight times using Eq.(56c). [*Ans.* (a) 1.50 hr to X, 1.12 hr to Y; (b) 0.833 hr from X, 1.12 hr from Y; (c) 0.093 hr; (d) 1.04.]

7. If the small car in Fig. 56G has an acceleration of 2.5 m/s², and the steel ball is dropped from a height of 0.5 m, find (a) the angle of descent, and (b) the lateral displacement of the ball as observed by the moving observer.

8. A merry-go-round is rotating with an angular velocity of 5 rpm. A 2-Kg ball starts rolling radially outward with a velocity of 4 m/s. Calculate (a) the Coriolis acceleration, (b) the Coriolis force, and (c) the average radius of its path on the floor. [*Ans.* (a) 4.18 m/s², (b) 8.36 N, (c) 3.82 m.]

9. A merry-go-round 16 m in diameter is rotating at a rate of 4 rpm. A boy on the periphery aims an arrow at a target diametrically opposite. If the arrow has a mass of 40 g and has a velocity of 100 m/s, find (a) the Coriolis acceleration, (b) the Coriolis force, (c) the average radius of the deflected path, and (d) the distance by which the arrow should miss the target.

10. A small spring gun, as shown in Fig. 56J, fires a

100-g projectile with a velocity of 15 m/s. If the table turns at 2.5 rps, find (a) the Coriolis acceleration, (b) the Coriolis force, and (c) the average radius of the deflected path. [*Ans.* (a) 471 m/s^2, (b) 47.1 N, (c) 0.478 m.]

11. A boy standing on one edge of a merry-go-round wishes to shoot an arrow to hit the center of a target diametrically opposite him. The merry-go-round is 20 m in diameter and turns at 5 rpm. The arrow is to have a speed of 80 m/s. Find (a) the Coriolis acceleration, (b) the radius of the path as seen by the boy, and (c) the distance he must advance his aim to hit the target.

12. A space-ship assembly simulates the acceleration due to gravity, *g*, by rotating two vehicles whose centers of mass are 100 m from the axis (see Fig. 14K). An astronaut in one vehicle releases an object 2 m above the floor of the craft. (a) How far does it appear to him to be deflected to one side? (b) Is the astronaut's body axis perpendicular to the floor? (c) Would a pendulum appear to hang straight down?

INTERFEROMETERS
AND LASERS

In this chapter we will study the *Michelson interferometer*, and then Fizeau's experiment by which the speed of light is found to be altered by a moving stream of water. The latter leads directly to the principles of the famous *Michelson–Morley experiment* on ether drift, which in turn leads to Einstein's theory of relativity.

We will then consider the *Fabry–Perot interferometer* as it applies to the hyperfine structure of spectrum lines, and finally to the principles of the recently developed instruments called *lasers*.

57.1. The Michelson Interferometer. The form of the Michelson interferometer generally found in the science laboratory is that shown in Fig. 57A. The optical parts consist of two mirrors,

Fig. 57A   *Diagram of the Michelson interferometer.*

M_1 and M_2, and two parallel plates of glass, G_1 and G_2. Oftentimes the rear side of plate G_1 is

lightly silvered (shown heavy in the figure) so that light coming from the source S is divided into (1) a reflected and (2) a transmitted beam of equal intensity. The light returning from M_1 passes through G_1 a third time before reaching the eye. The light returning from M_2 is reflected from G_1 and into the eye. The purpose of plate G_2 is to render the total path in glass equal for the two rays.

The mirror M_1 is mounted on a well-machined guide and can be moved along slowly by means of a screw V. When mirror M_2 is made exactly perpendicular to M_1 by screws on its back face, interference fringes similar to those found with a double slit may be seen, or photographed, at E. Photographs of typical fringes when mirror M_1 is at different distances are shown in Fig. 57B.

When monochromatic light is used as a source and the mirrors are in exact adjustment, circular fringes are observed as shown in photographs (a) and (b). If the mirrors are not exactly at right angles to each other, fringes like those in photographs (c) and (d) are obtained. If circular fringes are observed, and mirror M_1 is slowly moved along by the turn of the screw V, the circular fringe pattern will expand or contract; if it expands, new fringes will appear as a dot at the center, widen, and expand into a circle; and if it contracts, fringes grow smaller, become a dot, and vanish at the center. If straight or curved fringes are observed, the motion of M_1 causes the fringes to drift across the field at right angles to the fringe lines.

The expansion, contraction, or drift in the pattern for a distance of one fringe corresponds

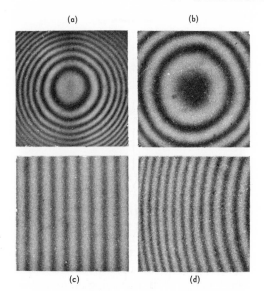

(a)　　　　(b)

(c)　　　　(d)

Fig. 57B *Interference fringe patterns as photo-graphed with a Michelson interferometer.*

to M_1 moving a distance of exactly $\frac{1}{2}$ wavelength of light. When M_1 moves back a distance of $\frac{1}{2}\lambda$, the total light path (1) increases a whole wavelength. If M_1 moves 1λ, the pattern will move two fringes because the total light path (1) has changed by 2λ. Any bright fringe that one ob-observes is caused by both beams coming together in phase. When the one path is changed

of any light source, one can then use the inter-ferometer to accurately measure distances.

It was by means of the Michelson interferom-eter that the standard meter was determined in terms of the wavelength of orange light, $\lambda = 6057.80$ Å of krypton, element 36.*

1 meter = 1,650,763.73 wavelengths
(for orange light of krypton)

57.2. Velocity of Light in Moving Matter. In 1859, the French physicist Armand Fizeau meas-ured the velocity of light in a moving stream of water and found that the light was carried along by the stream. A schematic diagram of his ap-paratus is shown in Fig. 57C.

Light from a monochromatic source S is sepa-rated into two beams by means of a lens L_1. These two beams pass through tubes A and B which contain water flowing rapidly in opposite directions. After reflection from M the beams traverse opposite tubes, so that upon arrival at L_1 one has traversed streams A and B in the direction of flow, while the other has traversed both tubes but always against the flow. Part of each beam is reflected by the half-silvered plate G and the two brought together at S′ where interference fringes are produced.

If the light travels faster by one path than the

Fig. 57C *Fizeau's experiment for measuring the velocity of light in a moving medium.*

by $\frac{1}{2}\lambda$, 1λ, $\frac{3}{2}\lambda$, etc., the two beams arriving at the same field points will again be in phase.

By counting the number of fringes required to move the mirror M_1 a given distance, the wavelength of light can be calculated. This would appear to be the most direct and accurate method for the wavelength measurements of different light sources. Knowing the accurate wavelength

other, the time will be different and the fringes formed at S′ will have shifted. Using tubes 1.5 m long and a water speed of 7.0 m/s, Fizeau found a shift of 0.46 of a fringe upon a reversal of the water stream. This shift corresponds to a de-

* Adopted as the international legal standard of length on October 14, 1960, by the General Conference on Weights and Measures in Paris, France.

crease in the speed of light in one direction, and an increase in the other, of about half the speed of the water. In other words, the moving water has a dragging effect upon the light waves.

In 1818, the French physicist Augustin Fresnel* derived a formula for this dragging effect, based upon the existence of what was then called the *ether*. His formula gives v' the increase in the velocity of light in any medium, due to the motion of the medium as

$$v' = v\left(1 - \frac{1}{\mu^2}\right) \qquad (57a)$$

where v is the velocity of the medium, and μ is the index of refraction. For water, with an index of 1.33, $v' = 0.43v$ in reasonably good agreement with Fresnel's observations.

57.3. The Michelson–Morley Experiment.

This, the most famous experiment in optics, was first performed by Michelson and Morley in 1881, in an effort to detect the motion of the earth through space. If the transmission of light through space requires an ether, that is, a medium for it to move in, then light should be dragged along by this ether as the earth moves along through space. In order to detect such a drift, the Michelson interferometer appeared to be the most sensitive instrument to use.

In principle the ether drift test consists simply of observing whether there is any shift of the interference fringes of light in the Michelson interferometer when the entire instrument is turned through an angle of 90°. Let us assume that the interferometer and the earth are at rest and that the ether is moving by with a velocity v as shown in Fig. 57D. If no ether drag is effective, light paths (1) and (2) will be out and back, as shown by the solid lines and arrows, and a set of interference bands like those shown in Fig. 57B will be observed.

* Augustin Fresnel (1788–1827), French physicist. Although starting his career as a civil engineer, Fresnel became interested in optics at the age of 26. His mathematical development of the wave theory of light and its complete validation of experiment have marked this man as an outstanding genius of the nineteenth century. His true scientific attitude is illustrated by a statement from one of his memoirs, "All the compliments that I have received from Arago, Laplace, and Biot never gave me so much pleasure as the discovery of a theoretic truth, or the confirmation of a calculation by experiment."

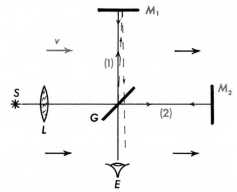

Fig. 57D   *The Michelson interferometer arrangement for detecting an ether drift.*

If we now suppose the light to be dragged along by an ether, the time it takes for light to traverse path (1) at right angles to the ether stream, and the time it takes to traverse path (2), first with and then against the stream, will both be increased.

The times to traverse paths (1) and (2) are given by Eqs.(56a) and (56b) as

$$t_{\perp} = \frac{2L}{\sqrt{c^2 - v^2}} \qquad t_{\parallel} = \frac{2Lc}{c^2 - v^2} \qquad (57b)$$

where c is the velocity of light *in vacuo*, and v is the very much slower drift velocity.

A little study of these equations will show that, while both times have been increased a slight amount, the increase is twice as large in the direction of motion. Furthermore, the ratio of the two times is given by

$$\boxed{\frac{t_{\perp}}{t_{\parallel}} = \sqrt{1 - \frac{v^2}{c^2}}} \qquad (57c)$$

An ether drift should, therefore, cause a shift in the fringes observed in the interferometer. Since neither the earth's motion, nor the ether, can be stopped, in an effort to observe this shift, a rotation of the interferometer through 90° should have a similar effect. By interchanging paths (1) and (2), the time difference $t_{\parallel} - t_{\perp}$ is reversed, and any fringe shift should be doubled.

Michelson and Morley made the light paths as much as 11 m long by reflecting the light back and forth between 16 mirrors, as shown in Fig.

57E. To prevent distortion by the turning of the instrument, the entire apparatus was mounted on a concrete block floating in mercury, and observations of the fringes were made as it ro-

57.4. The Fabry–Perot Interferometer. Unlike the Michelson interferometer that produces interference fringe patterns with two coherent beams of light, the Fabry–Perot interferometer

Fig. 57E *Miller's elaborate arrangement of the Michelson–Morley experiment to detect ether drift.*

tated slowly and continuously about a vertical axis.

If we assume the ether velocity v to be 18.6 mi/s (the speed of the earth in its orbit around the sun), and the speed of light c to be 186,000 mi/s, a shift of $\frac{1}{2}$ a fringe should have been observed. No shift as great as $\frac{1}{10}$ of this was observed. Such a negative result was so surprising and so disappointing that others have repeated the experiment.

The most exacting work was done by D. C. Miller who used Michelson and Morley's arrangement, but with optical paths of 64 m in place of 11 m. While Miller thought he found evidence for a shift of $\frac{1}{30}$ of a fringe, the latest analysis of Miller's data makes it probable that no shift exists.

produces interference with a large number of coherent beams. The principles of this device are shown in Fig. 57F.

Two optically flat glass or quartz plates, each partially silvered on one face only, are mounted in rigid frames. By means of fine screws the plates are adjusted until their two silvered surfaces are parallel to a high degree of precision. Light from an extended source S, upon passing through the interferometer undergoes reflection back and forth, and the emerging parallel rays are brought together to interfere in the focal plane of a lens.

In Fig. 57F a ray of light from the point P is shown incident on the first surface at an angle θ. Part of this light is reflected and part is transmitted. Part of the transmitted ray 1 is reflected at the second surface and part is transmitted.

Fig. 57F   *Diagram of the paths of light rays in a Fabry–Perot interferometer.*

Repeating this behavior at each mirrored surface it can be seen that rays 1, 3, 5, 7, etc., emerging as parallel rays have traveled successively greater distances. These numbers specify the number of times each ray traverses the gap of width d.

The *path difference* between successive rays 1, 3, 5, 7, etc., will be shown at the end of this section to be just $2d \cos \theta$. If this distance is exactly equal to a whole number of wavelengths, the emergent rays when brought together at the point P′ will all be in phase and produce a bright spot. For such a bright spot we can write

$$2d \cos \theta = n\lambda \qquad (57d)$$

where n is a whole number and λ is the wavelength.

For all rays from all points of the source incident at the same angle θ, identical phase relations will exist, and the lens will bring all sets of parallel rays to a focus at points lying on a circle in the focal plane of the lens. For those rays in the angle θ is such that the path difference

between successively reflected rays is $(n + \frac{1}{2})\lambda$, the waves in alternate rays will be out of step and destructively interfere to produce darkness. Hence the existence of bright and dark concentric rings on the screen indicates coherence as well as interference.

The interference ring patterns in Fig. 57G illustrate the difference between the kinds of fringes observed when (a) two beams of light are brought together, as in the Michelson interferometer and (b) when a large number of beams are brought together as with the Fabry–Perot interferometer.

Note that in Fig. 57F, for rays entering the interferometer parallel to the axis, that is, with $\theta = 0$, the multiply reflected rays will be brought together at the focal point F, and if these waves arrive in phase, a bright spot will be produced there, and

$$2d = n\lambda \qquad (57e)$$

The number n is called the *order of interference*, or in microwave terminology, the *principal*

(a)   (b)

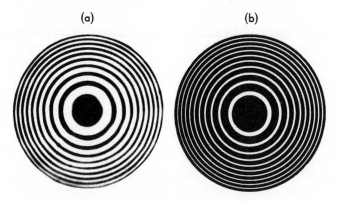

Fig. 57G   *Comparison of the types of fringes produced with (a) the Michelson interferometer and (b) the Fabry–Perot interferometer.*

oscillation mode of the cavity. For an interferometer with $d = 10$ cm, and green light $\lambda = 5000$ Å, $n = 400,000$ for the light emerging parallel to the axis.

To derive Eq.(57d) for the bright fringes of a Fabry–Perot interferometer, we refer to Fig. 57H. As ray 1 leaves the point A, ray 3 must

possible to determine the spin angular momenta and magnetic moments of many atomic nuclei (see Chapter 52).

The ability to resolve lines differing ever so slightly from one another in wavelength is attributed to the great length of the path difference between consecutive rays and the large number

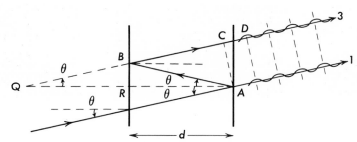

Fig. 57H *Geometry for calculating the path difference between two successive rays of a Fabry–Perot interferometer.*

travel the extra distance A to B to C to emerge in phase with ray 1. By extending the line BC back to the left, until it intersects the normal AR at the point Q, an isosceles triangle QBA is formed. Since this makes the line QB equal to AB, the total path difference

$$AB + BC = QC$$

Since QR = AR, and AR = d, we have

$$QA = 2d$$

Since the base of the right triangle QAC is the path difference QC, we obtain

$$QC = 2d \cos \theta$$

For bright fringes, QC must equal $n\lambda$, and this leads directly to Eq.(57d).

Equation (57d) shows that the highest order of interference occurs when $\theta = 0$, that is, for the most central fringe. As θ increases, $\cos \theta$ decreases, and the path difference QC decreases. If, for example, the central fringe is for $n = 400,000$, the next two fringes out will be $n = 399,999$ and $n = 399,998$, respectively.

57.5. Hyperfine Structure of Spectrum Lines. One of the principal uses of the Fabry–Perot interferometer has been that of resolving what is called the *hyperfine structure* of spectrum lines. Through the study of line structure it has been

of rays producing the interference fringes. Each wavelength produces its own set of fringes as given by Eq.(57d), and because bright fringes are very much sharper than the dark spaces between, several slightly different wavelengths can be seen as separate bright ring systems.

Since the spectrum of most light sources contains many lines, the ring system from a source to be studied is usually focused on the jaw faces of the slit of a prism spectrograph, and photographs are made with the slit wide open or with the slit about a millimeter or two wide.

Figure 57I is a reproduction of a section of the visible spectrum of mercury. In this relatively simple spectrum the overlapping of interference ring systems in (a) is confusing and the use of a slit to separate interference patterns as in (b) is clearly an improvement. In a complex spectrum like that of lanthanum, $Z = 57$, the slit must be narrowed still further to clearly separate most of the lines and see their ring structure (see Fig. 57J).

By tilting the Fabry–Perot interferometer so the center of the interference ring pattern is just off the lower end of the spectrograph slit, only half of each ring strip is observed. Occasionally it will be found that a line which appears sharp and single in an ordinary spectroscope will yield λ 4358   (a)   λ 5461   5770–90

blue   (b)   green yellow

Fig. 57I *Photographs of the visible spectrum of mercury made with a Fabry–Perot interferometer and a prism spectrograph. Spectrograph slit (a) wide open, and (b) 1 millimeter wide.*

ring systems that are complex. Examples are found in the lines marked X in the photograph, which upon close examination reveal at least seven components. Those marked A are single sharp lines. Line C is broad and probably composed of several unresolved lines.

A   A A A A   X X C

Fig. 57J *Photograph of a section of the lanthanum spectrum made with a Fabry–Perot interferometer and a prism spectrograph. (After D. E. Anderson.)*

Two line patterns selected from the Fabry–Perot spectrum of tantalum, $Z = 73$, and tungsten, $Z = 74$, have been enlarged and turned on their sides as shown in Fig. 57K. The upper pattern shows an eight-component line in the orange part of the spectrum at $\lambda = 5997$ Å, the structure being due to the fact that tantalum

atoms of atomic mass 181 have a nuclear spin of $\frac{7}{2} \frac{h}{2\pi}$ (see Table 71A).

The lower pattern shows a three-component line illustrating what is called *isotope structure.* Tungsten has five isotopes with the following relative abundance.

Isotope	180	182	183	184	186
Abundance, %	0.2	26.4	14.4	30.6	28.4

The even isotope 180 is quite rare and produces too faint a line to be seen.

The odd isotope 183 is known to produce a pattern of several lines, and because this pattern is spread over the three single lines produced by the three more abundant even isotopes, they are too faint to show in the reproduction. The innermost fringe of the three lines in each order is due to isotope 182.

To evaluate the differences in wavelength between the component lines of an otherwise single spectrum line we make use of the general equation, Eq.(57d). Any given fringe of a wavelength λ_1 is formed at such an angle that

$$2d \cos \theta_1 = n\lambda_1 \qquad (57f)$$

The next fringe out for this same wavelength is given by

$$2d \cos \theta_2 = (n - 1)\lambda_1 \qquad (57g)$$

HYPERFINE-STRUCTURE   TANTALUM $\lambda\,5997$

ISOTOPE-STRUCTURE   TUNGSTEN $\lambda\,5225$

Fig. 57K *Photographs of a section of the Fabry–Perot interferometer pattern of a single line from the spectrum of tantulum and tungsten.*

Suppose now that λ_1 has a component line λ_2 which has a slightly different wavelength than λ_1, and that this component in order n falls on order $n-1$ of λ_1. We can therefore write

$$2d \cos \theta_2 = n\lambda_2 \qquad (57h)$$

If we now let the small difference in wavelength $\lambda_1 - \lambda_2$ be written as $\Delta\lambda$, that is,

$$\Delta\lambda = \lambda_1 - \lambda_2$$

we may substitute $\lambda_1 - \Delta\lambda$ for λ_2 in Eq.(57h) and obtain

$$2d \cos \theta_2 = n(\lambda_1 - \Delta\lambda) \qquad (57i)$$

Equating right-hand sides of Eqs.(57g) and (57i) we find

$$\lambda_1 = n\Delta\lambda$$

and upon substituting the value of n from Eq. (57f) and solving for $\Delta\lambda$ we obtain

$$\Delta\lambda = \frac{\lambda_1{}^2}{2d \cos \theta_2}$$

Since θ_2 is practically zero, we can write $\cos \theta_2 = 1$, and obtain the very useful equation

$$\Delta\lambda = \frac{\lambda_1{}^2}{2d} \qquad (57j)$$

This is the wavelength interval between the centers of successive fringes and is independent of n. Knowing d and λ_1, we can calculate the wavelength difference of component lines lying in this small range from measured positions.

Example 1. The line pattern for $\lambda = 5225$ Å in Fig. 57K was made with a Fabry–Perot plate spacing of 5 cm. Find the wavelength interval between successive ring patterns of the same isotope.

Solution. The given quantities are $\lambda = 5225$ Å,

and $d = 5$ cm. First change 5 cm to angstroms, and then substitute in Eq.(57j)

$$\Delta\lambda = \frac{(5225 \text{ Å})^2}{2 \times 5 \times 10^8 \text{ Å}} = 0.0273 \text{ Å}$$

The interval between orders is 0.0273 Å, and the three components differ from each other by about one-quarter of this (see Problem 5 at the end of this chapter).

57.6. Lasers. The term *laser* derives its name from the description, *Light Amplification by Stimulated Emission and Radiation*. In principle the laser is a device that produces an intense, concentrated, and highly parallel beam of light. So parallel would be the beam from a visible light laser 1 ft in diameter that at the moon the beam would be no more than a mile wide.

Historically the laser is the outgrowth of the *maser*, a device using Microwaves instead of Light waves. The first successful maser was built by C. H. Townes at Columbia University in 1953. During the next seven years great strides were made in developing intense microwave beams, the principal contributions being made by the Bell Telephone Research Laboratories and the Lincoln Laboratories at the Massachusetts Institute of Technology.

The first successful laser, using a large synthetic ruby crystal, was built by T. H. Maiman of Hughes Aircraft Company Laboratories in the summer of 1960. Hundreds of extensive researches on laser development have been carried on since that time, and because such devices appear to have great potential in so many different fields of research and development, a brief account of their basic principles will be presented here.

Lasers are of three general kinds, those using solids, those using liquids, and those using gases. For the case of liquid or gas lasers, a Fabry–Perot interferometer, with silvered end plates like the ones shown in Fig. 57F, is filled with a fluid. In the solid laser, the ends of a crystal are polished and silvered as shown in Fig. 57L. Since

tion of light by a circular aperture [see Sec. 43.6, and Eq.(43k)].

57.7. Optical Pumping. A convenient method of describing laser action is to refer to an energy-level diagram of the electronic states involved in light absorption and emission. An energy-level diagram for the electrons in the atomic lattice of a ruby crystal is given in Fig. 57M. Here there are three sets of levels, the *normal state*, the *semi-*

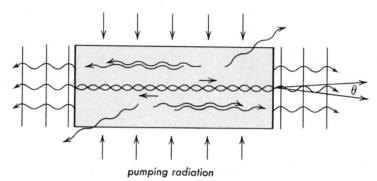

pumping radiation

Fig. 57L   *Diagram illustrating the coherent stimulation of light waves in a solid-state laser such as a ruby crystal.*

the first successful laser was made with a large single crystal of ruby, this device will be explained as representative of solid state lasers.

The atomic lattice structure of a ruby crystal has the properties of absorbing light of certain frequencies ν_0 and, of holding this absorbed energy for a period of time. Then by bouncing light of a different frequency ν_1 back and forth between the silvered ends, the excited atoms may be stimulated to emit their stored energy as light of the same frequency ν_1 and in exact phase with the original light waves. As these intensified waves bounce back and forth, they stimulate others, thus amplifying the original beam intensity.

Because the light waves emerging from the end of the laser are all in phase, the beam is said to be coherent, and the angular spread of the light is given by the relation

$$\theta = \frac{2.44\lambda}{d}$$

where θ is in radians, λ is the wavelength of light, and d is the diameter of the emergent beam. This equation arises from the treatment of the diffrac-

metastable states near the middle, and the top *wide-band energy levels*. (Pink ruby is a crystal lattice of aluminum and oxygen atoms, Al_2O_3, with a small amount of chromium ions as an impurity, 0.04% of Cr^{3+}.)

Fig. 57M   *Energy-level diagram of the energy states of a ruby crystal.*

Semi-metastable states are states in which electron transitions to lower levels are not entirely forbidden, as they are in ionized calcium, but there is a short or long delay in the electrons' jumping down to a lower level.

Normally an electron will remain in an excited state for about 10^{-8} s, before jumping to a lower state. In a metastable state, however, it may stay 10^{-5} s, up to several minutes, or more.

When a beam of white light enters a ruby crystal, strong absorption occurs in the blue and green part of the spectrum, and the transmission of only the red region is what gives the ruby its red color.

On shining a strong beam of blue-green light into a ruby crystal the absorption that takes place raises many electrons to the wide-band levels, as shown by the up arrow at the left in Fig. 57M. Because of internal atomic activity the electrons quickly drop down to the intermediate levels, not by the emission of photons, but by the conversion of energy into vibrational kinetic energy of the atoms forming the crystal lattice.

Once in the intermediate levels the electrons remain there for some time and randomly jump back to the normal state emitting visible red light. This *fluorescent light*, as it is called, enhances the red color of the ruby.

Since an incident beam of blue-green light steadily increases the number of electrons in the semi-metastable states, the process is called *optical pumping*. To greatly increase the electron populations in the middle levels, very intense light sources as well as efficient light-gathering systems are frequently used.

One of many systems developed for doing this is shown in Fig. 57N. By placing the exciting light source at one focus of an elliptical reflector and the laser at the other focus, high efficiency can be obtained.

In some lasers, where a steady light beam is required, the random emission of light within the gas, liquid, or solid mass will by chance find some of the waves emitted along the axis (see Fig. 57L). This light, because it may bounce back and forth many times between the highly reflective ends, will stimulate coherent emission parallel to itself and to the axis. These two waves traveling back and forth in step with each other now induce other emission, thereby giving rise

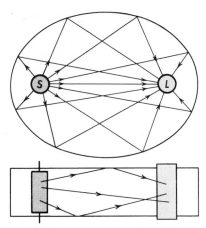

Fig. 57N *Elliptical reflector for concentrating light from a source S on a laser L.*

to a rapid growth or chain reaction. Thus by continuous pumping action from a separate light source, a large part of the stored energy is converted into a coherent beam of light of a different wavelength. Under these conditions the device is said to "laze" spontaneously.

If the silvered ends are not highly reflecting, too much light escapes from the ends and spontaneous lazing cannot occur. Under these conditions a beam of light of the stimulating frequency from another laser can be sent into the crystal where it is intensified. By modulating the input beam the greatly intensified output beam will be modulated accordingly. This modulation capability is one of the important properties that gives lasers their promising future applications to the field of communications.

57.8. The Helium–Neon Gas Laser. The first successful optical gas laser was set into operation by Javan, Bennett, and Heriott in 1961. Since that time many different gas lasers, using ten or more gas systems and several different excitation methods, have been made to operate. Because it was the first to function successfully, a helium–neon laser will be described here.

The gas laser shown in Fig. 57O is composed of a glass tube nearly a meter long containing a mixture of 1-mm-Hg pressure of helium and $\frac{1}{10}$-mm-Hg pressure of neon gas. The highly reflecting Fabry–Perot plates on the ends are so sealed as to prevent leakage and so mounted as

Fig. 57O   *Diagram of a helium–neon gas laser showing Fabry–Perot plates at the ends of the discharge tube, and a high-voltage, high-frequency electrical source for excitation.*

to be adjustable to a high degree of parallelism.

A high-voltage, high-frequency potential difference, such as that obtained from a Tesla coil, is applied by means of three metal bands around the outside of the tube.

Although there are ten times as many helium atoms present as there are neon atoms, the orange-red color of the gaseous discharge is characteristic of neon. The visible spectrum of helium contains strong lines in the red, yellow, green and blue, so the discharge in helium alone appears as white light. The spectrum of neon, on the other hand, has so many strong lines in the yellow, orange and red, and so few in the green, blue, and violet that its gaseous discharge appears orange-red. The neon spectrum also reveals a large number of strong lines in the near-infrared spectrum.

Simplified energy-level diagrams for helium and neon are shown in Fig. 57P for the purpose of explaining the atomic processes involved in laser action. The normal state of helium is a $^1S_0$

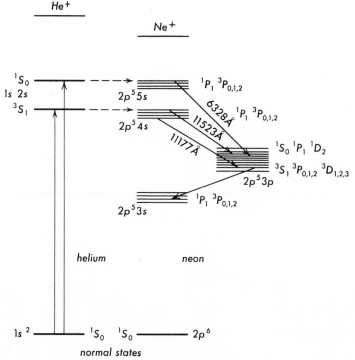

Fig. 57P   *Correlation diagram of the energy levels of helium and neon involved in the helium–neon gas laser.*

level arising from two electrons in 1s orbits. The excitation of one electron to a 2s orbit finds the atom in a $^3S_1$ or a $^1S_0$ state. Both of these are metastable, since transitions to the normal state are forbidden by selection rules (see Sec. 52.6).

Neon, with $Z = 10$, has ten electrons and in the normal state is represented by the configuration $1s^2\,2s^2\,2p^6$. When one of the $2p$ electrons is excited to a $3s$, $3p$, $3d$, $4s$, $4p$, $4d$, $4f$, $5s$, etc., orbit, triplet and singlet levels arise.

A subshell such as $2p^5$, lacking only one electron to form a closed subshell, behaves as though it were a subshell containing only one $2p$ electron. The number and designations of the levels produced are therefore the same as with two electrons.

As free electrons collide with helium atoms during discharge, one of the two bound electrons may be excited to 2s orbits, that is, to the $^3S_1$ or $^1S_0$ states. Since downward transitions are forbidden by radiation selection rules, these are *metastable states,* and the number of excited atoms increases. We therefore have optical pumping, out of the normal $^1S_0$ state and into the metastable states $^3S_1$ and $^1S_0$.

When a metastable helium atom collides with a neon atom in its normal state, there is a high probability that the excitation energy will be transferred to the neon, raising it to one of the $^1P_1$ or $^3P_0$, $^3P_1$, $^3P_2$ levels of $2p^5\,4s$ or $2p^5\,5s$. The small excess energy is converted to kinetic energy of the colliding atoms.

In this process, called a *collision of the second kind,* each helium atom returns to the normal state as each colliding neon atom is excited to the upper level of corresponding energy.

The probability of a neon atom being raised to the $2p^5\,3s$ or $2p^5\,3p$ levels by collisions of the second kind are extremely small because of the energy mismatch. The collision transfer, therefore, selectively increases the population of the upper levels of neon. Since selection rules permit transitions from these levels downward to the ten levels of $2p^5\,3p$, and these in turn to the four levels of $2p^5\,3s$, stimulated emission can speed up this process by laser action.

Light waves emitted within the laser at wavelengths such as 6328 Å, 11,177 Å, and 11,523 Å, will occasionally be emitted parallel to the tube axis. Bouncing back and forth between the parallel end plates, these waves will stimulate emission of the same frequency from other excited neon atoms, and the initial wave, with the stimulated wave, moves parallel to the axis and in phase.

Most of the amplified radiation emerging from the ends of the helium–neon gas laser are in the near-infrared region of the spectrum, between 10,000 Å and 35,000 Å. The most intense amplified wavelength in the visible spectrum being the red line at $\lambda = 6328$ Å. The strongest amplified line in the infrared is at $\lambda = 11,523$ Å.

PROBLEMS

1. A Fabry–Perot interferometer has its two silvered faces accurately spaced 2.5 mm apart. If green light of wavelength 6000 Å is sent through, and a 1-m focal-length lens is used on the far side to produce an interference ring pattern at the focal plane, find (a) the principal oscillation mode n, (b) the diameter of the $n - 1$ circular fringe, and (c) the equivalent wavelength spacing between adjacent rings.

2. A Fabry–Perot interferometer has its two silvered faces accurately spaced 1.8 cm apart. If blue light of wavelength 4500 Å is sent through, and a 1-m focal-length lens is used on the far side to produce an interference ring pattern at the focal plane, find (a) the principal oscillation mode n, and (b) the equivalent wavelength interval in angstroms between adjacent rings. [*Ans.* (a) 80,000, (b) 0.05625 Å.]

3. A ruby laser produces a beam of red light of wavelength 6943 Å, with a circular cross section $\frac{1}{8}$ in. in diameter. Find the diameter of this beam at a distance of 100 mi.

4. A ruby laser produces a beam of red light of wavelength 6943 A, with a circular cross section 1 cm in diameter. Find the diameter of this beam at a distance of 1000 Km. [*Ans.* 169 m.]

5. Use a millimeter scale and measure the distances between line components in the fringe pattern for $\lambda = 5997$ Å in Fig. 57K. Assuming that the Fabry–Perot plate separation was 7 cm, calculate (a) the wavelength interval between successive ring patterns and (b) the wavelength intervals between the strongest component and the other seven components.

RELATIVITY

The mention of the word "relativity" suggests the name of Albert Einstein,* the scientist to whom we are indebted for the now famous theory. To begin with, Einstein was a realist, and his theory rests upon physical facts which have been verified by repeated observations of well-planned experiments. Reference is made in particular to the Michelson–Morley experiment, described in Chapter 57.

Beginning in Chapter 56 we have seen that moving observers in each of two different frames of reference may make their own simultaneous measurements of some single event and by the use of transformation equations, determine the observations made by the other observer.

A frame of reference moving with constant velocity has been called an *inertial frame* because Newton's laws are obeyed within it. The term

* Albert Einstein (1879–1955), German–Swiss physicist, was born of Jewish parents at Ulm, Württemberg, on March 14, 1879. His boyhood was spent in Munich where his father, a dealer in chemicals, had settled in 1880. When the family moved to Italy in 1894, young Albert went to Switzerland to study. There he worked his way through school, finally taking his Ph.D. degree at the University of Zürich in 1902. He was appointed extraordinary professor of theoretical physics at the University of Zürich in 1909, and in 1913 he was called to Berlin as director of the Kaiser-Wilhelm Institute for Physics. While at this post, he was elected a member of the Prussian Academy of Sciences and a member of the Royal Society of London. In 1921 he received the Nobel Prize in physics and, in 1925, the Copley Medal of the Royal Society. From 1933 to 1945 he was with the Institute for Advanced Studies in Princeton, where he died. He is best known for his theory of relativity, the theory and explanation of Brownian motion, the theory of the photoelectric effect, and the quantum theory of radiant heat energy. Twice married, Einstein had several children. For his friends he was a quiet, sincere, and modest man who loved his pipe and violin and disliked formality.

inertial is used to distinguish such a frame from an accelerated frame in which a fictitious force appears to be ever present.

In transforming measurements from one inertial frame to another, distances and accelerations are found to have the same values whether viewed from one frame or the other. For these reasons *distance* and *acceleration* are said to be *invariant* (see Sec. 56.6). Observed velocities, on the other hand differ from one frame to another and are not invariant.

In deriving the Galilean–Newtonian transformation equations in Chapter 56, it was assumed that light travels with an infinite speed. This means that measurements could be made simultaneously from different frames. Since light has a finite speed, light itself should not be expected to be invariant; the speed of light should be different when measured from different inertial frames.

It should then be possible by accurately observing a single event from two inertial frames to determine this difference in the speed of light and find whether or not the two frames are moving through the ether at different rates.

This was the purpose of the Michelson–Morley experiment, and it failed.

58.1. Gedanken (Thought) Experiment. Imagine two space ships in the form of two giant rulers, perfectly straight and rigid, precisely marked and laid out side by side on the ground (see Fig. 58A). Six astronauts A, B, C, and A′, B′, C′, are stationed as shown, and all agree that rulers are the same length, and that the midpoints markings are truly at the midpoints.

The two space ships take off on a space voyage and later encounter each other in outer space for

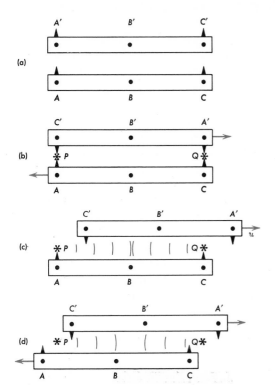

Fig. 58A *Diagrams of a "gedanken" experiment in which two space ships, in the form of two giant rulers, pass each other in free space.*

the purpose of seeing whether the two rulers are still of the same length. As they coast past each other on adjacent and parallel paths at a constant relative velocity *u*, electric sparks jump across between the points at the two opposite ends [see diagram (b)]. These sparks create light flashes of extremely short duration.

How will observers B and B′ interpret these light flashes? Before the two ships came into sight of each other there were no nearby objects against which B and B′ could determine their ship's motion. As the primed ruler passes, the light flashes are initiated, and B believes that these two events occurred at the two fixed points on his ship where A and C are located.

Since light travels with a constant speed of 3×10^8 m/s in free space, let us assume that the unprimed ruler is at rest and that the two light pulses do indeed reach observer B at the same time [see diagram (c)]. This means that the sparks occurred at an earlier time when B′ was

opposite B. Thus at the instant the two pulses reach B, B′ has already moved slightly past. Thus the P pulse has yet to reach B′, whereas the Q pulse has already passed B′. Then B′ must conclude that his primed ruler is longer than the unprimed one. Based on the hypothesis that B thinks the two rulers are still of the same length, B′ disagrees and thinks his own ruler is longer.

But this is impossible. The experiment is completely symmetrical and the two light signals do not arrive at B simultaneously.

Imagine the conditions to be those shown in diagram (d) in which both rulers are in motion and the light pulse P reaches B at the same time light pulse Q reaches B′. A short time Δt later, light pulse P reaches B′ and pulse Q reaches B. Since each observer sees that the light flash from the rear of his ship arrives later than the pulse from the front, each concludes that his ship is longer than the other. Which observer is right?

Since the experiment was absolutely symmetrical, we must conclude they are both right. If there were a tangible medium with respect to which the velocity of each ruler could be specified, and in which the speed of light were constant, one could take this into account and differentiate between the two answers. But the medium is a vacuum, there are no nearby objects, and it is just as meaningful to say one ship is at rest and the other is moving, as it is to say the opposite, or as it is to say they are both moving. Since a vacuum is intangible it is nonsense to talk about the velocity of an object relative to a vacuum.

If you, the reader, imagine yourself to be the observer B, it is very natural for you to consider you are on the stationary ruler and that the primed ruler is moving by at a velocity *u* [see diagram (c)]. It is also consistent with your common sense to conclude that you and B′ are both moving and that your ruler is longer because the P signal reaches you before the Q signal does [see diagram (d)]. But it is equally natural for me to imagine myself to be observer B′ and come to different conclusions that are equally consistent with common sense.

What makes this experiment seem to be

inconsistent is that in our every-day life we do not perceive airplanes becoming shorter as they speed down a runway on take-off, nor trains extending their length as they draw up to a stop at a station. The reason for this is that the speed of light is so great compared with the relative velocities of large familiar objects.

The important point of this "gedanken experiment" is to recognize that when there is relative motion between two observers, the time intervals measured between two events as well as lengths measured will differ.

The problem then becomes one of finding a set of equations that will enable the observer in one frame of reference to determine by calculation the measured observations of events as seen by another observer in another frame of reference.

58.2. The Lorentz–Fitzgerald Contraction.

From the time Michelson and Morley announced the negative results of their ether-drift experiment, scientists tried to explain why the experiment failed. An ingenious explanation was first advanced by Fitzgerald in 1890. If objects moving through space have to push against the immovable ether, he suggested, they would be compressed in the direction of motion. This compression would, therefore, shorten the Michelson interferometer arms holding the mirrors and might exactly compensate for an existing ether drift.

Lorentz,* the famous Dutch physicist, studied this problem from an atomic point of view. All matter, he proposed, is made up of atoms, and atoms are made up of charged particles that produce electric and magnetic fields. These fields must exert forces on the electromagnetic ether, thus causing the atoms and molecules in moving matter to be pushed closer together. Starting

* Hendrik A. Lorentz (1853–1928), Dutch physicist, was born at Arnheim on July 18, 1853. He was educated at the University of Leyden, where he was appointed professor of theoretical physics at the age of 25. Those who knew him never lost the opportunity of mentioning his charming personality and kindly disposition. Of his numerous contributions to science he is best known for (1) a set of four algebraic equations, known as the Lorentz transformation, equations which later came out of Einstein's special theory of relativity, and (2) for his theoretical explanation of the Zeeman effect. In 1922 he was awarded, jointly with Zeeman, the Nobel Prize in physics.

with the well-known principles of electricity and magnetism, Lorentz derived the following formula for the length of any object:

$$l' = l\sqrt{1 - \frac{v^2}{c^2}} \qquad (58a)$$

where v is the velocity of the object through the ether, l is its length when at rest in the ether, and c is the velocity of light. Note the resemblance of this equation to Eq.(56c). Suppose that an object is at rest, so that $v = 0$. Upon substitution of $v = 0$ in Eq.(58a), we find $l' = l$, which says the object's length l' will be just equal to its rest length l. If a rod were moving lengthwise with $\frac{3}{4}$ the speed of light, however, the substitution of $v = \frac{3}{4}c$ into the equation gives $l' = 0.66l$. This indicates that the moving rod is only $\frac{2}{3}$ as long as when it is at rest (see Fig. 58B).

Fig. 58B   *Diagram of the Lorentz–Fitzgerald contraction.*

It is interesting to see what this equation reveals if a rod could move lengthwise with the speed of light, i.e., with $v = c$. The result is $l' = 0$. This means that any object moving with the speed of light would be compressed to zero length. The velocity of light, therefore, becomes an upper limit for the velocity of any moving object.

The above formula, when applied to the cross arms of the interferometer used in the Michelson–Morley experiment (see Fig. 57E), shows that the arms are shortened by just the right amount to compensate for the expected drift [see Eq.(56c)]. This shortening of an object cannot be measured, for, if one attempts to measure the length of a moving object, the measuring stick must move with the same velocity, and an equal length of the stick shortens by the same amount.

58.3. Einstein's Special Theory of Relativity.

Einstein interpreted the failure of the Michelson–Morley experiment to mean that the velocity of light is invariant, that time and distance are relative, and that Galilean–Newtonian mechanics must be modified accordingly. Out of these modifications came the theory of relativity.

Relativity is divided into two parts. One part

sumption that the velocity of light is *invariant*.

The velocity of light in free space has the same value regardless of the motion of the source and the motion of the observer.

To see the meaning of this second statement, consider a reference frame and observer O at rest as shown in Fig. 58C. A source of light S is set

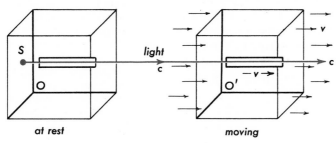

Fig. 58C *The velocity of light is the same to all observers, that is, it is invariant.*

is called the *special*, or *restricted*, *theory of relativity*, and the other is called the *general theory*. The special theory, developed by Einstein in 1905, deals with observers and their reference frames moving with constant velocities. The mathematics of the special theory is simple enough, and we will consider several of the relationships that are necessary for the satisfactory explanations of atomic phenomena.

The general theory, proposed by Einstein in 1915, deals with motions of bodies in accelerated frames of reference. The mathematics of the general theory is quite difficult, and the experimental evidence for its validity is not as well founded as for the special theory.

Since the Michelson–Morley experiment fails to provide a fixed frame of reference in space, Einstein's theory assumes that all such experiments will fail, and that at relatively high speeds the laws of Newton are not valid. Einstein's special theory of relativity shows that the laws of physics can be restated so that they will apply to any frame of reference, and that at low relative speeds these laws reduce to Newton's laws of motion. The first postulate for setting up these equations is:

The laws of physics apply equally well for all observers as long as they are moving with constant velocities.

The second postulate follows from the as-

up, and by means of an experiment the velocity of light is measured and found to be 3×10^8 m/s. Another observer O', moving with a velocity v with respect to O, allows the light from the same source S to pass through his apparatus. Upon measuring the velocity of this same light in his frame, he too finds 3×10^8 m/s.

For these two identical results to be consistent, Einstein derived new transformation equations. To do this he assumed that *distance* and *time* are relative, i.e., they are not *invariant*. His transformation equations may be written down and compared with the nonrelativistic equations as follows:

$$x' = x - vt \qquad x' = \gamma(x - vt) \qquad (58b)$$

$$t' = t \qquad t' = \gamma\left(t - \frac{vx}{c^2}\right) \qquad (58c)$$

nonrelativistic   **relativistic**

where γ is given by

$$\gamma = \frac{1}{\sqrt{1 - v^2/c^2}} \qquad (58d)$$

Note the similarity of these two sets of equations. By setting $v = 0$ in Eq.(58d), we get $\gamma = 1$, and the relativistic equations reduce to the nonrelativistic, or Newtonian, equations. The value of γ is just the ratio of the two *travel times* for the light paths in the Michelson–Morley experiment.

Classical laws such as Newton's laws of motion can be used in most applications of kinematics and dynamics to the motions of macroscopic bodies; but at speeds above 10% the speed of light, the relativistic equations should be used.

Since Eqs.(58b), (58c), and (58d) were first derived by Lorentz in 1895, their use in any problem is referred to as a *Lorentz transformation*. Lorentz arrived at the equations by assuming a contraction of moving objects in an ether, whereas Einstein in 1905 derived the equations by assuming the speed of light as *invariant*.

58.4. Relativistic Velocity Transformation.

This is the velocity transformation equation in the theory of relativity. It shows that velocity, as in Newtonian mechanics, too, is not *invariant*. Different observers find different velocities.

$$u' = u - v \qquad (58h)$$
$$\textbf{nonrelativistic}$$

Example 1. An observer on the earth (assumed to be an inertial frame of reference) sees a space ship P receding from him at 2×10^8 m/s and overtaking a space ship Q receding at 1.5×10^8 m/s. Find the relative velocity of (a) space ship Q as observed by P, (b) space ship P as observed by Q, and (c) space ship Q relative to space ship P as observed by O.

Solution. This example is shown schematically in Fig. 58D. The given quantities for (a) are $v = 2 \times 10^8$

Fig. 58D   *Diagram of two space ships receding from the earth with constant velocities.*

Suppose the velocity of a body in an observer's frame of reference is u, and we wish to calculate the velocity u' of that same body as measured by an observer moving with a velocity v. For this calculation we use the velocity transformation equations, Eq.(56i):

$$u' = \frac{x'_2 - x'_1}{t'_2 - t'_1} \quad \text{and} \quad u = \frac{x_2 - x_1}{t_2 - t_1} \quad (58e)$$

We now make use of the relativistic transformation equations, Eqs.(58b) and (58c), and substitute unprimed terms for each primed term in the first relation. This gives

$$u' = \frac{\gamma(x_2 - vt_2) - \gamma(x_1 - vt_1)}{\gamma(t_2 - vx_2/c^2) - \gamma(t_1 - vx_1/c^2)} \quad (58f)$$

Upon canceling the γ's, multiplying out, collecting like terms, dividing all terms by $t_2 - t_1$, substituting from the right-hand equation of Eq.(58e), and simplifying, we obtain*

$$\boxed{u' = \frac{u - v}{1 - uv/c^2}} \quad (58g)$$

relativistic

* The algebraic steps from Eq.(58e) to Eq.(58g) are left as a student exercise (see Problem 14).

m/s; $u = 1.5 \times 10^8$ m/s; and $c = 3 \times 10^8$ m/s. Upon substitution in Eq.(58g) we obtain

Part (a)

$$u' = \frac{1.5 \times 10^8 \text{ m/s} - 2.0 \times 10^8 \text{ m/s}}{1 - 1.5 \times 10^8 \times 2.0 \times 10^8/(3 \times 10^8)^2}$$

$$u' = \frac{-0.5 \times 10^8}{1 - 3 \times 10^{16}/9 \times 10^{16}} = -0.75 \times 10^8 \text{ m/s}$$

For (b) we reverse the velocity symbols; $u = 2 \times 10^8$ m/s and $v = 1.5 \times 10^8$ m/s. Upon substitution in Eq.(58g), we obtain

Part (b)

$$u' = \frac{2.0 \times 10^8 - 1.5 \times 10^8}{1 - 2.0 \times 10^8 \times 1.5 \times 10^8/(3 \times 10^8)^2}$$

$$u' = \frac{0.5 \times 10^8}{1 - 3 \times 10^{16}/9 \times 10^{16}} = +0.75 \times 10^8 \text{ m/s}$$

For (c) we take just the difference between the two velocities observed by O.

$$u' = 1.5 \times 10^8 - 2.0 \times 10^8 = -0.5 \times 10^8 \text{ m/s}$$

For solving problems using Eq.(58g), make a diagram similar to Fig. 58D, showing observer O, and his reference frame, at rest. The frame from which new observations are to be calculated is selected as body P, and is drawn to the right or left of O, and labeled with an appropriate arrow v. The body to be observed from P is now located in its appropriate position, to the right or left, and labeled Q with its appropriate arrow u.

The sign conventions for use in Eq.(58g) are as follows:

Velocities u or v to the right are positive.
Velocities u or v to the left are negative.
A positive u' signifies Q is moving to the right with respect to P.
A negative u' signifies Q is moving to the left with respect to P.

Example 2. Suppose space ship Q in Example 1 (Fig. 58D) is replaced by a beam of light moving from left to right, which observer O measures and finds to be $c = 3 \times 10^8$ m/s. What will the velocity of this same light be, as observed by space ship P?

Solution. The given quantities are $u = c$, $v = 2.0 \times 10^8$ m/s, and $c = 3 \times 10^8$ m/s. Upon first replacing u by c in Eq.(58g) and solving for u', we obtain

$$u' = \frac{u - v}{1 - uv/c^2} = \frac{c - v}{1 - cv/c^2} = \frac{c - v}{1 = v/c} = \frac{c - v}{\dfrac{c - v}{c}} = c$$

Hence the observer in P finds the velocity of light to be c regardless of his velocity. Hence the velocity of light is the same to all observers; it is *invariant*.

58.5. Relativistic Mass. Einstein's special theory of relativity shows that if the mass of an object is measured by two different observers, one moving with respect to the other, the results are different. Mass, therefore, is not invariant. Although the derivation will not be presented here, the special theory gives, for the transformation equation,

$$m = \gamma m_0 \tag{58i}$$

or

$$\boxed{m = \frac{m_0}{\sqrt{1 - v^2/c^2}}} \tag{58j}$$

relativistic

where m_0 is the mass of an object at rest in the observer's reference frame, and m is its mass when it is moving with a velocity v. A schematic diagram of a practical situation is shown in Fig. 58E in which the rest mass m_0 is not moving

Fig. 58E *Schematic diagram illustrating the relativistic increase in mass, and the Lorentz–Fitzgerald contraction, due to motion.*

with respect to you, the observer, while at the right the same mass m is shown moving with a velocity v.

Table 58A gives the values of the relativistic mass of objects for a large range of velocities.

TABLE 58A. RELATIVISTIC MASS FOR DIFFERENT VELOCITIES

Velocity ratio v/c in percent	1%	10%	50%	90%	99%	99.9%
Relative mass m/m_0	1.000	1.005	1.15	2.3	7.1	22.3

At 10% the speed of light (18,630 mi/s) the mass of a body is only $\frac{1}{2}$ of 1% greater than its rest mass. At 50% the speed of light the mass m has increased 15%, while at 99.9% the speed of light, it has jumped to over 22 times its rest mass. These values are in excellent agreement with experiments on high-speed atomic particles, a subject that will be considered in detail in later chapters.

It is important to note that, as the speed of any given mass increases, the mass rises slowly at first, and then much more rapidly as it approaches the speed of light. No object, however, can move with the speed of light, for by Eq.(58j) its mass would become infinite.

For low velocities v, Eqs.(58d) and (58j) are hard to evaluate, and the following approximation formula should be used*:

$$\frac{1}{\sqrt{1 - v^2/c^2}} \cong 1 + \frac{1}{2}\frac{v^2}{c^2} \tag{58k}$$

* The right side of this equation represents the first two terms of a mathematical series expansion, and for relatively low velocities v, the third and all succeeding terms are negligibly small:

$$1 + \frac{1}{2}\frac{v^2}{c^2} + \frac{3}{8}\frac{v^4}{c^4} + \frac{5}{16}\frac{v^6}{c^6} + \cdots$$

58.6. Einstein's Mass–Energy Relation. Just as sound, heat, and light are forms of energy, Einstein's special theory of relativity shows that mass is a form of energy. The expression giving the relation between mass and energy is an equation familiar to everyone. It is

$$E = mc^2 \qquad (58l)$$

relativistic

where m is the mass, c is the velocity of light, and E is the energy equivalence of the mass. The validity of this equation is now well established by hundreds of experiments involving atomic nuclei as well as the general subject called *atomic energy*.

If an object has a rest mass of m_0, it has stored within it a total energy m_0c^2. If the same mass is moving with a velocity v, its mass has increased to m and the total stored energy is mc^2. These two masses are related by Eq.(58j).

When a force F is applied to accelerate a given mass, the amount of work done is given by

$$W = F \times x$$

As a result of this *work done*, the object, whose rest mass is m_0, is moving with a velocity and has kinetic energy E_k:

$$F \times x = E_k \qquad (58m)$$

Applying the law of conservation of energy, we can write

$$m_0c^2 + E_k = mc^2$$

Solving for E_k, we obtain for the kinetic energy of a moving mass, the relation

$$E_k = mc^2 - m_0c^2 \qquad (58n)$$

Another form for this equation is obtained by substituting Eq.(58j) for m:

$$E_k = \frac{m_0c^2}{\sqrt{1 - v^2/c^2}} - m_0c^2 \qquad (58o)$$

or

$$E_k = m_0c^2\left[\frac{1}{\sqrt{1 - v^2/c^2}} - 1\right] \qquad (58p)$$

In the abbreviated notation,

$$E_k = m_0c^2(\gamma - 1) \qquad (58q)$$

The total energy of a moving particle is given by its rest mass, m_0c^2, plus the energy expended to give it motion, E_k. Using Eq.(58o) we can therefore write

$$E_{\text{total}} = \frac{m_0c^2}{\sqrt{1 - v^2/c^2}} \qquad (58r)$$

PROBLEMS

(Assume the speed of light to be 3×10^8 m/s, or 186,300 mi/s, in all of the following problems.)

1. Find the length of a meter stick moving lengthwise at a speed of 2.75×10^8 m/s. Assume a Lorentz–Fitzgerald contraction.

2. If a space ship 50 m long were to pass the earth traveling at 2.4×10^8 m/s, what would be its apparent length, assuming a Lorentz-Fitzgerald contraction? [*Ans.* 30 m.]

3. The brakeman on a freight train traveling 50 mi/hr is walking forward on top of one of the box cars at 3 mi/hr. A train just ahead of this one is traveling at 75 mi/hr. What is the velocity of the brakeman with respect to the engineer in the train ahead, to three significant figures, (a) in Newtonian mechanics, and (b) in special relativity?

4. A man on the ground observes a plane taking off on the airport runway at 120 m/s. A car traveling 32 m/s follows it down the runway. Find the relative velocity of the plane as seen by the driver of the car. [*Ans.* 88 m/s.]

5. An observer on the earth sees one space ship receding from the earth at 2.75×10^8 m/s overtaking another space ship receding from the earth at 2.50×10^8 m/s. What is the relative velocity of (a) the second ship as seen by the first, (b) the first ship as seen by the second, and (c) the relative velocity as seen from the earth?

6. An observer on the earth sees a space ship, receding from the earth at 2.0×10^8 m/s, launch a projectile ahead of it. As seen from the earth this projectile has a speed of 2.25×10^8 m/s. What is the velocity of the projectile with respect to the space ship as seen from (a) the space ship, and (b) the earth? [*Ans.* (a) 0.5×10^8 m/s, (b) 2.25×10^8 m/s.]

7. An earth observer sees a space ship approaching the earth at $\frac{2}{3}$ the speed of light. It launches an exploration vehicle which from the earth appears to be approaching at $\frac{3}{4}$ the velocity of light. What is the velocity of the vehicle with respect to the space ship as seen from (a) the space ship, and (b) the earth?

8. Two space ships are observed from the earth to be approaching each other, each with a velocity of $\frac{2}{3}$ the

speed of light. With what velocity is each space ship approaching the other, as seen from either ship? [Ans. 2.77×10^8 m/s, or 0.92 c.]

9. Atomic particles in the form of a beam have a velocity of 95% the speed of light. What is their relativistic mass as compared with their rest mass?

10. Atomic particles in the form of a beam have a velocity of 95% the speed of light. What is their relativistic mass compared with their rest mass? [Ans. $m/m_0 = 3.20$.]

11. An atomic particle has a rest mass of 6.4×10^{-25} Kg. Find its total mass energy when it is (a) at rest, and (b) when it has a velocity of 0.96 the speed of light.

12. Two atomic particles, each with a rest mass of 2.0×10^{-25} Kg, approach each other in head-on collision. If each has an initial velocity of 2.0×10^8 m/s, what is (a) the velocity of one atom as seen from the other, and (b) the relativistic mass of one as seen by the other? [Ans. (a) 2.77×10^8 m/s, (b) 5.10×10^{-25} Kg.]

13. If an atomic mass of 6.3×10^{-25} Kg were converted into energy, and all of it imparted as kinetic energy to another atomic particle with a rest mass of 2.5×10^{-25} Kg, what would be the atom's velocity?

14. Starting with Eq.(58e), carry out the algebraic steps necessary to obtain Eq.(58g).

15. A space ship P takes off from the earth and heads for a distant planet. Later a second ship Q takes off for the same planet. Sometime still later, space ship Q is observed from the earth to be receding at a speed of $\frac{3}{4}$ the speed of light. Space ship P as observed from ship Q is observed to be receding at $\frac{3}{4}$ the speed of light. With what speed is P receding from the earth? Assume all bodies lie along the same straight line.

16. Solve Problem 15, if the two observed speeds are $\frac{2}{3}$ the speed of light. [Ans. 2.77×10^8 m/s.]

17. Solve Eq.(58g) for u as the unknown.

ELECTRON OPTICS

There exists a remarkable similarity between optical systems of prisms and lenses, as they act upon light rays, and electric magnetic fields as they act upon streams of electrons. It is the purpose of this chapter to consider some of these similarities and to treat several practical applications of *electron optics*. To begin with, it is convenient to present one of the standard methods of producing a beam of electrons, and to give the formula for calculating electron velocity.

59.1. An Electron Accelerator. A schematic diagram of an electron accelerator is shown in Fig. 59A. The source of electrons is a cesium-

Fig. 59A *Electrons are accelerated by an applied potential difference V.*

oxide-coated cathode K, heated by a filament F. The cathode and filament are connected to the negative terminal, and the circular disk at the center to the positive terminal of a high-voltage battery V. Starting from rest at the cathode, the electrons are accelerated along the electric lines of force, acquiring at the anode A a velocity v.

By connecting the (+) terminal to the ground, the anode is brought to the potential of the surrounding walls of the room and the electrons are not attracted back toward A, but continue on with constant velocity. With a thin aluminum

foil at the end and a high applied voltage V, electrons may be projected into the air beyond.

One of the results of J. J. Thomson's experiments with cathode rays was the discovery that the velocity of electrons depends upon the *potential* applied between the anode and the cathode. The higher the voltage, the higher is the electron velocity.

$$Ve = \tfrac{1}{2}m_0v^2 \qquad (59a)$$

where V is the applied accelerating *potential* in volts, m_0 is the rest mass of the electron in kilograms, v the velocity in meters per second, and e the charge on the particle in coulombs.

Example 1. Calculate the velocity of electrons accelerated by a potential difference of 10,000 V. (The electronic charge $e = 1.60 \times 10^{-19}$ C, and $m = 9.1 \times 10^{-31}$ Kg.)

Solution. Direct substitution in the above equation gives

$$10,000 \times 1.6 \times 10^{-19} = \tfrac{1}{2}(9.1 \times 10^{-31}) \times v^2$$

from which

$$v = \sqrt{\frac{10,000 \times 1.6 \times 10^{-19} \times 2}{9.1 \times 10^{-31}}} = 0.59 \times 10^8 \text{ m/s}$$

This is approximately $\tfrac{1}{5}$ the speed of light. (Speed of light $c = 3 \times 10^8$ m/s.)

Instead of calculating the velocity of electrons in meters per second, it is customary to refer to their kinetic energy in terms of the applied voltage. For example, in the problem above the energy gained by the electrons is said to be 10,000 *electron volts* (10,000 eV, or 10 KeV). They are also sometimes referred to as 10,000-volt electrons.

If voltages greater than 255,000 V are used in Eq.(59a), the calculated velocities will be greater than the velocity of light. Consequently, for voltages of about 20,000 V or more, the relativistic formula should be used. From the formula for the kinetic energy of a high-speed mass, Eq.(58q), we obtain

$$Ve = m_0c^2(\gamma - 1) \qquad (59b)$$

where

$$\gamma = \frac{1}{\sqrt{1 - v^2/c^2}}$$

If Eq.(59b) is solved for v/c, one obtains the very useful equation,

$$\frac{v}{c} = \sqrt{1 - \left(\frac{1}{\dfrac{Ve}{m_0c^2} + 1}\right)^2} \qquad (59c)$$

59.2. Refraction of Electrons. When a moving electron, entering an electric field, makes an angle with the electric lines of force, it is bent in its path according to *Bethe's law of refraction* (see Fig. 59B). A correlation of this law with

The left-hand diagram shows two metal cylinders lined up end to end with fine wire screens across the ends marked A and B. The lower battery maintains a constant difference of potential $V_2 - V_1$ between these two screens.

Note in Eq.(50d) the reverse order of the velocities v_1 and v_2. When a ray of light enters a more dense medium, it is slowed down and at the same time bent toward the normal. Electrons, on the other hand, are deflected toward the normal when, in crossing a potential layer, they are speeded up. If the grid potentials are reversed, the electrons will be retarded in crossing the potential layer and they will be deflected away from the normal. In other words, *reverse the direction of the electrons, keeping their speed the same, and they will retrace their paths exactly.* Such a behavior is analogous to the very useful principle in geometrical optics that *all light rays are retraceable.*

To carry the refraction analogy a little further,

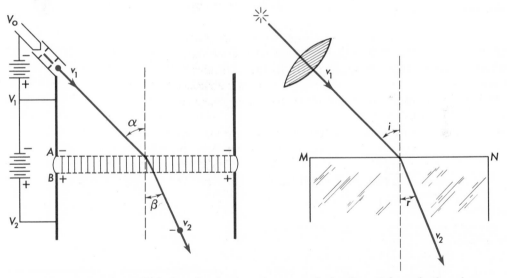

Fig. 59B   *The bending of light in refraction is analogous to the bending of the path of an electron.*

Snell's law in optics is indicated by the following parallel equations:

SNELL'S LAW	BETHE'S LAW	
$\dfrac{\sin i}{\sin r} = \dfrac{v_1}{v_2}$	$\dfrac{\sin \alpha}{\sin \beta} = \dfrac{v_2}{v_1}$	(59d)

consider the bending of electron paths by electrically charged bodies as shown in Fig. 59C. Attraction by the positively charged wire and repulsion by the negative produce a prismlike action in case (a). A negatively charged

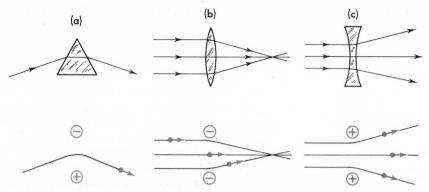

Fig. 59C   *Comparison of light optics with electron optics.*

metal ring produces a converging lenslike action in case (b); a positively charged ring produces a diverging lens action in case (c).

Since, by Eq.(59a), $v^2 \propto V$ and $v \propto \sqrt{V}$, the velocities v_1 and v_2 in Bethe's law of electron refraction may be replaced by $\sqrt{V_1}$ and $\sqrt{V_2}$, respectively, giving

$$\frac{\sin \alpha}{\sin \beta} = \frac{\sqrt{V_2}}{\sqrt{V_1}} \qquad (59e)$$

V_1 and V_2 are the potentials of the two grids A and B in Fig. 59B, taken with respect to the cathode source of electrons in the electron gun as zero.

59.3. Electron Lenses. An electron lens, known as a double-aperture system, is shown in Fig. 59D; it is to be compared in its action to parallel

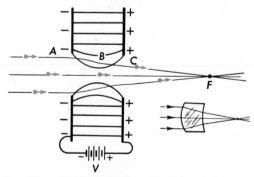

Fig. 59D   *Double-aperture electron lens and its optical analog.*

rays of light incident on a converging glass lens as shown at the lower right. While both are converging systems, the essential difference between the two is that whereas light rays are bent only at the two surfaces, electrons are refracted continuously as they pass through the potential layers.

The focal length of a glass lens is fixed in value by the radius of curvature of its two faces and the refractive index for the light used, but the focal length of an electron lens can be varied at will by altering v, the velocity of the electrons, and V, the voltage applied to the system. In this respect, the latter can be compared to the crystalline lens of the eye where the focal length can be changed by altering the lens curvature.

In the diagram, refraction for the upper path is greatest near A and, although it changes sign at some point near B, the gain in velocity due to the electric field produces a lesser deviation over the second half of the path, thereby causing convergence. If the electrons are reversed in direction on the right, they will retrace their paths and emerge parallel at the left. If the

Fig. 59E   *Symmetrical electron lens.*

electric field is reversed in direction, however, the electron paths will not be the same but the system will still act as a converging lens.

A second type of electron lens, known as a double-cylinder system, is shown in Fig. 59E. In passing through the potential gap, the electric field has a converging action for the first half of the distance and a diverging action during the second half. Because they spend a greater time in the first half of the converging field, and the force on a charged particle is independent of velocity, the impulse (force × time) is greater for the convergence interval than it is for the divergence interval.

By making the second cylinder larger than the first, as in Fig. 59F, the electric lines of force

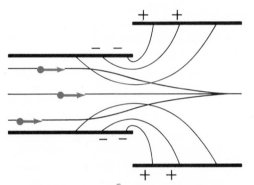

Fig. 59F   *Asymmetrical electron lens.*

spread out more in the second cylinder. Such spreading weakens the field in the larger cylinder and reduces the divergent action to bring the electrons to a shorter focus.

59.4. An Electron Gun. A narrow beam of high-speed electrons, all having as nearly as possible the same velocity, has many practical applications in the field of electronics and atomic research. A device for producing such beams is called an "electron gun" (see Fig. 59G).

Electrons from a small filament-heated cathode K are accelerated by a difference of potential V applied to the cylinders of an electrostatic lens system, A_1 and A_2. The purpose of the guard ring maintained at the potential of the cathode is to improve the properties of the lens action of the first aperture and thereby collect a maximum

Fig. 59G   *Electron gun.*

number of emitted electrons into the collimated beam.

The function of the second lens is to converge the bundle toward a focus and then introduce enough divergence to straighten the beam out into a narrow pencil. The velocity of the emergent beam is given by Eq.(59a) where V is the over-all voltage from cathode K to anode A_2.

59.5. The Cathode-Ray Oscilloscope. One of the simplest applications of an electron gun is to be found in every *cathode-ray oscilloscope*, an instrument whose purpose is to reveal the detailed variations in rapidly changing electric currents, potentials, or pulses (see Fig. 59H). In appearance this device looks like J. J. Thomson's cathode-ray tube (see Fig. 48F), and is actually the important element in one type of television receiver.

A cathode-ray oscilloscope is a vacuum tube containing *an electron gun* at one end, two pairs of *deflector plates* (or magnetic coils) near the middle, and a *fluorescent screen* at the other end. When an alternating voltage is applied to the *x plates*, the electron beam bends back and forth from side to side and, when applied to the *y plates*, it bends up and down. The luminous spot produced where the beam strikes the fluorescent screen traces out a horizontal line in the first instance and a vertical line in the second.

It is customary to apply a *saw-tooth potential difference* to the *x* plates [see Fig. 59I(a)] and the unknown potential difference to be studied, (b), to the *y* plates. The saw-tooth potential difference supplied by a special radio tube circuit, called a "sweep circuit," causes the beam spot to move from left to right across the screen at

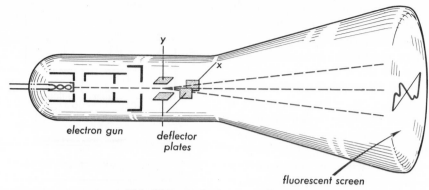

Fig. 59H *Cathode-ray oscilloscope.*

constant speed and then jump quickly back from right to left to repeat the motion, (c). When the vertical deflections occur at the same time, the spot draws out a graph of the varying potential difference as in diagram (d). By varying the sweep circuit frequency until it matches the frequency of the studied signal, repeated graphs

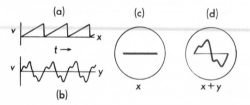

Fig. 59I *Potentials applied to a cathode-ray tube, and graphs appearing on a fluorescent screen.*

will be drawn out, one on top of the other, and persistence of vision and the fluorescent screen will present a stationary graph.

Green fluorescent screens are used for visual observation since the eye is most sensitive to this color; blue screens are used for photographic purposes since films and plates are most sensitive to blue.

The oscilloscope has many practical applications, and is to be found in every research laboratory as well as in every radio and television repair shop. Its principal function is to analyze, or diagnose, rapidly changing potential differences whose frequencies may be as low as a fraction of a cycle per second or as high as thousands of megacycles per second. Periodic or transient potential differences as small as a fraction of a microvolt may also be studied by first amplifying them with standard vacuum-tube or transistor circuits (see Chapters 54 and 55).

Another valuable feature of the oscilloscope is its ability to measure time intervals between electrical impulses less than a microsecond apart. One microsecond is equal to one-millionth of a second.

59.6. Infrared Telescope. A telescope for seeing objects in the dark illuminated by infrared light is diagramed in Fig. 59J. An image of the object to be observed is focused on the photocathode of the vacuum tube by means of an ordinary glass lens L. The cesium-oxide-coated cathode under infrared illumination emits photoelectrons which, accelerated to the right by

Fig. 59J *Ultraviolet and infrared telescope employing an electron-image tube.*

$A_1A_2A_3$ and A_4, are brought to a focus on the green fluorescent screen at the right. The visible light they produce there by their impact is then observed by means of a magnifying eyepiece.

Electron focusing is accomplished by varying the potential difference applied to the second anode A_2; the infrared light image is focused by moving the lens L; and the visible light image is focused by moving the eyepiece.

59.7. Magnetic Lenses. When electrons cross a magnetic field and their paths make an angle with the magnetic lines, they are deflected in spiral-like paths which, if properly controlled, may bring them to a focus. Such focusing properties of magnetic fields, illustrated by the cross section of a flat coil in Fig. 59K, were first

kind found with light and glass lenses arise. For this reason *diaphragms* are often used to confine electron beams to the center of the coil, as an *iris diaphragm* is used to confine light rays to the center of a lens.

59.8. Electron Microscope. The electron microscope, like the optical microscope, is an instrument used principally in the research laboratory for magnifying small objects to such an extent that their minutest parts may be observed and studied in detail. The importance of this device in the field of medical research cannot be overestimated. To illustrate, many viruses known to medical science as being responsible for certain human diseases lie beyond the range of the optical microscope. With the electron micro-

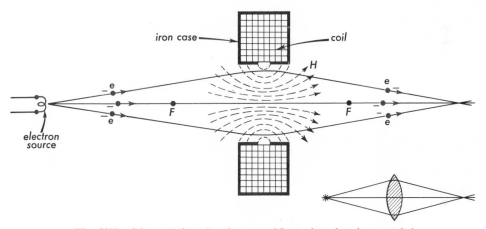

Fig. 59K   *Magnetic lens for electrons. (Optical analog, lower right.)*

demonstrated and proved mathematically by Busch in 1926. It can be shown that the focal length of such a lens, the magnetic field strength, and the electron velocity fit into well-known formulas in optics.

By encasing a flat coil in a hollow iron ring, the magnetic field becomes more concentrated and the refraction of electrons becomes more abrupt as they pass through the field. As a consequence the refraction more nearly resembles that of optical lenses. Still greater concentration is brought about by providing a small narrow gap on the inside of the iron casing, as shown in the diagram.

If electron paths diverge too far from the principal axis of a coil lens, aberrations of the

scope, magnifications of from 10 to 100 times that of the finest optical microscopes make many of these viruses, and some of their detailed structure, visible to the eye. While the highest magnification obtained with the best optical microscope is about 2000×, electron microscopes have already been made that give magnifications as high as 100,000×.

A schematic diagram of an electron microscope employing magnetic lenses is shown in Fig. 59L. At the bottom, a source of electrons is concentrated on the object (small arrow) by a condenser coil. Passing through or around the object, these electrons focus a magnified image of the object just below the projector coil. Only a small central section of these electrons pass

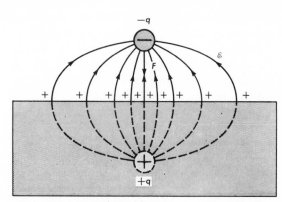

Fig. 59L *Optical microscope compared with an electron microscope.*

Fig. 59M *Diagram of the electric field between a negative charge −q and a good metallic conductor.*

into the projector coil, to be brought to focus in a further magnified image at the top. There the image of only a small section of the object can be seen directly on a fluorescent screen or can be photographed with ordinary photographic plates.

Electrons, like light waves, are stopped by metallic films; only when the films are extremely thin can transmitted rays be employed. For opaque objects the light, or electrons, may be

Coulomb forces of attraction and repulsion set up surface charges as shown. Under these conditions the electric field between the two takes the form shown by the solid lines.

A comparison of these lines with Fig. 29A(c) shows their general shape to be the same as though an equal but opposite charge +q was located an equal distance beyond the metal surface. In other words the field outside the

Fig. 59N *Electrons passing over a metallic diffraction grating at right angles to the surface grooves, generate electromagnetic waves of very short wavelength.*

reflected from the surface and only surface structures may be observed.*

59.9. Visible Light from Unbound Electrons. When an isolated charged body is located close to a metallic conductor as shown in Fig. 59M,

* For a more complete treatment of electron optics, see V. K. Zworykin, *et al.*, *Electron Optics and the Electron Microscope* (John Wiley & Sons, Inc., New York, 1945).

conductor is essentially that of an electric dipole. Furthermore, the total plus charge at the conducting surface is equal to $+q$ and exerts a force F on the isolated charge $-q$.

Suppose now that an electron moving with a velocity v passes close to a metallic conductor with a corrugated surface as shown in Fig. 59N. The field between the two will be the same as though an equal positive charge moved along with the same forward velocity v but oscillated up and down. Since the force on the electron varies with distance from the surface, it too moves up and down as shown and the accompanying field is the same as that of an oscillating electric dipole. As a result of these oscillations, electromagnetic waves will be radiated as if from a moving Hertzian dipole (see Sec. 54.5).

To calculate the frequency of the emitted radiation and the wavelength observed by a stationary observer, the principles of the Doppler effect must be employed. The top diagram in Fig. 59O represents the waves emitted in 1 s

Fig. 59O   *Geometry for derivation of doppler wavelength of electromagnetic waves from a moving electric dipole.*

from a stationary dipole source, and we can write

$$c = \nu \lambda_e \qquad (59f)$$

where c is the speed of light, ν is the source frequency, and λ_e is the wavelength.

The bottom diagram shows the same number of waves emitted in 1 s by the source as it moves toward the observer with a velocity v. Since the waves are crowded into a distance $c - v$, we may write

$$\nu \lambda = c - v \qquad (59g)$$

where λ is now the wavelength measured by the stationary observer. Substituting $\nu \lambda_e$ for c in this second equation, we obtain

$$\nu \lambda = \nu \lambda_e - v$$

and, therefore,

$$\lambda = \lambda_e - \frac{v}{\nu}$$

Since $\nu = c/\lambda_e$, substitution gives

$$\lambda = \lambda_e - \lambda_e \frac{v}{c}$$

from which,

$$\lambda = \lambda_e \left(1 - \frac{v}{c}\right)$$

If the observer is not in the forward direction but is in some direction making an angle θ with v, only the component of v should be used in this formula, and we write for the general case,

$$\lambda = \lambda_e \left(1 - \frac{v}{c} \cos \theta\right) \qquad (59h)$$

The first proposal that electromagnetic waves in the microwave and infrared region of the spectrum could be generated by projecting a beam of electrons over the surface of a diffraction grating was made by W. W. Salisbury* in 1949 (see Fig. 59P). The first experimental

electron
gun

grating

Fig. 59P   *Moving electron sources give rise to doppler effect and different wavelengths of light.*

generation of visible light by this method was performed by Smith and Purcel.†

If d represents the grating spacing, as shown in Fig. 59N, the vibration frequency of each moving electron will be given by

$$\nu = \frac{v}{d} = \frac{c}{\lambda_e}$$

Since this gives

$$\lambda_e = d \frac{c}{v}$$

direct substitution of dc/v for λ_e in Eq.(59h) yields

$$\lambda = d \left(\frac{c}{v} - \cos \theta\right) \qquad (59i)$$

* U. S. Patent No. 2, 634, 372, October 26, 1949.
† *Phys. Rev.*, **92** (November 15, 1953).

Example 2. A beam of 300,000 volt electrons is projected across a diffraction grating at right angles to the rulings. If the grating contains 20,000 lines/cm, find the wavelength of light emitted at right angles to the grating face.

Solution. The electron velocity v/c is first obtained by substituting $V = 3 \times 10^5$ V in Eq.(59c). This gives

$$\frac{v}{c} = 0.7765$$

Direct substitution of this value in Eq.(59i), gives

$$\lambda = 5 \times 10^{-7} \text{ m} \left(\frac{1}{0.7765} - 0 \right)$$

$$\lambda = 6.44 \times 10^{-7} \text{ m}$$

$$\lambda = 6440 \text{ Å}$$

This is red light.

QUESTIONS AND PROBLEMS

1. What is Bethe's law? In what way is it like Snell's law in optics? In what way is it different?

2. What kind of electric field will deviate an electron beam the way a glass prism deviates a light beam?

3. What are electron lenses? How are they made?

4. Make a diagram of an electron gun, using two hollow tubes of different diameter. Show the electric field and electron paths. Reverse the potentials, and assume a parallel beam again coming in from the left.

5. Make a diagram of a cathode ray oscilloscope. Label the principal parts. Briefly describe its action.

6. Make a diagram of your idea of an electron microscope. Label the principal elements.

7. What voltage applied to an electron gun will give electrons a velocity of 3×10^7 cm/s?

8. If 5000 V are applied to an electron gun, what will be the velocity of the electrons? [*Ans.* 4.19×10^7 m/s.]

9. Make a table of electron velocities for the following accelerating voltages: $V = 5$, 25, 90, 150, 300, and 600 V.

10. What voltage applied to an electron gun will produce electrons having a speed of 2000 mi/hr? [*Ans.* 2.25×10^{-6} V.]

11. Electrons accelerated by a potential $V_1 = 1200$ V enter an electric field between two grids as shown in Fig. 59B. If the angle of incidence is 40° and the potential across the grids is 600 V, find the angle of refraction.

12. If in Problem 11 the voltage across the grids is reversed, find the angle of refraction. [*Ans.* 65.3°.]

13. Electrons accelerated by a potential of 250 V enter an electric field as shown in Fig. 59B. If the angle of incidence is 50°, and the angle of refraction is 30°, find the potential difference between the grids.

14. If the angles are reversed in Problem 13, find the potential difference between the grids. [*Ans.* 106 V.]

15. Electrons from an electron gun enter a uniform magnetic field perpendicular to the lines of induction. If their circular path has a diameter of 25 cm and a potential of 250 V is applied to the gun, find the magnetic induction B.

16. Electrons are to be accelerated by an electron gun and then allowed to enter a uniform magnetic field. If the magnetic induction is 8×10^{-4} Wb/m², and the circular path is to have a radius of 5 cm, what voltage should be applied to the gun? [*Ans.* 140.5 V.]

17. Electrons accelerated by a potential $V = 1250$ V enter a uniform magnetic field in which the magnetic induction is 9×10^{-4} Wb/m². Moving at right angles to the field, what is the radius of their circular path?

18. Calculate the velocity of electrons accelerated by a potential of 500,000 V. [*Ans.* 2.59×10^8 m/s.]

19. Calculate the wavelength of the light emitted by the electron beam in Example 2 (this page) at an angle $\theta = 60°$. What is its color?

20. Calculate the wavelength of the light emitted by the electron beam in Example 2 (this page) at an angle of $\theta = 0$. In what part of the electromagnetic spectrum is this radiation? [*Ans.* 1.440×10^{-7} m, or 1440 Å. Extreme ultraviolet.]

21. A beam of electrons from an electron gun is made to pass over the surface of a diffraction grating having 12,000 lines/cm. If the electrons are accelerated by 100,000 V, find the wavelength of the light emitted at an angle of 30°.

22. An electron beam from an electron gun passes over the surface of a diffraction grating having 12,500 lines/cm. If the electrons are accelerated by 150,000 V, find the wavelength of the light emitted at an angle of 40°. [*Ans.* 6.488×10^{-7} m, or 6488 Å.]

RADIO, RADAR,
TELEVISION, AND MICROWAVES

This chapter is concerned with electromagnetic waves at the long-wavelength end of the electromagnetic spectrum. The basic relation involved is the well-known wave equation

$$c = \nu\lambda \qquad (60a)$$

where ν is the frequency, λ the wavelength, and c the speed of the waves. In a vacuum, c is the same for all electromagnetic waves and is equal to the speed of light:

$$c = 3 \times 10^8 \frac{m}{s} \qquad (60b)$$

A chart of the complete electromagnetic spectrum extending from the shortest known waves, the γ rays, to the longest known waves of radio is given in Fig. 60A. The long-wavelength end of this chart is seen to be divided into equally spaced bands with the designations shown in Table 60A.

TABLE 60A. RADIO WAVE BANDS

Band designation		ν	λ
VLF	very low frequency	3 Kc/s	100 Km
LF	low frequency	30 Kc/s	10 Km
MF	medium frequency	300 Kc/s	1 Km
HF	high frequency	3,000 Kc/s	100 m
VHF	very high frequency	30 Mc/s	10 m
UHF	ultra high frequency	300 Mc/s	1 m
SHF	super high frequency	3,000 Mc/s	10 cm
EHF	extremely high frequency	30,000 Mc/s	1 cm
		300,000 Mc/s	0.1 cm

The first four bands in this table are used for AM and FM radio communications of all kinds.

The VHF and UHF bands are used for television, while the SHF and EHF bands, called *microwaves*, are used principally for experiments of all kinds.

$$1000 \frac{cycles}{second} = 1 \frac{kilocycle}{second} = 1 \frac{Kc}{s}$$

$$1{,}000{,}000 \frac{cycles}{second} = 1 \frac{megacycle}{second} = 1 \frac{Mc}{s}$$

60.1. Long-Distance Reception. It has long been known that certain bands of radio waves travel farther at night than they do in the daytime. During daylight hours programs heard on standard broadcast bands, 550 to 1600 Kc/s, are generally received at distances up to 10 to 100 mi. At night, however, signals can be heard at 10 to 100 times these distances, but with intensities often varying in an erratic manner. Such variations are due to changing atmospheric conditions and are known as "fading." Fading is more pronounced at greater distances but improves considerably after the first hour or two after sundown, only to become worse again shortly before sunrise.

Short radio waves in the range 1.5 to 40 Mc/s travel great distances day or night but are strongly susceptible to changing atmospheric conditions. At one time of day, for example, communications between two greatly distant stations may be carried on over 20-m waves but not over 40-m waves. Later during the day the reverse may be true.

It is now known that the great distances spanned by radio are due to the reflection

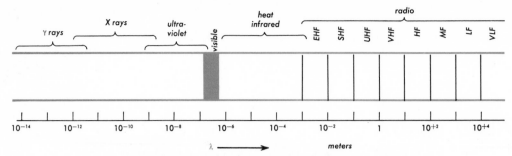

Fig. 60A *Electromagnetic spectrum showing wavelengths of radio bands.*

(actually refraction) of waves by a layer of electrically charged atoms and molecules in the upper atmosphere. The possible existence of such a layer was first postulated by O. Heaviside and A. E. Kennelly in 1902 to account for the propagation of waves around the earth's curved surface. The existence of such a layer was first demonstrated experimentally in 1925 by G. Breit, M. Tuve, and others, and its elevation shown to vary from 50 to 150 mi.

As illustrated in Fig. 60B, waves radiated upward from a transmitter T are bent back toward the earth where they are again reflected upward. The diagram indicates how the entire earth's surface might be covered with radio waves, the intensity of which should decrease with distance from the transmitter. At short distances of only a few miles a "ground wave," T to G in the figure, is heard as a strong steady signal day and night.

For some reason the Kennelly–Heaviside layer does not reflect the ultrahigh frequency waves used in *television* and *radar*. For this reason both are restricted to short-range operation, the waves traveling only in straight lines like visible light. To receive radar or television signals, therefore,

the receiver antenna must be within sight of the transmitting antenna. To cover a large area the transmitting antenna should be located high in the air atop a building, hill, or mountain peak.

60.2. Frequency Modulation. A majority of the standard broadcasting stations, as well as amateur and commercial radio stations, still employ *amplitude modulation* (AM). The audio-frequency currents from the microphone are used to vary the amplitude of the continuous oscillations and waves from the transmitter.

In frequency modulation (FM), the audio-frequency currents from the microphone are used to vary the frequency of the carrier wave yet keep its amplitude constant. Louder sounds with AM mean greater variations in amplitude while with FM they mean greater changes in frequency. The two are compared graphically in Fig. 60C.

While just as good reproduction of voice and music can be accomplished with AM as is possible with FM, the latter has the advantage of eliminating "static." Static is the term applied to those noises in radio reception directly attributed to local atmospheric disturbances. Frequent minor lightning discharges in the air induce undesirable current pulses in any radio

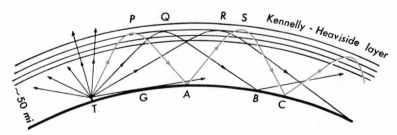

Fig. 60B *Radio waves are refracted (reflected) by the ionized gas layers high in the earth's atmosphere.*

(a) audio

(b) AM

(c) FM

Fig. 60C *Graphs comparing amplitude modulation (AM) with frequency modulation (FM) of radio waves.*

receiving antenna. When the receiver is designed to receive AM, these current pulses are amplified along with the broadcast and are heard as sharp cracking sounds or sometimes as a kind of "frying" noise. Where the receiver is designed for FM, however, the sudden current pulses picked up by the antenna do not change the frequency in any way and do not get through the *frequency discriminator circuit* to the audio amplifier. The resulting quietness to radio reception is remarkable and must be heard on a well-designed receiver to be fully appreciated.

60.3. Width of Radio Bands. The above discussion should not imply that the frequency of a carrier wave is unaltered by AM. Theory, confirmed by experimentation, shows that if a carrier wave of N cycles per second is amplitude modulated by a sound wave of n cycles per second, two new frequencies are produced, one $N - n$ and the other $N + n$. The first one is the beat note or difference frequency, whereas the other is a summation frequency not easily visualized from a graph like Fig. 60C.

When, for example, a carrier of 1 Mc/s is modulated by a sound of 5000 c/s, a receiver tuned to the carrier must also respond to 995,000 c/s and 1,005,000 c/s, and to hear all other sound frequencies between zero and 5000 c/s must respond to all frequencies between these two limits. Hence a frequency of 10,000 c/s ($N \pm 5000$ c/s) is required to transmit sounds from zero to 5000 c/s.

Transmitting stations must have their carrier frequencies 10,000 c/s apart to avoid interfering with each other; and receivers, when tuned to a given carrier, must not respond to frequencies of more than 5000 c/s up or down. To obtain higher-quality reception, 10,000 and even 15,000 c/s should be used. The latter would require a band width of 30,000 c/s and broadcasting stations would have to be at least 30,000 c/s apart. The desirability of high fidelity suggests shifting of all standard broadcast bands into the short-wave region (see Fig. 60A) where there is ample space for numerous stations 30,000 c/s apart. Although it is technically incorrect, it has become common practice to abbreviate the units "cycles per second" by just "cycles," and speak, for example of 20,000 cycles per second as 20,000 cycles.

60.4. The Scanning Process in Television. For years the sending of pictures by wire or radio has been an everyday occurrence. The fundamental principle involved in this process, and illustrated in Fig. 60D, is known as *scanning*. Every picture to be transmitted is scanned by an *exploring spot* which, starting at the top, moves in straight lines over the entire picture. The spot first moves from A to B, then from C to D, then E to F, etc., until the entire picture has been covered. Each time the spot reaches the right-hand side, it jumps back to the left and starts on the next line.

The exploring spot in any scanning device is so constructed that it generates an electric current proportional to the brightness of its instantaneous position. Such a pulsating current, called the *video signal*, is transmitted over wires or radio waves to the receiving station. There in a specially designed instrument a *reproducing spot*, whose brightness is proportional to the video signal amplitude, moves over a viewing screen in a path similar to that of the exploring spot. In this way the reproducing spot reconstructs the original picture.

It will be realized that the smaller the scanning and reproducing spots and the greater the number of lines, the better will be the details of the scanned picture being reproduced at the receiving end. The diagram shown here includes only 50 lines per picture as compared with 525 lines used in some standard (black and white) broadcasts.

If a single picture is to be sent by wire, as is generally the case in the *telephotographic newspaper service*, the scanning process requires from

Fig. 60D　*Illustration of the process of picture scanning.*

10 to 20 min. In television, however, it is standard practice to scan and transmit 30 distinct and separate pictures in every second of time. At the receiving station these pictures are rapidly flashed one after the other upon a viewing screen. All are still pictures differing progressively one from the next so that, due to persistence of vision, the motions seem smooth and continuous, just as with moving pictures.

To avoid spurious shadows and images the process of *interlacing* is employed. By this process each picture is scanned twice, first by

60.5. The Kinescope. In many respects the construction of a television receiver and its operation are similar to those of an ordinary radio receiver. The carrier wave from a nearby transmitter after being tuned in, detected, and amplified with conventional radio-tube circuits, is fed as a video signal into a kinescope in place of a loud-speaker. A kinescope is a large vacuum tube used for scanning and viewing the transmitted pictures.

A kinescope using electrostatic deflection plates for scanning is shown in Fig. 60E.

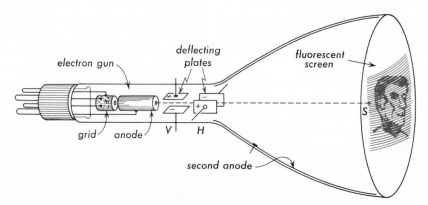

Fig. 60E　*Diagram of a kinescope, a typical vacuum tube used in a television receiver to reproduce pictures on a fluorescent screen.*

running the exploring spot over the odd numbered lines 1, 3, 5, 7, etc., and then over the even numbered lines 2, 4, 6, 8, etc.

Electrons from an electron gun at the left travel down the length of the tube to where, impinging upon a fluorescent screen, they produce a bright luminescent spot S. The purpose of deflecting plates V and H is to deflect the electron beam with the identical frequency and scanning motion of the transmitting station. Two special oscillator tubes and circuits in the receiver supply saw-tooth potentials (see Fig. 60F) to these

Fig. 60G   *Video signal current from a television tube.*

Fig. 60F   *Saw-tooth potentials applied to plates of the television tube to produce horizontal scanning A and B, and vertical scanning C and D. A horizontal deflection, B horizontal return, C vertical deflection, and D vertical return.*

plates; the high-frequency potentials to the H *plates* for horizontal scanning and the lower-frequency potentials to the V *plates* for vertical scanning.

The proper fluctuations in the intensity of the luminescent spot are brought about by applying

the receiver, act as a triggerlike mechanism to bring the reproducing spot to the top left of the screen at the proper time to start the next picture. In other words the transmitter sends out signals that enable the receiver to automatically keep "in step" with the pictures as they are sent.*

60.6. Radar. Radar was one of the most important electronic developments of World War II and may be defined as the art of determining by means of *radio echoes* the presence, distance, direction, and velocity of distant aircraft, ships, land masses, cities, and other objects. RADAR derives its name from the longer title "RAdio Detection And Ranging."

Basically, a complete radar station consists of a *transmitter*, a *receiver*, and an *indicator*. As shown by a schematic diagram in Fig. 60H, the

Fig. 60H   *Illustration of the principles of radar detecting and ranging.*

the video signal shown in Fig. 60G to the *grid* of the electron gun. This grid controls the flow of electrons through to the anode in the same way that the grid controls the current to the plate in an ordinary three-element radio tube.

For a small fraction of a second, between successive pictures being scanned for transmission, current pulses of a certain type and frequency are sent out from the sending station as part of the video signal. These, picked up by

transmitter sends out high-frequency radio waves which, traveling outward with the velocity of light, are reflected from a distant object. The small portion of the reflected waves returning toward the station is picked up and amplified by the receiver. The signal is then fed into any one of a number of indicating devices, some of which

* V. K. Zworykin and G. A. Morton, *Television: The Electronics of Image Transmission* (John Wiley & Sons, Inc., New York, 1954), 2nd ed.

are so complete as to give continuously the instantaneous *distance, direction,* and *relative velocity* of the object.

With one type of air-borne unit, ground objects can be observed on the screen of a kinescope even though fog or clouds intervene. Such systems are extremely useful in reducing the flying hazards that are always present during inclement weather.

The wavelengths of the waves used in radar are in the *microwave* region of the electromagnetic spectrum. They have wavelengths in the range of 1 cm to 10 cm.

60.7. The Pulsed System. Since a powerful transmitter must operate side by side with a supersensitive receiver, some provision is always made whereby the power from the transmitter is blocked out of the receiver. In most radar equipment this is accomplished by means of intermittent transmission, commonly called the *pulsed system.* According to this system, the transmitter is turned on for only a fraction of a second to send out a train of waves while the receiver is made very insensitive. When the transmitter goes off, the receiver is turned on to full sensitivity to receive the faint echo signal returning. When the receiver goes off, the transmitter comes on again to send out another wave train and repeat the above process hundreds of times per second.

A graph of the received pulses from an object 9 mi away is shown in Fig. 60I. Since the velocity

Fig. 60I　*Graph of transmitted pulses showing received pulse, or echo, from an object 9 mi distant.*

of radio waves is 186,300 mi/s, the same as light, the time interval between each transmitted pulse T and its echo R returning is a direct measure of the distance. If a frequency of 30,000 Mc/s is used, the wavelength is 1 cm and each pulse will contain thousands of waves. Rectified by the

receiver, an entire wave train appears as a voltage pulse as in the graph.

One type of *indicator* used for determining this time interval is a *cathode-ray oscilloscope* of the type shown in Fig. 59H. While the scanning spot is kept at constant intensity, a saw-tooth potential difference is applied to the horizontal sweep to make it move with constant speed across the fluorescent screen.

Electrical circuits are so arranged that the spot starts at the left just prior to the transmitter's emission of a pulse. When, a fraction of a second later, a pulse is initiated, a small part of the energy is applied as a vertical deflection of the spot, thereby producing a trace T as shown in Fig. 60J. When the returning echo signal arrives

Fig. 60J　*Trace of spot on cathode-ray tube as used in radar ranging.*

at the receiver, it too is applied as a vertical deflection, and a peak like the one at R_1 is produced. Upon reaching the right-hand end of the screen, the spot is extinguished and returned to the left, where it is again turned on and the above process repeated. As the spot retraces the same line many times every second, persistence of vision gives rise to the appearance of a steady trace.

If several different objects reflect waves of sufficient intensity to be picked up by the receiver, several peaks R_1, R_2, etc., will be seen on the indicator screen. In radar parlance, each such peak on the trace is called a *pip*, and its distance along the horizontal line from T is a direct measure of the time required for the signal to go out and return and is therefore a measure of the range of the object that caused it. Various methods of accurately measuring the distance interval have been developed.

If an object is coming toward or receding from a radar station, the frequency of the waves reflected from it will be increased or decreased, respectively, as in the Doppler effect. Hence by measuring the frequency change between the waves going out and those coming back, the velocity of approach or recession becomes known.

60.8. Wave Guides. The term "wave guide" is generally applied to a special class of metallic conductors having the property of conducting high-frequency oscillations from one place to another. To be more specific, it is a radio transmission line by which power generated at an oscillator can be transmitted to some utility point with little or no loss along the line.

Two types of wave guide commonly used at present are shown in Fig. 60K. The first, called a *coaxial cable* or *concentric line*, consists of a wire conductor insulated from, and running lengthwise through, the center of a tubular conductor. Power from any high-frequency source when connected to the central wire and tubular sheath, is propagated as waves through the dielectric between the two conductors.

The second is a hollow rectangular pipe called a *wave guide*. Power introduced as electromagnetic waves at one end is guided by the conducting walls to the other end. Each conductor is shown with a 90° bend to show that waves can be guided around corners.

Fig. 60K   *Wave guides commonly used in radar and television transmission lines: (a) coaxial cable, and (b) hollow conductor.*

While there is no limit to the frequency transmitted by coaxial lines, there is a lower limit for hollow wave guides. This lower limit, called the *cut-off frequency* or critical frequency, is the limiting case of a so-called *dominant mode* of vibration inside the guide and is analogous in some respects to the *fundamental vibration* of a given air column in sound. The dominant mode occurs in a rectangular pipe when the wider of the two dimensions b is $\frac{1}{2}$ a wavelength. The narrow dimension of the latter is not critical, but in practice is made to be about $\frac{1}{2}b$.

Since wave guides are comparable in cross section to the waves they propagate, and a coaxial cable will transmit any frequency no matter how low, the latter is generally used for waves longer than 10 cm, whereas hollow pipes are used with waves shorter than 10 cm. The power capacity of a hollow pipe, transmitting at its dominant mode, is greater than a coaxial cable of the same size.

Figure 60L shows an arrangement in which

Fig. 60L   *Radar antenna system for producing a nearly parallel beam.*

the high-frequency oscillations from an oscillator tube source (not shown) are fed through a coaxial cable C to a single dipole, or Hertzian doublet, D. Radiated waves from the doublet are reflected into a parallel beam by the mirror. Since the over-all length of a dipole must be equal to $\frac{1}{2}$ a wavelength, the two small rods for

10 cm waves would each be 2.5 cm, or 1 in., long.

Two commonly used methods of feeding waves into one end of a wave guide, or withdrawing them from the other end, are shown in Fig. 60M. *Probe coupling* illustrated at (a) and (d)

The reverse process takes place at (d) where the probe acts like a radio receiver antenna set into oscillation by the incoming waves.

In loop coupling (b) the surging charge in the loop constitutes a changing current that sets up magnetic lines of force threading through it. This

Fig. 60M   *Probe and loop coupling between wave guides and coaxial cables.*

shows the center wire of a coaxial cable protruding into a rectangular guide a short distance from the end. *Loop coupling* illustrated at (b) and (c) shows a single loop of wire protruding through the end wall of the guide. The size and position of the probe and loop are critically determined for each separate installation.

In probe coupling as at (a) the protruding wire becomes alternately positive and negative. By attraction and repulsion of electrons the metal surface above the probe acquires an opposite charge thereby giving rise to a periodically changing electric field $\mathcal{E}$ parallel to the probe. The surging charges in the probe simultaneously produce magnetic field lines B around the probe, perpendicular to the electric lines, hence the propagation through the guide of electromag-

changing magnetic field induces electric currents in the metal walls such that the bunching of charges above and below gives rise to a simultaneously reversing electric field $\mathcal{E}$. The net result is the same as with probe coupling; electromagnetic waves are propagated through the guide.

60.9. Wave Propagation in Guides. In sound, the resonance of an air column is described as the result of two waves traveling in opposite directions and stationary nodes and loops are formed. The propagation of electromagnetic waves in a wave guide, on the other hand, may be described in terms of two wave trains crisscrossing each other as they reflect back and forth between the walls of the conductor. For one of these modes, the so-called *dominant mode,* see Fig. 60N.

Fig. 60N   *The propagation of microwaves through a rectangular wave guide.*

netic waves with $\mathcal{E}$ and B perpendicular to each other (see Fig. 54G). The probe location is such that waves reflected from the end will be "in step" with those already moving down the guide.

The dotted lines in the "top" view represent wave fronts of the field $\mathcal{E}$, *dots* for the wave crests where the field is *up* out of the page, and *crosses* for the troughs where the field is *down* into the page. These two waves, traveling normal to their wave fronts with the velocity of light c, form resultant waves traveling lengthwise down the tube with a velocity V. The velocity V is always greater than the velocity of light and the wave length λ_g in the guide is always greater than the wave length λ outside. $V = \nu\lambda_g$.

As the b-dimension of the guide is reduced, the oblique wave fronts stay the same normal distance apart while the wave length λ_g and the velocity V increase, becoming infinite when $b = \frac{1}{2}\lambda$ (see Fig. 60O). Under this latter condi-

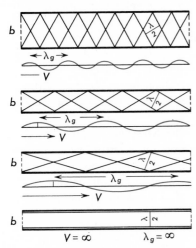

Fig. 60O *As a wave guide is narrowed down, the wavelength and wave velocity inside increases, becoming infinite when the critical width $b = \frac{1}{2}$.*

tion the two component wave fronts are parallel to the wave guide and the electric field at all points in the guide is rising and falling together. This is the resonant condition of the dominant mode, and the guide width b is at its minimum allowable value.

The velocity of the waves inside the guide, bouncing back and forth between opposite sides, is equal to the speed of light. The velocity V of the nodes and antinodes, however, is greater than c and is called the *phase velocity*. Energy cannot travel faster than c.

60.10. Scanning. In a majority of radar installations the receiver uses the same antenna as the transmitter, thereby requiring a rapid switching mechanism that connects the transmitter to the antenna, when a pulse is to be radiated, and

then to the receiver to pick up a possible echo signal (see Fig. 60P). Such dual use of one

Fig. 60P *Block diagram indicating a T–R box for alternately connecting the antenna reflector to the transmitter and receiver. Conical or spiral scanning is also indicated.*

antenna saves space and weight and eliminates the mechanical difficulty of making two directive antennas point in exactly the same direction while they are moved about.

In certain types of radar installation the transmitter beam is made to sweep back and forth across the ground or sky with a scanning motion similar to that used in television. In one system a spiral scanning motion adapts itself to total coverage of a given area. When the beam crosses the path of any reflecting object, an echo signal returns to the receiver where it is amplified and applied to the cathode beam of a kinescope. As the transmitter beam carries out its scanning motion, the cathode ray spot on the kinescope is made to traverse a similar path. At that instant, when an echo signal returns, the spot brightens, and its location on the screen locates the relative position of the object in the scanning field.

Because the reflector is rotated mechanically, the radar scanning speed is considerably slower than in television. Its usefulness, however, is unquestionable, for high above the clouds in a plane it is possible to observe the positions and shapes of many landmarks on the ground below, as well as other planes and turbulent air of violent storm centers ahead.

60.11. The Magnetron. The magnetron is a vacuum tube known to radar engineers as a powerful source of electromagnetic waves. A tube no larger than a man's hand, for example, is capable of delivering 100 KW in the form of 1 cm waves. A typical arrangement is shown in Fig. 60Q where the vacuum tube itself, in the

Fig. 60Q   *How a magnetron power tube is mounted in the strong field of a permanent magnet.*

shape of a pill box, is mounted between the poles of a small permanent magnet.

Diagrams showing the resonant cavities inside the tube are given in Fig. 60R. Electrons emitted

Fig. 60R   *Details of magnetron tube showing resonant cavities and their action on electrons and electric lines of force.*

by the hot cathode K are accelerated toward the ring-like plate by a potential of several thousand volts. The magnetic field urges the electrons to follow a spiral-like path, and at the same time causes them to bunch into clouds shaped like the arms of a windmill. These radial arms of spiraling electrons sweep clockwise around the main central cavity several billion times per second.

As the electron arms whirl around they repel the free electrons in the interstices between the small cavities, causing them to move alternately clockwise, then counterclockwise around their respective openings. These oscillatory surges of

negative charge make the metal interstices alternately positive, then negative, and at the same time set up electric and magnetic lines of force in the cavities and slots as shown. These fields extending into the central cavity slow down some electrons and speed up others to bunch them as stated above.

The high-frequency oscillating fields in each of the eight cavities constitute electrical energy which can be tapped through any one of the cavities by an opening leading into a wave guide as shown at the upper right. By pulsing the cathode to plate voltage thousands of times per second, bursts of microwaves are sent along the wave guide channel to some antenna system. Since the dominant mode of a cylindrical cavity occurs when the diameter is about 0.7λ, the smaller the diameter of the magnetron cavities, the shorter is the wavelength of the generated waves.*

60.12. The Klystron. Klystrons, like magnetrons, consist of electron vacuum tubes and circuits for generating and amplifying microwaves for radar and communication. A simple diagram of a klystron oscillator is shown in Fig. 60S.

Fig. 60S   *Diagram of the principal elements of a microwave klystron.*

A steady stream of electrons from an electron gun is made to pass by the opening of an input

---

* *Principles of Radar*, by M.I.T. Radar School Staff (McGraw-Hill Book Co., Inc., New York).

cavity resonator. Electric and magnetic field oscillations within this resonator give rise to oscillating potentials at the opening that speed up the electrons for one-half-cycle, and slow them down the other half. The fast electrons catch up with the slower ones causing a bunching of negative charges as shown in the diagram.

As regularly spaced bunches of electrons pass the output cavity, strong resonance occurs and intense voltage and field oscillations are produced within.

Microwave power is drawn from this resonator by means of an inductance loop as shown, a probe from a coaxial cable, or a waveguide of the appropriate dimensions (see Fig. 60M). A small amount of power is fed back through a phase changer to keep the input resonator operating with its proper phase and natural frequency.

When a klystron is used as an amplifier, feedback through a phase changer is not needed. The power derived from a klystron comes from the battery.

QUESTIONS AND PROBLEMS

1. What is RADAR? What do the letters stand for?

2. What is a pulsed radar system? Why is the operation intermittent?

3. How is the distance of an object determined? How is the velocity of a moving object determined?

4. What is a wave guide? How many kinds are there?

5. What is the process called scanning? What is a video signal?

6. What is meant by "interlacing"?

7. Radar waves of frequency 5×10^3 Mc/s are reflected from a paraboloidal metal reflector. Calculate the over-all length of the dipole used at its focal plane.

8. The dipole of a radar transmitter has an over-all length of 5 cm. Calculate the frequency in Mc/s. [Ans. 3000 Mc/s.]

9. A television transmitter broadcasts on a frequency of 108 Mc/s. Find the length of the dipole of the transmitting antenna.

10. A television receiver uses a straight dipole with an over-all length of 1.8 m. What is its natural frequency? [Ans. 83.3 Mc/s.]

11. A rectangular wave guide has a vertical opening of width $b = 2.0$ cm. If waves of frequency 0.8×10^{10} vib/s travel through the guide as shown in Fig. 60N, find (a) the wavelength λ_g and (b) the wave velocity V.

12. A rectangular wave guide as shown in Fig. 60N has a horizontal dimension $b = 1.5$ cm. If waves of frequency 1.5×10^{10} vib/s travel through the guide, find the wavelength λ_g and the wave velocity V. [Ans. (a) 2.65 cm, (b) 3.97×10^{10} cm/s.]

13. The dipole of a radar transmitter has an over-all length of 3.8 cm. Calculate the frequency in Mc/s.

14. A television receiver uses a straight dipole with an over-all length of 2.5 m. What is its natural frequency? [Ans. 60 Mc/s.]

15. A cross section of a rectangular wave guide has an opening of 7 mm by 16 mm. If waves of frequency 16,000 Mc/s are sent through the guide, find (a) the wavelength λ_g, and (b) the wave velocity V.

PHOTON COLLISIONS
AND ATOMIC WAVES

In the preceding chapters we have seen that light waves consist of small finite bundles of energy, called *quanta* or *photons*, and that they too, like atomic particles, may be made to collide with atoms of one kind or another. This was the case both in the *photoelectric effect* (Chapter 50) and in the production of X rays (Chapter 53). The first part of the present chapter deals with the *corpuscular nature of light*, and the last part with the *wave nature of atomic particles*.

This last statement suggests a sort of Dr. Jekyll and Mr. Hyde existence for light waves as well as for atoms. Under some conditions,

to take place. Acting like waves, the X rays may be scattered at different angles to produce a diffraction pattern (see Fig. 53F), or acting like particles, they may collide with atoms and eject electrons as in the photoelectric effect (see Chapter 50).

Even though a beam of X rays may contain waves all of the same frequency, not all of the ejected photoelectrons acquire the same velocity, but they are divided into several well-defined groups. These different groups are illustrated schematically by the lengths of the arrows in Fig. 61A.

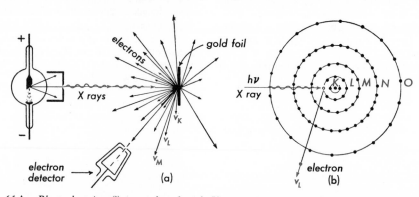

Fig. 61A *Photoelectric effect produced with X rays gives rise to electrons with several different velocities. (b) Detail of an X ray ejecting an L electron from a heavy atom.*

light and atoms may both act as though they were waves, whereas under other conditions they may both act like small particles.

61.1. Photoelectric Effect with X Rays. When a beam of X rays is allowed to shine on the surface of a thin sheet of metal like gold, several different phenomena may be observed

Careful measurements of the velocities of the photoelectrons, first made by Robinson and his collaborators in 1914, have shown that each velocity group is to be associated with the various shells of electrons within the atoms. The slowest electrons, all with the same velocity v_K, are ejected from the K shell, the next faster group with a velocity v_L from the L shell, the next group with a velocity v_M from the M shell, etc.

The closer an electron is to the nucleus [see diagram (b)], the greater is the attracting force and the greater is the force and energy necessary to liberate it from the atom. The velocity of the electrons in each group is given by Einstein's photoelectric equation,

$$hv = W + \tfrac{1}{2}mv^2 \qquad (61a)$$

where W, the work function, is the energy necessary to free an electron from any one of the different electron shells (see Sec. 50.6).

While all of the incident X-ray photons have the same energy hv, more energy W will be used in liberating a K electron than there will be in

where a K electron has been ejected, an L electron may jump into the vacated K shell, with the simultaneous emission of a K X ray. This may be followed immediately by an M electron's jumping into the vacated L shell and the emission of an L X ray.

61.2. The Compton Effect. While making a spectroscopic study of scattered X rays in 1923, A. H. Compton* discovered a new phenomenon, now known as the Compton effect. After considerable controversy with other experimenters, Compton proved quite conclusively that an X ray may collide with an electron and bounce off with reduced energy in another direction. This is analogous to the collision of two billiard balls.

Compton's historic experiment is illustrated schematically in Fig. 61B. X rays from a tube T

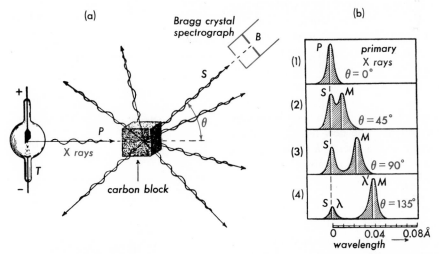

Fig. 61B   *The Compton effect. (a) Schematic diagram of Compton's experiment. (b) Graphs of the X-ray spectrum lines observed with a Bragg crystal spectrograph.*

liberating an L electron. This being the case, a photon liberating a K electron will have less energy left over for the electron than would another photon liberating an L electron from a similar atom. This experiment shows as well as one could wish that electrons exist in shells within the atom.

It should be pointed out that the energy W, used up in ejecting a photoelectron, is not lost by the atom but is later given out again in the form of X rays of various frequencies. In atoms

were made to strike one face of a small carbon block and scatter out in various directions. With an X-ray spectrograph at one side of the block, he measured the wavelength of the X rays S

* Arthur H. Compton (1892–1962), American physicist, born in Wooster, Ohio, on September 10, 1892. He received the degree of Doctor of Philosophy at Princeton University in 1920. In 1923 he discovered the change in wavelength of X rays when scattered by carbon, the phenomenon now known as the Compton effect. In recognition of this important discovery, in 1927 he was awarded the Nobel Prize in physics jointly with C. T. R. Wilson of England.

scattered in a direction θ. These wavelengths he then compared with those of the incident beam P.

The comparisons are illustrated by graphs in diagram (b). The top curve (1) represents the wavelength λ of the X rays in the beam P, before striking the block. The other three curves, (2), (3), and (4), represent the two wavelengths λ and λ' observed when the spectrograph is located at the angles $\theta = 45°$ $\theta = 90°$ and $\theta = 135°$ respectively. These graphs show that some of the scattered X rays have changed their wavelengths whereas others have not. They further show the important result that as the angle increases the change in wavelength of the modified rays M increases.

To explain the modified wavelengths M, Compton invoked the quantum theory of light and proposed that a single X-ray photon, acting as a material particle, may collide with a free electron and recoil as though it were a perfectly elastic sphere [Fig. 61C(a)]. Applying the law of conservation of energy to the collision, Compton assumed that the energy $\frac{1}{2}mv^2$ imparted to the recoiling electron must be supplied by the incident X-ray quantum $h\nu$. Having lost energy, the X ray moves off in some new direction with a lower frequency ν' and energy $h\nu'$. By applying conservation of energy, we obtain

$$h\nu = h\nu' + \tfrac{1}{2}mv^2 \qquad (61b)$$

Since in most cases the velocity of the recoiling electron is so near the velocity of light c, the relativistic equations must be applied. Using Eq.(58q) for the kinetic energy of a moving mass, we write

$$h\nu = h\nu' + m_0c^2(\gamma - 1) \qquad (61c)$$

where

$$\gamma = \frac{1}{\sqrt{1 - v^2/c^2}} \qquad (61d)$$

and m_0 is the *rest mass* of the electron.

As with two perfectly elastic balls, Compton also applied the law of conservation of momentum and derived an equation from which he could calculate the change in wavelength λ' of the scattered X ray. These calculated changes

were found to agree exactly with those observed by the experiment.

The fact that a beam of light has the equivalence of a momentum mv, and can exert a pressure on a wall on which it falls, has long been known. According to the quantum theory the momentum of a single photon is given by the energy $h\nu$ divided by the speed of light c,

$$\text{momentum of a photon} = \frac{h\nu}{c} \qquad (61e)$$

Compton's experiment is considered a proof of this equation.

Since momentum is a vector quantity, we construct a vector diagram as shown in Fig. 61C(b). The momentum of the X ray before

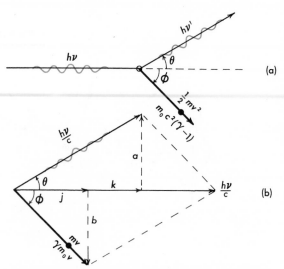

Fig. 61C *Vector diagrams for the collision between an X-ray photon and a free electron. The Compton effect.*

impact is $h\nu/c$, while its momentum after impact is $h\nu'/c$, and the momentum of the electron is mv.

For electrons close to the speed of light the momentum mv is written in the relativistic form γm_0v [see Eq.(58i)]. By resolving the two momenta into two components, we obtain a and k as components of $h\nu'/c$ and b and j as components of γm_0v.

Conservation of momentum requires the vector sum of j plus k to equal the initial momentum $h\nu/c$, and the vectors a and b to cancel each other. As equations,

$$\frac{h\nu}{c} = \frac{h\nu'}{c}\cos\theta + \gamma m_0 v \cos\phi \qquad (61f)$$

and

$$\frac{h\nu'}{c}\sin\theta = \gamma m_0 v \sin\phi \qquad (61g)$$

By combining Eqs.(61c), (61f), and (61g), and changing from frequencies ν and ν' to wavelengths by λ and λ', respectively, Compton derived the equation

$$\lambda' - \lambda = \frac{h}{m_0 c}(1 - \cos\theta) \qquad (61h)$$

The quantity $h/m_0 c$ is called the *Compton wavelength*, and is equal to 2.43×10^{-12} m. For those X rays that are scattered at an angle of 90°, the observed or calculated change in wavelength is just this amount and is the same for all X-ray wavelengths incident on the scatterer.

Compton's success is to be attributed to the exact agreement he found between the wavelength shift calculated from this application of the quantum theory and the values measured by experiment.

The first discoveries of the recoil electrons from the Compton effect were made by C. T. R. Wilson, and by Bothe and Becker. The existence of these collision products is readily shown by sending a beam of X rays through a Wilson cloud chamber just prior to its expansion (Fig. 61D).

Fig. 61D *Recoil electrons from X rays passing through the air in a Wilson cloud chamber. The Compton effect.* (After C. T. R. Wilson.)

When an X ray collides with a free electron the Compton effect can be expected, since the recoiling photon and electron are able to conserve energy and momentum. But when an X ray collides with an electron bound to an atom, the photoelectric effect takes place, since the atom can now recoil and conserve energy and momentum with the electron.

61.3. De Broglie's Electron Waves. In 1924 De Broglie, a French theoretical physicist, derived an equation predicting that all atomic particles have associated with them waves of a definite wavelength. In other words, a beam of electrons or atoms should, under the proper experimental conditions, act like a train of light waves or a beam of photons. The wavelength of these waves, as predicted by De Broglie, depends upon the mass and velocity of the particles according to the following relations:

$$\boxed{\lambda = \frac{h}{mv}} \qquad (61i)$$

This is known as *De Broglie's wave equation*. For an electron moving at high speed, the denominator mv is large and the wavelength is small. In other words, the faster an electron moves, the shorter the wavelength associated with it (see Fig. 61E).

Fig. 61E *Schematic diagram of a De Broglie wave.*

To acquire some concept of the relative wavelengths of electrons moving with different velocities, several values have been computed from De Broglie's equation (see Table 61A). The

TABLE 61A. WAVELENGTHS ASSOCIATED WITH ELECTRONS MOVING WITH DIFFERENT VELOCITIES ACCORDING TO DE BROGLIE'S WAVE EQUATION

V (applied voltage)	v (velocity mi/s)	$\frac{v}{c}$ (velocity %)	λ (wavelength Å)
1	370	0.20	12.23
10	1,100	0.62	3.87
100	3,700	1.98	1.22
1,000	18,000	6.26	0.38
10,000	36,000	19.50*	0.12
100,000	100,000	54.80*	0.03
1,000,000	175,000	94.10*	0.01

* These values take into account the increase in mass of the electron due to the theory of relativity [see Eq.(59b)].

velocities are listed in miles per second in column 2 and in percent of the velocity of light in column 3. The potential differences listed in column 1 are the voltages required by Eq.(59a) to give an electron any one of the velocities listed in columns 2 and 3. It will be noted that the wavelengths at the bottom correspond closely to those for X rays and γ rays.

61.4. The Davisson–Germer Experiment. The first experimental proof of the wave nature of atomic particles was demonstrated in 1927 by two American physicists C. J. Davisson and his collaborator, L. H. Germer. Their experiment is illustrated schematically in **Fig. 61F**. Electrons

Fig. 61F *The Davisson–Germer experiment. Electrons striking the surface layers of a crystal are diffracted at different angles just as if they were waves with a very short wavelength.*

from a hot filament are accelerated toward an anode, where, upon passing through a system of pinholes, they emerge as a narrow beam as indicated. This source acts as an electron gun from which electrons of any desired velocity may be obtained by applying the proper potential difference V.

Upon striking one of the polished faces of a nickel crystal, the electrons, acting like waves, are diffracted off in certain preferred directions. These preferred directions are located by means of a detector in which the electrons are collected

and their accumulated charge measured. The detector is mounted so that it may be turned to an angle θ, and the crystal is mounted so it may be turned about an axis parallel to the incident beam.

With the electron-beam incident perpendicular to the crystal surface shown in Fig. 61F, the preferred direction of diffraction for 54-volt electrons was found to be 50°. Under these conditions the surface rows of atoms parallel to AB act like the rulings of a diffraction grating, producing the first-order spectrum of 54-volt electrons at $\theta = 50°$. This is illustrated in a cross-section detail in **Fig. 61G**. The waves

Fig. 61G *Diagram of electron diffraction from the surface layer of a nickel crystal. The regular spacing of the atoms makes the crystal act like a diffraction grating.*

reflected from one row of atoms M must travel one whole wavelength farther than the waves from the adjacent row N.

61.5. Electron Diffraction Patterns. Experiments analogous to Von Laue's X-ray diffraction experiments were first performed in 1928 by the English physicist G. P. Thomson, and independently by the Japanese physicist Kikuchi (see Fig. 53F). A schematic diagram of their experimental apparatus is given in **Fig. 61H**. Electrons

Fig. 61H *Experimental arrangement for observing the diffraction of electron waves by thin films or crystals.*

of known velocity from an electron gun are projected at the front face of a thin metal film or crystal at C. A short distance farther on, the diffracted electrons strike a photographic plate where they produce patterns of the type reproduced in Fig. 61I.

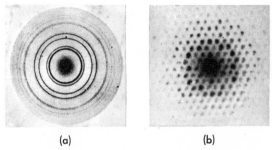

(a)   **(b)**

Fig. 61I *Photographs of electron diffraction patterns demonstrating the wave nature of electrons. (a) 36,000-volt electrons from a thin silver foil (after G. P. Thomson). (b) 68,000-volt electrons from a thin mica crystal (after Kikuchi).*

Kikuchi's photograph (b) was made by projecting 68,000-volt electrons through a thin mica crystal. In this instance we have the exact analog to the X-ray diffraction patterns of Friedrich, Knipping, and Von Laue (see Figs. 53F and 53G). The electrons, in passing through the crystal, are diffracted by the atom centers in such a way that the various crystal planes act like mirrors to reflect them the same as they do with X rays of an equivalent wavelength. Because high-speed electrons had to be used to penetrate the crystal, the diffraction spots are closer together; the reason for this is that the equivalent electron wavelength, $\lambda = 0.047$ Å, is about $\frac{1}{50}$ of the crystal spacing.

61.6. Electron Waves within the Atom. It is now known that the Bohr picture of the atom with sharply defined electron orbits is not correct. The newer and more accepted theories do not discard the Bohr theory entirely, but modify it to the extent that the electron does not behave as though it were a particle. The electron behaves as if it were made up of waves of the type described in preceding sections.

A very useful theory of the hydrogen atom was worked out independently by the two German physicists Heisenberg and Schrödinger

in 1925, and was later modified by the English theoretical physicist Dirac in 1928.*

Schrödinger, making use of De Broglie's idea of electron waves, pictures the single electron in the hydrogen atom as moving around the nucleus as a kind of *wave packet*. This wave packet is formed in somewhat the same way that standing waves are set up and maintained in sound waves.

We have seen in Sec. 25.2 how a stretched string may be set vibrating with a number of different natural modes. The frequencies ν of these different modes are called *harmonics* and are given by

$$\nu = n\nu_1 \qquad (61j)$$

where ν_1 is the frequency of the *first harmonic*, or *fundamental*, and

$$n = 1, 2, 3, 4, 5, \text{- - -} \qquad (61k)$$

To set up similar conditions in a Bohr circular orbit of hydrogen, we visualize the electron as a wave with a De Broglie wavelength long enough to extend more than once around the atom. With a complete overlap of waves the system should stabilize into one of standing waves. A little reasoning applied to such a system will show that each wave pattern should contain an even number of nodes and loops.

Since the circumference of a circle is $2\pi r$, and the De Broglie wavelength $\lambda = h/mv$, the conditions for standing waves may be written: Circumference $= n\lambda$,

$$2\pi r = n\frac{h}{mv} \qquad (61l)$$

where

$$n = 1, 2, 3, 4, 5, \text{- - -} \qquad (61m)$$

Multiplying both sides of this equation by $mv/2\pi$, we obtain,

$$mvr = n\frac{h}{2\pi} \qquad (61n)$$

which is exactly the equation first given by Bohr in his theory [see Eq.(51b)].

A schematic diagram of this standing-wave model for the first three orbits of hydrogen are shown in Fig. 61J. Note that the first orbit has

---

* For their contributions to the new theory of atomic structure, Heisenberg was granted the Nobel Prize in physics for the year 1932, while Schrödinger and Dirac were jointly granted the prize one year later.

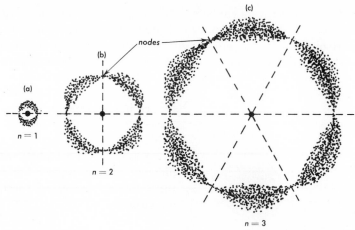

Fig. 61J　*Schematic diagrams of the waves of the orbital electron in the first three quantum states of the hydrogen atom.*

two nodes and a circumference of $1\lambda_1$, the second has four nodes and a circumference of $2\lambda_2$, and the third has six nodes and a circumference of $3\lambda_3$.

For increasing n, from 1 to 2 to 3, the wavelengths increase from $1\lambda_1$ to $2\lambda_1$ to $3\lambda_1$, the radii increase from $1r_1$ to $4r_1$ to $9r_1$, while the wave velocity decreases from $1v_1$ to $\frac{1}{2}v_1$ to $\frac{1}{3}v_1$.

61.7. The Schrödinger and Dirac Wave Equations. Introducing the De Broglie wavelength in a more general way into the theory of the hydrogen atom, Schrödinger, in Germany, in 1926 made a new and important contribution to atomic structure. His contribution is most briefly expressed by what is called the *Schrödinger wave equation.*

$$\nabla^2\psi + \frac{m^2v^2}{\hbar^2}\psi = 0 \qquad (61\text{o})$$

Two years later Dirac, in England, introduced the spin of the electron into this wave mechanics, and replaced Schrödinger's equation by four quite similar equations.

Although the methods used in solving these differential equations are beyond the scope of this book, we will discuss the results of the solutions since they lead to a better understanding of the structure and behavior of atoms.*

A vibrating string represents a one-dimen-

* For details of the solutions of Schrödinger's and Dirac's wave equations, see H. E. White, *Introduction to Atomic Spectra* (McGraw-Hill Book Co., Inc., 1934).

sional system of standing waves, and the integral numbers n specifying the allowed frequencies, as given by Eq.(61j), are analogous to the quantum numbers n of the allowed Bohr circular orbits [see Eqs.(25a) and (61j)].

When a thin metal plate is set into vibration, nodes and antinodes are formed, and we have a two-dimensional system of standing waves (see Fig. 25M). In all of the natural modes that may be produced with such plates, the nodes formed, whether they are radial, circular, or of any other shape, are even in number. Furthermore, the classical theory of vibrating plates shows that all natural modes may be presented by combinations of two series of whole numbers n and m.

Dirac's and Schrödinger's wave equations for the hydrogen atom are set up as models in which the electron may be thought of as spread out around the nucleus as a kind of cloud. Because of its wave nature, this negatively charged cloud takes the form of a three-dimensional system of standing waves.

The many vibration modes of such a cloud are called *spherical harmonics*, and the nodes they exhibit take the forms of lines, planes, cones, and spheres. In other words, the standing-wave patterns of the allowed states of hydrogen are more complex than those shown in Fig. 61J.

In our earlier studies we have seen that the energy involved in vibrations is proportional to the square of the amplitude (see Sec. 22.11).

Since ψ in any of the wave equations represents the amplitude of the electron-cloud vibrations at any point P, the square of the amplitude ψ^2 has been interpreted to be proportional to the charge density of the cloud at that point.

To visualize the different allowed vibration states of the cloud, it is convenient to locate the nodes and loops in *polar coordinates* (see Fig. 61K). The vertical line MN represents a fixed

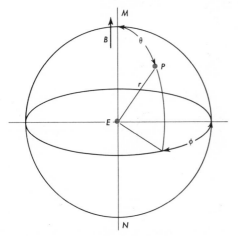

Fig. 61K   *Diagram illustrating the position of a point P in polar coordinates.*

direction in space and is set up by imagining the atom located in a magnetic field B and then slowly reducing the field intensity to zero. Any point in the space is then located with respect to this line, and the nucleus at the center, by specifying the values of ϕ, θ, and r.

It is not surprising to learn that the solutions of the wave equation give the exact same energies for the various allowed states of the hydrogen atom, as does the Bohr theory of orbits [see Eq.(51k)].

$$E = -\frac{2\pi^2 m e^4 k^2}{n^2 h^2} \qquad (61p)$$

where n takes integral values only. Furthermore all allowed states are determined by four quantum numbers [see Eq.(52r)].

$$\left.\begin{array}{l} n = 1, 2, 3, 4, 5, \cdots \infty \\ l = 0, 1, 2, 3, 4, \cdots n-1 \\ j = \tfrac{1}{2}, \tfrac{3}{2}, \tfrac{5}{2}, \tfrac{7}{2}, \tfrac{9}{2}, \cdots l+\tfrac{1}{2} \\ m = \pm\tfrac{1}{2}, \pm\tfrac{3}{2}, \pm\tfrac{5}{2}, \pm\tfrac{7}{2}, \cdots \pm j \end{array}\right\} \quad (61q)$$

We will now see how these allowed states may be represented by graphs, and how closely these graphs may be correlated with the simpler but less accurate orbital models of Bohr.

THE D_ϕ DENSITY DISTRIBUTION. For any fixed value of θ the total charge density is a constant for all values of ϕ from 0° to 360° (see Fig. 61L).

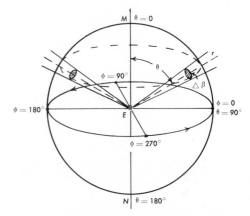

Fig. 61L   *Diagram in polar coordinates illustrating the symmetry of the D_ϕ density distribution of the electron cloud in hydrogen.*

This means that if we select a small angle $\Delta\beta$ making an angle θ with the polar axis, and sum all of the charge within it from $r = 0$ to $r = \infty$, an equal amount of charge will be found within as we rotate it around the axis.

$$D_\phi = \text{constant} \qquad (61r)$$

We say, therefore, that the D_ϕ distribution is symmetrical around the polar axis for all values of n, l, j, and m.

THE D_θ DENSITY DISTRIBUTION. The electron cloud density is not constant for all values of the azimuth angle θ, except for the s and p states where $j = \tfrac{1}{2}$. For all other values of j and m the charge density varies with θ.

If in Fig. 61L we turn the small solid angle $\Delta\beta$ from $\theta = 0°$ through 90° and on to $\theta = 180°$, the total negative charge found within this narrow cone at the different angles θ varies according to the polar graphs shown in Fig. 61M.

These graphs, shown as solid lines at the right of each polar axis, should now be rotated 360° around the axis, to produce a three-dimensional surface. The dashed lines on the left in each

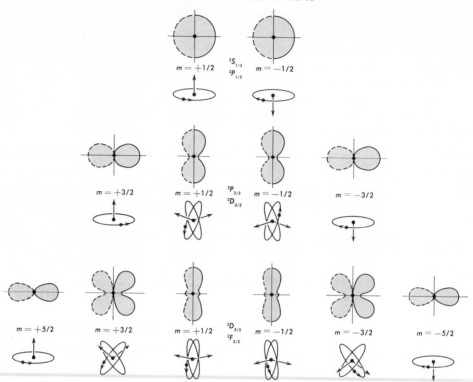

Fig. 61M   *The D_θ charge-density distribution of the electron cloud for several of the lower states of the hydrogen atom, according to the Dirac wave equations.*

figure are drawn in to show this surface in cross section, and the polar symmetry of the D_ϕ distribution.

It is important to note that the electron cloud is not confined to the color-shaded areas inside these graphs. The length of any straight line, drawn from the center of any one of these diagrams to any point on its surface, is proportional to the charge found in the small solid angle $\Delta\phi$ when its axis is at that angle θ.

The corresponding Bohr orbits are shown below each density graph for comparison purposes only. Rotating the orbit around the polar axis corresponds to the space quantization and orbit precession described in Sec. 52.8.

The two top figures, representing all of the s and p states of the hydrogen atom with $j = \frac{1}{2}$, ($^2S_{1/2}$ and $^2P_{1/2}$), are spherically symmetrical. The first and fourth diagrams in the second row, when rotated, are similar in shape to smoke rings, while the second and third, when rotated, are similar to dumbbells. These angular distri-

butions are the same for all principal quantum numbers n.

THE D_r DENSITY DISTRIBUTION. The D_r density distribution specifies the relative amount of the electron charge to be found at a distance r from the nucleus. If we sum up the total charge within a thin spherical shell of thickness Δr and of radius r, and repeat the summing process for many other shells of the same thickness but different r, we can plot graphs as shown in Fig. 61N.

In the case of the 3s graph, for the $3^2S_{1/2}$ state, for example, the maximum at $r = 12r_1$ means that more of the electron's charge is found to be at that distance than at any other. The points $r = 2r_1$ and $r = 7r_1$, where the curve goes almost to zero, correspond to spherical nodes within the electron cloud. The value r_1 is the radius of the first Bohr circular orbit, and is equal to 0.528 Å.

It should be noted that all graphs go to zero only at $r = 0$ and at $r = \infty$. The cor-

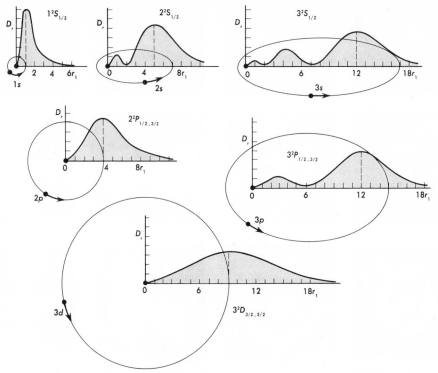

Fig. 61N   *The D_r density distribution of the electron cloud for several of the lower states of the hydrogen atom, according to the Schrödinger wave equation.*

responding Bohr–Sommerfeld electron orbits are shown below each density-distribution curve for comparison purposes. Note how closely each charge-density graph and its corresponding orbit compare with each other in size.

Photographs representing a number of the possible states of a single electron are shown in Fig. 61O. These are not pictures of real atoms but are made to represent them. They were made by *time-exposure photography* of a specially designed mechanical top whose shape and spinning motion combines the D_ϕ, D_θ, and D_r distributions described above.

Where the electronic charge density is large, the figure is white; where it is zero or nearly zero at the nodes, the figure is dark. The three-dimensional distributions can be visualized by imagining each photograph to be rotating about a vertical axis through the center. The relative sizes of these patterns are given approximately by n^2.

Even though the new theory of the hydrogen

atom is an improvement upon the older Bohr orbit theory, and gives a more satisfactory explanation of all known phenomena, it is difficult to form a mental picture of what an atom might look like. Indeed, the modern theoretical physicist goes so far as to say that the question, "What does an atom look like?" has no meaning much less an answer. There are others, however, who still maintain that only those things that can be pictured are the things that are understood and that all mental thought processes are made in terms of things we detect by sight, sound, and touch.

There are some scientists who continue to think of the electron as a particle rather than a wave, and to interpret the quantity ψ^2 as a probability factor. Following this interpretation, the graphs in Figs. 61M and 61N represent the relative probability of finding the electron at any given time in that direction and at that distance, respectively. In other words, there are regions in the space around the nucleus where the prob-

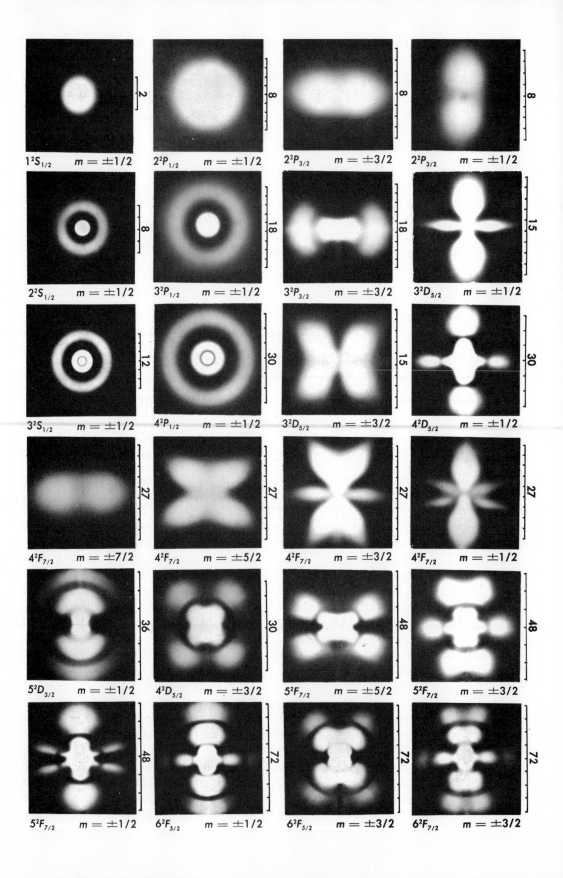

$1\,^2S_{1/2}$ $m = \pm 1/2$	$2\,^2P_{1/2}$ $m = \pm 1/2$	$2\,^2P_{3/2}$ $m = \pm 3/2$	$2\,^2P_{3/2}$ $m = \pm 1/2$
$2\,^2S_{1/2}$ $m = \pm 1/2$	$3\,^2P_{1/2}$ $m = \pm 1/2$	$3\,^2P_{3/2}$ $m = \pm 3/2$	$3\,^2D_{5/2}$ $m = \pm 1/2$
$3\,^2S_{1/2}$ $m = \pm 1/2$	$4\,^2P_{1/2}$ $m = \pm 1/2$	$3\,^2D_{5/2}$ $m = \pm 3/2$	$4\,^2D_{5/2}$ $m = \pm 1/2$
$4\,^2F_{7/2}$ $m = \pm 7/2$	$4\,^2F_{7/2}$ $m = \pm 5/2$	$4\,^2F_{7/2}$ $m = \pm 3/2$	$4\,^2F_{7/2}$ $m = \pm 1/2$
$5\,^2D_{3/2}$ $m = \pm 1/2$	$4\,^2D_{5/2}$ $m = \pm 3/2$	$5\,^2F_{7/2}$ $m = \pm 5/2$	$5\,^2F_{7/2}$ $m = \pm 3/2$
$5\,^2F_{7/2}$ $m = \pm 1/2$	$6\,^2F_{5/2}$ $m = \pm 1/2$	$6\,^2F_{5/2}$ $m = \pm 3/2$	$6\,^2F_{7/2}$ $m = \pm 3/2$

ability of finding the electron at any given instant is high, and other regions like the nodes where the probability is very low or zero.

61.8. The New Atomic Picture. Although the Bohr atom has been replaced by the more satisfactory model of a *nucleus surrounded by electron waves*, it is still customary, for convenience only, to talk about electron *shells* and *orbits*. The reason for this is that there is a close analogy between the old and the new models. When the Bohr–Stoner scheme of the building up of the elements is extended to the new theory of electron waves, the electrons are found to distribute their charge in such a way that something analogous to shells is formed.

This is illustrated by the graph for a rubidium atom, atomic number 37, in Fig. 61P. The

Fig. 61P   *Diagrams comparing the new and the old theories of atomic structure, according to wave mechanics and the Bohr–Stoner model.*

shaded area above represents the distribution of the charge of 37 electrons on the new theory, and the lower orbital model represents the electron shells on the old theory. The new model is represented by a graph because it is spherically symmetrical in space, while the old model is represented by orbits because it is confined to one plane. Proceeding out from the nucleus it is seen that the charge rises to several maxima at

distances corresponding closely to the discrete K, L, M, N, and O shells of the orbital model. In other words, the new atom also has a shell-like structure.

61.9. Heisenberg's Uncertainty Principle. The quantum theory description of a light beam as being made up of discrete packages of energy $h\nu$, called photons, would seem to rest upon our ability to determine for a given photon both the *position* and the *momentum* that it possesses at a given instant. These are usually thought of as measurable quantities of a material particle. It was shown by Heisenberg, however, that for particles of atomic magnitude it is in principle impossible to determine both position and momentum simultaneously with perfect accuracy. If an experiment is designed to measure one of them exactly, the other will become uncertain, and vice versa.

An experiment can measure both position and momentum but only within certain limits of accuracy. These limits are specified by the *uncertainty principle* (sometimes called the *principle of indeterminacy*), according to which

$$\Delta x \cdot \Delta p = \hbar \qquad (61s)$$

Here Δx and Δp represent the variations of the value of position and the corresponding momentum of a particle which must be expected if we try to measure both at once, i.e., the uncertainties of these quantities ($\hbar = 1.0544$ J s).

The uncertainty principle is applicable to photons, as well as to all material particles from electrons up to sizable bodies dealt with in ordinary mechanics. For the latter, the very small magnitude of $\hbar$ renders Δx and Δp entirely negligible compared to the ordinary experimental errors encountered in the measuring of its position x and its momentum p.

When p is very small, as it is for an electron or a photon, the uncertainty may become a large percent of the momentum itself, or else the uncertainty in the position is relatively large.

Fig. 61O   *Electron-density distribution figures representing the single electron states of the hydrogen atom. The rotation of each figure about a vertical axis through its center generates the three-dimensional distribution. The scale on the right of each figure gives the dimensions in angstrom units. 1 angstrom unit = 10^{-10} meters.*

According to Bohr the uncertainty principle of Heisenberg provides complementary descriptions of the same phenomenon. That is, to obtain the complete picture of any event we need both the wave and corpuscular properties of matter, but because of the uncertainty principle it is impossible to design an experiment that will show both of them in all detail at the same time. Any one experiment will reveal the details of either the wave or corpuscular character, according to the purpose for which the experiment is designed.

The interference fringes in Young's double-slit experiment, shown in Fig. 43I, constitute one of the simplest manifestations of the wave character of light. Identical fringe patterns, however, can be obtained by sending a beam of electrons or protons through the same slits. On the wave theory a small part of the incident wave goes through one slit and another small part goes through the other, and these when they come together produce constructive and destructive interference at different areas on the screen (see Fig. 61Q).

If on the corpuscular theory, however, a photon $h\nu$, or a particle m, goes through one slit, how can it be affected by the other slit, and hence go to one of the appropriate fringe areas on the screen, and never to one of the zero points?

To answer this question let us suppose small sensitive detectors, such as scintillation counters (see Figs. 64H and 64I), are placed behind the two slits as shown in Fig. 61Q. These detectors

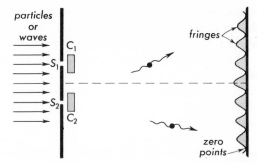

Fig. 61Q   *Young's double-slit experiment modified to demonstrate both wave and corpuscular properties of matter.*

C_1 and C_2 can register each photon or particle that goes through one slit or the other. But, in so doing, the fringe pattern will have been destroyed because of the deflections suffered by the corpuscles in producing scintillations. Because of a change in direction the momentum p is changed so that its new momentum is uncertain.

Hence, when we use slit detectors to make Δx small, we introduce a large change in momentum p, and destroy the fringe pattern. When we do without the slit counters to restore the fringe pattern making Δp small, Δx becomes large because we do not know what slit the corpuscle went through.

Some philosophers regard the uncertainty principle as one of the profound principles of nature. Physicists, on the other hand, are inclined to believe it to be an expression of our inability thus far to formulate a better theory of radiation and matter.

PROBLEMS

1. Calculate the momentum of an X ray having a wavelength of 0.25×10^{-10} m.

2. What would be the De Broglie wavelength of a 2000-Kg car moving along the highway at 30 m/s? [*Ans.* 1.1×10^{-38} m.]

3. Find the wavelength associated with an electron moving with $\frac{1}{15}$ the speed of light.

4. Calculate the wavelength associated with a proton moving with $\frac{1}{20}$ the speed of light. [*Ans.* 2.64×10^{-14} m.]

5. Find the wavelength of an α particle accelerated by a potential difference of 20,000 V.

6. The equivalent wavelength of a moving electron is 0.25×10^{-10} m. What voltage applied between two grids will bring it to rest? [*Ans.* 2400 V.]

7. If 5000 V are applied as an accelerating potential difference to an electron gun, what is the equivalent wavelength of the electrons?

8. The electron beam in a television receiver tube is accelerated by 12,000 V. What is the De Broglie wavelength of the electrons? [*Ans.* 0.112 Å.]

9. Briefly explain the Davisson–Germer experiment. What was observed and what were the conclusions?

10. If the electron beam in a TV picture tube is accelerated by 10,000 V, what is the De Broglie wavelength? [*Ans.* 1.23×10^{-11} m.]

11. Calculate the momentum of each photon in a beam of visible green light, $\lambda = 5000$ Å.

12. Find the momentum of each photon in a beam of violet light, $\lambda = 4000$ Å. [*Ans.* 1.66×10^{-27} Kg m/s.]

13. Find the speed of an electron whose wavelength is equivalent to 0.75 Å.

14. X rays of wavelength 0.82 Å fall on a metal plate. Find the wavelength associated with the photoelectrons emitted. Neglect the work function of the metal. [*Ans.* 0.0997 Å.]

15. Plot a polar graph for the θ distribution of the electron density distribution for the hydrogen atom state $j = \frac{3}{2}$, $m = \frac{3}{2}$. Assume $D_\theta = \sin^2 \theta$.

16. Plot a polar graph for the D_θ distribution of the electron density distribution for the hydrogen atom state $j = \frac{3}{2}$, $m = \frac{1}{2}$. Assume $D_\theta = 3 \cos^2 \theta + 1$.

17. Plot a polar graph for the D_θ distribution of the electron density distribution for the hydrogen atom state $j = \frac{5}{2}$, $m = \frac{1}{2}$. Assume $D_\theta = 5 \cos^4 \theta - 2 \cos^2 \theta + 1$.

18. Using a pencil, crayon, or water colors, make a shaded sketch or picture, similar to the photographs in Fig. 61O, to represent the $3^2P_{3/2}$, $m = \pm\frac{1}{2}$, states of hydrogen. Make an approximate scale.

19. Using a pencil, crayon, or water colors, make a shaded sketch or picture, similar to the photographs in Fig. 61O, to represent the $5^2D_{5/2}$, $m = \pm\frac{1}{2}$, states of hydrogen. Make an approximate scale.

20. Using a pencil, crayon, or water colors, make a shaded sketch or picture, similar to the photographs in Fig. 61O, to represent the $6^2F_{7/2}$, $m = \pm\frac{3}{2}$, states of hydrogen. Make an approximate scale.

21. Using a pencil, crayon, or water colors, make a shaded sketch or picture, similar to the photographs in Fig. 61O, to represent the $5^2D_{5/2}$, $m = \pm\frac{3}{2}$, states of hydrogen. Draw an approximate scale.

RADIOACTIVITY

Radioactivity may be defined as a spontaneous disintegration of the nucleus of one or more atoms. The phenomenon was discovered originally by Becquerel* in 1896 and is confined almost entirely to the heaviest elements in the periodic table, elements 83 to 102. What Becquerel discovered was that uranium, element 92, gave out some kind of rays that would penetrate through several thicknesses of thick black paper and affect a photographic plate on the other side. When the same phenomenon was confirmed several months later by Pierre and Marie Curie,† these rays became known as Becquerel rays.

* Antoine Henri Becquerel (1852–1908), French physicist. Born in Paris on December 15, 1852, Antoine succeeded to his father's chair at the Museum of Natural History in 1892. In 1896 he discovered radioactivity, the phenomenon for which he is most famous. The invisible but penetrating rays emitted by uranium and other radioactive elements are now called Becquerel rays. For these researches he was granted the Nobel Prize in physics in 1903.

† Pierre Curie (1859–1906) and Marie Curie (1867–1936), French physicists. Pierre Curie was educated at the Sorbonne where he later became professor of physics. Although he experimented on piezoelectricity and other subjects, he is chiefly noted for his work on radioactivity performed jointly with his wife, Marie Sklodowska, whom he married in 1895. Marie was born in Poland on November 7, 1867, where she received her early scientific training from her father. Becoming involved in a student's revolutionary organization, she left Poland for Paris where she took a degree at the university. Two years after the discovery of radioactivity by Becquerel, Pierre and Madame Curie isolated polonium and radium from pitchblende by a long and laborious physical-chemical process. In 1903 they were awarded the Davy Medal of the Royal Society, and (jointly with Becquerel) the Nobel Prize in physics. Professor Curie, who was elected to the Academy of Sciences in 1905, was run over and killed by a carriage in 1906. Succeeding him as professor at the university, Madame Curie in 1911 was awarded the Nobel Prize in chemistry. She has the rare distinction of having had a share in the awards of two Nobel Prizes.

62.1. Discovery of Radium. Unlike the discovery of many new phenomena, the discovery of radium by Pierre and Madame Curie in 1898 was brought about intentionally by a set of carefully planned experiments. Having found that pitchblende was active in emitting Becquerel rays, the Curies chemically treated a ton of this ore in the hope of isolating from it the substance or element responsible for the activity. The first concentrated radioactive substance isolated was called *polonium* by Madame Curie, a name chosen in honor of her native country, Poland. Five months later came the isolation of a minute quantity of *radium*, a substance that was a powerful source of Becquerel rays. Continued experiments by the Curies, and others, soon led to the isolation of many other substances now recognized as radioactive elements. Some of the more common of these are *ionium, radon,* and *thorium.*

62.2. The Properties of Becquerel Rays. It is to the experimental genius of Rutherford* that we owe the complete unraveling of the mystery surrounding the nature of Becquerel rays. As the result of an extensive series of experiments, Rutherford and his co-workers discovered that

* Lord Rutherford (1871–1937), British physicist, was born in New Zealand where he attended the university. In 1898 he became Macdonald professor of physics at McGill University, Montreal, Canada, and in 1907 professor of physics at Manchester University. In 1919 he became professor and director of experimental physics at the University of Cambridge, and in addition held a professorship at the Royal Institution in London. He is most famous for his brilliant researches establishing the existence and nature of radioactive transformations and the electrical structure of the atom. For this work and until the time of his death in 1937 he was acclaimed by many as the greatest living experimental physicist. He was awarded the Nobel Prize in chemistry in 1908, and was knighted in 1914.

these penetrating rays are of three quite different kinds. A simplified experiment demonstrating this is illustrated in Fig. 62A. A small sample of radium is dropped to the bottom of a small drill

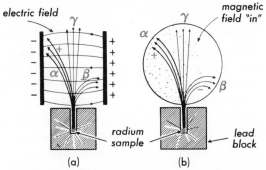

Fig. 62A *The bending of Becquerel rays in (a) an electric field, and (b) a magnetic field.*

hole made in a block of lead. This produces a narrow beam of rays emerging from the top of the block, since rays entering the walls of lead are absorbed before reaching the surface. When electrically charged plates are placed at the side of this beam as shown in diagram (a), the paths of some rays are bent to the left, some to the right, and some are not bent at all. A magnetic field as shown in diagram (b) exhibits the same effect. Paths bending to the left indicate positively charged particles called *α rays* or *α particles*, those bending to the right indicate negatively charged particles called *β rays* or *β particles*, and those going straight ahead indicate no charge and are called *γ rays* or photons.

Rutherford, by a series of experiments, was able to show that each *α* ray is in reality a *doubly ionized helium atom*, i.e., a helium atom with both of its electrons removed. Such a particle is nothing more than a bare helium nucleus with double the positive charge of a hydrogen nucleus or proton, and a mass number or atomic weight four times as great. The *β rays* he found are ordinary electrons with a mass of $\frac{1}{1836}$ the mass of a *proton* or $\frac{1}{7360}$ the mass of an *α particle*, while *γ rays* are electromagnetic waves of about the same or a little higher frequency than X rays. Although *γ* rays all travel with exactly the velocity of X rays and visible light, *α* rays

are ejected with a speed of from $\frac{1}{10}$ to $\frac{1}{100}$ the velocity of light; *β* particles move faster than *α* particles, some of them traveling with 99% the velocity of light.

62.3. Identification of Alpha Particles. The first conclusive evidence that alpha particles are helium nuclei was obtained by Rutherford and Royds in England in 1909. A special glass tube as shown in Fig. 62B was used for this purpose.

Fig. 62B *Special discharge tube used in proof that alpha particles are helium nuclei.*

A thin-walled glass tube A containing radon gas was sealed inside a thick-walled tube B containing mercury. At the top was a glass capillary tube C with two metal electrodes D and E sealed through the glass as shown.

Tubes B and C were evacuated through the side tube P, and then mercury was raised to the level shown. After maintaining this condition for some time, some of the alpha rays emitted by the radon gas atoms passed through the thin glass walls of tube A to be collected in tube B.

Here these particles acquire electrons and become neutral atoms. After standing for six days the mercury was raised to the level L, forcing the helium into the capillary. A high voltage was applied to the electrodes, and the light from the discharge was observed with a spectroscope. The line spectrum observed was found to be identical with that obtained when a discharge was sent through another tube containing regular helium gas.

62.4. Ionizing Power. When Becquerel rays penetrate matter in the gaseous, liquid, or solid state, they do not continue to move indefinitely, but are brought to rest slowly by ionizing atoms all along their path. Being ejected from their radioactive source with tremendously high speeds, all three types of rays collide with electrons and knock them free from atoms. They are, therefore, *ionizing agents*. The relative number of ionized atoms created along the path of an α particle, however, is much greater than the number created by a β particle or γ ray. If, in traveling the same distance in a given material, a γ ray produces one ionized atom, a β particle will, on the average, produce approximately 100, and an α particle will produce about 10,000. Thus α particles are powerful ionizing agents, while γ rays are not.

As stated above, an α particle, ejected from a radioactive atom, is only a nucleus of a helium atom and lacks the two electrons necessary to make of it a neutral atom. As this particle speeds through matter, it picks up and loses electrons at a rapid rate. No sooner does an electron become attached than it is swept off again by other atoms. Finally, upon coming to rest, however, each α particle collects and retains two electrons, becoming a *normal helium atom*.

62.5. Penetrating Power. At each collision with an atom, Becquerel rays lose, on the average, only a small part of their initial energy. Usually an α particle or β particle will make several thousand collisions before being brought to rest. At each collision, some of the kinetic energy is expended in ionizing the atom encountered while giving that same atom a certain amount of kinetic energy. Since α particles produce the greatest number of ions in a given path,

they penetrate the shortest distance and therefore have the poorest penetrating power. The penetrating powers of the three kinds of rays are roughly inversely proportional to their ionizing power.

	α	β	γ
Relative ionizing power	10,000	100	1
Relative penetrating power	1	100	10,000

62.6. Methods of Detecting Becquerel Rays. There are several well-known methods for detecting and measuring radioactivity; the most common of these are

Electroscopes	Geiger–Müller counters
Electrometers	Scintillation counters
Cloud chambers	Ionization chambers
Bubble chambers	Photographic emulsions
Semiconductors	Spark chambers

We have already seen how X rays passing through an electroscope cause the charge to disappear and the gold leaf to fall. This same action may be demonstrated with α, β, and γ rays. The stronger the source of rays or the nearer the sample is brought to the electroscope, the more rapid is the discharge. Experiments show that, if the walls of the electroscope are too thick, only the γ rays get through to produce ionization on the inside. For this reason specially designed electroscopes made with thin windows of light material like aluminum are used for measuring α and β rays.

The Braun type of electrometer is convenient for demonstration purposes. This device uses a lightweight metal pointer, pivoted a trifle above its center of gravity and insulated from its ring support by a nonconductor l as shown in Fig. 62C. In principle, the electrometer operates exactly like an electroscope; when charged positively or negatively, the needle rises and the pointer indicates the acquire potential on a scale.

If a radioactive source is brought close to the knob or terminal of a charged electrometer, the needle slowly returns to the vertical, or no charge, position. The α particles produce many ions in the air close to the source; oppositely charged ions are drawn toward the knob and there neutralize the charge.

62.7. The Wilson Cloud Chamber. In 1912

Fig. 62C *Diagram of a Braun-type electrometer—used here to detect radioactivity.*

C. T. R. Wilson devised a method by which one may actually observe the paths of α and β particles. As will be seen in the following chapters, this method is used extensively in modern atomic physics as a means of studying many different atomic processes. The device by which this is accomplished consists of an expansion chamber in which water vapor is made to condense upon ions produced by the high-speed particles that have previously passed through it.

To begin with, the conditions under which water in the vapor state will condense into fog-drops are quite critical. These conditions are (1) there must be water vapor present, (2) there must be dust particles or ions on which the drops can form, and (3) the temperature and pressure must be brought to a definite value. That water drops will condense only upon ions or dust particles can be demonstrated with an ordinary glass jar containing a little water as shown in Fig. 62D. If allowed to stand for a short period of time, some of the water will evaporate and fill the bottle with vapor. Ions are next formed in the bottle by momentarily inserting a small gas flame as shown in diagram (a). Compressed air is then injected into the bottle through a tube, so that when the stopper is quickly removed the sudden expansion will produce a dense fog as shown in diagram (b). If the flame is not first inserted to produce ions, no appreciable fog can be formed.

The purpose of the compressed air and subsequent expansion of the chamber is to lower the temperature, thus causing the air to become supersaturated with water vapor. Under these conditions the vapor will condense on all ionized molecules present.

When an α or β particle shoots through the air, positive and negative ions are formed all along its path. The removal, by collision, of each electron from a neutral atom or molecule leaves a positively charged ion. The electron that at-

Fig. 62D *Experiment demonstrating the formation of fog drops on ions in a glass jar.*

taches almost immediately to another neutral atom or molecule forms a negatively charged ion. If immediately after an α particle has gone through a cloud chamber an expansion takes place, fogdrops will form on the newly created ions, revealing clearly the path the particle has taken. As illustrated by the photographs in Fig. 62E, such α-ray tracks are straight and quite

Fig. 62F   *Diagram of a small laboratory-type Wilson cloud chamber.*

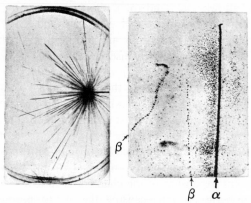

Fig. 62E   (*a*) *α-ray tracks from radium as seen in a Wilson cloud chamber.* (*b*) *One α-ray and two β-ray tracks.* [After C. T. R. Wilson, *Proc. Roy. Soc.* (*London*), **87**, 292 (1912).]

dense, whereas the β-ray tracks are crooked and sparsely lined with drops. The β rays, being very light particles, are easily deflected by collision, while the relatively heavy α particles "plow" right through thousands of atoms with only an occasional deflection.

Gamma rays are never observed in a cloud chamber, since they produce so few ions. In passing through several feet of air a single γ ray will, on the average, produce only one or two ions. This is not enough to produce a recognizable cloud track. If a very strong source of γ rays is available, however, their presence can be observed in a cloud chamber by the chance collisions some of them have made with electrons. These recoiling electrons are called "Compton electrons" and were explained in Sec. 61.2, and shown in Fig. 61D.

A diagram of a simple type of Wilson cloud chamber is shown in Fig. 62F. The arrangement is made from an ordinary flat-bottomed flask with a rubber bulb attached to the neck. A tiny

deposit of radium or polonium is inserted in the end of a thin-walled glass tube as indicated. When the rubber bulb is squeezed to compress the air in the top, and then released to cause an expansion, fogdrops will form on the ions created by the α particles. The battery and the wires leading to the wire ring in the top of the chamber and the water below are for the purpose of quickly removing ions previously formed in the chamber. This clears the field of view for newly formed tracks.

Another type of cloud chamber, one that is readily made in any laboratory workshop, is shown in Fig. 62G. This is the so-called *diffusion cloud chamber*, a device that is continuously sensitive to track formation. A glass cylinder separates and insulates a shallow metal pan below from a metal ring and glass disk above. The bottom pan contains alcohol and rests on a slab of dry ice (solid CO_2).

A blotter, extending 80% of the way around the walls, rests with its lower edge in the alcohol. Evaporated alcohol around the warm upper edge of the blotter mixes with the air and slowly settles as it cools. In the dotted region, alcohol vapor is saturated and small droplets will form on any ions present. Alpha particles shooting

Fig. 62G   *Cross-section diagram of a diffusion cloud chamber.*

out through this space create positive and negative ions, and hence tracks are observed.

A potential difference of 100 V or so between the bottom pan and the top ring will clear the field of ions so that newly formed tracks are not masked by a dense fog of droplets. A strong source of light shining through the 20% open space through the blotter wall illuminates the tracks, thus making them visible.

62.8. Isotope Designations. Within a period of a few years following the discovery of radioactivity, a large number of radioactive elements were found. Soon after J. J. Thomson's discovery of isotopes in 1912, it was realized that the actual number of radioactive elements was few in number and that the many different kinds of activities are to be attributed to the isotopes of only a few elements.

The early designations and the present-day assignments of radioactive isotopes are given in Tables 72A and 72B. Note for example that Ra A, Ra C′, Ac A, Ac C′, Th A, and Th C′ are all isotopes of the 84th element, *polonium.*

It is common practice among scientists today to designate all isotopes of all elements in an abbreviated from. The isotopes of radium, for example, are written

$$_{88}Ra^{223} \quad _{88}Ra^{224} \quad _{88}Ra^{225} \quad _{88}Ra^{226} \quad _{88}Ra^{228}$$

instead of

Ac X   Th X   Ra   Ms I

The subscript to the left of the chemical symbol gives the value of the atomic number Z, i.e., the number of positive charges on the nucleus, the number of orbital electrons in the neutral atom, and the position of the element in the periodic table. The superscript on the right gives the atomic mass number A, i.e., the whole number nearest in value to the atomic mass when

that quantity is expressed in atomic mass units (amu).

62.9. Range. The range of an α particle is defined as the distance such a particle will travel through dry air at normal atmospheric pressure. In a partial vacuum where there are fewer air molecules per centimeter to bump into, the distance traveled before coming to rest will be greater, whereas in air under higher than normal atmospheric pressure there are more molecules per centimeter and the distance will be diminished. Experiments show that some radioactive elements eject α particles with a higher speed than others. The higher the initial speed, the greater is the range. The range of the α particles from $_{88}Ra^{226}$ is 3.39 cm, whereas the range of those from $_{84}Po^{212}$ is 8.62 cm.

The ranges of α particles in general have been determined in three different ways: (1) by the Wilson cloud chamber, (2) by the number of ions produced along the path, and (3) by scintillations produced on a fluorescent screen.

In the Wilson cloud-chamber photograph of Fig. 62H, α particles of two different ranges are observed. The radioactive sample used to obtain this picture was a mixture of $_{83}Bi^{212}$ and $_{84}Po^{212}$. The shorter tracks with a 4.79 cm range are due to the α particles from $_{83}Bi^{212}$ which disintegrate to become $_{81}Tl^{208}$, and the longer tracks of 8.62 cm range are due to the α particles from $_{84}Po^{212}$ which disintegrate to become lead (see Table 72B).

When one measures the number of ions produced along the path of an α particle, curves similar to those in Fig. 62I are obtained. At the end of each track the number is seen to reach a maximum and then drop to zero within a very short distance. This maximum on the graph is called the "Bragg hump" in honor of W. H.

Fig. 62H   *Wilson cloud-chamber tracks from $_{83}Bi^{212}$ and $_{84}Po^{212}$. (After Rutherford, Chadwick, and Ellis.) (Courtesy of Cambridge University Press.)*

Bragg, who discovered the phenomenon. The maximum number of ions is therefore produced just before the particles are stopped i.e., where they are moving at relatively low speeds. The point at which the ion density drops rapidly to zero gives the range as shown in the figure. Al-

Fig. 62I   *Graphs of the relative number of ions produced at various points along the path of an α particle (a) from $_{83}Bi^{212}$, and (b) from $_{84}Po^{212}$.*

though the experimental method by which ion density is usually determined will not be presented here, another method is presented. This is the well-known method of counting fogdrops. An enlarged photograph of a cloud track, as reproduced in Fig. 62J, reveals the individual fogdrops separated sufficiently to enable the number of drops per centimeter of path to be counted. In measurements of this kind, it is

Fig. 62J   *Enlarged photograph of a cloud-chamber track showing individual fog drops. (After Brode.)*

assumed that each ion produces one fogdrop.

The third method used in measuring the range is illustrated in Fig. 62K. When each α particle

Fig. 62K   *Experimental method of measuring the range of α particles.*

strikes a fluorescent screen, a tiny flash of light is produced. These flashes, called *scintillations*, are observed by means of a microscope. When the sample is moved farther and farther away, by pulling the rod R back, a point is reached where scintillations are no longer observed. The distance *d*, where the α particles just fail to reach the screen, is a direct measure of the range.

62.10. Range of Alpha Particles—Experiment. A simple laboratory experiment for measuring the range of α particles is shown in Fig. 62L. It involves the use of a radioactive source obtained from any physics supply house, a Braun-type electrometer, and an ionization chamber made from ordinary sheet metal. The ionization chamber, about the size of the most common tin can, has a hole in the bottom and a sliding disk plunger for a top. The radioactive source on the Braun electrometer, and a small metal clamp is used to ground the needle to the frame when it swings about 3 cm from its zero position. A 600-V radio battery of small capacity is a convenient source of high potential.

The plunger distance *r* is first set at about 8 cm. In this position the needle rises steadily, hits a small metal clamp stop, and quickly drops back to zero. The needle rises again and drops

Fig. 62L *An experimental arrangement for measuring the range of α particles.*

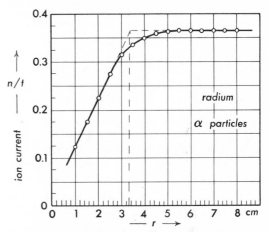

Fig. 62M *Graph of the ion current from the α particle range experiment (see Fig. 62L).*

to that shown in Fig. 62M is obtained. The drop in ion current at distances less than the *range* is due to the fact that α particles hit the plunger before they reach the end of their range in air

back quickly at a regular rate, due to the continual collection of charge from the ions in the chamber above. With a stop watch the time t required for any given number n of discharges of the needle is recorded. The plunger is then lowered 5 mm and the discharge time again measured. This process is repeated for distances diminishing by 5-mm steps, and the discharge rate determined.

The quantity n/t for each setting of the plunger distance r is a direct measure of the ion current, that is, to the number of ions produced per second. If n/t is plotted against r, a curve similar

and are prevented from creating their full quota of ions. The leveling-off of the current at larger values of r signifies that all α particles reach the end of their range in air and create their full ion quota. From the intersection of the dotted lines the α-particle range is found to be approximately 3.3 cm, in good agreement with the accurately known value of 3.39 cm.

The ranges of α particles from some of the natural radioactive elements are given in Chapter 63, Tables 63A and 63B.

QUESTIONS

1. Who discovered radioactivity? What were the circumstances?

2. Who discovered radium, polonium, and thorium?

3. What names are given to the different radioactive rays? Who unraveled this mystery?

4. What are α rays, β rays, and γ rays?

5. What are the relative ionizing powers and penetrating powers of the different rays?

6. What is a Wilson cloud chamber? How does it work?

7. What kinds of particles do not leave tracks in a Wilson cloud chamber? Why not?

8. Define or briefly explain each of the following: (a) scintillations, (b) the Bragg hump, (c) penetrating power, (d) ionizing power, and (e) an ionized atom.

9. What is meant by the range of an α particle?

10. From your knowledge of atomic structure explain how an α particle loses energy as it passes through matter, such as a gas.

11. Draw a graph showing how the specific ionization along the path of an α particle varies with distance. Indicate the range of the particle on the plot.

12. Why does the α particle-range graph of Fig. 62M round off at the top instead of showing a sharp break in the curve?

13. What effect would β and γ rays from an radium source have upon the measured ion current and the α-particle range measurements described in Sec. 62.9?

14. What is the purpose of the dry ice in the operation of a diffusion cloud chamber (see Fig. 62G)?

DISINTEGRATION
AND TRANSMUTATION

We have seen in the preceding chapter how the heaviest elements in the periodic table spontaneously emit three kinds of radiation, *alpha particles* which are positively charged helium nuclei, *beta particles* which are negatively charged electrons, and *gamma rays* which are electromagnetic waves of extremely high frequency called photons. Such emission is called *radioactivity*.

63.1. Transmutation by Spontaneous Disintegration. A careful study of radioactivity indicates that α, β, and γ rays originate from within the nucleus of the atom and are the result of a nuclear disintegration. When a radium atom disintegrates by ejecting an α particle, the nucleus loses a net positive charge of 2. Since the number of positive charges on the nucleus determines the exact number of electrons outside of the atom, and this in turn determines the chemical nature of an atom, the loss of an α particle, with two positive charges, leaves a new chemical element. Thus a *radium atom*, for example, in disintegrating, changes into a new atom called *radon*. We say that there has been a *transmutation*. Not only does a nucleus lose a double charge by emitting an α particle and thereby *drops down two places in atomic number*, but it also loses a weight of four mass units and thus *drops down four units in atomic weight*, or four *atomic mass units*.

The disintegration of radioactive nuclei may be written in the form of simple equations, as follows. For radium

$$_{88}\text{Ra}^{226} \rightarrow {}_{86}\text{Rn}^{222} + \alpha \qquad (63a)$$

or

$$_{88}\text{Ra}^{226} \rightarrow {}_{86}\text{Rn}^{222} + {}_2\text{He}^4 \qquad (63b)$$

As another example, for polonium

$$_{84}\text{Po}^{210} \rightarrow {}_{82}\text{Pb}^{206} + {}_2\text{He}^4 \qquad (63c)$$

When a nucleus like $_{82}\text{Pb}^{214}$ disintegrates by ejecting a β particle (an electron) to become $_{83}\text{Bi}^{214}$, the nuclear positive charge *increases by one unit*. Such a transmutation yields a new element one atomic number higher in the chemical table. Since an electron weighs only $\frac{1}{1836}$ part of a hydrogen atom or proton, the change in mass due to a β particle leaving a nucleus is too small to change the atomic mass number. Although the loss in weight is measurable, it changes the atomic weight so slightly that for most purposes of discussion it can be, and is, neglected. For $_{82}\text{Pb}^{214}$

$$_{82}\text{Pb}^{214} \rightarrow {}_{83}\text{Bi}^{214} + {}_{-1}\text{e}^0 + \gamma \text{ ray}$$

In each equation the sum of the subscripts on the right side of the equation is equal to the subscript on the left. The same is true for the superscripts. The designation $_2\text{He}^4$ represents the α particle, and $_{-1}\text{e}^0$ represents the β particle. In nearly all radioactive disintegrations where a β particle is emitted, one finds a γ ray also. In such cases, as shown by the example, $_{82}\text{Pb}^{214}$ ejects a β particle and a γ ray to become $_{83}\text{Bi}^{214}$, a nucleus higher in atomic number by unity, but with the same mass number.

A γ ray, like the β ray particle, changes the weight of a nucleus by a negligible amount, and, since it has no charge, it does not alter either the atomic number or the mass number.

63.2. Half-Life. *The half-life of a radioactive element is the time required for half of a given quantity of that element to disintegrate into a new element.* For example, it takes 1600 years for $\frac{1}{2}$ of a given quantity of $_{88}Ra^{226}$ to change into $_{86}Rn^{222}$. In another 1600 years, $\frac{1}{2}$ of the remainder will have disintegrated, leaving $\frac{1}{4}$ of the original amount. The half-life of $_{88}Ra^{226}$ is therefore said to be 1600 years.

The rate at which a given quantity of a radioactive element disintegrates, that is, *decays*, is found by observing the activity of a given sample over a period of time and plotting a graph of the type shown in Fig. 63A. Here, for $_{84}Po^{210}$, the

rate of polonium decay

Fig. 63A   *Decay curve for the radioactive element polonium. $_{84}Po^{210}$ has a half-life of 140 days.*

activity drops to $\frac{1}{2}$ of its original value in 140 days. In another 140 days it again drops to half value, etc. The term activity may be defined as the number of rays given off per second of time, or as the number of ionized atoms produced each second by the rays.

The only difference between the decay curve of one element and that of another is the horizontal time scale to which they are plotted. To turn Fig. 63A into a decay curve for $_{84}Ra^{226}$, the times 140, 280, 420 days, etc., need only be changed to read 1600, 3200, 4800 years etc., respectively. Since, therefore, all radioactive decay curves follow the same law, one does not have to wait for half of a given sample to disintegrate to be able to calculate how long it will be before half will have changed. This would require too many years of waiting for some elements.

A decay curve for the radioactivity of any given substance is best shown on what is called a *semilog graph*. Such a graph involves the use of

cross-section paper in which the spacings on the horizontal scale are uniform, while on the vertical scale they are proportional to the logarithms of numbers. Such cross-section paper can be purchased, or made by using the B or C scale on the slipstick of a slide rule.

In Fig. 63B, the fractions $\frac{1}{1}$, $\frac{1}{2}$, $\frac{1}{4}$, $\frac{1}{8}$, $\frac{1}{16}$, etc., are plotted on semilog graph paper with the polonium *time scale* plotted horizontally. Note that a straight line is the result. If a semilog graph is plotted for the activity of any other radioactive element, it too will be a straight line, but with a different slope.

Suppose that for a given sample of radioactive material the initial number of particles given off per minute is N_0. After a time t, the number of atoms yet to disintegrate will have decreased and the reduced number of particles given off per minute will be N. Hence, the ratio N/N_0 will decrease with time t. If the logarithm of the inverse ratio N_0/N is plotted against t, as shown by the dotted line in Fig. 63B, it too will produce a straight line. The latter shows that the Napierian logarithm of N_0/N is proportional to t. We can therefore write

$$\ln \frac{N_0}{N} = \lambda t \qquad (63d)$$

where λ is the proportionality constant and is called the *decay constant*.

To find the half-life of an element from the semilog graph we find the point where $N = \frac{1}{2}N_0$, and call the corresponding time the *half-life T*. For this graph point, Eq.(63d) gives

$$\ln \frac{N_0}{\frac{1}{2}N_0} = \lambda T \qquad (63e)$$

or

$$\ln 2 = \lambda T \qquad (63f)$$

Looking up the Naperian logarithm of 2, we find 0.693 (see Appendix IV). Hence

$$0.693 = \lambda T \qquad (63g)$$

or

$$T = \frac{0.693}{\lambda} \qquad (63h)$$

This is the relation between the decay constant λ and the half-life T of any element.

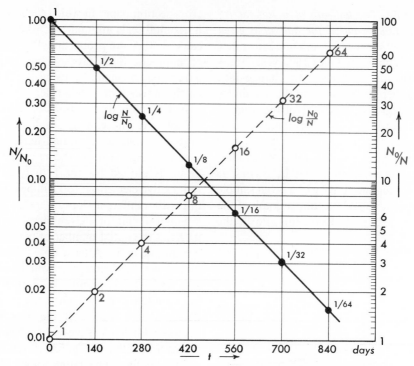

Fig. 63B   *Semilog graphs of the α particle activity of polonium, $_{84}Po^{210}$.*

Example 1. A count-rate meter is used to measure the activity of a given sample. At one instant the meter shows 4750 counts per minute (cpm). Five minutes later it shows 2700 cpm. Find (a) the decay constant, and (b) the half-life.

Solution. To find the decay constant λ, use Eq. (63d). We first find

$$\frac{N_0}{N} = \frac{4750}{2700} = 1.760$$

To find the logarithm to the base e of any number we can look up the logarithm to the base 10 of the number, and multiply by 2.3026. From a table of ordinary logarithms, we find

$$\log 1.760 = 0.2455$$

Multiplying this by 2.3026, we obtain

$$\ln 1.760 = 0.5653$$

Using Eq.(63d), we obtain

(a) $\lambda = \dfrac{0.5653}{5 \text{ min}} = 0.1131 \text{ min}^{-1}$

Substituting in Eq.(63h), we obtain

(b) $T = \dfrac{0.693}{0.1131} = 6.1 \text{ min}$

The mean life of a radioactive element is defined as the average time single atoms or particles exist before disintegrating, and is given by the reciprocal of the decay constant.

$$\tau = \frac{1}{\lambda}$$

As shown by Eq.(63h) the half-life T is just slightly over $\frac{2}{3}$ the mean life τ:

$$T = 0.693\tau$$

63.3. Radioactive Series. It was Rutherford and his colleagues who discovered that when one radioactive atom disintegrates by ejecting an α or β particle, the remaining atom is still radioactive and may sooner or later eject another particle to become a still different atom. This process they found to continue through a series of elements, ending up finally with a type of atom that is stable and not radioactive. It is now known that nearly all natural disintegration processes, occurring among the heaviest elements of the periodic table, finally end up with *stable lead atoms,* atomic number 82.

TABLE 63A. URANIUM-238 SERIES

Element	Symbol	Atomic no.	Mass no.	Particle ejected	Range in air	Half-life
Uranium	$_{92}U^{238}$	92	238	α	2.70 cm	4.5×10^9 yr
Thorium	$_{90}Th^{234}$	90	234	β	....	24.5 days
Protoactinium	$_{91}Pa^{234}$	91	234	β	....	1.14 min
Uranium	$_{92}U^{234}$	92	234	α	3.28	3×10^5 yr
Thorium	$_{90}Th^{230}$	90	230	α	3.19	83,000 yr
Radium	$_{88}Ra^{226}$	88	226	α	3.39	1600 yr
Radon	$_{86}Rn^{222}$	86	222	α	4.12	3.82 days
Polonium	$_{84}Po^{218}$	84	218	α	4.72	3.05 min
Lead	$_{82}Pb^{214}$	82	214	β	....	26.8 min
Bismuth	$_{83}Bi^{214}$	83	214	α, β	....	19.7 min
Polonium	$_{84}Po^{214}$	84	214	α	6.97	10^{-6} s
Thallium	$_{81}Tl^{210}$	81	210	β	....	1.32 min
Lead	$_{82}Pb^{210}$	82	210	β	....	22 yr
Bismuth	$_{83}Bi^{210}$	83	210	β	....	5 days
Polonium	$_{84}Po^{210}$	84	210	α	3.92	140 days
Lead	$_{82}Pb^{206}$	82	206	stable	....	infinite

There are at least four known radioactive series or chains of elements, one starting with uranium-238, a second with thorium-232, a third with uranium-235, and a fourth with plutonium-241. The first and fourth of these series are given in Tables 63A and 63B. All four series are given in a graphical tabulation in Table 72A and Table 72B.

When a uranium atom $_{92}U^{238}$ of mass number 238 and atomic number 92 disintegrates by ejecting an α particle, the remainder is a new atom, $_{90}Th^{234}$, of mass number 234 and atomic number 90. When a $_{90}Th^{234}$ atom disintegrates by ejecting a β particle to become $_{91}Pa^{234}$, the mass number remains unchanged at 234, while the atomic number increases by 1 to become 91.

TABLE 63B. PLUTONIUM SERIES*

Element	Symbol	Atomic no.	Mass no.	Particle ejected	Range in air	Half-life
Plutonium	$_{94}Pu^{241}$	94	241	β	..	...
Americium	$_{95}Am^{241}$	95	241	α	4.1†	500 yr
Neptunium	$_{93}Np^{237}$	93	237	α	3.3†	2.25×10^6 yr
Protoactinium	$_{91}Pa^{233}$	91	233	β	..	27.4 days
Uranium	$_{92}U^{233}$	92	233	α	3.3†	1.63×10^5 yr†
Thorium	$_{90}Th^{229}$	90	229	α	3.3	7×10^3 yr
Radium	$_{88}Ra^{225}$	88	225	β	..	14.8 days
Actinium	$_{89}Ac^{225}$	89	225	α	4.4	10 days
Francium	$_{87}Fa^{221}$	87	221	α	5.0	4.8 min
Astatine	$_{85}At^{217}$	85	217	α	5.8	0.018 s
Bismuth	$_{83}Bi^{213}$	83	213	$\beta(94\%)$ $\alpha(4\%)$	4.6	47 min
Polonium	$_{84}Po^{213}$	84	213	α	7.7	10^{-6} s
Lead	$_{82}Pb^{209}$	82	209	β	..	3.3 hr
Bismuth	$_{83}Bi^{209}$	83	209	stable	..	infinite

* See J. M. Cork, *Radioactivity and Nuclear Physics* (D. Van Nostrand Co., Inc., Princeton, New Jersey, 1957).
† See F. Hagemann, L. I. Katzin, M. H. Studier, A. Ghiorso, and G. T. Seaborg. *Phys. Rev.*, **72**, 252 (August 1947).

This increase of 1 positive charge is attributed to the loss of 1 negative charge. These processes of successive disintegration continue until $_{82}Pb^{206}$, a *stable* lead atom, is the end result.

As explained in Secs. 49.4 and 62.8, all atoms with the same atomic number but different mass number are called isotopes of the same element. For example, $_{82}RaB^{214}$, $_{82}ThB^{212}$, $_{82}AcB^{211}$, $_{82}RaD^{210}$, $_{82}Pb^{209}$, $_{82}Pb^{208}$, $_{82}Pb^{207}$, and $_{82}Pb^{206}$ are isotopes of the same chemical element, lead (see Tables 72A and 72B). Even though the first five of these are radioactive, i.e., unstable, the other three are stable. Chemically they behave exactly alike and are separated only with difficulty. The isotopes 214, 210, and 206 belong to the uranium-238 series; 212 and 208 belong to the thorium series; 211 and 207 belong to the uranium-235 series; and 209 belongs to the neptunium series.

63.4. Daughter Products. When an element disintegrates by emitting α or β rays, it produces a new chemical element. Such "offspring" atoms are referred to as the *daughter element*, an element which itself may or may not be radioactive. Consider as an example the radioactive element radon, $Z = 86$. Of the several known isotopes of this element (see Table 72B), isotope 220 is a derivative of the thorium series beginning with $_{90}Th^{232}$.

Thoron-220 is a gas and is α-active, that is, it disintegrates by giving off α particles. The daughter product, polonium-216, is α-active, and has an extremely short half-life of 0.158 s. The daughter product of this element, however, has the relatively long half-life of 10.6 hr. The reactions involved here are as follows:

$$_{86}Rn^{220} \rightarrow {}_{84}Po^{216} + {}_2He^4 \quad (T = 54.5 \text{ s})$$
$$_{84}Po^{216} \rightarrow {}_{82}Pb^{212} + {}_2He^4 \quad (T = 0.158 \text{ s}) \quad (63i)$$
$$_{82}Pb^{212} \rightarrow {}_{83}Bi^{212} + {}_{-1}e^0 \quad (T = 10.6 \text{ hr})$$

If a given quantity of $_{86}Rn^{220}$ gas is confined to a closed vessel, the gas nuclei that disintegrate will tend to accumulate as $_{84}Po^{216}$. Not much of this daughter product can accumulate, however, since with the short half-life of 0.158 s, most of the nuclei quickly disintegrate into $_{82}Pb^{212}$. In the period of 10 to 15 min, few of these $_{82}Pb^{212}$ nuclei disintegrate, and they do accumulate. A graph of this decrease of parent element $_{86}Rn^{220}$ and the accumulation of daughter element $_{84}Po^{216}$ and its daughter element $_{82}Pb^{212}$ is shown in Fig. 63C.

63.5. Half-Life Experiment. A relatively simple experiment for measuring the half-life of a

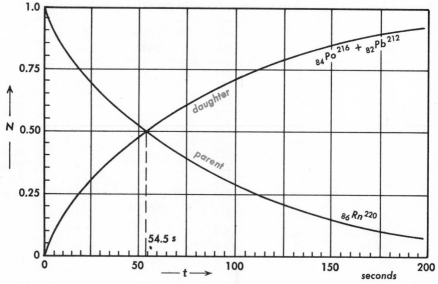

Fig. 63C   *Decay curve for $_{86}Rn^{220}$ (radon) and the growth curve for the daughter products,* $_{84}Po^{216} + {}_{82}Pb^{212}$.

Fig. 63D *Simple apparatus for determining the half-life of a radioactive gas like radon, $_{86}Rn^{220}$.*

radioactive element is shown in Fig. 63D. Radon gas $_{86}Rn^{220}$ from a small glass vessel A, injected into an ionization chamber C, is detected by the ion current I as it flows through the electrometer E into the ground G.

Immediately upon squeezing the rubber bulb B and injecting the radon, the electroscope needle rises and falls, discharging intermittently through the stop S. The time t is recorded from a seconds clock each time a discharge occurs, and these are recorded against the discharge number n. A typical set of recorded times is plotted in Fig. 63E. The leveling-out of the graph after some time signifies that little radon gas is left, and a reasonably horizontal line is drawn at $n = 14$ as the last discharge that could be obtained. Coming down, therefore, to the point $N = 7$, where the activity was at half value, the time $t = 56$ s is read from the graph as the half-life of $_{86}Rn^{220}$.

The decay curve of Fig. 63E can be plotted as a semilog graph by plotting the difference between the line $N = 14$ and the curve value at each 10-s interval, and plotting these as shown in Fig. 63F. When the best possible straight line is drawn through the points, the half-value point comes at $t = 56$ s.

Mathematically, this value can be computed from the graph and Eq.(63d) as follows. At time

Fig. 63E *Experimental decay curve for radon ($_{86}Rn^{220}$), obtained using the apparatus shown in Fig. 63D.*

Fig. 63F *Semilog graph for finding the half-life of radon, $_{86}Rn^{220}$.*

$t = 0$ we obtain $N_0 = 14$. Choosing any other point far down on the graph, such as the one at $t = 150$ s, we find $N = 2.2$. Dividing one value by the other gives $N_0/N = 6.36$. Looking up this number in a table of logarithms we find ln $6.36 = 18.50$ (see Appendix IV). Substitution of this value in Eq. (63e), along with $t = 150$ s, gives as the value for the decay constant:

$$\lambda = \frac{1.850}{150} = 0.0123$$

When this is substituted in Eq.(63h), we obtain

$$T = \frac{0.693}{0.0123} = 56.3 \text{ s}$$

as the half-life.

63.6. Different Forms of Energy. Einstein, in working out the theory of relativity, arrived at a number of simple equations concerning the nature of the physical world. One of these equations, having to do with the increase in mass of a moving object, was presented in Sec. 58.5. It is important at this point to consider this mass–energy equation again:

$$E = mc^2 \qquad (63j)$$

where m is the mass, c is the velocity of light, and E is the energy equivalent.

From this relation we can predict that mass can be turned into energy, or energy into mass. In other words, mass is a form of energy, for if a quantity of mass m could be annihilated, a definite amount of energy E would become available in some other form. To illustrate this, suppose that a 1-g mass could be completely annihilated and the liberated energy given to some other body in the form of kinetic energy:

$$E = 1 \times 10^{-3} \text{ Kg} \times 9 \times 10^{16} \text{ m}^2/\text{s}^2$$
$$= 9 \times 10^{13} \text{ J}$$

In the English system of units this is equivalent to 7×10^{13} ft-lb or enough energy to propel the largest battleship around the world.

The annihilation of mass then is a source of undreamed-of energy. In the following chapters we will see that disintegration is one means whereby mass can be annihilated or created through planned laboratory experiments.

In the following chapters we will see that if an atom, a part of an atom, or an electron is annihilated, the energy may either be transformed into kinetic energy and given to another atomic particle in the form of a velocity, or it may appear as a γ ray of specified frequency ν and energy $h\nu$. To find the equivalence between mass energy, γ = ray energy, and kinetic energy, all of the following quantities are equated to each other:

$$\boxed{E = mc^2 = h\nu = \tfrac{1}{2}m_0v^2 = Ve} \quad (63k)$$

It is customary among physicists to express each of these energies in terms of V in volts. Thus one speaks of a one-million volt γ ray, a three-million volt electron, or a 12.5-million volt proton, etc. This terminology is used for convenience only, and denotes the value of V in the above equation which, with the electronic charge substituted for e, gives the energy of the γ-ray photon, or the energy of the moving atomic particle. For all energies, m in the second term is the relativistic mass given by Eq.(58j), and the fourth term is the kinetic energy of any particle whose rest mass is m_0. At very high velocities the fourth term must be replaced by the relativistic kinetic energy $m_0c^2(\gamma - 1)$ [see Eq.(58q)].

When an atomic nucleus ejects an α or β particle, the mass of that nucleus diminishes not only by the rest mass of the ejected particle, but by an amount called the *annihilation energy*. A small part of the nuclear mass is annihilated and given to the ejected particle as kinetic energy.

While the annihilated mass varies from isotope to isotope, it is usually less than 1% of one atomic mass unit.

As a convenient figure to use in disintegration problems, we will calculate the energy equivalent to the annihilation of unit atomic mass, namely, 1.66×10^{-27} Kg. Using the second and last terms of Eq.(63k), we find

$$\boxed{Ve = mc^2} \quad (63l)$$

$$V = \frac{1.66 \times 10^{-27} \times 9 \times 10^{16}}{1.60 \times 10^{-19}}$$

$$= 931,000,000 \text{ V}$$

The annihilation energy of 1 amu = 931 million electron volts. Abbreviated,

$$1 \text{ amu} = 931 \text{ MeV} \quad (63m)$$

When a γ ray is ejected from a nucleus, it carries with it an energy $h\nu$. This energy may be expressed by the mass equivalence as given by the second and third terms of Eq.(63k), or by the voltage equivalence as given by the third and fifth terms. It is customary to use the latter relation and write

$$\boxed{Ve = h\nu} \quad (63n)$$

Example 2. A γ ray has a wavelength of 4.5×10^{-13} m. Find its energy equivalence in million electron volts.

Solution. Using the wave equation $c = \nu\lambda$, and substituting c/λ for ν in Eq. (63n), we obtain

$$V = \frac{hc}{e\lambda}$$

Substituting, we find that

$$V = \frac{6.62 \times 10^{-34} \times 3 \times 10^8}{1.60 \times 10^{-19} \times 4.5 \times 10^{-13}}$$

$$= 2.75 \times 10^6$$
$$V = 2.75 \text{ MeV}$$

It is common practice to express the initial energy of α particles by specifying either their range in air or their energy equivalence in MeV. This applies to other high-speed particles as well,

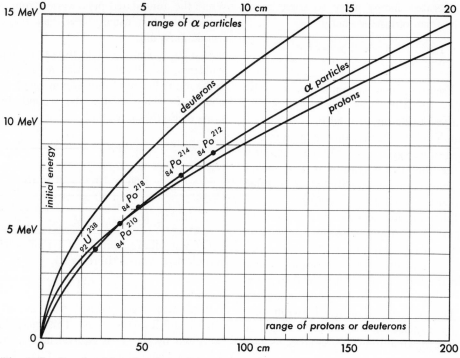

Fig. 63G *Graphs giving the range of protons, deuterons, and α particles for different initial energies in million electron volts.*

particles such as protons and deuterons which are the nuclei of the two hydrogen isotopes. A graph like the one shown in Fig. 63G is useful for converting the observed range of an α particle to its equivalent energy in MeV, or vice versa.

QUESTIONS AND PROBLEMS

1. What is spontaneous disintegration?

2. What is transmutation? What change takes place in the nucleus of an atom when an α particle is emitted? What change takes place when a β particle is emitted?

3. What is meant by the half-life of a radioactive isotope?

4. What is meant by the range of radioactive rays? Which of the three kinds of rays should have the greatest range?

5. What is the abbreviated designation for atomic nuclei?

6. Write down the nuclear reaction, in the abbreviated form, for the emission of an α particle by an ionium nucleus (atomic number 90) (see Table 72A).

7. Write down the nuclear reaction for the emission of an α particle by radon-222 (atomic number 86) (see Table 72A).

8. Write down the nuclear reaction for α-particle emission by uranium-238 (see Table 72A).

9. Write the nuclear reaction for the emission of a β particle by actinium-227 (see Table 72B).

10. Write the nuclear reaction for the emission of a β particle by radium B (see Table 72A).

11. If the activity of a radioactive sample drops to $\frac{1}{8}$th of its initial value in 1 hr and 20 min, what is its half-life?

12. If the activity of a radioactive sample drops to $\frac{1}{32}$ of its initial value in 7.5 hr, find its half-life. [*Ans.* 1.5 hr.]

13. How long will it take a sample of radon to decrease to 10% if its half-life is 3.82 days? Find your answer by plotting a decay curve.

14. How long will it take a sample of radium D to decrease to 10% if its half-life is 22 years? [*Ans.* 73.1 y.]

15. If the activity of a radioactive sample drops to $\frac{1}{64}$ of its initial value in 6 hr and 45 min, find its half-life.

16. The activity of a radioactive sample drops to $\frac{1}{32}$ of its initial value in 54 hr. Find its half-life. [*Ans.* 10.8 hr.]

17. How long will it take for the activity of a sample of

radon-222 to decrease to 5.8%? Determine your answer by graphing the time-decay curve.

18. How long will it take for the activity of a sample of francium-221 to decrease to $\frac{1}{10}$ of 1%? [*Ans.* 47.8 min.]

19. What radioactive atoms are isotopes of bismuth? Give symbols, atomic numbers, and mass numbers (see Tables 72A and 72B).

20. If 5 lb of lead could be completely annihilated, how many joules would be produced? [*Ans.* 20.4 × 10^{16} J.]

21. Calculate the mass equivalent to an energy of (a) 16 MeV, (b) 45 MeV, and (c) 3.8 MeV.

22. If the following masses could be annihilated, how much energy, in MeV, is created? (a) 0.0216 atomic mass unit, (b) 0.0589 atomic mass unit. [*Ans.* (a) 20.1, (b) 54.8.]

23. At one instant a count-rate meter shows a radioactive sample emitting 3000 cpm. Ten minutes later the activity has dropped to 1200 cpm. Find (a) the decay constant, and (b) the half-life.

24. In recording the activity of a given radioactive sample, a count-rate meter indicates 6250 cpm. Two minutes later the meter shows the activity has dropped to 4840 cpm. Calculate (a) the decay constant, and (b) the half-life. [*Ans.* (a) 0.149 min^{-1}, (b) 4.65 min.]

BETA AND
GAMMA RAYS

Beta rays emitted by the natural radioactive elements have been studied by many people. It was Becquerel who first found them to be comparable to cathode rays. Today we know them as electrons. One of the greatest mysteries of atomic physics has been the origin of these particles. The great mass of experimental evidence shows that most of them come from the nucleus, yet they do not exist in the same form inside any of the known nuclei. Furthermore, unlike α particles and γ rays, they do not emerge from the nuclei with the same energy and range, but with a wide band of velocities.

64.1. Beta-Ray Spectrograph. This is an instrument by which one can experimentally determine the velocity of β particles from a radioactive source. Figure 64A is a diagram of one such

Fig. 64A *Diagram of a β-ray spectrograph.*

instrument, developed in principle by Robinson in England. Beta particles from a small radioactive source A, consisting of a fine wire with a deposit of material on its surface, are allowed to

pass through a slit S. With the entire vacuum tube located in a uniform magnetic field, the β particles follow circular paths and are brought to focus on a photographic plate P or at the open slit of an ionization chamber C. Each of the three semicircular paths in any one group shown in the diagram has the same radius and diameter. The focusing action indicated can be demonstrated by using a compass and drawing several semicircles with the same radius, but slightly displaced centers. The velocity of any group of electrons is given by Eq.(48e), as

$$Bev = \frac{mv^2}{r} \tag{64a}$$

where r is the path radius, B the magnetic induction, and e, m, and v the electron's charge, mass, and velocity, respectively.

If the field B is constant, and a photographic plate P is located as shown in the figure, its development after a time t will result in a photograph like the drawing in Fig. 64B. In addition

Fig. 64B *Diagram of a β-ray spectrogram.*

to a darkened background all along the plate, one finds several lines parallel to the slit. The background indicates β particles present with all different velocities, while the lines signify groups with discrete and definite velocities. Not all spectrograms with such a continuous background contain these lines, however.

In some β-ray spectrographs, the β particles are collected in an ionization chamber C as shown in Fig. 64A. Different velocities are determined by slowly and continuously changing the magnetic induction B. This is accomplished by changing the current I in the field coils F. If measurements of electrometer current are recorded for different values of B, a graph similar to that shown in Fig. 64C can be plotted.

signifies a velocity limit or maximum. As shown by Table 64A, such end-point energies have different values for different isotopes.

64.2. The Neutrino Postulate. In 1931 Pauli, of Germany, suggested that in β-ray emission all nuclei of the same isotope emit the same amount of energy, and that this is the *end-point energy* shown in Fig. 64C (see also Table 64A). To account for the observed fact that some β particles emerge with much less energy than others, he made the following postulate. The

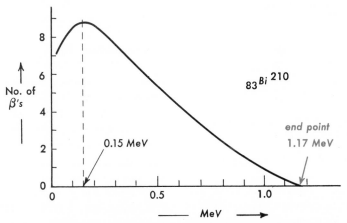

Fig. 64C   *Graph of β-ray energies from $_{83}Bi^{210}$.*

The measured ion current is plotted as the number of β particles, and the coil current I is plotted as the energy the particles would have to enter the slit at C. This curve, which is for the radioactive bismuth isotope $_{83}Bi^{210}$, shows β particles with a maximum energy at 0.15 MeV, and an *end-point* energy of 1.17 MeV. The end point, or cut-off, at the high-energy end of this curve,

emission of a β particle by any nucleus is accompanied by a companion particle having a variable energy E. While the β particle is an ordinary negatively charged electron, the companion particle, now called a *neutrino*, has no charge. In some respects a neutrino is like a photon; it has no rest mass, it has energy E, and it travels with the speed of light c. Hence, the reaction for β emission by a nucleus like $_{83}Bi^{210}$, can be written

$$_{83}Bi^{210} \rightarrow {}_{84}Po^{210} + {}_{-1}e^0 + \bar{\nu}_e \qquad (64b)$$

where $_{-1}e^0$ represents the beta particle and $\bar{\nu}_e$ represents the neutrino. Since there are now known to be several kinds of neutrinos, the e subscript indicates its association with an electron and the bar over it signifies it is an antiparticle.

The neutrino postulate has served another important function in atomic processes; it permits the retention of the law of conservation of mo-

TABLE 64A. END-POINT ENERGIES FOR β RAYS

Nuclide	End point E	Half-life
$_{82}Pb^{214}$	0.72 MeV	26.8 min
$_{83}Bi^{210}$	1.17 MeV	4.8 day
$_{87}Fr^{223}$	1.20 MeV	21.0 min
$_{88}Ra^{225}$	0.320 MeV	15 day
$_{89}Ac^{228}$	1.55 MeV	6.1 hr
$_{90}Th^{231}$	0.21 MeV	25.6 y
$_{90}Th^{234}$	0.193 MeV	24 day

mentum. All even-numbered nuclei, *even A*, are known to have an angular momentum given by an integral quantum number, $I = 0, 1, 2, 3, 4, \ldots$, all odd-numbered nuclei, *odd-A*, are known to have an angular momentum given by a half-integral quantum number, $I = \frac{1}{2}, \frac{3}{2}, \frac{5}{2}, \frac{7}{2} \ldots$. Furthermore, all electrons are known to have a spin angular momentum given by a half-integral quantum number, $s = \frac{1}{2}$. By assigning the neutrino a spin angular momentum equal in magnitude to that of the electron, the two spins can either cancel each other as shown in Fig. 64D, or add together, thus keeping the nuclear

nucleus

Fig. 64D *Each β particle from a nucleus is accompanied by a neutrino.*

spin integral or half-integral valued as the case may be.

Only recently have experiments been performed that appear to establish the existence of these phantom particles, neutrinos. Since nuclei are composed of neutrons and protons, the two ejected particles are created by the nucleus, a neutron transforming into a proton as it emits an electron of mass m_0, charge $-e$, and spin $\frac{1}{2}\hbar$, and a neutrino of energy E, no charge, and spin $\frac{1}{2}\hbar$ [see Eq (52h)].

64.3. Conservation of Nuclear Energy. The simultaneous emission of a β particle and a neutrino from the nucleus of an atom requires energy. The disintegrating nucleus gives up not only the mass of the two particles but some additional mass which it converts into kinetic energy. By adding up all this energy in the form of mass, the total loss in the mass of an atom can be calculated.

Consider as an example the β emission of $_{83}Bi^{210}$ as represented by Eq.(64b). The masses of the two atoms involved are known to be

$$_{83}Bi^{210} \; 209.984110 \text{ amu}$$
$$_{84}Po^{210} \; \underline{209.982866 \text{ amu}}$$
$$\Delta m = 0.001244 \text{ amu}$$

To convert this mass into MeV, we multiply Δm by the value 931 MeV given by Eq.(63m), which gives

$$E = 1.17 \text{ MeV}$$

This is just the end-point energy derived from experiment and shown in Fig. 64C. The mass of the ejected electron need not be included here, since the two masses above are for the neutral atoms. $_{83}Bi^{210}$ has 83 orbital electrons included in its mass of 209.984110 amu, while $_{84}Po^{210}$ includes 84 electrons. When $_{83}Bi^{210}$ ejects an electron from the nucleus, the daughter product $_{84}Po^{210}$ picks up a stray electron to become a neutral atom.

64.4. Gamma Rays. For many radioactive elements the emission of an α or β particle from a nucleus is immediately followed by the emission of a γ ray. It has been shown by crystal diffraction spectrographs that γ rays are electromagnetic waves and that they consist of sharp lines of discrete wavelengths. Just as visible light, and ultraviolet and infrared radiation as well as X rays are known to be emitted from the outer structure of the atom by an electron's jumping from one energy level to another, so γ rays are believed to arise from a transition of a nucleon from one energy state to another within the nucleus. (Neutrons and protons as constituents of nuclei are called *nucleons.*)

There is good evidence that γ rays are emitted by the daughter element, that is, that they are preceded by particle emission. A good example is to be found in the case of $_{82}Pb^{210}$. This nucleus is the lead isotope with a beta half-life of 22 years. The reaction is written

$$_{82}Pb^{210} \rightarrow \; _{83}Bi^{210} + \; _{-1}e^0 + \bar{\nu}_e + \gamma \text{ ray} \quad (64c)$$

These emissions are represented on a nuclear energy-level diagram in Fig. 64E. When a $_{82}Pb^{210}$ nucleus emits a β particle and a neutrino, the end-point energy is found to be 18,000 electron volts (18 KeV). This leaves a $_{83}Bi^{210}$ nucleus in what is called an *excited state* or energy level. A transition down to the ground level is accompanied by the emission of a γ ray with an energy $h\nu$. This energy is equivalent to 47 KeV. Although it is not shown in this diagram, this nu-

Fig. 64E   *Energy-level diagram illustrating β-ray emission followed by γ-ray emission.*

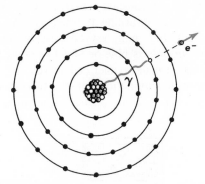

Fig. 64F   *Orbital electron ejected by a γ-ray from the same atom's nucleus. Internal conversion.*

cleus, too, is radioactive and emits another β ray to become $_{84}Po^{210}$ [see Eq.(64b)].

64.5. Internal Conversion. When a γ ray is emitted by a disintegrating nucleus, it must of necessity pass some of the outer electrons on its way out of the atom. Upon passing close to one of the electrons, a photoelectric action may occur whereby the γ ray is absorbed and an electron is emitted. Energetically this process must follow the photoelectric equation, Eq. (50a),

$$h\nu = W + \tfrac{1}{2}mv^2 \qquad (64d)$$

Part of the γ-ray energy $h\nu$ is used to pull the electron away from the atom, and the remainder is imparted to it as kinetic energy. As a rule this kinetic energy is relatively large, and $\tfrac{1}{2}mv^2$ must be replaced by the relativistic form $m_0c^2(\gamma - 1)$ [see Eq.(58q)].

Since the energy required to remove an electron from an atom will differ from one shell to another, the electrons can be expected to have any one of several discrete energies. The definite sharp lines shown in Fig. 64B supply the evidence for this assumption. Furthermore, the experimentally determined energies check exactly with those determined from X rays as shown in Fig. 61A. The process just described is illustrated schematically in Fig. 64F, and is called internal conversion (IC).

If by internal conversion an electron is ejected from the innermost K shell, leaving a vacancy there, another electron from the L shell or M

shell falls in to take its place and, in so doing, emits an X ray. Confirmation of such a process is assured since the measured wavelengths of such X rays are identical with those emitted by the same element in an X-ray tube.

64.6. Scintillation Counters. A scintillation counter is a sensitive device used in nuclear physics studies for the detection and measurement of high-energy atomic radiation. In principle it is based upon the earliest discoveries in radioactivity that α particles upon striking a fluorescent material, like zinc sulfide, produce a tiny flash of light (see Fig. 62K). These flashes, called *scintillations*, can be seen by the dark-adapted eye, or they can be detected by a photomultiplier tube and amplified.

It is now well known that when high-energy-charged atomic particles pass through certain transparent materials, fluorescent light is produced all along the path (see Fig. 64G). As the fast-moving particle collides with atoms and

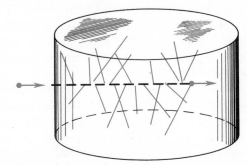

Fig. 64G   *Diagram of the fluorescent light developed by an atomic particle traversing a transparent crystal or plastic fluor.*

molecules, electrons are raised to excited energy levels and in returning to their ground states emit light. For many crystals and plastics this *fluorescent light* is blue or violet in color, while for others it is ultraviolet or infrared.

A typical scintillation counter tube is shown in Fig. 64H. A block of fluorescent material is

Fig. 64H   *Scintillation detector tube using a photomultiplier tube with a fluorescent block.*

mounted on the flat end of a special photomultiplier tube and then encased in a thin-walled, light-tight aluminum shield. When a particle traverses the fluor, the light ejects electrons from the photocathode by the photoelectric effect. The charge multiplication built up by the eight or more dynodes makes a sizable voltage pulse that activates some electronic counting device (see Fig. 64I).

When γ rays are to be detected, the fluorescent materials frequently used are crystals of sodium iodide, NaI, and cesium iodide, CsI. For high-energy β rays, such plastics as polystyrene, impregnated with anthracene, are used. These are inexpensive and very effective and can be quite large in size. For α particles with their relatively low penetrating power, a thin layer of zinc sulfide

Fig. 64I   *One type of scintillation counter with a count-rate meter, two ranges, and an on–off switch.*

deposited on the photomultiplier tube or a plastic surface is commonly used.

The principal advantages of scintillation counters over other detectors of nuclear radiation are these. (1) They operate in air or in a vacuum; (2) they deliver an electrical impulse which is proportioned to the energy lost by the traversing particle; and (3) they can count at amazingly high speeds.

While the duration of a single pulse from a NaI crystal counter will last about one microsecond, the pulse time from an anthracene counter can be as short as one thousandth of a microsecond (10^{-9} s).

64.7. Cerenkov Radiation. In 1934 Cerenkov, in Russia, discovered that fast-moving electrons, such as β particles from radioactive materials, will produce light within a transparent medium if their velocity is greater than the speed of light in that medium. In a medium like glass or plastic, the speed of light is about $\frac{2}{3}$ to $\frac{3}{4}$ the speed of light in a vacuum, yet many β particles are ejected at speeds greater than this, and some of them are close to $c = 3 \times 10^8$ m/s.

The phenomenon of Cerenkov radiation is analogous to (a) the production of the V-shaped wave from a ship when the ship travels through water at a speed greater than the wave velocity or (b) the shock waves from a missile traveling through the air at a speed greater than sound.

In Fig. 64J a particle is shown generating a conical wave as it travels with a velocity V through a medium of refractive index μ. While the conical wave front makes an angle with the particle's direction, the light travels outward at right angles to the wave front.

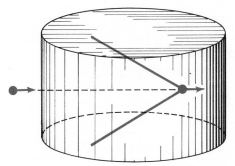

Fig. 64J *The conical wave from a high-speed atomic particle in a transparent medium: Cerenkov radiation.*

The principle of Cerenkov radiation is frequently used to detect high-energy atomic particles. A Cerenkov counter has the same general construction as shown in Fig. 64H, except that the fluor is replaced by a transparent medium, liquid or solid, and with a refractive index specified for the particular particle speeds to be detected.

64.8. Semiconductor Detectors. Recent experiments show that semiconducting materials like those used in transistors are useful detectors of α rays and other heavy atomic particles. One type of semiconductor detector used is shown in Fig. 64K. A thin layer of gold metal is deposited on

silicon
crystal   to amplifier

Fig. 64K *Semiconductor detector using silicon.*

the two surfaces of a thin wafer of very pure silicon and the two conducting surfaces are connected to a 1- to 20-V battery and amplifier. When a charged particle enters the crystal, free electrons and holes develop, increasing the number of free electric charges. The sudden current

pulse thereby created is amplified and then measured or counted.

64.9. Radiation Absorption. As high-energy-charged particles travel through matter in the solid, liquid, or gaseous state, their energy is gradually dissipated in a number of different ways, principally by the excitation and ionization of atoms and molecules. Gamma rays on the other hand, have a far greater range because they have no electric charge. Unless their energy is over 1 MeV, their absorption is due to the photoelectric effect or the Compton effect. In either case, ions are formed in the process, and, in relation to those produced by charged particles, are far apart.

A diagram representing the absorption of γ rays is presented in Fig. 64L. If I_0 represents the

Fig. 64L *Diagram illustrating the absorption of γ rays by matter.*

intensity of the beam as it enters the medium, there will be some depth d_1 at which the intensity will have dropped to $\frac{1}{2}I_0$. Imagine now that we divide the medium into layers, each of thickness d_1. The beam intensity $\frac{1}{2}I_0$ entering the second layer will be reduced to $\frac{1}{2}$ of this initial value and emerge to enter the third layer with an intensity $\frac{1}{4}I_0$. Upon traversing the third layer, the entering beam $\frac{1}{4}I_0$ will be reduced to half value, or to $\frac{1}{8}I_0$, etc.

If we now plot a graph of the beam intensity I against the number of absorbing layers, or the depth x, we obtain the curve shown in Fig. 64M. While the absorption curves for different γ-ray energies, and different absorbers, are not identical, they are alike in that they follow the same law. Just as in the case of the half-lives of radioactive isotopes (see Fig. 63B), if we plot the absorption on a semilog graph, we obtain a straight line. From this straight line we can write

$$\ln \frac{I_0}{I} = \mu x \qquad (64e)$$

The proportionality constant μ is often called the *absorption coefficient* and represents the fraction of the beam absorbed from the beam per centimeter path. The calculation of μ can be

Fig. 64M   *Absorption curve for γ rays.*

made from the experimental data by selecting any two values of I from the straight-line section of such a semilog graph.

64.10. Radiation Absorption. If a beam of β and γ rays, emitted by a radioactive source, are allowed to enter an absorbing medium, the β rays are absorbed within a much shorter distance than are the γ rays. A schematic diagram of the relative absorptions is shown in Fig. 64N.

Suppose we perform an experiment, using a small sample of radium as a radiation source, a scintillation counter as a detector, and aluminum or lead sheets as absorbers (see Fig. 64O). Radiation from a radium source S, in passing through

absorbers at A, enters the fluor block C, and the signal developed is amplified by the photomultiplier tube PM.

The number of counts per minute (C/M), detected by the scintillation counter, is shown here being recorded with an electronic amplifier called a *scaler*.

Fig. 64N   *Schematic diagram showing the relative absorption of β and γ rays.*

The five circles represent the end view of electronic tubes, each having ten small pins. Only one pin at a time in each tube will glow orangered in color, the light arising from a neon gas discharge around it. Each pulse from the scintillator will cause the glow to jump to the next pin clockwise in tube "1." When the tenth pulse arrives and the glow jumps from pin 9 to 0, the glow in the next tube "10" will jump from pin 0 to pin 1. The next time around for tube "1," the glow in tube "10" will jump to 2, thus indicating a total count of 20. This process continues, thus activating the third tube for hundreds, the fourth for thousands, etc. The reading showing in the diagram is 12,631.

By depressing the RESET switch, all five tubes

Fig. 64O   *Scintillation tube with scaler counter for radiation absorption measurements.*

return to their zero positions. To determine the number of counts per minute from any setting, the COUNT switch is raised at the same time the button on a stop-watch is pressed. At the end of one minute, by the watch, the COUNT switch is depressed, stopping the counting process. The total counts are then read directly from the tubes.

Such scalers as these are usually equipped with a dual-purpose milliammeter as shown at the right. When the accompanying switch is thrown to the V position, the knob N can be turned to adjust and set the total voltage applied to the photomultiplier tube. When it is thrown to the C/M position, the meter pointer will read directly the counts per minute. As one observes this meter for a fixed set of counting conditions, the pointer will fluctuate about some median position, and the observer must estimate the

average value. It is for this reason that, for accuracy, the tube readings are preferred.

With no absorbers in place, and the source far removed from the scintillation counter, stray radiation from nearby objects and cosmic rays can and should always be measured and recorded as "background C/M." After the source is inserted in the holder, absorbers are inserted one at a time between the source and the counter, and the C/M determined for each. The results of this experiment, using first a series of lead absorbers and then a series of aluminum absorbers, are shown on a semilog graph in Fig. 64P.

Since β rays from a radioactive source have a range of velocities, the upper part of each graph is curved. At the point where each curve straightens out, the β rays are completely absorbed and

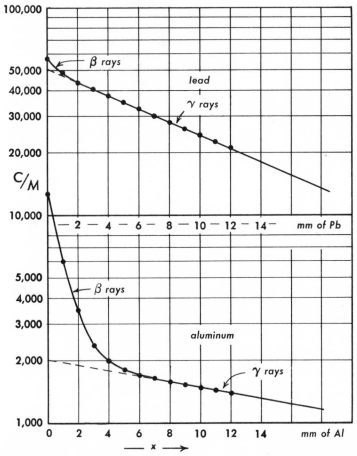

Fig. 64P   *Semilog graphs of β-ray and γ-ray absorption by lead (Pb) and aluminum (Al).*

only the more penetrating γ rays are left. The straight section signifies that γ-ray absorption follows Eq.(64e), and that absorption coefficients can be determined for both lead and aluminum.

PROBLEMS

1. Write down the reaction for the disintegration of $_{82}Pb^{210}$ (see Table 72A).

2. Write down the reaction for the disintegration of $_{84}Po^{215}$ (see Table 72B).

3. Atoms of $_{89}Ac^{228}$ emit β particles with an end-point energy of 1.55 MeV. (a) Write down the reaction and (b) find the loss in nuclear mass due to this particle and the neutrino (see Table 64A).

4. Atoms of $_{90}Th^{231}$ emit β particles with an end-point energy of 0.21 MeV. (a) Write down the reaction and (b) find the loss in nuclear mass due to the emission of this particle and the neutrino (see Table 64A). [Ans. (b) 0.00023 amu.]

5. Atoms of $_{82}Pb^{210}$ have a mass of 209.984177 amu, and emit β particles followed by a γ ray as shown in Fig. 64E. (a) Write down the reaction, and (b) find what the atomic mass is of the daughter product.

6. An electron has a kinetic energy equivalent of 2 MeV. What is its velocity relative to the velocity of light, v/c [see Eq.(59c)]? [Ans. 97.9%.]

7. An electron has a velocity of 99.8% the speed of light ($v/c = 0.998$). Calculate its equivalent energy in MeV.

8. Calculate the absorption coefficient of aluminum for γ rays as given by the experimental graph in Fig. 64P. [Ans. 0.032 mm^{-1}.]

9. Calculate the absorption coefficient of lead for γ rays as given by the experimental graph in Fig. 64P.

10. Atoms of the radioactive isotope $_{90}Th^{234}$ have a mass of 234.04357 and a half-life of 24 days. Sixty-five percent of these nuclei emit β particles with an energy of 193 KeV, while 35% emit 100-KeV β particles, followed by a γ ray. Either way they become the same daughter element $_{91}Pa^{234}$. (a) Make a single energy-level diagram for these changes. (b) Write down the two different reactions. (c) Find the γ-ray energy in amu. (d) What is the mass of the daughter atom? [Ans. (c) 0.0001 amu. (d) 234.04336 amu.]

11. Atoms of the radioactive isotope $_{88}Ra^{225}$ have a mass of 225.023518 amu and a half-life of 15 days. Sixty-three percent of these nuclei emit a β particle with an energy of 280 KeV, followed by a γ ray, while 37% emit a 320-KeV β particle with no γ ray. Either way they become the same daughter element $_{89}Ac^{225}$. (a) Make a single energy-level diagram for these two disintegration modes. (b) Write down the two reactions. (c) Find the γ-ray energy in amu. (d) What is the mass of the daughter atom?

ATOMIC COLLISIONS
AND NUCLEAR DISINTEGRATION

The continual search of the scientists for some knowledge of the ultimate particles into which all matter may be subdivided has led within the last 60 years to the discovery of still smaller particles than molecules and atoms: protons, neutrons, mesons, neutrinos, etc. These discoveries are only the first steps toward solving the age-old mystery of why all solids, large or small, do not fall apart.

65.1. Rutherford's Scattering Experiments. As early as 1903 P. Leonard sent cathode rays through thin films of metal and measured their penetration and absorption in matter. He concluded from his experiments that the mass associated with solid matter is not distributed uniformly throughout the body, but is concentrated upon myriads of tiny isolated centers which he called *dynamids*. It was for these experiments that he was awarded the Nobel Prize in physics in 1905.

During the following decade Sir Ernest Rutherford, and his collaborators H. Geiger and E. Marsden, performed a series of ingenious experiments on the scattering of α particles, the results of which implied that the positive charge and mass of every atom are confined to a particle smaller than 10^{-12} cm in diameter. Historically this marks the beginning of the idea of a nuclear atom proposed formally by Niels Bohr several years later. A schematic diagram of the scattering experiments is given in Fig. 65A.

High-speed α particles from the radioactive element radon, confined to a narrow beam by a hole in a lead block, were made to strike a very thin gold foil F. While most of the α particles go straight through the foil as if there were nothing there, some of them collide with atoms of the foil and bounce off at some angle. The latter phenomenon is known as *Rutherford scattering*.

Fig. 65A   *Diagram of the Rutherford scattering experiments.*

The observations and measurements made in the experiment consisted of counting the number of particles scattered off at different angles θ. This was done by the scintillation method of observation. Each α particle striking the fluorescent screen S produces a tiny flash of light, called a *scintillation*, and is observed as such by the microscope M. With the microscope fixed in one position the number of scintillations observed within a period of several minutes was counted; then the microscope was turned to another angle, and the number was again counted for an equal period of time.

In the schematic diagram of Fig. 65B, α particles are shown passing through a foil three atomic layers thick. Although the nuclear atom was not known at the time the experiments were performed, each atom is drawn in the figure with the positively charged nucleus at the center

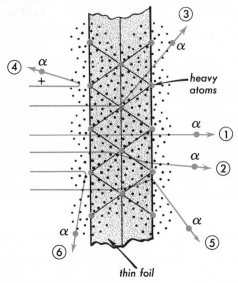

Fig. 65B *Schematic diagram of α particles being scattered by the atomic nuclei in a thin metallic film.*

and surrounded by a number of electrons. Since most of the film is *free space*, the majority of the α particles go through with little or no deflection as indicated by ray (1). Other α's like (2) passing relatively close to an atom nucleus are deflected at an angle of a few degrees. Occasionally, however, an almost *head-on collision* occurs as shown by (4) and the incoming α particle is turned back toward the source.

As an α particle approaches an atom, as represented by ray (6) in Fig. 65B, it is repelled by the heavy positively charged nucleus and deflected in such a way as to make it follow a curved path. The magnitude of the repulsive force is at all times given by Coulomb's law [see Eq.(26a)]:

$$F = k \frac{QQ'}{r^2} \qquad (65a)$$

Whatever the force of repulsion may be at one distance r, it becomes 4 times as great at $\frac{1}{2}$ the distance, 9 times as great at $\frac{1}{3}$ the distance, 16 times as great at $\frac{1}{4}$ the distance, etc. We see,

therefore, that at very close range the mutual repulsion of the two particles increases very rapidly and finally becomes so great that the lighter α particle is turned away. The repelling force, still acting, gives the particle a push, causing it to recede with the same velocity as that with which it approached. The actual trajectory is in every case a hyperbolic orbit with the nucleus at the focus (see Fig. 65C).

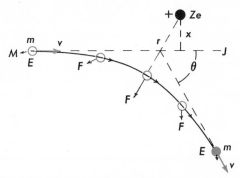

Fig. 65C *Diagram of the deflection of an α particle by a nucleus: Rutherford scattering.*

65.2. The Rutherford Scattering Experiments.

To see how the principles of mechanics and Coulomb's law, Eq.(65a), are applied to the deflection of α particles passing by an atomic nucleus, we refer to Fig. 65C. The α particle of mass m, charge $2e$, moving with a velocity v along the line MJ would, in the absence of Coulomb's law, pass within a distance x of a relatively heavy nucleus of charge Ze. Owing to the mutual repulsion of the two positive charges, the force F, expressed by

$$F = k \frac{Ze \cdot 2e}{r^2} \qquad (65b)$$

and acting on the α particle at all points, gives rise to a hyperbolic trajectory as shown.

Approaching along one asymptote, and receding along the other, the α particle is deflected through a total angle θ.

By applying these principles to find the numbers of particles scattered at different angles Rutherford obtained the following formula:

$$N = N_0 \frac{nt(Ze)^2(2e)^2}{2^4 r^2 (\frac{1}{2}mv^2)^2 \sin^4 \frac{1}{2}\theta} \qquad (65c)$$

N = number of α's striking the screen
N_0 = number of α's striking the foil
n = number of atoms per unit volume
t = foil thickness
Z = atomic number
e = charge on electron
$\frac{1}{2}mv^2$ = kinetic energy of α particle
θ = angle scattered

While this formula looks quite complicated, it can be separated into parts as follows:

1. Foil thickness $N \propto t$
2. Kinetic energy $N \propto 1/(\frac{1}{2}mv^2)^2$ (65d)
3. Scattering angle $N \propto 1/\sin^4 \frac{1}{2}\theta$
4. Nuclear charge $N \propto (Ze)^2$

Repeated experiments with different films made of light and heavy elements, like copper, silver, and gold, showed that the relative number of the wide-angle deflections increases with atomic weight. From all of these results and numerous calculations, Rutherford came to the following conclusions.

1. An increase in film thickness t increases proportionately the number of target nuclei to be hit, and hence the number of particles scattered out.
2. The greater the energy or velocity of the incident particle, the smaller will be the angle through which it will be deflected.
3. A single impact can deflect a particle through a large angle and by head-on collision reverse its direction.
4. Increased deflections resulting from foils of increasing atomic number Z are the result of stronger Coulomb forces arising from increased nuclear charge Ze.
5. Deflections resulting from nuclear collisions are perfectly elastic and obey the laws of conservation of mechanical energy and momentum.
6. All of the positive charge of an atom is confined to a particle smaller than 10^{-12} cm in diameter.
7. Practically all of the weight of an atom is confined to this same particle.
8. The amount of positive charge in atomic units is approximately equal to half the atomic weight.

Although an α particle (mass number 4) is light compared with an atom of a metal like gold (mass number 197), it is 7000 times heavier than a single electron. For this reason the electrons surrounding the atomic nucleus are pushed to either side as the α particle goes speeding through, and they have little effect upon the shape of the trajectory.

A graph representing the force of repulsion between an α particle and a positively charged nucleus is illustrated in Fig. 65D. Diagram (a)

(a)

(b)

Fig. 65D   *Graphs representing the repulsion between a positively charged nucleus and an α particle. (a) Coulomb's law giving the repelling force F, and (b) the potential curve giving the energy.*

shows the rapid increase in force as the distance decreases, while diagram (b) shows the rapid rise in potential energy. The potential energy between two electric charges is given by Eq.(29j):

$$E_p = k\frac{QQ'}{r}$$ (65e)

The reason for giving this equation, and the potential-energy curve in Fig. 65D, is that an interesting mechanical model for demonstrating

Rutherford scattering can be derived from it. Such a model is illustrated in Fig. 65E, where the

Fig. 65E   *Mechanical model of an atomic nucleus for demonstrating Rutherford scattering.*

circular peak at the right represents the nucleus of an atom and has a form generated by rotating curve (b) of Fig. 65D, about its vertical axis at $r = 0$.

Marbles representing α particles roll down a chute and along a practically level plane where they approach the potential hill. Approaching the hill at various angles, the marbles roll up to a certain height and then off to one side or the other. The paths they follow, if watched from above, are *hyperbolic* in shape. Approaching the hill in a head-on collision, the ball rolls up to a certain point, stops, then rolls back again. Thus the potential energy of the α particle close to the nucleus is analogous to the potential energy of a marble on the hillside, and the electrostatic force of repulsion is analogous to the component of the downward pull of gravity.

65.3. Elastic Collisions Between Atoms. Collisions between free atomic particles were first studied by Rutherford with apparatus as shown in Fig. 65F. A long glass tube, containing a small

then permitted to travel through the gas to the other end of the tube where, upon passing through a thin aluminum foil to a fluorescent screen S, they could be observed as scintillations in the field of view of a microscope M. This is exactly the arrangement used by Rutherford in measuring the range of α particles from different radioactive elements (see Fig. 62K).

With air in the tube T and $_{84}Po^{214}$ as a source of α particles, scintillations could be observed with the screen as far back as 7 cm. With hydrogen in the tube it was found that the distance d could be greatly increased. Inserting thicker and thicker aluminum foils between F and S in front of the fluorescent screen, the range of the particles was calculated to be equivalent to 28 cm of air.

The conclusion Rutherford drew from this result was that an α particle occasionally collides with a hydrogen atom, much as a large ball collides with a lighter one, imparting to it a greater velocity and hence a greater penetrating power. Of the many recoil hydrogen atoms from collisions with α particles, some undergo head-on collisions and go shooting off in a forward direction with over half again (more accurately 1.6 times) the speed of the incident α particle.

The enormous increase in range is due principally to a higher velocity. Each hydrogen nucleus, called a *proton*, is stripped of its orbital electron, and, with only a single positive charge, produces fewer ions per centimeter of path than

Fig. 65F   *Rutherford's apparatus used in observing atomic collisions between α particles from radium and the atoms of a gas like hydrogen, helium, nitrogen, oxygen, etc.*

sample of radioactive material R, was first thoroughly evacuated by means of a vacuum pump and then filled with a gas of known constitution. Alpha particles from the radioactive source were

an α particle with its double positive charge. Curiously enough, protons or α particles having the same velocity have about the same range. The reason for this is that, whereas an α particle has double the charge of a proton and produces more ions per centimeter of its path, which tends to slow it down more rapidly, it also has four times the mass and therefore four times the energy. The range curves in Fig. 63G show that for

that the angle between the two recoiling particles is 90°, a right angle.

Most elastic collisions between atoms are not head-on collisions, but ones in which the incident particle strikes the other a glancing blow. When

(a)   (b)   (c)

Fig. 65G *Wilson cloud-chamber photographs of collisions between α particles and (a) a hydrogen atom, (b) a helium atom, and (c) an oxygen atom. (After Rutherford, Chadwick, and Ellis.)*

protons and *α particles* with the same kinetic energy, the protons have about ten times the greater range.

A more convincing study of such atomic collisions can be made with a Wilson cloud chamber. In the thousands of cloud-chamber photographs of the ion tracks made by α particles from radioactive elements, one occasionally observes forked tracks of the type reproduced in Fig. 65G. When each of these pictures was taken, the cloud chamber contained different gases. For photograph (a) the cloud chamber contained hydrogen, for (b) it contained helium, and for (c) it contained oxygen. Schematic diagrams of these same collisions are illustrated in Fig. 65H. Note in (b)

an α particle having a mass of 4 units collides with a hydrogen atom of 1 unit, the α particle is deviated only a little from its path, whereas the hydrogen atom nearly always recoils off at quite a large angle. This is in agreement with the laws of conservation of energy and momentum applied to two perfectly elastic spheres.

When an α particle collides with a helium atom, both particles have the same mass of 4 units each, and the two always glance off at right angles to each other. The laws of mechanics show that for a head-on collision between perfectly elastic spheres of equal mass, one moving and one at rest, the incident particle is stopped by the collision and the second body goes on in the forward direction with all of the velocity.

When an α particle collides with an oxygen atom having a mass of 16 units, the oxygen atom recoils to one side with a relatively low velocity, and the α particle glances off to the other side with a high or low velocity depending upon the angle of recoil. The oxygen atom with its greater mass and charge ionizes more particles per centimeter path and therefore leaves a heavier track.

(a)   (b)   (c)

Fig. 65H *Diagrams of collisions between α particles and other nuclei of different mass.*

Atomic collisions involving such high velocities take place between the heavy nuclei of the atoms and are little affected by the light orbital electrons. If a nucleus is hit hard by a collision, it will be partially or wholly denuded of its electrons. When it comes to rest, it will soon pick up enough electrons to make it a neutral atom again.

65.4. The Discovery of Nuclear Disintegration. Upon repeating the range experiments illustrated in Fig. 65F with a heavy gas in the tube T, Rutherford made a new and startling discovery in 1919. When nitrogen gas (atomic weight 14) was admitted to the tube, scintillations could be observed at a distance of 40 cm or more from the source. No such long-range particles had ever been observed before. What were these long-range particles? They could not be electrons or γ rays, for these were not capable of producing visible scintillations. Rutherford allowed the new rays to pass through a magnetic field and discovered from their deflection that they had the mass and charge of protons. In other words, the long-range particles were hydrogen nuclei.

Rutherford was not long in coming forward with the correct explanation of the phenomenon. An α particle, near the beginning of its range where its velocity is high, may make a head-on collision with a nitrogen nucleus and be captured. This capture is then followed immediately by a disintegration in which a proton is ejected with high speed. The process is illustrated in

before   capture   disintegration

Fig. 65I   *The disintegration of a nitrogen nucleus by a high-speed α particle.*

Fig. 65I, and the transformation can be represented by the following simple reaction:

$$_2\text{He}^4 + {_7}\text{N}^{14} = ({_9}\text{F}^{18}) = {_8}\text{O}^{17} + {_1}\text{H}^1 \quad (65f)$$

When the α particle, with a charge of $+2$ and

mass 4, collides with the nitrogen nucleus with a charge of $+7$ and mass 14, they form a single particle with a charge of $+9$ and mass 18. Since an atom with a nuclear charge of $+9$ would be expected to have all the chemical properties of *fluorine*, atomic number 9, the newly formed nucleus is labeled $_9\text{F}^{18}$.

An examination of the table of isotopes, however (see Appendix VII), shows that no such isotope exists in nature. The reason becomes apparent when it is realized that such a combination of particles is not stable. A fluorine nucleus of mass 18 is unstable and disintegrates by discharging a proton, a particle with a charge of $+1$ and a mass of 1. This leaves behind a residual nucleus with a charge of $+8$, and a mass of 17. Under atomic number 8 in the same Appendix VII, an oxygen isotope of mass 17 is seen to have been found in nature.

Thus the above disintegration process started with two stable nuclei, *helium* and *nitrogen*, and out of them were created two new stable nuclei, *oxygen* and *hydrogen*. This is called a *transmutation* of elements. Because the intermediate step indicates only a momentary existence of a fluorine nucleus, $_9\text{F}^{18}$, this step is often omitted from any discussion of the above process and the disintegration reaction simply written

$$_2\text{He}^4 + {_7}\text{N}^{14} = {_8}\text{O}^{17} + {_1}\text{H}^1$$

Such transformation reactions are like equations and must balance: first, the total amount of charge must remain the same, and second, the mass numbers must balance. The first of these is accomplished by having the sum of the subscripts on one side of the reaction equal to the sum of the subscripts on the other side, and the second by having the sum of the superscripts the same on both sides. In every known atom the subscript, representing the nuclear charge, is the sole factor determining the chemical element to which the atom belongs.

65.5. Chadwick's Identification of the Neutron. In 1932 Chadwick, in England, performed an experiment for which he was awarded the Nobel Prize in physics in 1935. As diagramed in Fig. 65J his experiment consisted of bombarding a beryllium target with α particles. Penetrating

Fig. 65J *The experiment by which Chadwick discovered the neutron. The penetrating rays are neutrons and α particles.*

particles emerging from the beryllium were permitted to impinge upon a block of paraffin from which protons were found to emerge with high speed. From energy calculations he was able to show that the penetrating rays were uncharged particles with the mass of protons; these he called *neutrons*. The disintegration taking place in the metal target is the following (see Fig. 65K):

$$_2\text{He}^4 + {}_4\text{Be}^9 = {}_6\text{C}^{12} + {}_0n^1 \qquad (65g)$$

The α particle, $_2\text{He}^4$, makes a collision and unites with a beryllium nucleus, $_4\text{Be}^9$, causing a

Fig. 65K *The neutron process discovered by Chadwick. See Fig. 65J.*

disintegration; whereupon a neutron, $_0n^1$, is expelled with high velocity. The residual particle with a charge of +6 and mass of 12 units is a stable carbon nucleus such as found in nature.

The penetrating rays from the beryllium block in Fig. 65J are mostly neutrons which, in bombarding the paraffin block, collide elastically with hydrogen atoms, knocking them out on the other side. An elastic head-on collision between two particles of the same weight, like a neutron and proton, finds the entire velocity of one transferred to the other; the neutron is stopped and the proton goes on. The protons, having a positive charge, can be observed by their tracks in a Wilson cloud chamber, whereas neutrons cannot.

The reason fast neutrons have such a high penetrating power is that they are not slowed down by ionizing atoms as they pass close by them. A proton, electron, or α particle has a charge and can ionize atoms by attracting or repelling electrons from a distance, but a neutron without a charge cannot do this. It must make a direct collision with another particle to be slowed down or stopped.

Neutrons can now be produced in such intense beams that they are often used in place of X rays wherever radiations of high penetrating power are desired.

65.6. The Nucleus Contains Neutrons and Protons. Since the time of Chadwick's identification of the neutron as an elementary particle, our ideas concerning the nucleus of the atom have had to be modified. We now believe that the nucleus contains two kinds of particles, neutrons and protons. Each neutron has a mass of one unit and no charge, whereas each proton has a mass of one unit and a positive charge of one unit. This differs from the older idea that the nucleus contains protons equal in number to the atomic weight and enough electrons to neutralize the surplus charge in excess of the amount specified by the atomic number.

Since only the proton has a charge, any given nucleus of atomic number Z and mass number M is now believed to have Z protons and $M - Z$ neutrons, and in a neutral atom the number of protons is believed to be equal to the number of orbital electrons. The nuclear particles of a few of the elements of the periodic table are given in Table 65A, as examples.

Schematic diagrams of the nucleus of five different atoms are given in Fig. 65L.

65.7. Atomic Masses Are Not Whole Numbers.

TABLE 65A. NEUTRONS AND PROTONS IN THE
NUCLEI OF A FEW ELEMENTS

Atom	Protons	Neutrons
$_1H^1$	1	0
$_1H^2$	1	1
$_2He^4$	2	2
$_3Li^6$	3	3
$_3Li^7$	3	4
$_4Be^9$	4	5
$_4Be^{10}$	4	6
$_5B^{11}$	5	6
$_7N^{13}$	7	6
$_8O^{16}$	8	8
$_{11}Na^{23}$	11	12
$_{29}Cu^{65}$	29	36
$_{80}Hg^{200}$	80	120
$_{92}U^{238}$	92	146

When an α particle collides with the nucleus of an atom and produces a disintegration as shown in Fig. 65I, the total energy before collision must be equal to the total energy after col-

$_1H^1$	$_1H^2$	$_2He^4$	$_3Li^7$	$_8O^{16}$
proton	deuteron	α particle	lithium	oxygen
$Z=1$	$Z=1$	$Z=2$	$Z=3$	$Z=8$
$M=1$	$M=2$	$M=4$	$M=7$	$M=16$

Fig. 65L   The number of protons and neutrons in the nuclei of hydrogen, deuterium, helium, lithium, and oxygen.

lision. To verify this, all forms of energy involved in the process must be included: (1) *the kinetic energy of all particles*, (2) *the energy of a γ ray if one is involved*, and (3) *the mass energy*. The latter is necessary since disintegration experiments show that the total mass of the two colliding particles is not in general equal to the total mass after disintegration. To test this change, it is necessary that we know the exact masses of all atoms individually.

Recent mass spectrographic measurements by Aston, Bainbridge, and others (see Chapter 49) show that the masses of atoms are not exactly whole-number values as previously suspected and given in Appendix VIII. A list of the most

recent mass determinations of some of the lighter elements of the periodic table is given in Appendix IX. These values are all based upon the carbon isotope 12 as having a mass of exactly 12.000000.

65.8. Conservation of Energy in Nuclear Disintegrations. To illustrate the law of conservation of energy as it applies to nuclear disintegrations, consider Rutherford's first experiment, shown in Figs. 65F and 65I, where α particles from $_{84}Po^{214}$ passing through nitrogen gas make collisions with, and disintegrate, nitrogen nuclei. The total energy of any two particles before impact will be the sum of the masses of the two nuclei, $_2He^4 + {}_7N^{14}$, plus their kinetic energy E_{k1}. The total energy after impact will be the sum of the masses of the two nuclei, $_8O^{17}$ and $_1H^1$, plus their kinetic energy E_{k2}. If we insert accurately known masses, the reaction becomes

$$_2He^{4.002604} + {}_7N^{14.003074} + E_{k1}$$
$$= {}_8O^{16.999133} + {}_1H^{1.007825} + E_{k2} \quad (65h)$$

It is customary to express the energies E_{k1} and E_{k2} in *mass units* or in million electron volts, MeV. The kinetic energy before impact is confined to the α particle from $_{84}Po^{214}$, which has been measured and found to be equivalent to 7.7 MeV. Dividing this value by 931, from Eq.(63m), gives the equivalent of 0.00827 mass unit. Adding mass-energy for both sides of Eq.(65f), we must obtain the same total.

Using mass values given in Appendix IX we obtain,

$_2He^4 =$	4.002604	$_8O^{17} =$	16.999133
$_7N^{14} =$	14.003074	$_1H^1 =$	1.007825
$E_{k1} =$	0.008270	$E_{k2} =$	?
Total $=$	18.013948		18.013948

(65i)

Simple addition and subtraction show that, to yield the proper sum for the right-hand column, E_{k2} must be equal to 0.006990 mass unit. Multiplying by 931 gives, this time, 6.51 MeV as the energy liberated. This is the liberated energy utilized in the "explosion" which drives the proton and oxygen nuclei apart.

In general, when an atomic nucleus disintegrates by splitting up into two particles, the annihilation energy is divided between them. Experiments show that this division takes place according to the ordinary laws of mechanics, that *the kinetic energies of the two particles are approximately inversely proportional to their respective masses.*

When, in the above example, the available

chance, disintegrations might occur. In 1932 Cockcroft and Walton announced that they had successfully disintegrated lithium atoms with protons accelerated by relatively low voltages. Their apparatus is schematically represented in Fig. 65M.

Fig. 65M   *Schematic diagram of the Cockcroft–Walton experiment. Lithium is disintegrated by 150,000-volt protons.*

energy is divided between an oxygen nucleus of mass 17 and a proton of mass 1, the $_8O^{17}$ nucleus acquires an energy of 0.36 MeV, and the proton an energy of 6.15 MeV. A proton with this kinetic energy and velocity has a range of 49 cm in air. Recent repetitions of Rutherford's experiment give measured ranges of 48 cm and an energy of 6 MeV, in good agreement with the calculation.

Graphs showing the ranges of protons, deuterons, and α particles for different energies are drawn in Fig. 63G.

65.9. The Cockcroft–Walton Experiment. Believing that the disintegration of atomic nuclei might be accomplished by using other than α particles as projectiles, Rutherford instigated in 1930 the construction of a high-voltage, dc generator at the Cavendish Laboratory. The purpose of this *million-volt* source of potential difference was to accelerate hydrogen nuclei, *protons*, to high speeds and then cause them to strike known substances. In this way he hoped to produce new and various kinds of disintegrations.

Becoming impatient with the relatively slow progress of the project, however, Rutherford suggested to Cockcroft and Walton that lower voltages be tried in the meantime to see if, by

Electrons from a hot filament F, passing through hydrogen gas in the region of A, ionize many hydrogen atoms. These protons with their positive charge are then accelerated toward the other end of the tube by a potential difference V of 150,000 V. Upon passing through the opening C and a window W, they emerge from the acceleration chamber as a narrow beam of protons.

This tube, acting as a "proton gun," is aimed at a target consisting of lithium metal. Cockcroft and Walton observed and measured α particles emanating from the metal with a range of 8 cm, an energy equivalent to 8.5 MeV. Considering the relatively low energy of the bombarding protons of only 0.15 MeV, this is a tremendous release in atomic energy. The transmutation taking place here is written as follows:

$$_1H^1 + {_3Li^7} + E_{k1} = {_2He^4} + {_2He^4} + E_{k2} \quad (65j)$$

This reaction, illustrated in Fig. 65N, shows a proton, $_1H^1$, of energy $E_{k1} = 0.15$ MeV, entering a lithium nucleus, $_3Li^7$, to form a new but unstable beryllium nucleus, $_4Be^8$. Being unstable, this compact structure of eight particles splits up into two α particles which are driven apart with great violence. Since the measured energy of each α particle is equivalent to 8.5 MeV, each disinte-

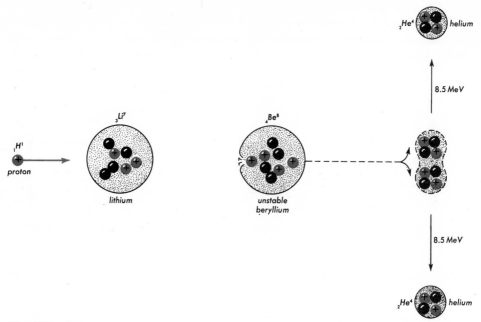

Fig. 65N   *Disintegration of a lithium nucleus by a proton of 0.15 MeV energy: the Cockcroft–Walton experiment.*

gration involves the liberation of 17.0 MeV energy. The source of energy is to be found in the annihilation of a part of the total atomic mass.

The loss in mass can be calculated from the table of atomic weights, given in Appendix IX. Listing the involved masses in two columns and adding, we obtain

$$_1H^1 = 1.007825$$
$$_3Li^7 = 7.016005 \qquad _2He^4 = 4.002604$$
$$E_{k1} = \underline{0.000161} \qquad _2He^4 = \underline{4.002604}$$
$$8.023991 \qquad 8.005208$$

E_{k1} is the mass equivalent to the energy of the incident proton and is obtained by dividing 0.15 MeV by 931 [see Eq.(63m)]. The difference between the two sums, $8.023991 - 8.005208 = 0.018783$ mass unit, represents the loss in mass by the disintegration. When multiplied by 931,

this gives 17.48 MeV as the liberated energy, a value in good agreement with the experimentally determined value of 17.0 MeV.

It might be thought that such a disintegration as the one described above could be used as a source of energy, but as yet it has not been feasible to use it so. While each nuclear collision and disintegration liberates at least one hundred times as much energy as that supplied to the proton, it takes many particles to make a few collisions. In other words, only a small percentage of the proton bullets hit the tiny nuclear targets as they pass through matter. Most of them are slowed down by electron collisions and the ionization of atoms. To a proton bullet the lithium nuclei, as targets in the lithium metal, present an area millions of times smaller than the space between them.

QUESTIONS AND PROBLEMS

1. If, in Rutherford's scattering experiments, the number of α particles observed at an angle $\theta = 50°$ is 28/min, how many per minute should be observed at 25° and 145°?

2. When the scintillation microscope used in a

Rutherford scattering experiment is set at an angle $\theta = 30°$, the number of α particles observed is 3000/hr. How many per hour should be observed at 60° and at 150°? [*Ans.* 216, and 16.]

3. If, in Rutherford's experiments, scintillations are

observed at an angle of 30° for a silver foil, 200 α particles are counted in 1 min. How many counts per minute would be observed if the foil were replaced by foils of equal thickness made of (a) aluminum, (b) copper, and (c) gold?

4. Complete the following disintegration reactions:

$$_1H^2 + {}_8O^{16} \rightarrow {}_{+2}He^4 \qquad _1H^2 + {}_5B^{10} \rightarrow {}_{+0}n^1$$
$$_2He^4 + {}_{13}Al^{27} \rightarrow {}_{+1}H^1 \qquad _1H^1 + {}_3Li^6 \rightarrow {}_{+2}He^3$$

5. From the known masses of the atoms in the reactions of Problem 4, find the energy liberated by each disintegration in MeV. Assume the incident energy of the lighter nucleus in each reaction to be 35 MeV.

6. From the graphs plotted in Fig. 63G, write down the ranges of the following particles: (a) 10-MeV protons, (b) 13-MeV protons, (c) 12-MeV α particles, (d) 10-MeV deuterons, and (e) 8-MeV α particles. [*Ans.* (a) 116 cm, (b) 182 cm, (c) 14.1 cm, (d) 67 cm, (e) 7.3 cm.]

7. If the following mass is annihilated, and 90% of it goes into kinetic energy of an α particle, find the range of the particle in air at normal atmospheric pressure: (a) 0.01328 amu, and (b) 0.007284 amu.

8. Briefly explain the experiment by which Chadwick discovered the neutron. Make a diagram.

9. Give a brief description of the Rutherford experiment in which the first nuclear disintegrations were discovered.

10. Make a table of the following atoms giving the number of protons and neutrons in each nucleus: Ba^{138}, Ca^{44}, Fe^{56}, I^{127}, and Au^{197}.

11. The range of protons in air is found to have the following values: (a) 5 cm, (b) 14 cm, (c) 70 cm, and (d) 150 cm. Find their energies in MeV.

12. Deuterons from a radioactive source are found to have three definite ranges: (a) 10 cm, (b) 75 cm, and (c) 115 cm. Determine their energies from Fig. 63G. [*Ans.* (a) 3.4 MeV, (b) 10.7 MeV, (c) 13.5 MeV.]

13. Alpha particles from a radioactive material are found to have three ranges: (a) 3.5 cm, (b) 5.8 cm, and (c) 12.8 cm. Find their energies using Fig. 63G.

14. In a nuclear disintegration process, a mass of 0.00820 amu is annihilated and 95% of the liberated energy is imparted as kinetic energy to an alpha particle. Find (a) its energy in MeV, and (b) its range. [*Ans.* (a) 7.25 MeV, (b) 6.5 cm.]

COSMIC RAYS

Karl K. Darrow has described the subject of cosmic rays "as unique in modern physics for the minuteness of the phenomena, the delicacy of the observations, the adventurous excursions of the observers, the subtlety of the analysis, and the grandeur of the inferences." It is impossible for anyone to say when and by whom cosmic rays were first studied. From the time of the discovery of radioactivity by Becquerel (in 1896) and the discovery of radium by the Curies only a few months later, the radioactive rays from the ground, air, and outer space have been investigated by many scientists. Extending over a period of some 50 years, these investigations have led to some of the most interesting and important discoveries in the structure of atomic nuclei.

66.1. Early Experiments. It has long been known that a charged electroscope, if left standing for some little time, will discharge regardless of how well the gold leaf is insulated. Realizing that the rays from radioactive materials can be stopped by a sufficient thickness of heavy matter, Rutherford and Cooke (in Canada, 1903) surrounded an electroscope with a thick wall of brick and found very little decrease in the rate of discharge. McLennan and his co-workers (also in Canada) lowered an electroscope into a lake, hoping that the thick layer of water would screen off the rays. This experiment, like the other, failed.

In 1910 Glockel, with an electroscope, rose nearly 3 mi in a balloon in order to get away from the ground radiation, but to his astonishment he found that the rate of discharge did not decrease, but increased, the higher he went. The same effect was observed by Hess (in Austria, 1911) and Kolhörster (in Germany, 1914). Rising to heights as great as $5\frac{1}{2}$ mi, both of these ob-

servers independently found that the intensity of these unknown radiations became greater the higher they went.

Because in one of his scientific publications concerning these results Hess suggested the possibility that some kind of penetrating rays were entering the earth's atmosphere from outer space, he is usually credited with the discovery of cosmic rays. For this reason he was granted the Nobel Prize in physics for the year 1936

66.2. Millikan and Bowen's Discovery. Soon after World War I (1922), R. A. Millikan, with the help of I. S. Bowen, constructed several small, self-recording string electroscopes. Making use of their war-time experiences with sounding balloons, they sent these electroscopes high into the stratosphere by fastening each one to two sounding balloons. As shown in Fig. 66A, the string electroscope E consists of two gold-covered quartz fibers insulated and mounted with their ends together. When they are charged, the fibers spread apart in mutual repulsion, and as they discharge they slowly come together.

Daylight, passing through a narrow vertical slit S in the instrument case, casts a shadow of the center section of the fibers on a rotating disk D which contains a photographic film. As the film turns slowly and the fibers come together, they leave a double trace, as indicated in the diagram. On the same film, a small oil manometer recorded the height of ascent and a small thermometer recorded the temperature. The film was driven by a watch W, the whole apparatus weighing only 7 oz. On one of the best record flights, only one of the balloons burst at a height of 10 mi and the other brought the instruments safely to earth.

Like the earlier results obtained by other ex-

Fig. 66A *Diagrams of one of the sensitive electroscopes sent up into the stratosphere by Millikan and Bowen to measure cosmic rays. (a) Schematic diagram, (b) scale drawing of entire instrument 6 in. high.*

perimenters, Millikan and Bowen found the ionization to increase with increasing altitude. After extending the observations of previous workers to higher altitudes, Millikan and Bowen became convinced, and announced their belief, that the rays were coming from interstellar space.

66.3. The Penetration of Cosmic Rays. In order to determine the nature of the new rays, Millikan and his co-workers, Otis, Cameron, and Bowen, in the fall of 1922 began an extensive

study of the penetrating power of cosmic rays. Since cosmic rays penetrate our atmosphere of many miles of air, how far might they penetrate beyond?

Self-recording electroscopes were lowered to various depths in snow-fed lakes as illustrated schematically in Fig. 66B. Measurements taken at Arrowhead Lake in Southern California (at an elevation of 5100 ft) agreed approximately with those taken at Muir Lake near Mt. Whitney

Fig. 66B *Illustrating the lowering of self-recording electroscopes into deep, snow-fed lakes to measure the absorption of cosmic rays by the water.*

(at an elevation of 11,800 ft), provided one took into account the increased air path for the lower elevation. The extra mile and a quarter of air is equivalent in weight to 6 ft of water.

As cosmic rays penetrate deeper and deeper below the surface of water, their number decreases, until at a depth of 100 ft the intensity is reduced to about one ten-thousandth of that at the surface. With very sensitive electroscopes, cosmic radiation capable of penetrating 2000 ft of water has more recently been detected. This is a far greater penetrating power than that possessed by any known X rays or γ rays from radioactivity.

66.4. The Geiger–Müller-Tube Counter. There are at least nine methods of observing and measuring cosmic rays. These are

    (a) Geiger–Müller-tube counters
    (b) Wilson cloud chambers
    (c) Ionization chambers
    (d) Photographic emulsions
    (e) Scintillation counters
    (f) Bubble chambers
    (g) Electroscopes
    (h) Semiconductors
    (i) Spark chambers

The Geiger–Müller tube, named after its inventors, is one of the simplest electrical instruments ever designed (see Fig. 66C). It consists

Fig. 66C *Diagram of a Geiger–Müller tube.*

of an open-ended copper cylinder from 1 to 25 in. long, fitted inside a thin-walled glass cylinder with a fine tungsten wire stretched along the middle. After the tube has been partially evacuated (a pressure of from 5 to 10 cm of mercury is

convenient), a potential difference of about 1000 V is applied, the positive to the center wire and the negative to the cylinder.

When a single cosmic ray or high-speed particle from a radioactive source goes through a Geiger–Müller tube, ions are created by the freeing of electrons from air molecules. These freed electrons are attracted by the positively charged wire and move toward it, acquiring within a very short distance a high velocity of their own. Because of this velocity they, too, can ionize other atoms, thus freeing more electrons.

This multiplication of charges repeats itself in rapid succession, producing within a very short interval of time an *avalanche of electrons toward the central wire*. This sudden surge of charge is equivalent to a small current impulse along the electrical circuit. When this current has been intensified by an amplifier, it may be made to operate an electric switch, a radio loud-speaker, or any kind of electrical device.

Quite frequently, the impulses of a Geiger–Müller tube are made to operate a small counting device. Each cosmic ray particle passing through the tube is therefore counted automatically. The number of counts received per second depends upon the size of the counter tube. An average-sized tube 1 in. in diameter and several inches long, at sea level, gives from 50 to 100 counts per minute.

A common form of Geiger counter is shown in Fig. 66D. It consists of a G–M-counter tube about 10 cm long connected to a box containing

Fig. 66D *Geiger counter instrument complete with G–M tube and counting-rate meter.*

vacuum-tube circuits, a small loud-speaker, and a counting-rate meter M.

Dial (1) operates the speaker and permits the individual ray pulses to be heard. Dial (2) turns on the vacuum tubes as in any radio or TV receiver, and turning it clockwise increases the voltage supplied to the G–M tube. Dial (3) has three position points to which it can be turned. The position marked volts connects the meter M so that it shows the voltage on the G–M tube. When in the ×1 position, under C/M, the meter M directly reads counts per minute, and in the ×10 position the meter reading should be multiplied by 10.

66.5. Directional Effects. To observe the direction of the greatest cosmic-ray intensity, a cosmic ray telescope is used. Such a telescope is made by connecting two or more Geiger–Müller tubes *in coincidence*, and mounting them on a common support some distance apart. Tubes in coincidence are so connected electrically that a current will flow in the accompanying electric circuit only when both tubes discharge at the same time.

When one tube is set above the other, as shown in Fig. 66E(a), a single cosmic ray, on going

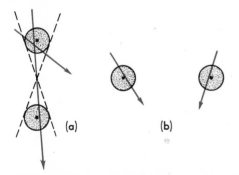

Fig. 66E *Diagram of two Geiger counters. Connected in coincidence, they form a cosmic-ray telescope.*

through both cylinders, will cause a current pulse and a count to be made. If, however, a particle goes through one and not the other, no count is recorded. Experiments at sea level show that, when the telescope is mounted in the horizontal position (b), few counts are made, whereas when it is mounted in a vertical direction many more

counts are recorded. The interpretation to be made, therefore, is that cosmic rays come principally from overhead.

As a verification of the telescope method, a Wilson cloud chamber is frequently inserted between two Geiger counter tubes as shown in Fig. 66F, and a photograph of the path of each cos-

Fig. 66F *With a Wilson cloud chamber mounted between two Geiger tubes connected in coincidence, the cosmic rays are made to take their own picture.* (After R. B. Brode.)

mic ray is taken. Thousands of such photographs are made automatically by having a single cosmic ray take its own picture. This is accomplished by allowing the sudden electric current from the counter tubes, produced by a ray in transit, to open and close a camera shutter, to cause the cloud chamber to expand, and to flash a light, illuminating the fog track that forms.

The compiled experimental results of various observers taken at different elevations are illustrated by the curves in Fig. 66G. Near the city of

Fig. 66G *The intensity of cosmic rays increases with altitude up to a height of 10 to 15 mi, and then decreases.*

In the reproduction of Fig. 66F, either one of the two cosmic rays would have tripped the electrical devices and taken the picture. It should be noted that both rays passed right through a 0.5-in. lead plate without being deviated. Cloud-chamber pictures are not photographs of cosmic rays, but of the path traversed by the rays.

66.6. The Altitude Effect. The results of airplane and balloon flights into the stratosphere have shown that the intensity of cosmic rays increases up to a height of from 12 to 15 mi, and then decreases again. In 1935 Stevens and Anderson,* for example, rose to a height of nearly 14 mi carrying with them, among other scientific instruments, Geiger–Müller tube counters. With these instruments they measured the cosmic-ray intensity at various altitudes on both their ascent and descent.

* Capt. A. W. Stevens and O. A. Anderson, *National Geographic Magazine*, **69**, 693 (1936).

Omaha, at a magnetic latitude of 51°N, the maximum is found at a height of 15 mi where an intensity 170 times as great as that at sea level has been measured. From that altitude to the highest points that observations have been made, about 17 mi, there is a gradual decrease in total intensity.

The four different curves in the figure show, from altitude measurements made by observers all over the world, that in nearing the magnetic equator the cosmic-ray intensity decreases at high altitudes, as well as at sea level.

66.7. Primaries and Secondaries. Experimental observations show that the cosmic rays entering our atmosphere are almost entirely composed of positively charged atomic nuclei. Of these so-called *primary cosmic rays*, 89% are protons, and another 10% are about 90% α particles and 10% heavier nuclei like carbon, nitrogen, oxygen, iron, etc. (see Table 66A in Sec. 66.13).

Upon entering the atmosphere, a high-energy primary particle soon collides with another atomic nucleus, splitting one or both particles into a number of smaller nuclear fragments, each one of which carries away some of the primary's energy. These high-speed particles in turn collide with other nuclei, further dividing their energy to produce other high-speed particles. All of these rays, with the exception of the primary particle, are called *secondary cosmic rays.*

One of the results of cosmic-ray collision processes is the creation of very high frequency and highly penetrating gamma rays. These photons, too, are included in the classification, Secondary Cosmic Rays.

At a height of some 15 mi, about ten to fifteen times as many secondary cosmic rays exist as have entered the atmosphere as primaries. At this level, where more than $\frac{9}{10}$ of the earth's atmosphere still lies below, as many rays are observed moving in a horizontal direction as in the vertical. From the diagram presented in Fig. 66H it becomes quite clear why the primaries are difficult to distinguish from the far greater number of secondaries.

At lower altitudes the total intensity decreases,

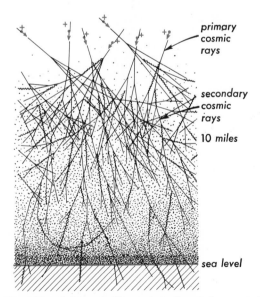

Fig. 66H *Schematic illustration of secondary cosmic rays produced from primaries entering the earth's atmosphere.*

since many of the secondaries produced above are stopped by collision. In other words, so much energy is lost by successive collisions that the energy is gradually absorbed as heat motion by the air molecules. By the time sea level is reached, the remaining rays consist principally of a few high-speed secondaries and primaries. Even at sea level, some of these rays have enough energy left to penetrate several hundred, and even several thousand feet of earth and water.

It should be borne in mind that, between collisions of the type indicated in Fig. 66H, each cosmic-ray particle is continually being slowed down as it "plows through" thousands of air molecules, knocking electrons free to produce ions. These are the ions on which fogdrops form, revealing the path in a cloud chamber.

Although γ rays also lose energy by collisions with atoms to produce Compton electrons, the γ rays themselves do not leave visible tracks in a Wilson cloud chamber. The reason for this is that collisions are few and far between, and the resulting fogdrops are too far apart.

66.8. The Latitude Effect. By the year 1930, studies of cosmic-ray intensities by Millikan indicated that the number of cosmic rays arriving at the earth's surface was constant at all latitudes. This led him to the conclusion that the primary cosmic radiation entering the atmosphere must be γ rays of very high energy. He reasoned that, if they were charged atomic particles, they would be deflected by the earth's magnetic field, and fewer would reach the earth near the magnetic equator.

In 1931 the Dutch physicist Clay, sailing from Amsterdam in the Northern Hemisphere to Batavia, Dutch Guiana, in the Southern Hemisphere, carried Geiger counters with him aboard ship. Measuring the cosmic-ray intensity daily en route, he obtained the results shown by the graph in Fig. 66I. The curve shows that as one proceeds from magnetic north to magnetic south, at sea level, the cosmic-ray intensity remains quite constant, until a magnetic latitude of about 42° is reached. In this region the intensity begins to drop appreciably, reaches a minimum at the equator, and rises again to symmetrical intensities in the Southern Hemisphere.

Fig. 66I   *Graph of the cosmic-ray intensity at various latitudes of the earth's surface.*

66.9. Effect of the Earth's Magnetic Field. The decrease in cosmic-ray intensity at the earth's magnetic equator (see Fig. 66I) is now explained as being due to the earth's magnetic field. This is illustrated in Fig. 66J. The paths of all charged

these belts by Van Allen and his colleagues at State University of Iowa was made from instruments carried into space by American earth-circling satellites. These belts surround the earth, except at the regions of the magnetic poles, the outer one being caused largely by the slower particles, protons and electrons, from the sun. The inner Van Allen belt is formed by more energetic particles from outer space, and is centered about 2500 mi above the magnetic equator.

If the primary energy is very large, little deflection will occur, and particles like a and b will reach our atmosphere and perhaps the ground. At somewhat lower energies they will be deflected back into space as c and d. At still lower energies they may follow paths like e, f, and g.

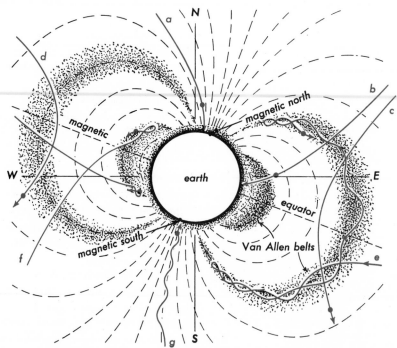

Fig. 66J   *The behavior of primary cosmic rays in the earth's magnetic field. The shaded arches are the Van Allen belts.*

particles crossing the earth's magnetic field are bent by a force that is perpendicular to the direction of the field.

Because of these forces, many charged particles from the sun and outer space are trapped by the field in two belts. The recent discovery of

Particle e spirals around the field lines and follows them in toward the earth. As the field gets stronger, a point is reached where the particle is turned back, and spiraling around the field lines approaches the earth again on the other side. Such particles running back and forth are trapped; they account for the large number of ionized particles that form the Van Allen belts.

Slow particles, such as g, entering the earth's field parallel to the lines of force from far away, will be guided by the field and reach the earth's surface. A day or two after an active display of solar flares, so many particles become trapped in the outer Van Allen belt that they spill out into the earth's atmosphere, creating auroras. Since particles with only the highest of energies can get down to the earth's atmosphere near the magnetic equator, the cosmic-ray latitude effect is well understood.

66.10. Discovery of the Positron. The positron, or positive electron, was discovered by Anderson in 1932 by photographing the tracks of cosmic rays in a Wilson cloud chamber. Under the influence of a strong magnetic field applied perpendicular to the face of the cloud chamber, positively charged particles should bend to the

Fig. 66K *Wilson cloud-chamber photographs of pair production. An X ray coming close to the nucleus of an atom produces a pair of electrons, one positive and one negative.* (a) *Discovery of a positron* (after Anderson), (b) *three pairs of electrons produced by X rays* (after Anderson), (c) *pair produced in air by X rays* (after Lauritson and Fowler), (d) *pair produced in air by X rays from* $_{81}Tl^{208}$ (after Simons and Zuber).

right and negatively charged particles should bend to the left. In order to be certain that those bent one way were not all coming from above, and those bent the other way were particles of the same kind and charge coming from below, Anderson inserted a block of lead in the chamber to slow down the particles. Under these conditions photographs similar to the one shown in (a) of Fig. 66K were obtained.

Here Anderson could be quite certain, from the curvature of the track on each side of the lead, that the particle entered from the side shown above, for in passing through the lead plate it could only have been slowed down and not speeded up. Knowing the direction of motion, the direction of the field, and the direction of bending, Anderson concluded that such a particle had a positive charge.

Comparing the track with well-known electron tracks and α particle tracks, he concluded that the new particle had about the same mass as the electron. Later experiments continued to give more positive proof of the existence of a positive electron. Now, very strong beams of positrons can be produced in the laboratory.

It should be pointed out here that near sea level most cosmic rays come from above, whereas a few come from other angles and the horizontal, and some even from below.

66.11. Creation of Electron Pairs. Soon after Anderson's discovery of the positron, several theoretical physicists attempted to calculate the conditions under which a positron might exist in nature. An extension of the quantum theory of the electron, proposed earlier by P. Dirac, led them to the prediction that if a high-energy photon, i.e., a high-frequency γ ray, were to come close enough to the nucleus of an atom, the electric field of the nucleus would be strong enough to annihilate the γ ray and create in its place a *pair of particles, an electron and a positron.* These two particles, the theory predicts, should have the same mass, and equal but opposite charges. A schematic diagram of pair production is given in Fig. 66L.

Blackett, Anderson, and others, looking for such pairs in a cloud chamber, soon found them exactly as predicted. Gamma rays from a radioactive element like $_{81}Tl^{208}$, in passing through matter, were observed to produce pairs of electrons. Three photographs of such incidents are shown in Fig. 66K. In (b) three different pairs are seen emerging from the points marked X on the lower side of a lead plate, and in (c) and (d) a pair is seen having been produced apparently in mid-air. As usual the γ rays that produced these pairs do not show up in the cloud chamber.

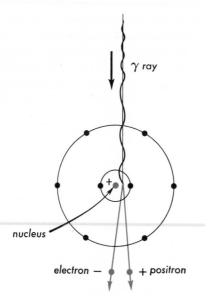

Fig. 66L *Schematic diagram of electron pair production.*

When an electron pair is created, *conservation of energy and momentum* requires the two particles to move almost straight forward. Without a magnetic field applied to the cloud chamber, the particles travel side by side in almost parallel paths, but with a magnetic field the path of the positron bends to one side and that of the electron to the other.

The reason positrons were not discovered earlier in the history of physics is that they do not exist long in the free state. As soon as a positron meets with an electron, the two are annihilated. Because a positron can annihilate an electron it is called an *antiparticle*.

Experiments indicate that all electrons and positrons spin around an axis through their center of mass. There is good evidence that when a

positron and an electron come close together, they frequently combine by revolving around each other like a double star, with their spin axes parallel to one another. As such a pair they are called *positronium*.

Positronium is very short lived, for soon the two particles disintegrate completely; in their place γ rays are created. If the particles were spinning in the same direction, they would disintegrate into three γ rays of different energies, whereas, if they were spinning in opposite directions, they would produce two γ rays. Conservation of energy and momentum requires each of these latter rays to have an energy of $\frac{1}{2}$MeV [see Eq.(63k)]. As reactions we can write, for pair production

$$\gamma \rightarrow e^- + \bar{e}^+ \qquad (66a)$$

and for pair annihilation into two gamma rays,

$$e^- + \bar{e}^+ \rightarrow \gamma + \gamma \qquad (66b)$$

The bar over any given symbol signifies that it is an antiparticle. The subject of particles vs antiparticles is given in detail in Chapters 74 and 75.

66.12. Cosmic-Ray Showers. Out of hundreds and hundreds of cloud-chamber photographs of cosmic rays, the experimenter is occasionally rewarded with a picture of a cosmic-ray shower. Instead of one or two tracks in the picture, he finds anywhere from half a dozen or more to several hundred. As shown by the photographs in Fig. 66M, most of the tracks of a shower seem to come from one localized region, usually within a solid piece of matter like a lead plate or the wall of the cloud chamber.

An extensive study of showers by both the experimental and theoretical physicists has led to the conclusion that each shower is produced by a single, high-energy cosmic ray. A charged particle of very high energy upon entering a solid block of matter, where atoms are packed very close together, carries out the multiple-collision process illustrated in Fig. 66H. Here, within a short distance of 1 or 2 cm of lead, enough atoms are encountered to yield many secondaries. These secondaries, emerging from the lower face of the metal, result in the observed photographs.

Fig. 66M *Wilson cloud-chamber photographs of cosmic-ray showers.* (The first three photographs are reproduced through the courtesy of R. B. Brode and the last three through the courtesy of C. D. Anderson and the *Physical Review.*)

In a thin sheet of metal, relatively small showers are usually found, whereas with a thick metal block showers of many tracks are occasionally photographed. The first five photographs in Fig. 66M were taken without a magnetic field so that the tracks are all straight, while the last photo was taken with a magnetic field. The bending of three tracks to the right and three to the left indicates equal numbers of positrons and electrons.

In photograph (a), a single high-speed particle is seen to enter the lead plate from above and to produce some twenty or more secondary particles, each with enough energy to get through and into the air space below. In (b), two small showers of particles enter the top surface of the lead plate, whereas a single larger shower emerges from the bottom. Apparently one or two of the particles at the center of the one shower above have the necessary high energy to produce the lower shower, whereas the others of lower energy are stopped by the lead. Note particularly the

fanning out of the rays below. In (c), a small shower of very high energy particles enters the chamber from above, having been produced far above the cloud chamber in a shower-producing process, probably by a single particle of extremely high energy. As some of these secondaries pass through the lead, each produces a shower of its own.

Direct evidence that some showers originate with a single high-energy particle is shown in Fig. 66N. Here, in a cloud chamber with 13 equally spaced lead plates, a relatively large shower is seen to have grown from only one or possibly two particles at the top. Not only does this avalanche grow in numbers with each traversal of a lead plate, but the relatively small spread of the tracks indicates how nearly each new particle recoils along with the others in the forward direction. In this picture, one observes in the small space of several inches the process that, in Fig. 66H, requires several miles of air.

66.13. Mesons. The presence in cosmic rays

Fig. 66N *Cloud-chamber photograph showing cascade shower of cosmic rays developed in 13 lead plates, each 1.3 cm thick.* (Courtesy, Wm. B. Fretter.)

of charged particles having a mass several hundred times that of an electron, yet considerably lighter than a proton, was discovered by Anderson and Nedermeyer in 1938. These particles, called *mesons*, are of several kinds, and experimental data taken in balloons and airplanes show that most of them are produced high in the atmosphere by the collisions of primary cosmic rays with air nuclei.

High in the atmosphere high-energy atomic particles collide with atomic nuclei, and as a result transfer large amounts of energy by knocking out protons, neutrons, and π mesons, as shown in Fig. 66O.

When a high-energy proton collides with a nucleus transferring energy to another proton within, the following typical reactions occur,

$$p + p \rightarrow p + p + \pi^+ + \pi^0 + \pi^- \quad (66c)$$

and

$$p + p \rightarrow p + n + \pi^+ + \pi^+ + \pi^- \quad (66d)$$

When the incoming proton collides and trans-

Fig. 66O *Primary cosmic ray produces π mesons by nuclear collision.*

fers a large amount of energy to a neutron the following typical reactions occur

$$p + n \rightarrow p + p + \pi^+ + \pi^- + \pi^- \quad (66e)$$

and

$$p + n \rightarrow p + n + \pi^+ + \pi^0 + \pi^- \quad (66f)$$

The π mesons, each with a mass of about 275 m_e, along with other nucleons, recoil forward with speeds close to that of light (m_e = mass of an electron). The term nucleon is here applied to only those particles believed to exist in atomic nuclei and consist of protons and neutrons.

The possible existence of mesons and their spontaneous disintegration were first predicted by Yukawa* in 1935, and first photographed by Williams and Roberts in 1940.

All charged π mesons are now known to have a half-life of 2×10^{-8} s, and each one decays into a charged μ particle called a *muon*, and a lightweight neutral particle called a *neutrino* (see Sec. 64.2).

The neutrino ν is an uncharged particle, postulated first by Pauli in order to explain nuclear phenomena in keeping with the fundamental

* H. Yukawa, *Proc. Phys. Math. Soc.*, Japan, **17**, 48 (1935).

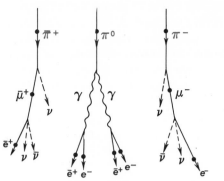

Fig. 66P *π mesons disintegrate into μ mesons, γ rays, electrons, and neutrinos.*

laws of the conservation of energy and of momentum.

The decay of π mesons, more commonly called *pions*, may be written as interactions as follows:

$$\pi^- \rightarrow \mu^- + \bar{\nu}_\mu \qquad (66g)$$
$$\bar{\pi}^+ \rightarrow \bar{\mu}^+ + \nu_\mu \qquad (66h)$$

The uncharged π mesons are very unstable. With a half-life of less than 10^{-14} s, they decay into two γ rays. In the upper atmosphere these γ rays create cascade showers of electrons by electron pair-production and bremsstrahlung (see Fig. 66N).

The decay of a neutral pion can be written

$$\pi^0 \rightarrow \gamma + \gamma \qquad (66i)$$

It is now well known that muons decay, with half-lives of 2×10^{-6} s, into electrons and neutrinos, as shown in Figs. 66P and 66Q. The decay of the muons may be written as follows:

$$\mu^- \rightarrow e^- + \bar{\nu}_e + \nu_\mu \qquad (66j)$$
$$\bar{\mu}^+ \rightarrow \bar{e}^+ + \nu_e + \bar{\nu}_\mu \qquad (66k)$$

In the above reactions we see that there are four different kinds of neutrinos, ν_μ, $\bar{\nu}_\mu$, ν_e, and $\bar{\nu}_e$. These particles will be treated in detail in Chapters 74 and 75. The neutrino subscripts indicate the electrons and muons with which

Fig. 66Q *Wilson cloud chamber photographed in a magnetic field of 8000 gauss showing decay of a π meson into a μ meson and of the μ meson into a positron.*

they were associated, while the bar over a particle signifies it is an *antiparticle*.

Many of the charged μ mesons, with their mass of about 210 m_e, traverse the atmosphere before decaying, and reach the surface of the earth. At sea level the charged cosmic rays are about 70% μ mesons and 29% electrons and positrons, with about 1% heavier particles like protons, deuterons, α particles, etc.

In traversing solid matter, negatively charged π mesons frequently slow down to such a speed that, upon an encounter with a nucleus, they are

Fig. 66R   *"Star" in photographic emulsion showing the explosion of a nucleus resulting from the capture of a slow π meson.* (Courtesy, C. F. Powell's laboratory, University of Bristol, England.)

attracted by the + charge and captured. In this process the meson mass is transformed into energy exciting the nucleus to such a state that it literally explodes by shooting out a number of heavier particles like protons, deuterons, α particles, etc. Figure 66R shows such a "star" event in a photographic emulsion.

Recent studies of cosmic-ray tracks made in photographic emulsions and cloud chambers indicate the presence of particles with various other masses and charges (to be discussed in Chapter 74).

Most recent cosmic-ray observations at high altitudes and at sea level show the following:

TABLE 66A. COMPOSITION OF PRIMARY AND
SECONDARY COSMIC RAYS

Primaries		Sea level	
H	89%	μ Mesons	70%
He	9%	e^+ and e^-	29%
Li, Be, B	0.5%	Heavier particles	1%
C, N, O	0.5%		
Ne, Mg, Si	0.1%		
Fe	0.03%		

QUESTIONS

1. Make a diagram of a Geiger–Müller tube counter, and briefly explain how it is able to be used to detect atomic particles of high energy.

2. Who was awarded the Nobel Prize in physics for the discovery of cosmic rays? What was his experimental observation?

3. How does the intensity of cosmic rays vary with altitude?

4. Explain why the intensity of cosmic rays is a minimum near the equator. Make a diagram.

5. How was the positron discovered, and by whom?

6. Under what conditions are electron pairs created?

7. What is a cosmic-ray telescope, and how is it made?

8. What are primary cosmic rays, and of what are they composed?

9. What are the secondary cosmic rays, and of what are they composed?

10. Make a list of all the atomic particles found in cosmic rays.

11. Make diagrams to show the disintegration of π mesons.

ATOMIC PARTICLE ACCELERATORS

At the time Cockcroft and Walton were performing their first disintegration experiments (see Fig. 65M), E. O. Lawrence,* an American physicist, and his assistant S. L. Livingston were developing a new type of atomic accelerator which soon attracted the attention of the leading physicists the world over. So successful was this "atomic machine gun" in producing high-speed atomic projectiles for disintegration experiments that a new and larger instrument was soon constructed and put into operation. Because the principles of this accelerator involved the cyclic motion of charged atomic particles in a uniform magnetic field, the device was appropriately called a *cyclotron*. Today a cyclotron of considerable size occupies a most prominent posi-

---

* Ernest O. Lawrence (1901–1958), American experimental physicist. After an early education in South Dakota, Lawrence . obtained the A.B. degree at the University of South Dakota in 1922, the master's degree at Minnesota in 1923, and the Ph.D. at Yale University in 1925. After two years as National Research Fellow he became, at the early age of 26, Assistant Professor of Physics at Yale University. The following year he was appointed Associate Professor of Physics at the University of California, and in 1930 was made full Professor. Having built up the Radiation Laboratory at the same institution, he became its Director in 1936. In 1937 he was awarded the Comstock Prize of the National Academy of Sciences, the Cresson Medal of the Franklin Institute, and the Hughes Medal of the Royal Society of London. Lawrence was a member of the National Academy of Sciences and was noted principally for his invention and development of the cyclotron and its application to the production of induced radioactivity. For these discoveries he was granted the Nobel Prize in 1939. During World War II he directed one of the main research projects leading to the isolation of uranium-235 used in atomic bombs.

tion in many of the leading physics laboratories of the world.

One of the early cyclotrons built at the University of California, called the "sixty-inch," is an instrument capable of producing intense beams of protons, deuterons, or α particles having energies of 10, 20, and 40 MeV, respectively. The purpose of these high-speed particles, as is the case with all such instruments, is to subject various known substances to bombardment and thus produce disintegrations and transmutations of all kinds.

67.1. The Lawrence Cyclotron. Although the operation of a large cyclotron requires an elaborate outlay of apparatus and equipment, the principles upon which it operates are quite simple. As a means of explaining these principles, cross-section diagrams of a cyclotron are shown in Figs. 67A and 67B.

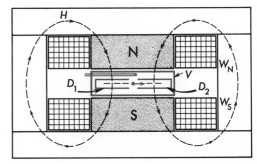

Fig. 67A   *Cross-section diagram of a cyclotron.*

The very heart of the instrument consists of two short, hollow, half-cylinders, D_1 and D_2, mounted inside of a vacuum chamber V, between

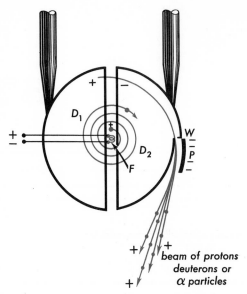

Fig. 67B   *Detailed diagram of the "dees" of a cyclotron.*

the poles of a powerful electromagnet, and connected on the outside to the two terminals of a high-frequency alternating-current generator. This generator is really a shortwave radio transmitter supplying energy to the "dees" (D_1 and D_2) instead of to the antenna.

When a trace of hydrogen gas is admitted to the evacuated chamber, the hot-wire filament F ionizes some of the hydrogen atoms, thereby producing the protons to be used as atomic bullets. At the particular instant when D_1 is charged positively and D_2 is charged negatively, a proton in the neighborhood of F will be accelerated toward D_2. Moving through the strong magnetic field of the huge magnet, this positively charged particle traverses a circular path as shown in the diagram.

If, after making a half-turn, the potential difference is reversed so that D_1 becomes negatively charged and D_2 positively charged, the proton will be attracted by one and repelled by the other, causing it to increase its speed. With added speed it therefore moves in the arc of a larger circle as shown.

After this second half-turn, the potential difference again reverses, making D_1 positive and D_2 negative, and again the proton speeds up.

Thus, as the potentials reverse periodically, the proton travels faster and faster, moving in ever-expanding circles, until, reaching the outer edge, it passes through a narrow open window W.

Upon leaving W all protons must pass close to a negatively charged plate P where, by attraction, their paths are straightened out and they become a separated beam of projectiles. Whatever substance is to be bombarded is then placed in this beam, and the disintegrated fragments are studied by means of various detective devices.

The fundamental principle that makes the cyclotron work at all is the fact that *the time required for a charged particle to make one complete turn within the dees is the same for all speeds.* The faster a particle travels the larger is the circle it must traverse, thus keeping the time constant. Hence, with a constant frequency of the alternating current supply, some particles may be just starting their acceleration near the center while others farther out have already acquired higher speeds. The result is a pulsed stream of protons emerging from the window W.

If the ac voltage applied between the *dees* of the cyclotron is 200,000 V, with each half-turn a particle obtains an added velocity equivalent to 200,000 V. If a proton makes 25 complete revolutions before leaving the chamber at W, it will have acquired a velocity equivalent to 200,000 times 25 times 2, or 10,000,000 V. Here, then, is a beam of 10 MeV protons acquired by the application of a potential difference only $\frac{1}{50}$ as great.

Deuterium is a gas composed of atoms of mass 2, the heavy isotope of hydrogen (see Appendix VII). A deuterium atom without its one and only orbital electron is called a *deuteron*. When hydrogen in the evacuated chamber of the 60-in. cyclotron is replaced by *deuterium* and the magnetic field strength is doubled, a beam of high-energy deuterons is obtained. Having twice the mass, but the same unit positive charge as protons, these particles acquire twice as much energy. If helium gas is used in place of deuterium, many of the atoms become doubly ionized at the source and after acceleration emerge from the cyclotron window as alpha particles with an energy of about 40 MeV. By increasing or decreasing the frequency of the potential applied to the dees, and properly adjusting the magnetic field, protons, deuterons, or α particles of 10, 20, and 40 MeV, respectively, can be produced.

Some of the details of the cyclotron shown in Fig. 67A are as follows: The dimension, 60 in., refers to the diameter of the poles of the cyclotron magnet; this in turn limits the size of the dees and therefore the maximum energy available in the form of atomic projectiles. Most of the instrument's total weight of 200 tons lies in the solid iron core and the pole pieces located inside the field windings. The latter, consisting of many turns of thick copper wire, are encased in tanks W_S and W_N through which cooling fluid is continually circulated.

A photograph of an 11-MeV deuteron beam from the Harvard University cyclotron is shown in Fig. 67C. From the point where the particles

Fig. 67C *Photograph by Paul Donaldson of an 11-MeV deuteron beam from the Harvard cyclotron.* (Courtesy, Harvard University Press and A. K. Solomon.)

emerge from the cyclotron window at the left center to where they come to rest in mid-air at the lower right, they ionize the air molecules and atoms, causing them to emit visible light.

67.2. Theory of the Cyclotron. The theory of the cyclotron involves simple classical laws describing the motion of a charged particle in a uniform magnetic field. By Eq.(48e), the force

on a particle in a magnetic field is given by Bev, and this is equal to the centripetal force mv^2/r:

$$Bev = \frac{mv^2}{r} \qquad (67a)$$

Here e is the charge on the particle in coulombs, m is its mass in kilograms, v is its velocity in meters per second, and r is the radius of its circular path in meters. To find the time required for any charged particle to make one complete circle the formula $x = vt$ from mechanics is employed. The distance traveled in one turn is represented by x, and T represents the time:

$$T = \frac{x}{v} = \frac{2\pi r}{v} \qquad (67b)$$

By solving Eq.(67a) for v, and substituting Eq.(67b), we obtain

$$v = \frac{Ber}{m} \qquad \text{and} \qquad T = \frac{2\pi}{B} \cdot \frac{m}{e} \qquad (67c)$$

The right-hand equation shows that the *period T* is independent of r and v and for like particles (that is, the same e and m) varies with the magnetic induction B. The alternating potential difference E applied to the cyclotron dees must therefore match in frequency the particles' motion due to the field B. It is customary in practice to apply a fixed frequency to the dees and adjust the current in the magnetic field coils until resonance occurs. In the 60-in. cyclotron, $B = 1.6$ Wb/m² or 16,000 G.

67.3. The Van de Graaff Generator. This machine, developed in 1931 by R. Van de Graaff at Princeton University, employs the principle of the electrostatic generator discovered many years ago. A typical installation, as shown in Fig. 67D, consists of a large hollow sphere, supported on insulating columns and charged by a belt conveying electrical charges from a battery at ground potential and depositing it inside the sphere. The fabric conveyor belt, a foot or more in width and running over well-aligned rollers, travels about 60 mi/hr.

As the belt passes between the metallic surface and row of needle points at P, electrons from the points jump toward the positive electrode and are caught by the belt. Upon entering the sphere at the top, the electrons jump to the needle

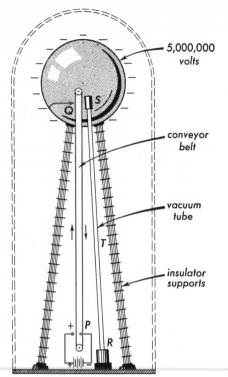

Fig. 67D   *Diagram of a Van de Graaff generator of high voltage.*

1941 by D. W. Kerst at the University of Illinois, is an electron accelerator capable of producing electron beams of high energy as well as X rays of extremely high penetrating power. This ingenious device differs from the cyclotron in at least two fundamental respects: first, the electrons are accelerated by a rapidly changing magnetic field, and, second, the circular orbit of the particles has a constant radius.

A cross-section diagram of a 20-MeV betatron is shown in Fig. 67E. A glass vacuum tube in the

Fig. 67E   *Cross-section diagrams of an electron accelerator, called a betatron.*

points Q where they go quickly to the outside surface of the sphere. The "spraying" of electrons *to* and *from* the points is assured by keeping the battery potential high (about 50,000 V) to maintain a "brush discharge." As more and more electrons arrive at the sphere, its negative potential rises higher and higher until leakage into the surrounding air and through the insulators becomes equally fast.

Atomic particles to be accelerated are generated inside a vacuum-tube source S inside the sphere. Starting at the top of a long straight vacuum tube T, electrons are accelerated downward toward ground potential, where, acquiring the full energy of the available voltage, they are allowed to bombard whatever target is being studied. Where installations are designed for accelerating protons, deuterons, or α particles, the battery potential is reversed and the sphere acquires a high positive potential with respect to the ground.

67.4. The Betatron. The *betatron*, invented in

shape of a *doughnut* and containing an *electron gun* is mounted between the poles of an electromagnet. An alternating current (180 c/s) applied to the coils causes some of the magnetic lines of force to pass through the vacuum tube at the electron orbit and the remainder through the orbit center, as shown below. Electrons are injected only at the beginning of each quarter cycle when the field begins to increase in the "up" direction. The increasing field through the center of the orbit gives rise to an electromotive force, tangent to the orbit, speeding up the electrons; whereas the increasing field at the orbit is just sufficient to increase the centripetal force and keep the electrons from spiraling outward. The stability of such an orbit is brought about by properly shaping the pole faces of the magnet, adjusting the frequency and strength of the magnetic field, and injecting the electrons at the proper voltage at the appropriate time.

During World War II, a 350-ton betatron was constructed by the General Electric Company and put into use as a source of extremely penetrating X rays. In this instrument electrons accelerated to 100-MeV energy, and impinging upon a target, give rise to X rays capable of penetrating many feet of solid iron and lead.

67.5. The Synchro-Cyclotron. The firm belief that new and fundamental discoveries in nuclear physics can be made with atomic projectiles having greater and greater energies has led scientists and engineers in various institutions to combine their efforts in groups to design and construct larger and larger atomic accelerators. One such instrument is the synchro-cyclotron shown in Fig. 67F.

The fundamental differences between this and the orthodox cyclotron are the use of one dee in place of two and the use of an applied alternating-current potential whose frequency is made to rise and fall periodically instead of remaining constant. The principles of operation are illustrated in Fig. 67G. Starting at the center, protons, deuterons, or α particles are made to move in circles of increasing radius, the acceleration taking place as they enter and leave the lips of the dee. At the outer edge they are deflected out of the field, as in the cyclotron, or allowed to strike a suitable target inside the vacuum chamber.

The theory of the synchro-cyclotron* is based upon "phase stability," a principle fundamental to nearly all high-energy accelerators. This relatively new idea can be derived from the well-founded theory that, as a particle is accelerated and approaches the speed of light, continued acceleration increases the mass, while the speed approaches a nearly constant value. In other words, as more and more energy is given to a

* The theory of phase stability of atomic accelerators of high energy was first developed in 1945 by V. Veksler [*J. Phys.*, USSR, **9**, 153 (1945)], and independently by E. M. McMillan [*Phys. Rev.* **68**, 143 (1945)].

particle, more and more of it is stored as *increased mass* and less and less as *increased speed*.

To apply this principle to an accelerator like the synchro-cyclotron, consider the conditions that exist when a positively charged particle in a uniform magnetic field is moving with constant speed in an orbit of constant radius and at the same time in synchronism with an applied high-frequency potential difference. Such an orbit is represented by the dotted circle in Fig. 67G, with the particle entering and leaving the lips of the dee at A and B when the potential (see graph below) is zero. By Eq.(67a), $Bev = mv^2/r$. Since, from mechanics, angular velocity $\omega = v/r$, and the frequency of revolution $f = \omega/2\pi$, direct substitution in Eq.(67a) gives $m = Be/2\pi f$. Multiplying both sides of this equation by the square of the speed of light c^2 gives

$$mc^2 = \frac{Bec^2}{2\pi f}$$

where mc^2 represents the total energy E of the particle,

$$E = \frac{Bec^2}{2\pi f} \tag{67d}$$

It may be shown from these equations that mc^2 includes the *rest mass* m_0c^2 of the particle, and that to increase E the magnetic induction can be *increased* as in the betatron and synchrotron (see Sec. 67.6), or *the frequency can be decreased* as in the synchro-cyclotron.

Returning now to the high-speed but stationary orbit AB in Fig. 67G, assume that a particle is a little early in entering the dee. Arriving there, as shown by A′ in the graph below, the dee has a negative potential a′ and the particle is accelerated by attraction. Being accelerated, the mass increases with little increase in speed. Owing principally to increased mass, the particle now describes a larger circle, and the next time around it has dropped back to arrive more nearly at the time of *zero potential*. Hence, if the magnetic induction B were to be increased or the frequency f were to be decreased, the particle might be made to continually enter and leave the dee ahead of the zero phase and receive a forward push each time around.

If a particle gets behind the zero phase (A to

Fig. 67F *Photograph of the 184-in., 4000-ton, synchro-cyclotron at the University of California, Berkeley, California.*

Fig. 67G *Illustration of "phase stability" as applied to the synchro-cyclotron.*

A″ in the graph), it will not receive a forward pulse and, moving with nearly constant speed, will permit a decreasing frequency of an applied potential difference to catch up and get ahead again. Hence phase stability is assured and forward impulses will occur as the particle spirals outward with increasing energy.

In the 184-in. synchro-cyclotron, the high-frequency potential difference is applied to the dee stem at P and the variable capacitor C, composed of a fast rotating set of "fan blades" passing between a set of stationary blades, varies the frequency up and down through relatively wide limits. In producing 200 MeV deuterons, the frequency of the dee potential rises and falls 120 times/second between the limits of 12.5 and 8.5 Mc/s.

The positive ions are pulsed into the center of the dee when the frequency is 11.3 Mc/s, and they arrive at the outer edge when it has dropped to about 9.6 Mc/s. Having made 10,000 turns around the chamber in a period of only one-thousandth of a second, the deuterons have an energy of 300 MeV. The target, located inside the vacuum chamber, is therefore bombarded by pulses coming at the rate of 120 per second.

A drop from 11.3 to 9.6 Mc/s decreases f [see Eq.(67d)] by about 15%, thereby increasing a deuteron's energy E and mass m by 15%, or 0.3 atomic mass unit (amu). Such an increase, by Eq.(63m), is equivalent to 300 MeV.

67.6. The Synchrotron. This device is an electron accelerator employing the principles of the *cyclotron* and *phase stability*. A cut-away diagram of such an instrument is shown in Fig. 67H. As in the betatron, electrons are injected into a doughnut-shaped vacuum chamber by an electron gun. Operating first as a betatron, the electrons are accelerated in an orbit of fixed radius by a rapidly increasing magnetic field. The rising field is produced by discharging a large capacitor bank through the magnet coils. Part of the field goes through the relatively small *flux bars* near the orbit center, and part through the pole faces and vacuum chamber.

As the electrons quickly approach the speed of light, their mass begins to increase rapidly; from about 2 MeV on, they move at almost constant speed (between 98% and 100% the speed of light). Increasing energy is added in this *second phase* by an alternating potential difference applied to the *sector dee* shown in the diagram. Instead of decreasing the frequency, as in the synchro-cyclotron, the magnetic induction B is

Fig. 67H   *Cross-section diagrams of a 300-MeV synchrotron.*

several were constructed, they have not proved satisfactory until recently. Applying the principles of tubular wave guides and resonant cavities, L. Alvarez and his collaborators, immediately after World War II, constructed the first successful linear accelerator. Since a giant machine employing the same principles is soon to be built at Stanford University, the ideas involved are of considerable importance.

A cut-away diagram of part of the Alvarez lineac is given in Fig. 67I. Protons are initially produced and accelerated to 4 MeV by a pressure Van de Graaff generator (see Fig. 67D) and then injected at that energy into one end of a 40-ft tank, as shown at the upper left. Once inside they are further accelerated as they pass through a series of "drift tubes," and arrive at the other end with an energy of about 40 MeV.

The tank cavity within the copper lining, fed by 30 radar transmitting oscillators, is set resonating at its *dominant mode* at a frequency of 200 Mc/s. The "standing-wave" conditions set up are such that the electic field ε is parallel to the tube axis and is everywhere rising and falling together. The lengths of the drift tubes gradually increase so that the protons cross each gap when the field ε is to the right, and are inside the tubes, in a field-free space, when the field is to the left. It now seems possible that additional tank sections can be added end to end to this system to

increased [see Eq.(67d)] and as the electron *mass* increases, the stronger field maintains the beam orbit constant.

Upon reaching a maximum energy of 300 MeV, for example, the electrons, with a mass some 600 times their *rest mass*, are caused to spiral inward to strike a tungsten target, where they produce 300-MeV X rays.

67.7. The Linear Accelerator. Although linear accelerators were proposed as early as 1929, and

Fig. 67I   *Diagrams showing the first section of a linear accelerator.*

obtain almost any desired energy. Calculations indicate 1 MeV per lineal foot can be expected from such a system.

67.8. Billion Electron Volt Accelerators. The design and construction of an instrument capable of accelerating particles to energies of billions of electron volts (BeV) involve many problems. Not the least of these is the economic factor concerned primarily with the initial cost of such an instrument as well as its subsequent maintenance.

A number of accelerators producing particles of 1 BeV or more are now in operation and others of greater and greater energy are being planned.

IN OPERATION (1965)

Pasadena, California	1.1 BeV (electrons)
Ithaca, New York	1.3 BeV (electrons)
Berkeley, California	6.2 BeV (protons)
Dubna, Russia	10 BeV (protons)
Geneva, Switzerland	28 BeV (protons)
Brookhaven, Long Island	32 BeV (protons)
Cambridge, Massachusetts	7.5 BeV (electrons)
Argonne, Illinois	12.5 BeV (protons)

PLANNED OR UNDER CONSTRUCTION

Palo Alto, California   15–45 Bev (electrons)

The basic design of one of these large instruments, the 6.2 BeV *bevatron*, is shown in Fig. 67J.

The magnet arrangement consists of four quadrant segments spaced so that the particle orbits are quarter-circles connected by 20-ft straight sections. The electrical power supplied to the 10,000-ton magnet is provided by a motor generator with a large flywheel. During buildup of the magnetic field, a peak power of 100,000 KW is drawn from the flywheel and stored in the magnet. As the field is reduced between beam pulses, the generator acts as a motor and returns energy to the flywheel.

The protons from a source S are first accelerated to 10 MeV by a linear accelerator, and then injected into the 385-ft race track proper. As they pass through the accelerator electrode in one of the straight sections and are speeded up by the high-frequency potential differences, the magnetic field increases at the proper rate to keep the beam in the same orbit. The output beam consists, as it does in all high-energy accelerators, of a series of pulses. From the time of injection, each pulse of protons takes about 2 s to acquire its final speed, and in so doing makes about four million revolutions of the orbit and travels about 300,000 mi.

Fig. 67J   *Berkeley Bevatron designed to produce 6.2 BeV protons.*

QUESTIONS AND PROBLEMS

1. What is a cyclotron? What is its purpose? What does it accelerate?

2. What is deuterium? Is deuterium the same as hydrogen?

3. What is a Van de Graaff generator? What is it frequently used for? Can it be used to accelerate protons and electrons?

4. What does the abbreviation "MeV" stand for? What does the abbreviation "BeV" stand for?

5. What is a betatron? Where do you think it got its name?

6. Approximately what is the highest energy to which atomic particles have been accelerated in the laboratory?

7. If the frequency of the potential applied to the dees of a cyclotron is 8.5×10^6 c/s, what must be the magnetic induction B to accelerate α particles?

8. Calculate the frequency of the oscillating potential that must be applied to a cyclotron in which deuterons are accelerated. Assume the magnetic induction has a constant value of 25,000 G. [Ans. 19.0 Mc/s.]

9. The frequency applied to the dees of a cyclotron is 7.6 Mc/s. What must be the magnetic induction B if protons are to be accelerated?

10. What total accelerator voltage will give protons a velocity of 99% the speed of light? [Ans. 6.67 BeV.]

TRANSMUTATION
OF THE ELEMENTS

The use of high-speed atomic particles, whether they come from radioactive materials, from cyclotrons, or from cosmic rays, has led in recent years to the discovery of many secrets that lie hidden within the atomic nucleus. While the thousands of experiments performed have led to the discovery of many new elementary particles, several hundred radioactive isotopes of the known elements have been produced by the process of nuclear bombardment.

68.1. Proton and Deuteron Disintegrations. When high-energy protons or deuterons are used to bombard different known elements, various disintegration products are formed. An experimental arrangement in which the cyclotron acts as the source of high-speed particles is shown in Fig. 68A. To determine the nature of

cyclotron

Fig. 68A *Experimental arrangement generally used for bombarding known substances with high-speed deuterons from the cyclotron and for detecting the disintegration products with an ionization chamber as a detector.*

the disintegration taking place within the substance under bombardment, it is common practice to identify the penetrating rays emerging

from the other side by the use of suitable detectors.

Numerous experiments have shown that the disintegration products to be looked for may be *protons, α particles, neutrons, γ rays, mesons, electrons, positrons,* etc. For some of these penetrating rays, one kind of detector may be more suitable than another. The *scintillation counter,* for example, is particularly useful in detecting γ rays and electrons, whereas the *Wilson cloud chamber* and *ionization chamber* are useful in detecting protons, α particles, or neutrons.

The detector shown at the right in Fig. 68A represents an ionization chamber. When a Wilson cloud chamber is used to identify disintegration products, charged particles can be identified by the density of their fog tracks, and their energy can be determined by the curvature of the tracks when a magnetic field is applied. This is illustrated in Fig. 68H for positrons. Once the nature of the emerging rays from a bombarded target is known, the recoil product of the disintegration also becomes known by writing down a reaction equation. Six examples of such reaction equations are given by the following:

Q values, MeV

$$_1H^1 + _9F^{19} = _8O^{16} + _2He^4 \qquad 8.113 \qquad (68a)$$
$$_1H^1 + _5B^{11} = _6C^{12} + \gamma \text{ ray} \qquad 15.955 \qquad (68b)$$
$$_1H^2 + _7N^{14} = _6C^{12} + _2He^4 \qquad 13.574 \qquad (68c)$$
$$_1H^2 + _8O^{16} = _7N^{14} + _2He^4 \qquad 3.110 \qquad (68d)$$
$$_1H^2 + _3Li^6 = _3Li^7 + _1H^1 \qquad 5.028 \qquad (68e)$$
$$_1H^2 + _4Be^9 = _5B^{10} + _0n^1 \qquad 4.362 \qquad (68f)$$

It is customary to omit the *mass energy* of the bombarding particle from the left-hand side of all reaction equations and to designate the total energy liberated by the disintegration as shown at the right above. The values of Q given above therefore represent the experimentally determined values of the energy over and above that supplied by the incident projectile.

Consider the fifth reaction, which can be taken to represent an experiment in which a beam of 2 MeV deuterons from the cyclotron bombards a target of lithium metal. From the other side of the target a stream of high-energy protons would be detected. If they are sent through a Wilson cloud chamber in a magnetic field, for example, their tracks could be identified as proton tracks and their energy determined by the curvature of the tracks to be 6.0 MeV. The lithium atoms in the target would recoil with the remaining 1 MeV. When the accurate weights of the four nuclei involved are taken into account, there is a total loss of 0.00540 atomic mass units. Multiplying by 931, this is equivalent to 5.0 MeV energy. This value plus the energy of the incident bombarding particle gives 7.0 MeV.

As a second example consider Eq.(68f) in which deuterons, bombarding beryllium metal, produce high-speed neutrons and recoiling boron nuclei. This particular disintegration is important experimentally because it is used as a means of obtaining intense beams of neutrons for use as projectiles in other disintegrations. The nuclear changes are illustrated schematically in Fig. 68B.

The available energy from the loss in mass alone is equivalent to 4.4 MeV; so that, if deuterons with an energy of 7 MeV are used to bombard the beryllium target, the available energy becomes 11.4 MeV, 1 MeV going to the recoil boron nucleus and approximately 10.4 MeV to the neutron.

The table of accurately known masses of nuclides given in Appendix IX includes a column 3 of excess mass values in MeV. These values represent the difference between the mass of each nuclide and its *mass number*. These numbers have been multiplied by 931 to give the equivalent energy in MeV in column 4.

As a practical matter column 3 of mass excess energies is very useful. Consider as an illustration the following example.

Example 1. Find the Q value for the reaction shown in Eq.(68e), using the mass energies given in column 3 of Appendix IX.

Solution. The energy equivalents for each of the two nuclides in collision are first added to obtain

$_1H^2$	13.135 MeV
$_3Li^6$	14.089 MeV
	27.224 MeV

The energy equivalents for the two product nuclides are next added to obtain

$_3Li^7$	14.908 MeV
$_1H^1$	7.288 MeV
	22.196 MeV

The difference between these totals gives directly

$$Q = +5.028 \text{ MeV}$$

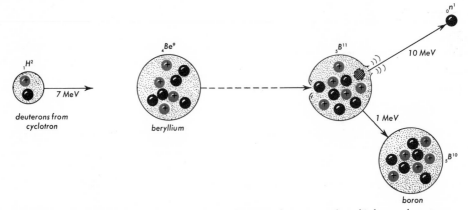

Fig. 68B *Deuteron disintegration of a beryllium nucleus to produce high-speed neutrons.*

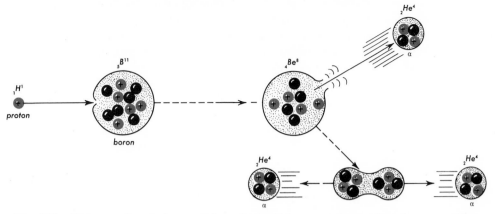

Fig. 68C *Disintegration of a boron nucleus of mass 11 by a proton to produce three α particles.*

68.2. Multiple Disintegrations. A study of certain disintegration experiments shows that some of the unstable nuclei created by the capture of a proton or deuteron by a stable nucleus split up into more than two stable nuclei. Examples of this arise when boron is bombarded by protons and when nitrogen is bombarded by deuterons. In the case of boron (see Fig. 68C), the proton is first captured by a $_5B^{11}$ nucleus to form an unstable carbon nucleus, $_6C^{12}$. This composite structure, as we will see in a later chapter, has too much mass to be a stable $_6C^{12}$ nucleus, and it disintegrates by the expulsion of an α particle with several million volts energy, leaving behind a beryllium nucleus, $_4Be^8$:

$$_1H^1 + _5B^{11} = _4Be^8 + _2He^4 \qquad (68g)$$

This nuclear combination is still unstable and splits apart into two more α particles:

$$_4Be^8 = _2He^4 + _2He^4$$

When the phenomenon was first observed, it was thought that all three α particles came apart simultaneously, but further observations showed that first one and then two were ejected. The total energy liberated has been measured to be about 11 MeV, which checks almost exactly with the value obtained from the loss in mass.

68.3. Branch Disintegrations. It so happens that when certain atoms are bombarded with high-speed particles, two or more disintegration processes may subsequently take place. As an illustration of this phenomenon of *branch dis-* *integration*, consider the proton bombardment of beryllium in which the following two types of disintegration have been identified:

$$_1H^1 + _4Be^9 = _3Li^6 + _2He^4 \qquad (68h)$$
$$_1H^1 + _4Be^9 = _5B^{10} + \gamma \text{ ray} \qquad (68i)$$

When a proton is captured by a beryllium nucleus to form an unstable boron nucleus, $_5B^{10}$, there are two ways in which it may split up. The instability of the boron in the first place is due to the presence of too much mass. Such an atom is said to be in an *excited state*, for by the emission of a γ ray it gives up its surplus energy and becomes a stable $_5B^{10}$ nucleus, or by splitting up into two particles it gives up its surplus in the form of kinetic energy to become $_2He^4$ and $_3Li^6$, two stable nuclei.

An abbreviated notation for nucleus reactions is illustrated by the following examples:

$$_1H^1 + _9F^{19} = _8O^{16} + _2He^4 \qquad F^{19}(p, \alpha)O^{16}$$
$$_1H^2 + _7N^{14} = _6C^{12} + _2He^4 \qquad N^{14}(d, \alpha)C^{12}$$
$$_1H^2 + _3Li^7 = _2He^4 + _2He^4 + _0n^1 \qquad Li^7(d, 2\alpha n)$$

68.4. Discovery of Induced Radioactivity. The discovery of induced radioactivity was made in 1934 by F. Joliot and I. Curie Joliot.*

For years the Curie–Joliots, as they are now

* Irene Curie, daughter of the most famous woman physicist, Marie Curie, is the wife of Frederick Joliot. Because of the now famous name of Curie, the physicists of the world hyphenate the name and call them Mme. Curie–Joliot and M. J. F. Joliot, or for short the Curie–Joliots. For years they worked with radioactive substances in the famous laboratory of the late Mme. Marie Curie at the Radium Institute in Paris.

often called, had been exposing various substances to the α rays from naturally radioactive elements and had been studying the various disintegrations that took place. In the specific instance referred to above, they bombarded aluminum with α *particles from polonium* and measured the energies of the ejected neutrons by the recoiling of protons from paraffin (see Fig. 68D). They observed that, even after the po-

α particles　　neutrons　　protons

polonium source　　aluminum　　paraffin　　detector

positrons

after bombardment

Fig. 68D　*Experimental arrangement used by the Curie–Joliots when they discovered induced radio-activity.*

lonium source was taken away, the detector continued to respond to some kind of penetrating radiation. Upon investigating the nature of these rays, they found positively charged electrons coming from the aluminum.

Repeating the experiments to make certain of the results, they came to the conclusion that, under the bombardment of α particles, the aluminum had become radioactive in its own right. What was happening has since been verified: α particles striking aluminum nuclei are captured, and the resulting nuclei disintegrate with the violent ejection of neutrons:

$$_2He^4 + {}_{13}Al^{27} = [{}_{15}P^{30}] + {}_0n^1 \qquad (68j)$$

The newly created recoil particles, with a charge of $+15$ and mass 30 have been identified as phosphorus nuclei which are not stable but radioactive. Spontaneously disintegrating, these radioactive phosphorus nuclei $_{15}P^{30}$ shoot out positrons, leaving behind them stable silicon atoms of charge $+14$ and mass 30:

$$[{}_{15}P^{30}] = {}_{14}Si^{30} + {}_1\bar{e}^0 + \nu_e \qquad (68k)$$

The *half-life* of this activity, which measures the rate of decay of the phosphorus into silicon

(for the meaning of half-life see Sec. 63.2), is only 2.5 min. The emission of a positively charged electron is accompanied by a neutrino, just as in the case of β emission. Oftentimes, however, the neutrino is omitted from the reaction since it carries no charge and no rest mass.

Although the mass of the electron is not zero, it is so small compared with unit mass (the mass of one electron, it will be remembered, is $\frac{1}{1836}$th of the mass of the proton) that e is written with a zero superscript. According to this notation of a positron is written $_1e^0$ and an electron $_{-1}e^0$.

Because the phosphorus does not all disintegrate immediately, it has been possible to identify the activity as coming from the newly created phosphorus atoms in the following way. A piece of aluminum metal, immediately after being bombarded, is dissolved in hydrochloric acid together with some ordinary inactive phosphorus, and then a standard chemical separation is made. Testing each part separately, the radioactivity is found to be present with the phosphorus residue, and not with the aluminum.

68.5. The Discovery of Radioactive Sodium. Immediately after the discovery of induced radioactivity by the Curie–Joliots, Lawrence bombarded sodium with 2-MeV deuterons from the cyclotron and found that it too, like aluminum, became radioactive (see Fig. 68E). Upon

(a)　　　　　　(b)

deuterons　　protons　　　electrons and γ rays

sodium chloride

during bombardment　　after bombardment

Fig. 68E　*Experimental arrangement used by Lawrence in discovering radioactive sodium.*

testing for the nature of the rays given off during bombardment, Lawrence found protons with an energy of about 7 MeV. When the sodium target was removed from the deuteron beam, as shown in diagram (b), and then tested for activity, it was found to be emitting both electrons and γ rays. The bombarding reaction, therefore, is

$${}_1H^2 + {}_{11}Na^{23} = [{}_{11}Na^{24}] + {}_1H^1 \qquad (68l)$$

followed by the radioactive decay of the unstable sodium nuclei,

$$[{}_{11}Na^{24}] = {}_{12}Mg^{24} + {}_{-1}e^0 + \bar{\nu}_e + \gamma \text{ ray} \qquad (68m)$$

The first stage of the disintegration process is shown at the left in Fig. 68F, and the radioactive decay is shown at the right.

Fig. 68F   *The production and disintegration of radiosodium.*

The residual nucleus $_{11}Na^{24}$ of the first disintegration is called *radiosodium*. Having a charge of $+11$ and mass of 24, it must be an isotope of sodium not found in nature. Since measurements of the activity of radiosodium give a *half-life* of only 15 hr, it is clear why such atoms are not found in nature. If they were formed some time in the ages past, they would all have disintegrated by this time.

An energy-level diagram for the decay of radioactive sodium is shown in Fig. 68G. The left-hand energy scales are given equally well in

Fig. 68G   *Energy-level diagram for radioactive decay of sodium-24.*

amu or in MeV. After emitting an electron, the nuclear charge increases by unity, and we have a magnesium nucleus in an excited state or energy level. With two successive transitions in which 2.75-MeV and 1.37-MeV γ rays are emitted, the nucleus becomes a stable system, a normal isotope of magnesium $_{12}Mg^{24}$.

Up to the present time more than 600 different kinds of radioactive atoms have been produced in the laboratory. Two examples, in addition to those already given, are illustrated by the following reactions:

$$\begin{aligned} {}_1H^2 + {}_{15}P^{31} &= [{}_{15}P^{32}] + {}_1H^1, \\ [{}_{15}P^{32}] &= {}_{16}S^{32} + {}_{-1}e^0 + \bar{\nu}_e \quad (68n) \end{aligned}$$

$$\begin{aligned} {}_1H^2 + {}_6C^{12} &= [{}_7N^{13}] + {}_0n^1, \\ [{}_7N^{13}] &= {}_6C^{13} + {}_1\bar{e}^0 + \nu_e \quad (68o) \end{aligned}$$

The first of these reactions forms *radioactive phosphorus* $_{15}P^{32}$ which is *electron active* with a half-life of 15 days.

A cloud-chamber photograph of the positrons emitted by radioactive nitrogen $_7N^{13}$ is reproduced in Fig. 68H. The magnetic field bends all

Fig. 68H   *Photograph of the Wilson cloud-chamber tracks of positrons ejected by radio nitrogen, $_7N^{13}$.*

the rays in the same direction, indicating that all are positive charges. The low-density fogdrops forming the tracks indicate particles with the mass of an electron.

68.6. Electron Capture. Many radioactive nuclei, when created by some collision process, are unstable to the extent of one extra positive charge. Although many such nuclei disintegrate and become stable by the emission of a positron, others draw to them an orbital electron from the K shell of the same atom. Inside the nucleus this negative charge neutralizes a positive charge, whereas outside an L or M electron jumps into the K shell vacancy with the simultaneous emission of a characteristic X ray (see Fig. 68I).

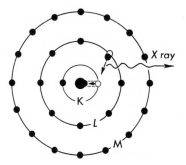

Fig. 68I   *Unstable nucleus captures an electron from the K shell of orbital electrons. As a consequence, an X ray is emitted.*

Beryllium-7 and gallium-65 are specific examples of unstable nuclei in which *K capture* occurs. The reactions for these are

$$_4\text{Be}^7 + _{-1}e^0 = {}_3\text{Li}^7 + \bar{\nu}_e$$
$$_{31}\text{Ga}^{65} + _{-1}e^0 = {}_{30}\text{Zn}^{65} + \bar{\nu}_e \qquad (68p)$$

An energy-level diagram involving the radioactive decay of actinium-226 is shown in Fig. 68J. This nucleus is β-active; 80% of its atoms

Fig. 68J   *Energy-level diagram of the two-way radioactive decay of actinium-226.*

disintegrating by emitting β particles with an end-point energy of approximately 1 MeV, each followed by the emission of one or two γ rays

to become thorium-226. The other 20% of the atoms capture an electron from the K shell, and immediately emit one or two γ rays to become radium-226.

Electron capture (E.C.) changes one of the nuclear protons into a neutron, and the atomic number drops by unity from 89 to 88. The emission of a β particle changes one of the neutrons into a proton, and the atomic number increases by unity from 89 to 90. In some few isotopes, E.C. is the only means of radioactive decay.

68.7. Nuclear Stability. We now know that if we bombard targets with atomic particles of sufficiently high energy, every known stable element can be converted into radioactive isotopes of that element or of neighboring elements. Furthermore, a number of isotopes can be produced for any one element, some with masses smaller than any of its stable isotopes, and some with greater masses. In the case of copper, for example, the following isotopes have been produced.

Copper Z = 29

MASS	ACTIVITY	HALF-LIFE		
58	β^+	3 s		
59	β^+	81 s		
60	β^+	24 min		
61	β^+	3.3 hr		
62	β^+	10 min		
63	Stable	—	70%	
64	$\beta^-/\beta^+ = 2$	12.8 hr	42%	E.C.
65	Stable	—	30%	
66	β^-	5.1 min		
67	β^-	58 s		
68	β^-	32 s		

The first five isotopes have too many protons to be stable nuclides, and by positron emission convert a proton into a neutron and become an isotope of nickel. The last three isotopes have too few protons, and by electron emission convert a neutron into a proton and become an isotope of zinc.

Isotope $_{29}\text{Cu}^{64}$, lying between two stable isotopes, is an interesting combination of nucleons, since these nuclei are found to decay in any one of four different ways. All four processes are

Fig. 68K *Energy-level diagram of a four-way radioactive decay of copper-64.*

illustrated in an energy-level diagram in Fig. 68K.

Approximately 38% of the copper-64 nuclei decay by the emission of a β^- and a neutrino, to become zinc-64:

$$_{29}Cu^{64} = {}_{30}Zn^{64} + {}_{-1}e^0 + \bar{\nu}_e \quad +0.573 \text{ MeV}$$

The β^- end-point energy of 0.573 MeV corresponds to a decrease in nuclear mass of 0.000616 amu. *The masses of all nuclides include the masses of all orbital electrons for the neutral atoms.* When $_{29}Cu^{64}$ ejects an electron from the nucleus, the daughter product $_{30}Zn^{64}$ picks up a stray electron to become a neutral atom. The term *nuclide* is applied to any known assembly of nuclear particles called a nucleus.

Approximately 42% of the copper-64 nuclei decay by *electron capture* with the simultaneous emission of a neutrino:

$$_{29}Cu^{64} + {}_{-1}e^0 = {}_{28}Ni^{64} + \nu_e \quad +1.678 \text{ MeV}$$

The end-point energy of this process is 1.678 MeV, and the neutrino spin of $\frac{1}{2}\hbar$ compensates for the spin of $\frac{1}{2}\hbar$ given the nucleus by the captured electron.

Some 19% of the copper-64 nuclei emit a β^+ and a neutrino to become stable nuclei, nickel-64:

$$_{29}Cu^{64} = {}_{28}Ni^{64} + {}_1\bar{e}^0 + \nu_e \quad +0.656 \text{ MeV}$$

The end-point energy for these positrons is 0.656 MeV. The difference between the two end-point energies of 1.678 MeV and 0.656 MeV, or 1.022 MeV, is just the mass-energy equivalence of two

electrons. When $_{29}Cu^{64}$ ejects a positron from the nucleus, the daughter product also drops one of its orbital electrons to become a neutral atom. The mass-energy equivalence of one electron ($m = 0.00549$ amu) is 0.511 MeV.

Finally, a few copper-64 nuclei, approximately 0.6%, capture an orbital electron and emit a neutrino, leaving the daughter product, $_{28}Ni^{64}$ in an *excited state*. This process is immediately followed by the emission of a 1.34-MeV gamma ray:

$$_{29}Cu^{64} + {}_{-1}e^0 = {}_{28}Ni^{64} + \nu_e + \gamma \text{ ray} \\ + 1.678 \text{ MeV}$$

The end-point energy for this electron capture process alone is only 0.338 MeV.

A small section of a chart of the known nuclides of all the elements is shown in Fig. 68L.* Each square represents one nuclide, and includes such information as relative abundance, atomic number, mass, half-life, activity, etc. *Isotopes,* nuclides having the same number of protons, lie along a horizontal line. *Isotones,* nuclides having the same number of neutrons, lie along vertical lines. *Isobars,* nuclides having the same number of nucleons, i.e., the same A, lie along 45° lines. The small shaded rectangles represent the stable nuclides; all others are radioactive.

The stability of every nucleus is associated with the relative numbers of neutrons and pro-

* A complete "Chart of the Nuclides" including all known nuclides may be obtained by writing to General Electric Co., Knolls Atomic Power Laboratory, Schenectady, New York.

Fig. 68L   *A typical section from a "Chart of Nuclides," published by the Knolls Atomic Power Laboratory, operated by the General Electric Company, under the direction of Naval Reactors, U. S. Atomic Energy Commission. Revised 1964.*

Fig. 68M   *Neutron–proton diagram of stable nuclei.*

tons bound together. If N represents the number of neutrons and Z the number of protons in any nucleus, and we plot a graph for all the known stable nuclides, we obtain a chart like the one shown in Fig. 68M. It will be noted that along any isobaric line, constant A $(A = Z + N)$, there is only one nuclide for *odd A*. There are only two exceptions to this rule, and these are found at $A = 113$ and $A = 123$. These pairs are

$$_{48}Cd^{113} \quad \text{and} \quad _{49}I^{113}$$
$$_{51}Sb^{123} \quad \text{and} \quad _{52}Te^{123}$$

For *even A*, there are usually two, and occasionally three, stable nuclides having the same A.

If, in Fig. 68M, we plotted vertically upward out of the page, as a third dimension, the accurately known atomic masses M for all known stable as well as radioactive nuclides, we would obtain a kind of valley running diagonally up the chart, with the lowest points near the center of the stable nuclides. This is illustrated by a cross-section diagram in Fig.

Fig. 68N   *Atomic mass relations for nuclides with A = 87: Odd Z and even N nuclides fall on the same parabola with even Z and odd N.*

68N for $A = 87$. These are the isobars given in the second column from the right in Fig. 68L:

$_{35}Br^{87}$	86.927310 amu	β^-
$_{36}Kr^{87}$	86.919311 amu	β^-
$_{37}Rb^{87}$	86.915410 amu	β^-
$_{38}Sr^{87}$	86.915130 amu	Stable
$_{39}Y^{87}$	86.916820 amu	E.C.
$_{40}Zr^{87}$	86.920330 amu	β^+
$_{41}Nb^{87}$	86.926380 amu	β^+

Note that the only stable nuclide, $_{38}Sr^{87}$, lies deepest in the valley curve.

Figure 68O is a typical atomic mass graph for isobars of *even A*. The isobars of *even Z* and *even N* fall on the lower parabola and therefore represent more tightly bound nuclear structures than the *odd Z odd N* isobars.

Among the stable nuclides there are 54 pairs of *even–even* isobars and only two cases of three. The latter are: $_{50}Sn^{124}$, $_{52}Te^{124}$, $_{54}Xe^{124}$, and $_{54}Xe^{136}$, $_{56}Ba^{136}$, $_{58}Cs^{136}$.

The isobar parabolas given in Fig. 68O are drawn from the following known masses:

$_{38}Sr^{92}$	91.916650 amu	β^-
$_{39}Y^{92}$	91.914730 amu	β^-
$_{40}Zr^{92}$	91.911130 amu	Stable
$_{41}Nb^{92}$	91.913210 amu	E.C.
$_{42}Mo^{92}$	91.912720 amu	Stable
$_{43}Tc^{92}$	91.919100 amu	β^+

68.8. The Mechanics of Recoiling Particles. When a nucleus disintegrates by ejecting a particle, classical laws of mechanics are found to apply to the resultant motions. Consider, for example, a radioactive nucleus as shown in Fig. 68P.

If the compound nucleus is initially at rest, and the masses of the two fragments after disintegration are m_1 and m_2, conservation of momentum requires that

$$m_1v_1 = m_2v_2 \qquad (68q)$$

If an amount of energy E is liberated by the

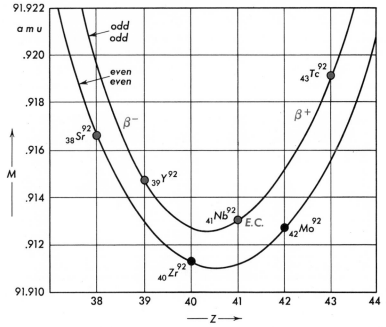

Fig. 68O   *Atomic mass relations for nuclides with A = 92: Odd Z and odd N nuclides form one parabola and even Z and even N nuclides form another.*

disintegration process, the law of conservation of energy requires that

$$E = E_1 + E_2 \qquad (68r)$$

where

$$E_1 = \tfrac{1}{2}m_1v_1^2$$

and

$$E_2 = \tfrac{1}{2}m_2v_2^2$$

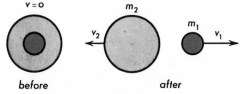

Fig. 68P   *Mechanics involved in the disintegration of a compound nucleus.*

The ratio of the two energies is, therefore,

$$\frac{E_1}{E_2} = \frac{\tfrac{1}{2}m_1v_1^2}{\tfrac{1}{2}m_2v_2^2} \qquad (68s)$$

If we solve Eq.(68q) for v_1, we can substitute m_2v_2/m_1 for v_1 in Eq.(68s), and obtain

$$\frac{E_1}{E_2} = \frac{m_2^2}{m_1m_2} \qquad (68t)$$

Example 2. If an energy of 20 MeV is liberated in a reaction in which the nuclear recoil mass is 100 times the mass of the ejected particle, find (a) the energy ratio of the two recoiling particles, and (b) the energy given each particle.

Solution. Since $m_2 = 100m_1$, direct substitution in Eq.(68t) gives

(a) $\qquad \dfrac{E_1}{E_2} = 100 \qquad$ or $\qquad E_1 = 100E_2$

By substituting $100E_2$ for E_1, and 20 MeV for E, in Eq.(68r), we obtain

$$20 \text{ MeV} = 100E_2 + E_2$$

or $\qquad\qquad E_2 = 0.20 \text{ MeV}$

and $\qquad\qquad E_1 = 19.8 \text{ MeV}$

In all such nuclear reactions the momentum imparted to both bodies is always equal, yet approximately 99% of the energy in this example is carried away by the lighter particle. In other words, conservation of energy and momentum divides the energy approximately inversely as the masses.

If the compound nucleus is moving with a velocity v at the time of disintegration, the above equations apply to a *center of mass* point continuing on with the same initial velocity v.

68.9. Medical Applications. Since the time of its discovery, radiosodium has found numerous containing the "tagged" atoms; at various times thereafter thin sections of tissue from the plant or animal are placed in direct contact against a photographic film. After several hours of exposure to any possible rays from "tagged" atoms in the section, the film is developed. Figure 68Q

Fig. 68Q   *Radioautograph of the type used in medical studies, showing selective absorption of phosphorus by the liver and spleen.*

and important applications in many branches of science. It has, for example, been used as a means of tracing certain organic and inorganic chemicals passing through the human body, through plants, and through chemical experiments of one kind or another. To give a simple example, one can show, by drinking water containing radiosodium in the form of common table salt (NaCl), that within 2 min some of it has entered the blood stream and has been distributed to all parts of the body. The presence of the salt in the finger tips or the toes can be demonstrated by detecting the electrons and γ rays from the sodium with a scintillation counter. Similar experiments can be performed with trees and plants to see how rapidly their roots take up certain plant foods and distribute them to the leaves and branches. At the present time radiophosphorus 32, because of its chemical properties and its comparatively long half-life, is being used in a number of medical researches as a possible cure for certain diseases, as well as for tracing the migration of phosphorus through the body.

One useful medical technique is the use of radioactive elements to obtain *radioautographs*. A plant or animal is given a single dose of liquid shows at the left a thin cross section of the mouse, previously fed radiophosphorus [see Eq.(68n)], and at the right the resulting radioautograph of this same section. The dark areas indicate the uptake of phosphorus by the *spleen* and *liver* sections, and nowhere else.

Figure 68R shows an *X ray* and *strontium radioautograph* of a section of an amputed leg from a patient with osteogenic sarcoma (bone

Fig. 68R   *X-ray and radioautograph of a human leg.* (Courtesy, Dr. J. G. Hamilton.)

cancer). The patient received radiostrontium orally two days before removal of the extremity. The X ray shows the bone tumor at the upper end of the tibia, while the radioautograph shows selective deposits of strontium in the tumor, with small amounts in the surrounding bone and relatively little in the soft tissues. These studies indicate that radiostrontium may prove useful in clinical therapy.

Since the process of life is one of continual change, there is a rapid turnover of elements in living systems. When common molecules are chemically formed with one or more of their atoms radioactive, they are said to be tagged. In living systems, such as the various organs of the body, these tagged molecules can change places with others of like kind. In time, however, these molecules disappear by natural elimination processes or by decay.

If $_{15}P^{32}$ is taken orally, for example, one finds that after four hours 44% is in the bones, 25% in the muscles, and 2.4% in the blood. When $_{53}I^{131}$ is taken orally, turnover studies show that 80 times as much iodine has been taken up by the thyroid as by any other per gram mass of the body.

A typical graph of the behavior of radioactive elements by living systems is shown in Fig. 68S.

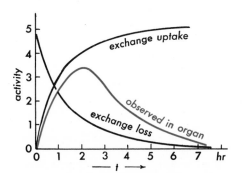

Fig. 68S *Typical exchange curves for radioactive molecules in living systems.*

68.10. Radiation Damage. Energy absorbed by the passage of radiation through matter gives rise to structural changes called *radiation damage*. The nature and amount of damage produced is closely related to the number of ion pairs created, and this in turn depends upon the absorbing material and the characteristics of the radiation.

Since biological effects vary widely between body tissues and different types of radiation, it is customary to measure radiation absorption by the number of ion pairs produced in air. The exposure of specimens to any and all kinds of radiation is measured in terms of a unit called the *roentgen*.

ROENTGEN. The roentgen unit, abbreviated 1 R, is that quantity of X or γ radiation that produces one electrostatic unit of negative, or positive, charge in 0.001293 grams of dry air. Under standard conditions air has a density of 0.001293 g/cm^3, and one coulomb = 3×10^9 esu. Since the charge of a single electron, or ion, is 1.60×10^{-19} C, the roentgen can also be defined as the quantity of X or γ radiation which, under standard conditions, produces in air:

$$\frac{1}{3 \times 10^9 \times 1.6 \times 10^{-19}} = 2.08$$
$$\times 10^9 \text{ ion pairs/cm}^3$$

Experimental measurements show that on the average it takes 32.5 eV to produce one ion pair. Consequently,

$$1 \text{ R} = 2.08 \times 10^9 \times 32.5 = 67.6 \text{ BeV}$$

This energy is equivalent to 0.108×10^{-7} J, or 0.108 ergs. In one gram of air 1 R would produce

$$\frac{0.108 \text{ ergs}}{0.001293} = 83.5 \text{ ergs}$$

This same radiation will produce 93 ergs per gram of water (the main constituent of tissue), approximately 40 ergs/gm in fat, and 900 ergs/gm in bone.

ROENTGEN EQUIVALENT, PHYSICAL (rep). This is a unit applied to statements of dose of ionizing radiation not covered by the definition of the roentgen. One *rep* has been defined as the dose that produces an energy absorption of 93 ergs per gram of tissue for the particular radiations in question.

ROENTGEN EQUIVALENT, MAN (rem). A dose of any ionizing radiation producing the same biological effect in tissue as that produced by 1 *roentgen* of high-voltage X radiation is called

1 *rem*. The roentgen is frequently divided into one thousand equal parts called the *milliroentgen:*

$$1 \text{ roentgen} = 1000 \text{ milliroentgens}$$
$$1 \text{ R} = 1000 \text{ mR}$$

RADIATION DOSE. The total radiation entering a specified area or volume is called the radiation dose and is measured in *roentgens per hour* or *milliroentgens per hour.*

One effect of penetrating radiation is to bring about gene mutation. Such mutations are of greatest concern to the individual man or woman from birth through the reproductive years. In human beings this is assumed to be about 30 years. Experiments show that a total of 50 R per person received during the reproduction period of 30 years doubles the number of mutations that occur naturally in the absence of radiation.

The amount of radiation to which an individual can be subjected with no adverse effects is called a *permissible dose.* This is generally accepted to be 250 mR per week, or 6.25 mR per hr based on a 40 hr working week.

CURIE. The *curie*, as a unit of radioactivity, was originally defined as the number of disintegrations per second emanating from one gram of radium. Because of experimental difficulties the unit was redefined by the International Commission on Radiological Units (July 1953) as follows: The curie is a unit of radioactivity defined as the quantity of any radioactive nuclide in which the number of disintegrations per second is 3.700×10^{10}. The *millicurie*, mCi, and *microcurie*, μCi, are smaller units in frequent use. Medical doses are usually expressed in millicurie-hours.*

* See D. J. Hughes, *Pile Neutron Research* (Addison-Wesley Publishing Co., Inc., Reading, Massachusetts).
References: J. Cork, *Radioactivity and Nuclear Physics* (D. Van Nostrand Co., Inc., Princeton, New Jersey); H. Semat, *Introduction to Atomic Physics* (Farrar and Rinehart, New York); R. D. Evans, *The Atomic Nucleus* (McGraw-Hill Book Co., Inc., New York).

PROBLEMS

1. When 8-MeV α particles bombard Na^{23}, protons are observed being ejected. (a) Write down the disintegration equation, and (b) find the energy liberated.

2. If a 4-MeV deuteron on N^{14} produces a proton, what is the energy liberated? Assume that 94% of the energy goes into the proton. What will be (a) its maximum energy, and (b) its range in air (see Fig. 63G)? [*Ans.* (a) 11.8 MeV, (b) 157 cm.]

3. When 15-MeV deuterons bombard B^{10}, protons, neutrons, and α particles are observed as disintegration products. Assuming these are branch disintegrations, write down the three reactions and give the liberated energies.

4. If 6-MeV deuterons on N^{14} produce C^{12} and α particles, (a) how much energy is liberated? If the available energy is divided between the two particles in the inverse ratio of their respective masses, what is (b) the maximum energy of the α particles, and (c) their range in air? [*Ans.* (a) 19.6 MeV, (b) 14.7 MeV, (c) 20 cm.]

5. If 25-MeV protons are incident on Be^9, α particles are observed emitted as high-speed disintegration products. (a) Write down the reaction, and (b) find the energy liberated. If the liberated energy is divided between the disintegration products in the inverse ratio of their respective masses, what is (c) the energy of the α particles, and (d) their maximum range in air?

6. If the accurately known mass of copper-64 is 63.929761 amu, find the accurate masses of the stable isobars nickel-64 and zinc-64 (see Fig. 68K). [*Ans.* nickel-64, 63.927959 amu; zinc-64, 63.929145 amu.]

7. Cesium-130 is a radioactive isotope with a half-life of 30 min. Some of the atoms decay by positron emission with an end-point energy of 1.97 MeV, while the others decay by electron emission with an end-point energy of 0.44 MeV. Write down the reactions, and draw an energy-level diagram (see Fig. 68J).

8. There are five isobars of mass number $A = 104$, whose masses are known from measurements. They are as follows:

$_{44}Ru^{104}$	103.912000	Stable
$_{45}Rh^{104}$	103.912610	β^-
$_{46}Pd^{104}$	103.910170	Stable
$_{47}Ag^{104}$	103.914450	β^+
$_{48}Cd^{104}$	103.913800	β^+

(a) Plot an atomic-mass graph for these nuclides similar to that shown in Fig. 68O. (b) At what value of Z do you find the minimum mass for the even–even isobars? (c) Extrapolate to find the approximate mass of $_{43}Tc^{104}$. [*Ans.* (b) 45.6. (c) 103.925 amu.]

9. There are five isobars of mass number $A = 134$, whose masses are known from measurements. They are as follows:

$_{53}I^{134}$	133.916020	β^-
$_{54}Xe^{134}$	133.911884	Stable
$_{55}Ba^{134}$	133.912930	E.C. and β^-
$_{56}La^{134}$	133.910870	Stable
$_{57}Ce^{134}$	133.914570	E.C. and β^+

(a) Plot an atomic-mass graph for these nuclides similar to that shown in Fig. 68O. (b) At what value of Z do you find a minimum mass for the even–even isobars? (c) Extrapolate to find the approximate mass of $_{58}Pr^{134}$ and (d) the approximate mass of $_{52}Te^{134}$.

10. There are five isobars of mass number $A = 124$, whose masses are known from measurements. They are as follows:

$_{50}Sn^{124}$	123.911740	Stable
$_{51}Sb^{124}$	123.912340	β^-
$_{52}Te^{124}$	123.909420	Stable
$_{53}I^{124}$	123.912610	E.C. and β^+
$_{54}Xe^{124}$	123.912560	Stable

(a) Plot an atomic-mass graph for these nuclides similar to that shown in Fig. 68O. (b) At what value of Z do you find the minimum mass for the even–even isobars? (c) Extrapolate to find the approximate masses of $_{49}In^{124}$ and $_{55}Cs^{124}$. [*Ans.* (b) $Z = 51.8$. (c) 123.923 amu, and 123.924 amu, respectively.]

11. If a boron-11 nucleus is at rest when it liberates a neutron, and the total energy liberated is 16 MeV, find (a) the energy ratio of the two recoiling particles, and (b) the energy of each particle in MeV.

12. If a neon-20 nucleus is at rest when it liberates a proton, and the total energy liberated is 12 MeV, find (a) the energy ratio of the two recoiling particles, (b) the energy of each particle, and (c) the range of the proton. [*Ans.* (a) 19.8. (b) 0.6 MeV and 11.4 MeV. (c) 145 cm.]

NEUTRON AND GAMMA-RAY REACTIONS

While the bombardment of all targets by high-energy-charged atomic particles, such as protons, deuterons, and alpha particles, is found to produce disintegrations and transmutations of various kinds, it is also possible to bring about similar reaction with neutrons and gamma rays.

69.1. Neutron Reactions. The first disintegrations produced by high-speed neutrons as atomic projectiles were announced in 1932 by the English physicist Feather. Immediately following Chadwick's discovery of these neutral particles, Feather allowed neutrons from beryllium (see Fig. 69A) to enter a Wilson cloud chamber containing pure nitrogen gas. Numerous expansions of the chamber and the simultaneous clicks of a camera shutter gave many photographs of the ion tracks left by recoiling nitrogen atoms.

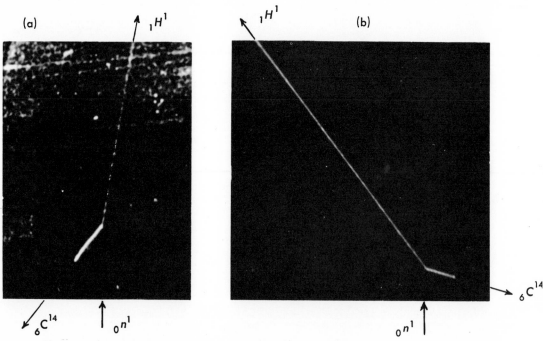

Fig. 69A *Cloud-track photographs of neutron disintegrations of nitrogen.* (After Feather and Rasetti.)

Although most of the photographs indicated elastic collisions between nitrogen atoms and neutrons, an occasional photograph showed a forked track, indicating a disintegration of a nitrogen nucleus:

$$_0n^1 + _7N^{14} = _6C^{14} + _1H^1 \qquad (69a)$$

Two photographs of several such disintegrations are reproduced in Fig. 69A. Although hundreds of neutrons enter the cloud chamber every second, they do not ionize atoms as charged particles do, and hence leave no tracks. When a head-on nuclear collision occurs, however, the disintegrated nuclei, possessing as they do high speeds and positive charges, leave a trail of ions behind them. The fork in each photo shows a proton track of considerable length originating at the same point as the more dense, short-ranged track of the recoiling carbon nucleus.

Strong sources of neutrons are produced by inserting a thin plate of beryllium metal in the intense beam of deuterons coming from the cyclotron as shown in Fig. 69B. The disinte-

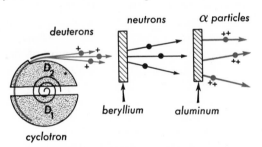

Fig. 69B *Experimental arrangement for producing intense beams of neutrons by bombarding beryllium with deuterons. The neutrons are then used as projectiles for further disintegrations, as illustrated here for aluminum.*

gration process, giving rise to the neutrons, is the reaction Eq.(68f).

Into such a beam of chargeless particles, numerous substances of known chemical constitution have been inserted, and the disintegration products studied with suitable detectors. To illustrate by an example, suppose that a thin sheet of aluminum is inserted into the beam of neutrons as shown in the figure. In this particular instance, α particles are observed emerging from

aluminum, thus enabling one to write down the following neutron reaction:

$$_0n^1 + _{13}Al^{27} = _{11}Na^{24} + _2He^4 \qquad (69b)$$

Thus *radioactive sodium*, produced originally by the deuteron bombardment of ordinary sodium, is here produced by a different reaction [see Eq.(68l)]. As proof of the result, the bombarded aluminum target is found to be β-ray and γ-ray active with a half-life of 15 hr. There are at least two other known disintegration processes by which radiosodium is produced: one by the neutron bombardment of silicon, and the other by the α-particle bombardment of magnesium.

This is but one example of the many known radioactive elements that can be manufactured in four different ways. As a matter of fact, with sufficiently energetic atomic bullets, it is now possible to produce hundreds of atomic nuclei not found in nature. While most of them have short half-lives and do not last very long, there are many with long half-lives, some extending into thousands of years.

Examples of other neutron disintegrations are illustrated by the following reactions:

$$_0n^1 + _9F^{19} = _7N^{16} + _2He^4 \qquad (69c)$$
$$_0n^1 + _{20}Ca^{42} = [_{19}K^{42}] + _1H^1$$
$$[_{19}K^{42}] = _{20}Ca^{42} + _{-1}e^0 + \bar{\nu}_e \quad (69d)$$

Equation (69d) represents a typical case of the capture of a neutron to form a radioactive isotope $_{19}K^{42}$ which, by the ejection of an electron, reverts back to the original stable element, $_{20}Ca^{42}$. Many such reactions are known, particularly among the heavier elements in the first half of the periodic table.

When 100- to 200-MeV deuterons from a large cyclotron strike almost any target, neutrons with energies of 100 MeV or more are produced. Figure 69C is a Wilson cloud-chamber photo showing the result of a 100-MeV neutron impact with an oxygen nucleus. The paths of the recoiling fragments, four α particles, are bent in the magnetic field.

Not all disintegration processes liberate more energy than that required to produce them. This is illustrated by the following example:

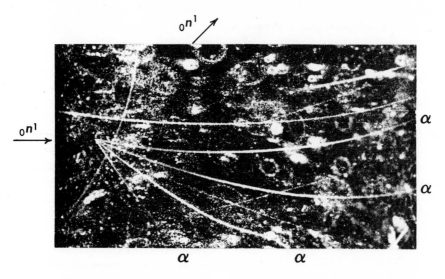

Fig. 69C *Wilson cloud-chamber photo showing the result of a 100-MeV neutron impact on an oxygen nucleus.* (Courtesy, W. Powell.)

$$_0n^1 + {_6}C^{12} = {_4}Be^9 + {_2}He^4$$
$$Q = -5.7 \text{ MeV} \quad (69e)$$

To carry out this disintegration, the bombarding neutrons must have an energy of 5.7 MeV or greater. The sum of the masses produced is greater by this amount than those that went to make them. This is an example of what is called a fast-neutron reaction. This reaction is the reverse of the reaction by which neutrons were first produced in large quantity [see Sec. 65.5 and Eq.(65g)].

69.2. Slow Neutron Reactions. The fact that neutrons, slowed down to very low speeds, have the ability to disintegrate certain atoms was first discovered and investigated by the Italian physicist, Enrico Fermi, and his collaborators. A neutron approaching the nucleus of an atom does not experience a repulsive force, as does a proton, deuteron, or α particle, and consequently its chances of penetration into a nucleus and of being captured by it are relatively large. It is for this reason that slowly moving neutrons are able to bring about disintegrations that slowly moving charged particles cannot.

The customary method of producing *slow neutrons* is to surround a source of fast neutrons with paraffin or some material containing large quantities of hydrogen or deuterium. As neutrons pass through this "moderator" material, elastic collisions with hydrogen nuclei continually slow them down, until at a distance of several centimeters from the source most of them have lost all of their original energy. What little energy they do have is picked up by regular thermal collisions with other atoms.

Since their resultant motions become quite the same as the random motions of the atoms and molecules of the moderator, they are called *thermal neutrons*. Thermal neutrons are defined as neutrons in equilibrium with the substance in which they exist, commonly, neutrons of kinetic energy of 0.0253 eV. Compared with fast neutrons moving with almost the speed of light, like those from a target of beryllium bombarded by the beam from a cyclotron, thermal neutrons have a velocity of only 2200 m/s. This is essentially the velocity of hydrogen molecules in a gas at normal temperature and pressure.

One of the many known slow-neutron reactions is one in which boron-10 captures a neutron and ejects an α particle:

$$_0n^1 + {_5}B^{10} \longrightarrow {_3}Li^7 + {_2}He^4 \quad (69f)$$

69.3. A Thermal-Neutron Source. A very good laboratory source of thermal neutrons can be made with a small quantity of radium and beryllium. The radium sample is surrounded by a thin jacket of beryllium metal and an outer jacket of lead, and then this unit is imbedded at the center of several cubic feet of paraffin (see Fig. 69D). The α particles from radium produce neutrons by the reaction

$$_2\text{He}^4 + {}_4\text{Be}^9 \rightarrow {}_6\text{C}^{12} + {}_0n^1 \qquad Q = 5.6 \text{ MeV}$$

The fast neutrons given off by the beryllium metal bounce around in the paraffin, quickly

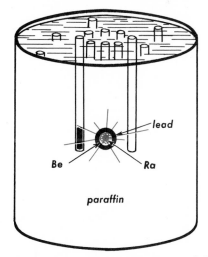

Fig. 69D   *Diagram of a Ra–Be source of thermal neutrons for laboratory experiments.*

slowing down to thermal velocities, while the unwanted β and γ rays from the radium are absorbed by the lead.

Any source to be radiated by slow neutrons is placed in a holder and lowered through any one of several ports shown in the top surface.

An effective demonstration of slow-neutron reactions can be made by rolling a thin sheet of silver metal into a hollow cylinder, about 1 in. in diameter and 4 in. long, and subjecting it to the Ra–Be source (Fig. 69D). After several minutes the cylinder is withdrawn and quickly placed around a Geiger-counter tube, or near the fluor of a scintillation counter. The activity detected will be strong at first and then will slowly die out over a period of several minutes.

If a scaler counting system like the one shown in Fig. 64O is employed, and the number of counts registered on the tube faces is recorded at 10 s intervals, a decay curve like the one shown in Fig. 69E can be plotted. Such a graph with two distinct straight sections is found to be a composite of two half-life curves, one for 24 s and the other for 2.3 min. These two half-lives are attributed to the two stable isotopes of silver, one of mass 107 amu and one of 109 amu.

The capture of a neutron by each of these nuclides produces the radioactive isotopes, silver-108 and silver-110. Both of these are electron active, and produce stable cadmium nuclides as follows:

$$_{47}\text{Ag}^{108} \rightarrow {}_{48}\text{Cd}^{108} + {}_{-1}e^0 + \bar{\nu}_e \qquad (2.3 \text{ min})$$
$$_{47}\text{Ag}^{110} \rightarrow {}_{48}\text{Cd}^{110} + {}_{-1}e^0 + \bar{\nu}_e \qquad (24.2 \text{ s})$$

The procedure for finding the two half-lives from the graph in Fig. 69E is to start with the lower straight section and extrapolate back to zero time. This straight line is then subtracted from the upper curve at two points of time, such as $t = 0$ and $t = 100$ s, and the other straight line drawn in as shown. The summation of these two straight lines should produce the observed curve. Note that the straight lines drop to half their initial values at $t = 24$ s and $t = 138$ s.

Another effective demonstration of slow-neutron reactions is to roll a thin sheet of indium metal into a hollow cylinder, subject it to the slow neutron source (Fig. 69D), and then place it over a Geiger-counter tube or scintillation counter. Like silver, it too will show a strong activity at first and then die out over a period of several minutes.

Indium has two stable isotopes, $_{49}\text{In}^{113}$ and $_{49}\text{In}^{115}$. Upon neutron capture they will become the radioactive isotopes, $_{49}\text{In}^{114}$ and $_{49}\text{In}^{116}$. Both of these nuclides decay by electron emission into stable tin isotopes. $_{49}\text{In}^{116}$ decays in either one of two ways, as follows:

$$_{49}\text{In}^{114} \rightarrow {}_{50}\text{Sn}^{114} + {}_{-1}e^0 + \bar{\nu}_e \qquad (72 \text{ s})$$
$$_{49}\text{In}^{116} \rightarrow {}_{50}\text{Sn}^{116} + {}_{-1}e^0 + \bar{\nu}_e \qquad (54 \text{ min})$$
$$_{49}\text{In}^{116} \rightarrow {}_{50}\text{Sn}^{116} + {}_{-1}e^0 + \bar{\nu}_e \qquad (13 \text{ s})$$

The longer-lived In^{116} is an excited state of the nucleus, called an *isomeric state*, and beta decay with an end-point energy of 1 MeV is followed by several gamma rays. The shorter-lived I^{116} is the normal state of the nucleus, and beta decay with an end-point energy of 2.9 MeV takes it directly to the normal state of Sn^{116} without the emission of gamma rays.

atoms in solids and suggests the possibilities of diffraction, as in the case of X rays and Laue patterns (see Figs. 53F and 53G).

The diffraction of strong beams of neutrons by the atoms of a crystal has been studied by

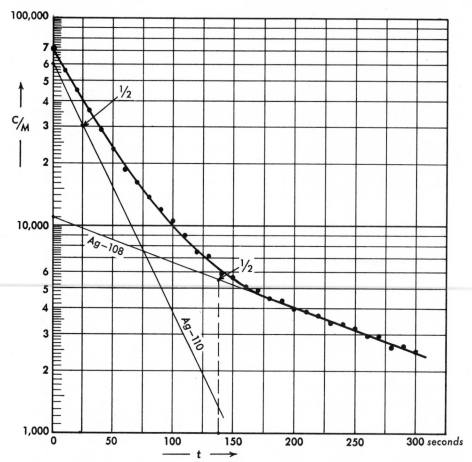

Fig. 69E   *Semilog graph of the β rays from the two silver isotopes, made active by thermal neutrons.*

69.4. Neutron Diffraction. We have seen in a preceding chapter that wave properties are associated with all moving bodies. The De Broglie wavelength of any mass m is given by Eq.(61i) as

$$\lambda = \frac{h}{mv} \qquad (69g)$$

which for thermal neutrons with a velocity of 2200 m/s gives $\lambda = 1.8 \times 10^{-10}$ meters, or 1.8 Å. This value is comparable to the spacings of

many people. Wollan and Shull, using a sodium chloride crystal and an experimental arrangement similar to that shown for X rays in Fig. 53F, obtained the picture reproduced in Fig. 69F. Since neutrons have little or no effect upon photographic films, the front face of the film was covered with a sheet of indium metal 0.5 mm thick.

Neutrons captured by the indium nuclei produce radioactive isotopes, as shown in the preceding section. These unstable isotopes disintegrate, with the emission of electrons. Electrons do affect a photographic emulsion and upon development produce the spots shown.

Fig. 69F   *Neutron diffraction pattern of sodium chloride.* (Courtesy, E. O. Wollan and C. G. Shull.)

Neutrons, like X rays, therefore, become useful tools in the study of the atomic structure of matter.

69.5. Photon Interactions. The term "photon interaction" refers to the disintegration of atomic nuclei brought about by photons. In general, the photons to be used must have a very high energy $h\nu$, and this means their frequency ν must be high and their wavelength λ short: $(c = \nu\lambda)$.

X rays and γ rays are electromagnetic waves in character, and both are composed of photons. The terms X ray or γ ray only signify their origin and, in reactions with nuclei, are of no consequence.

Instead of specifying a photon by giving its frequency ν, it is customary in nuclear reactions to express its energy in electron volts. By the general energy equation, Eq.(63k), we have

$$Ve = h\nu \quad \text{or} \quad V = h\nu/e \quad (69h)$$

For reference purposes, only the following wavelengths and frequencies are calculated from this equation.

PHOTON RELATIONS

V (volts)	λ (m)	ν (1/s)
1 KeV	1.24×10^{-9}	2.4×10^{17}
1 MeV	1.24×10^{-12}	2.4×10^{20}
1 BeV	1.24×10^{-15}	2.4×10^{23}

To obtain sources of high-energy photons, it is common practice to use γ rays from radioactive sources, or to produce X rays with the high-energy electron beam of a betatron or synchrotron. $_{81}Tl^{208}$, for example, produces 2.62-MeV γ rays that are useful for many kinds of experiments.

As an example of the production of high-energy photons with the beam from a large electron accelerator, consider the 1.3-BeV electrons of the Cornell synchrotron (see Fig. 69G).

Fig. 69G   *Photons produced by the electron beam from a synchrotron are used to study photon reactions in a cloud chamber.*

Each time the beam in this machine is allowed to strike a metal target inside the vacuum chamber, the 1.3-BeV electrons produce X rays of extreme penetrating power. Target composition is of little importance in this process, since the phenomenon called "Bremsstrahlung" is responsible for the high-energy X-ray beam that emerges (see Fig. 53M). In such a beam one finds a continuous band of photons ranging in energy from practically 0 up to 1.3 BeV.

As such a beam is made to traverse any form of matter, there are several processes by which

Fig. 69H   *The three major processes responsible for the absorption of high-energy photons in matter.*

- Photoelectric effect
- Compton effect
- Pair production

For photons of low energy the photoelectric effect is chiefly responsible for absorption. As the energy increases, the Compton effect becomes more and more important until, at energies of 1 MeV, pair production sets in and eventually becomes predominant.

A diffusion cloud-chamber photograph of a Compton recoil electron and an electron pair is shown in Fig. 69I. The hundreds of photons that passed through this gas-filled cloud chamber, from left to right, left no tracks since they were electrically neutral. One photon, however, collided with an atomic electron near the upper center of the field, and the forward recoiling

the rays are absorbed or scattered from the beam. These, as shown in Fig. 69H, are:

Fig. 69I   *Cloud-chamber photograph showing a Compton recoil electron (circle) and an electron pair (V track) produced by photons. (Courtesy, Cornell Laboratory.)*

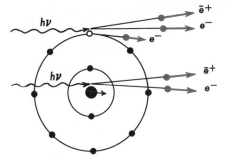

Fig. 69J *High-energy photons can produce electron pairs by collision with a nucleus or an orbital electron.*

electron, in the magnetic field applied to the chamber, made $1\frac{3}{4}$ turns around a circle. Another photon, coming close to a nucleus at the upper left, created an electron pair. From the curvatures of the tracks it is clear that the positron curving upward had more energy than the Compton electron, but less energy than its electron associate.

whereas with the far heavier nucleus the recoil is so small that a track is seldom observed.

A cloud-chamber photograph showing an electron triplet and an electron pair is reproduced in Fig. 69K.* Of the many photons traversing the chamber from left to right, one came extremely close to an atomic electron, and there in the strong electric field created a pair, the positron bending upward, the slower electron downward, and the still slower recoiling electron spiraling around in a small circle. The second photon coming close to the nucleus of a hydrogen atom produced another pair, the positron bending upward and the electron downward. Note the tiny recoil track of the nucleus.

69.6. Photon-Deuteron Interactions. If a cloud chamber is filled with deuterium, that is, with gas in which all molecules are composed of the heavy hydrogen atoms, $_1H^2$, interesting photon interactions can be observed. One process is

Fig. 69K *Cloud-chamber photograph showing an electron triplet and an electron pair produced by high-energy photons (see Fig. 69J). (Courtesy, Cornell University.)*

The production of a pair of electrons by a photon passing close to an atomic nucleus can also occur in the region close to an electron (see Fig. 69J). In both of these processes, the force exerted by the photon on the charged particle during the pair creation causes that particle to recoil forward. Because of its relatively small mass, the electron recoil may be large enough to appear as a third track in a cloud chamber, as

shown in Fig. 69L. A deuteron, the nucleus of a deuterium atom, is composed of one neutron and one proton.

If a photon collides with the neutron of a deuteron, it may produce a proton p and a

* The photographs in Figs. 69I, 69K, 69M, 69O, and 69Q where supplied by the diffusion cloud chamber research group, B. Chasan, G. Cocconi, V. Cocconi, E. Hart, R. Schectman, and D. White, at Cornell University.

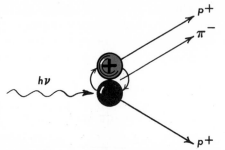

Fig. 69L　*One type of reaction produced by photon collisions with deuterons (see Fig. 69M).*

pi-minus meson, π^-, as shown. Since the two particles leave so quickly after the collision, the remaining "spectator proton" continues on with whatever momentum it had at the moment of impact. The reaction for this can be written

$$h\nu + d \rightarrow p + \pi^- + \underbrace{p}_{spectator} \qquad (69i)$$

Such an explanation accounts for the cloud-chamber event shown in Fig. 69M. A photon

Fig. 69M　*Cloud-chamber photograph showing one type of photon reaction (see Fig. 69L). (Courtesy, Cornell Laboratories.)*

entering from the left collides with the neutron of a deuteron. The neutron is split into a proton

---

p and a π^- meson, with the low momentum "spectator proton" stopping in the chamber.

Since it is generally accepted that a proton or deuteron has unit positive charge, and neutrons and neutrinos have none, their charge exponents are usually omitted in reactions.

69.7. Photo Production of Meson Pairs. If a high-energy photon comes close enough to a proton in a nucleus, a π meson pair may be created in much the same way that an electron pair is produced with a photon of lower energy. If the nucleus is a deuteron, as shown in Fig. 69N, the proton recoils from the impact while

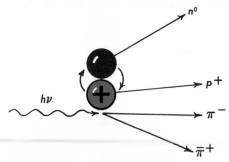

Fig. 69N　*Diagram of a photon collision with the proton of a deuteron, producing a pair of π mesons (see Fig. 69O).*

the neutron continues on with whatever momentum it had at the moment of impact.

As a reaction, we can write,

$$h\nu + d \rightarrow p + \pi^- + \pi^+ + \underbrace{n}_{spectator} \qquad (69j)$$

This reaction accounts for the cloud-chamber event shown in Fig. 69O. A photon, entering from the left, comes close to the proton of a deuteron. A pair of π mesons is created, the proton recoils under the impact, and the neutron "spectator," not being able to form a track, goes on in some unknown direction.

In all such reactions the conservation laws of energy, momentum, and charge must hold. Measurements of track curvatures give velocities and momenta of particles, and calculations are made to see that the conservation of energy and momentum hold. We have seen previously that approximately 1 MeV is required to create an

Fig. 69O *Photograph of a photon collision with the proton of a deuteron, producing a pair of π mesons.* (Courtesy, Cornell Laboratories.)

electron pair. Since a π meson has a mass 275 times that of an electron, an energy of approximately 275 MeV is required to create a pair of π mesons. This is the threshold energy for meson pair-production.

Another interesting reaction involving the impact of a high-energy photon with a deuteron is one in which the processes shown in Figs. 69L and 69N are combined. As shown schematically in Fig. 69P, a photon collides with the neutron,

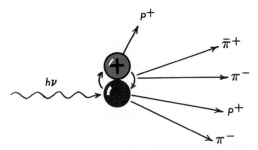

Fig. 69P *Diagram of a photon collision with a deuteron, splitting the neutron and producing a pair of π mesons (see Fig. 69Q).*

splits it apart into a proton, p, and a π^- meson, and simultaneously creates a π meson pair, while the proton "spectator" continues on with its relatively low energy. The reaction is written

$$h\nu + d \rightarrow p + p + \pi^- + \pi^+ + \pi^- \quad (69k)$$

All five of these particles have a charge and may be identified in the cloud-chamber event reproduced in Fig. 69Q. The laboratory-meas-

Fig. 69Q *Cloud chamber photograph of a photon collision with a deuteron, splitting the neutron and producing . a pair of π mesons.* (Courtesy, Cornell Laboratories.)

ured angles, the ionization along the tracks of the five particles, as well as the momentum calculations, readily verify the dynamics of this event.

69.8. Mean Life of a Neutron. Numerous laboratory experiments show that a free neutron has an average life of about 17 min, or 1000 s, before it spontaneously decays. The neutron decays into a proton, an electron, and an antineutrino. In the form of a reaction,

$$n \rightarrow p + e^- + \bar{\nu}_e \quad (69l)$$

In relation to the time scale in which atomic particles interact with each other during a collision (about 10^{-8} to 10^{-15} s), the mean life of a neutron is extremely long.

The mean life of a neutron is so long that even a thermal neutron will, on the average, travel more than 1000 mi before decaying. A 2 MeV neutron will travel 10 million miles.

By comparing the decay of a neutron with the radioactive decay of unstable nuclei, we can speak of the above equation as one of beta decay.

QUESTIONS AND PROBLEMS

1. Charged particles show their tracks in a Wilson cloud chamber. Neutrons and γ rays do not. Why?

2. How are strong beams of neutrons produced? Can neutrons be accelerated in a cyclotron?

3. When silicon-28 is bombarded by neutrons, protons are found coming from the target. Write down the resultant reaction.

4. When neutrons collide with oxygen-16 nuclei, α particles are observed to be given off. Write down the reaction.

5. (a) If radioactive phosphorus-32 is produced by the neutron bombardment of sulfur-32, what is the reaction equation? (b) What happens to the phosphorus-32?

6. How are photons with an energy of 1 BeV produced in the laboratory? Make a diagram and explain the atomic process involved.

7. What are thermal neutrons? What are slow neutrons? What are their velocities in m/s?

8. Make a diagram of a radium–beryllium source of thermal neutrons. Explain the function of each substance used.

9. When slow neutrons are captured by lanthanum-139, the resulting nuclei give off electrons with an end-point energy of 1.43 MeV. Write down the two reactions.

10. If the mass of iodine-127 is 126.9109 amu, find the masses of the two other nuclei resulting from slow-neutron capture described in Problem 9. [*Ans.* (a) $I^{128} = 127.9199$, (b) $Xe^{128} = 127.9181$.]

11. If indium metal is subjected to thermal neutrons for some time and then placed close to a scintillation counter, the initial counting rate is found to be 48,000 cpm. Plot a semilog graph for the activity from this metal for the succeeding 5 min. Note that the activity will be due almost entirely to $_{49}I^{114}$.

12. If a photon in coming close to a nucleus were to create a pair of protons, what would the threshold energy be in electron volts? (Note: Proton mass is 1.007276 amu.) [*Ans.* 1.876 BeV.]

SPECIAL ATOMIC
AND NUCLEAR EFFECTS

It is well known from detailed observations of spectrum lines that whether radiant energy arises from the external structure of atoms or from the nucleus, the breadths of most lines are independent of the spectrograph used to observe them. In many cases narrow and broad lines are observed in the same spectrum. The sharp and diffuse series of the optical spectra of the alkali metals and alkaline earth elements are good examples of this. Although special sources of light have been devised that are capable of sharpening most lines to within the limits of the resolving power of the finest spectrographs, some lines have resisted all efforts to make them narrow.

In this chapter we are concerned with the principal causes of the observed breadth of lines, and with certain atomic and nuclear processes associated with the emission and absorption of photons. The principal causes for the breadth of spectrum lines are:

- Doppler effect
- Natural breadth
- Stark effect

70.1. Doppler Broadening. One of the most classical of all atomic phenomena is the Doppler principle as it applies to the observed frequencies of light. This is well illustrated by certain lines in the solar spectrum shown in Fig. 46J. The light emitted from atoms on the side of the sun approaching the earth are shifted to higher frequencies, while light emitted from atoms on the side receding from the earth are shifted to lower frequencies.

Quite similar effects are well known to exist in the case of an electrical discharge tube where, owing to thermal agitation, most of the atoms emitting light have high velocities. The random motions of the atoms and molecules in a gas, however, produce a net broadening of the line with no apparent shift in its central maximum.

Figure 70A gives a classical representation of

Fig. 70A   *Diagram of the Doppler effect for light emitted by excited atoms, receding from, and approaching the slit of a stationary spectrograph.*

two identical atoms emitting photons of the same frequency ν_0 while they are moving with respect to the slit of a spectrograph. The wavelength emitted by the atom receding from the spectrograph is lengthened, while that emitted by the approaching atom is shortened. Although the velocity of light c is the same for both waves, the frequency of the waves passing through the slit will be different in the two cases. From the theory of relativity the observed frequency will be given by

$$\nu = \nu_0 \frac{\sqrt{1 - (v^2/c^2)}}{1 - (v/c)}$$

This is the relativistic Doppler equation, where ν is the observed frequency, ν_0 is the emitted frequency, and v is the relative velocity of the atom with respect to the spectrograph, $+v$ for an approaching atom and $-v$ for a receding atom.

By a mathematical expansion this equation can be written in the more useful form of a series, as follows:

$$\nu = \nu_0 \left(1 + \frac{v}{c} + \frac{1}{2}\frac{v^2}{c^2} + \frac{1}{2}\frac{v^3}{c^3} + \cdots\right) \quad \text{(70a)}$$

For velocities that are less than 1% the speed of light, the third and succeeding terms of this series are extremely small and can be neglected. The equation then becomes

$$\nu = \nu_0 \left(1 + \frac{v}{c}\right) \quad \text{(70b)}$$

which is just the Doppler formula derived for sound waves. For velocities where v is high and not greatly different from c, the first three or four terms are also required for calculations and the Doppler formula from Newtonian mechanics is not valid.

Since the emitting atoms and molecules of a gas are moving with random velocities, the thousands of photons entering the slit of a spectrograph produce a broadened spectrum line having an intensity contour like that shown in Fig. 70B.

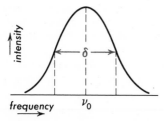

Fig. 70B   *Intensity contour of a spectrum line broadened by the Doppler effect.*

The frequency spread of this line is called the *half-intensity breadth*, and is given by the formula

$$\delta = 1.67 \frac{\nu_0}{c}\sqrt{\frac{2RT}{m}} \quad \text{(70c)}$$

The half-intensity breadth is defined as the interval between two points where the intensity drops to half its maximum value. In Eq.(70c) R is the general gas constant, T is the absolute temperature of the gas, and m is the atomic weight. This equation shows that the Doppler broadening is (1) proportional to the frequency ν_0, (2) proportional to the square root of the temperature, and (3) inversely proportional to the square root of the atomic weight. As an illustration of the use of Eq.(70c), consider the following example:

Example 1. Find the Doppler half-intensity breadth of the sodium yellow line $\lambda = 5890$ Å if the light source temperature is 500°K.

Solution. The general gas constant can be found in any book of tables of physical constants and has the value 8.32 joules/mole/K°, and the molecular weight of sodium is 23×10^{-3} Kg/mole.* By direct substitution in Eq.(70c), we obtain

$$\delta = \frac{1.67}{5.89 \times 10^{-7}\,\text{m}}\sqrt{\frac{2 \times 8.32\,\dfrac{\text{Kg m}^2}{\text{mole K° s}}\,500\text{K°}}{23 \times 10^{-3}\,\dfrac{\text{Kg}}{\text{mole}}}}$$

$$\delta = \frac{1.67}{5.89 \times 10^{-7}\,\text{m}}\sqrt{3.62 \times 10^5\,\frac{\text{m}^2}{\text{s}^2}}$$

$$\delta = 1.68 \times 10^9\,\frac{\text{vib}}{\text{s}}$$

To change this to wave numbers, divide by $c = 3 \times 10^{10}$ cm/s.

$$\delta = 0.056\,\text{cm}^{-1}$$

Since $\lambda = 5890$ Å corresponds to a wave-number frequency of 16,980 cm^{-1}, the wave-number breadth of 0.056 cm^{-1} corresponds to a wavelength breadth of only

$$\delta_\lambda = \frac{0.056 \times 5890}{16,980} = 0.0194\,\text{A}$$

Experimental observations are in keeping with Eq.(70c); to produce sharper lines in any given spectrum the temperature must be lowered. Furthermore the lines produced by the lighter elements in the periodic table are in general broader than those produced by the heavy elements.

* A mole is defined as a mass of a substance equal to the molecular weight. Since sodium has an atomic weight of 23, 1 mole of pure sodium weighs 23 grams. The number of molecules in one mole of a substance is given by Avogadro's number, i.e., 6.02×10^{23} molecules. This is the number of sodium atoms in 23 g of sodium metal.

Figure 70C is a graph of the same spectrum line produced by a high-temperature source such as an electric spark, and a low-temperature source such as a liquid-air-cooled gaseous discharge.

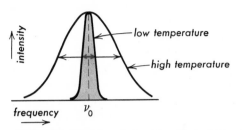

Fig. 70C *Comparison of Doppler line widths for spectrum lines from a hot and cold light source.*

70.2. Natural Breadths of Spectrum Lines. According to quantum mechanics, an energy-level diagram of an atom is not to be thought of as a set of sharp discrete levels but a sort of continuous distribution of energy possibilities with pronounced peaks as shown in Fig. 70D. This

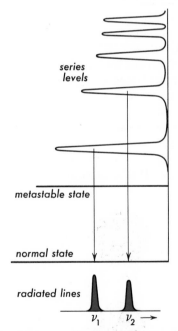

Fig. 70D *Schematic diagram illustrating the natural breadths of atomic energy levels and spectrum lines.*

is a kind of graph in which the energy is plotted vertically and the probability of an electron's

being excited to an upper level is plotted horizontally.

When an electron is excited to an upper level, it has a high probability of arriving at an energy value at or near one of the peaks before it returns to the normal state and emits light. Since there is a high probability it may go slightly higher or lower than the center of each peak, the spectrum lines arising from transitions to lower levels will give rise to a so-called *natural breadth* of the observed spectrum lines.

The longer an electron remains in an excited state, the greater is the probability it will arrive at the peak energy value before jumping back down. For this reason *metastable states*, with their relatively long average lifetime t, will be quite narrow, as is the *normal state*. The shorter the average lifetime in an excited state, the wider it will be. The natural half-value widths of energy levels are given by the simple relation

$$\delta_n = \frac{1}{2\pi t} \qquad (70d)$$

where for many levels in neutral atoms, t is approximately 10^{-8} s. For the yellow lines of the sodium spectrum the natural half-intensity breadth is only 0.000116 Å, a value a hundred times smaller than the Doppler width from normal gas discharge tubes.

In most spectrum lines the natural width is so narrow as to be completely masked by Doppler broadening.

An explanation of the natural breadth of energy levels is to be found in *Heisenberg's uncertainty principle* (see Sec. 61.8). Instead of writing $\hbar$ as the product of *momentum times velocity*, it may be written as the product of *energy times time:* $\hbar = 1.0544 \times 10^{-34}$ J s:

$$\Delta E \times \Delta t = h \qquad (70e)$$

In this equation ΔE represents the uncertainty of the energy when the uncertainty of the time is Δt. If an atom remains in the normal state for a long time, the uncertainty of the energy value is small and the level is sharp. If the electron is excited to an upper level where it remains for an extremely short time, the uncertainty of the energy value is greater and the level is widened.

In other words, an electron excited toward an upper level may have little time to settle into the peak position before jumping down again.

70.3. The Stark Effect. Although the splitting up of spectrum lines in a magnetic field was discovered by Zeeman as early as 1897, some 16 years elapsed before anyone succeeded in showing that a similar effect is produced when a source of light is placed in an electric field.

In 1913 J. Stark demonstrated that every line of the Balmer series of hydrogen, when the source was located in a uniform electric field of 100,000 V/cm, is split into a number of components. A greatly enlarged photograph of the red hydrogen line $\lambda = 6562$ Å is shown in Fig. 70E.

Fig. 70E   *Observed Stark-effect pattern for the red line of hydrogen, H_α, $\lambda = 6562$ Å.*

The origin of the Stark effect is to be found in energy levels themselves. In an electric field many of the energy levels that are otherwise single are split up into a number of component levels. As in the Zeeman effect, where the atoms are in a magnetic field, the levels form a pattern that is symmetrical about the field-free level. The stronger the electric-field intensity, the wider is the splitting.

Not all levels of the same atoms are split the same amount in any given field. Some levels are widely spaced, while others are close together and some remain single. In general the widest splitting occurs for levels arising from non-penetrating electron orbits. These are the orbits of valence electrons that are nearly circular on the orbital model and correspond to the D and F levels of the elements in the first two columns of the periodic table.

In an ordinary arc, where no external electric field is applied to the light source, many ions are produced which upon collision with other atoms give rise to strong electric fields. The effect of these intermolecular heterogeneous fields is to produce varying amounts of splitting of the energy levels of atoms, resulting in a broadening of the observed spectrum lines. This is the origin of the diffuseness of the so-called *diffuse series* of lines observed in many spectra. The sharp series, on the other hand, involves levels that show little or no splitting in strong electric fields.

70.4. Gamma-Ray Spectrum Lines. Gamma rays emitted by radioactive nuclei, like visible light emitted by the external electron structure of atoms, show a finite breadth when photographed with an appropriate γ-ray spectrograph. Gamma-ray spectrographs are identical in principle and similar in construction to X-ray spectrographs, and γ-ray spectrograms are similar in appearance to X-ray spectrograms (see Figs. 53I and 53J). In a gas at room temperature, radioactive atoms, like stable atoms, move about with different velocities. The emission of γ rays by randomly moving nuclei will, therefore, give rise to a Doppler broadening as shown in Fig. 70B.

Because γ rays have extremely high frequencies, their photon energies $h\nu$ and momenta $h\nu/c$ are thousands of times greater than for visible light, and upon emission by a nucleus give rise to an appreciable recoil energy and momentum. This is illustrated schematically in Fig. 70F.

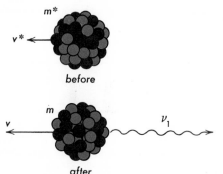

Fig. 70F   *Diagram of γ-ray frequency change due to Doppler effect and nuclear recoil.*

Before disintegration the excited nucleus of mass m^* is moving with a random velocity v^*. As a result of γ-ray emission the recoiling nucleus acquires additional momentum and the γ ray loses momentum. Momentum balance therefore requires

$$m^*v^* = mv + \frac{h\nu_1}{c} \qquad (70f)$$

before   after

Conservation of energy also applies to the process, giving

$$E^*_n = E_n + E_\gamma$$

or

$$\tfrac{1}{2}m^*v^{*2} = \tfrac{1}{2}mv^2 + h\nu_1 \qquad (70g)$$

before   after

It is important to note that the frequency ν_1 is not the frequency ν_0 that would be observed if the nuclear mass were at rest.

Since the nuclei producing any given line all have the same mass, and emit γ rays of the same energy $h\nu_0$, the observed frequency loss r due to recoil and the broadening δ due to the Doppler effect have the result shown in Fig. 70G. If a

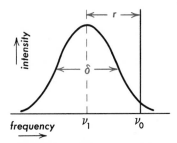

Fig. 70G *Frequency–intensity graph for γ-ray emission showing Doppler width δ and recoil frequency shift r.*

nuclear mass could be steadily increased, momentum and energy balance would still hold, but the energy of nuclear recoil would decrease, and the maximum of ν_1 would approach ν_0.

70.5. Optical and Gamma-Ray Resonance Absorption. When a beam of yellow light from a sodium lamp is made to pass through a glass vessel containing sodium vapor, strong absorption occurs. The atomic processes taking place under these conditions are a kind of resonance phenomenon commonly observed with sound waves.

A good demonstration in sound is shown in Fig. 70H. Two tuning forks with exactly the same natural frequency, that is, with the same pitch, are mounted on separate sounding boards. Fork A is set vibrating for a moment and then stopped. Fork B will then be found to be vibrating.

Fig. 70H *An experiment for demonstrating resonance between two identical tuning forks.*

Each sound pulse that emerges with each wave from fork A passes by the other fork, pushing with just the right frequency to set fork B vibrating. Such resonance absorption will fail if there is a frequency mismatch between the second fork and the passing waves. If fork A is moved rapidly away from or toward fork B, such a mismatch due to the Doppler effect will prevent resonance.

An analogous demonstration of resonance absorption with visible light is shown in Fig. 70I. Light from a sodium lamp in passing

Fig. 70I *An experiment for demonstrating resonance between sodium atoms.*

through a sodium flame of a Bunsen burner casts a pronounced dark shadow on a nearby screen. A small piece of asbestos paper soaked in common table salt, NaCl, and placed in an ordinary gas flame can be used to produce an abundance of free sodium atoms.

The atomic process of resonance absorption taking place in this experiment is shown in Fig. 70J. An excited atom in the sodium lamp emits, for example, a wave $\lambda = 5890$ Å by the downward transition from the $3^2P_{3/2}$ excited level to the $3^2S_{1/2}$ normal state (see Fig. 52G).

Fig. 70J *Energy-level diagram illustrating light emission and resonance absorption between two sodium atoms.*

This wave on coming close to a normal sodium atom in the flame will be absorbed and raise the single valence electron to the $3^2P_{3/2}$ level. This second atom will in turn emit the same frequency again, to be absorbed by another atom in the flame, or to escape from the flame in some random direction. Because re-emission will be in a random direction and seldom in the original direction from the lamp, a shadow will be cast.

When an experiment analogous to this is performed with gamma rays, various difficulties are encountered. Because an appreciable amount of the energy of a gamma ray emitted by a radioactive atom is given up to the recoiling nucleus, the frequency of the emitted wave is reduced sufficiently from ν_0 to cause a mismatch between the gamma-ray frequency ν and the natural frequency ν_0 of another nucleus of the same isotope (see Fig. 70G). Furthermore, the recoil of a second nucleus resulting from a gamma-ray impact would give rise to an even greater mismatch.

Intensity–frequency graphs for gamma emission and absorption by identical nuclides are given in Fig. 70K. If the radioactive source, and the target on which the γ rays impinge, are at the same temperature, the Doppler broadening will be the same for both.

The area of overlap of the two curves indicates conditions where resonance absorption might

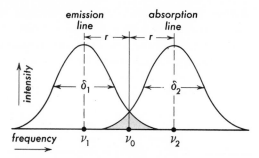

Fig. 70K *Frequency–intensity graphs for γ-ray emission and absorption lines, showing Doppler widths δ, recoil shifts r, and overlap frequencies.*

be expected to occur. For example, a point at ν_0 corresponds to an event in which a radioactive nucleus is approaching the target at the time of emission and has sufficient kinetic energy to compensate for the energy loss required for recoil. If this emitted γ ray of frequency ν_0 encounters a normal target nucleus moving toward the oncoming wave with an appropriate kinetic energy, resonance absorption can occur. The small overlap area would indicate, however, that resonance absorption under the conditions described should be very small.

70.6. The Mossbauer Effect. The phenomenon of resonance absorption with γ rays was predicted by W. Kuhn in 1921 and first observed by P. B. Moon in 1951. A major breakthrough occurred in 1958, when the phenomenon of recoilless nuclear resonance absorption was discovered by R. L. Mossbauer.

This new absorption effect provided a means for eliminating the energy losses by recoil, both at the source and at the receiver. As an additional feature of the discovery, gamma-ray spectrum lines of extreme narrowness have been produced, which may be useful for other research experiments.

According to the principles described in Sec. 70.4, the loss of energy to a recoiling nucleus could be suppressed by rigidly fastening the emitting nuclei, as well as the absorbing nuclei, to an infinitely heavy mass. An experimental method for doing this is the binding of nuclei to a crystal lattice.

To reduce Doppler broadening, the γ-ray source and absorber are cooled to extremely low temperatures. This is accomplished by immersing the radioactive crystal source and the crystal absorber in a liquid helium bath.

At temperatures close to absolute zero, atomic vibrations within the crystal lattice are reduced to practically zero, so that during emission or absorption the atoms have little or no motion. Under these conditions Doppler broadening is reduced to practically zero and the observed line reveals its natural line breadth (see Figs. 70C and 70D).

The elimination of atomic vibrations within the crystal lattice has another important effect. Atomic vibrations are quantized, that is, vibration energies have discrete values which may be represented by spaced energy levels. When atoms are in their lowest vibrational energy state, as they are when the crystal is at absolute zero, the recoil energy of a gamma ray is not always sufficient to raise an atom to the next vibrational state. Under these conditions the binding of a nucleus with its neighbors is such that an appreciable part of the crystal lattice takes up any γ-ray recoil momentum. Because the crystal mass is so large, the recoil energy is practically zero, and the value of r in Fig. 70K is reduced to zero. Gamma-ray emission or absorption under these conditions is said to be *recoilless*.

With the Doppler effect and nuclear recoil both reduced to zero, only the natural line breadths are involved in nuclear resonance absorption.

A diagram of Mossbauer's apparatus is shown in Fig. 70L. Gamma rays from a source at M pass through a narrow channel C and a thin

target A, to where they fall on a scintillation counter S. The lead shielding around the source and the detector is for the purpose of reducing all extraneous radiation to a minimum.

To detect resonance absorption in A, the source is set into rotation as indicated by an arrow and the detector turned on only when the source is moving in line with the absorber. This motion introduces a Doppler shift d, that is, a slight increase or decrease in the frequency of the gamma rays. The effect is illustrated by shifting the red curve in Fig. 70M to the right or to the

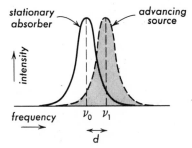

Fig. 70M *Graphs of the natural breadths of γ-ray lines from radioactive crystals at low temperatures near absolute zero.*

left. The mismatch in frequency between the γ rays from the moving source and the nuclei in the stationary absorber reduces the number of photons absorbed. The faster the source moves toward or away from the target, the greater the Doppler shift is and the greater the number of γ rays reaching the counter.

Figure 70N is a graph from Mossbauer's

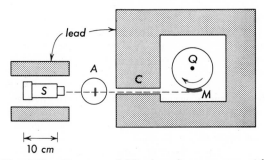

Fig. 70L *Diagram of Mossbauer's apparatus with which he discovered recoilless emission and absorption of γ rays.*

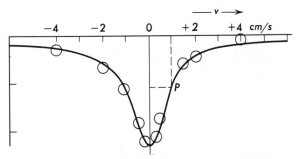

Fig. 70N *Transmission of the 0.129 MeV γ radiation through a resonance absorber of iridium-191, measured at different velocities of the source. (After Mossbauer.)*

original experiment, performed by using the 0.129-MeV gamma rays from iridium-191. Note that the greatest absorption occurs when the source is at rest. Observe also the extremely low velocities required to produce a Doppler mismatch in frequency. The latter is a clear indication of the narrowness of γ-ray spectrum lines and shows that one is observing natural line breadths rather than Doppler broadening (see Figs. 70B and 70D). The mean lifetime of the Ir^{191} transition can be calculated from the half-width of the curve in Fig. 70N and Eq.(70e).

To make this calculation we first find the γ-ray frequency ν_0 by means of the equation $Ve = h\nu$.

$$\nu_0 = \frac{Ve}{h} = \frac{1.29 \times 10^5 \times 1.6 \times 10^{-19}}{6.6 \times 10^{-34}}$$

$$= 3.13 \times 10^{19} \frac{\text{vib}}{\text{s}}$$

The half-width at half-intensity of the resonance curve in Fig. 70N, point P, is approximately 1 cm/s, or 1×10^{-2} m/s. If we now use the Doppler formula, Eq.(70b), to find the corresponding change in frequency $\Delta\nu$, where $\Delta\nu = \nu - \nu_0$, we obtain

$$\Delta\nu = \nu_0 \frac{v}{c} = 3.13 \times \frac{10^{19} \times 1 \times 10^{-2}}{3 \times 10^8}$$

$$= 1.04 \times 10^9 \frac{\text{vib}}{\text{s}}$$

Since $E = h\nu$, we can write $\Delta E = h\,\Delta\nu$, and use Eq.(70e) to find Δt:

$$\Delta t = \frac{h}{\Delta E} = \frac{h}{h\,\Delta\nu} = \frac{1}{\Delta\nu}$$

or

$$\Delta t = \frac{1}{1.04 \times 10^9} = 9.6 \times 10^{-10} \text{ s}$$

The mean life of this gamma-ray energy state is, therefore, 9.6×10^{-10} s.

The nuclear energy levels of Ir^{191} involved in Mossbauer's experiment are shown in Fig. 70O.

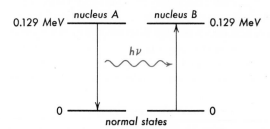

Fig. 70O *Energy-level diagram illustrating γ-ray emission and resonance absorption between two iridium-191 nuclei.*

Many experimenters have confirmed Mossbauer's discovery and recoilless γ-ray transitions have been observed in fifteen or more radioactive nuclei. For his discovery Mossbauer was awarded, jointly with Hofstader, the 1961 Nobel Prize in physics (see Appendix XII).

PROBLEMS

1. A distant star is found to be approaching the earth at a speed of 2.700×10^6 m/s. Its spectrum shows that its surface contains a large amount of calcium. In the laboratory the violet line from a calcium discharge tube has a wavelength of 3968.000 Å. Find (a) the frequency of this violet light, (b) the difference between this frequency and the frequency of the light coming from the star, (c) this frequency difference in wave numbers, and (d) the wavelength shift in angstroms. Carry both frequencies to seven significant figures.

2. A distant star is found to be approaching the earth at a speed of 4.5×10^6 m/s. Its spectrum reveals that its surface is composed largely of hydrogen. In the laboratory the red line of the Balmer series, observed with a hydrogen discharge tube, has a wavelength of 6562 Å. What is (a) the frequency of this laboratory light, (b) the difference between this frequency and the frequency of the light

coming from the star, (c) this same frequency shift in wave numbers, and (d) the wavelength shift in angstroms? [*Ans.* (a) 4.57×10^{14} vib/s. (b) 6.86×10^{12} vib/s. (c) 229 cm^{-1}. (d) 98.4 Å.]

3. When the spectrum lines from a distant star are measured, they are all found to be shifted to shorter wavelengths than when they are produced in the laboratory. The yellow line of sodium, for example, is not at its normal wavelength of 5890 Å, but at 5840 Å. Find (a) the frequency of the normal sodium light, (b) the frequency of the light from the star, (c) the frequency difference, and (d) the velocity of the star with respect to the earth. Carry both frequencies to six significant figures.

4. When the spectrum of the light from a distant star is observed and measured, the lines are found to be shifted to shorter wavelengths than when they are produced in the laboratory. The green line of iron, for example, is not

at its normal wavelength of 5270 Å, but at 5240 Å. Find (a) the frequency of the normal green line, (b) the frequency of the corresponding line from the star, (c) the frequency difference, and (d) the velocity of the star with respect to the earth. [*Ans.* (a) 5.692×10^{14} vib/s. (b) 5.725×10^{14} vib/s. (c) 3.3×10^{12} vib/s. (d) 1.74×10^6 m/s.]

5. Find the Doppler half-intensity breadth of the hydrogen red line $\lambda = 6562$ Å, if the light source is at 2000°K: (a) in vib/s, (b) in wave numbers, and (c) in angstroms.

6. Find the Doppler half-intensity breadth of the mercury green line $\lambda = 5461$ Å, if the light source is at 1000°K; (a) in vib/s, (b) in wave numbers, and (c) in

angstroms. [*Ans.* (a) 8.81×10^8 vib/s. (b) 0.0294 cm^{-1}. (c) 0.00877 Å.]

7. If the Mossbauer experiment is performed with a 5-MeV gamma ray from a radioactive source and the half-width at half-intensity of the resonance curve (see Fig. 70N) is 2.2 cm/s, find (a) the frequency of the gamma ray, (b) the Doppler shift in vib/s, and (c) the mean life of the gamma-ray state.

8. If the Mossbauer experiment is performed with a 1.80-MeV gamma ray from a radioactive source and the half-width at half-intensity of the resonance curve (see Fig. 70N) is 1.2 cm/s, find (a) the frequency of the gamma ray, (b) the Doppler shift in vib/s, and (c) the mean life of the gamma-ray state. [*Ans.* (a) 4.36×10^{20} vib/s. (b) 1.74×10^{10} vib/s. (c) 5.75×10^{-11} s]

THE ATOMIC NUCLEUS

Although the disintegrations of different nuclei give rise to many different kinds of particles or units of energy, it would appear that we need assume only two kinds of particles existing within the nucleus—*neutrons* and *protons*. If this is correct, our task becomes the difficult one of explaining not only the disintegration mechanism of an unstable nucleus but the binding forces that hold a stable nucleus together. An answer to the latter question will serve as a starting point for the following presentations.

71.1. Nuclear Binding Forces. According to the *neutron–proton theory* of the atomic nucleus (see Fig. 71A), the deuteron nucleus contains

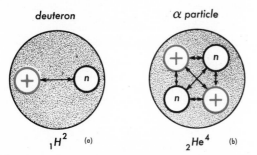

Fig. 71A *Schematic diagram of the nucleus for (a) a deuterium atom, and (b) a helium atom.*

only one neutron and one proton. Let us compare, therefore, the mass of one free proton and one free neutron with their mass when combined as a deuteron (for masses, see Appendix IX):

Neutron mass	$_0n^1$ =	1.008665
Hydrogen mass	$_1H^1$ =	1.007825
	Sum =	2.016490
Deuteron mass	$_1H^2$ =	2.014103

The difference in mass of 0.002387 atomic mass unit (amu) is not due to inaccurate measurements of mass but is a real difference to be accounted for as the annihilation energy that binds the two particles together. When a neutron and proton come together to form a deuteron, a small part of their mass—namely, 0.002387 amu (equivalent to 2.22 MeV energy)—is radiated from the newly formed nucleus. At close approach, in other words, the two particles attract each other so strongly that once together, it takes the equivalent of a little more than 2 MeV of energy to pull them apart. This has been confirmed by a nuclear photoelectric effect, an experiment in which γ rays of 2.22 MeV energy or greater are found to break up deuterium nuclei into their constituent parts, while γ rays of lower energy have no effect. How neutrons and protons attract each other when very close together is a question of great importance, for we now realize that the stability of all the universe as we know it depends upon these forces.

Consider as a second example, the attractive forces between the four nucleons of a helium nucleus, i.e., the two neutrons and two protons of an α particle as shown in Fig. 71A. By combining the masses of the four free particles and comparing them with the mass of the helium atom, we obtain

$$2_0n^1 + 2_1H^1 = 4.032980 \text{ amu}$$
$$He^4 = \underline{4.002604 \text{ amu}}$$
$$\text{Mass difference} = 0.030376 \text{ amu}$$
$$E = 28.3 \text{ MeV}$$

This value of 28.3 MeV indicates a binding energy of approximately 7 MeV per nucleon, a value considerably higher than 2.2 MeV for the deuteron. This is a measure of the energy that

Fig. 71B *Binding energy per nucleon for the lightest elements in the periodic table.*

must be expended in breaking the attractive bonds shown in the diagram.

are given in the preceding chapter. One process not described there, and called the *nuclear photoelectric effect*, is shown in Fig. 71D. A photon of energy $h\nu$, passing close to a nucleus, is absorbed; part of the energy is used to remove a neutron or proton from the nucleus, and the remainder given to the particle as kinetic energy [see Eq.(50a)]:

$$h\nu = W + \tfrac{1}{2}mv^2 \qquad (71a)$$

The work function W, as we have seen above, is about 8 MeV and is essentially the energy required to create the extra mass needed by the nucleon to set it free.

71.2. The Packing Fraction. An informative method of displaying the mass differences and

Fig. 71C *Binding energy per nucleon for the stable isotopes of the periodic table.*

If we make similar calculations for other nuclides near the beginning of the periodic table, and plot a graph of the binding energy per nucleon, E/A, where A is the mass number, we obtain Fig. 71B. If this same procedure is carried out for the entire periodic table, a graph like the one shown in Fig. 71C is obtained. By drawing a horizontal line across the upper part of the graph at 8 MeV, as shown by the colored line, we obtain a kind of average binding energy per nucleon for nearly all the elements. This value is approximately the difference between unit atomic mass and the mass of a free neutron or proton.

Collisions between high-energy photons and nuclei, giving rise to several kinds of reactions,

binding energies of stable nuclei is to plot a graph of all packing fractions. The *packing*

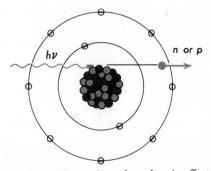

Fig. 71D *The nuclear photoelectric effect.*

fraction P of any nuclide is obtained from the relation

$$P = \frac{M - A}{A} \qquad (71b)$$

where $M - A$ for any nuclide is called its *mass defect:*

$$M = \text{mass of nuclide}$$
$$A = \text{mass number} \qquad (71c)$$

In other words, P is the difference between the average nucleon mass for that nuclide and unit atomic mass. It will be seen in Fig. 71E that the

all the way to zero separation, however, for as the two charges come very close together we know, from what has been said in the preceding section, there must be an attraction. Gamow proposed, therefore, that at close approach there is another law of force that comes into play and that this force is one of attraction for neutrons as well as protons and is very strong.

Since Coulomb's law is known to hold quite accurately at large distances, this added factor is called a *short-range force.* Graphs of Coulomb's law for repulsion and the short-range for at-

Fig. 71E　*Graph of the packing fraction for stable nuclei.*

very light and the heavy nuclides have an average mass per nucleon greater than unity, whereas those near the middle of the graph have a mass per nucleon less than unity. In the next chapter we shall see that these differences are directly related to the availability of nuclear energy.

71.3. The Nuclear Potential Barrier. Early in the development of ideas concerning nuclear disintegration, Gamow proposed a model by which one might represent the atomic nucleus. This model is based upon the forces acting between two positive charges and is an extension of the nuclear model described in Sec. 65.2, and illustrated in Figs. 65D and 65E.

Picture again a proton or an α particle, with its positive charge, approaching a positively charged nucleus. As the two charges come closer and closer together, they repel each other with greater and greater forces as given by Coulomb's law. This repulsion cannot continue to increase

traction are shown in Fig. 71F. Note that when the particle is at the distance shown, 9×10^{-13} cm, Coulomb's law of repulsion is predominant,

Fig. 71F　*The two force laws for a positive charge close to a nucleus.*

whereas, at a distance less than 2×10^{-13} cm, the short-range force of attraction predominates. Since both of these forces are effective for all distances, they should be combined into one graph as shown by the F curve in Fig. 71G. If

Fig. 71G   *Graphs of the force and potential energy of a positively charged particle close to a nucleus.*

instead of the force F we plot the potential energy stored between the two particles, we obtain the E_p curve shown by the dotted line. Such a curve represents what is called the *potential barrier* of the nucleus. The highest point of the barrier is frequently called the edge of the nucleus which, for heavy atoms in the periodic table, occurs at, and gives a nuclear radius of, from 1 to 8×10^{-13} cm (see Table 73A).

A very good model of the nucleus, having the form of a *well* or the *crater of a volcano*, can be made by rotating the dotted line around the vertical axis. When this is done we obtain the cross-section diagram in Fig. 71H. With this model the electrical potential energy, E_p, between the two positively charged particles is analogous to the potential energy of a ball at any point on the side of the hill, and the electrostatic force of repulsion is analogous to the force of gravity.

71.4. Bohr's Nuclear Model. In 1937 Niels Bohr, the famous Danish physicist, made another outstanding contribution to modern physics when he improved Gamow's model of the nucleus by extending what is sometimes called the *waterdrop model* of the nucleus. Bohr and his collaborator Kalkar imagined the many particles

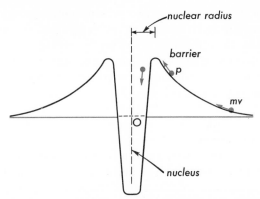

Fig. 71H   *A graphical model of the atomic nucleus as proposed by Gamow. The potential barrier of a nucleus to an approaching positive charge is analogous to the crater of a volcano.*

in a heavy nucleus as moving about within a spherical enclosure with motions analogous to the molecules in a drop of water. The surface of the spherical enclosure, which is the top of the potential barrier as represented in Fig. 71I, is analogous to the surface tension which holds a small waterdrop to its spherical form.

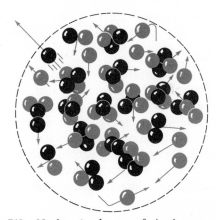

Fig. 71I   *Nucleus in the act of ejecting a neutron, based upon the Bohr–Gamow waterdrop model.*

Just as the rapid motion of the molecules in water is a measure of the temperature, so Bohr speaks of the rapid motion of the neutrons and protons within the spherical boundary of the nucleus as a sort of *pseudotemperature*. To explain disintegration, the analogy is drawn that the ejection of a particle from the nucleus is like the evaporation of a water molecule from a drop of water. Just as a rise in temperature brings about a more rapid evaporation of water, so an increase in the motions within the nucleus gives rise to a higher probability of disintegration.

In a stable nucleus, the particles within are moving about with very little kinetic energy and are in the analogous state of a relatively low temperature. When a high-speed particle from outside penetrates the potential barrier, it is accelerated toward the center of the nucleus and acquires a very high kinetic energy before it collides with one or more of the particles inside. Soon the energy becomes divided among the many particles, and the nucleus takes on a higher temperature state. The potential-well model of this same condition is shown in Fig. 71J.

Fig. 71J   *Well model representing an unstable nucleus.*

Now, as the particles move about inside, there is a certain probability or chance that, within a given interval of time, some one particle will be hit by several particles, giving it a sufficiently high velocity in an outward direction to permit an escape through the potential barrier. The more rapid the internal motions, that is, the higher the temperature, the greater is this chance of escape.

A direct disintegration may be described in this way: If upon entering the nucleus a high-speed particle like a proton adds sufficient energy to give the nucleus a high temperature, another particle like a neutron or an α particle may be ejected immediately. Since such an ejected particle has to be supplied with a certain minimum energy to get free, the remaining particles will be slowed down, and the nucleus will have a lower temperature.

71.5. Nuclear Demonstration Models. A demonstration model illustrating the capture of a high-speed proton or an α particle by a nucleus, prior to disintegration, is shown in Fig. 71K. Marbles rolled down the incline represent the speeding-up of atomic projectiles by an accelerator like the cyclotron. Approaching the potential barrier, a marble may roll part way up and then be deflected off to one side, illustrating elastic scattering of the kind observed by Rutherford. If the initial velocity is high enough the marble may go over the top of the barrier and drop into the crater opening at the top, representing a capture prior to disintegration.

A demonstration of what happens inside the nucleus is illustrated by another model as shown in Fig. 71L. In this case the vertical scale of the barrier has of necessity been reduced, i.e., flattened out. When a marble is rolled down the incline and into the group of marbles at the center of the barrier, there may be several collisions before another particle usually goes bouncing out on the other side. This corresponds to a direct disintegration where one particle like a proton goes in and a neutron comes out.

If a single particle does not emerge, most of the

Fig. 71K   *Mechanical model of a nucleus for demonstrating the capture of a high-speed proton, deuteron, or α particle, prior to disintegration.*

Fig. 71L *Mechanical model of a nucleus for demonstrating (a) the increased kinetic energy of nuclear particles after a capture and (b) the chance probability of radioactive decay or disintegration by the ejection of a particle.*

Fig. 71M *A graphical model of the nucleus as it is presented to an approaching neutron or proton.*

particles inside take on random motions, colliding with each other much the same as do the molecules or atoms in a gas or liquid. To prevent friction from stopping them (there is no friction in an atom), the marbles are continually agitated by a small pin protruding from underneath the barrier. This pin is mounted slightly off center at the end of the shaft of a small electric motor. If the motor is left running for some time, a single marble will eventually be hit by several particles moving in the same direction and will recoil with sufficient speed to carry it over the barrier and out. This corresponds to a disintegration or radioactive decay, which takes place according to the *laws of chance*, and to the resultant drop in "temperature" of the nucleus.

The faster the motor runs, the greater is the internal agitation and chance of ejection, and the shorter is the so-called half-life of the element.

71.6. Nuclear Model for Neutron Disintegrations. When a neutron approaches a nucleus prior to a disintegration, it does not encounter a potential barrier of the type already described for protons and α particles. A neutron has no charge, so that at large distances it is not repelled by the positively charged nucleus. It may, therefore, approach a nucleus with very little speed of its own and be captured when it comes too close. At very close range the short-range attractive force shown in Fig. 71F sets in, and draws the two together.

To an approaching neutron, the nucleus acts as though it were a pit into which the particle will fall. This is illustrated by the flat potential curve in Fig. 71M. The marble rolling along the horizontal plane toward the pit represents the influence of the nucleus upon the neutron's

motion, whereas the marble rolling up the hill (dotted line) represents the influence of the same nucleus upon the motion of a proton. A mechanical model patterned after Fig. 71K, and made with the neutron-barrier shape, offers an excellent demonstration of neutron scattering and capture.

71.7. Nuclear Spin. Approximately $\frac{1}{3}$ of all known stable nuclei, and many of the radioactive nuclides, are known to have a mechanical moment p_J and a magnetic moment μ_J. The earliest evidence for a nuclear spin, as it is called, was found in atomic spectra. Many spectrum lines show a fine structure which in Sec. 52.4 was explained as being due to electron spin. Many of these fine-structure lines show a still finer structure, now known to be due to a nuclear spin (see Sec. 57.5, and Figs. 57J and 57K).

As an additional example of this *hyperfine structure*, as it is called, several of the spectrum lines of the element praseodymium are shown in Fig. 71N. In a normal spectrogram these look like single lines, but under the high dispersion and magnification shown here, each line reveals six hyperfine components. The six components signify that the nucleus of praseodymium has a spin angular momentum $p_J = \frac{5}{2}\hbar$ and a large magnetic moment.

The angular momenta of nuclei in general are given by

$$p_J = J\hbar \qquad (71d)$$

where J is the nuclear spin quantum number, and $\hbar$ represents unit angular momentum given by $h/2\pi$ [see Eq.(52b)]. Quantitative experiments show that this *quantum number, J,* can take half-integral as well as whole-number values (see Table 71A).

$$\lambda = 4382 \qquad 4672 \qquad 4877 \qquad 4651 \qquad 4685 \qquad 4578 \text{ Å}$$

Fig. 71N Photographs of the hyperfine structure of a few of the spectrum lines of the element praseodymium, Z = 59. Wavelengths are in Angstrom units; structure produced by nuclear spin.

The magnetic moments of nuclei in general are extremely small as compared with those associated with electrons in the outer structures of atoms. For all nuclei the magnetic moment is given by the relation

$$\mu_J = g\hbar \frac{e}{2M} \qquad (71e)$$

where the g factor varies from nucleus to nucleus, $\hbar$ is unit angular momentum, and M is the mass of the proton. The last two factors involve fixed atomic constants, and combined are called the *nuclear magneton*. One nuclear magneton is given by

$$\mu_n = \hbar \frac{e}{2M} \qquad (71f)$$

or

$$\mu_n = 5.050 \times 10^{-27} \text{ ampere meters}^2$$

The g factor therefore gives the nuclear magnetic moment in nuclear magnetons. *Note that one nuclear magneton is $\frac{1}{1836}$ of one Bohr magneton* [see Eq.(52f)].

A list of a few nuclides in Table 71A shows typical values of the nuclear spin quantum number J, and the measured magnetic moments in nuclear magnetons.

71.8. Proton and Neutron Spin. Every proton, whether it is bound to an atom or is free, has a spin angular momentum of $\frac{1}{2}\hbar$ (see Fig. 71O):

$$p_{\text{proton}} = \tfrac{1}{2}\hbar \qquad (71g)$$

Having a positive charge, the magnetic field around a proton is parallel to its mechanical moment, instead of oppositely directed as is the case with an electron (see Fig. 52F). Furthermore, since the mass of a proton is 1836 times the mass of an electron, it maintains the same angular momentum by spinning much slower, and this reduces its magnetic moment to a

TABLE 71A. TYPICAL NUCLEAR SPINS AND MAGNETIC MOMENTS

	J	g Factor
$_1\text{H}^1$	$\frac{1}{2}$	+2.792
$_1\text{H}^2$	1	+0.857
$_3\text{Li}^6$	1	+0.82
$_3\text{Li}^7$	$\frac{3}{2}$	+3.26
$_4\text{Be}^9$	$\frac{3}{2}$	−1.18
$_5\text{B}^{10}$	3	+1.80
$_7\text{N}^{14}$	1	+4.01
$_8\text{O}^{16}$	0	0
$_8\text{O}^{17}$	$\frac{5}{2}$	−1.89
$_8\text{O}^{18}$	0	0
$_{23}\text{V}^{51}$	$\frac{7}{2}$	+5.15
$_{25}\text{Mn}^{55}$	$\frac{5}{2}$	+3.47
$_{50}\text{Sn}^{119}$	$\frac{1}{2}$	−1.05
$_{55}\text{Cs}^{135}$	$\frac{7}{2}$	+2.73
$_{73}\text{Ta}^{181}$	$\frac{7}{2}$	+2.1
$_{80}\text{Hg}^{198}$	0	0
$_{80}\text{Hg}^{199}$	$\frac{1}{2}$	+0.50
$_{80}\text{Hg}^{200}$	0	0
$_{80}\text{Hg}^{201}$	$\frac{3}{2}$	−0.56
$_{83}\text{Bi}^{209}$	$\frac{9}{2}$	+4.08

relatively small value. The magnetic moment of a proton is found by precision experimental measurements to be

$$\mu_{\text{proton}} = 2.792 \text{ nuclear magnetons} \qquad (71h)$$

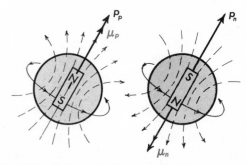

Fig. 71O Schematic diagrams showing proton and neutron spins and associated magnetic moments.

The neutron, like the proton and electron, has a spin angular momentum of $\frac{1}{2}\hbar$:

$$p_{neutron} = \frac{1}{2}\hbar \qquad (71i)$$

Having no net charge, the neutron might well be expected to have zero magnetic moment. Experimentally, however, its spin does produce a magnetic field, and one that is oppositely directed to angular momentum (see Fig. 71O). The neutron's magnetic moment is

$$\mu_{neutron} = -1.913 \text{ nuclear magnetons} \qquad (71j)$$

A negative magnetic moment is a clear indication that the neutron is a complex particle containing negative and positive charges in equal amounts, and that the negative charge is, on the average, farther from its axis of rotation.

71.9. The Deuteron. The deuteron is a nuclear particle composed of one proton and one neutron. Its known spin of $J = 1$ (see Table 71A) indicates that the spins of the two particles are parallel to each other as shown in Fig. 71P.

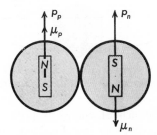

Fig. 71P *Schematic diagram of the deuteron, showing proton and neutron spins parallel and magnetic moments opposing.*

Since the two magnetic moments are oppositely directed, the resultant magnetic moment of the combination should be 2.792 − 1.913, or 0.879 nuclear magnetons. Precision measurements, however, show that μ_d is slightly smaller than this, and is

$$\mu_{deuteron} = 0.857 \text{ nuclear magnetons} \qquad (71k)$$

71.10. Nuclear Shell Model. A reasonably successful theory* of nuclear spins and magnetic

* For their development of the theory of the nature of the shell structure of the atomic nucleus, Maria Goeppert-Mayer of California, J. Hans D. Jensen of Heidelberg, and Eugene Wigner of Princeton were jointly awarded the 1963 Nobel Prize in physics.

moments is based upon the electron spin–orbit model so successful in explaining the outer structure of atoms (see Sec. 52.5). Experimental evidence for this idea stems in large measure from a classification of all stable nuclides as to their odd or even numbers of protons and neutrons (see Table 71B).

While all nucleons have a spin of $\frac{1}{2}\hbar$, neutrons and protons appear to pair off with opposing spins, thus canceling both the mechanical moments and magnetic moments. While the positive magnetic moments (see Table 71A) are probably

TABLE 71B. CLASSIFICATION OF KNOWN
STABLE NUCLIDES

Z protons	N neutrons	Known stable nuclides	Nuclear spin J
odd	odd	4	1, 2, 3, 4
odd	even	50	$\frac{1}{2}, \frac{3}{2}, \frac{5}{2}, \frac{7}{2}, \frac{9}{2}$
even	odd	55	$\frac{1}{2}, \frac{3}{2}, \frac{5}{2}, \frac{7}{2}, \frac{9}{2}$
even	even	165	0

due to *odd protons*, and the negative magnetic moments to *odd neutrons*, the wide range in values and the half-integral values of J in the *odd–even* and *even–odd* nuclides suggests orbital motions.

By analogy with the electron structure of atoms, orbital quantum numbers $l = 0, 1, 2, 3, \ldots$, for $s, p, d, f, g, \ldots$, respectively, are assigned to all nucleons. If the odd orbital nucleon is a proton, its positive charge and spin will give rise to two positive magnetic moments (see Fig. 71Q). If l and s are parallel as in the diagram, so that $j = l + s$, the magnetic moments will add; if l and s are oppositely directed,

Fig. 71Q *Schematic diagrams of proton and neutron orbits around nuclei.*

$j = l - s$, the magnetic moments will subtract.

For a proton the orbital angular momentum is given by

$$p_l = l\hbar$$

and the associated orbital magnetic moment by

$$\mu_l = l\hbar \frac{e}{2M}$$

By adding or subtracting the spin magnetic moment μ_{proton} [see Eq.(71h)], we obtain the expected total nuclear magnetic moment μ_J. While experimentally determined values of μ_J do not agree exactly with the values calculated by this simple model, they are in surprisingly good agreement.

If the orbital nucleon is a neutron, its orbital motion cannot give rise to an orbital magnetic moment (see Fig. 71Q). Neutron spin, however, does have a negative magnetic moment, and the magnitude of its contribution to the entire nucleus will depend upon its orientation with respect to the nuclear spin axis.

Some success with the application of the Pauli exclusion principle, applied to the filling of proton and neutron subshells, has been achieved (see Sec. 52.9). The experimental evidence that such closed subshells exist in nuclei is to be found in a number of nuclear properties. If the binding energy, angular momentum, or magnetic moment is plotted against proton number Z or neutron number N, discontinuities occur when either Z or N has the value 2, 8, 14, 20, 28, 50, 82, and 126. While these so-called "magic numbers" seem to represent closed shells and subshells, much is yet to be learned about the structure of atomic nuclei.

71.11. Mesic Atoms. Because of the Coulomb attractive forces between unlike charges, negatively charged mesons have a far greater probability of being captured by atomic nuclei than have their positively charged antiparticles (see Fig. 74P). There is a certain probability that as π^- and μ^- particles pass through matter they may be captured in any one of a number of outside orbits to form a kind of Bohr atom.

All equations derived for hydrogen can be applied to such mesic atoms by replacing the proton charge $+e$ by the nuclear charge $+Ze$, where Z is the atomic number. When this is done, Eq.(51c) for the radius of circular orbits becomes

$$r = \frac{n^2 h^2}{4\pi^2 me^2 kZ} \qquad (71l)$$

where m is the particle mass and n is the principal quantum number. The innermost orbit for hydrogen and its electron, where $n = 1$ and $Z = 1$, has a radius $r_1 = 5.28 \times 10^{-9}$ cm.

Since the radius varies inversely as the mass of the orbiting particle, the radius of the allowed orbits, $n = 1, 2, 3, 4$, etc., for π and μ mesic atoms will be about $\frac{1}{273} r_1 n^2$ and $\frac{1}{207} r_1 n^2$, respectively. Around a proton, the π^- orbit, $n = 1$, would have a radius of 1.93×10^{-11} cm, and for $n = 2$ a radius four times this. In an atom like $_{35}\text{Br}^{79}$, the innermost π^- orbit would be only $1/35 \times 273$, or $\frac{1}{9555}$ as large as the normal hydrogen atom, and the meson would be just skimming the surface of the nucleus with a radius of 5.53×10^{-13} cm (see Fig. 71R).

Fig. 71R *Schematic orbital diagram of a π mesonic atom—phosphorus, $_{15}P^{31}$—in the $n = 1$ circular orbit.*

Since the orbital energy is proportional to the particle mass m [see Eq.(51k)], transitions between orbits will have energies $h\nu$ comparable to X rays. X rays arising from jumps from the $n = 2$ to $n = 1$ orbits of π^- mesic atoms were first observed in 1952 by Cemak, McGuire, Platt, and Schulte. These were produced by a beam of π^- mesons from the University of Rochester cyclotron traversing the beryllium, carbon, and oxygen target.

Similar observations were made by Rainwater and Fitch in 1953 for μ^- particles from a cyclotron. Confirmation of the origin of these X rays is attributed to the agreement between measured X-ray wavelengths and those calculated from the Bohr formula.*

* For more details of nuclear structure, see R. D. Evans, *The Atomic Nucleus* (McGraw-Hill Book Co., Inc., New York, 1955).

PROBLEMS

1. Using the atomic masses given in Appendix IX, calculate the binding energy per nucleon for (a) chlorine-35, and (b) silver-107.

2. Using the atomic masses given in Appendix IX, calculate the binding energy per nucleon for (a) phosphorus-31, and (b) aluminum-27. [*Ans.* (a) 8.33 MeV, (b) 8.30 MeV.]

3. Calculate the packing fraction for (a) sodium-23, and (b) argon-40. See Appendix IX for atomic masses.

4. Calculate the packing fraction for (a) lithium-7, and (b) calcium-42.

5. Substitute the values of the atomic constants in Eq.(71f) and calculate the value of the nuclear magneton (see Appendix I).

6. Calculate the ratio between the angular velocity of electron spin and proton spin. Assume uniform homogeneous spheres of equal size. [*Ans.* 1836.]

7. If the odd proton in a nucleus were in a d orbit, with its spin directed parallel to l, what would you expect (a) the nuclear spin value J, and (b) the nuclear magnetic moment μ_J to be?

8. If the odd proton in a nucleus were in a g orbit, $l = 4$, with its spin parallel to l, what would you expect (a) the nuclear spin value J, and (b) the nuclear magnetic moment μ_J, to be? [*Ans.* (a) $J = \frac{9}{2}$, (b) 6.792 nuclear magnetons.]

9. Calculate the radius of the μ^- orbit, $n = 1$, for a calcium atom.

10. Calculate the radius of the π^- orbit, $n = 1$, for the nuclide $_{20}\text{Ca}^{40}$. [*Ans.* 9.7×10^{-13} cm.]

11. Calculate the radius of the π^- orbit, $n = 1$, for the nucleus shown in Fig. 71R.

FISSION AND FUSION

In 1937 Fermi, Segré, and their collaborators subjected uranium to the bombardment of neutrons. From the radioactivity produced they believed they had succeeded, for the first time, in producing a series of new elements, 93, 94, 95, etc., beyond uranium 92. The reason for their belief was that the uranium, after bombardment, gave off electrons with a number of different half-lives. If one attributed these different half-lives to the successive disintegrations of the same atoms, a single nucleus should emit several electrons, one after the other. With each emission the nuclear charge would increase by unity, thus producing an atom of higher and higher atomic

and his two associates Lise Meitner and F. Strassmann made a new and important discovery. After bombarding uranium metal with neutrons they carefully performed a series of chemical separations of the uranium sample to determine the element to which the newly produced radioactivity belonged. To their amazement they found the radioactive atoms to be identical chemically with a number of different elements, nearly all of which are near the center of the periodic table. In other words, a uranium nucleus, after the capture of a single neutron, seemed to be splitting apart into two nearly equal fragments, as illustrated in Fig. 72A.

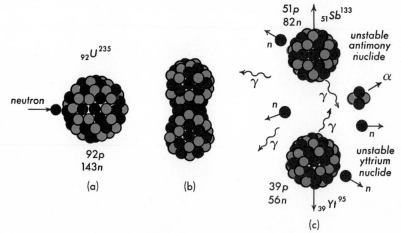

Fig. 72A   *Diagrams of the fission of a uranium nucleus into two unstable nuclides, four neutrons, four gamma rays, and one alpha ray.*

number. Similar observations were later made by the Curie–Joliots, in France.

72.1. The Discovery of Fission. In 1939, just prior to World War II, Otto Hahn in Germany,

In the few weeks that followed this discovery, many observers in different laboratories the world over not only confirmed the results, but extended the observations by studying in detail the products of the disintegrations. To explain the phenomenon in simple words, consider the details of the process illustrated in Fig. 72A. An original uranium nucleus, $_{92}U^{235}$, with its 92 protons and 143 neutrons, is shown in (a) as it captures a slowly moving neutron.

In diagram (b), the newly formed nucleus is unstable and starts to separate into two nearly equal parts. Because this process resembles cell division in the science of biology, the phenomenon is called *fission*. In coming apart, the uranium nucleus, behaving like the analogous water-drop, splashes out small drops, that is, alpha particles, neutrons, and γ rays. So great is the energy liberated by this explosion of the nucleus that each of the two heavy nuclei fly apart in opposite directions with tremendous speeds. That they do so has been confirmed by many Wilson cloud-chamber photographs, one of which is reproduced in Fig. 72B.

To obtain this photograph the cloud chamber contained a thin film of material coated with uranium. The fission of one uranium nucleus reveals two tracks of the same density, showing clearly that the particles traveled outward in opposite directions. The heavy forks near the ends of the tracks are characteristic of highly charged fission fragments that have made several collisions with other nuclei before coming to rest.

Not all of the uranium nuclei divide into antimony and niobium as shown in Fig. 72A, but into any one of many pairs of fragments corresponding to elements near the center of the periodic table. The experimental evidence seems to favor pairs of slightly unequal mass, accompanied by from one to five or more neutrons, as shown in diagram (c).

Numerous measurements of the masses of fission fragments have made it possible to construct the graph shown in Fig. 72C. The fission

Fig. 72B *Wilson cloud-chamber photograph showing a pair of fission fragments recoiling in opposite directions. Note the δ-ray forks near the ends. Fission was produced by a neutron beam from a cyclotron.* (Courtesy, I. K. Bogg.)

Fig. 72C *Semilog graph showing the fission fragment yield for slow neutrons on uranium-235.*

fly apart, two neutrons, an alpha particle, and two gamma rays splash out as shown. Within less than a millisecond after separation, each of the two massive fragments is shown ejecting another neutron and a gamma ray. All four of the neutrons are called *prompt neutrons*. As a reaction we may write,

$$_0n^1 + {}_{92}U^{235} \rightarrow$$
$$_{51}Sb^{133} + {}_{39}Yt^{95} + {}_2He^4 + 4({}_0n^1) + 4\gamma$$

Although the two massive fragments, $_{51}Sb^{133}$ and $_{39}Yt^{95}$, are not stable, they will collide with other atoms and slow down to thermal energies before continuing to decay toward stability. To become stable, each massive fragment undergoes a series of beta emissions until it becomes a stable nucleus. This is illustrated for $_{51}Sb^{133}$ in Fig. 72D. The reaction shown in this figure may be written,

$$_{51}Sb^{133} \underset{\beta}{\rightarrow} {}_{52}Te^{133} \underset{\beta}{\rightarrow} {}_{53}I^{133} \underset{\beta}{\rightarrow} {}_{54}Xe^{133} \underset{\beta}{\rightarrow} {}_{55}Cs^{133}$$

The diagram starts at the left immediately after the nuclide $_{51}Sb^{134}$ has emitted a prompt neutron leaving behind $_{51}Sb^{133}$. With a half-life of 5 min $_{51}Sb^{133}$ emits an electron and becomes $_{52}Te^{133}$. With a half-life of 60 min $_{52}Te^{133}$ emits an electron to become $_{53}I^{133}$. This process continues until $_{54}Xe^{133}$ emits an electron to form the stable nucleus $_{55}Cs^{133}$. The neutrino and gamma rays emitted with each beta decay are not shown.

A similar series of beta emissions could occur with the other fission fragment.

$$_{39}Yt^{95} \underset{\beta}{\rightarrow} {}_{40}Zr^{95} \underset{\beta}{\rightarrow} {}_{41}Nb^{95} \underset{\beta}{\rightarrow} {}_{42}Mo^{95}$$

The final nuclide is a stable isotope of molybdenum.

fragment yield is plotted vertically to a logarithmic scale, and the mass number A is plotted horizontally to a uniform scale. The curve is seen to rise sharply between $A = 75$ and 90 and to drop equally fast between $A = 145$ and 160. The most probable values for the mass numbers of the two fragments are 95 and 139 with a minimum of $\frac{1}{10}$ of 1% at $A = 117$.

In general, fission fragments are not stable nuclei but contain an excess number of neutrons.

As an illustration of typical fission events, consider what happens to the two fragments shown in Fig. 72A. As they first separate and

Fig. 72D *Disintegration series starting with unstable antimony, one of the fragments of the fission of a uranium-235 nucleus.*

As proof that the above series is produced by fission, previously bombarded uranium has been chemically analyzed for elements near the center of the periodic table. After each chemical separation is performed, a test of the β-ray activity is made by a measurement of the half-life. A comparison of this measured half-life with the values already known for the same element from other disintegration experiments has made it possible to identify some of the radioactive nuclei produced. Such tests, for example, have been made by Wu* for the series of four elements in Fig. 72D. Note the increasing half-lives she identified for this series, indicating increased stability as the stable nucleus cesium is approached.

In carrying out such a series of beta decays, some fission fragments suddenly emit a neutron to become stable. In Fig. 72D, for example, the $_{54}Xe^{133}$ nucleus may emit a neutron, in place of an electron, to form a stable xenon nucleus, $_{54}Xe^{132}$. Similarly in the $_{39}Yt^{95}$ series the $_{40}Zr^{95}$ nucleus may emit a neutron to become stable zirconium $_{40}Zr^{94}$.

Because such neutrons are emitted a relatively long time after fission, they are called *delayed neutrons*. About 99% of the neutrons ejected as the result of fission are prompt neutrons while only one out of a hundred are delayed neutrons.

72.2. Fission Energy. The energy liberated in the fission of uranium is due largely to the U-235 isotope. Uranium found in the earth's crust has three principal isotopes with the following relative abundance:

U-238	99.280%	4.51 × 10⁹ y
U-235	0.714%	7.10 × 10⁸ y
U-234	0.006%	2.48 × 10⁵ y

All three of these nuclides are radioactive and decay by α emission (see Tables 72A and 72B).

When a slow or fast neutron is captured by a U-235 nucleus, the two fission fragments as well as the neutrons fly apart with a tremendous amount of kinetic energy. This energy release can best be illustrated by graphs. In Fig. 72E the number of fission fragments from a given quantity of U-235 is plotted vertically, and their ki-

*C. S. Wu (Mrs. C. L. Yuan), *Phys. Rev.*, **58**, 925 (1940).

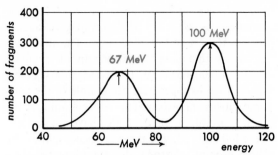

Fig. 72E *Graph of the energies of the fission fragments from uranium-235.*

netic energy in MeV is plotted horizontally. The result is a double-peaked curve with maxima at 67 MeV and 100 MeV. While the greatest probability is for a particle of 100 MeV, the areas under the two peaks represent the total numbers of particles produced, and these are approximately equal.

When U-235 nuclei undergo fission as the result of slow-neutron capture, the average number of neutrons liberated is found to be 2.5 neutrons per fission. Some may yield as many as five neutrons, but two and three are the most probable numbers. When the initial kinetic energies of prompt neutrons are measured, a graph of the kind shown in Fig. 72F is obtained. Although the

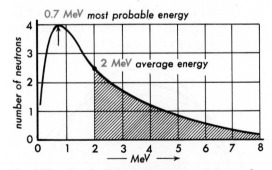

Fig. 72F *Graph of the prompt neutron energies from uranium-235 fission.*

maximum probability is for a neutron of 0.7 MeV, the median energy is approximately 2.0 MeV.

The average γ-ray energy emitted in the fission of U-235 is approximately 23 Mev.

A rough calculation of the average energy liberated in the fission of U-235 can be made from known atomic masses. For U-235, the atomic mass, $M = 235.043933$ amu, gives a mass defect $M - A$ of 0.043933 amu. The incoming neutron with a mass of 1.008665 amu has a mass defect of 0.008665 amu. The average mass defect $M - A$ for isotopes near the middle of the periodic table is approximately -0.094 amu. If the fission products, for example, have mass numbers 100 and 133, and these are accompanied by three prompt neutrons, the mass balance gives the following:

BEFORE FISSION		AFTER FISSION	
U-235	235.043933	2 frag.	232.812000
n	1.008665	3 n	3.025995
	236.052598		235.837995

The total mass converted is the difference, 0.214603 amu. After multiplying by 931 Mev/amu, we find the energy released to be 200 MeV. This value is consistent with the measured energies given in Figs. 72E and 72F. For the two fragments the average measured energy is 171 MeV. For the three neutrons the average measured energy is 6 MeV. These, added to the γ-ray energy release of 23 MeV, give a measured total of 200 MeV.

72.3. Bohr's Liquid Drop Model. It was Bohr who first proposed that a heavy nucleus behaves like a liquid drop, and that fission may be explained as the result of oscillations brought about by the impinging neutron (see Fig. 72G). Attractive forces between nucleons, like the attractive forces between liquid molecules, give rise to surface tension and the spheroidal state. As raindrops grow in size while falling through the air, their spherical stability decreases; they respond more readily to disruptive forces of the air stream and break up into smaller drops. A similar instability could be expected in heavy nuclei where the attractive forces give rise to a similar kind of surface tension.

Consider a nucleus like $_{92}U^{235}$, containing 92 protons and 143 neutrons, closely packed so that attractive forces between neighboring nucleons are all the same. This nucleus should be slightly larger than six nucleons in diameter, as shown in Fig. 72A(a). Each nucleon in the interior of such a system will be in contact with, and therefore will be bound by, 12 others, as shown in Fig. 72H. Since the binding energy U

Fig. 72H *With a large number of closely packed spheres, each will be in contact with twelve others: six around, three above, and three below.*

between each pair of nucleons belongs equally to both, the total binding energy of each nucleon should be $6U$:

$$B_v = +6U \qquad (72a)$$

This quantity B_v applies only to the interior of the nucleus and is called the *volume binding energy*. Experimentally, B_v is about 14 MeV per nucleon for heavy nuclides.

Nucleons on the surface of the sphere are attracted by only half as many neighbors as those on the interior. For this reason the *surface binding energy* per nucleon should be approximately half as great as the volume binding energy. As

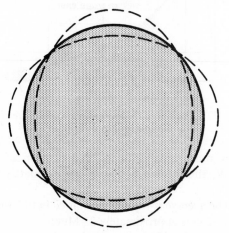

Fig. 72G *Diagram of the oscillations of a waterdrop. Bohr's model for the nuclei of heavy atoms.*

more and more particles are added to build up larger and larger nuclides, the number inside and on the surface both increase, but the number inside increases more rapidly. The surface area of a sphere is proportional to the square of the radius, while the volume is proportional to the cube of the radius.

If, therefore, we assign the volume binding

necessary to ensure stability. However, since subshells of neutrons and protons are filled according to the Pauli exclusion principle (see Sec. 71.10), the excess neutrons must be placed in higher energy levels. Being in higher energy levels means they are less tightly bound to the nucleus, thus reducing the average binding energy per nucleon.

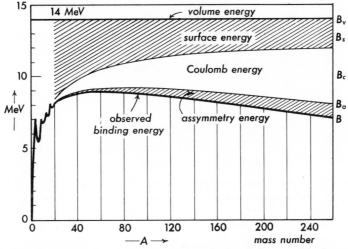

Fig. 72I *Graph of the binding energy factors for the liquid-drop model of atomic nuclei.*

energy B_v to all nucleons, we must subtract some surface binding energy B_s to take care of surface nucleons. The relative amount to be subtracted will decrease as A, the total number of nucleons, increases (see Fig. 72I).

While the short-range forces of attraction between nucleons account for nuclear stability, the weaker Coulomb forces between protons are also present. Since these Coulomb forces are repulsive, the binding energy per nucleon is further reduced. The amount by which it is reduced is called the *Coulomb energy*.

Finally, the total binding energy is also reduced in heavy nuclei by the preponderance of neutrons. If we tried to construct a heavy nucleus out of equal numbers of protons and neutrons, the repulsive Coulomb forces between protons would not be overcome by the attractive short-range forces between all nucleons, and the nucleus would be unstable. The excess number of neutrons provides the additional attractive forces

Hence there are four factors affecting the stability of nuclei:

$+B_v$ = volume binding energy
$-B_s$ = surface binding energy
$-B_c$ = Coulomb energy
$-B_a$ = asymmetric energy

The curves and their shaded areas in Fig. 72I show how, starting with the volume binding energy of 14 MeV for each nucleon, each of the other three factors reduces this value in going to heavier and heavier nuclides. This gives only a rough accounting of the experimentally determined curve shown by the heavy line, and reproduced from Fig. 71C.

72.4. The Transuranic Elements. All elements with atomic numbers greater than 92 are called the *transuranic elements*. The first transuranic element, neptunium, atomic number 93, was identified in 1939 by McMillan and Abelson. A beam of neutrons incident on a target of uranium metal gave rise to several known nuclear reactions. A neutron captured by one of the most abundant nuclei, U-238, forms U-239 and a γ ray, followed by β emission, to yield neptunium, element 93:

$$_0n^1 + {}_{92}U^{238} \rightarrow {}_{92}U^{239} + \gamma \text{ ray}$$
$$_{92}U^{239} \rightarrow {}_{93}Np^{239} + {}_{-1}e^0 + \bar{\nu}_e + \gamma$$

Ten different radioactive isotopes of neptunium are now known. Ranging in mass number from 231 to 240, isotope $_{93}Np^{237}$ emits α particles and has the longest half-life, 2.2 million years. While slow or fast neutron capture by U-238 is almost always followed by β emission, about one out of a hundred fast neutrons will cause fission.

Plutonium (Pu), element 94, was first identified by Kennedy, McMillan, Seaborg, Segrè, and Wahl, as arising from the spontaneous emission of β particles from $_{92}Np^{239}$:

$$_{92}Np^{239} \rightarrow {}_{94}Pu^{239} + {}_{-1}e^0 + \bar{\nu}_e + \gamma$$

Schematic diagrams of the above processes are given in Fig. 72J. Fifteen different radio-

$_{96}Cm^{240}$ and $_{96}Cm^{242}$, formed by (α, n) and $(\alpha, 3n)$ reactions. These nuclei are α emitters with half-lives of one month and five months, respectively. $_{95}Am^{241}$ was first discovered arising from a relatively long-lived β emitter, $_{94}Pu^{241}$, and emits α particles with a half-life of about 500 years.

Ten radioactive isotopes of americium are now known. Ranging in mass number from 237 to 246, $_{95}Am^{243}$ has the longest half-life of 8000 years and emits α particles.

Thirteen radioactive isotopes of curium are now known. Ranging in mass number from 239 to 250, several isotopes have long half-lives. These are

$_{96}Cm^{245}$	α-active	9320 y
$_{96}Cm^{247}$	α-active	4×10^7 y
$_{96}Cm^{248}$	α-active	4.7×10^5 y

Berkelium (Bk), element 97, was discovered in 1949 by Thompson, Ghiorso, and Seaborg. $_{95}Am^{241}$ bombarded by 35-MeV α particles yields $_{97}Bk^{243}$. K capture with a half-life of 4.7 hr turns

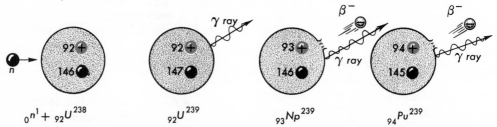

$$_0n^1 + {}_{92}U^{238} \qquad {}_{92}U^{239} \qquad {}_{93}Np^{239} \qquad {}_{94}Pu^{239}$$

Fig. 72J *Neutron capture by uranium-238 produces, by radioactive β decay, neptunium and plutonium.*

active isotopes of plutonium are now known. Ranging in mass numbers from 232 to 246, several have long half-lives:

$_{94}Pu^{239}$	α-active	24,360 y
$_{94}Pu^{240}$	α-active	6760 y
$_{94}Pu^{242}$	α-active	380,000 y
$_{94}Pu^{244}$	α-active	7.6×10^7 y

Americum (Am), element 95, and curium (Cm), element 96, were discovered in 1944 by Seaborg, James, Morgan, and Ghiorso, in collaboration with Hamilton. A sizable quantity of $_{94}Pu^{239}$ was bombarded in the Berkeley cyclotron by 40-MeV helium nuclei and two isotopes,

99.9% of these nuclei into $_{96}Cm^{243}$, with 0.1% emitting α particles to become $_{95}Am^{239}$.

Eight radioactive isotopes of berkelium are known. Ranging in mass number from 243 to 250, $_{97}Bk^{247}$ has a half-life of 1000 years and is α-active.

Californium (Cf), element 98, was discovered in 1950 by Thompson, Street, Ghiorso, and Seaborg. $_{96}Cm^{242}$ bombarded by 35-MeV α particles yields $_{98}Cf^{244}$. With a half-life of 45 min, $_{98}Cf^{244}$ ejects α particles with an energy of 7.1 MeV to produce $_{96}Cm^{240}$.

Eleven radioactive isotopes ranging in mass number from 244 to 254 are known. Isotope

$_{98}Cf^{251}$ has the longest half-life, 800 years, and is α-active.

Einsteinium (E), element 99, and fermium (Fm), element 100, were discovered as a joint project by 16 scientists.

In November 1952 the first full-scale thermonuclear explosion was detonated on an island in the Pacific Ocean. The explosion produced a mile-wide crater in the coral island site, and the radioactive cloud rose ten miles and reached a diameter of approximately 100 miles. Drone planes, radio-controlled, flew through this cloud collecting samples for laboratory study. Among other things it was found that some of the uranium nuclei not undergoing fission had captured as many as 17 neutrons, and formed $_{92}U^{255}$. This very heavy isotope proceeds to give off electrons one after the other, each one raising the nuclear charge by one. Elements 99 and 100 were identified by their predicted chemical properties.

Ten radioactive isotopes of einsteinium are now known, and range in atomic mass number from 246 to 255. Isotope $_{99}E^{254}$ has the longest half-life, 480 days, and is α-active.

Ten radioactive isotopes of fermium are now known. They range in atomic mass number from 248 to 256. Isotope $_{100}Fm^{253}$ has the longest half-life, 7 days, and is α-active.

Mendelevium (Mv), element 101, was discovered by Ghiorso, Harvey, Chappin, Thompson, and Seaborg in 1955. Two radioactive isotopes, $_{101}Md^{255}$ and $_{101}Md^{256}$, are known. The half-life of $_{101}Md^{256}$ is approximately one hour. This nuclide was produced by bombarding einsteinium-253 with helium nuclei from a cyclotron beam.

Element 102, now called nobelium after Alfred Nobel, the father of the Nobel Prize awards, was first discovered with certainty by Ghiorso, Sikkeland, Walton and Seaborg in 1958. A very small quantity of curium was bombarded by carbon ions from a heavy-ion accelerator. The high-speed carbon nuclei are captured by the curium-246 nuclei, in the following reaction

$$_{6}C^{12} + {}_{96}Cm^{246} \rightarrow {}_{102}No^{254} + 4_0n^1$$

Four isotopes of nobelium have now been identified and are $_{102}No^{253}$, $_{102}No^{254}$, $_{102}No^{255}$, and $_{102}No^{256}$.

Element 103, now called lawrencium after Ernest Lawrence, the inventor of the cyclotron, was discovered by Ghiorso, Sikkeland, Larsh, and Latimer, in 1961. A 3-mg target of californium was bombarded by boron ions $_5B^{10}$ and $_5B^{11}$. A typical reaction is,

$$_{5}B^{11} + {}_{98}Cf^{252} \rightarrow {}_{103}Lw^{257} + 6_0n^1$$

It is interesting to trace out the genetic relationships of the entire group of transuranium elements and see how they link up with the natural radioactive elements. All of the known nuclides fall naturally into four main series as shown in Tables 72A and 72B. The four principle activities common to all series are alpha emission (α), beta emission (β^-), electron capture (E.C.), and spontaneous fission (S.F.). While small percentages of some transuranium nuclides spontaneously fission, note that practically all californium-254 and fermium-256 nuclei decay in this way.

It is now known that all heavy nuclei, starting approximately with Th-232, are fissionable, i.e., under proper excitation conditions they split apart with great violence into almost equal pair fragments. Some of them, like U-233, U-235, and Pu-239, fission by the capture of a slow neutron as well as a fast neutron, whereas others like U-238 and Pu-241 fission only by the capture of fast neutrons. The capture of a slow neutron by U-238 is followed by β decay to produce Np and Pu, whereas fast-neutron capture is followed by fission.

72.5. Photofission of Heavy Nuclei. The fission of uranium and thorium initiated by γ rays was first discovered by Haxley, Schoupp, Stevens, and Wells in 1941. These experimenters bombarded a uranium target with 6.2-MeV γ rays and observed fission fragments. Later experiments by others have shown that photofission can be demonstrated with many of the heavy elements, and that the threshold energy for nuclides Th-230, U-233, U-235, U-238, and Pu-239 is just over 5 MeV.

The discovery that some nuclei undergo fission spontaneously was made by Petrzhak and Flerov in 1940. Many of the heavier isotopes of the transuranic elements show spontaneous fission.

72.6. The Meson Theory of the Nucleus. The

TABLE 72A *The 4n + 1 and 4n + 2 series of nuclides connecting the natural radioactive elements with the man-made transuranium elements.*

Series 4n + 1   Series 4n + 2

			Series 4n + 1	Series 4n + 2
81	thallium	Tl	209 (2.2m)	RaC″ 210 (1.32m) RaE″ 206
82	lead	Pb	213 209 (3.2h) stable [209]	RaB 214 (26.8m) RaD 210 (19y) stable [206]
83	bismuth	Bi	213 (47m)	RaC 214 (20m) RaE 210 (5d)
84	polonium	Po	217 213 (4.2μs)	RaA 218 (3m) RaC′ 214 (158μs) RaF 210 (138d)
85	astatine	At	217 (0.018s) 213	218 214
86	radon	Rn	221 217	Rn 222 (3.8d) 218
87	francium	Fr	221 (4.8m) 217	222 218
88	radium	Ra	225 (15d) 221	Ra 226 (1622y) 222
89	actinium	Ac	225 (10d) 221	222
90	thorium	Th	233 229 (7340y) 225	UX₁ 234 (24d) Io 230 (8×10⁴y) 226
91	protactinium	Pa	237 233 (27d) 229 225	234 (UX₂ 1.2m) 230 226
92	uranium	U	237 233 (1.6×10⁵y) 229	238 (4.5×10⁹y) → 234 (U II 2.5×10⁵y) → 230
93	neptunium	Np	241 237 (2.1×10⁶y) 233	238 234
94	plutonium	Pu	245 241 (13y) 237 233	246 242 (3.8×10⁵y) → 238 (86y) → 234
95	americium	Am	245 241 (458y) 237	246 242 238
96	curium	Cm	249 245 (9300y) 241	250 → 246 (5480y) → 242 → 238
97	berkelium	Bk	249 (314d) 245	250 246
98	californium	Cf	253 249 (360y) 245	254 (100%) 250 (13.2y) → 246
99	einsteinium	Es	253 (20d) 249	254 (60d) 250 246
100	fermium	Fm	253 (4.5d) 249	254 (3.2h) → 250 (30m)
101	mendelevium	Md		
102	(nobelium)	No	253	254 (3s)
103	lawrencium	Lw	257 (8s)	

(diagram legend: α, E.C., S.F., β⁻)

---

possible existence of mesons was first proposed by the Japanese mathematical physicist Yukawa in 1935. He proposed that the short-range forces between protons and neutrons inside the nucleus are to be attributed to relatively smaller particles.

According to Yukawa, nucleons emit and absorb mass-quanta, called *mesons*, just as elec-trons in the outer structure of the atom emit and absorb photons. The fact that the nuclear forces extend over only a short range can be shown to mean that the meson, unlike the massless photon, would have a finite rest mass. Furthermore, some mesons are charged, and some are neutral (see Fig. 660).

The present concept of nucleons is that they consist of some sort of common core surrounded by a pulsating cloud of π mesons called *pions*.

(see Fig. 72K). This diagram might well represent a deuteron, with both spins in the same direction to give $I = 1$, and the negative pion

TABLE 72B   *The 4n + 3 and 4n series of nuclides connecting the natural radioactive elements with the man-made transuranium elements.*

Since pions are charged +, 0, or −, the rapid jumping back and forth between nucleons changes the nucleon identity equally fast and at the same time binds the two nucleons together

charge at a greater distance from the center of the neutron to produce its negative magnetic moment (see Fig. 71P).

To liberate two pions as free particles, suffi-

Fig. 72K *Schematic diagram of the meson clouds around each of two nucleon cores, the charge exchange accounting for the strong attractive force U.*

cient energy must be imparted to the nucleus to create their rest mass of 270 m_e each, or a total of 0.503 BeV (see Fig. 69N).

The exchange of a single pion between two nucleons may be written

$$n \rightleftarrows p + \pi^-$$
$$p \rightleftarrows n + \bar{\pi}^+$$

72.7. Fusion. Measurements of solar radiation reaching the earth each day not only make it possible to calculate the surface temperature of the sun but also to determine its total radiation. The fact that the sun, over a period of many years, shows no signs of cooling off, has long been an unsolved mystery. With the discovery of nuclear disintegration and the development of methods of producing many new types of atoms, this mystery has in a measure been recently solved.

Although there is no direct way known of observing the interior of a star like our sun, mathematical calculations based upon well-established physical laws show that down deep within such a mass the temperature is so extremely high that matter must be a conglomeration of atoms, electrons, and light waves, all moving about at tremendously high speeds.

Near the center of the sun where the temperature is about 20 million degrees, the atoms are stripped of their electrons and the light waves produced are of such high frequencies that they should be classified as γ rays and X rays. Here, where the average particle velocity is so high, nuclear reactions must be taking place on a large scale and the liberated energy must be filtering up through to cooler and cooler layers as light waves of lower and lower frequency. At

the surface, most of the radiations escaping are of sufficiently low frequency to be classified as *visible, ultraviolet,* and *infrared.*

A careful study of all known nuclear reactions led Bethe in 1938 to propose the following set of chain processes as those most probably responsible for the generation of energy at the sun's central core:

$$
\begin{aligned}
&(1) \ _1H^1 + {}_6C^{12} = {}_7N^{13} + \gamma \text{ ray} \\
&(2) \hspace{3.2cm} {}_7N^{13} \rightarrow {}_6C^{13} + {}_1\bar{e}^0 + \nu_e \\
&(3) \ _1H^1 + {}_6C^{13} = {}_7N^{14} + \gamma \text{ ray} \\
&(4) \ _1H^1 + {}_7N^{14} = {}_8O^{15} + \gamma \text{ ray} \\
&(5) \hspace{3.2cm} {}_8O^{15} \rightarrow {}_7N^{15} + {}_1\bar{e}^0 + \nu_e \\
&(6) \ _1H^1 + {}_7N^{15} = {}_6C^{12} + {}_2He^4
\end{aligned}
\qquad \text{(72b)}
$$

By summing up the equations it will be seen that four hydrogen atoms are consumed and that two positrons, three γ rays, and one helium nucleus, are created. The other nuclei cancel out, since the original carbon atom in the first reaction is returned unaltered in the last reaction. Hence hydrogen is burned and helium is liberated. The loss in mass for each such cycle of reactions is, therefore, as follows:

$$
\begin{aligned}
4_1H^1 &= 4.031300 \\
_2He^4 &= 4.002604 \\
2_1e^0 &= 0.001098
\end{aligned}
$$

Subtracting gives $4.031300 - 4.002604 - 0.001098 = 0.027598$ amu. This is equivalent to 25.7 MeV energy.

More recent experiments and calculations* indicate that the proton–proton cycle given below is of even greater importance in the creation of solar and stellar energy than the above carbon cycle:

$$_1H^1 + {}_1H^1 \rightarrow {}_1H^2 + {}_1\bar{e}^0 + \nu_e + 0.93 - 2 \text{ MeV} \tag{72c}$$

$$_1H^1 + {}_1H^2 \rightarrow {}_2He^3 + \gamma \text{ ray} + 5.5 \text{ MeV} \tag{72d}$$
$$_2He^3 + {}_2He^3 \rightarrow {}_2He^4 + 2_1H^1 + 12.8 \text{ MeV} \tag{72e}$$

The net result is the same as before; four hydrogen atoms have been converted into one helium atom. Note that since two $_2He^3$ nuclei are involved in the reaction, Eq.(72e), two proton reactions of the type of Eqs.(72c) and (72d)

---

* See "Nuclear Reactions in Stars" by E. E. Salpeter, *Phys. Rev.,* **88,** 547 (1952).

are required to form one $_2He^4$ nucleus. Six protons are used and two are returned.

The rates at which these reactions should take place are not only consistent with the temperature of 20 million degrees, calculated from other considerations, but hydrogen and helium are known to be the most abundant elements of which stars are made.

In order for the sun to radiate 3.8×10^{26} joules of energy per second, Einstein's equation $E = mc^2$ shows that mass must be annihilated at the rate of 4.2×10^9 Kg/s (or 4,500,000

tons/s). While this result indicates that the sun is losing mass at a tremendous rate, the amount is small when compared with the sun's total mass of 1.98×10^{30} Kg. To illustrate, in one million years the sun should lose one ten-millionth of its total mass.†

† For a more complete treatment of nuclear energy, see S. Glasstone, *Sourcebook on Atomic Energy* (D. Van Nostrand Co., Inc., Princeton, New Jersey). For more details of the general subject of nuclear physics, see R. D. Evans, *The Atomic Nucleus* (McGraw-Hill Book Co., Inc., New York).

QUESTIONS AND PROBLEMS

1. Make a diagram like Fig. 72A, showing a plutonium-239 nucleus capturing a slow neutron and undergoing fission. Assume that four prompt neutrons are emitted, and that the fragments have initial charges of 139 and 97, respectively.

2. If one of the fission fragments of U-235 is the radioactive isotope xenon-140, what stable isotope will it become if a series of β particles ensues? Make a diagram like Fig. 72D. [*Ans.* $_{57}La^{139}$.]

3. If one of the fission fragments of U-235 is the radioactive isotope krypton-92, what stable isotope will it become if a series of β-decays takes place? Make a diagram like Fig. 72D.

4. If one of the fission fragments of U-235 is the radioactive isotope krypton-95, what stable isotope will it become if a series of β particles ensues? Make a diagram like Fig. 72D. [*Ans.* $_{42}Mo^{95}$.]

5. If a small quantity of americium-244 is bombarded

by deuterons and β particles are emitted, what is the reaction?

6. When americium-243 is bombarded by deuterons from a cyclotron, α particles are emitted. What is the reaction? [*Ans.* $_1H^2 + {}_{95}Am^{243} \rightarrow {}_{94}Pu^{241} + {}_2He^4$.]

7. What are the reactions by which neptunium and plutonium were discovered?

8. If nuclei are composed of closely packed spherical shells of nucleons, how many nucleons are required to form a nucleus with three complete shells around one nucleon at the center? Assume nucleon centers to lie on the surface of a sphere. [*Ans.* 176.]

9. If nucleons have a diameter of 2.2×10^{-13} cm, what is the diameter of the nucleus fermium-254?

10. (a) How many surface nucleons are there in Problem 8? (b) How many interior nucleons are there? [*Ans.* (a) 113. (b) 63.]

NUCLEAR ENERGY

Not long after the discovery of fission in 1939, it became evident to many scientific groups in America and in Europe that if a sufficient quantity of pure uranium-235 (U-235) could be isolated from its more abundant isotope uranium-238 (U-238), it might have explosive powers many times greater than anything heretofore known. The reasons for believing this appeared at the time to be somewhat as follows.

73.1. A Chain Reaction. Suppose that a given mass of uranium metal, all composed of U-235 atoms, was brought together into one lump. The first cosmic ray that penetrated this mass and produced a neutron might well set off the chain reaction shown schematically in Fig. 73A. A U-235 nucleus would capture the neutron and in splitting apart with great violence would liberate

one or more additional neutrons. These in turn would be quickly absorbed by other nearby atoms, which in turn would split up, at the same time liberating other neutrons. Hence a rapidly growing kind of avalanche might occur, a kind which, if fast enough, would have the characteristics of an explosion.

A graph showing the rate of growth of such a chain process is given in Fig. 73B. Since even the

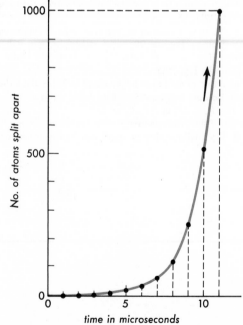

Fig. 73B *Growth curve of fission in pure uranium-235.*

Fig. 73A *Schematic diagram of a chain reaction in pure uranium-235.*

slowest of neutrons in solid matter will have average speeds of hundreds of thousands of centimeters per second, about the same as hydrogen atoms in a gas at ordinary temperatures, and since many neutron collisions will, on the average, occur within several centimeters, the graph shows how quickly the growth reaches gigantic proportions. The *time* scale is of the order of microseconds.

The escape of neutrons from any quantity of uranium is a *surface effect* depending on the area of the surface, whereas fission capture occurs throughout the body and is therefore a *volume effect*. If the assembled mass of uranium is too small, the probability that most neutrons liberated by fission would escape through the surface before being captured might well be so large that a growing chain reaction cannot occur. Since the volume of a sphere increases with the cube of the radius while the surface area increases with the square of the radius, the *probability of escape* would decrease with increasing size. In other words, if the uranium mass were too small, the growth process shown in Figs. 73A and 73B would be cut off before it became very large, and only if the mass were greater than some critical value would an explosion take place.

Consider, therefore, a large quantity of U-235 in two or more units, each smaller than the critical size, and separated by a short distance (see Fig. 73C). Because of the relatively large

Fig. 73C   *A schematic diagram of a hypothetical atomic explosion device, based upon a fast chain reaction in pure uranium-235 or plutonium-239.*

surface area of each unit, neutrons readily escape and a chain reaction cannot develop. Suddenly, an explosive like TNT is detonated behind the separated blocks, driving them together as indicated at the center of the diagram. Neutrons entering this greater-than-critical mass from a

Ra–Be source will now initiate a rapid chain reaction which results in a violent explosion. The tremendous energy release of such a device can only be fully realized by those who have actually seen and heard one detonated.

The first atomic bomb ever produced was assembled by scientists under the direction of the University of California, and was successfully detonated at Alamogordo, New Mexico, on July 16, 1945. This device was composed of practically pure U-235. Many of the atomic devices exploded since that time have used plutonium-239 as the fissionable material, and peaceful uses of all kinds are now being studied by many.

One such promising development makes use of the tremendous amount of heat energy liberated. Repeated explosions underground can be confined to relatively small volumes of space, and the heat can be tapped off through some heat-transfer system, such as circulating steam pipes.

73.2. Nuclear Radius and Geometrical Cross Section. Many experiments concerned with the collisions between atomic particles indicate that a nucleus may be considered a conglomerate of closely packed spheres of the same size. The average nucleon radius is now believed to be

$$r_0 = 1.2 \times 10^{-15}\,\text{m} \qquad (73a)$$

If spheres of this size are packed together into a ball-like structure as shown in Fig. 73A(a), the approximate radius of the combination will be given by

$$R = r_0 \sqrt[3]{A} \qquad (73b)$$

where the number of nucleons is given by the mass number A. For a uranium nucleus, U-238, for example, $A = 238$ and $R = 7.4 \times 10^{-15}$ m, a value only six times that of the proton.

The concept of nuclear cross section is one of considerable importance in nuclear studies. If a nucleus is set up as a target for other atoms to hit, its *geometrical cross section* serves as a reasonably good measure of the target size, and is given by

$$\sigma_g = \pi R^2 \qquad (73c)$$

For U-238 this cross section is approximately

$$\sigma_g = 1.73 \times 10^{-28}\,\text{m}^2$$

The unit area for nuclei has been arbitrarily set at 1×10^{-28} m², and is called the *barn*. The geometrical cross section for U-238, for example, would be written $\sigma_g = 1.73$ barns:

$$1 \text{ barn} = 1 \times 10^{-28} \text{ m}^2$$
$$1 \text{ barn} = 1 \times 10^{-24} \text{ cm}^2 \qquad (73d)$$

Calculated cross sections for a few nuclides are given in Table 73A, along with the heights of the nuclear barrier B for incident α particles (see Fig. 71H).

TABLE 73A. NUCLEAR RADII, GEOMETRICAL CROSS SECTIONS, AND POTENTIAL BARRIER HEIGHTS

Nuclide	R (10^{-15} m)	σ_g (barns)	B (MeV)
$_2\text{He}^4$	1.9	.11	2.4
$_8\text{O}^{16}$	3.2	0.32	6.0
$_{30}\text{Zn}^{64}$	4.8	0.72	14.0
$_{48}\text{Cd}^{113}$	5.8	1.06	19.0
$_{100}\text{Fm}^{252}$	7.6	1.82	29.0

73.3. Cross Sections and Mean Free Path. When neutrons are incident upon some material, each nucleus within the target area does not always behave as though its cross section is a constant. For example, in the capture of a neutron prior to radioactive decay, the nuclear size may appear to be quite different from its calculated geometric cross section. For fast neutrons, a nuclear cross section might be relatively small, while for slow neutrons it may be quite large.

With this explanation we see that cross section is not a target area in the literal sense, but is a figurative concept expressing the *interaction probability*.

The probability of interaction between a neutron and a nucleus is called the *microscopic cross section* σ, and is regarded as the effective target area of a nucleus. If a beam of neutrons is incident on 1 cm³ of material, the total effective target area will be $n\sigma$, where n is the total number of atoms per cm³ (see Fig. 73D). This product is called the *macroscopic cross section*, and is designated Σ.

$$\Sigma = n\sigma \qquad (73e)$$

The total cross section σ_t of a single nuclide

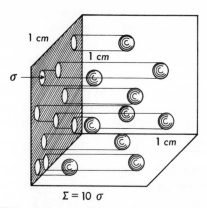

Fig. 73D   *Diagram showing the microscopic cross section and the meaning of the macroscopic cross section.*

is the sum of several cross sections, one for each different kind of process that alters the bombarding particles' energy or momentum:

$$\sigma_t = \sigma_s + \sigma_c \qquad (73f)$$

where σ_s is the effective nuclear area that produces measurable scattering, and σ_c is the effective area for radiative capture. A nuclear capture process whose prompt result is the emission of electromagnetic radiation only is called *radiative capture*. The designation σ_c therefore represents the *radiative capture cross section*. If fission is also one of the effects of capture, as it is with some of the heaviest nuclides like U-235 and Pu-239, we have

$$\sigma_t = \sigma_s + \sigma_c + \sigma_f \qquad (73g)$$

As an illustration of these various σ's, the cross sections for U-235 for fast neutrons (2 MeV) and thermal neutrons (0.0253 eV) are given in Table 73B. U-235 is one of a number of exceptional nuclei, for most cross sections are

TABLE 73B. CROSS SECTIONS FOR PURE U-235

Cross sections in barns	Fast neutrons 2 MeV $\left(\begin{array}{c}2 \times 10^7 \\ \text{m/s}\end{array}\right)$	Slow neutrons 0.0253 eV $\left(\begin{array}{c}2200 \\ \text{m/s}\end{array}\right)$
Scattering $\sigma_s =$	5.0	10
Capture $\sigma_c =$	0.25	107
Fission $\sigma_f =$	1.27	580

small and comparable with geometrical cross sections. The whole subject of nuclear energy and the design of nuclear reactors and explosives is very dependent upon the smallness of the cross sections of some elements and the largeness of others.

The average distance a neutron travels between nuclear events is given by the reciprocal of the macroscopic cross section. This average distance is called the *mean free path:*

$$\text{Mean free path } \lambda = \frac{1}{\Sigma} \qquad (73\text{h})$$

Example 1. Find (a) the total macroscopic cross section, and (b) the mean free path for 2-MeV neutrons in pure U-235.

Solution. From Table 73B, and by Eq.(73g), we obtain

$$\sigma_t = 6.52 \text{ barns}$$

To find n for Eq.(73e), we take the density of uranium metal, $\rho = 18.7 \times 10^3$ Kg/m³, and divide by the mass in Kg of one uranium atom. Since unit atomic mass is 1.66×10^{-27} Kg (see Appendix I), the mass of one U-235 atom is

$$M = 235 \times 1.66 \times 10^{-27} = 3.90 \times 10^{-25} \text{ Kg}$$

Dividing ρ by M, gives

$$n = \frac{18.7 \times 10^3}{3.9 \times 10^{-25}} = 4.79 \times 10^{28} \frac{\text{atoms}}{\text{m}^3}$$

$$n = 4.79 \times 10^{22} \frac{\text{atoms}}{\text{cm}^3}$$

Substituting σ_t and n in Eq.(73e), we obtain

$$\Sigma_t = 4.79 \times 10^{22} \frac{\text{atoms}}{\text{cm}^3} \times 6.52 \times 10^{-24} \text{ cm}^2$$

or   (a) $\Sigma_t = 0.312 \text{ cm}^{-1}$

To find the mean free path, Eq.(73h) gives

(b) $\lambda_t = 3.21 \text{ cm}$ (73i)

By using the separate value σ_s, σ_c, or σ_f alone, and the procedure given in Example 1, the mean free paths for scattering, radiative capture, or fission alone can be calculated. For the scattering and fission of U-235 by 2 MeV neutrons, for example,

$$\lambda_s = 4 \text{ cm} \qquad (73\text{j})$$

and

$$\lambda_f = 16 \text{ cm} \qquad (73\text{k})$$

Since the scattering cross section of U-235 is four times the fission cross section, secondary neutrons will collide several times with U-235 nuclei before producing fission. A schematic diagram of this process is illustrated in Fig. 73E.

Fig. 73E   *Elastic scattering of a neutron by a nucleus.*

73.4. Neutron Scattering. There are, in general, two ways in which particles may be scattered by impacts with atomic nuclei; one is by *elastic scattering*, and the other is called *inelastic scattering*. In cases of elastic scattering, the total kinetic energy as well as the total momentum before impact are equal, respectively, to the total kinetic energy and the total momentum after impact. In mechanics this means that the coefficient of restitution $r = 1$.

If a fast neutron collides elastically with a light particle like a proton, deuteron, or an α particle, considerable energy may be imparted to the recoiling nuclide. If the neutron collides with a heavy nucleus, on the other hand, conservation laws show that little kinetic energy can be imparted to the recoiling heavy nucleus and that the neutron will rebound in some new direction with most of its original energy (see Fig. 73E).

If, therefore, fast neutrons are to be slowed down to relatively low velocities by elastic scattering, materials composed of large quantities of atoms of low atomic weight, such as hydrogen, will be most effective. Any material used for this purpose is called a *moderator*.

Since the function of a moderator is to reduce the speeds of fast neutrons to low velocities by elastic collisions, the material used to do this will best serve its purpose if the nuclei scatter elastically and have small capture cross sections. Furthermore, the lighter the atoms the greater will be the recoil energy of the moderator nuclei when they do collide, and the fewer will be the impacts necessary to reduce the neutrons to thermal energies (see Table 73C).

Element	No. of impacts
Hydrogen	18
Deuterium	25
Beryllium	87
Carbon	115
Uranium	2160

Capture cross sections of a few moderators are given in Table 73D.

TABLE 73D. NEUTRON CAPTURE CROSS SECTIONS OF MODERATORS AND STRUCTURAL MATERIALS

Element	σ_c (barns)
Hydrogen	0.33
Deuterium	0.00046
Carbon	0.0032
Beryllium	0.010
Aluminum	0.23
Zirconium	0.18
Molybdenum	2.4
Iron	2.5
Copper	3.6

Note the extremely low cross section and atomic mass of the first four elements.

When fast neutrons collide with uranium nuclei, either U-235 or U-238, some of them are scattered inelastically, while others are captured. The inelastic scattering process is illustrated in Fig. 73F. In passing close to one of these heavy nuclei, a considerable amount of energy is taken from the neutron, and the nucleus is raised to an excited state. The neutron leaves the nucleus in some new direction, with perhaps less than half its initial kinetic energy.

The excited nuclei, in returning to their normal state, emit γ rays. While inelastic impacts always obey the law of conservation of momentum, thus giving rise to the heavy-particle recoil shown, *conservation of kinetic energy does not hold.*

73.5. Explosive Chain Reactions. Uranium metal as it is usually refined is composed of three radioactive isotopes.

URANIUM ISOTOPE	RELATIVE ABUNDANCE
$A = 238$	99.280%
235	0.714%
234	0.006%

Since both U-235 and U-238 undergo fission with fast neutrons, one might think ordinary uranium in a large enough mass might explode. One good reason for believing this is that fission cross sections for both isotopes are about the same for fast neutrons. (σ_f for U-235 is 1.27 barns; see Table 73B.) Another reason is that fast neutrons might be expected to shorten the time between fission events.

The reason that ordinarily refined uranium in a mass of any size will not explode is that the scattering cross sections are larger than fission cross sections, thus making the mean free path between scattering events relatively small. After one or two inelastic impacts with uranium nuclei, the secondary neutrons have lost most of their initial energy of 2 MeV, and the fission capability of U-238 has dropped to an extremely low value. The fission cross section of U-238 for slow neutrons is practically zero.

Since the fission cross section for U-235 increases as the neutron velocity decreases and becomes extremely large at thermal energies (see Table 73B), only relatively pure U-235 can develop an explosive chain reaction. Thermal-neutron cross sections for fissionable nuclides are given in Table 73E.

73.6. Critical Mass Factors. For a mass of fissionable material like pure U-235 or Pu-239 to be explosive, the time between fission events must be very small, and relatively few neutrons must escape through the surface, or be lost some-

Fig. 73F *Inelastic scattering of a neutron by a uranium nucleus.*

TABLE 73E. THERMAL NEUTRON CROSS SECTION
FOR FISSIONABLE MATERIALS
(in barns, at 2200 m/s)

Nuclide	σ_s	σ_c	σ_f
U-235	10	107	580
Pu-239	9.6	315	750
U-233	—	52	533
U-238	8.3	3.50	0

where by capture. A schematic diagram of possible paths of neutrons between two consecutive fission events is shown in Fig. 73G.

Fig. 73G *Schematic diagram of inelastic scattering between fission events in uranium-235 or plutonium-239.*

Starting out as fast neutrons, the neutrons lose considerable energy with each inelastic impact. As the neutron velocity decreases, the U-235 fission cross section increases and fission capture becomes more and more probable.

To find the time T_f between fission events, we note that the velocity of 2 MeV neutrons is approximately 2×10^7 m/s, while the average velocity of thermal neutrons (0.0253 eV) is 2.2×10^3 m/s. If we adopt a geometric average velocity of 2×10^5 m/s, and an average mean free path for scattering of 4 cm, as given by Eq.(73j), *the average time between scattering events will be*

$$T_s = \frac{0.04 \text{ m}}{2 \times 10^5 \text{ m/s}} = 2 \times 10^{-7} \text{ s} \quad (73l)$$

Allowing an average of five scattering events before fission capture, we obtain

$$T_f = 1 \times 10^{-6} \text{ s} \quad (73m)$$

Owing to the random directions of the inelas-

tic scattering (see Fig. 73G) the average diffusion distance or *straight-line* distance between fission events is from 5 to 8 cm.

The critical mass for a nuclear explosive device should lie somewhere between the size of a marble (2 cm diameter) and the size of a basketball (24 cm diameter). Visualize, therefore, two spheres of pure U-235 or Pu-239, one large and one small, as shown in Fig. 73H. It is clear that

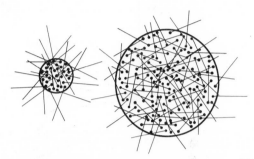

Fig. 73H *Schematic diagram of pure uranium-235, or plutonium-239, showing escape of most of the neutrons for a subcritical size, and capture of most of the neutrons for greater than critical size.*

if the average straight-line distance between fission events is 6 cm (see Fig. 73G) few neutrons will be captured in the small sphere, while many will be captured in a mass the size of a basketball.

Whether or not any mass will sustain a chain reaction at all is determined by what is called the *reproduction factor*. The reproduction factor k is given by the ratio,

$$k = \frac{\text{rate of neutron production}}{\text{rate of neutron disappearance}} \quad (73n)$$

If the rate of neutron production equals the rate at which neutrons disappear, the mass is said to be *critical*, and $k = 1$.

Curves showing the growth in an assembly where k is slightly greater, and slightly smaller, than unity are given in Fig. 73I. Since one generation of neutrons requires about 1 μs [see Eq.(73m)], the horizontal scale can represent time in microseconds.

In five generations the curve $k = 1.1$ rises to 1.61, since

$1.1 \times 1.1 \times 1.1 \times 1.1 \times 1.1 = 1.61$ neutrons

In ten generations this same curve rises to

Fig. 73I *Growth curves for neutrons with reproduction factors barely above and below critical,*
k = 1.

$(1.1)^{10}$ or 2.59 neutrons, and in 100 generations to $(1.1)^{100}$ or 1×10^5 neutrons. In 1000 generations, or approximately $\frac{1}{1000}$ of a second, the number rises to approximately 1×10^{41} neutrons. Since this represents more atoms than would be available in any given assembly, 1000 generations would not materialize.

In pure U-235, or Pu-239 the size of a marble, the reproduction factor is approximately 0.1, while for a sphere the size of a basketball, $k = 2.4$.

The relation between the reproduction factor k and the number of neutrons produced x, is given by

$$k^n = x \qquad (73o)$$

where n is the number of generations. Taking the logarithm of both sides of Eq.(73o) gives

$$\log k^n = \log x$$

or

$$n \log k = \log x \qquad (73p)$$

73.7. Nuclear Reactors. A nuclear reactor,

formerly called an atomic pile, is an apparatus in which nuclear fission can be maintained as a self-supporting yet controlled chain reaction. It is a kind of furnace in which uranium is the fuel burned, and many useful products such as heat, neutrons, and radioactive isotopes are products.

Reactors are of many kinds, sizes, and shapes, the two principal ingredients of them being a quantity of fissionable material, and a moderating substance for slowing down the neutrons to thermal velocities. A reactor is often designated according to the moderator, or coolant, used within it. Because of the immensity of the subject, only the simplest elements of these devices will be described here, and these as illustrations of the basic principles of many others.

A self-sustaining chain reaction cannot be maintained in pure uranium alone, no matter how large the mass. By properly combining or surrounding the metal with a moderator, however, the 2-MeV neutrons produced in the fission of U-235 can be slowed down by elastic scattering to thermal energies of 0.0253 eV. At these relatively low velocities of 2200 m/s, the fission cross section of U-235 has the enormous value of 580 barns (see Table 73B).

The cross sections of a few nuclear fuels at thermal energy are given in Table 73E.

The first self-sustaining chain reaction ever created by man was put into operation at the University of Chicago on December 2, 1942. This device consisted of a huge "pile" of small carbon blocks, carefully laid together to form one solid mass about the size of a normal school room. During construction, lumps of pure uranium metal were inserted at regular intervals throughout the mass.

A schematic diagram of a pile constructed of large carbon blocks is shown in Fig. 73J. Long

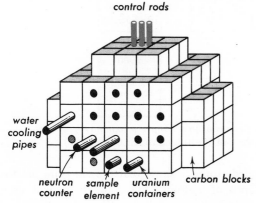

control rods

water cooling pipes

neutron counter sample element uranium containers carbon blocks

Fig. 73J   *Uranium pile of carbon blocks used to produce plutonium-239 and many other radioactive atomic nuclei. (Concrete protective walls are not shown.)*

cylindrical holes through the blocks provide for the insertion or removal of fuel elements, control rods, detecting devices, samples to be irradiated, etc. The fuel elements consist of pure uranium metal sealed in thin-walled aluminum cylinders.

The distance between uranium fuel elements in the moderator material is of importance in reactor design. The slowing-down distances for three commonly used moderators are as follows:

Ordinary water,	H_2O	5.7 cm
Heavy water,	D_2O	11.0 cm
Carbon blocks,	C	19.0 cm

When, within the uranium metal, a few U-235

nuclei undergo fission, fast neutrons are liberated. Most of these enter the surrounding carbon (the moderator), where they collide elastically with carbon nuclei and slow down. Eventually, many of them enter the uranium metal as thermal neutrons and are captured by U-235 nuclei to cause fission. A diagram showing this process is given in Fig. 73K.

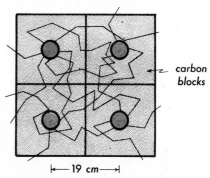

carbon blocks

|←— 19 cm —→|

Fig. 73K   *Diagram showing moderator action in an atomic reactor. Elastic collisions of neutrons with carbon nuclei slows the neutrons to thermal energies.*

Not all neutrons produced within a reactor result in capture by U-235. Some are lost by escape through the surface, some by radiative capture by U-235 as well as U-238, and some by capture by structural materials and fission products.

The neutron balance in a natural uranium reactor, operating at the critical rate $k = 1$, is shown in Fig. 73L. Of the millions of fast neutrons produced in the reactor in each microsecond, the diagram starts with 1000 fast neutrons at the center, and shows what might reasonably happen to them in regenerating 1000 more fast neutrons. The average number of neutrons produced per fission is 2.5. This factor is directly involved in the bottom four squares where it is used in accounting for reproduction. It should be noted that 60% of the neutrons disappear by other than fission processes.

If the reproduction factor k of the reactor assembly is greater than unity [see Eq.(73n)], the total number of neutrons will rise, and along with it the temperature. To prevent the temperature from rising too high, control rods, which

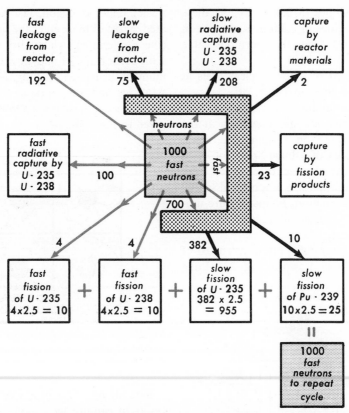

Fig. 73L   *A block diagram showing the balance of neutrons in a natural uranium reactor that is just critical.* (Calculated numbers by courtesy of Westinghouse Electric Corp.)

are strong neutron absorbers, are lowered into the central core.

The most widely used control rods, or plates, contain boron or cadmium. Both of these elements have enormous capture cross sections for slow neutrons. When *normal cadmium metal* is subjected to thermal neutrons, the *average cross section* is 2500 barns. Experiments with sepa-

rated isotopes show that the six principal isotopes of cadmium have the individual cross sections shown in Table 73F.

Direct experimental evidence for the large cross section of Cd-113 is shown in Fig. 73M.

Fig. 73M *Normal cadmium mass spectrogram (above) and isotopes altered by neutron absorption (below).* (After Dempster.)

TABLE 73F. THERMAL NEUTRON CAPTURE
CROSS SECTIONS FOR CADMIUM ISOTOPES

Isotope (A)	Abundance (%)	Cross section (barns)
110	12.4	0.20
111	12.7	0.26
112	24.1	0.03
113	12.3	20,000
114	28.9	0.14
116	7.6	1.5

The upper photograph is a mass-spectrograph record of the five principal stable isotopes of cadmium made with the metal as normally refined. The lower reproduction is a similar record made with cadmium metal after it had been subjected to intense neutron irradiation in a reactor. Note that the isotope 113 is missing and that isotope 114 is enhanced. The capture of a neutron by Cd-113 produces Cd-114.

An excellent demonstration can be made by placing a piece of metallic silver in a thin-walled box made of cadmium metal and subjecting it to a Ra–Be neutron source as shown in Fig. 69D. After some time the silver is removed from the cadmium box and placed near a Geiger or scintillation counter. No counts will be recorded. If the silver metal is subjected to the neutrons without the cadmium shield, it will show considerable β activity, as expected.

73.8. Power Reactors o⁻ Nuclear Power Plants. To utilize the natural heat developed in a uranium reactor as a source of great power has long been recognized as a feasible enterprise. The basic principles of one type of "power reactor" are shown in Fig. 73N. A quantity of enriched

pushed in a little farther to absorb more neutrons, while to raise the temperature they are pulled out a little farther.

Because of the harmful effects of the intense neutron radiation upon men and equipment, it is not reasonable to vaporize a liquid directly as in a steam boiler; it is better to circulate a fluid through the shielded reactor and heat-exchanger, as shown in the diagram.

The hot liquid flowing through the heat-exchanger vaporizes a more volatile liquid like water; the resulting hot gas or steam under pressure drives a turbine of special design. The turbine in turn drives an electric generator, developing power that can be used to light our cities and factories or to drive ships and submarines through the water and large planes through the air.

One of the problems connected with such power reactors is the effect of the intense neutron radiation on the metal structures. The neutrons change some atoms and permanently dis-

Fig. 73N *Schematic diagram of one type of nuclear power plant.*

uranium, in the form of a pure metal or in the form of a solution of soluble salt in water forms the center of the heat energy source.

The energy released by fission produces great quantities of heat, and the rising temperature is regulated to a predetermined value by cadmium rods. To reduce the fission rate, and thereby lower the temperature, the control rods are

place others from their normal positions in the crystal lattice of the solids, and as a result weaken certain crucial mechanical parts. Intensive studies of the properties of various materials under conditions likely to be encountered in power reactors are continually carried on in our research laboratories.

Another important problem concerns the nature of the coolant; it must be able to withstand high temperatures and must not absorb neutrons and become radioactive to any appreciable extent; yet it must be efficient in the transfer of heat in both the reactor and the heat exchanger. Certain metals with low melting points appear to be most promising in these and other respects.

73.9. Swimming-Pool Reactor. The swimming-pool type of reactor derives its name from the fact that a large tank of ordinary water is used as a protective shield for the operating personnel. Figure 73O is a cut-away diagram of a typical

Fig. 73O *Cross-section diagram of a "swimming pool" type of reactor, showing fuel elements, carbon moderator, and access channels and equipment at the bottom. (Courtesy, General Atomics.)*

reactor of this kind, and one that is designed as a multipurpose instrument. The several fuel elements at the bottom of the tank are in the form of small cylindrical rods; each is composed of a solid homogeneous alloy of uranium and zirconium hydride moderator, clad in their aluminum cylinders. The uranium is enriched to 20% of U-235. The three control rods are of boron carbide.

Full physical and visual access to the core is possible at all times from the top, as shown in Fig. 73P. Samples to be irradiated by neutrons can be lowered into the water in the region of the core, and an observer can readily see the blue glow of the water around it, which is caused by the Cerenkov radiation.

A rotary specimen rack ("lazy susan") located just above the large carbon or graphite moderator block, provides a water-tight facility for radioactive isotope production. A pneumatic tube running to the bottom of the tank permits a sample element, in a small container called a *rabbit*, to be subjected to neutrons and quickly removed for the measurement of very short half-lives.

73.10. Uncontrolled Fusion. We have seen in Sec. 73.7 how the sun, and other stars, by means of certain nuclear reaction cycles and temperatures of millions of degrees, are able to fuse protons into α particles (hydrogen into helium), with the simultaneous emission of great quantities of energy. While all of the ingredients needed in these reactions are plentiful on the earth's surface, and can be purified and assembled in the research laboratory, the temperature of several million degrees required to cause them to fuse cannot be produced by any of the standard laboratory methods.

Here the atomic bomb employing the process of fission has come to our aid and made such temperatures possible. When an atomic bomb, containing U-235 or Pu-239, explodes, the temperature reached at the central core, although it may last only a small fraction of a second, is comparable to that reached at the center of the sun.

While superatomic bombs containing hydrogen and other light elements have been highly successful, the exact materials used, their proportions, the physical size and shape of the devices, and the mechanical and electrical systems involved are all classified by governments as secret military information. These same government agencies, however, do conduct, through their civilian directed laboratories, scientific research projects on the peaceful uses of nuclear explosions.

Fig. 73P *Photograph looking down through the water to the principal elements at the bottom of a "swimming pool" type of reactor.* (Courtesy, General Atomics.)

In the interest of knowledge itself, it should be said that through the study of explosive reactions we can learn more of nature's fathomless mysteries. We can look, for example, at some of the lightest of nuclides and select several reactions that look promising from an energy standpoint. Five promising reactions involving the hydrogen and lithium isotopes are

$$_1H^2 + {_1H^2} \rightarrow {_2He^3} + {_0n^1} \quad + \quad 4.0 \text{ MeV}$$
$$_1H^2 + {_1H^3} \rightarrow {_2He^4} + {_0n^1} \quad + \quad 17.6 \text{ MeV}$$
$$_1H^2 + {_3Li^6} \rightarrow {_2He^4} + {_2He^4} + 22.1 \text{ MeV}$$
$$_1H^1 + {_3Li^7} \rightarrow {_2He^4} + {_2He^4} + 17.5 \text{ MeV}$$
$$_0n^1 + {_3Li^6} \rightarrow {_2He^4} + {_1H^3} \quad + \quad 4.6 \text{ MeV}$$

Note the particularly large energies released with the fusion of deuterium with tritium, deuterium with lithium-6, and hydrogen with lithium-7.

Lithium is relatively abundant on the earth, and lithium-6 can be separated in reasonable quantities from its more abundant isotope, lithium-7. Tritium, $_1H^1$, on the other hand, is a radioactive isotope of hydrogen not found in nature, because of its relatively short half-life of 12.2 years. It is only produced in quantities, at considerable expense, in atomic reactors.

73.11. Controlled Fusion. The conviction on the part of many physicists that controlled fusion is possible has led, these past few years, to the expenditure of a great deal of scientific manpower and money.

In principle one would visualize a jet of fusible

material, such as deuterium, being fed from a nozzle into a cavity where, upon fusion, great quantities of energy in the form of heat would be continuously generated and tapped off.

From the very start of all projects working on this problem, it has been realized that, owing to the temperature requirements of millions of degrees, no material walls can be close to the region in which fusion is to be consummated. This has led many to the use of a gaseous discharge called a *plasma*, held suspended in space by the magnetic lines of force of an electromagnet.

A plasma is an electrically neutral stream or mass of ionized atoms, molecules, and electrons and may be produced in various ways. A high-current arc, such as that used in a searchlight, is a good plasma source. Plasma in many devices is confined by what has been termed a *magnetic bottle*. Visualize, as shown in Fig. 73Q, a stream of ionized atoms injected into the central region of a hollow solenoid. Moving with the high speeds of ions in a hot gas, these particles spiral around in the field with the lines of force acting as guides.

As particles spiral into the stronger field at either end, the force components drive them back again toward the center. By increasing and decreasing the currents in the field coils A, B, and C, the field shape can be modified at will and the plasma widened or narrowed. By decreasing the field at the right and progressively increasing

the field from left to right, the plasma can be transported lengthwise from one tube to another.

If all fields are increased, the plasma volume is compressed and the temperature rises. A rising temperature means higher ion velocities and greater probability that impacts will produce

Fig. 73Q *Schematic diagram of a plasma held suspended in a magnetic field: a "magnetic bottle."*

fusion. If the field is decreased at one end and increased at the other, the plasma may be quickly moved along the cylinder axis, thus constituting a jet. Plasma jet studies by various aircraft and other research laboratories offer promising results for the near future. While much has been learned from the various controlled-fusion study projects, there is still much to be discovered before successful power sources are realized. There are many who now believe that greater research effort should be placed on studies of the basic principles of the plasma itself and that eventual rewards will be well worth the effort.

PROBLEMS

1. Since the critical size for a uranium-235 explosion lies between a marble and a basketball, find (a) the ratio of these sphere diameters, (b) the ratio of their surface areas, (c) the ratio of their volumes, and (d) the ratio of volume to surface area (see Sec. 73.6 for sizes).

2. Find (a) the radius and (b) the geometrical cross section for the nucleus of silver-109. [*Ans.* (a) 5.73×10^{-15} m. (b) 1.03 barns.]

3. Find (a) the radius and (b) the geometrical cross section for the nucleus of mercury-202.

4. If the reproduction factor for fission in a mass of U-235 is 1.20, how many secondary neutrons will be produced in (a) 5 generations, (b) 10 generations, (c) 100 generations, and (d) 1000 generations? (Note: Use logarithms.) [*Ans.* (a) 2.49. (b) 6.19. (c) 8.28×10^7. (d) 1.52×10^{79}.]

5. If the reproduction factor for fission in a mass of Pu-239 is 1.38, how many secondary neutrons will be produced in (a) 5 generations, (b) 10 generations, and (c) 100 generations? (Note: Use logarithms.)

6. The reproduction factor in a mass of U-235 is 1.05. (a) How many neutron generations will occur in 2 ms, and (b) how many secondary neutrons will be released? [*Ans.* (a) 2000. (b) 2.39×10^{42}.]

7. The reproduction factor in a mass of Pu-239 is 1.26. (a) How many neutron generations will occur in $\frac{1}{10}$ of a millisecond, and (b) how many secondary neutrons will be released?

8. (a) Find the total macroscopic cross section for thermal neutrons in pure U-235. (b) Find the total mean free path. [*Ans.* (a) 33.4 cm^{-1}. (b) 0.299 mm.]

9. (a) Find the macroscopic fission cross section for

thermal neutrons in pure U-235. (b) Find the corresponding mean free path.

10. (a) Find the total macroscopic fission cross section for thermal neutrons in pure Pu-239. (b) Find the corresponding mean free path. (Assume the density of Pu to be 17 g/cm³.) [*Ans.* (a) 46.0 cm⁻¹. (b) 0.21 mm.]

11. (a) Find the macroscopic scattering cross section for thermal neutrons in pure Pu-239. (b) Find the corresponding mean free path. (Assume the density of Pu to be 17 g/cm³.)

12. Calculate the average cross section in barns for thermal neutrons on the six cadmium isotopes given in Table 73F. [*Ans.* 2460 barns.]

ELEMENTARY PARTICLES

For many decades now, physicists have been searching for the ultimate particles of which all matter is composed. From the atom and its electron structure, the search has extended into the nucleus, and from the nucleus to the structure of nucleons themselves.

The purpose behind the planning and building of atomic accelerators that will produce higher and higher energies, reaching into the BeV and hundreds of BeV ranges, has been, and continues to be, the hitting of nuclei harder and harder. When a nucleon is hit by a very high energy particle, a variety of particles are frequently produced.

The questions concerning the origin and nature of these particles present challenging problems to experimentalist and theorist alike. Do these particles exist in some strange form within the nucleus, or are they created from the release of mass and impact energy? If they are created, what is the mechanism involved? How long do they last, and what becomes of their energy?

In this chapter we will take a brief look at some recent discoveries and observations in "high-energy physics," in the hopes that such glimpses may instill some interest and give you, the reader, some clue as to what new experiments might be performed that would shed new light on these "elementary particles."

74.1. Elementary Particles. With the discovery of the neutron by Chadwick in 1932, the number of elementary particles became four in number: the *electron*, the *proton*, the *neutron*, and the *photon*. The first three are the atomic particles of which atoms are built, while the photon is the quantum unit of radiation emitted or absorbed by the electrons in the outer structure of atoms or by the particles within the nucleus.

The photon can only exist when traveling with the speed of light, and because of its motion possesses energy $h\nu$. By the mass–energy relation, $E = mc^2$, a photon also has mass $h\nu/c^2$. It possesses mass by virtue of its motion, for at rest it would have no energy and no mass.

The electron, proton, and neutron, on the other hand, have a definite rest mass m_0 and a rest energy m_0c^2. When they are set into motion, their mass increases, and their total energy is given by mc^2.

74.2. Antiparticles. The positron, discovered by Anderson in 1932, is a positively charged electron. We have seen in Sec. 66.11 how electron pairs can be created and how a free positron in coming together with an electron is annihilated with the energy appearing in the form of two γ rays. It is this very property that gives the positron the name *antiparticle*—it destroys itself along with an electron and becomes another form of energy.

We have also seen in Fig. 69N that, when a high-energy photon comes close to the nucleus, mesons may be produced. If a pair of mesons is produced, one positive and one negative, one is the antiparticle of the other. These π-mesons may react with other nuclei or they may decay into muons as shown in Fig. 66Q. The muons in turn may decay into electrons and positrons, or they may be captured by some other nucleus.

The discovery of the positron, three pions $\bar{\pi}^+$, π^0, and π^-, the two muons μ^+ and μ^-, along with the two neutrinos ν and $\bar{\nu}$, raised the number of elementary particles by 1947 to twelve.

The number of known particles expanded rapidly between 1947 and 1954, and there were added four new groups of heavier particles that became known collectively as "strange particles." In the order of increasing mass these were called K particles, Λ particles, Σ particles, and Ξ particles.

Although the proton carries a positive charge its symbol is usually written p. A bar over any symbol represents an antiparticle. For example, $\bar{e}^+$ represents an antielectron, or positron.

74.3. K Particles. These elementary particles belong to the meson class, have a mass of about 970 electron masses, yet have no spin angular momentum. Being heavier by far than π mesons they have more possible methods, or modes, of decay. K^+ particles have a mean life of 1.2×10^{-8} s and decay with the following modes. For a definition of mean life, see Sec. 63.2.

$$
\begin{aligned}
K^+ &\to \bar{\mu}^+ + \nu_\mu & 59\% \\
K^+ &\to \bar{\pi}^+ + \pi^0 & 26\% \ (\theta \text{ mode}) \\
K^+ &\to \bar{\pi}^+ + \bar{\pi}^+ + \pi^- & 5\% \ (\tau \text{ mode}) \\
K^+ &\to \bar{\mu}^+ + \nu_\mu + \pi^0 & 4\% \\
K^+ &\to \bar{e}^+ + \nu_e + \pi^0 & 4\% \\
K^+ &\to \bar{\pi}^+ + \pi^0 + \pi^0 & 2\%
\end{aligned}
\tag{74a}
$$

The K^0 and $\bar{K}^-$ particles have similar decay modes, and the K^0 has a mean life of 1×10^{-10} s. These particles are frequently called *kaons*.

74.4. Λ⁰ Particles. All Λ^0 particles are neutral; that is, they have no charge. Their mass is approximately 2185 electron masses, which means they are heavier than nucleons. Since their mass is about 75 electron masses heavier than a proton plus a pion, it is not surprising to find that when they decay they carry out the following reactions.

$$
\begin{aligned}
\Lambda^0 &\to p + \pi^- \\
\Lambda^0 &\to n + \pi^0 \\
\Lambda^0 &\to p^- + \bar{\pi}^+
\end{aligned}
\tag{74b}
$$

Λ^0 particles have a mean life of 2.5×10^{-10} s.

All elementary particles heavier than nucleons are called *hyperons*, and by including protons and neutrons they are called *baryons*.

74.5. Σ Particles. These baryons are of three kinds, Σ^+, Σ^0, and Σ^-, and have a mass of approximately 2335 m_e. They have a spin angular momentum of $\frac{1}{2}\hbar$, and decay with a mean life of 10^{-10}, by the following modes,

$$
\begin{aligned}
\Sigma^+ &\to p + \pi^0 \\
\Sigma^+ &\to n + \bar{\pi}^+ \\
\Sigma^- &\to n + \pi^- \\
\Sigma^0 &\to \Lambda^0 + \gamma
\end{aligned}
\tag{74c}
$$

74.6. Ξ Particles. These baryons are about 130 electron masses heavier than $\Lambda + \pi$ and belong to the baryon class. They also have a spin of $\frac{1}{2}\hbar$ and decay principally by the following modes:

$$
\begin{aligned}
\Xi^- &\to \Lambda^0 + \pi^- \\
\Xi^0 &\to \Lambda^0 + \pi^0
\end{aligned}
\tag{74d}
$$

74.7 Photographic Emulsions. When a photon or ionizing particle traverses the sensitive emulsion of a photographic film, the clear silver bromide crystal grains that are penetrated are turned into black silver upon development by regular film-developing processes.

Since the sensitive emulsion on most film is extremely thin, satisfactory emulsions up to 1 mm in thickness, containing about 80% silver bromide, were first developed by C. F. Powell in England. These can be stacked in layers to build up larger volumes, exposed to high-energy nuclear beams, or cosmic rays, and then developed (see Fig. 74A). By studying consecutively

Fig. 74A *Numbered stack of extra-thick photographic emulsions used in photographing high-energy nuclear events.*

numbered films separately, under a suitable measuring microscope, one can observe nuclear collision events and make measurements of the different particles, their directions, ranges, track densities, etc.

Track densities vary widely with particle *charge* and *velocity*, as shown in Fig. 74B. The energies required of various particles to travel 1 mm in an average nuclear emulsion are

e	0.7 MeV	p	14.0 MeV
μ	5.5 MeV	d	20.0 MeV
π	6.1 MeV	α	55.0 MeV

Because emulsion densities are far greater than the gas in a cloud chamber, the track ranges are extremely small. This high-density and short-range feature is particularly useful, therefore, to the study of nuclear events involving very high speed particles.

The procedure used for displaying emulsion tracks is to make enlargements of microscope photographs of neighboring sections, and to piece the photographic prints together as shown in Fig. 74C. These print assemblies were made from a stack of 46 emulsions, 15 cm × 15 cm, exposed at high altitude over England in 1952.

The first assembly (a) shows a "star" of tracks in emulsion 17, one track being that of a K^+ as indicated. Six cm along this track in the emulsion (this corresponds to 60 ft on the enlarged scale shown here) we come to assembly (b) from emulsion 6. There the K^+ disintegrated by the τ mode into π mesons [see Eq.(74a)]. Two cm along the π^- track, in assembly (c), the pion was captured by a heavy nucleus, resulting in a nuclear explosion. Among the secondary products

Fig. 74B *Charged particle tracks in a photographic emulsion showing differences in track density.* (Courtesy, C. F. Powell, P. H. Fowler, and D. H. Perkins, from *The Study of Elementary Particles*, Pergamon Press Ltd.)

were four singly charged particles and a $_3Li^8$ nucleus. The latter, on reaching the end of its range, emitted a β particle forming $_4Be^8$ which

Fig. 74C *Five directly related events traced through a photographic emulsion stack.* (Courtesy of C. F. Powell, P. H. Fowler, and D. H. Perkins, from *The Study of Elementary Particles*, Pergamon Press Ltd.)

spontaneously splits up into two α particles to produce the "hammer track" shown.

About 3 cm along the $\bar{\pi}^+$ track, in assembly (d), the pion decays into a $\bar{\mu}^+$ and a neutrino ν_μ. A short distance along this track, in assembly (e), the $\bar{\mu}^+$ decays into a positron $\bar{e}^+$, a neutrino ν_e, and an antineutrino $\bar{\nu}_\mu$.

The nuclear-emulsion photograph in Fig. 74D shows a "star" of 22 tracks. A primary cosmic

Fig. 74D *Photographic-emulsion star produced by a cosmic-ray proton. (Courtesy of C. F. Powell, P. H. Fowler, and D. H. Perkins, from The Study of Elementary Particles, Pergamon Press Ltd.)*

ray, a proton, enters from the top, and collides with a silver or bromine nucleus in the emulsion, causing an explosion. Most of the tracks were made by π mesons, and the others probably by Kaons and protons.

While the number of stars of this general nature is small relative to other kinds of nuclear events observed in emulsions, a great many have been observed and studied.

74.8. The Bubble Chamber. The bubble chamber, invented in 1952 by D. H. Glaser, has become one of the most valuable instruments for studying the minute details of high-energy nuclear events. In a cloud chamber, fogdrops form on the ions produced by charged atomic particles that have just previously traversed the gas-filled chamber. In the bubble chamber, the ions, formed by charged particles traversing the liquid,

form local heat centers in which tiny gas bubbles develop and grow.

The basic principles of the bubble chamber involve the superheating of a liquid and the bubbles that form in the process of boiling. Water, for example, boils at 100°C at standard atmospheric pressure. If the pressure is increased as in a pressure cooker, boiling will not begin until a higher temperature is reached. If the pressure is then suddenly reduced, boiling begins with the sudden formation of tiny bubbles that grow quickly in size.

A simplified diagram of a bubble chamber is shown in Fig. 74E. A box with thick glass walls,

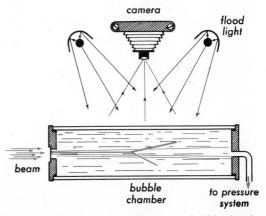

Fig. 74E *Cross-section diagram of a bubble chamber showing track illumination, camera, and incident-particle beam.*

filled with a liquid, is connected to a pressure system and then heated to some predetermined temperature. High-energy particles enter the liquid through a thin window. A sudden release of a valve in the pressure system is quickly followed by the flash of floodlights and the snap of a camera shutter. If the chamber is operating properly, and events are correctly timed, sharply defined trails of bubbles that have formed on the paths of ions made by the traversing particles will be photographed (see Figs. 74H, 74I, 74J, 74K, and 74L).

The extensive use of liquid hydrogen in bubble chambers has been particularly effective in the study of elementary and strange particle events. The difficulties of handling liquid hydrogen at -253°C in large bubble chambers have been overcome by L. Alvarez and his colleagues at the University of California over a period of several years. Liquid hydrogen is particularly useful in that it provides a high concentration of "target protons," the simplest of atomic nuclei, and at the same time greatly shortens the distance between events that would be required in the gas-filled space of a cloud chamber (see Figs. 74F and 74G).

Wiegand, and Ypsilantis at the University of California. The discovery came as the result of long-range plans laid for the purpose of answering the question, "Is there in nature, or can there be created by a strong interaction, a negatively charged particle with the mass of a proton?" One of the principal objectives in building the 6.2-BeV proton accelerator in 1953 was to find an answer to this question. Protons accelerated

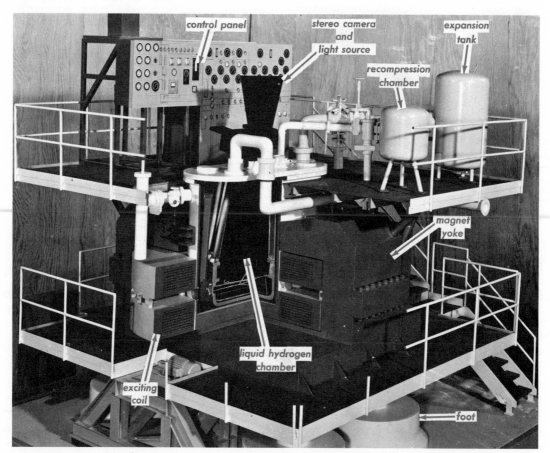

Fig. 74F *Cutaway model of the 72-inch liquid-hydrogen bubble chamber at the Lawrence Radiation Laboratory.*

It is customary to locate a bubble chamber in the strong field of a large electromagnet so that particle charge and momentum relations can be obtained from track curvature (see Figs. 74H and 74I).

74.9. Antiprotons. The existence of antiprotons was discovered in 1955 by Chamberlain, Segrè,

to a high enough energy should, in colliding with heavier nuclei, impart sufficient energy to create, if such were possible, a pair of protons, one plus, the other minus.

The first antiprotons were discovered as high-energy, negatively charged particles emerging from a copper target in the proton beam of the bevatron and having all of the anticipated properties. By means of a strong magnet the antiprotons were bent away from the protons and into a scintillation counter. Today antiproton

74.10. Baryon Reactions. An antiproton event involving the production of a baryon–antibaryon pair is reproduced in Fig. 74I. As shown in the legend diagram, an antiproton from the beva-

Fig. 74G   *Cross-section diagram of the 72-inch liquid-hydrogen bubble chamber.*

events are commonly observed and studied by means of a bubble chamber.

Figure 74H is a photograph in which an antiproton entered the liquid hydrogen bubble chamber from the left. Near the center of the picture it interacted with a proton, and both particles were annihilated in the production of four pairs of π mesons. Since the bubble chamber operated in the uniform field of a strong electromagnet, the π^- tracks curve clockwise, and the $\bar{\pi}^+$ tracks curve counterclockwise. The $\bar{\pi}^+$ that curved back to the left and down decayed into a $\bar{\mu}^+$ and an $\bar{e}^+$ as shown in the accompanying legend diagram.

The reactions for this event are written as follows:

$$\bar{p}^- + p \rightarrow 4\pi^- + 4\bar{\pi}^+$$
$$\bar{\pi}^+ \rightarrow \bar{\mu}^+ + \nu_\mu \qquad (74e)$$
$$\bar{\mu}^+ \rightarrow \bar{e}^+ + \nu_e + \bar{\nu}_\mu$$

tron target enters the bubble chamber at the left and interacts with a proton.

The track disappears at this point because the interaction with a proton in the liquid hydrogen produces a neutral lambda–antilambda pair. With only a short lifetime of about 10^{-10} s, each of these Λ^0 particles disintegrates, one into π^- and p, and the other into $\bar{p}^-$ and $\bar{\pi}^+$. The antiproton is captured by another proton at the upper right and is immediately annihilated in the production of two pion pairs. The reactions for these events are

$$\bar{p}^- + p \rightarrow \bar{\Lambda} + \Lambda$$
$$\Lambda \rightarrow p + \pi^-$$
$$\bar{\Lambda} \rightarrow \bar{p}^- + \bar{\pi}^+ \qquad (74f)$$
$$\bar{p}^- + p \rightarrow 2\bar{\pi}^+ + 2\pi^-$$

As high-energy protons from a large accelerator traverse any target material whatever, a

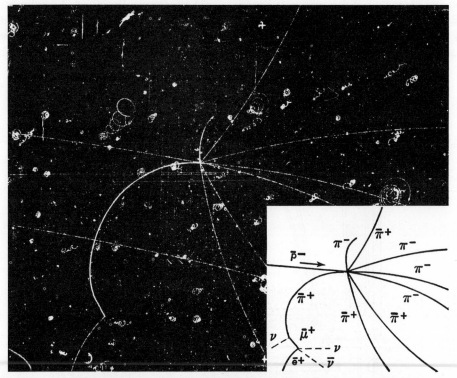

Fig. 74H   *Pi-meson star produced by the proton capture of an antiproton in a liquid-hydrogen bubble chamber.* (Courtesy, L. Alvarez and colleagues.)

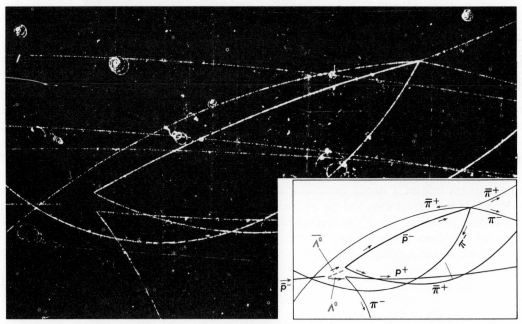

Fig. 74I   *Bubble-chamber photograph and legend diagram of correlated events involving two antiprotons, two* Λ° *particles, and seven* π *mesons.* (Courtesy, L. Alvarez and colleagues.)

considerable number of π mesons are produced along with other particles. These charged mesons, $\bar{\pi}^+$ or π^-, can be channeled, by bending in a magnetic field, to any other area for experimentation. Directed into a bubble chamber, for example, their reactions with protons can be studied.

Figure 74J is a photograph in which a π^- enters a liquid-hydrogen bubble chamber from

The bubble-chamber photograph in Fig. 74K(a) shows a series of related events involving 14 particles: $\bar{\pi}^+$, $2\pi^0$, $2\pi^-$, p, n, K^+, Σ^+, $\bar{\mu}^+$, $\bar{e}^+$, $\bar{\nu}$ and 2ν. As shown by the labeled diagram in Fig. 74K(b), one of the high-energy π^--particles enters from the left and interacts with a proton. This interaction produces Σ^- and K^+ particles. The Σ^- decays into a π^- and a neutron, while the K^+ decays into a $\bar{\pi}^+$ and two (not showing)

Fig. 74J   *Bubble-chamber photograph with π^-, p, K^0, Λ^0, $\bar{\pi}^+$, and π^- tracks, all in one related event. Legend diagram at upper right.* (Courtesy, L. Alvarez and colleagues.)

the left. As shown in the legend diagram, interaction with a proton cancels the charges and ends the track by creating two neutral particles.

These two recoiling particles K^0 and Λ^0 do not produce tracks in the chamber but, having short lifetimes, quickly disintegrate. The neutral K particle decays into a pair of pions, $\bar{\pi}^+$ and π^-, while the Λ-particle decays into a proton and a π^-. As reactions

$$\pi^- + p \rightarrow K^0 + \Lambda^0$$
$$K^0 \rightarrow \bar{\pi}^+ + \pi^- \qquad (74g)$$
$$\Lambda^0 \rightarrow p + \pi^-$$

π^0's. The $\bar{\pi}^+$ decays into a $\bar{\mu}^+$ and then $\bar{e}^+$ in the customary way.

The reactions involved may be written

$$\pi^- + p \rightarrow \Sigma^- + K^+$$
$$\Sigma^- \rightarrow \pi^- + n$$
$$K^+ \rightarrow \bar{\pi}^+ + \pi^0 + \pi^0 \qquad (74h)$$
$$\bar{\pi}^+ \rightarrow \bar{\mu}^+ + \nu_\mu$$
$$\bar{\mu}^+ \rightarrow \bar{e}^+ + \nu_e + \bar{\nu}_\mu$$

The photograph reproduced in Fig. 74L shows K^- tracks entering from the left. In the upper left, one of these particles collides with a carbon

Fig. 74K(a) *Bubble-chamber photograph (in liquid hydrogen) of correlated events involving Σ^- and K^+ particles. See legend diagram below. (Courtesy, L. Alvarez and colleagues.)*

Fig. 74L *Propane bubble-chamber photograph of an event involving K mesons and a Ξ particle. (Courtesy, Wilson Powell and colleagues.)*

nucleus and produces three charged particles, as shown by the three-pronged fork. Energy and momentum calculations from the measured tracks show that the reaction is

$$\bar{K}^- + {}_6C^{12} \rightarrow K^+ + \Xi^- + p + {}_4Be^{10} \quad (74i)$$

The lower prong of the fork is the K^+ particle, which decays into a neutrino ν_μ and a $\bar{\mu}^+$ recoiling down to the left:

$$K^+ \rightarrow \bar{\mu}^+ + \nu_\mu$$

The middle prong of the fork is the Ξ^- particle which at the bend in the middle of the picture decays into a π^- and a Λ^0:

$$\Xi^- \rightarrow \pi^- + \Lambda^0$$

The neutral Λ^0-particle, recoiling to the right, creates no track but quickly decays into a π^-

and a p to form the V-shaped track at the right:

$$\Lambda^0 \rightarrow \pi^- + p$$

74.11. Spark-Chamber Detectors. One of the most recent instruments developed for use in the study of high-energy nuclear reactions is known as the *spark chamber*. This device is composed of a stack of equally spaced conducting plates as shown by the cross-section diagram in Fig. 74M.

A typical chamber will have 25 to 100 plates,

Fig. 74K(b) *Labeled track pattern for bubble-chamber photograph in Fig. 74K(a).*

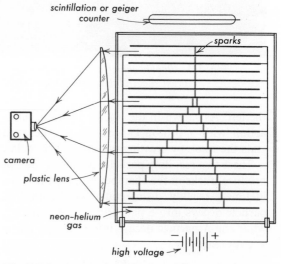

Fig. 74M *Cross-section diagram of a spark-chamber detector used for observing high-energy nuclear reactions involving elementary particles.*

each about 1 mm thick and 1 m square, and accurately spaced about 6 mm apart. Alternate plates are connected together and the two sets connected to a 10,000 to 15,000 V dc source. The airtight vessel in which the plates are mounted contains pure helium, or a mixture of approximately 90% neon and 10% helium, at a pressure of 1 atmosphere.

When a high-energy charged particle enters such a chamber, a detector outside the chamber, or inside, triggers the high voltage to the plates, and opens the camera shutter. Traversing the chamber a charged particle produces many ion pairs along its path, and sparks jump between the pairs of oppositely charged plates as indicated. A large lens, cut from clear plastic, makes it possible for a camera to photograph the light from sparks between all plates. A second large lens and camera "looking into" an adjacent side of the box permits the simultaneous taking of two pictures, thereby recording stereoscopic photos of each event.

A photograph of a proton scattered by a carbon nucleus is shown in Fig. 74N. This picture shows only one of several events diagramed above. A beam of $\bar{\pi}^+$ mesons, produced by the 6.3-BeV proton beam of the bevatron, passes through a target containing hydrogen. Upon collision with another proton, a K^+ meson and a Σ^+ baryon are produced. The K^+ decays into a $\bar{\mu}^+$ and a neutrino [see Eq.(74a), fourth equation]. The Σ^+ decays into a proton and a π^0 [see Eq.(74c), first equation]. The proton, detected as it enters the carbon plate spark chamber, is photographed as shown. The horizontal and vertical white lines in the photo are the image of a grid used for making measurements.

74.12. Omega Meson. The ω^0 is an atomic particle composed of three π mesons, and was first detected by Alvarez, Maglic, Rosenfeld, and Stevenson in 1961. Antiproton reactions in a hydrogen bubble chamber frequently give rise to four-pronged tracks of the kind shown in Fig. 74O. Momentum and energy measurements of many such events clearly show that two pairs of oppositely charged pions are responsible for the four emergent tracks. Frequently, however, one pair of pions is produced and the remaining

Fig. 74N *Spark chamber photograph of the scattering of a proton by a carbon nucleus.* (Courtesy of E. F. Beal, Bruce Cork, D. Keefe, P. G. Murphy, and W. A. Wenzel, and the Lawrence Radiation Laboratory.)

mass quickly decays (in about 10^{-22} s) into three pions, $\bar{\pi}^+ + \pi^0 + \pi^-$. Before decaying, this uncharged particle, with a mass of 1540 m_e, is called an ω^0 particle. The alternate reactions for this event are

$$\bar{p}^- + p \rightarrow 2\bar{\pi}^+ + 2\pi^-$$

or

$$\bar{p}^- + p \rightarrow \bar{\pi}^+ + \pi^- + \omega$$

followed by

$$\omega \rightarrow \bar{\pi}^+ + \pi^0 + \pi^-$$

An excellent illustration of the decay of a $\bar{\pi}^+$ into a $\bar{\mu}^+$ and $\bar{e}^+$ is shown at the lower right in Fig. 74O (see Fig. 66P).

In the upper right in Fig. 74O, a π^- is captured by a proton to produce a neutron and a π^0. Normally a π^0 decays into γ rays, but about one out of eighty such neutral particles converts one of the γ rays into an electron pair. Such a *Dalitz pair*, as it is called, is shown by the oppositely

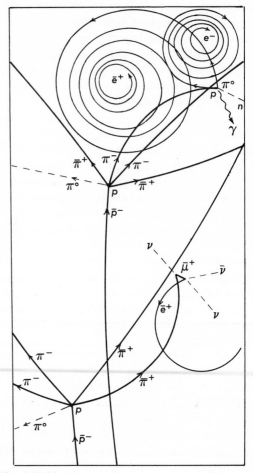

Fig. 74O(a) *Photograph of antiproton reactions in a hydrogen bubble chamber showing meson pairs in the kind of reaction that first led to the identification of the ω meson.* (Courtesy of the Lawrence Radiation Laboratory, and L. W. Alvarez and associates.)

Fig. 74O(b) *Legend diagram for Fig. 74O(a) showing the uncharged trackless particles as dotted lines.*

directed spirals. The reactions for this event are

$$\pi^- + p \rightarrow \pi^0 + n$$
$$\pi^0 \rightarrow \bar{e}^+ + e^- + \gamma \text{ ray}$$

74.13. Particle Classification. The energy-level diagram in Fig. 74P represents an orderly array of 89 *strongly interacting* and *elementary particles* known today. Some of these particles were predicted before they were identified in laboratory experiments.

The vertical column of symbols and numbers on the right gives the *particle designations* suggested for general adoption by Chew, Gell-

Mann, and Rosenfeld, along with the *rest-mass energy* in millions of electron volts, MeV, and the particles *spin angular momentum J* in units of $\hbar$. The numbers in the third row across the top give the *baryon number*, or *atomic mass*, *A*, and the numbers in the fourth row give the *particle charge Q* in units of the electronic charge *e*. All mesons (center) and leptons (bottom) have mass number $A = 0$.

One scale on the left gives the rest mass in multiples of the electronic mass m_e, and the other scale the rest mass in MeV. The specifically labeled dots, with the exception of ω^0, represent the 30 so-called elementary particles identified prior to 1957. Note that the left half of the table is a mirror image of the right half.

Fig. 74P *Energy-level diagram of strongly interacting and elementary particles as compiled by Geoffrey F. Chew, Murray Gell-Mann, and Arthur H. Rosenfeld. (Scientific American, February 1964)*

$$m_e c^2 = 0.511 \text{ MeV}$$

The photon $h\nu$, the π^0, and the η^0 are placed on the center line because they differ from all the rest in one respect: each of these particles acts as its own antiparticle.

The very interesting idea put forward that some distant galaxies in the heavens might be made up of antimatter might well be true. In such a galaxy, all hydrogen atoms would be made of antiprotons and positrons, and the protons and electrons would be their antiparticles. Thus Fig. 74P carries a double meaning, and *either half represents the antiparticles for the other half.*

74.14. Nuclear Spin and Isotopic Spin. The concept of nuclear spin J was introduced in Sec. 71.7 to explain the hyperfine structure of spectrum lines as well as the measured magnetic moments of neutrons and protons. The neutrino was then introduced into β decay in order to maintain the conservation laws of energy, momentum, and angular momentum.

In writing down nuclear reactions as equations, the *law of conservation of electrical charge* is always imposed as part of the balancing process. Since elementary particles carry a charge of $+1$, 0, or -1, Heisenberg was the first to apply quantum numbers to charge and refer to the concept as *isotopic spin.*

While both words in this term are misnomers, they arose from the idea that pairs of particles like nucleons, and triplets like the π mesons, may be thought of as isotopes and that their charges, differing from each other by unity, suggest space quantization like electron spin and orbit in a magnetic field (see Fig. 52P).

Chew, Gell-Mann, and Rosenfeld use the symbol I to represent the isotopic spin quantum number proposed by Heisenberg.

Within the nucleus, short-range forces between neutrons and protons are exactly alike, but the ever-present Coulomb forces between protons removes this symmetry and we are able to differentiate between the two different kinds of nucleons. In an effort to formulate a theory of these differences, particle charge has been likened to a vector, here called isotopic spin, and differences in charge have been compared with the space

quantization of a spin vector in a field (see Fig. 74Q).

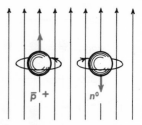

Fig. 74Q *Schematic diagram of isotopic spin, a kind of charge quantization for elementary doublets like the neutron and proton.*

By this analogy a nucleon may be thought of as a particle with an isotopic spin of $I = \frac{1}{2}$ and a *spin average* or center of $\overline{Q} = +\frac{1}{2}$. If the particle spin lines up with the spin average, we have a proton with isotopic spin $I = +1$; if it lines up in the opposite direction we have a neutron with isotopic spin $I = 0$.

The isotopic spin of antinucleons is $I = -\frac{1}{2}$, and with a spin average or center of $\overline{Q} = -\frac{1}{2}$, this gives $Q = 0$ for the antineutron and $Q = -1$ for the antiproton.

The pions form a triplet, with charges $+1$, 0, -1. This particle is therefore assigned an isotopic spin of $I = 1$. Applying the concept of space quantization to this vector magnitude, we obtain three possible orientations as shown in Fig. 74R. These three positions, centered at

Fig. 74R *Schematic diagram of isotopic spin, a kind of charge quantization for elementary triplets like π mesons.*

charge $\overline{Q} = 0$, give $Q = +1$, 0, and -1, corresponding to π^+, π^0, and π^-.

It would seem that this fiction of comparing electrical charge with spin orientation in a field might have some basic foundation and that additional experimental data will lead to a more acceptable theory of the basic concept we call electric charge.

74.15. Particle Symbols and Quantum Numbers. It will be observed in Fig. 74P that all particles occur in families, or charge multiplets: *singlets, doublets, triplets,* and *quadruplets.* Within each multiplet, particles differ only in electrical charge Q.

Only ten different patterns of baryons and mesons are known or predicted and each is represented by a different set of three quantum numbers, A, Y, and I.

QUANTUM NUMBER A, called the *baryon number*, has the value $+1$, 0, or -1 for all particles, and represents the familiar atomic mass number long used for nuclei. For uranium-238, $A = 238$, etc.

QUANTUM NUMBER Y, called the *hypercharge*, is assigned the whole number value given by twice the average charge of a multiplet.

$$Y = 2\overline{Q} \tag{74j}$$

For the nucleon doublet p^+ and n^0, for example, the average charge $\overline{Q} = (1 + 0)/2 = +1/2$. This gives $Y = 2\overline{Q} = +1$.

QUANTUM NUMBER I, called *isotopic spin*, gives the number of particles in a multiplet. The multiplicity is given by

$$M = 2I + 1 \tag{74k}$$

For Δ particles, for example, $I = \frac{3}{2}$ and the multiplicity $M = 2 \times \frac{3}{2} + 1 = 4$.

The quantum numbers assigned each of the ten known family patterns are given in Table 74A.

As an example of the proposed symbolism, a particle designated N^0, 939, $\frac{1}{2}$, is a *neutron* with quantum numbers $A = 1$, $Y = 1$, $I = \frac{1}{2}$, $J = \frac{1}{2}$, and a rest-mass energy of 939 MeV. Similarly a particle designated $\overline{\Sigma}^-$, 1193, $\frac{1}{2}$, is an *antisigma baryon* with quantum numbers $A = -1$, $Y = 0$, $I = 1$, $J = \frac{1}{2}$, and a rest mass of 1193 MeV. A particle designated $\overline{K}^0$, 496, 0, is an antiparticle *kappa* with quantum numbers $A = 0$, $Y = -1$, $I = \frac{1}{2}$, $J = 0$, and rest-mass energy of 496 MeV.

All baryons and mesons, along with their anti-

TABLE 74A. ELEMENTARY PARTICLE QUANTUM NUMBERS

Baryons		A	Y	I	S
Lambda	Λ	1	0	0	-1
Omega	Ω	1	-2	0	-3
Nucleon	N	1	1	$\frac{1}{2}$	0
Xi	Ξ	1	-1	$\frac{1}{2}$	-2
Sigma	Σ	1	0	1	-1
Delta	Δ	1	1	$\frac{3}{2}$	0

Mesons		A	Y	I	S
Eta	H	0	0	0	0
Kappa	K	0	1	$\frac{1}{2}$	1
Pi	π	0	0	1	0

Antibaryons		A	Y	I	S
Lambda	$\overline{\Lambda}$	-1	0	0	1
Omega	$\overline{\Omega}$	-1	$+2$	0	3
Nucleon	$\overline{N}$	-1	-1	$\frac{1}{2}$	0
Xi	$\overline{\Xi}$	-1	$+1$	$\frac{1}{2}$	2
Sigma	$\overline{\Sigma}$	-1	0	1	1
Delta	$\overline{\Delta}$	-1	-1	$\frac{3}{2}$	0

Antimesons		A	Y	I	S
Eta	$\overline{H}$	0	0	0	0
Kappa	$\overline{K}$	0	-1	$\frac{1}{2}$	-1
Pi	$\overline{\pi}$	0	0	1	0

particles, are frequently referred to as *strange particles*. The quantum number called the *strangeness number S* was introduced in 1957 to predict which new particles might be produced by impact, that is, by strong interactions. It is now known that the strangeness number assigned to each particle family is related to the hypercharge quantum number Y and baryon number A as follows:

$$S = Y - A$$

The strangeness number for the predicted and recently found particle Ω^-, 1676, $\frac{3}{2}$, for example, is $S = -2 - 1 = -3$.

74.16. Conservation Laws. Throughout the many chapters of this book we have encountered practically all of the fundamental laws of nature, conservation laws, Newton's laws, Keppler's laws, Kirchhoff's laws, gas laws, Ohm's law, Wien's law, and many others. These laws are not to be looked upon as laws of nature so much as they are as a means of describing the way nature behaves.

Nature it seems has chosen only one law and the job of the scientist is to find it. Perhaps someday we will.

Thus far in the history of science man has come up with a number of laws he considers basic. Of these fundamental laws, those classified by the word *conservation* should be listed at the top. Some quantities in nature seem to be conserved in some kinds of processes and not in others, while other quantities seem to be conserved in all situations and under all circumstances.

The following is a list of the seven laws found to hold in all particle interactions.

Law 1. *The total energy, including mass, remains constant.*

Law 2. *The total linear momentum remains constant.*

Law 3. *The total angular momentum remains constant.*

Law 4. *The total charge remains constant.*

Law 5. *The total electron family number remains constant.*

Law 6. *The total muon family number remains constant.*

Law 7. *The total baryon number remains constant.*

Everything that can happen without violating these laws does happen. The first four laws have been employed in establishing all the reactions given in the preceding chapters. The last three laws will now be explained and we will see how they apply to elementary particle interactions.

The electron family is composed of four elementary particles, the electron e^-, the electron neutrino ν_e, the positron $\bar{e}^+$, and the positron neutrino $\bar{\nu}_e$. The first two are particles and each has the electron family number $+1$, while the second two are antiparticles and each has the electron family number -1. All other particles have electron family number 0.

The muon family is composed of four elementary particles, the negative muon μ^-, the muon neutrino ν_μ, the antimuon $\bar{\mu}^+$, and the antimuon neutrino $\bar{\nu}_\mu$. The first two are particles and each has the muon family number $+1$, while the second two are antiparticles and each has the muon family number -1. All other particles have muon family number 0.

Example 1. Apply the conservation laws of charge, muon number, and electron number to the natural decay of a negative pion.
Solution. For this reaction, see Eq.(66g).

$$\pi^- \rightarrow \mu^- + \bar{\nu}_\mu$$

Charge No.	$-1 = -1 + 0$
Muon No.	$0 = +1 - 1$
Electron No.	$0 = \quad 0 + 0$

The π^- and μ^- are both particles with numbers as shown. With these as fixed numbers, the muon family law shows that the neutrino must be an antiparticle. Since none of the particles in this decay are members of the electron family, all electron numbers are zero.

Example 2. Apply the charge, muon, and electron number conservation laws to the positive muon decay.
Solution. For this reaction see Eq.(66k).

$$\bar{\mu}^+ \rightarrow \bar{e}^+ + \bar{\nu}_\mu + \nu_e$$

Charge No.	$+1 = +1 + 0 \ + 0$
Muon No.	$-1 = \quad 0 - 1 \ + 0$
Electron No.	$0 = -1 + 0 \ + 1$

The balancing of charge is straight forward and self-explanatory. Since the positive muon is an antiparticle it has a muon family number -1. To balance this, one of the neutrinos must be a muon antineutrino with muon number -1. Since the positron is an antiparticle, its electron number of -1 must be balanced by an electron neutrino with an electron number $+1$.

We have seen in the preceding chapter that all particles having a mass equal to or greater than the nucleon are called *baryons*. Furthermore the baryon number is none other than what we have previously called the *atomic mass number A*. For most of the elementary particles known today A has the value $+1$ or -1.

In applying the baryon law to interactions we count all baryons as having baryon number $+1$, and their corresponding antibaryons as having baryon number -1 (see Sec. 74.15).

Example 3. Apply the charge, electron, muon, and baryon conservation laws to the decay of the neutron.

Solution. By Eq.(69l) the decay of the neutron gives rise to a proton, an electron, and an antineutrino.

$$n \rightarrow p^+ + e^- + \bar{\nu}_e$$

Charge No.	$0 =$	$+1$	-1	$+0$
Electron No.	$0 =$	0	$+1$	-1
Muon No.	$0 =$	0	$+0$	$+0$
Baryon No.	$1 =$	1	$+0$	$+0$

Note that both the neutron and proton have baryon number $+1$, but appear on opposite sides of the equation. The electron number law shows that the neutrino must belong to the electron, and it must be an antineutrino to balance the equation.

An eighth conservation law involving all kaons and baryons is concerned with another set of quantum numbers called *strangeness numbers.* Stated simply,

Law 8. The total strangeness number remains constant.

While this law holds for all strong interactions brought about by high-energy collisions with or between baryons, *it does not hold for the natural decay of the particles produced.* For strangeness numbers see Eq.(74l) and Table 74A.

Example 4. Apply the charge, baryon, and strangeness conservation laws to the reaction shown in Fig. 74K, and written in Eq.(74g).

Solution.

$$\pi^- + p^+ \rightarrow \Sigma^- + K^+$$

Charge No.	$-1 + 1$	$=$	$-1 + 1$
Baryon No.	$0 + 1$	$=$	$1 + 0$
Strangeness No.	$0 + 0$	$=$	$-1 + 1$

Since the K^+ particle has baryon number 0, the Σ^- particle must have baryon number $+1$, and is therefore a real particle. Since the Σ^- has a strangeness number -1, the K^+ must have a strangeness number $+1$. Therefore it cannot be an antiparticle.

Example 5. Apply the charge, baryon, and strangeness laws to the decay of a Σ^- particle [see Eq.(74c)].

Solution.

$$\Sigma^- \rightarrow n + \pi^-$$
$$-1 = 0 - 1$$
$$1 = 1 + 0$$
$$-1 \neq 0 + 0$$

This typical violation of the strangeness law which occurs in the decay of hyperons is the reason these particles were originally called *strange particles.*

PROBLEMS

1. Calculate the threshold energy for the production of a proton pair.

2. Calculate the threshold energy for the production of four pairs of π mesons (see Fig. 74H). [*Ans.* 110 MeV.]

3. Make a legend diagram of the 3-pronged event shown in Fig. 74L. Label each track with the appropriate particle symbols.

4. An atomic particle is designated Σ^-, 1385, $\frac{3}{2}$. Write down the values of the quantum numbers $Y, A, I, J, S,$ and M, and specify the mass in units of the electronic mass m_e.

5. An atomic particle is designated Ω^-, 1676, $\frac{3}{2}$.

Write down the values of the quantum numbers $Y, A, I, J, S,$ and M, and give the particles mass in units of the electronic mass m_e.

6. What are the values of the quantum numbers $Y, A, I, J, S,$ and M for an atomic particle designated $\bar{N}^+, 1512, \frac{3}{2}$? Write down its mass in units of the electronic mass m_e.

7. What are the quantum numbers $Y, A, I, J, S,$ and M, for an atomic particle designated $\bar{\Delta}^{-2}, 1920, \frac{7}{2}$? Write down the mass in units of the electronic mass m_e.

8. Apply the conservation laws of charge, muon number, and electron family number to the natural decay of a positive pion.

9. Apply the conservation laws of charge, muon number, and electron family number to the negative muon decay.

10. Apply the conservation laws of charge and baryon number to the first reaction given in Eq.(74f).

11. Apply the conservation laws of charge, baryon, and strangeness number to the first reaction in Eq.(74g).

12. Apply the conservation laws of charge, baryon, and strangeness number to the first reaction in Eq.(74h).

13. Apply the conservation laws of charge and baryon number to the reaction given by Eq.(74i)

FIELD THEORY
AND WORLD LINES

The concepts of electric and magnetic fields were first introduced in the theory of electricity and magnetism by Faraday and Maxwell over 100 years ago. While electric fields were proposed to explain the forces between charged bodies, gravitational fields were later introduced to explain the long-range forces between astronomical bodies (see Fig. 14B).

75.1. Field Theory of Atomic Particles. It was Einstein, through his theory of relativity, who first postulated that all fields around every body or particle should be considered as something real.

The emission of a photon by one excited atom and its subsequent absorption by another are clear indications that electromagnetic fields may be suddenly created or destroyed in chunks. Electrons with their electric and magnetic fields move in the field of a nucleus to which they are attached. Suddenly a chunk of electromagnetic field, a photon, is emitted. Later this chunk of field is absorbed by another similar system of fields, another atom.

Although the dual nature of particles and waves, as described in Chapter 61, is difficult to comprehend, each elementary chunk of energy, whatever its form, may be regarded as a localized region containing some kind of field. All events in the world may then be described as the interactions between various kinds of these localized fields.

The creation of a positron in pair production, for example, may be thought of as the creation of a chunk of positive field. As the positron recedes, this field travels through space as a wave, and at some later time collides with the localized field of an electron, and both fields vanish.

At the spot where these charged particle fields disappeared there is created two electromagnetic fields (photons) propagated through space with the speed of light c.

The idea that elementary particle events involve different kinds of fields, acting on one another at a distance, is becoming more and more an acceptable theory. Thus far, however, no one has been able to bring together all of the various kinds of fields into one successful *unified field theory*.

For this reason it is customary to describe all events in the universe, from the strong short-range forces between certain elementary atomic particles to the long-range gravitational forces between astronomical bodies, as arising from the interactions between four different kinds of fields. Listed in the order of decreasing intensity these are:

> *strong fields*
> *electromagnetic fields*
> *weak fields*
> *gravitational fields*

Around all charged baryons all four of these fields may be assumed to exist. A schematic diagram, based on classical theory and representing a proton, is shown in Fig. 75A.

Although the intensity of all fields decreases to zero only at infinity, their lines are shown terminating at different distances from the center. While the intensity of each field increases with decreasing distance from the center, the strong

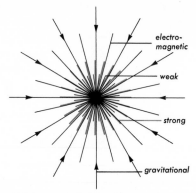

Fig. 75A *Schematic diagram of the various kinds of elementary particle fields around a charged baryon.*

atomic world forces us to accept a new picture of elementary particles.

When quantum theory is applied to the strong field around a baryon, like the proton, the classical picture of radial field lines is replaced by a field of mesons as shown in Fig. 75B(a).

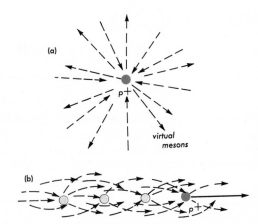

Fig. 75B *Schematic diagrams showing the virtual meson field around a proton, (a) stationary, and (b) moving.*

field is by far the strongest at distances less than about 10^{-15} m.

At distances a little greater than 10^{-15} m the strong field drops off rapidly and the Coulomb field, associated with the particle's charge, predominates (see Fig. 71G). While little is known about the properties and extent of the weak field, gravitational fields are known to extend great distances into the space surrounding astronomical bodies.

For each uncharged baryon the electromagnetic field is absent, while for each muon and electron the strong short-range field is absent. For each photon the strong and weak fields are absent, while for neutrinos the strong and electromagnetic fields are absent.

When a low-energy proton collides with another proton at rest, the Coulomb fields interact at some distance and the two particles recoil before their strong fields get close enough together to produce an observable effect. This is *elastic*, or *Rutherford, scattering*.

When a high-energy proton makes a head-on collision with another proton, however, the particles override the Coulomb forces and the strong fields interact at close range. Whatever transformations are brought about as the result of this collision the event is referred to as a *strong interaction*.

75.2. The Quantum Theory of Fields. In spite of our limited imaginations in describing particle fields, the successes of the mathematics of quantum theory in explaining observations in the

Charged and uncharged pions and other mesons are assumed to be shooting out and in, i.e., from and to the central core. These are to be thought of as *virtual mesons* which reveal their *real* properties when, as the result of a collision, one or more of them escape.

If the proton is moving at high velocity as in diagram (b), mesons may be visualized as leaving the particle at one point in its path, and rejoining it at some other point farther along.

When quantum theory is applied to the electromagnetic field around an electron or muon, the classical picture of radial field lines is replaced by the emission and absorption of photons as shown in Fig. 75C(a). These electromagnetic waves are to be thought of as virtual photons which reveal their real properties only when, as the result of a high-energy collision, one or more escape. If the electron is moving with a high velocity as in diagram (b), the photons may be visualized as leaving the particle at one point in its path and rejoining it at some later point farther along.

Very little is known about weak fields and gravitational fields of elementary particles. What is known has been gleaned from events involving particles that exhibit neither strong fields nor electromagnetic fields. These are the neutrinos; they have baryon number zero and no charge.

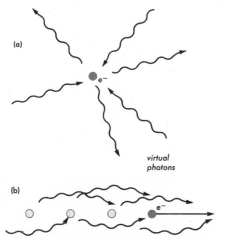

Fig. 75C *Schematic diagrams showing the virtual photon field around an electron, (a) stationary, and (b) moving.*

By analogy it is assumed that the field around each neutrino is to be attributed to the radiation and absorption of virtual atomic particles that have yet to be detected.

In an attempt to explain why the sun is able to exert an inward force on a planet to hold it in its orbit, theoretical physicists have invented a particle called the *graviton*. Around each elementary particle, or large mass of particles, virtual gravitons are pictured being continually emitted and absorbed. Two separated particles are then pictured as exchanging gravitons, and through this exchange realize attractive forces. For large masses of particles these are the forces given by Newton's law of gravitation.

75.3. World Lines. The method of depicting elementary-particle events by means of space–time graphs was introduced by R. Feynman in 1949. As an introduction to the meaning of these useful graphical pictures, consider the flight of an airplane from one city to another as shown in Fig. 75D. The time t is plotted vertically, and the distance x is plotted horizontally.

We now represent the plane's history by the solid line ABCD. Parked at the ramp at the Washington Airport, time t is advancing in the direction A to B. The plane takes off, and moving both in time and space, traces out the world line B to C. Landing in New York and coming to rest on the ramp, the plane again moves only in time, and its world line CD is straight upward.

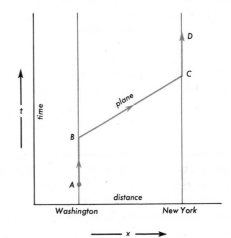

Fig. 75D *World-line graph of a plane flight from Washington to New York.*

Note there is no such thing as standing still in a space–time graph. A city like Washington moves through time and continually traces out its vertical world line. If one places a ruler horizontally across the bottom of the diagram and then pushes it upward with uniform speed across the diagram, the intersection of the world lines with the ruler edge gives a description of the plane's motion with respect to the two cities.

A narrow horizontal slot in a strip of cardboard is more effective than a ruler. If the strip is moved downward with uniform speed, the dots seen in the slot represent an equally valid motion, namely, that of the plane on its return flight.

Turning now to the world of elementary particles, we may trace the world lines of a simple and well-known event (see Fig. 75E). The diagram represents the emission of a photon by an excited atom.

Initially at rest the atom traces out a vertically straight world line. Upon the emission of a pho-

Fig. 75E *World-line graph for the emission of a photon by an atom.*

ton with the speed of light, the atom recoils to the left as shown. The slower a particle moves, the more nearly vertical is its world line, while the faster it moves the more nearly horizontal is its world line.

Since no particle can travel from one place to another with infinite speed, no world line can be horizontal. Photons and neutrinos provide the most nearly horizontal world lines since they travel with the speed of light c.

Figure 75F represents the decay of a negative pion

$$\pi^- \rightarrow \mu^- + \bar{\nu}_\mu$$

The dot at the vertex A indicates the time at which the world line of the pion ends and the world lines of the muon and antineutrino begin.

Fig. 75F *World-line graph for the decay of a pion into a muon and a neutrino.*

75.4. Strong Interactions. The strong binding forces known to exist within the nucleus are attributed to the mesons that jump back and forth between the neutrons and protons. When a neutron collides with a proton in free space, the two particles at close approach may exchange one or more mesons and each recoil with a different mass and charge.

Consider the collision event involving two nucleons as shown in Fig. 75G. As the neutron approaches the proton, their strong fields interact at close approach of about 10^{-13} cm, a π^- meson is transferred to the proton, and the two particles recoil.

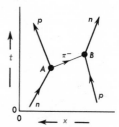

Fig. 75G *World line diagram of a strong interaction. At the close approach of a neutron and proton, a negative pion makes a transition from neutron to proton.*

The world-line diagram indicates, however, that this single event probably takes place in two steps. At close approach of about 10^{-13} cm at A the neutron emits a π^- meson. A short time later at point B the π^- meson combines with the proton converting into a neutron. The two reactions may be written:

$$n \rightarrow p^+ + \pi^-$$
$$\pi^- + p^+ \rightarrow n.$$

The approximate time interval for this event to take place may be calculated from Heisenberg's uncertainty principle [see Eq.(61s)].

$$\Delta E \times \Delta t = \hbar \qquad (75a)$$

The change in energy ΔE is just the total mass energy of the exchanged π^-.

$$\Delta E = mc^2 = 275 \times 9.1 \times 10^{-31} \times 9 \times 10^{16}$$
$$\Delta E = 2.25 \times 10^{-11} \text{ joules}$$

Solving Eq.(75a) for Δt, and substituting, we obtain

$$\Delta t = \frac{\hbar}{\Delta E} = \frac{1.05 \times 10^{-34}}{2.2 \times 10^{-11}} = 5 \times 10^{-22} \text{ seconds}$$

75.5. Electromagnetic Interactions. Electromagnetic interactions are confined to events in which the interacting particle fields are electromagnetic in character. Electrons, positrons, and photons fall into this category and none of them possess the strong fields so characteristic of nucleons and hyperons.

In the process called Bremsstrahlung, an electron passing through the nonhomogeneous field close to a nucleus or an electron is deflected in its path as it emits a photon (see Fig. 53M).

In the photoelectric effect a photon is absorbed by an electron, the latter recoiling from the impact. World-line diagrams for both of these events are shown in Fig. 75H.

If the relative velocities of the electrons are low, the photon energy ΔE will be small and the wavelength may correspond to visible light. If, however, the relative velocities are close to the speed of light, the photon energy ΔE will be large and the wavelength may correspond to X rays (see Problems 2 and 3).

A world-line diagram for the annihilation of an electron–positron pair is shown in Fig. 75J.

Fig. 75H   *World-line diagrams for (a) the electron emission of a photon as in bremsstrahlung, and (b) the absorption of a photon by an electron as in the photoelectric effect.*

Fig. 75J   *World-line diagram of an electron–position annihilation yielding two photons.*

By combining these two diagrams we obtain a world-line diagram representing the elastic scattering between two electrons (see Fig. 75I). According to classical theory, when two elec-

The electron field, at close approach to the positron field, emits a photon at point A. The photon flies away and the recoiling electron later combines with the positron and creates another photon. As a reaction

$$e^- + \bar{e}^+ = \gamma + \gamma \qquad (75b)$$

75.6. Weak Interactions. Typical of the events classified as weak interactions are those involving radioactive beta decay. Consider the well-known decay of a free neutron.

The neutron with its half-life of 11.7 min decays into a proton, an electron, and an antineutrino (see Fig. 75K).

The neutron initially at rest suddenly explodes

Fig. 75I   *World-line diagram of the elastic collision of two electrons.*

trons approach each other they exert equal and opposite forces on one another. These forces give rise to the changes in the energy and momentum of both electrons. If one electron loses energy the other gains an equivalent amount.

According to quantum theory, when the overlapping photon fields of the two electrons are sufficiently great, the one electron loses energy ΔE by emitting a photon at A. A short time Δt later the other electron absorbs the photon, thereby gaining the energy ΔE.

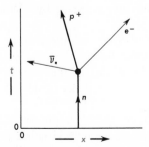

Fig. 75K   *World-line graph for the decay of a free neutron into a proton, electron, and an antineutrino.*

into three particles as shown. The reaction is

$$n \rightarrow p^+ + e^- + \bar{\nu}_e \qquad (75c)$$

Note that the world line of the antineutrino has the same slope as a photon.

If the antineutrino later encounters a proton, there is a small probability that it will be captured in what is called the *inverse beta-decay process.*

$$\bar{\nu}_e + p^+ \rightarrow n + \bar{e}^+ \qquad (75d)$$

While the electron appears in the neutron decay process, the laws of charge conservation and electron family conservation require the creation of a positron in the capture process.

The neutron's average life of 11.7 min means that for the inverse beta-decay process to occur, the field of an antineutrino must be close to that of a proton for that length of time.

Since the antineutrino travels with the speed of light, it will not stay close enough to a proton for capture to occur. In 11.7 min a neutrino will travel nearly twice the distance from the earth to the sun. It is for this reason that neutrions have great penetrating power, and that all matter as well as free space is assumed to be packed full of neutrinos.

Although neutrinos are seldom captured by nucleons, their short-range weak field is postulated in order to account for their occasional absorption.

75.7. Gravitational Interactions. The fact that astronomical bodies attract each other over distances of many millions of miles is one of the great mysteries of nature. If one calculates the electrostatic force between a proton and an electron and then compares it with the gravitational force between the same two bodies, he finds the electrostatic force is greater by a factor of 2.3 $\times$ 10^{39}.

In spite of this vast difference in the magnitudes of these force fields, the success of the quantum mechanics in the atomic world suggests the possible existence of new particles called *gravitons* (see end of Sec. 75.3).

By analogy with the photon field around charged bodies, we may visualize the existence of gravitons around each mass (see Fig. 75C).

The world-line diagram in Fig. 75L shows how the emission of a graviton from the sun to a planet gives rise to a force, first on the planet and then on the sun. Billions of gravitons per second, traveling in both directions between the two bodies, are assumed to account for the great total force of attraction.

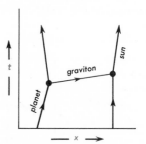

Fig. 75L   *World-line diagram for the exchange of a graviton between a planet and the sun.*

75.8. Time Reversal Invariance. Suppose an astronaut on his way to a distant galaxy takes motion pictures of our solar system to show the hosts he visits. The hosts at the distant galaxy, being familiar with the laws of mechanics and gravitation, would conclude that what they observed obeyed all natural laws.

But had the film been run backward they would have been equally satisfied since the motion is consistent with the same laws of motion. This is the principle of *time-reversal invariance.* Under a hypothetical reversal of time, all the laws of nature remain unchanged.

Although the time reversal of a complicated event like the explosion of a shell into many fragments may be quite improbable, and for practical purposes next to impossible, the time reversal of events in the world of elementary particles appears to be valid and many of them are observed to happen.

Note how well time reversal works on all world-line diagrams in Figs. 75D, 75E, 75F, 75H, and 75I. When time reversal is applied to Fig. 75K, the coming together of three particles simultaneously is highly improbable, yet is an allowed event and in the center of the sun may readily take place.

An examination of the two diagrams in Fig. 75H suggests the possibility of reversing the time of the photon and obtaining a different but allowed event.

To illustrate how this may be carried out, we start with diagram (a) and reverse the arrowhead of the photon. This diagram is now a twisted version of diagram (b). To bring it into accord with diagram (b) we rotate the new world line of the photon around the vertex until it points forward in time.

When this principle of time reversal is applied to a single charged particle in an observed event the rule is to reverse the charge as well as the particle–antiparticle classification. Such a process is illustrated in Fig. 75M.

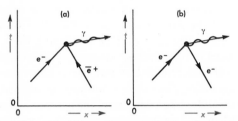

Fig. 75M *World-line diagrams showing the principle of time reversal applied to a single particle. Positron–electron annihilation becomes photon emission as in bremsstrahlung.*

Diagram (a) shows the event pictured at vertex B in Fig. 75J. We now reverse the direction of the positron arrowhead, reverse the charge from plus to minus, and the classification from antiparticle to particle.

The result now looks like a twisted version of Fig. 75H(a). To bring it into agreement with observations we swing this newly labeled arrow around the vertex to obtain the same kind of event shown in Fig. 75H(a).

Feynman concluded from this kind of process that the electron–photon vertex is a fundamental principle of nature and that it may be used to represent all known electromagnetic interactions between electrons, positrons, and photons.

Furthermore, the mathematical description of an electron field moving forward in time is identical with the description of a positron field propagating backward in time, and vice versa.

75.9. Parity. Parity is a mathematical treatment of what is best described as a mirror sym-

metry of many natural phenomena. Up until recently it was believed that the mirror image of any physical phenomenon or laboratory experiment is just as true to nature as the direct image itself. This is consistent with the principle called *conservation of parity*.

According to the conservation of parity, it was believed that if one observed an experiment by looking in a mirror and was not told he was looking in a mirror, there would be no way in which he would know it. As an example of parity, many crystalline structures show mirror symmetry. With many cubic crystals there is no question, since the image and mirror image have identical structures.

Diagrams of two kinds of quartz crystals found in nature are shown in Fig. 75N. One,

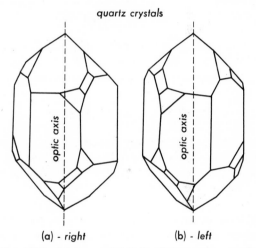

quartz crystals

(a) - right   (b) - left

Fig. 75N *Right- and left-handed quartz crystals. Each is a mirror image of the other.*

called right-handed quartz, has its silicon and oxygen atoms lined up in clockwise spirals around the axis, while the left-handed quartz is a mirror image of the other and has its molecules lined up in a counterclockwise direction. One will rotate plane-polarized light clockwise as it traverses the crystal along the optic axis, while the other will rotate it counterclockwise. The existence of both of these crystals is consistent with the conservation of parity.

The first serious question regarding the conservation of parity arose in the minds of two young theoretical physicists, Yang and Lee, when they pointed out in 1956 that K^+ mesons can decay into two pions (θ mode) or three pions (τ mode) [see Eq.(74a)]. An experiment suggested by Yang and Lee to test for parity was carried out by Wu, Ambler, Hayward, Hoppes, and Hudson. This experiment showed that, when radioactive cobalt-60 nuclei were lined up with their spin axes parallel to each other, more β particles were emitted along this axis in one direction than in the other.

To realize the significance of this result, consider the common decay of a $\bar{\pi}^+$ meson into a $\bar{\mu}^+$ and a ν_μ. The $\bar{\pi}^+$ has zero spin, while the $\bar{\mu}^+$ and ν_μ have spins of $\frac{1}{2}$. To conserve angular momentum, the two particles must fly apart spinning in opposite directions as shown in Fig. 75O.

Fig. 75O Schematic diagram showing the left-handed, or negative, helicity of $\bar{\mu}^+$ and ν particles in the decay of $\bar{\pi}^+$ mesons.

Moving in the direction of the arrows, both are advancing, as would left-handed screws. The mirror image in (b), which is apparently forbidden by nature, shows both particles advancing as right-handed screws. *A spinning particle advancing as a right-handed screw is said to have positive helicity; advancing as a left-handed screw it is said to have negative helicity.*

From the observed spin directions of β particles, it is now known that all *neutrinos have negative helicity* while *antineutrinos have positive helicity.* With this rule and spin conservation, we see from Fig. 75P that in π^- decay both μ^- and $\bar{\nu}_\mu$ have positive helicity.

It should be pointed out that helicity has meaning for neutrinos only, since they move with the speed of light. To an observer moving

Fig. 75P Schematic diagram showing the right-handed, or positive, helicity of μ^- and $\bar{\nu}$ particles in the decay of π^- mesons.

faster than a muon, for example, the spin direction would appear to be the reverse of that seen by an observer moving slower than the muon.

If all the particles in one or the other of the two mirror images of Figs. 75O and 75P are changed to their corresponding antiparticles, the resulting interaction becomes the real interaction of the other. Thus there is an over-all symmetry between the two decay reactions.

When a $\bar{\mu}^+$ decays in the customary way into a positron, a neutrino, and an antineutrino, helicity for the neutrinos as well as the $\bar{\mu}^+$ is already fixed. What helicity is imparted to the electron and the $\bar{\mu}^+$ will depend on the relative directions of all recoiling particles. If the neutrinos go off together as shown in Fig. 75Q, the

Fig. 75Q Schematic diagram of $\bar{\mu}^+$ decay showing the helicity of particles where the two neutrinos move off in the same direction.

positron must recoil with negative helicity. If the antiprotons recoil in opposite directions, the positron, to conserve spin, can have either positive or negative helicity. Drawings for these cases will be left as exercises for the student.

If a distant world is made of antimatter, there is no known way whereby we on the earth can determine this. Furthermore, though μ^- and $\bar{\mu}^+$ have positive and negative helicity, respectively, there is no information we could impart to a man on a distant world that would tell him which is which.

75.10. Mean Lives of Elementary Particles. The discovery of so many elementary particles in recent years has greatly complicated all previous theories of the atomic nucleus. The fundamental questions arising in the minds of the physicists include not only the different properties of the individual particles but the way they fit into the structure of the atomic nucleus. At the present stage of development, in trying to unravel the many mysteries concerning elementary particles, some important questions stand out.

Are all of the particles listed in Fig. 74P really elementary, or are some of them just composites of others? Could it be that some of the stars in the universe, or entire galaxies, are made of antimatter, with hydrogen atoms composed of antiprotons and positrons, etc.? Why are elementary charges limited to values of $+1$, 0, and -1?

Every physicist believes that some day we will know the answers to these and many other questions about the nature of elementary particles, the building blocks of the universe.

One interesting aspect of the nature of the particles themselves concerns their *mean life* (see Table 75A).

The best and most direct means of determining the lifetime of any identified particle is to measure the length of the track it produces in a cloud chamber, bubble chamber, or photographic emulsion, and determine its velocity from conservation laws or the curvature of its path in a magnetic field. The lifetime τ is then given by the distance traveled divided by the velocity.

The lifetime determined in this way is the time the particle existed in the laboratory frame of reference. To find τ_0, the lifetime of the particle in its own moving frame of reference, the special theory of relativity must be used. Starting with the transformation equation, Eq.(58c), we write τ_0 for t' and τ for t,

$$\tau_0 = \gamma \left(\tau - \frac{vx}{c^2} \right)$$

TABLE 75A. MEAN LIVES OF THE UNSTABLE ELEMENTARY PARTICLES

Particle	Mean life (s)
Ξ^+	1.3×10^{-10}
Ξ^0	1.5×10^{-10}
Ξ^-	1.3×10^{-10}
Σ^+	0.8×10^{-10}
Σ^0	1.0×10^{-9}
Σ^-	1.6×10^{-10}
Λ^0	2.5×10^{-10}
n	1.0×10^3
K^+	1.2×10^{-8}
K^0	1.0×10^{-10}
K^-	1.2×10^{-8}
π^+	2.5×10^{-8}
π^0	2.2×10^{-16}
π^-	2.5×10^{-8}
$\bar{\mu}^+$	2.2×10^{-6}
μ^-	2.2×10^{-6}

In this equation x represents the distance traveled, and τ the time of travel in the laboratory frame of reference. Placing

$$x = v\tau$$

and

$$\gamma = 1 \bigg/ \sqrt{1 - \frac{v^2}{c^2}}$$

we obtain

$$\tau_0 = \tau \sqrt{1 - \frac{v^2}{c^2}} \tag{75e}$$

This formula has been verified with high accuracy up to velocities of 99.5% the speed of light, and with approximately 10% accuracy at velocities up to 99.95% the speed of light.

Consider for example the events shown in Fig. 74J in which a Λ^0 particle existed long enough to travel 8 cm before decaying into a proton, p^+, and a negative pion, π^-. Traveling this distance with 70% the speed of light (energy = 0.45 BeV), its lifetime is given by (8 $\times$ 10^{-2} m)/(2.1 $\times$ 10^8 m/s), or $\tau = 3.8 \times 10^{-10}$ s. This is the lifetime in the laboratory frame of reference.

In the frame of the moving Λ^0 particle, the real lifetime τ_0 is found by direct substitution in Eq.(75e).

$$\tau_0 = 3.8 \times 10^{-10} \sqrt{1 - (0.70)^2}$$
$$\tau_0 = 2.7 \times 10^{-10} \text{ s}$$

There is an upper limit, however, to the determination of lifetimes by this direct method. For high-energy particles traveling with 70% the speed of light, an observed track of only 3 μ in a photographic emulsion corresponds to a time $\tau = (3 \times 10^{-6} \text{ m})/(2.1 \times 10^8 \text{ m/s})$, or 1.4×10^{-14} s. In the reference frame of the moving particle, the real lifetime $\tau_0 = 1 \times 10^{-14}$ s.

One of the most interesting questions that has arisen out of modern physics concerns the real existence of the very short-lived elementary particles. Since particles such as Λ, Σ, Ξ, and ω are known to have mean lives of one-thousandth of a millionth of a second or less, do we have a right to say they exist long enough to call them particles at all?

One approach to finding an answer to this question is to graphically represent the lifetime of a few commonly recognized natural phenomena or bodies of matter, and to compare the time scales of their existence. The generally accepted lifetime of the earth, from the time of its creation to the present, is 4.5×10^9 y, or 1.4×10^{17} s. This interval of time is represented by the colored line at the top in Fig. 75R.

Since we admit the earth was created sometime in the past, we must also admit that time existed before this event, and that time must be extended to infinity in the past. While the earth still exists at the present, and will sometime come to an end in the future, time must continue on with succeeding astronomical events and by logical reasoning we find it necessary to extend the time scale to plus infinity. The line is therefore infinitely long in both directions.

Paleontologists agree that mammals have inhabited this earth for approximately two million years, or about 6×10^{14} s. On the earth's time scale this is but a tiny dot, but by a 200-fold expanded scale as in the second line, we can show the finite span of 6×10^{14} s as the colored line. This scale like the one above it, extends to

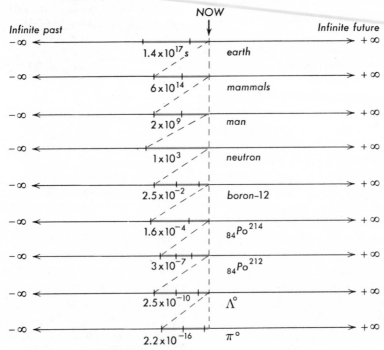

Fig. 75R *Comparison of time-scale graphs for natural bodies from the earth to elementary particles.*

infinity in the past as well as to infinity in the future.

The average life span of individual man is approximately 70 y, or 2×10^9 s. On the mammalian scale this is but a dot, but by expanding the scale ten-thousand-fold or more, we obtain the scale shown in the third line of the diagram. It is on this colored line that all the events of our entire life may be represented timewise.

The mean life of a free neutron is approximately 11.7 min, or 700 s, yet on the time scale of man this is so short an interval that it becomes a mere dot. Since intense beams of neutrons can be produced with atomic accelerators, and atomic reactors, in the laboratory, and many different kinds of events involving them at great distances from their origin are observed, their existence is just as real as the existence of man.

Let us now carry these time scales down several more steps, through the short-lived radio-active isotopes like boron-12, $_{84}Po^{214}$ and $_{84}Po^{212}$, until we reach the time scale of a π^0 meson, 2.2×10^{-16} s. Here on a sufficiently expanded time scale the interval looks like all the others. It has a finite length representing creation at the left and radioactive decay on the right. The scale extends infinitely far into the past like all the others, and it extends infinitely far into the future.

If we now step down to the ω particle with a mean life of 10^{-22} s, the time of its existence had to be determined from reasonably well developed theory. Moving with three-quarters the speed of light, after its creation, this particle exists long enough to travel five to ten nuclear diameters before decaying into three π mesons. It will therefore be left to you the reader to decide whether particles with such short lifetimes really exist, and whether or not there is a limit to the shortness of any time scale.

PROBLEMS

1. Two protons approaching each other are elastically scattered. Construct a world-line diagram for this interaction assuming an exchange of a neutral pion.

2. Calculate the interaction time for the elastic scattering of two electrons where the exchanged photon is visible green light $\lambda = 5 \times 10^{-7}$ m (see Fig. 75H).

3. Calculate the interaction time for the elastic scattering of two electrons where the exchanged photon has a wavelength in the gamma-ray region of the electromagnetic spectrum, $\lambda = 1 \times 10^{-11}$ m.

4. Make a world-line diagram for the decay of a carbon-14 nuclide.

5. Make a world-line diagram for the decay of a phosphorus-30 nuclide.

6. Construct a world-line diagram for the absorption of a photon by an atom.

7. Construct a world-line diagram for the decay of a positive pion.

8. Construct a world-line diagram for the decay of a negative muon.

9. Construct a world-line diagram for the decay of a positive muon.

10. In Fig. 74J(a), a π^- meson and proton come together and create a K^0 and Λ^0. (a) Show that strangeness numbers are conserved by writing numbers under the reaction symbols. (b) Could the same two original particles have created a Σ^+ and K^-? [Ans. (a) $0 + 0 = 1 - 1$. (b) No.]

11. Write down the first reaction in Eq.(74g), and then replace each particle by its antiparticle. Do the conservation laws (a) obey the baryon law #7, and (b) the strangeness law #8?

12. Write down the first reaction in Eq.(74h), and then replace each particle by its antiparticle. Do the conservation laws (a) obey the baryon law #7, and (b) the strangeness law #8? [Ans. (a) yes, (b) yes.]

13. Apply the law of conservation of baryons and conservation of strangeness number to show why the strongly reacting particles in Fig. 74J(a) could not have resulted in the reaction $\pi^- + p \rightarrow \Sigma^0 + \Lambda^0$.

14. Apply the laws of conservation of baryon number and strangeness number, and show why the strong reaction in Fig. 74J(a) could not have been $\bar{p}^- + p \rightarrow \Lambda^0 + K^0$. [Ans. Baryons are conserved.]

15. If the measured distance the K^0 particle travels in Fig. 74J is 2.5 cm, and the speed of the particle is 50% the speed of light, find (a) the lifetime of the particle in the laboratory frame of reference, and (b) the real lifetime.

16. If the measured distance a Λ^0 particle travels in a bubble chamber is 9.5 cm, between its creation and its decay into a proton and a π^- meson, and it has a velocity of 65% the speed of light, find (a) its laboratory lifetime, and (b) its real lifetime. [Ans. (a) 4.9×10^{-10} s. (b) 3.7×10^{-10} s.]

17. If the measured distance the Λ^0 particles traveled in Fig. 74I is 2.5 cm, and the speed of the particles is 45% the speed of light, what is their lifetime in (a) the laboratory frame of reference, and (b) in their own frame of reference?

18. If the measured distance a Σ^0 particle travels in a bubble chamber is 120 cm, between its creation and its

decay into a Λ^0 and a γ ray, and the particle speed is 75% the speed of light, find its lifetime in the laboratory frame of reference, and (b) its real lifetime. [*Ans.* (a) 5.3×10^{-9} s. (b) 3.5×10^{-9} s.]

19. A Σ^+ track in a bubble chamber was measured to be 8 cm long, and from the curvature of its track in a magnetic field, its velocity was 80% the speed of light. Find (a) its lifetime in the laboratory, and (b) its real lifetime.

20. The Ξ^- particle in Fig. 74L has a speed of 80%

the speed of light and exists long enough to travel 5 cm before decaying into a Λ^0 and a π^-. Find its lifetime (a) in the laboratory frame of reference, and (b) its real lifetime. [*Ans.* (a) 2.1×10^{-10} s. (b) 1.3×10^{-10} s.]

21. A Λ^0 particle in Fig. 74L has a speed of 60% the speed of light and travels a distance of 3.5 cm before decaying into a proton and a π^- meson. Find its lifetime (a) in the laboratory frame of reference, and (b) its real lifetime.

Appendix I—Values of the General Physical Constants
(after Du Mond)

Planck's constant of action............................	$h = 6.6238 \times 10^{-34}$ Js
Electronic charge......................................	$e = 1.6019 \times 10^{-19}$ C
Electronic charge......................................	$e = 4.8022 \times 10^{-10}$ esu
Specific electronic charge............................	$e/m = 1.7598 \times 10^{11}$ C/Kg
Specific proton charge................................	$e/M_p = 9.5795 \times 10^{7}$ C/Kg
Electronic mass.......................................	$m = 9.1072 \times 10^{-31}$ Kg
Mass of atom of unit atomic weight....................	$M = 1.6600 \times 10^{-27}$ Kg
Mass of proton..	$M_p = 1.6722 \times 10^{-27}$ Kg
Ratio mass proton to mass electron....................	$M_p/m = 1836.1$
Wien's displacement-law constant......................	$C = 0.28976$ cm deg
Velocity of light.....................................	$c = 299{,}790$ Km/s
Square of velocity of light...........................	$c^2 = 8.9874 \times 10^{10}$ Km^2/s^2
Unit atomic angular momentum..........................	$\hbar = 1.0544 \times 10^{-34}$ Js
Bohr magneton...	$\mu_B = 9.273 \times 10^{-24}$ Am
Avogadro's number.....................................	$N = 6.0254 \times 10^{26}$/Kg mol
Energy equivalent of electron mass....................	$mc^2 = 0.51097$ MeV
Energy of unit atomic mass............................	$E = 931.34$ MeV

Appendix II—Abbreviations Used in this Text

ampere(s)	A	megavolt	MV
ampere turn(s)	A-turn	megawatt	MW
angstrom unit(s)	Å	meter	m
atomic mass number	A	microampere	μA
atomic mass unit(s)	amu	microcurie	μC
atomic number	Z	microfarad	μF
barn	b	microhenry	μH
billion electron volts	BeV	micromicrofarad	$\mu\mu$F
or giga electron volts	GeV	micron	μ
British thermal unit	Btu	microwatt	μW
calorie	cal	mile	mi
centimeter	cm	millimeter	mm
coulomb	C	million electron volts	MeV
decibel	db	millisecond	ms
farad	F	millivolt	mV
foot	ft	milliwatt	mW
gauss	G	minute	min
gram	g	nanosecond	ns
henry	H	newton	N
horsepower	hp	ohm	Ω
hour	hr	radian	rad
inch	in.	revolutions/second	rps
joule	J	second	s
kilocalorie	Kcal	slug	sl
kilocycles/second	Kc/s	thousand electron volts	KeV
kilometers	Km	volt	V
kilogram	Kg	watt	W
kilovolt	KV	weber	Wb
kilowatt	KW	year	y
megacycles/second	Mc/s		

Appendix III

TRIGONOMETRIC FUNCTIONS (*Natural*)

Angle	Sine	Cosine	Tangent	Angle	Sine	Cosine	Tangent
0°	0.000	1.000	0.000				
1°	.018	1.000	.018	46°	.719	.695	1.036
2°	.035	0.999	.035	47°	.731	.682	1.072
3°	.052	.999	.052	48°	.743	.669	1.111
4°	.070	.998	.070	49°	.755	.656	1.150
5°	.087	.996	.088	50°	.766	.643	1.192
6°	.105	.995	.105	51°	.777	.629	1.235
7°	.122	.993	.123	52°	.788	.616	1.280
8°	.139	.990	.141	53°	.799	.602	1.327
9°	.156	.988	.158	54°	.809	.588	1.376
10°	.174	.985	.176	55°	.819	.574	1.428
11°	.191	.982	.194	56°	.829	.559	1.483
12°	.208	.978	.213	57°	.839	.545	1.540
13°	.225	.974	.231	58°	.848	.530	1.600
14°	.242	.970	.249	59°	.857	.515	1.664
15°	.259	.966	.268	60°	.866	.500	1.732
16°	.276	.961	.287	61°	.875	.485	1.804
17°	.292	.956	.306	62°	.883	.470	1.881
18°	.309	.951	.325	63°	.891	.454	1.963
19°	.326	.946	.344	64°	.899	.438	2.050
20°	.342	.940	.364	65°	.906	.423	2.145
21°	.358	.934	.384	66°	.914	.407	2.246
22°	.375	.927	.404	67°	.921	.391	2.356
23°	.391	.921	.425	68°	.927	.375	2.475
24°	.407	.914	.445	69°	.934	.358	2.605
25°	.423	.906	.466	70°	.940	.342	2.747
26°	.438	.899	.488	71°	.946	.326	2.904
27°	.454	.891	.510	72°	.951	.309	3.078
28°	.470	.883	.532	73°	.956	.292	3.271
29°	.485	.875	.554	74°	.961	.276	3.487
30°	.500	.866	.577	75°	.966	.259	3.732
31°	.515	.857	.601	76°	.970	.242	4.011
32°	.530	.848	.625	77°	.974	.225	4.331
33°	.545	.839	.649	78°	.978	.208	4.705
34°	.559	.829	.675	79°	.982	.191	5.145
35°	.574	.819	.700	80°	.985	.174	5.671
36°	.588	.809	.727	81°	.988	.156	6.314
37°	.602	.799	.754	82°	.990	.139	7.115
38°	.616	.788	.781	83°	.993	.122	8.144
39°	.629	.777	.810	84°	.995	.105	9.514
40°	.643	.766	.839	85°	.996	.087	11.43
41°	.656	.755	.869	86°	.998	.070	14.30
42°	.669	.743	.900	87°	.999	.052	19.08
43°	.682	.731	.933	88°	.999	.035	28.64
44°	.695	.719	.966	89°	1.000	.018	57.29
45°	.707	.707	1.000	90°	1.000	.000	∞

Appendix IV

COMMON LOGARITHMS

(To obtain Naperian logarithm of a number multiply these logarithms by 2.3026.)

N	0	1	2	3	4	5	6	7	8	9
0	....	0000	3010	4771	6021	6990	7782	8451	9031	9542
1	0000	0414	0792	1139	1461	1761	2041	2304	2553	2788
2	3010	3222	3424	3617	3802	3979	4150	4314	4472	4624
3	4771	4914	5051	5185	5315	5441	5563	5682	5798	5911
4	6021	6128	6232	6335	6435	6532	6628	6721	6812	6902
5	6990	7076	7160	7243	7324	7404	7482	7559	7634	7709
6	7782	7853	7924	7993	8062	8129	8195	8261	8325	8388
7	8451	8513	8573	8633	8692	8751	8808	8865	8921	8976
8	9031	9085	9138	9191	9243	9294	9345	9395	9445	9494
9	9542	9590	9638	9685	9731	9777	9823	9868	9912	9956
10	0000	0043	0086	0128	0170	0212	0253	0294	0334	0374
11	0414	0453	0492	0531	0569	0607	0645	0682	0719	0755
12	0792	0828	0864	0899	0934	0969	1004	1038	1072	1106
13	1139	1173	1206	1239	1271	1303	1335	1367	·1399	1430
14	1461	1492	1523	1553	1584	1614	1644	1673	1703	1732
15	1761	1790	1818	1847	1875	1903	1931	1959	1987	2014
16	2041	2068	2095	2122	2148	2175	2201	2227	2253	2279
17	2304	2330	2355	2380	2405	2430	2455	2480	2504	2529
18	2553	2577	2601	2625	2648	2672	2695	2718	2742	2765
19	2788	2810	2833	2856	2878	2900	2923	2945	2967	2989
20	3010	3032	3054	3075	3096	3118	3139	3160	3181	3201
21	3222	3243	3263	3284	3304	3324	3345	3365	3385	3404
22	3424	3444	3464	3483	3502	3522	3541	3560	3579	3598
23	3617	3636	3655	3674	3692	3711	3729	3747	3766	3784
24	3802	3820	3838	3856	3874	3892	3909	3927	3945	3962
25	3979	3997	4014	4031	4048	4065	4082	4099	4116	4133
26	4150	4166	4183	4200	4216	4232	4249	4265	4281	4298
27	4314	4330	4346	4362	4378	4393	4409	4425	4440	4456
28	4472	4487	4502	4518	4533	4548	4564	4579	4594	4609
29	4624	4639	4654	4669	4683	4698	4713	4728	4742	4757
30	4771	4786	4800	4814	4829	4843	4857	4871	4886	4900
31	4914	4928	4942	4955	4969	4983	4997	5011	5024	5038
32	5051	5065	5079	5092	5105	5119	5132	5145	5159	5172
33	5185	5198	5211	5224	5237	5250	5263	5276	5289	5302
34	5315	5328	5340	5353	5366	5378	5391	5403	5416	5428
35	5441	5453	5465	5478	5490	5502	5514	5527	5539	5551
36	5563	5575	5587	5599	5611	5623	5635	5647	5658	5670
37	5682	5694	5705	5717	5729	5740	5752	5763	5775	5786
38	5798	5809	5821	5832	5843	5855	5866	5877	5888	5899
39	5911	5922	5933	5944	5955	5966	5977	5988	5999	6010
40	6021	6031	6042	6053	6064	6075	6085	6096	6107	6117
41	6128	6138	6149	6160	6170	6180	6191	6201	6212	6222
42	6232	6243	6253	6263	6274	6284	6294	6304	6314	6325
43	6335	6345	6355	6365	6375	6385	6395	6405	6415	6425
44	6435	6444	6454	6464	6474	6484	6493	6503	6513	6522
45	6532	6542	6551	6561	6571	6580	6590	6599	6609	6618
46	6628	6637	6646	6656	6665	6675	6684	6693	6702	6712
47	6721	6730	6739	6749	6758	6767	6776	6785	6794	6803
48	6812	6821	6830	6839	6848	6857	6866	6875	6884	6893
49	6902	6911	6920	6928	6937	6946	6955	6964	6972	6981
50	6990	6998	7007	7016	7024	7033	7042	7050	7059	7067
N	0	1	2	3	4	5	6	7	8	9

COMMON LOGARITHMS (*Cont.*)

N	0	1	2	3	4	5	6	7	8	9
50	6990	6998	7007	7016	7024	7033	7042	7050	7059	7067
51	7076	7084	7093	7101	7110	7118	7126	7135	7143	7152
52	7160	7168	7177	7185	7193	7202	7210	7218	7226	7235
53	7243	7251	7259	7267	7275	7284	7292	7300	7308	7316
54	7324	7332	7340	7348	7356	7364	7372	7380	7388	7396
55	7404	7412	7419	7427	7435	7443	7451	7459	7466	7474
56	7482	7490	7497	7505	7513	7520	7528	7536	7543	7551
57	7559	7566	7574	7582	7589	7597	7604	7612	7619	7627
58	7634	7642	7649	7657	7664	7672	7679	7686	7694	7701
59	7709	7716	7723	7731	7738	7745	7752	7760	7767	7774
60	7782	7789	7796	7803	7810	7818	7825	7832	7839	7846
61	7853	7860	7868	7875	7882	7889	7896	7903	7910	7917
62	7924	7931	7938	7945	7952	7959	7966	7973	7980	7987
63	7993	8000	8007	8014	8021	8028	8035	8041	8048	8055
64	8062	8069	8075	8082	8089	8096	8102	8109	8116	8122
65	8129	8136	8142	8149	8156	8162	8169	8176	8182	8189
66	8195	8202	8209	8215	8222	8228	8235	8241	8248	8254
67	8261	8267	8274	8280	8287	8293	8299	8306	8312	8319
68	8325	8331	8338	8344	8351	8357	8363	8370	8376	8382
69	8388	8395	8401	8407	8414	8420	8426	8432	8439	8445
70	8451	8457	8463	8470	8476	8482	8488	8494	8500	8506
71	8513	8519	8525	8531	8537	8543	8549	8555	8561	8567
72	8573	8579	8585	8591	8597	8603	8609	8615	8621	8627
73	8633	8639	8645	8651	8657	8663	8669	8675	8681	8686
74	8692	8698	8704	8710	8716	8722	8727	8733	8739	8745
75	8751	8756	8762	8768	8774	8779	8785	8791	8797	8802
76	8808	8814	8820	8825	8831	8837	8842	8848	8854	8859
77	8865	8871	8876	8882	8887	8893	8899	8904	8910	8915
78	8921	8927	8932	8938	8943	8949	8954	8960	8965	8971
79	8976	8982	8987	8993	8998	9004	9009	9015	9020	9025
80	9031	9036	9042	9047	9053	9058	9063	9069	9074	9079
81	9085	9090	9096	9101	9106	9112	9117	9122	9128	9133
82	9138	9143	9149	9154	9159	9165	9170	9175	9180	9186
83	9191	9196	9201	9206	9212	9217	9222	9227	9232	9238
84	9243	9248	9253	9258	9263	9269	9274	9279	9284	9289
85	9294	9299	9304	9309	9315	9320	9325	9330	9335	9340
86	9345	9350	9355	9360	9365	9370	9375	9380	9385	9390
87	9395	9400	9405	9410	9415	9420	9425	9430	9435	9440
88	9445	9450	9455	9460	9465	9469	9474	9479	9484	9489
89	9494	9499	9504	9509	9513	9518	9523	9528	9533	9538
90	9542	9547	9552	9557	9562	9566	9571	9576	9581	9586
91	9590	9595	9600	9605	9609	9614	9619	9624	9628	9633
92	9638	9643	9647	9652	9657	9661	9666	9671	9675	9680
93	9685	9689	9694	9699	9703	9708	9713	9717	9722	9727
94	9731	9736	9741	9745	9750	9754	9759	9763	9768	9773
95	9777	9782	9786	9791	9795	9800	9805	9809	9814	9818
96	9823	9827	9832	9836	9841	9845	9850	9854	9859	9863
97	9868	9872	9877	9881	9886	9890	9894	9899	9903	9908
98	9912	9917	9921	9926	9930	9934	9939	9943	9948	9952
99	9956	9961	9965	9969	9974	9978	9983	9987	9991	9996
100	0000	0004	0009	0013	0017	0022	0026	0030	0035	0039
N	0	1	2	3	4	5	6	7	8	9

Appendix V—The Slide Rule

A slide rule is a simple mechanical device used for carrying out the arithmetic processes of *multiplication* and *division*. Since slide rules are easy to use, and inexpensive ones are quite adequate for most purposes, every physics student should acquire a slide rule and learn how to use it.

The beginner should select a straight inexpensive rule about ten inches in length and one that contains four and not more than six scales. The scales most commonly used are the A, B, C, and D scales as shown in Fig. A. Note that the slide rule consists of the slide rule *body*, and two movable parts we will call the *slipstick* and the *slider*.

Significant Figures. Before learning to use a slide rule we should clearly understand the meaning of the term *significant figures*. The three lists of numbers in columns I, II, and III below will help to illustrate its meaning.

The first significant figure of a number is the first numeral that is not zero. The last significant figure is the last numeral that is not zero.

Most slide rules are capable of handling the multiplication and division of numbers to three significant figures only. Furthermore, the answers are correct only to three significant figures.

I	II	III
Two significant figures	**Three significant figures**	**Four significant figures**
24	374	5279
6.9	21.5	63.08
0.37	6.05	0.1062
0.053	0.00328	0.04503
4600	546000	692700

If numbers like those in column III are to be used in any slide-rule calculation, they should be reduced to three significant figures. These particular numbers would, therefore, be assumed to have the values 5280, 63.1, 0.106, 0.0450, and 693000, respectively. Since many of the measurements made in the science laboratory are accurate to only three significant figures, the use of a slide rule is usually, but not always, sufficient and justified.

The C and D Scales. In making your first critical examination of your slide rule, note that there are four fundamental scales, and that they are marked at the left end of the rule by A, B, C, and D (see Fig. A). Since multiplication and division are usually carried out with the two identical C and D scales, we shall examine the entire length of these scales in three sections and see how to determine any position of the slider hairline.

Consider the left-hand section of the C and D scales from the left index 1 to

Fig. A.

hairline

slider

slipstick

slide-rule body

A B C D

the principal number 2, as shown in Fig. B. Note that the interval is divided into ten divisions representing tenths, and each of these into ten divisions representing hundredths.

Fig. B.

If the slider hairline were located in the position shown by the arrow at the left, its position would be written down as 1.14. Similarly, the second arrow position represents the reading 1.37. The third arrow position appears to be halfway between 1.53 and 1.54; hence we do what is called *interpolate* and write 1.535. Interpolation is a process of inserting or finding intermediate values by making a reasonable estimate as to an exact value. Since interpolation is nothing more than a good guess, the reading 1.535 is hardly better than three significant figures would indicate. Applying the interpolation process to the fourth arrow position, we could write 1.950, with the understanding that the last figure 0 may not be correct.

Although a decimal point has been inserted after the first digit of each arrow position in Fig. B, it could just as readily be placed before the first digit, after the second digit, or after the third digit, etc. In other words the left index 1 can represent any of the numbers 1, 10, 100, 1000, etc. If we let this index represent 10, the right-hand number 2 will represent 20, and the arrow positions would be read as 11.4, 13.7, 15.35, and 19.50. If we let the left index represent 100, the right-hand number 2 will represent 200, and the arrow positions would read as 114, 137, 153.5, and 195.0.

Set the slider of your rule at random between the principal numbers 1 and 2, and then practice reading its position until you feel confident you are reading it correctly.

We are now ready to examine the center section of the C and D scales between the index numbers 2, 3, and 4. Note in Fig. C, and on your own rule, that each of the two intervals

Fig. C.

is divided into tenths, and each subdivision into fifths. In other words, the smallest intervals, as marked, each represent 2/10 of a subdivision. Suppose we wanted to locate the position 2.36 on these scales. The first significant figure indicates that the position lies between 2 and 3. Set the hairline of your rule on 2. The second significant figure 3 indicates that the position is between the third and fourth subdivision, while the third significant figure 6 shows it is 6/10 or 3/5 of the distance between these two subdivisions. Hence the left arrow is properly located at 2.36.

Since the index numbers 3, 4, and 5 can also represent the numbers 30, 40, and 50, or 300, 400, and 500, the arrow positions could represent 23.6, 31.5, and 37.4, or 236, 315, and 374, respectively.

Finally we can examine the right-hand section of the C and D scales between the index numbers 4, 5, 6, 7, 8, 9, and 1 (see Fig. D). Between each pair of numbers are ten subdivisions and each subdivision is divided into halves or $\frac{5}{10}$. Note carefully the positions of the arrows and be sure you can read any position of your slider hairline when it is located any place on the C and D scales.

Fig. D.

Multiplication. To multiply two factors, carry out the four following steps: (1) Set the slider hairline on your first number on the D scale. (2) Move the slipstick so the left-hand index 1 of the C scale is exactly under the hairline. (3) Move the slider hairline to your second number on the C scale. (4) Read your answer on the D scale under the hairline.

Suppose for example you want to find the product 3 × 2. While you don't need the slide rule to find the answer, the performance of such a simple operation will clarify the method (see Fig. E). (1) Set the slider hairline on 3 of the D scale. (2) Move the slipstick and bring

Fig. E.

the left index 1 of the C scale to the hairline. (3) Move the slider to the second number 2 on the C scale. (4) Read the answer as 6 on the D scale.

A little study will show the slide-rule settings for the products 30 × 20, 3 × 20, 30 × 2300 × 20, etc., would all be the same as the above. The numeral 6 is the correct first numeral for all answers, but the number of zeros to be added must be determined by inspection.

Fig. F.

Consider the procedure for obtaining the product of 24.0 × 1.5. (1) Set the slider hairline exactly on the fourth subdivision line beyond the 2 of the D scale. This position represents 24.0. (2) Move the left-hand index 1 of the C scale to the hairline. (3) Move the slider to the fifth subdivision between 1 and 2 on the C scale. (4) The answer is under the hairline on the D scale and appears exactly at the sixth subdivision beyond 3 or 360. To locate the decimal point, inspect the two original numbers. One-and-a-half times 24 cannot be as small as 3.60 nor as large as 360. Therefore it must be 36.0. Similarly the product 24.0 × 2 is 48.0 as shown by the hairline position at the right in Fig. F.

Find the product 3.8 × 56.5. When the above steps are carried out for this product, the answer will be found to lie beyond the right-hand end of the D scale. In such cases one moves the right-hand index 1 of the C scale to the first number 3.8 on the D scale (see Fig. G). Moving the slider to the left, until the hairline is on the second number 56.5 on the C scale, the answer is read off the D scale as 215.

Fig. G.

The Decimal Point. To find the decimal point in any problem, substitute round numbers for those appearing in the problem and determine the position of the decimal point by approximation. For example, in the last problem round off the number 3.8 to 4, and the number 56.5 to 60. The product 4 × 60 by mental arithmetic is 240, so the answer is 215 and not 21.5 or 2150.

Division. Division on the slide rule is just the reverse of multiplication.

Rule. To divide one number by the other, carry out the following steps: (1) Set the slider hairline on the dividend, or numerator, on the D scale. (2) Move the slipstick until the divisor, or denominator, on the C scale lines up with the hairline. (3) The quotient, or answer, is under the C index at one end of the slipstick or the other. In simple terms, line up the numerator on the D scale with the denominator on the C scale, and the answer is under the C-scale index.

For example, find the quotient for 6/2. (1) Set the slider hairline on 6 of the D scale (see Fig. E). (2) Bring the 2 of the C scale to the hairline. (3) The answer 3 is now under the C index on the D scale. Note that the fraction 6/2 is just upside down on the rule.

As a second example find the quotient of 215/56.5 (see Fig. G). Set the hairline on 215 of the D scale and then line up 56.5 of the C scale. The answer 3.8 is on the D scale under the C index at the right. Note again that the fraction is lined up but inverted at the hairline position.

To find the decimal point in the last problem, round off the numbers and use mental arithmetic. For the number 215 write 200 and for 56.5 write 50. The quotient for 200/50 is 4. The answer, therefore, is 3.8 and not .38 or 38.

Square and Square Roots. To find the square of a number, one multiplies that number by itself. To find the square root of a number requires the carrying out of a complicated arithmetic process. With the slide rule these operations are relatively simple.

To find the square of a number, use the following rules: (1) Set the slider hairline to the number on the D scale. (2) Read the answer under the hairline on the A scale.

Inspection of Fig. A shows that directly above 2 on the D scale we find its square, or 4, on the A scale. Directly above 3 on the D scale is its square, or 9, on the A scale. Directly above 4 on the D scale (the position of the slider hairline shown) we find its square, or 16, on the A scale.

Fig. H.

To find the square root of a number, the reverse process is used: (*1*) *Set the hairline at the number on the A scale.* (*2*) *Read the square root on the D scale under the hairline.* Always use the left half of the A scale for numbers with an odd number of figures in front of the decimal point, and the right half for those with an even number of figures before the decimal point.

In Fig. H the hairline settings are shown for finding the square roots of 4.80 and 820. The two answers are shown on the D scale as 2.19 and 28.6.

Summary

The slide rule is most frequently and conveniently used for multiplication, division, squares, and square roots. A 10-in. rule is capable of an accuracy to three significant figures. The first significant figure of a number is the first numeral that is not zero. The last significant figure is the last numeral that is not zero.

Multiplication and division are most accurately performed on the longer C and D scales, whereas squares and square roots are found by using the A and D scales.

Problems

1. Express each of the following numbers to three significant figures only: (a) 6497, (b) 38.27, (c) 0.43927, (d) 0.06008, (e) 349.8.

2. Express each of the following numbers to three significant figures only: (a) 2359, (b) 64.32, (c) 0.4953, (d) 0.007647, (e) 987.7.

3. Find the product of each of the following: (a) 2.5 × 3, (b) 2.5 × 3.7, (c) 1.6 × 5.0, (d) 6 × 3.5, (e) 4.7 × 5.8.

4. Find the product of each of the following: (a) 2.7 × 3, (b) 3.4 × 2.1, (c) 2.3 × 2.9, (d) 5.6 × 3.4, (e) 4.3 × 8.7.

5. Find the product of each of the following:

(a) 3 × 26.4, (b) 28 × 35, (c) 29 × 17, (d) 13.5 × 6. (e) 17.2 × 21.6.

6. Find the product of each of the following: (a) 2.5 × 17, (b) 32 × 1.7, (c) 19 × 14, (d) 26.2 × 1.75, (e) 23.2 × 9.4.

7. Find the quotient of each of the following: (a) 6/5, (b) 25/4, (c) 38/7, (d) 64/3, (e) 72/2.7.

8. Find the quotient of each of the following: (a) 7/2, (b) 32/5, (c) 56/4.2, (d) 26/3.4, (e) 8.5/4.6.

9. Find the quotient of each of the following: (a) 35/6.2, (b) 67/5.9, (c) 325/28, (d) 430/270, (e) 675/780.

Appendix VI

Trigonometry of the Right Triangle. Of the mathematics to be encountered in this book, none involves more than the simplest equations in algebra and the three most common functions in trigonometry, *sine*, *cosine*, and *tangent*. These, however, are quite generally used and a brief review of the trigonometric functions is not out of place here. The principal use of the sin, cos, and tan occurs in problems where the solution requires the solving of a right triangle.

As shown in Fig. 1 the small letters a, b, and c represent the lengths of the sides of the triangle and the capital letters A, B, and C represent their corresponding opposite angles. Angle $C = 90°$.

By definition

$$\sin = \frac{\text{side opposite}}{\text{hypotenuse}}, \qquad \cos = \frac{\text{side adjacent}}{\text{hypotenuse}},$$

$$\tan = \frac{\text{side opposite}}{\text{side adjacent}}.$$

Fig. 1

(It would be well to memorize these definitions and from them and Fig. 1 practice writing down the following equations:)

$$(1) \quad \sin A = \frac{a}{c} \qquad\qquad (2) \quad \cos A = \frac{b}{c} \qquad\qquad (3) \quad \tan A = \frac{a}{b}$$

$$(4) \quad \sin B = \frac{b}{c} \qquad\qquad (5) \quad \cos B = \frac{a}{c} \qquad\qquad (6) \quad \tan B = \frac{b}{a}.$$

Each of these equations is a relation between one angle and two sides of the triangle. By transposing they take on another useful form. Equations (1) and (2), for example, become

$$(7) \quad a = c \sin A \qquad\qquad (8) \quad b = c \cos A.$$

If two of the sides of any right triangle are known, the other side and the two acute angles can be calculated from the above equations. This is done by making use of trigonometric tables of sin, cos, and tan given in Appendix III for all angles between 0° and 90°.

Example: For a given right triangle, angle $C = 90°$, the side $a = 6$ cm, and side $c = 12$ cm. Find angle A, angle B, and side b.

Solution: Using Eq. (1) and substituting, $\sin A = 6/12 = 0.5$. Looking up 0.500 in the sin column of Appendix III, the angle 30° is read. Since the sum of the three angles in any triangle is 180°,

$$(9) \quad A + B + C = 180°.$$

Subtraction gives angle $B = 60°$. Applying Eq. (8), $b = c \cos A$, we look up the cos of 30° in the tables and find 0.866, which substituted for cos A gives $b = 12 \times 0.866 = 10.39$ cm.

737

When two of the sides of a right triangle are known, the other side can also be calculated from the theorem that the square on the hypotenuse equals the sum of the squares of the other two sides.

$$(10) \quad c^2 = a^2 + b^2.$$

When in a right triangle, one of the acute angles is known, only the length of one side need be known to calculate the lengths of the other two sides.

From the definitions of the sin, cos, and tan in Eqs. (1), (2), and (3) it will be noted that the tan is equal to the sin divided by the cos.

$$(11) \quad \tan \theta = \frac{\sin \theta}{\cos \theta}.$$

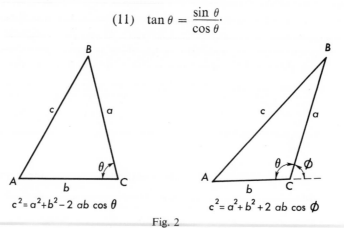

Fig. 2

Solution of Any Triangle. Many times in the solving of a physics problem it becomes necessary to solve an oblique triangle (see Fig. 2). Where two sides and the included angle of such a triangle are known, the **Law of Cosines** may be used to calculate the other side.

$$(12) \quad c^2 = a^2 + b^2 - 2ab \cos \theta.$$

If the included angle is less than 90° as shown in diagram (a), the values of a and b and $\cos \theta$ are substituted directly into Eq. (12) and the value of the side c calculated. If the angle θ is greater than 90°, as in diagram (b), the supplementary angle ϕ is found and Eq. (13) used.

$$(13) \quad c^2 = a^2 + b^2 + 2ab \cos \phi.$$

In reality Eqs. (12) and (13) are one and the same equation since $\phi = 180° - \theta$. In the special case $\theta = 90°$, the cosine term becomes zero, since $\cos 90° = 0$, and both formulas reduce to Eq. (10), as they should.

In words, the *Law of Cosines* states: *the square of any side of a triangle is equal to the sum of the squares on the other two sides minus twice their product multiplied by the cosine of the included angle.*

When three sides of a triangle are known, the angles can all be determined from Eq. (12). Transposing all but $\cos \theta$ to the same side of the equation,

$$(14) \quad \cos \theta = \frac{a^2 + b^2 - c^2}{2ab}.$$

With this as a general formula for angle θ, similar equations for all three angles of any triangle may be written,

$$(15) \quad \cos A = \frac{b^2 + c^2 - a^2}{2bc}, \qquad \cos B = \frac{c^2 + a^2 - b^2}{2ca},$$

$$\cos C = \frac{a^2 + b^2 - c^2}{2ab}.$$

A negative value for the cosine calculated from these equations means that the angle is greater than 90°. Its value can be found by looking in the tables for the angle whose sine has the same positive value, and then add 90°. For example, suppose $\cos A$ equals -0.5. Looking up the angle whose sine is $+0.500$ we find 30°. Angle A is therefore $30° + 90°$ or 120°.

If two angles and the included side of an oblique triangle are known, the other two sides are readily calculated from the well-known **Law of Sines.**

$$(16) \quad \frac{a}{\sin A} = \frac{b}{\sin B} = \frac{c}{\sin C}.$$

Any two terms from these equalities give an equation with only one unknown.

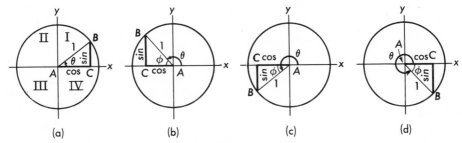

Fig. 3

The trigonometric functions sin, cos, and tan apply not only to angles between 0° and 90° but to larger angles as well. How they apply is illustrated in Fig. 3 where four circles of unit radius are drawn. Diagram (a) shows a right triangle ABC with angle θ in the first quadrant. It follows from the definitions of the sin and cos given by Eqs. (1) and (2) that

$$\sin \theta = BC/AB, \qquad \text{and} \qquad \cos \theta = AC/AB.$$

Since $AB = 1$, the $\sin \theta$ becomes just the length of the line BC. From Eq. (11), the $\tan \theta = BC/AC$.

All angles between 90° and 180° lie in the second quadrant, and are represented by θ in diagram (b). Similarly, angles between 180° and 270° lie in the third quadrant as illustrated in diagram (c), and angles between 270° and 360° lie in the fourth quadrant as illustrated in diagram (d). In all quadrants the length of the line $BC = \sin \theta$, the length of the line $AC = \cos \theta$, and the ratio $BC/AC = \tan \theta$.

To find the numerical values of the functions for all angles greater than 90°, the angle ϕ is first determined by finding the difference between θ and 180° and/or 360°, as the case may be. The values of $\sin \phi$, $\cos \phi$, and $\tan \phi$ are then read from the Tables in Appendix III. In the second quadrant the sin, being in the $+$ direction, is positive, whereas the cos, being in the $-x$ direction, is negative. In the third quadrant the sine and cosine are both negative, whereas in the fourth quadrant the sine is negative and the cosine positive.

Examples: let $\theta = 150°$. Find $\sin \theta$, $\cos \theta$, and $\tan \theta$. Subtracting from 180° gives $\phi = 30°$. From the tables in Appendix III, $\sin 30° = 0.500$, $\cos 30° = 0.866$, and $\tan 30° = 0.577$, giving $\sin 150° = 0.500$, $\cos 150° = -0.866$ and $\tan 150° = -0.577$.

Problems in Trigonometry

1. Find the number of degrees in the following angles: (a) $\sin \theta = 0.342$, (b) $\sin \theta = 0.809$, (c) $\cos \theta = 0.530$, (d) $\cos \theta = 0.454$, (e) $\tan \theta = 0.520$, and (f) $\tan \theta = 1.881$.

2. Find the sin, cos, and tan for the following angles: (a) 32.6°, and (b) 84.3°. [Ans. (a) 0.539, 0.842, 0.639; (b) 0.995, 0.0993, 10.02.]

3. Find the sin, cos, and tan for the following angles: (a) 118°, (b) 205°, and (c) 325°.

4. Find the angle θ for each of the following: (a) $\cos \theta = -0.249$, (b) $\sin \theta = -0.618$, and (c) $\tan \theta = -2.023$. [Ans. (a) 104.4° or 255.6°, (b) 116.3° or 306.3°, (c) 218.2° or 321.8°.]

5. One of the acute angles of a right triangle is 33° and the shortest side is 5 m long. Find the lengths of the other two sides and the remaining angle.

6. One of the acute angles of a right triangle is 48° and the hypotenuse is 6 m long. Find the other angle and the lengths of the other two sides. [Ans. 42°, 4.01 m, 4.46 m.]

7. A right triangle has sides of length: 3 ft, 4 ft, and 5 ft. Make a diagram to scale and measure the angles. Calculate the angles and compare them with those measured.

8. If the hypotenuse of a right triangle is 16 m long and one side is 10 m long, what is the length of the remaining side and the size of the two acute angles? [Ans. 12.5 m, 38.7°, and 51.3°.]

9. From a point on the level ground 180 ft from the base of a flag pole, an observer sights the top at an angle of 48° 24′. How high is the flag pole?

10. A base line 160 m long is measured along the beach; from its ends a rock can be seen some distance off shore. If the angles that the lines of sight from the ends make with the base line are 90° and 72.5°, how far from shore is the rock? [Ans. 508 m.]

11. A base line 20 m long is measured along the bank of a river, and from its ends a tree on the oppo-site bank is sighted. If the angles that these lines make with the base line are 65.5° and 72.6°, what is the width of the river? Make a diagram to scale.

12. To find the distance to a mountain peak, a base line 2 mi long is measured out on level ground in the valley below. From each end of this line the peak is sighted through a surveyor's telescope, and the lines of sight are found to make angles of 74.5° and 67.2° with the base line. Find the distance to the peak from the ends of the base line. Make a diagram to scale. [Ans. (a) 2.97 mi, (b) 3.11 mi.]

13. A ship in distress is sighted from two light-houses 10 mi apart. From the first lighthouse the line of sight to the ship is found to make an angle of 125° with the line of sight to the second lighthouse, while from the second the line of sight is found to make 48° with the line of sight to the first lighthouse. How far is the ship from the nearest lighthouse? Make a diagram to scale.

14. When the sun is 35.4° above the horizon, the shadow of a tall tree is found to be 260 ft long, as measured along level ground from the base of the tree. How high is the tree? [Ans. 185 ft.]

15. Two sides of a triangle are 24.8 m and 32.6 m, respectively, and the included angle is 35.5°. Find the length of the other side, and the values of the other two angles.

16. Two sides of a triangle are 5.7 m and 8.4 m, respectively, and the included angle is 115°. Find the length of the other side, and the values of the other two angles. [Ans. 12.0 m, 39.4°, and 35.6°.]

17. From a point on level ground 150 ft from the base of a flag pole, an observer sights the top at an elevation angle of 35°. How high is the flag pole? [Ans. 105 ft.]

18. A base line 400 ft long is measured along the ocean shore, and from the end a rock can be seen offshore. If the angles that the lines of sight make with the base line are 90° and 75°, how far off shore is the rock? [Ans. 1490 ft.]

Appendix VII—Complete List of the Stable Isotopes of the Chemical Elements

Atomic weights are based on the atomic mass of $C^{12} = 12$ even (see Sec. 49.7).

AT. NO.	ELEMENT	SYM.	ISOTOPES, MASS NO.	AT. WT.
1	hydrogen........	H	**1**, (2)	1.00797[a]
2	helium.........	He	**4**, (3)	4.0026
3	lithium.........	Li	6, **7**	6.939
4	beryllium.......	Be	9	9.0122
5	boron..........	B	10, **11**	10.811[a]
6	carbon.........	C	**12**, (13)	12.01115[a]
7	nitrogen........	N	**14**, (15)	14.0067
8	oxygen.........	O	**16**, (18), (17)	15.9994[a]
9	fluorine........	F	19	18.9984
10	neon..........	Ne	**20**, (21), **22**	20.183
11	sodium........	Na	23	22.9898
12	magnesium.....	Mg	**24**, 25, 26	24.312
13	aluminum.....	Al	27	26.9815
14	silicon........	Si	**28**, 29, 30	28.086[a]
15	phosphorus.....	P	31	30.9738
16	sulfur.........	S	**32**, 33, 34	32.064[a]
17	chlorine.......	Cl	**35**, 37	35.453[b]
18	argon.........	Ar	(36), (38), **40**	39.948
19	potassium......	K	**39**, (40), 41	39.102
20	calcium........	Ca	**40**, (42), (43), 44	40.08
21	scandium.......	Sc	45	44.956
22	titanium........	Ti	46, 47, **48**, 49, 50	47.90
23	vanadium......	V	**51**	50.942
24	chromium.....	Cr	50, **52**, 53, 54	51.996[b]
25	manganese......	Mn	55	54.9380
26	iron..........	Fe	54, **56**, 57, (58)	55.847[b]
27	cobalt.........	Co	59	58.9332
28	nickel.........	Ni	**58**, 60, 61, 62 (**64**)	58.71
29	copper........	Cu	**63**, 65	63.54
30	zinc..........	Zn	**64**, 66, 67, 68, (70)	65.37
31	gallium........	Ga	**69**, 71	69.72
32	germanium.....	Ge	70, 72, 73, **74**, 76	72.59
33	arsenic........	As	75	74.9216
34	selenium.......	Se	(74), 76, 77, 78, **80**, 82	78.96
35	bromine.......	Br	**79**, 81	79.909[b]
36	krypton.......	Kr	(78), 80, 82, 83, **84**, 86	83.80

[a] Atomic weights so designated are known to be variable because of natural variations in isotopic composition. The observed ranges are: Hydrogen ± 0.00001; Boron ± 0.003; Carbon ± 0.00005; Oxygen ± 0.0001; Silicon ± 0.001; Sulfur ± 0.003.

[b] Atomic weights so designated are believed to have the following experimental uncertainties: Chlorine ± 0.001; Chromium ± 0.001; Iron ± 0.003; Bromine ± 0.002; Silver ± 0.003.

37	rubidium	Rb	**85,** *87*	85.47
38	strontium	Sr	(84), 86, 87, **88**	87.62
39	yttrium	Yt	**89**	88.905
40	zirconium	Zr	**90,** 91, 92, 94, 96	91.22
41	niobium	Nb	**93**	92.906
42	molybdenum	Mo	92, 94, 95, 96, 97, **98,** 100, 102	95.94
43	technetium	Tc	*99*	97.2
44	ruthenium	Ru	96, 98, 99, 100, 101, **102,** 104	101.07
45	rhodium	Rh	**103**	102.905
46	palladium	Pd	(102), 104, 105, **106,** 108, 110	106.4
47	silver	Ag	107, **109**	107.870[b]
48	cadmium	Cd	106, (108), 110, 111, **112,** 113, 114, 116	112.40
49	indium	In	113, **115**	114.82
50	tin	Sn	112, (114), (115), 116, 117, 118, 119, **120,** 122, 124	118.69
51	antimony	Sb	**121, 123**	121.75
52	tellurium	Te	(120), 122, 123, 124, 125, 126, **128,** 130	127.60
53	iodine	I	**127**	126.9044
54	xenon	Xe	(124), (126), 128, **129,** 130, 131, 132, 134, 136	131.30
55	cesium	Cs	**133**	132.905
56	barium	Ba	(130), (132), 134, 135, 136, 137, **138**	137.34
57	lanthanum	La	**139**	138.91
58	cerium	Ce	(136), (138), **140,** 142	140.12
59	praseodymium	Pr	**141**	140.906
60	neodymium	Nd	**142,** 143, **144,** 145, 146, (148), (150)	144.24
61	prometeum	Pm		146.0
62	samarium	Sa	144, 147, 148, 149, 150, **152,** 154	150.35
63	europium	Eu	**151, 153**	151.96
64	gadolinium	Gd	155, **156,** 157, **158,** 160	157.25
65	terbium	Tb	**159**	158.924
66	dysprosium	Dy	161, 162, 163, **164**	162.50
67	holmium	Ho	**165**	164.930
68	erbium	Er	**166,** 167, 168, 170	167.26
69	thulium	Tm	**169**	168.934
70	ytterbium	Yb	171, 172, 173, **174,** 176	173.04
71	lutecium	Lu	**175**	174.97
72	hafnium	Hf	176, 177, 178, 179, **180**	178.49
73	tantalum	Ta	**181**	180.948
74	tungsten	W	182, 183, **184, 186**	183.85
75	rhenium	Re	185, **187**	186.2
76	osmium	Os	186, (187), 188, 189, 190, 192	190.2
77	iridium	Ir	191, **193**	192.2
78	platinum	Pt	(192), 194, **195,** 196, 198	195.09
79	gold	Au	**197**	196.967
80	mercury	Hg	(196), 198, 199, 200, 201, **202,** 204	200.59
81	thallium	Tl	203, **205**	204.37
82	lead	Pb	204, 206, 207, **208**	207.19
83	bismuth	Bi	**209**	208.98

Although some of them are found in nature, elements 84 and up are unstable. For their isotopes see Tables 72A and 72B.

Appendix VIII—Relative Masses of One Stable Isotope for Each of the Elements

Based on $O^{16} = 16$ and $C^{12} = 12$.

These values are taken from Everling, König, Mattauch, and Wapstra, *Nucl. Phys.* **18**, 529 (1960); and König, Mattauch, and Wapstra, *Nucl. Phys.* **31**, 18 (1962).

Space is left between third and fourth decimal place to facilitate reading.

SYMBOL	O^{16} = 16 EVEN	C^{12} = 12 EVEN	SYMBOL	O^{16} = 16 EVEN	C^{12} = 12 EVEN
$_1H^1$	1.008 1456	1.007 8252	$_{51}Sb^{121}$	120.942 190	120.903 750
$_2He^4$	4.003 8761	4.002 6036	$_{52}Te^{128}$	127.945 370	127.904 710
$_3Li^7$	7.018 236	7.016 005	$_{53}I^{127}$	126.944 697	126.904 352
$_4Be^9$	9.015 051	9.012 186	$_{54}Xe^{129}$	128.945 765	128.904 784
$_5B^{11}$	11.012 805	11.009 3051	$_{55}Cs^{133}$	132.947 340	132.905 090
$_6C^{12}$	12.003 8150	12 even	$_{56}Ba^{138}$	137.948 860	137.905 010
$_7N^{14}$	14.007 5262	14.003 0744	$_{57}La^{139}$	138.950 220	138.906 060
$_8O^{16}$	16 even	15.995 9149	$_{58}Ce^{140}$	139.949 760	139.905 280
$_9F^{19}$	19.004 444	18.998 4046	$_{59}Pr^{141}$	140.952 186	140.907 390
$_{10}Ne^{20}$	19.998 7964	19.992 4404	$_{60}Nd^{142}$	141.952 493	141.907 478
$_{11}Na^{23}$	22.997 081	22.989 773	$_{61}Pm^{143}$	142.956 240	143.910 800
$_{12}Mg^{24}$	23.992 670	23.985 045	$_{62}Sm^{144}$	143.957 400	143.911 650
$_{13}Al^{27}$	26.990 113	26.981 535	$_{63}Eu^{153}$	152.969 230	152.920 720
$_{14}Si^{28}$	27.985 822	27.976 927	$_{64}Gd^{156}$	155.971 810	155.922 240
$_{15}P^{31}$	30.983 611	30.973 763	$_{65}Tb^{159}$	158.974 800	158.924 300
$_{16}S^{32}$	31.982 232	31.972 074	$_{66}Dy^{164}$	163.980 200	163.928 100
$_{17}Cl^{35}$	34.979 972	34.968 855	$_{67}Ho^{165}$	164.982 000	164.929 600
$_{18}Ar^{40}$	39.975 089	39.962 384	$_{68}Er^{166}$	165.984 700	165.931 900
$_{19}K^{39}$	38.976 101	38.963 714	$_{69}Tm^{169}$	165.985 500	165.932 700
$_{20}Ca^{40}$	39.975 294	39.962 589	$_{70}Yb^{177}$	176.999 710	176.943 940
$_{21}Sc^{45}$	44.970 811	44.955 916	$_{71}Lu^{177}$	176.998 710	176.942 450
$_{22}Ti^{48}$	47.963 491	47.947 948	$_{72}Hf^{180}$	180.002 330	179.945 120
$_{23}V^{51}$	50.960 174	50.943 978	$_{73}Ta^{181}$	181.003 700	180.646 180
$_{24}Cr^{52}$	51.957 027	51.940 514	$_{74}W^{184}$	184.007 630	183.949 150
$_{25}Mn^{55}$	54.958 123	54.941 293	$_{75}Re^{187}$	187.014 410	186.954 980
$_{26}Fe^{56}$	55.952 714	55.934 932	$_{76}Os^{189}$	189.017 290	188.957 220
$_{27}Co^{59}$	58.951 925	58.933 189	$_{77}Ir^{193}$	193.023 680	192.962 340
$_{28}Ni^{58}$	57.953 761	57.935 342	$_{78}Pt^{195}$	195.026 450	194.964 460
$_{29}Cu^{63}$	62.949 600	62.929 594	$_{79}Au^{197}$	197.029 171	196.966 552
$_{30}Zn^{64}$	63.949 469	63.929 145	$_{80}Hg^{202}$	202.034 840	201.970 630
$_{31}Ga^{69}$	68.947 594	68.925 682	$_{81}Tl^{205}$	205.039 627	204.974 462
$_{32}Ge^{74}$	73.944 660	73.921 150	$_{82}Pb^{206}$	206.039 940	205.974 460
$_{33}As^{75}$	74.945 400	74.921 580	$_{83}Bi^{209}$	209.046 856	208.980 417
$_{34}Se^{80}$	79.941 919	79.916 512	$_{84}Po^{214}$	214.063 224	213.995 192
$_{35}Br^{81}$	80.942 069	80.916 344	$_{85}At^{217}$	217.073 639	217.002 405
$_{36}Kr^{84}$	83.938 181	83.911 504	$_{86}Rn^{222}$	222.085 948	222.015 365
$_{37}Rb^{85}$	84.938 700	84.911 710	$_{87}Fr^{221}$	221.084 440	221.014 176
$_{38}Sr^{88}$	87.933 560	87.905 610	$_{88}Ra^{226}$	226.097 210	226.025 360
$_{39}Y^{89}$	88.933 690	88.905 430	$_{89}Ac^{227}$	227.099 990	227.027 814
$_{40}Zr^{90}$	89.932 900	89.904 320	$_{90}Th^{232}$	232.111 980	232.038 211
$_{41}Nb^{93}$	92.935 550	92.906 020	$_{91}Pa^{234}$	234.117 770	234.043 370
$_{42}Mo^{98}$	97.936 640	97.905 510	$_{92}U^{238}$	238.126 440	238.050 760
$_{43}Tc^{99}$	98.938 400	98.907 300	$_{93}Np^{239}$	239.128 937	239.052 938
$_{44}Ru^{102}$	101.936 110	101.907 720	$_{94}Pu^{240}$	240.130 292	240.053 974
$_{45}Rh^{103}$	102.937 520	102.903 800	$_{95}Am^{241}$	241.133 325	241.056 689
$_{46}Pd^{106}$	105.936 870	105.903 200	$_{96}Cm^{242}$	242.135 750	242.058 800
$_{47}Ag^{107}$	106.938 960	106.904 970	$_{97}Bk^{245}$	245.144 150	245.066 240
$_{48}Ca^{112}$	111.928 410	111.902 840	$_{98}Cf^{246}$	246.147 000	246.068 780
$_{49}In^{115}$	114.940 600	114.904 070	$_{99}Es^{249}$	249.155 400	249.076 220
$_{50}Sn^{120}$	119.940 250	119.902 130	$_{100}Fm^{252}$	252.162 790	252.082 650

Appendix IX—Table of Isotopes and Their Properties

(s = second; m = minute; h = hour; d = day; y = year)

Based upon carbon-12 as 12 even.

SYMBOL	ATOMIC MASS (amu)	MASS EXCESS MeV	ABUND. OR ACTIVITY	HALF-LIFE
$_{-1}e^0$	0.000 549	0.511	—	stable
$_1p^1$	1.007 276	6.774	—	stable
$_0n^1$	1.008 665	8.071	β^-	13 m
$_1H^1$	1.007 825	7.288	**99.985**	stable
H^2	2.014 103	13.135	**0.015**	stable
H^3	3.016 049	14.949	β^-	12.2 y
$_2He^3$	3.016 030	14.931	**0.00013**	stable
He^4	4.002 604	2.425	**99.9999**	stable
He^5	5.012 296	11.453	$\alpha + n$	inst.
He_6	6.018 900	17.604	β^-	0.82 s
$_3Li^5$	5.012 541	11.681	$\alpha + p$	inst.
Li^6	6.015 126	14.089	**7.52**	stable
Li^7	7.016 005	14.908	**92.48**	stable
Li^8	8.022 488	20.947	β^-	0.86 s
Li^9	9.027 300	25.400	β^-	0.17 s
$_4Be^6$	6.019 780	18.430	β^+	0.4 s
Be^7	7.016 931	15.770	E.C.	53.6 d
Be^8	8.005 308	4.944	2α	inst.
Be^9	9.012 186	11.350	**100**	stable
Be^{10}	10.013 535	12.607	β^-	2.5×10^6 y
$_5B^8$	8.024 612	22.924	β^+	0.6 s
B^9	9.013 335	12.420	$2\alpha + p$	inst.
B^{10}	10.012 939	12.052	**18.6**	stable
B^{11}	11.009 305	8.667	**81.4**	stable
B^{12}	12.014 353	13.369	β^-	0.022 s
$_6C^{10}$	10.016 830	15.670	β^+	19.1 s
C^{11}	11.011 433	10.649	β^+	20.5 m
C^{12}	12.000 000	0	**98.892**	stable
C^{13}	13.003 354	3.124	**1.108**	stable
C^{14}	14.003 242	3.020	β^-	5.6×10^3 y
C^{15}	15.010 600	9.873	β^-	2.3 s

SYMBOL	ATOMIC MASS (amu)	MASS EXCESS MeV	ABUND. OR ACTIVITY	HALF-LIFE
$_7N^{12}$	12.018 709	17.426	β^+	0.012 s
N^{13}	13.005 739	5.345	β^+	10.1 m
N^{14}	14.003 074	2.864	**99.635**	stable
N^{15}	15.000 108	0.101	**0.365**	stable
N^{16}	16.006 089	5.672	β^-	7.36 s
N^{17}	17.008 449	7.869	β^-	4.14 s
$_8O^{14}$	14.008 597	8.008	β^+	74 s
O^{15}	15.003 072	2.861	β^+	2.0 m
O^{16}	15.994 915	−4.736	**99.76**	stable
O^{17}	16.999 133	−0.807	**0.04**	stable
O^{18}	17.999 160	−0.782	**0.20**	stable
O^{19}	19.003 577	3.332	β^-	29.4 s
O^{20}	20.004 071	3.792	n	13.6 s
$_9F^{17}$	17.002 098	1.954	β^+	66 s
F^{18}	18.000 950	0.884	β^+	1.87 h
F^{19}	18.998 405	−1.486	**100**	stable
F^{20}	19.999 986	−0.013	β^-	11.2 s
F^{21}	20.999 972	−0.026	β^-	5 s
$_{10}Ne^{18}$	18.005 715	5.323	β^+	1.6 s
Ne^{19}	19.001 892	1.762	β^+	19 s
Ne^{20}	19.992 440	−7.041	**90.92**	stable
Ne^{21}	20.993 849	−5.729	**0.26**	stable
Ne^{22}	21.991 385	−8.025	**8.82**	stable
Ne^{23}	22.994 475	−5.146	β^-	40.2 s
Ne^{24}	23.993 597	−5.964	β^-	3.4 m
$_{11}Na^{20}$	20.008 890	8.280	β^+	0.3 s
Na^{21}	20.997 638	−2.200	β^+	23 s
Na^{22}	21.994 435	−5.183	β^+, E.C.	2.6 y
Na^{23}	22.989 773	−9.526	**100**	stable
Na^{24}	23.990 967	−8.414	β^-	15.0 h
Na^{25}	24.989 920	−9.390	β^-	60 s
$_{12}Mg^{23}$	22.994 135	−5.463	β^+, E.C.	11 s
Mg^{24}	23.985 045	−13.930	**78.60**	stable
Mg^{25}	24.985 840	−13.189	**10.11**	stable
Mg^{26}	25.982 591	−16.215	**11.29**	stable
Mg^{27}	26.998 346	−14.581	β^-	9.45 m
Mg^{28}	27.983 880	−15.015	β^-	21.4 h
$_{13}Al^{24}$	24.000 090	0.090	β^+	2.1 s
Al^{25}	24.990 414	−8.928	β^+	7.6 s
Al^{26}	25.986 900	−12.201	β^+, E.C.	10^5 y
Al^{27}	26.981 535	−17.199	**100**	stable
Al^{28}	27.981 908	−16.851	β^-	2.3 m
Al^{29}	28.980 442	−18.217	β^-	6.6 m
$_{14}Si^{27}$	26.986 701	−12.387	β^+, E.C.	4.9 s
Si^{28}	27.976 927	−21.491	**92.27**	stable
Si^{29}	28.976 491	−21.897	**4.68**	stable
Si^{30}	29.973 761	−24.440	**3.05**	stable
Si^{31}	30.975 349	−22.961	β^-	2.6 h
Si^{32}	31.974 020	−24.200	β^-	7×10^2 y

SYMBOL	ATOMIC MASS (amu)	MASS EXCESS MeV	ABUND. OR ACTIVITY	HALF-LIFE
$_{15}P^{28}$	27.991 740	−7.690	β^+	0.28 s
P^{29}	28.981 816	−16.937	β^+	4.4 s
P^{30}	29.978 320	−20.193	β^+	2.5 m
P^{31}	30.973 763	−24.438	**100**	stable
P^{32}	31.973 908	−24.303	β^-	14.3 d
P^{33}	32.971 728	−26.334	β^-	24.4 d
P^{34}	33.973 340	−24.830	β^-	12.4 s
$_{16}S^{31}$	30.979 599	−19.002	β^+	2.6 s
S^{32}	31.972 074	−26.012	**95.054**	stable
S^{33}	32.971 461	−26.583	**0.740**	stable
S^{34}	33.967 865	−29.932	**4.190**	stable
S^{35}	34.969 034	−28.843	β^-	87.1 d
S^{36}	35.967 091	−30.653	**0.016**	stable
S^{37}	36.971 040	−26.980	β^-	5.0 m
S^{38}	37.971 220	−26.800	β^-	6 m
$_{17}Cl^{32}$	31.986 030	−13.010	β^+	0.31 s
Cl^{33}	32.977 446	−21.008	β^+	2.4 s
Cl^{34}	33.973 764	−24.437	β^+	32.4 m
Cl^{35}	34.968 855	−29.010	**75.4**	stable
Cl^{36}	35.968 312	−25.516	β^-, E.C.	3.2 y
Cl^{37}	36.965 898	−31.766	**24.6**	stable
Cl^{38}	37.968 002	−29.804	β^-	37.5 m
Cl^{39}	38.968 003	−29.803	β^-	55.5 m
Cl^{40}	39.970 400	−27.500	β^-	1.4 m
$_{18}Ar^{35}$	34.975 275	−23.030	β^+	1.83 s
Ar^{36}	35.963 548	−30.227	**0.337**	stable
Ar^{37}	36.966 772	−30.950	E.C.	34.1 d
Ar^{38}	37.962 725	−34.720	**0.063**	stable
Ar^{39}	38.964 321	−33.233	β^-	2.6×10^2 y
Ar^{40}	39.962 384	−35.037	**99.600**	stable
Ar^{41}	40.964 508	−33.058	β^-	1.83 h
Ar^{42}	41.963 043	−34.423	β^-	3.5 y
$_{19}K^{38}$	37.969 090	−28.791	β^+	7.7 m
K^{39}	38.963 714	−33.798	**93.08**	stable
K^{40}	39.964 008	−33.524	**0.0119**	10^9 y
K^{41}	40.961 835	−35.548	**6.91**	stable
K^{42}	41.962 417	−35.006	β^-	12.5 h
K^{43}	42.960 731	−36.577	β^-	22.4 h
K^{44}	43.962 040	−35.360	β^-	22.0 m
$_{20}Ca^{39}$	38.970 706	−27.286	β^+	1.0 s
Ca^{40}	39.962 589	−34.846	**96.97**	stable
Ca^{41}	40.962 279	−35.135	E.C.	2×10^5 y
Ca^{42}	41.958 628	−38.536	**0.64**	stable
Ca^{43}	42.958 780	−38.394	**0.145**	stable
Ca^{44}	43.955 490	−41.458	**2.06**	stable
Ca^{45}	44.956 189	−40.807	β^-	164 d
Ca^{46}	45.953 689	−43.136	**0.0033**	stable
Ca^{47}	46.954 512	−42.370	β^-	4.9 d
Ca^{48}	47.952 363	−44.371	**0.185**	10^{16} y
Ca^{49}	48.955 662	−41.298	β^-	8.8 m

For atomic masses in *amu* and mass excess energies in *Mev*, for isotopes in the remainder of the periodic table, see *Nuclear Physics*, March-April, pp. 28–42, 1962, by L. A. König, J. H. E. Mattauch, and A. H. Wapstra.

Appendix X—The Periodic Table of Chemical Elements

I	II	III	IV	V	VI	VII	VIII		
1 H 1.0080							2 He 4.0026		
3 Li 6.939	4 Be 9.0122	5 B 10.811	6 C 12.011	7 N 14.007	8 O 15.999	9 F 18.998	10 Ne 20.183		
11 Na 22.990	12 Mg 24.312	13 Al 26.981	14 Si 28.086	15 P 30.974	16 S 32.064	17 Cl 35.453	18 Ar 39.948		
19 K 39.102	20 Ca 40.08	21 Sc 44.956	22 Ti 47.90	23 V 50.942	24 Cr 51.996	25 Mn 54.938	26 Fe 55.847	27 Co 58.933	28 Ni 58.71
29 Cu 63.54	30 Zn 65.37	31 Ga 69.72	32 Ge 72.59	33 As 74.922	34 Se 78.96	35 Br 79.909	36 Kr 83.80		
37 Rb 85.47	38 Sr 87.62	39 Yt 88.905	40 Zr 91.22	41 Nb 92.906	42 Mo 95.94	43 Tc . . .	44 Ru 101.07	45 Rh 102.905	46 Pd 106.4
47 Ag 107.870	48 Cd 112.40	49 In 114.82	50 Sn 118.69	51 Sb 121.75	52 Te 127.60	53 I 126.904	54 Xe 131.30		
55 Cs 132.905	56 Ba 137.34	57 La 138.91	72 Hf 178.49	73 Ta 180.95	74 W 183.85	75 Re 186.2	76 Os 190.2	77 Ir 192.2	78 Pt 195.09
79 Au 196.97	80 Hg 200.59	81 Tl 204.37	82 Pb 207.19	83 Bi 208.98	84 Po . . .	85 At . . .	86 Rn . . .		
87 Fr . . .	88 Ra . . .	89 Ac . . .	90 Th 232.04	91 Pa . . .	92 U 238.03	93 Np . . .	94 Pu . . .	95 Am . . .	96 Cm . . .

58 Ce 140.12	59 Pr 140.91	60 Nd 144.24	61 Pm . . .	62 Sm 150.35	63 Eu 151.96	64 Gd 157.25	65 Tb 159.2	66 Ds 162.50	67 Ho 164.93	68 Er 167.26	69 Tm 168.93	70 Yb 173.04	71 Lu 174.97
90 Th 232.04	91 Pa . . .	92 U 238.03	93 Np . . .	94 Pu . . .	95 Am . . .	96 Cm . . .	97 Bk . . .	98 Cf . . .	99 E . . .	100 Fm . . .	101 Md . . .	102 (No) . . .	103 Lw . . .

Atomic weights are given on the carbon-12 equal 12 even.

Appendix XI—Electron Subshells

The table shows the order in which the electron subshells are filled in, in the building up of the elements of the periodic table. Atomic weights are given with respect to carbon-12 as 12 even.

n+l+1	Sub-Shells	1	2	3	4	5	6	7	8	9	10	11	12	13	14
1	1s	1.0080 H 1	4.003 He 2												
2	2s	6.939 Li 3	9.012 Be 4												
3	2p	10.81 B 5	12.000 C 6	14.007 N 7	15.999 O 8	18.998 F 9	20.183 Ne 10								
3	3s	22.990 Na 11	24.312 Mg 12												
4	3p	26.98 Al 13	28.08 Si 14	30.974 P 15	32.064 S 16	35.453 Cl 17	39.948 Ar 18								
4	4s	39.102 K 19	40.08 Ca 20												
5	3d	44.96 Sc 21	47.90 Ti 22	50.94 V 23	51.996 Cr 24	54.94 Mn 25	55.85 Fe 26	58.93 Co 27	58.71 Ni 28	63.54 Cu 29	65.37 Zn 30				
5	4p	69.72 Ga 31	72.59 Ge 32	74.92 As 33	78.96 Se 34	79.91 Br 35	83.80 Kr 36								
5	5s	85.47 Rb 37	87.62 Sr 38												
6	4d	88.90 Y 39	91.22 Zr 40	92.91 Nb 41	95.94 Mo 42	(99) Tc 43	101.1 Ru 44	102.91 Rh 45	106.4 Pd 46	107.870 Ag 47	112.40 Cd 48				
6	5p	114.82 In 49	118.69 Sn 50	121.75 Sb 51	127.60 Te 52	126.90 I 53	131.3 Xe 54								
6	6s	132.90 Cs 55	137.34 Ba 56												
7	4f	138.91 La 57	140.12 Ce 58	140.91 Pr 59	144.24 Nd 60	(145) Pm 61	150.35 Sm 62	151.96 Eu 63	157.25 Gd 64	158.92 Tb 65	162.50 Dy 66	164.93 Ho 67	167.2 Er 68	168.93 Tm 69	173.04 Yb 70
7	5d	174.97 Lu 71	178.5 Hf 72	180.95 Ta 73	183.92 W 74	186.2 Re 75	190.2 Os 76	192.2 Ir 77	195.09 Pt 78	196.97 Au 79	200.59 Hg 80				
7	6p	204.37 Tl 81	207.19 Pb 82	208.98 Bi 83	210 Po 84	(210) At 85	222 Rn 86								
7	7s	(223) Fr 87	226.05 Ra 88												
8	5f	227 Ac 89	232.04 Th 90	231 Pa 91	238.03 U 92	(237) Np 93	(242) Pu 94	(243) Am 95	(245) Cm 96	(245) Bk 97	(248) Cf 98	(253) Es 99	(254) Fm 100	(256) Mv 101	No 102
8	6d	Lw 103	104	105	106	107	108	109	110	111	112				

1901 Röntgen, Wilhelm Conrad (1845–1923), German. *Discovery of X rays.*

1902 Lorentz, Hendrik Antoon (1853–1928), Dutch, and
Zeeman, Pieter (1865–1943), Dutch. *Zeeman Effect.*

1903 Becquerel, Henri Antoine (1852–1908), French. *Discovery of Radioactivity.*
Curie, Pierre (1859–1906), French, and
Curie, Marie Sklodowska (1867–1934), Polish chemist in France. *Studies of Radioactivity.*

1904 Lord Rayleigh (John William Strutt) (1842–1919), English. *Studies of Gases.*

1905 Lenard, Philipp (1862–1947), German. *Studies of Cathode Rays.*

1906 Thomson, Sir Joseph John (1856–1940), English. *Discharges through Gases.*

1907 Michelson, Albert A. (1852–1931), American. *Precision Optical Instruments.*

1908 Lippmann, Gabriel (1845–1921), French. *Interference Color Photography.*

1909 Marconi, Guglielmo (1874–1937), Italian, and
Braun, Ferdinand (1850–1918), German. *Development of Wireless.*

1910 Van der Waals, Johannes D. (1837–1923), Dutch. *Gas Laws.*

1911 Wien, Wilhelm (1864–1928), German. *Heat Radiation Laws.*

1912 Dalen, Gustaf (1869–1937), Swedish. *Automatic Lighting of Lighthouses.*

1913 Kamerlingh-Onnes, Heike (1853–1926), Dutch. *Liquid Helium and Low Temperatures.*

1914 Von Laue, Max Theodor Felix (1879–1960), German. *Diffraction of X rays.*

1915 Bragg, Sir W. H. (1862–1942), English, and his son
Bragg, W. L. (1890–   ), English. *Crystal Structure.*

1917 Barkla, Charles G. (1877–1944), English. *Characteristic X rays of the Elements.*

1918 Planck, Max (1858–1947), German. *Quantum Theory of Radiation.*

1919 Stark, Johannes (1874–1957), German. *The Stark Effect of Spectrum Lines.*

1920 Guillaume, Charles E. (1861–1938), Spanish. *Study of Nickel–Steel Alloys.*

1921 Einstein, Albert (1879–1955), German. *Theory of Relativity and the Photoelectric Effect.*

1922 Bohr, Niels (1885–1962), Danish. *Theory of Atomic Structure.*

1923 Millikan, Robert A. (1868–1953), American. *Charge on Electron and Photoelectric Effect.*

1924 Siegbahn, Karl M. (1886–   ), Swedish. *X-ray Spectroscopy.*

1925 Franck, James (1882–   ), German, and
Hertz, Gustav (1887–   ), German. *Electron Impact on Atoms.*

1926 Perrin, Jean B. (1870–1942), French. *Discovery of the Equilibrium of Sedimentation.*

1927 Compton, Arthur H. (1892–1962), American. *Compton Effect.*
Wilson, Charles T. R. (1869–1959), English. *Wilson Cloud Chamber.*

1928 Richardson, Owen Willans (1879–1959), English. *Studies of Thermal Ions.*

1929 De Broglie, Louis V. (1892–   ), French. *Wave Character of Electrons.*

1930 Raman, Sir Chandrasekhara V. (1888–   ), Indian. *Raman Effect.*

1932 Heisenberg, Werner (1901–   ), German. *Creation of Quantum Mechanics.*

1933 Schrödinger, Edwin (1887–   ), German, and
Dirac, P. A. M. (1902–   ), English. *Atomic Theory.*

1935 Chadwick, James (1891–   ), English. *Discovery of the Neutron.*

1936 Hess, Victor F. (1883–   ), Austrian. *Discovery of Cosmic Rays.*
Anderson, Carl D. (1905–   ), American. *Discovery of Positron.*

1937 Davisson, Clinton J. (1881–   ), American and
     Thompson, George P. (1892–   ), English. *Electron Diffraction by Crystals.*
1938 Fermi, Enrico (1901–1954), Italian. *Slow-Neutron Reactions.*
1939 Lawrence, Ernest O. (1901–1958), American. *Development of Cyclotron.*
1940, 1941, 1942, not awarded
1943 Stern, O. (1888–   ), German. *Magnetic Moment of Proton.*
1944 Rabi, I. I. (1898–   ), American. *Magnetic Moments of Nuclei.*
1945 Pauli, W. (1900–1958), Swiss. *Pauli Exclusion Principle.*
1946 Bridgman, P. W. (1882–1961), American. *Physical Effects of High Pressures.*
1947 Appleton, Sir Ed. V. (1892–   ), English. *Exploration of the Ionosphere.*
1948 Blackett, P. M. S. (1897–   ), English. *Discoveries in Cosmic Radiation.*
1949 Yukawa, H. (1907–   ), Japanese. *Theoretical Prediction of Mesons.*
1950 Powell, C. F. (1903–   ), English. *Photographic Cosmic-Ray Studies.*
1951 Cockcroft, Sir J. D. (1897–   ), English, and
     Walton, E. T. S. (1903–   ), English. *First Transmutation of Atomic Nuclei.*
1952 Bloch, Felix (1905–   ), American. *Nuclear Magnetic Moments.*
     Purcell, Ed. M. (1912–   ), American. *Radio Astronomy.*
1953 Zernike, Frits (1888–   ), Dutch. *Phase Contrast Microscope.*
1954 Born, Max (1882–   ), German. *Quantum Mechanics, and Wave Functions.*
     Bothe, Walther (1891–1957), German. *Quantum Mechanics, and Wave Functions.*
1955 Kusch, P. (1911–   ), American, and
     Lamb, W. E. (1913–   ), American. *Microwave Spectroscopy and Atomic Structure.*
1956 Shockley, W. (1910–   ), American,
     Brattain, W. H. (1902–   ), American, and
     Bardeen, J. (1908–   ), American. *Semiconductors, and Their Application to Transistors.*
1957 Yang, C. N. (1922–   ), American, and
     Lee, T. D. (1926–   ), American. *Studies of the Concept of Parity in Atomic Physics.*
1958 Cerenkov, P. A. (1904–   ), Russian,
     Tamm, I. E. (1895–   ), Russian, and
     Frank, I. M. (1908–   ), Russian. *Discovery and Study of Cerenkov Radiation.*
1959 Segrè, E. (1905–   ), American, and
     Chamberlain, O. (1920–   ), American. *Discovery of the Antiproton.*
1960 Glaser, D. A. (1926–   ), American. *The Bubble Chamber.*
1961 Hofstadter, Robt. (1916–   ), American, and
     Mossbauer, R. L. (1930–   ), German. *Nuclear Radiation and Absorption.*
1962 Landau, L. D. (1908–   ), Russian. *Mathematical explanation of very low temperature phenomena.*
1963 Goeppert-Mayer, Maria (1906–   ), American, and
     Jensen, J. Hans D. (1906–   ), German. *Nuclear Shell Model.*
     Wigner, E. (1902–   ), American. *Theoretical Work on Symmetry and Parity.*
1964 Townes, C. H. (1915–   ), American,
     Basov, N. (1922–   ), Russian, and
     Prokhorov, A. (1916–   ), Russian. *Development of Lasers and Masers.*
1965 Feynman, R. P. (1918–   ), American,
     Schwinger, J. S. (1918–   ), American, and
     Tomonaga, S. (1906–   ), Japanese. *Research in Quantum Electrodynamics.*

Appendix XIII—Powers of Ten Notation and Algebra

In speaking of the size and shape of an object or the time interval between the occurrence of two events, it is convenient to express very large numbers and very small decimals in an abbreviated form. This is done principally to conserve time and space. It is convenient for the astronomer in the study of stars, on the one hand, and the physicist and chemist in the study of atoms on the other. The abbreviations in common use are based upon powers of tens as follows:

$$10 = 10^1 \qquad\qquad 1 = 10^0$$
$$100 = 10^2 \qquad\qquad 0.1 = 10^{-1}$$
$$1000 = 10^3 \qquad\qquad 0.01 = 10^{-2}$$
$$10,000 = 10^4 \qquad\qquad 0.001 = 10^{-3}$$
$$100,000 = 10^5 \qquad\qquad 0.0001 = 10^{-4}$$
$$1,000,000 = 10^6 \qquad\qquad 0.00001 = 10^{-5}$$

The abbreviated form on the right side of each equation is mathematically correct. For example,

$$10^3 = 10 \times 10 \times 10 = 1000$$

and

$$10^{-3} = \frac{1}{10^3} = \frac{1}{1000} = 0.001$$

In every case, *the exponent is seen to give directly the number of digits the decimal point is moved from unity*, positive integers specifying the number of places the decimal point is moved to the right to make large numbers, and negative integers specifying the number of places it is moved to the left to make small fractions. To illustrate the use of this system, suppose we say that a truck weighs three million grams. This can be written

$$3,000,000 \text{ g} = 3 \times 1,000,000 \text{ g}$$
$$= 3 \times 10^6 \text{ g}$$

In the abbreviated notation the mass is therefore written 3×10^6 g. If more than one numeral occurs, any one of several abbreviations might be written. For example, in the case of large numbers,

$$840,000,000 = 84 \times 10,000,000 = 84 \times 10^7$$

or

$$840,000,000 = 8.4 \times 100,000,000 = 8.4 \times 10^8$$

In the case of small numbers, on the other hand,

$$0.0024 = 2.4 \times 10^{-3}, \text{ or } 24 \times 10^{-4}$$

To illustrate the advantages of this abbreviated notation, the mass of the *earth* and the mass of an *electron* are found by experiment to be as follows:

$$\text{mass of the earth,} \quad m = 5.97 \times 10^{24} \text{ Kg}$$
$$\text{mass of an electron,} \ m = 9.11 \times 10^{-31} \text{ Kg}$$

If these are written down in complete decimal form they would appear as follows:

mass of the earth = 5,970,000,000,000,000,000,000,000 Kg

mass of the electron = 0.000,000,000,000,000,000,000,000,000,000,911 Kg

At a meeting held by the International Union for Pure and Applied Physics a few years ago, the following symbolism was adopted for general use:*

10^3	Kilo	K		10^{-3}	milli	m
10^6	Mega	M		10^{-6}	micro	μ
10^9	Giga	G		10^{-9}	nano	n
10^{12}	Terra	T		10^{-12}	pico	p

One of the reasons for adopting these notations was that B, for billion, stands for 10^9 in the United States, and for 10^{12} in Great Britain. Because the term "billion" is so thoroughly entrenched in the minds of scientists in the United States, only a few have adopted G and T, while the change from k to K for *one thousand* is becoming more common.

The multiplication and division of large and small numbers in the abbreviated notation involves the addition and subtraction of exponents.

Rule 1. When a power number is changed from numerator to denominator, or vice versa, the sign of the exponent is changed. For example,

$$\frac{5}{2 \times 10^{-6}} \text{ equals } \frac{5 \times 10^6}{2}$$

Rule 2. When two power numbers are multiplied, their exponents are added. For example,

$$3 \times 10^5 \times 2 \times 10^4 = 3 \times 2 \times 10^{5+4} = 6 \times 10^9$$

Again,

$$3 \times 10^{17} \times 2 \times 10^{-12} = 3 \times 2 \times 10^{17-12} = 6 \times 10^5$$

Rule 3. When one power number is divided by another, their exponents are subtracted. For example,

$$\frac{8 \times 10^9}{2 \times 10^4} = \frac{8 \times 10^{9-4}}{2} = 4 \times 10^5$$

Again,

$$\frac{6 \times 10^{-7}}{3 \times 10^{-2}} = \frac{6 \times 10^{-7+2}}{3} = 2 \times 10^{-5}$$

Problems

1. Write each of the following in powers of ten notation, and then express the answers in powers of ten notation: (a) $6000 \times 30,000$, (b) $58,000 \times 0.002$, (c) $345 \times 0.0004 \div 0.00002$, and (d) $0.00042 \times 0.00000007 \div 0.006$.

2. Solve each of the following problems and find the answers in powers of ten notation: (a) $5 \times 10^3 \times 4 \times 10^8$, (b) $3.2 \times 10^7 \times 7 \times 10^{-4}$, (c) $6.5 \times 10^3 \times 5 \times 10^4 \div 2 \times 10^{-5}$, and (d) $1.8 \times 10^{-6} \times 4 \times 10^{-15} \div 9 \times 10^{-28}$. [*Ans.* (a) 2×10^{12}, (b) 2.24×10^4, (c) 1.625×10^{13}, and (d) 8×10^6.]

3. Solve each of the following problems and express the answers in powers of ten notation: (a) $2.6 \times 10^6 \times 5.0 \times 10^2$, (b) $4 \times 10^{18} \times 3.5 \times 10^{-8}$, (c) $3 \times 10^5 \times 8 \times 10^7 \div 4 \times 10^4$, and (d) $5 \times 10^{-3} \times 6 \times 10^{11} \div 3 \times 10^{-4}$.

4. Write each of the following in powers of ten notation; express the answers in powers of ten: (a) $30,000 \times 2500$, (b) 3800×0.00004, (c) $5,200,000 \times 20,000 \div 0.0004$, and (d) $0.00081 \times 7000 \div 0.003$. [*Ans.* (a) 7.5×10^7, (b) 15.2×10^{-2}, (c) 2.6×10^{14}, and (d) 1.89×10^3.]

* See *Physics Today*, **9**, 23 (1956); **10**, 30 (1957).

5. If a 1-lb weight were made only of particles having the mass of an electron, of how many particles would it be composed?

6. The sun's mass is 1.98×10^{33} g. To how many earth masses is this equivalent? [*Ans.* 3.32×10^5.]

7. Calculate the number of seconds in one week, and express the answer in powers of ten.

8. Calculate the number of seconds in a life span of 50 years, and express the answer in powers of ten. [*Ans.* 1.58×10^9 s.]

9. Find the sum of 5 yd and 3 m in (a) yards, (b) meters, and (c) centimeters.

10. Find the sum of 150 in. and 325 cm in (a) yards, (b) meters, and (c) centimeters. [*Ans.* (a) 7.62 yd, (b) 7.06 m, and (c) 706 cm.]

11. Find the difference between 10 mi and 20 Km in (a) miles, and (b) kilometers.

12. Find the difference between 25 Km and 15 mi in (a) miles, and (b) kilometers. [*Ans.* (a) 0.534 mi, (b) .860 Km.]

13. Calculate the distance to the moon in meters if the distance is 239,000 mi. Express your answer in powers of ten.

14. Calculate the distance to the sun in kilometers if the distance is 90,000,000 mi. [*Ans.* 1.448×10^8 Km.]

15. Solve each of the following and give each answer in powers of ten: (a) $3 \times 10^5 \times 10^6$, (b) $2.5 \times 10^4 \div 5 \times 10^{-2}$, (c) $3.9 \times 10^8 \times 5 \times 10^{-3}$, (d) $4.2 \times 10^{-6} \div 7 \times 10^{-2}$, and (e) $6 \times 10^{-2} \div 1.5 \times 10^4$.

16. Solve each of the following and give each answer in powers of ten: (a) $3.2 \times 10^5 \times 6.0 \times 10^2$, (b) $4.2 \times 10^3 \div 2.0 \times 10^{-2}$, (c) $8.6 \times 10^6 \times 5 \times 10^{-2}$, (d) $6 \times 10^{-6} \div 1.2 \times 10^{-2}$, and (e) $12 \times 10^{-3} \div 3 \times 10^4$. [*Ans.* (a) 1.92×10^8, (b) 2.1×10^5, (c) 4.3×10^5, (d) 5×10^{-4}, and (e) 4×10^{-7}.]

17. Solve each of the following and give each answer in powers of ten: (a) $4 \times 10^{-2} \times 3.2 \times 10^6 \div 8 \times 10^4$, (b) $2.2 \times 10^{-3} \times 5 \times 10^{-2} \div (4 \times 10^2 \times 5 \times 10^{-4})$, (c) $9.2 \times 10^6 \times 3 \times 10^7 \div 6 \times 10^{-8}$, and (d) $3.4 \times 10^{-5} \times 2.8 \times 10^{-2} \div 8 \times 10^7$.

INDEX